AA Lifestyle Guides in association with
Millennium & Co

WIN one
Fabulous 'Weekends Away' for two
in 5 Free Prize Draws

see overleaf for terms & conditions

Enjoy a break with a difference with Millennium & Copthorne Hotels. Choose from any one of the 17 exclusive 4-star hotels around the UK, offering the highest standard of accommodation, food and leisure facilities.
The recipe for a perfect weekend away.

For more information on Millennium & Copthorne Hotels, call 0845 30 20001, quoting "AA Lifestyle Guides".

HOW TO ENTER

Just complete (in capitals please) and send off this card or alternatively, send your name and address on a stamped postcard to the address overleaf (no purchase required). Entries are limited to one per household and to residents of the UK and Republic of Ireland over the age of 18. This card will require a stamp if posted in the Republic of Ireland. **Closing date 6 September 2002.**

MR/MRS/MISS/MS/OTHER, PLEASE STATE: _____

NAME: _____

ADDRESS: _____

_____

_____

POSTCODE: _____

TEL. NOS: _____ E-MAIL: _____

Are you an AA Member?   Yes/No

Have you bought this or any other AA Lifestyle Guide before?   Yes/No

If yes, please indicate the year of the last edition you bought:

AA Hotel Guide	_____	AA Caravan & Camping (Europe)	_____
AA Bed and Breakfast Guide	_____	AA Britain Guide	
AA Restaurant Guide	_____	AA Days Out Guide	_____
AA Pub Guide	_____	Other, please state	_____
AA Caravan & Camping (Britain & Ireland)	_____		

If you do not wish to receive further information or special offers from AA Publishing please tick the box ☐

We may use information we hold about you to write to, or telephone, you about other products and services offered by us and our carefully selected partners. Information may be disclosed to other companies in the Centrica plc group (including those using the British Gas, Scottish Gas, Goldfish and AA brands) but we can assure you that we will not disclose it to third parties. Tick the box if you do NOT wish to hear about other products and services.'

DO02

Terms and Conditions

1. Four winners will be drawn from each of the five prize draws to take place on 04 January, 08 March, 03 May, 05 July and 06 September 2002.

2. Closing date for receipt of entries is midday on the relevant draw date. Final close date for receipt of entries is 06 September 2002.

3. Entries received after any draw date other than the final one will go forward into the next available draw. Each entry will only be entered in one draw. Only one entry per household accepted.

4. Winners will be notified by post within 14 days of the relevant draw date.

5. Prizes must be booked within 3 months of the relevant draw date. Prizes are not transferable and there is no cash alternative.

6. This prize cannot be used in conjunction with any other discount, promotion or special offer.

7. Each prize consists of two nights' accommodation and full traditional breakfast for two adults sharing a standard twin/double room in a UK Millennium or Copthorne Hotel. Supplements may be charged for feature or family rooms. All accommodation is subject to availability.

8. Millennium & Copthorne Hotels provide all hotel accommodation, services and facilities and the AA is not party to your agreement with Millennium & Copthorne Hotels in this regard.

9. No purchase required

10. The prize draw is open to anyone resident in the UK or the Republic of Ireland over the age of 18, other than employees of the Automobile Association or Millennium & Copthorne Hotels, their subsidiary companies or their families or agents.

11. For a list of winners, please send a stamped, self addressed envelope to AA Lifestyle Guide Winners 2002, AA Publishing, Fanum House (4), Basingstoke, Hants, RG21 4EA.

12. If this card is posted in the Republic of Ireland, it must have an appropriate stamp.

13. Once a prize weekend has been booked, cancellation will invalidate the prize.

BUSINESS REPLY SERVICE
Licence No BZ 343

PLEASE NOTE: Requires a stamp if posted in Republic of Ireland

AA Lifestyle Guide 2002 Prize Draw

AA PUBLISHING
FANUM HOUSE (4)
BASING VIEW
BASINGSTOKE
HANTS RG21 4EA

AA

The Days Out

Guide 2002

AA Lifestyle Guides

Produced by AA Publishing

A CIP catalogue record for this book is available from the British Library

Directory generated by the AA Establishment Database, Information Research, AA Hotel Services

Design by Nautilus Design UK Ltd, Basingstoke, Hampshire

Cover artwork by Sue Climpson, Whitchurch, Hampshire

Cover pictures: Castle Howard, AA Photo Library/ P. Bennett; Stratford-upon-Avon, AA Photo Library/ J. Welsh; Littlecote, AA Photo Library/W. Voysey; Legoland Windsor, Pictures Colour Library

Advertisement Sales: advertisingsales@theAA.com
Lifestyle Guides: lifestyleguides@theAA.com

Typeset/Repro by Avonset, 11 Kelso Place, Lower Bristol Road, Bath BA1 3AU

Printed in Italy by Rotolito Lombarda SpA

The contents of this book are believed correct at the time of printing. Nevertheless, the Publisher cannot be held responsible for any errors or omissions or for changes in the details given in this guide or for the consequences of any reliance on the information provided in the same. We have tried to ensure accuracy in this guide but things do change and we would be grateful if readers would advise us of any inaccuracies they may encounter.

OS Ordnance Survey® This product includes mapping data licensed from Ordnance Survey® with the permission of the Controller of Her Majesty's Stationery Office ©Crown copyright 2001. All rights reserved. Licence number 399221

Northern Ireland mapping reproduced by permission of the Director and Chief Executive, Ordnance Survey of Northern Ireland, acting on behalf of the Controller of Her Majesty's Stationery Office ©Crown copyright 2001. Permit No. 1674

Republic of Ireland mapping based on Ordnance Survey Ireland by permission of the Government. Permit No. MP006901 ©Government of Ireland.

Maps prepared by the Cartographic Department of The Automobile Association

Published by AA Publishing, which is a trading name of Automobile Association Developments Limited whose registered office is Millstream, Maidenhead Road, Windsor, Berkshire, SL4 5GD Registered number 1878835.

ISBN 0 7495 3190 8

How to Use *this Guide*

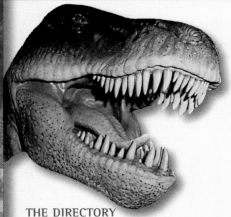

THE DIRECTORY

The directory is arranged in counties, then in alphabetical location order within each county. Each county has an introductory page that gives general information on the county as well as details of selected events and festivals. (These pages may mention places, landmarks or streets that do not have an entry in the directory.)

❶ MAP REFERENCES & ATLAS

Map references for establishments are based on the National Grid, and can be used with the Atlas at the back of this book, or with any AA Atlas of Britain.
First is the map page number, followed by the National Grid reference. To find the location, read the first figure horizontally and the second figure vertically within the lettered square.

❷ DIRECTIONS are given after the address of

each establishment or attraction and where shown have been provided by the places of interest themselves.

ABBREVIATED ENTRIES

Some attractions have abbreviated entries and the line 'Details not confirmed for 2002'. These are entries that were unable to provide the relevant information in time for publication. Please ring the establishment for up-to-date details.

❸ TELEPHONE NUMBERS have the STD code

shown before the telephone number. (If dialling Northern Ireland from England use the STD code, but for the Republic you need to prefix the number with 00353.)

❹ OPENING TIMES quoted in the guide are

inclusive - for instance, where you see Apr-Oct, that place will be open from the beginning of April to the end of October.

❺ FEES quoted for the majority of entries are

current. If no price is quoted, you should check with the establishment concerned before you visit. Places which are open 'at all reasonable times' are usually free, and many places which do not charge admission at all may ask for a voluntary donation. Remember that prices can go up, and those provided to us by the attractions are provisional for 2002.

Sample entry

🏛 **ANY TOWN**   **Map 03 SP27 —❶**
ANY PLACE
ZE17 5ZE (off A14 at junc with B760 signed Old Weston) —❷
❸— ☎ **01002 293002** 🖨 **01002 293007**
e-mail: anyplace@demon.co.uk

A wildlife breeding centre, dedicated to the practical conservation of endangered species including gibbons, marmosets, lemurs, wildcats, meerkats, Britain's only group of breeding sloths and many more. There is also a large and varied bird collection, with several species unique to this location. Over 120 species in all. Other attractions include a children's play area, and undercover viewing of many mammals.

❹— **Times:** summer daily 10.30-6; winter daily 10.30-4. (Closed Xmas)
❺— **Fees:** £3 (£1.50 children and OAP) **Facilities:** P 🍵 ♿ toilets for disabled, shop ⊗ ————————————————❻

❻ FACILITIES
This section includes parking, dogs allowed, refreshments etc. See page 6 for a key to Symbols and Abbreviations used in this guide.

VISITORS WITH DISABILITIES should look for the wheelchair symbol showing where all or most of the establishment is accessible to the wheelchair-bound visitor. We strongly recommend that you telephone in advance of your visit to check the exact details, particularly regarding access to toilets and refreshment facilities. Guide dogs are usually accepted where the establishments show the 'No Dogs' symbol - unless stated otherwise. For the hard of hearing induction loops are indicated by a symbol.

CREDIT & CHARGE CARDS are now taken by a number of establishments for admission charges. To indicate which accept credit cards we have used this symbol at the end of the entry. 💳

PHOTOGRAPHY is restricted in some places and there are many where it is only allowed in specific areas. Visitors are advised to check with places of interest on the rules for taking photographs and the use of video cameras.

SPECIAL EVENTS are held at many of these establishments, and although we have listed a few of the more important ones on the county introduction pages, we cannot hope to give details of them all, so please ring the places of interest for details of exhibitions, themed days, talks, guided walks and more.

Key to SYMBOLS AND ABBREVIATIONS

SYMBOLS

In order to give you as much information as possible in the space available, we have used the following symbols in the guide:

	ENGLISH	FRANÇAIS	DEUTSCH	ITALIANO	ESPAÑOL
☎	Telephone number	Numéro de téléphone	Telefonnummer	Numero telefonico	Número telefónico
▤	Fax number				
♿	Suitable for visitors in wheelchairs	Les invalidens fauteuils roulants pourrant y accéder	Für Rollstuhltahrer zugänglich	Accessibile agli handicappeti	Acondicionado para visitantes en silla de reudas
🅿	Parking at Establishment	Stationnement à l'établissement	Parken an Ort und Stelle	Parcheggio in loco	Aparcamiento en el establecimiento
🅿	Parking nearby	Stationnement tout près	Parken in der Nähe	Parcheggio nelle vicinanze	Aparcamiento cerca del
☕	Refreshments	Rafraîchissements	Erfrischungen	Snack-bar	Refrescos
✕	Restaurant	Restaurant	Restaurant	Ristorante	Restaurante
🐕	No dogs	Chiens non permis	Hundeverbot	Cani non accettati	Se prohiben los perros
🚌	No coaches	Les groupes en cars pas admis	Keine Reisebusgesellschaften	Non si accettano comitive in pullman	Non se admiten los grupos de viajeros en autobús
⊕	Cadw (Welsh Historic Monuments)	Cadw Monument ancien (Pays de Galles)	Cadw Historiches Gebaude (Walisland)	Cadw Monumento storico (Galles)	Cadw Monumento histórico (Gales)
✳	English Heritage	English Heritage	English Heritage	English Heritage	English Heritage
✿	National Trust	National Trust	National Trust	National Trust	The National Trust
♛	National Trust for Scotland	National Trust en Ecosse	National Trust in Schottland	National Trust per la Scozia	The National Trust de Escocia
▮	Historic Scotland				

ABBREVIATIONS

In the same way, we have abbreviated certain pieces of information:

	ENGLISH	FRANÇAIS	DEUTSCH	ITALIAN	ESPAÑOL
BH	Bank Holidays	Jours fériés	Bankfeiertage	Festività nazionale	Días festivos (bancos y comercio)
PH	Public Holidays	Jours fériés	Feiertage	Festività nazionale	Días festivos
Etr	Easter	Pâques	Ostern	Pasqua	Semana Santa
ex	except	sauf	ausser	eccetto	excepto
IR£	Irish punts	Punts irlandais	Punts Irisch	Punts irlandesi	Punts irlandeses
Free	Admission free	Entrée gratuit	Freier eintritt	Ingresso gratuito	Entrada gratuita
£1	Admission £1	Entrée £1	Eintritt £1	Ingresso £1	Entrada £1
ch 50p	Children 50p	Enfants 50p	Kinder 50p	Bambini 50p	Niños 50p
ch 15 50p	Children under 15 50p	Enfants de moins de 15 ans 50p	Kinder unter 15 Jahren 50p	Bambini sotto i 15 anni 50p	Los niños de menores de 15 años 50p
Pen	Senior Citizens	Retraites	Rentner	Pensionati	Jubilados
Party	Special or reduced rates for parties booked in advance	Tarifs spéciaux ou réduits pour groupes réservés d'advance	Sondertarife oder Ermässigungen für im voraus bestellte Gesellschaften	Tariffe speciali o ridotte per comitive che prenotano in anticipo	Tarifas especiales o reducidas para los grupos de viajeros que reserven de anternano
Party 30+	Special or reduced rates for parties of 30 or more booked in advance	Tarifs spéciaux ou réduits pour groupes de 30 ou plus réservés d'advance	Sondertarife oder Ermässigungen für im voraus bestellte Gesellschaften von wenigstens 30 Personen	Tariffe speciali o ridotte per comitive di 30 o più persone che prenotano in anticipo	Tarifas especiales o reducidas para grupos de 30 viajeros, o más, que reserven de anternano

more
to discover

Explore over 400 historic properties from stately homes to majestic castles and romantic ruins.

Re-live the past
See our properties come to life with action-packed re-enactments of historic events, music and drama.

A past to remember
We guarantee an eventful and memorable day out for all.

The Angel of Peace Descending on the Chariot of War, Wellington Arch, London

Stonehenge

Tintagel Castle

Dover Castle

Osborne House & Gardens

Family Days Out

By Julia Hynard

Great British days out are as varied as the great British family. Whether you're toting a toddler or tempting a teenager to spend some quality time with you, there's an immense amount to choose from. The most successful of the attractions have cross-generational appeal, with a range of facilities for the adventurous spirit, the enquiring mind, the hungry body and the aching feet. For details of opening times, admission prices, facilities and access, look up the attraction's full entry in the book.

can play a virtual reality cave game. Gloomy Wood is the spooky forest setting for a very haunted house, while Cred Street is a more gentle area including Barney's Playground, Barney's Theatre and Toyland Tours. Children will also want to visit the enchanting Storybook Land, Adventure Land and Old MacDonald's, a working farm.

If this is all a little too exciting, relax and enjoy the landscaped gardens, boating lake and aerial cable car rides with views over the estate.

Legoland, (p18) Windsor, also among the UK's top attractions, is particularly child-centred. It offers plenty to fill your day in themed areas such as the Imagination Centre, Duplo Gardens, My Town, Wild Woods and Castleland. There are more than 50 rides, and other attractions include the Life on Mars show, a kids' driving school and panning for gold. The opportunity to play with huge quantities of Duplo/Lego bricks, including state-of-the-art robotic components, and to see spectacular animated Lego constructions in Miniland, is a particular draw for kids. Legoland

Below: Alton Towers

THRILLS & SPILLS

The UK's most popular theme park, **Alton Towers (p198)** in Staffordshire, has it all. Set in 200 acres around the original stately home (now undergoing renovation), it offers the biggest range of innovative and terrifying thrill rides in the country in the X-Sector and Forbidden Valley. These include the notorious Nemesis, Oblivion, Submission, and a spectacular new generation coaster promised for the 2002 season.

More rides are to be found in Katanga Canyon (themed around an African village), in Merrie England, with its ever popular log flume and 3D cinema, and the prehistoric Ug Land, where you

also has an aerial monorail, the Sky Rider, from where you can see the sights and take the weight off your feet.

THE CALL OF THE WILD

Flamingo Land (p257) (North Yorkshire) is a rather cosy name for a major tourist attraction that combines all the excitement of the theme park with a fully-fledged zoo. The white knuckle rides on offer include the The Terroriser, The Bullet, The Wild Mouse, and Magnum Force – an astonishing triple loop rollercoaster, the first of its kind in Europe – along with a traditional carousel and fun rides for smaller children. The zoo is home

The Eden Project

to over 1,000 animals, including tigers, monkeys, penguins and meerkats ... oh and the eponymous flamingos, the largest flock in the country.

Daily shows are an additional attraction, including Professor Bubbles with his dream machine, and all the family can enjoy the Little Monster's Den of Mischief.

Children are not always enthusiastic garden visitors, but the sheer scale of **The Eden Project (p40)** in Cornwall is sure to impress them with its massive geodesic biomes creating a 'global garden' in a huge china clay pit, over 50 metres deep. To give you an idea of the size, the pit could accommodate 35 football pitches and some of the largest biomes (giant conservatories) could hold the Tower of London. Three of the world's climate zones are recreated: the humid tropics, the warm temperate regions, and the temperate zone, representing what you might find in the rainforest, southern Africa or Britain.

The message is one of conservation and sustainable development, showcasing the fabulous plant life of the world and our dependence on it. Children will particularly enjoy adventure trails through the rainforest, and discovering the source of many of the materials we use in our everyday lives.

continued

FAMILY DAYS OUT

Ironbridge

INDUSTRIAL HERITAGE

For a blast from the industrial past check out the award-winning **Ironbridge Gorge Museums (p188)** at Telford, Shropshire. Nine museums over an area of 80 acres around the Ironbridge Gorge include the first ever Iron Bridge, cast by Abraham Darby III in 1779, which still spans the River Severn, with an interpretive exhibition in the tollhouse. The others are:

Blists Hill Victorian town – shops, factories, houses and a cast of characters in Victorian dress
Broseley Pipeworks – preserved clay tobacco pipe works
Coalbrookdale Museum of Iron – the great Darby furnace and display of iron products
Coalport China Museum – national collections of Caughley and Coalport china, a children's gallery and demonstration workshops
Darby Houses – the homes of the industrial community of Coalbrookdale
Jackfield Tile Museum – gas-lit galleries of decorative tiles, with workshops and geological exhibition

LIVING HISTORY

Encouraging the family to imbibe a little culture is easy at **Madame Tussaud's (p140)** in London, where figures from history and celebrities from sports, the arts and media are brought (almost) to life in the world-renowned waxwork collection founded in Paris in 1770. During the French Revolution, Madame Tussaud (née Anne Marie Grosholtz) and her uncle Philippe Curtius were forced, as wax modellers, to make death masks of those who fell victim to the guillotine, many of whom were personal friends. These masks formed the basis of the infamous Chamber of Horrors, still a favourite today. Another feature of the modern Tussaud's experience is the Spirit of London, a ride through 400 years of London history.

A similar 'journey through time' is offered at the **Jorvik Viking Centre (p263)** at York where time cars carry visitors through a time tunnel from World War II back to Norman times and on to a full-scale reconstruction of 10th-century Coppergate. On the same theme Dublin's **Viking Centre (p368)** provides an interactive simulation of 'Dyflin', where visitors can chat to the locals, watch them at work and experience authentic sounds and smells of life in Viking Dublin.

The **Ulster American Folk Park (p363)** in Omagh draws on transatlantic cultural links and tells the story of mass emigration from Ulster to America in the 18th and 19th centuries. The 70-acre park is made up of three main areas: the Old World, based around the restored farmhouse of Thomas Mellon who left for Pennsylvania in 1818; the dockside, complete with emigrant ship, and the New World, where log houses furnished in period style give a flavour of the emigrant's life in America.

Ironbridge

Museum of the Gorge – a Gothic-style riverside warehouse housing an exhibition on the history of the gorge
Tar Tunnel – put on a hard hat and go down the tunnel to discover the source of natural bitumen
There is a huge amount to see, and you can pay to visit individual museums or get a 'passport' for them all.

Ironbridge

The history of another major, if declining, industry is preserved at the **Scottish Mining Museum,** (p310) in a Victorian colliery at Newtongrange. Former miners lead guided tours, and visitors are equipped with special helmets incorporating remote-controlled headphones. Features of the museum are the fully accessible three-storey visitor centre with exhibitions, interactive displays and audio-visual presentations, the hands-on operations centre, pithead, largest winding engine in Scotland, and reconstructed underground roadway and coalface capturing the atmosphere of the working pit.

Wales commemorates its traditional industries with the **South Wales Miners Museum** (p346) in the Afan Argoed Countryside Centre, and the **Welsh Slate Museum (p341)** at

R R S Discovery

VOYAGE OF DISCOVERY

The **Discovery Point (p299)** on the quayside at Dundee is a must for any family with a spirit of adventure. It is another award-winning attraction, with spectacular exhibits and special effects, centring on Captain Scott's polar exploration ship, RRS Discovery, one of the last wooden three-masted ships built in Britain.

Further south, in Edinburgh, the latest scientific input has been employed to produce a new style of visitor attraction in **Our Dynamic Earth. (p289)** In a virtual journey around the planet you can experience the big bang, ice age and tropical rainstorms; plunge the depths of the oceans and soar above the mountains, and get to grips with the past and the future of our Earth.

The UK's only attraction dedicated to space, the **National Space Centre (p126)** is located in a stunningly futuristic tower building in Leicester. Five themed galleries use the latest technology to take you on a space voyage of discovery, including space rockets, satellites and hands-on activities. The domed space theatre is the venue for some great shows, including some suitable for younger children. If scientific discovery is your thing, then **Techniquest (p333)** in Cardiff Bay is billed as the UK's number one attraction of its kind. Aiming to make science fun, the 3,000-square-metre development features a 30-seat hollow sphere planetarium (where you can see the stars by day), a laboratory, discovery room, 100-seat science theatre, and no less than 160 hands-on exhibits to inform, challenge, and entertain the visitor.

Dynamic Earth

Llaberis, set amid beautiful scenery on the shores of Llyn Padarn. Highlights of the latter are the largest working waterwheel in mainland Britain, a 3D multi-media presentation on the work and lives of the quarrymen, the restored machinery, and quarrymen's houses furnished to represent significant period's in the industry's history.

Multiple awards have been heaped upon another industrial museum, the **Verdant Works (p300)** in the city of Dundee. This working jute mill provides an all-weather attraction with interactive exhibits, a film show and original working machinery. A social history gallery recalls the lives of those caught up in what was once the world centre of jute manufacture, and charts the industry's subsequent decline.

National Space Centre

FAMILY DAYS OUT

Never in a thousand years will you believe what's happened over the last ten centuries.

THE STORIES and intrigue which surround Warwick Castle make it one of the most popular tourist destinations in Britain. Over the past ten centuries this impressive fortress has survived the most turbulent times in English history. Now discover its secrets for yourself.

Beyond the portcullis, encounter treachery in the 'Kingmaker' attraction which allows you to see how a 15th century army prepare for battle. Pick up a sword or try on a helmet and see just how soldiers lived and died on the battlefield in our 'Death or Glory' attraction. Then, find out why the Castle became a favourite retreat for important figures of late Victorian society in 'A Royal Weekend Party'. Every day throughout the summer there's a unique opportunity to witness mediaeval life at the Mediaeval Festival. See the daily life of craftsmen and enjoy the programme of entertainment including birds of prey and fighting knights. Making a visit to Warwick Castle one of the most exciting days out in history.

WARWICK CASTLE

Bedfordshire

One of England's smallest counties, Bedfordshire contains the picturesque villages of Woburn and Old Warden, and the large towns of Luton and Bedford. There's plenty of countryside to explore on foot or by bike, and plenty to see and do in Bedfordshire's towns and villages.

EVENTS & FESTIVALS

March
tbc Bedfordshire Festival of Music, Speech & Drama, various venues in Bedford

May
1st Ickwell May Festival, The Maypole, Ickwell Green
tbc Bedford River Festival (entertainment, parade, fête, raft races)

July
6th-7th Popular Flying Association International Air Rally & Exhibition, Cranfield Airfield, Cranfield

August
3rd Proms in the Park, Bedford Park

September
14th-15th Bedfordshire Steam & Country Fayre, Old Warden Park, near Biggleswade

October
5th Bedford Beer Festival, Bedford Corn Exchange
tbc National Apple Day at Bromham Mill (apples, cider, apple bobbing, farmers market & entertainment)

November
tbc Bedford Fireworks Display, Rugby Ground, Goldington Road, Bedford

December
tbc Bedford Victorian Fayre, Bedford town centre

Top: the picturesque Green of Ickwell.

For many travellers, Luton is the gateway to London and Eastern England. London Luton Airport offers an increasing number of international flights, but that's not all there is to this bustling town. Once a centre for hat manufacture, Luton has a variety of attractions including gardens, museums, parks and a unique collection of horse-drawn carriages. Not far from the town there stands the magnificent Luton Hoo, a 19th-century house (now a hotel) with 1,500 acres of `Capability' Brown garden and a collection of art connected with the Russian royal family.

The county has some charming sights, set among its many small villages. Woburn is one of these, and is known not only for its Abbey and Safari Park, but also its fine Georgian houses and antique shops. At Shuttleworth, not far from Old Warden, the Swiss Garden is an ideal place to spend a quiet afternoon. In its ten-acre spread there are trees and shrubs from all over the world, as well as a tiny thatched Swiss cottage.

Dunstable boasts the Norman Church of St Peter, with medieval additions that include a 14th-century chancel screen. Ampthill, between Luton and Bedford, is full of fascinating architecture, including Avenue House and the 14th-century Church of St Andrew, which houses a cannon-ball monument to Richard Nicolls, a local man who named New York (after his patron the Duke of York) in 1664.

AMPTHILL
Map 04 TL03
HOUGHTON HOUSE
(1m NE off A421)
Times: Open all reasonable times. **Facilities:** 🅿 & ⚑ *Details not confirmed for 2002*

BEDFORD
Map 04 TL04
BEDFORD MUSEUM
Castle Ln MK40 3XD (close to town bridge and Embankment)
☎ 01234 353323   🖷 01234 273401
e-mail: bmuseum@bedford.gov.uk

The museum is devoted to local history and natural history, with 19th-century room sets and displays of birds and mammals, agriculture, archæology, fossils and minerals. There is a changing programme of children's activities, temporary exhibitions and special events. Please telephone for details.
Times: Open all year, Tue-Sat 11-5, Sun 2-5. (Closed Mon ex BH Mon afternoon, Good Fri & Xmas). **Fee:** £2.10 (ch, pen & con free). Fri free for everyone. Annual ticket £8.40. **Facilities:** 🅿 (50 mtrs) & (lift available on request, subject to staff availability) toilets for disabled shop 💢 (ex guide dogs)

CECIL HIGGINS ART GALLERY & MUSEUM
Castle Ln MK40 3RP (in the centre of the town, just off the Embankment)
☎ 01234 211222   🖷 01234 327149
e-mail: chag@bedford.gov.uk

A recreated Victorian mansion, with the rooms arranged as though the house was lived in. Includes bedroom with furniture designed by Victorian architect William Borges. The adjoining gallery has an outstanding collection of ceramics, glass and changing exhibition of prints, drawings and watercolours.
Times: Open all year, Tue-Sat 11-5, Sun & BH Mon 2-5. (Closed Mon, Good Fri, 25-26 Dec & 1 Jan). **Fee:** £2.10 (ch & concessions free) includes entry to Bedford Museum. Free to all visitors Fri
Facilities: 🅿 (50 yds) pay & display 💺 & toilets for disabled shop 💢 (ex guide dogs) 🐾

ELSTOW
Map 04 TL04
MOOT HALL
MK42 9XT (signposted off Elstow Road)
☎ 01234 266889   🖷 01234 228531
Times: Open 2 Apr-Oct, Tue-Thu, Sat, Sun 2-5 (Closed Mon ex BH's & Fri). Phone to confirm. **Facilities:** 🅿 & shop 💢 *Details not confirmed for 2002*

LEIGHTON BUZZARD
Map 04 SP92
LEIGHTON BUZZARD RAILWAY
Pages Park Station, Billington Rd LU7 4TN (0.75m SE on A4146 signposted in and around Leighton Buzzard. Nr rdbt junc with A505 Dunstable-Aylesbury)
☎ 01525 373888   🖷 01525 377814
e-mail: info@buzzrail.co.uk

Originally built to serve the local sand industry in 1919, this railway has run a steam passenger service since 1968. With the largest collection of narrow gauge locomotives in Britain, the Leighton Buzzard Railway is an important part of Britain's railway heritage.
Times: Open Mar-Oct, Sun & BH wknds; Jul, Wed; Aug, Tue-Thu, Sat & BH wknds. **Fee:** Return ticket £5 (ch 2-15 £2, pen £4 & ch under 2 free). Party 10+. **Facilities:** 🅿 💺 & (platform & train access for wheelchairs) toilets for disabled shop 🐾

LUTON
Map 04 TL02
JOHN DONY FIELD CENTRE
Hancock Dr, Bushmead LU2 7SF (signposted from rdbt on A6, at Barnfield College on New Bedford Rd)
☎ 01582 486983   🖷 01582 422805
e-mail: tweent@luton.gov.uk

The John Dony Field Centre is a purpose built study centre for exploring the landscapes, plants and animals of the Luton area. Featuring permanent displays of local archæology, natural history and the management of the local nature reserve, it explains how ancient grasslands and hedgerows are conserved and follows 4000 years of history from Bronze Age to modern times.
Times: Open all year, Mon-Fri 9.30-4.45, Sun 9.30-1. Closed BHs. **Fee:** Free. **Facilities:** 🅿 & toilets for disabled 🐾 (ex guide/hearing dogs)

LUTON MUSEUM & ART GALLERY
Wardown Park, Old Bedford Rd LU2 7HA (Follow brown signs from the town centre & N of Luton)
☎ 01582 546722 & 546739   🖷 01582 546763
e-mail: burgessl@luton.gov.uk

A Victorian mansion, with displays illustrating the natural and cultural history, archæology and industries of the area, including the development of Luton's hat industry, and the Bedfordshire and Hertfordshire Regimental Collections. Due to refurbishment, some galleries may be affected during 2001-2002, telephone 01582 546722 for further details before travelling.
Times: Open all year, Tue-Sat 10-5, Sun 1-5 (Closed Xmas, 1 Jan & Mon). **Fee:** Free. **Facilities:** 🅿 💺 & (parking adjacent to entrance, lift to 1st floor) toilets for disabled shop 🐾 (ex guide dogs & hearing dogs)

STOCKWOOD CRAFT MUSEUM & GARDENS
Stockwood Country Park, Farley Hill LU1 4BH (signposted from M1 junct 10 and from Hitchin, Dunstable, Bedford and from Luton town centre)
☎ 01582 738714 & 546739   🖷 01582 546763
e-mail: burgessl@luton.gov.uk

The Museum is set in period gardens which incorporate the Ian Hamilton Finlay Sculpture Gardens. The Mossman collection of horse-drawn vehicles traces the history of transport from Roman times to the 1940s. Craft demonstrations are held at weekends in the summer. Please telephone for details of special events.
Times: Open all year; Mar-Oct, Tue-Sat 10-5, Sun & BH Mons 10-6; Nov-Mar, weekends 10-4. (closed Xmas & 1 Jan) **Fee:** Free.
Facilities: 🅿 💺 ✕ licensed & (stair lift, parking, induction loop, automatic door) toilets for disabled shop 🐾 (ex guide & hearing dogs)

⛪ OLD WARDEN
Map 04 TL14

THE SHUTTLEWORTH COLLECTION
Old Warden Aerodrome SG18 9EP (2m W from rdbt on
A1, Biggleswade by-pass)
☎ 01767 627288 📠 01767 627745
Times: Open all year, daily 10-4 (3pm Nov-Mar). Closed 10 days at
Xmas, up to and including 1 Jan. **Facilities:** 🅿 ✗ licensed ♿
(passageways between hangars are ramped) toilets for disabled shop
🎋 *Details not confirmed for 2002*

⛪ SANDY
Map 04 TL14

RSPB NATURE RESERVE
The Lodge SG19 2DL (1m E, on B1042 Potton Rd)
☎ 01767 680541 📠 01767 683508
e-mail: jo.davies@rspb.org.uk

The headquarters of the Royal Society for the
Protection of Birds. The house and buildings are not
open to the public, but there are waymarked paths and
formal gardens, and two species of woodpecker,
nuthatches and woodland birds may be seen, as may
muntjac deer. Another feature is the specialist wildlife
garden created in conjunction with the Henry
Doubleday Association.
Times: Open daily dawn-dusk. Visitor Centre 9-5.15. **Fee:** Members
free. Non-members £3.50 (ch 50p, concessions £1.50) Family £6.
Facilities: 🅿 ♿ (partial access) toilets for disabled shop 🎋 (ex guide
dogs) 🍴

⛪ SILSOE
Map 04 TL03

WREST PARK HOUSE & GARDENS
MK45 4HS (0.75 mile E off A6)
☎ 01525 860152

The formal gardens designed over 150 years ago form a
serene and beguiling setting for this elegant 19th-
century mansion.
Times: Open Apr-Sep, wknds & BH's 10-6 (Oct 10-5). Last admission
one hour before closing time. **Fee:** £3.50 (ch 5-15 £1.80, under 5's
free, con £2.60). Personal stereo tour included in price.
Facilities: 🅿 🍴 🎋 (in certain areas) ⛺

⛪ WHIPSNADE
Map 04 TL01

WHIPSNADE WILD ANIMAL PARK
LU6 2LF (signposted from M1 junct 9 & 12)
☎ 01582 872171 📠 01582 872649

Set in 600 acres of countryside, Whipsnade is home to
over 2,500 creatures, and is one of the largest wildlife
conservation centres in Europe. Visitors can see tigers,
elephants, penguins, giraffes, bears, chimps, hippos
and more. Free daily demonstrations include the
Elephant Walk, Birds of the World, sealions and
penguin feeding.
Times: Open all year, daily. (Closed 25 Dec). Telephone 01582 872171
for opening times. **Fee:** £10.70 (ch 3-15, pen & student £8). Car entry
£8.50. **Facilities:** 🅿 (charged) 🍴 ♿ (free entry for disabled cars)
toilets for disabled shop 🎋 🍴

⛪ WOBURN
Map 04 SP93

WOBURN ABBEY
MK17 9WA
☎ 01525 290666 📠 01525 290271
e-mail: enquiries@woburnabbey.co.uk

Standing in 3000 acres of parkland, this palatial 18th-
century mansion was originally a Cistercian Abbey, and
the Dukes of Bedford have lived here since 1547. The
art collection includes works by Canaletto, Rembrandt,
Van Dyck, and Gainsborough. 14 state apartments are
on view, and the private apartments are shown when
not in use. Special events are held during the year,
including a Craft Fair and a De-Havilland Tiger Moth
Fly-In.
Times: Open Jan-25 Mar; Abbey Sat & Sun only 11-4, Deer park 10.30-
3.45; 26 Mar-1 Oct; Abbey weekdays 11-4, Sun & BH 11-5; 2-31 Oct Sat
& Sun only; Deer Park weekdays 10-4.30, Sun & BH 10-4.45.
Fee: Abbey & Deer Park £7.50 (ch over 12yrs £3.00, pen £6.50). Family
ticket £19-£21.50. Deer Park only car & passengers £5. Motorcycles &
passengers £2. **Facilities:** 🅿 🍴 ✗ licensed ♿ (wheelchairs
accommodated by prior arrangement) toilets for disabled shop 🎋 🍴

WOBURN SAFARI PARK
Woburn Park MK17 9QN (Signposted from M1 junct 13)
☎ 01525 290407 📠 01525 290489
e-mail: wobsafari@aol.com

Set in the 3000 acres of parkland belonging to Woburn
Abbey, Woburn Safari Park has an extensive collection
of many species. The safari road passes through an
African plains area stocked with eland, zebra, hippo
and rhino, then through well-keepered tiger and lion
enclosures and on past bears and monkeys. Animal
encounters, sea lion and parrot shows, and elephant
displays, are all popular attractions. The large leisure
complex also offers a boating lake, adventure
playgrounds, railway train, walk-through aviary,
squirrel monkey exhibit and 'the Australian Walkabout',
with friendly wallabies.
Times: Open daily, 10 Mar-28 Oct, 10-5. **Fee:** £12.50 (ch3-17 £9, pen
£9.50). Ch under 3 free. From 21Jul-3Sep prices increase by extra 50p
during Bedfordshire School Holidays) **Facilities:** 🅿 ✗ licensed ♿
toilets for disabled shop 🎋 (guide dogs-leisure area,book) 🍴

Berkshire

Berkshire is a narrow county of wide variety, reaching from the edge of London on its eastern boundary to the relative isolation of the Lambourn Downs in the west, containing towns as diverse as Reading and Hungerford, Newbury and Windsor.

Waterways play an important part in Berkshire's character and history, not least the River Thames which forms the county's border with Oxfordshire. The Kennet, a tributary of the Thames that was partially converted into the Kennet and Avon Canal, had a major role in the growth and success of both Reading and Newbury, and flows the length of the county from Reading until it peters out somewhere in Wiltshire. Both of these rivers, as well as The Bourne and the River Pang, flow through some of England's prettiest countryside. The charm of these scenes has been preserved in one of Britain's best-loved children's books. Kenneth Graham used the river banks around Cookham as the setting for *The Wind in the Willows* in 1908. Cookham is also known as the birthplace of eccentric artist, Sir Stanley Spencer (1891-1959), whose work includes Christ Carrying the Cross and various religious murals. His birthplace and a gallery of his work are in the town.

Reading is the largest and liveliest town in Berkshire and has played an important role in the county's history. The town was founded by the Saxons and its 12th-century abbey was once a major pilgrimage site. Alfred defeated a Viking invasion nearby, and the town was also the home of the English Parliament for a while. During the Industrial era Reading was famous for Bacon, Biscuits and Beer – The Three B's, and the Huntley & Palmer biscuit factory can still be seen among the new office blocks and apartments near the centre of town.

Top: Bisham Church

⚒ BASILDON
Map 04 SU67

BASILDON PARK
Lower Basildon RG8 9NR (7m NW of Reading on W side of A329)
☎ 0118 984 3040 📠 0118 984 1267
e-mail: tbdgan@smtp.ntrust.org.uk

This 18th-century house, built of Bath stone, fell into decay in the 20th century, but has been beautifully restored by Lord and Lady Iliffe. The classical front has a splendid central portico and pavilions, and inside there are delicate plasterwork decorations on the walls and ceilings. The Octagon drawing room has fine pictures and furniture, and there is a small formal garden.
Times: House open Apr-Nov, Wed-Fri 1-5.30; Sat, Sun & BH Mon 1-5.30 (Closed Good Fri). Park & garden Apr-4 Nov, 12-5.30.
Fee: House & grounds £4.30, family ticket £10.50; Grounds only £1.80, family ticket £4.50. **Facilities:** 🅿 ✖ licensed ⅰ (driven buggy) toilets for disabled shop ⅰ (ex on lead in grounds) ⅰ

BEALE PARK
Lower Basildon RG8 9NH (Exit M4 Junct 12, follow brown tourist signs to Pangbourne, A329 toward Oxford)
☎ 0118 984 5172 📠 0118 984 5171
e-mail: bealepark.bun.co.uk

Beale Park's late eccentric owner, Gilbert Beale was so fond of Indian peacocks that by the time of his death in 1967, there were over 300 of them on the site. Today the park specialises in the captive breeding of rare birds. A new owlery is under construction, and there are meerkats and wild boar to be seen, plus there is the chance to ride on the steam railway.
Times: Open Mar-Dec. **Fee:** £4.50 (ch under 3 & disabled ch free, ch 3-16 £3, stu, disabled adult & helper £2.25 pen £3.50). Family (2ad+2ch) £13, (1ad+3ch) £12. **Facilities:** 🅿 ⅰ ⅰ (wheelchair available, parking) toilets for disabled shop ⅰ (ex guide dogs)

⚒ ETON
Map 04 SU97

DORNEY COURT
Dorney SL4 6QP (signposted from M4 junct 7, via B3026)
☎ 01628 604638 📠 01628 665772
e-mail: palmer@dorneycourt.co.uk

An enchanting brick and timber manor house (c1440) in a tranquil setting. With tall Tudor chimneys and a splendid great hall, it has been the home of the present family since 1510.
Times: Open BH Mons in May; Sun 1.30-4.30. Aug every afternoon ex Sat 1.30-4.30. **Fee:** £5 (ch £3, under 9's free). **Facilities:** 🅿 ⅰ garden centre ⅰ (ex guide dogs)

⚒ MAIDENHEAD
Map 04 SU88

COURAGE SHIRE HORSE CENTRE
Cherry Garden Ln, Maidenhead Thicket SL6 3QD (off A4 0.5m W of A4/A423/A423M jct)
☎ 01628 824848 📠 01628 828472
Times: Open Mar-Oct, daily 10.30-5. Last admission 4pm.
Facilities: 🅿 ⅰ ✖ ⅰ (wheelchair available) toilets for disabled shop
Details not confirmed for 2002 🚩

⚒ NEWBURY
Map 04 SU46

WEST BERKSHIRE MUSEUM
The Wharf RG14 5AS (from London take M4 junct 13, then Southbound on A34 for 3m, follow signs for town centre.
☎ 01635 30511 📠 01635 38535
e-mail: heritage@westberks.gov.uk
Times: Open all year: Apr-Sep, Mon-Fri (Wed during school hols only) 10-5, Sat 10-4.30. Oct-Mar, Mon-Sat (Wed during school hols only) 10-4. (Closed Sun & BHs). **Facilities:** 🅿 (15yds) ⅰ shop ⅰ (ex guide dogs) *Details not confirmed for 2002*

⚒ READING
Map 04 SU77

MUSEUM OF ENGLISH RURAL LIFE
University of Reading, Whiteknights Park RG6 6AG (2m SE on A327)
☎ 0118 931 8660 📠 0118 975 1264
e-mail: info@rhc.ac.uk
Times: Open all year, Tue-Sat, 10-1 & 2-4.30. (Closed BH's & Xmas-New Year). **Facilities:** 🅿 ⅰ shop ⅰ *Details not confirmed for 2002*

THE MUSEUM OF READING
The Town Hall, Blagrave St RG1 1QH
☎ 0118 939 9800 📠 0118 939 9881
Times: Open all year, Tue-Sat 10-5, Sun & BH 2-5. **Facilities:** 🅿 (200m) ⅰ ✖ licensed ⅰ (lifts parking space) toilets for disabled shop ⅰ (ex guide dogs) *Details not confirmed for 2002* 🚩

⚒ RISELEY
Map 04 SU76

WELLINGTON COUNTRY PARK
RG7 1SP (signposted off A33, between Reading & Basingstoke)
☎ 0118 932 6444 📠 0118 932 6445

350 acres of woodland and meadows, set around a lake in peaceful countryside. There is a collection of farm animals, a deer park and a miniature railway. You can also fish and boat on the 35-acre lake. Attractions also include crazy golf, an adventure playground and a new sandpit.
Times: Open all year Mar-Oct, daily 10-5.30, Nov-Feb wknds 10-4.30.
Fee: £4.30 (ch £2.20) **Facilities:** 🅿 ⅰ ⅰ (fishing platform & nature trail for disabled) toilets for disabled shop 🚩

⚒ WINDSOR
Map 04 SU97

FROGMORE HOUSE
Home Park SL4 1NJ (entrance from B3021 between Datchet & Old Windsor)
☎ 01753 831118 (recorded info)
🖥 01753 832290

The present building dates back to 1618, and residents have included Charles II's architect, Hugh May, who built it, Queen Charlotte, Queen Victoria and Queen Mary. An original mural, discovered only recently during redecoration, can be seen on the stairway.
Times: Open Tue-Thu 7 Aug-27 Sep (pre-booked tours only).
Fee: Tours £6.50. **Facilities:** shop ⚹ 🍴

HOUSEHOLD CAVALRY MUSEUM
Combermere Barracks, St Leonards Rd SL4 3DN
☎ 01753 755203
Times: Open all year Mon-Fri (ex BH) 9-12.30 & 2-4.30. **Facilities:** ♿ shop ⚹ *Details not confirmed for 2002*

LEGOLAND WINDSOR
Winkfield Rd SL4 4AY (on B3022 Windsor to Ascot road well signposted from M3 junct 3 & M4 junct 6)
☎ 08705 040404 🖥 01753 626300
e-mail: www.legoland.co.uk

Set in 150 acres of Windsor Great Park, Legoland Windsor offers over 40 hands-on activities, with rides, themed playscapes and more Lego bricks that you would ever dream possible. The cities of Europe, recreated in Lego, can be seen in Miniland.
Times: Open daily 10 Mar-4 Nov (Closed 11-12, 18-19 & 25-26 Sep 2-3, 9-10, & 16-17Oct). **Fee:** £18.50 (ch 3-15, £15.50, pen £12.50) Groups 20+. Tickets can be booked in advance by telephoning 08705 040404. **Facilities:** 🅿 🍴 ✗ licensed ♿ (signing staff, wheelchairs, parking) toilets for disabled shop ⚹ (ex guide dogs) 🍴

ST GEORGE'S CHAPEL
SL4 1NJ (M4 junct 6 & M3 junct 3)
☎ 01753 865538 🖥 01753 620165

Begun in 1475 by Edward IV, and completed in the reign of Henry VIII, the chapel is a fine example of Perpendicular architecture, with large windows adding to the effect of light and spaciousness. The fan vaulting on the ceiling is magnificent, and the chantries and intricate carving on the choir stalls all add to this superb building.
Times: Open Mon-Sat 10-4. (Closed 26 & 27 Apr, 16-19 Jun, 24-25 Dec & occasionally at short notice). Closed Sun worshippers very welcome. **Fee:** Free entry to the Chapel is included in the price of entry to Windsor Castle. **Facilities:** ♿ shop ⚹

SAVILL GARDEN (WINDSOR GREAT PARK)
Wick Ln, Englefield Green TW20 0UU (Signposted off A30 between Egham & Virginia Water)
☎ 01753 847518 🖥 01753 847536
e-mail: savillgarden@crownestate.org.uk

The magnificent 35-acre garden lies within Windsor Great Park. It has spectacular woodland displays in spring, sweeping herbaceous borders in summer, fiery autumn colours and misty winter vistas. The garden's temperate house is a year-round delight.
Times: Open all year, daily 10-6 (10-4 Nov -Feb). (Closed 25-26 Dec).
Fee: £5 (ch 6-16 £2, pen £4.50) Apr & May; £4 (ch 6-16 £1, pen £3.50) Jun-Oct; £3 (ch 6-16 £1, pen £2.50) Nov-Mar. Ch 1-5 free. Party 10+.
Facilities: 🅿 🍴 ✗ licensed ♿ (wheelchairs available) toilets for disabled shop garden centre (ex guide dogs) 🍴

WINDSOR CASTLE
SL4 1NJ (M4 junct 6 & M3 junct 3)
☎ 01753 831118 🖥 01753 832290
e-mail: windsorcastle@royalcollection.org.uk

Covering 13 acres, this is the official residence of HM The Queen and the largest inhabited castle in the world. Begun as a wooden fort by William the Conqueror, it has been added to by almost every monarch since. The Upper Ward includes the State Apartments, magnificently restored following the fire of 1992, and the Lower Ward where St George's Chapel is situated. The Doll's House designed for Queen Mary in the 1920s by Lutyens, is also on display.
Times: Open all year, daily except Good Friday & 25-26 Dec. Nov-Feb 10-4 (last admission 3), Mar-Oct 10-5.30 (last admission 4). As Windsor Castle is a royal residence the opening arrangements may be subject to change at short notice. **Fee:** £11 (ch 17 £5.50, under 5's free, over 60's £9) Family ticket £27.50 (2ad+2ch). **Facilities:** 🅿 (400yds) ♿ (ramps) toilets for disabled shop ⚹ (ex guide dogs) 🍴

Bristol

Bristol was once one of the South of England's major ports but is now perhaps better known for its contributions to contemporary art and music. It is an ancient city with a modern outlook, and centuries of history are waiting, ready to be explored by the curious visitor.

For centuries ships sailed from Bristol to every part of the known world in search of new produce and markets, opening up international trade routes. In 1497 John Cabot (Giovanni Caboto), a Genoese pilot set sail from Bristol and within months had discovered North America. Four centuries later the Cabot Tower was built in commemoration. In 1843 Brunel launched his SS Great Britain, the largest iron ship then built. She now sits, rescued and restored, in the dock where she was constructed.

Clifton Suspension Bridge is 702ft (214m) long and spans the Avon gorge, which is over 200 ft (60m)deep. The Bridge was designed by Isombard Kingdom Brunel and took a while to build. Work started in 1836, but due to financial problems was not completed until 1864, five years after Brunel had died. The bridge remains a fitting monument to Victorian engineering.

The city's cathedral was founded as an Augustinian monastery and contains examples of Norman, early-English, Gothic and Victorian architecture. Other important church buildings include St Mary Redcliffe, which was built in the Middle Ages and carries a massive tower with a 285ft (87m) spire.

Post-war rebuilding of the blitz-damaged city centre has meant that Bristol's current identity is less defined by its history than by its recent contributions to popular culture and art. Redevelopment of the disused dockland has led to the creation of art spaces such as the Arnolfini and the Watershed, which are at the forefront of uncovering new talent.

EVENTS & FESTIVALS

May
6th North Somerset Show, Ashton Court Estate, Long Ashton
tbc Bristol Motor & Classic Car Show, Ashton Court Estate, Long Ashton

July
6th St Pauls Carnival, St Pauls, Bristol
27th-28th Bristol Harbour Regatta (provisional)
tbc Bristol Community Festival, Ashton Court Estate, Long Ashton

August
8th-11th Bristol Balloon Fiesta, Ashton Court Estate, Long Ashton
tbc Bristol Flower Show, The Downs

September
7th-8th International Kite Festival, Ashton Court Estate, Long Ashton

October
6th Bristol Half Marathon (provisional)
3rd-30th Poetry Festival, various venues in Bristol

November
tbc Firework Fiesta, Durdham Downs, Bristol
tbc Christmas lights switch on, Bristol city centre

Top: Clifton Suspension Bridge

🏛 BRISTOL   Map 03 ST57

ARNOLFINI
16 Narrow Quay BS1 4QA
☎ 0117 929 9191   📄 0117 925 3872
e-mail: arnolfini@arnolfini.demon.co.uk

Arnolfini is one of Europe's leading centres for
contemporary art, presenting new and innovative work
in the visual arts, performance, dance and film.
Times: Open Mon-Wed, Fri-Sat 10-7, Thu 10-9, Sun & BH's 12-7.
(Closed Xmas) **Fee:** Admission to galleries free. Charge made for
cinema and performances. **Facilities:** 🅿 5mins walk 🍷 ✕ licensed &
toilets for disabled shop 🎡 (ex guide dogs) 🍴

@ BRISTOL
Anchor Rd, Harbourside BS1 5DB (from city centre, A4
to Anchor Rd. Located on left opposite Cathedral)
☎ 0845 345 1235   📄 0117 915 7200
e-mail: information@at-bristol.org.uk

A new leisure complex that brings science and nature
to life. It comprises three world-class attractions:
Explore, Wildwalk, and an IMAX Theatre. Explore: an
interactive journey through science, nature and the
human brain and body. Wildwalk: a walk through a
living rainforest, guided by multimedia technologies,
and, the four storeys high, IMAX Theatre.
Times: Open all year, daily 10-6. (Closed 25 Dec). **Fee:** Ticket for 3
attractions £15.50 (ch £11, concessions £13). Family ticket £50.
Facilities: 🅿 (charged) 🍷 ✕ licensed & toilets for disabled shop 🎡
(ex guide dogs) 🍴

BLAISE CASTLE HOUSE MUSEUM
Henbury Rd, Henbury BS10 7QS (off B4057)
☎ 0117 950 6789   📄 0117 959 3475
e-mail: general-museum@bristol-city.gov.uk
Times: Open Apr-Oct, Sat-Wed, 10-5. **Facilities:** 🅿 & shop 🎡
Details not confirmed for 2002

BRISTOL CITY MUSEUM & ART GALLERY
Queen's Rd BS8 1RL
☎ 0117 922 3571   📄 0117 922 2047
e-mail: general-museum@bristol-city.gov.uk
Times: Open all year, daily 10-5. **Facilities:** 🅿 (NCP 400 yds) 🍷 &
(lift) toilets for disabled shop 🎡 *Details not confirmed for 2002*

BRISTOL INDUSTRIAL MUSEUM
Prince's Wharf, Prince St, City Docks BS1 4RN
☎ 0117 925 1470   📄 0117 729 7318
e-mail: general-museum@bristol-city.gov.uk
Times: Open Apr-Oct, Sat-Wed 10-5; Nov-Mar, Sat & Sun 10-5.
Facilities: 🅿 (charged) & toilets for disabled shop 🎡 *Details not
confirmed for 2002*

BRISTOL ZOO GARDENS
Clifton BS8 3HA (Follow brown signs)
☎ 0117 973 8951   📄 0117 973 6814
e-mail: information@bristolzoo.org.uk

Over 300 species of wildlife in beautiful gardens. Seal
and Penguin Coasts with underwater viewing join
favourites such as Gorilla Island, Bug World, Twilight

World and Reptile House. There is a 'hands-on' Activity
Centre, special events and feeding time talks.
Times: Open all year, daily (ex 25 Dec) from 9am. Closing times
approx 5.30pm (summer) 4.30pm (winter). **Fee:** £8.40 (ch 3-14 £4.80,
pen £7.40). Party. **Facilities:** 🅿 (charged) ✕ licensed & (wheelchairs
for use in zoo grounds) toilets for disabled shop 🎡 🍴

GEORGIAN HOUSE
7 Great George St, off Park St BS1 5RR
☎ 0117 921 1362   📄 0117 922 2047
e-mail: general-museum@bristol-city.gov.uk
Times: Open Apr-Oct, Sat-Wed, 10-5. **Facilities:** 🅿 🎡 *Details not
confirmed for 2002*

HARVEYS WINE MUSEUM
12 Denmark St BS1 5DQ (City Centre)
☎ 0117 927 5036   📄 0117 927 5001

Explore a world of wine at Harveys 13th-century
cellars, and discover the delights of tasting from a
range of sherries, ports, wines and champagnes.
Times: Open all year **Fee:** Open to pre-booked parties only
Facilities: 🅿 (5 mins walk) (parking meters) ✕ licensed shop 🎡 🍴

JOHN WESLEY'S CHAPEL(THE NEW ROOM)
36 The Horsefair, Broadmead BS1 3JE (M32 towards
Broadmead) ☎ 0117 926 4740

The oldest Methodist chapel in the world, built in 1739
and extended in 1748. Above the chapel are the
preacher's rooms where John Wesley, Charles Wesley
and the early Methodist preachers stayed.
Times: Open all year, Mon-Sat 10-4. **Fee:** Free. **Facilities:** 🅿 (250yds)
🍷 & shop 🎡 (ex guide dogs) 🍴

MARITIME HERITAGE CENTRE
Gas Ferry Rd BS1 6UN (follow brown signs 'Anchor')
☎ 0117 926 0680   📄 0117 925 5788
e-mail: commerical@ss-great-britain.com

Exploring 200 years of Bristol shipbuilding, with special
reference to Charles Hill & Son, and their predecessor,
James Hillhouse. At the Great Western Dock the
museum forms part of the *SS Great Britain* and John
Cabot's *Matthew* experience.
Times: Open all year, daily 10-5.30, 4.30 in winter. (Closed 24 & 25
Dec). **Fee:** Admission is for the museum, the SS Great Britain & the
Matthew £6.25 (ch £3.75, pen £5.25). Family ticket (2 adults & 2 ch)
£16.50. Party 20+. **Facilities:** 🅿 (charged) 🍷 & toilets for disabled
shop 🎡 (ex guide dogs) 🍴

SS GREAT BRITAIN
Great Western Dock, Gas Ferry Rd BS1 6TY
☎ 0117 926 0680   📄 0117 925 5788
Times: Open all year daily 10-5.30, 4.30 in winter. (Closed 24 & 25
Dec). **Facilities:** 🅿 (charged) 🍷 & shop 🎡 *Details not confirmed
for 2002* 🍴

Buckinghamshire

Visitors to Buckinghamshire cannot fail to be enchanted by the majestic sweep of the Chiltern Hills, and fascinated by the history and heritage of the county's many attractive towns and villages.

Richly wooded in the west but mainly windswept and bare near Ivinghoe in the east, the Chilterns extend in a line from Goring in the Thames Valley, across the breadth of Buckinghamshire, to a point near Hitchin in Hertfordshire. Its highest point is the 835ft Coombe Hill near Wendover, which is also the site of a Boer War memorial. Many of the chalk downs are crowned with ancient beech groves. Walkers can get to grips with the Chilterns by walking the North Bucks Way – 30 miles from Wolverton to Chequers near Great Missenden.

Chequers Court plays an important role as the official country residence of the British Prime Minister. It was given to the nation by Lord Lee of Fareham in 1921. The building was constructed in the 16th century, sits in 1,000 acres of farms and woodland, and fittingly, contains some valuable Cromwellian relics.

Buckinghamshire is famous for its pretty villages and any one of them would make a visit here worthwhile. Not only are they pretty, but many have strong historical connections. Jordan is the site of the most famous of all Quaker Meeting Houses, which was built in 1688. British Prime Minister Benjamin Disraeli lived at Hughenden Manor in Hughenden; John Milton, author of *Paradise Lost*, lived in a cottage near Chalfont St Giles; Florence Nightingale lived at Claydon House near Buckingham; and jazz couple Johnny Dankworth and Cleo Laine live at Wavedon.

Top: Bletchley Park, HQ of the Enigma code-breaking operation in WWII

EVENTS & FESTIVALS

February
Shrove Tuesday Olney Pancake Day Race

April
6th-7th April Stowe Kite Festival, Stowe Park, Buckingham (provisional)

May
4th-5th Marlow Spring Regatta, Marlow
4th-5th Milton Keynes Garden Show

June
2nd Coombe Hill Run, Wendover
tbc Milton Keynes City Spectacular & Carnival,
tbc Milton Keynes International Festival

July
6th North Bucks Show, Stowe Park, Buckingham (provisional)
tbc Buckingham Festival
tbc Music & Fireworks, Stowe Park, Buckingham
tbc Street Children Festival, Higginson Park, Marlow

August
29th Bucks County Show, Weedon Park, Aylesbury
tbc Music & Fireworks, Stowe Park, Buckingham

September
8th Thames Valley Grand Prix Raft Race, Marlow
21st Marlow Carnival, Marlow

November
tbc Milton Keynes Free Firework Display

🏛 BEACONSFIELD   Map 04 SU99
BEKONSCOT MODEL VILLAGE
Warwick Rd HP9 2PL (2.7m M40 junc 2, 4m M25 junc 16)
☎ 01494 672919 🖹 01494 675284
e-mail: bekonscot@dial.pipex.com

A miniature world, depicting rural England in the 1930s. A Gauge 1 model railway meanders through six little villages, each with their own tiny population. **Times:** Mid Feb-end Oct daily 10-5. **Fee:** £4.50 (ch £2.75, pen & students £3.50). Party 13+. **Facilities:** 🅿 🍴 🚻 (wheelchair loan) toilets for disabled shop 🕨 (ex guide dogs) 🍽

🏛 CHALFONT ST GILES   Map 04 SU99
CHILTERN OPEN AIR MUSEUM
Newland Park, Gorelands Ln HP8 4AB (M25 junct 17, M40 junct 2. Follow brown signs)
☎ 01494 871117 & 875542 🖹 01494 872774

Saved from demolition and moved brick by brick to Newland Park, this collection of old buildings includes barns, granaries and even a tin chapel. Step back in time and get a feel of the 1940s in a fully furnished Prefab, or experience 50AD at the Iron Age House. Demonstrations including brick making, rug making, blacksmithing and storytelling. Regular living history re-enactments. **Times:** Open Apr-29 Oct, daily 10-5. **Fee:** £5.50 (ch 5-16 £3, concessions £4.50) Family ticket (2 adults & 2 ch) £15. **Facilities:** 🅿 🍴 🚻 (Braille guide books & taped guides available, wheelchairs) toilets for disabled shop 🕨 (ex on lead) 🍽

MILTON'S COTTAGE
Dean Way HP8 4JH (0.5m W of A413. 3m N of M40 junct 2)
☎ 01494 872313
e-mail: pbirger@clara.net

A timber-framed, 16th-century cottage, with a charming garden, the only surviving home in which John Milton lived and worked. He completed Paradise Lost and started Paradise Regained here. First editions of these works are among the many rare books and artefacts on display. **Times:** Open Mar-Oct, Tue-Sun 10-1 & 2-6. Also open Spring & Summer BH. **Fee:** £2.50 (ch 15 £1). Party 20 or over £2 each. **Facilities:** 🅿 ✕ licensed 🚻 (special parking area closer to cottage) shop 🕨 (ex guide dogs)

🏛 CLIVEDEN   Map 04 SU98
CLIVEDEN
SL6 0JA (2m N of Taplow)
☎ 01628 605069 🖹 01628 669461
e-mail: tclest@smtp.ntrust.org.uk

The 375 acres of garden and woodland overlook the River Thames, and include a magnificent parterre, topiary, lawns with box hedges, and rose and water

gardens. The palatial house, home of the Astors, is now a hotel, The Great Hall and French Dining Room can be visited on certain afternoons. **Times:** Open Grounds 15 Mar-31 Oct daily 11-6, Nov-Dec daily 11-4 (Woodlands open all year 11-6). House Apr-Oct, Thu & Sun 3-6 by timed ticket. (Last admission 5.30) **Fee:** Grounds: £5. House: £1 extra. Family ticket £12.50. **Facilities:** 🅿 ✕ licensed 🚻 powered vehicle & wheelchairs available, parking near house toilets for disabled shop 🕨 (ex in woodland) 🐾 🍽

🏛 HIGH WYCOMBE   Map 04 SU89
WYCOMBE LOCAL HISTORY & CHAIR MUSEUM
Castle Hill House, Priory Av HP13 6PX (signposted by brown tourism sign from A404 (Amersham Hill) N of High Wycombe town centre)
☎ 01494 421895 🖹 01494 421897
e-mail: enquiries@
wycombemuseum.demon.co.uk

Situated in an 18th-century house, set in attractive grounds. The displays explore the history of the Wycombe area, focusing on the chair making industry, with interactive displays, and changing exhibitions. **Times:** Open all year, Mon-Sat 10-5, Sun 2-5. Closed on BHs except special events - ring for details. **Fee:** Free. **Facilities:** 🅿 🍴 🚻 (large print guides, special parking/drop off point) toilets for disabled shop 🕨 (ex guide dogs)

🏛 HUGHENDEN   Map 04 SU89
HUGHENDEN MANOR
HP14 4LA (1.5m N of High Wycombe, on W side of A4128)
☎ 01494 755573 🖹 01494 463310
Times: House open 1-30 Mar, Sat & Sun only. Apr-Oct, Wed-Sun & BH Mon 1-5. Last admission 4.30. Gardens same dates as house 12-5. Park open all year. (closed on Good Friday) **Facilities:** 🅿 ✕ licensed 🚻 (braille leaflet and taped guide) toilets for disabled shop 🕨 (ex in park & car park only) 🐾 *Details not confirmed for 2002*

🏛 LONG CRENDON   Map 04 SP60
COURTHOUSE
HP18 9AN (2m N of Thame, via B4011)
☎ 01494 528051 🖹 01494 463310

Probably built as a wool store in the early 1400s, but also used as a manorial courthouse until the late 19th century, this timber-framed building stands out, even in this picturesque village. Although the windows and doors have been altered and the chimney stack is Tudor, the magnificent timber roof is original. **Times:** Open, Upper storey Apr-Sep, Wed 2-6, Sat, Sun & BH Mons 11-6. **Fee:** £1. **Facilities:** 🅿 (street) 🕨 🐾

🏛 MIDDLE CLAYDON   Map 04 SP72
CLAYDON HOUSE
MK18 2EY (Off A413 in Padbury, follow National Trust signs. Entrance by north drive only).
☎ 01296 730349   🖷 01296 738511
e-mail: tcdgen@smtp.ntrust.org.uk

The rather sober exterior of this 18th-century house gives no clue to the extravagances that lie inside, in the form of fantastic rococo carvings. Ceilings, cornices, walls and overmantels are adorned with delicately carved fruits, birds, beasts and flowers by Luke Lightfoot. The Chinese room is particularly splendid.
Times: Open Apr-4 Nov, Sat-Wed 1-5pm (Closed Thu & Good Fri). Last admission 4.30pm. **Fee:** £4.30 (ch £2.15) Family ticket £10.50. **Facilities:** 🅿 💺 ✗ ♿ (Braille guide) toilets for disabled 🍴 (ex guide dogs or in park) 🐾

🏛 QUAINTON   Map 04 SP72
BUCKINGHAMSHIRE RAILWAY CENTRE
Quainton Rd Station HP22 4BY (Off A41 Aylesbury to Bicester Road. 7m NW of Aylesbury)
☎ 01296 655720 & 655450 (info)
🖷 01296 655720

The Centre houses an interesting and varied collection of about 20 locomotives with 40 carriages and wagons from places as far afield as South Africa, Egypt and America. Items date from the 1800s up to the 1960s. Visitors can take a ride on full-size and miniature steam trains and stroll around the 20-acre site to see locomotives and rolling stock. The Centre runs locomotive driving courses for visitors. Regular 'days out with Thomas' events take place throughout the year.
Times: Open with engines in steam Apr-Oct, Sun & BH Mon; Jul-Aug, Wed; 10.30-5.30. Dec Sat & Sun Santa's Magical Steamings-advanced booking recommended. Also open for static viewing Sun, Nov & Mar 11-4 & Sat, Apr-Oct 11-4. **Fee:** Steaming Days; £4 (ch & pen £3). Family ticket £12. BH wknds £5 (ch & pen £4). Family ticket £15. Static viewing; £2.50 (ch & pen £1.50). **Facilities:** 🅿 💺 ♿ toilets for disabled shop 🛍

🏛 STOWE   Map 04 SP63
STOWE GARDENS
MK18 5EH (3m NW of Buckingham)
☎ 01280 822850   🖷 01280 822437
e-mail: tstejw@smtp.ntrust.org.uk

One of the supreme creations of the Georgian era, the first, formal layout was adorned with buildings by Vanbrugh, Kent and Gibbs. In the 1730s Kent designed the Elysian Fields in a more naturalistic style, and it's one of the earliest examples of the reaction against formality, which lead to the evolution of the landscape garden.
Times: Open 3 Mar-28 Oct (closed 26 May), Wed-Sun, 10-5.30, last admission 4; 1-23 Dec, Wed-Sun, last admission 3. Open all BH Mons. **Fee:** £4.60 (ch £2.30). Family ticket £11.50 **Facilities:** 🅿 ✗ licensed ♿ (manual wheelchairs unsuitable,powered batricars available) toilets for disabled shop 🐾

STOWE HOUSE
MK18 5EH (From London M1 to Milton Keynes. 3m NW Buckingham)
☎ 01280 818282   🖷 01280 818186
e-mail: sses@stowe.co.uk

Set in the National Trust's landscaped gardens, Stowe is a splendid 18th-century mansion. The leading designers of the day were called in to lay out the gardens, and leading architects - Vanbrugh, Gibbs, Kent and Leoni - commissioned to decorate them with garden temples. The house is now a major public school.
Times: Open 8 Jul-Aug, Wed & Thu 2-5. Fri-Sun 10-1. 14-23 Dec Fri & Sat 10-1. Please tel for further details on group bookings and other dates. **Fee:** £3 (ch £1.50). **Facilities:** 🅿 ♿ toilets for disabled shop 🍴 (ex guide dogs)

🏛 WADDESDON   Map 04 SP71
WADDESDON MANOR
HP18 OJH (gates off A41, 6m NW of Aylesbury)
☎ 01296 653211, 653226 & 653203
🖷 01296 653212
e-mail: twmsep@smtp.ntrust.org.uk

This French Renaissance-style château was built in the 1870s for Baron Ferdinand de Rothschild. It houses one of the world's finest collections of French 18th-century decorative arts: Savonnerie carpets, Sèvres porcelain, Beauvais tapestries and furniture, as well as important portraits by Gainsborough and Reynolds and works by

contd.

17th-century Dutch and Flemish masters. The wine cellars and the garden with its Rococo-style aviary, shrubberies and woodland are also open to the public. **Times:** Open, Grounds & Aviary only, Mar-23 Dec, Wed-Sun & BH Mon 10-5. House 28 Mar-4 Nov, Wed-Sun & BH Mon 11-4. Entrance by timed ticket. **Fee:** Grounds & Aviary £3 (ch £1.50). Family ticket £7.50. 7 Nov-23 Dec free. House - £7 (ch £6). Tickets bookable in advance at booking charge of £3 per transaction (tel 01296 653226). **Facilities:** ☐ ✗ licensed ⅙ (wheelchairs available, braille guide, parking) toilets for disabled shop ⚱ (ex guide dogs in grounds) ⚘ ◥

⬛ WEST WYCOMBE   Map 04 SU89
West Wycombe Caves
HP14 3AJ (on A40)
☎ 01494 524411 (office) & 533739 (caves)
▤ 01494 471617
Times: Open all year, Mar-Oct, daily 11-6; Nov-Feb, Sat & Sun 1-5.
Facilities: ☐ ⚱ ⅙ toilets for disabled shop garden centre ⚱ (ex guide dogs) *Details not confirmed for 2002*

West Wycombe Park
HP14 3AJ (S of A40)
☎ 01628 488675
Times: Open, House & grounds Jun-Aug, Sun-Thu 2-6. Grounds only Apr-end May, Sun & Wed 2-6 & Etr, May Day & Spring BH Sun & Mon 2-6. Last admission 5.15. Entry by timed tickets on wkdays. Parties must book in advance. **Facilities:** ☐ ⅙ (partial access to ground floor & gardens) ⚱ (ex on lead in car park) ⚘ *Details not confirmed for 2002*

⬛ WING   Map 04 SP82
Ascott
LU7 0PS (0.5m E of Wing, 3m SW of Leighton Buzzard on S side of A418)
☎ 01296 688242 ▤ 01296 681904
e-mail: info@ascottestate.co.uk

A National Trust property since 1946, Ascott holds an exceptional collection of paintings, Chinese porcelain and English and French furniture. The 30-acre garden is a fine example of Victorian gardening and the grounds are stunning at any time of year.
Times: House & Gardens: 24 Apr-23 May, 7 Aug-14 Sep daily 2-6 (ex Mon). Gardens: 30 May-1 Aug every Wed & last Sun in month & 19 & 26 Sep 2-6. **Fee:** House & Garden £5.60 (ch £2.80). Gardens only: £4 (ch £2). National Trust members free. **Facilities:** ☐ ⅙ (wheelchairs available, all parts accessible with assistance) toilets for disabled ⚱ ⚘

Cambridgeshire

The City of Cambridge is the place that most visitors will want to visit most, and who can blame them? Its ancient colleges, air of learning and rich history are guaranteed to be of interest to anyone looking for a special taste of England, yet there is much more to the county.

Much of Cambridgeshire is unspoilt and ideal for exploration. Many of the peat-black Fens have been reclaimed over the centuries, and beautiful rivers such as the Ouse and the Nene, as well as miles of canal, are great for those looking for relaxation. 605 acres of undrained fenland at Wicken Fen are run by the National Trust as a nature reserve.

Walkers are well catered for, with over 3,000 miles of public footpaths to explore. Routes include the Fen Rivers Way, the Nene Way, and the Hereward Way. This latter covers 43 miles of lowland, and is named after Hereward, who made a brave stand against Norman conquest in 1071.

But Cambridgeshire isn't all peace and quiet. Peterborough has modern arcades as well as lots of old streets that have been pedestrianised. Huntingdon, Ely, Wisbech, St Neots and St Ives have all retained something of the atmosphere of the English market town, complete with family-run shops and busy market days.

The county also has connections with historical figures. Katherine of Aragon is buried in Peterborough cathedral, Wisbech is home to the Octavia Hill Birth place Museum, commemorating the life and work of one of the founders of the National Trust, and Oliver Cromwell was born in Huntingdon.

A forgotten chapter in the county's history concerns Coprolite-digging, "the extraction of phosphatised clay nodules for fertiliser" which caused a "coprolite rush" between 1850 and 1890.

Top: The Folly, Wimpole Park

EVENTS & FESTIVALS

January
12th Whittlesey Straw Bear Festival

March
16th-17th National Shire Horse Show, Peterborough
23rd-24th Daffodil Weekend, Thriplow

May
6th Stilton Cheese Rolling
10th-12th St Neots Folk Festival (provisional)
tbc Duxford Air Show

June
1st Strawberry Fair, Cambridge (provisional)
14th-16th East of England Show, Peterborough
29th-30th Hemingford Abbots Open Gardens & Flower Festival Weekend
tbc Charles Wells Cambridge Folk Festival, Cambridge
tbc Children's Festival Family Day, Jesus Green, Cambridge

July
4th-8th Wisbech Rose Fair
13th World Pea Shooting Championships, Ely (provisional)
tbc Ely Folk Week, Ely

August
1st-24th Cambridge Shakespeare Festival
20th-25th Peterborough Beer Festival

September
tbc Duxford Air Show

October
13th The World Conker Championships, Peterboro'

🏛 CAMBRIDGE   Map 05 TL45

CAMBRIDGE & COUNTY FOLK MUSEUM
2/3 Castle St CB3 0AQ (Turn off A14 on A3019,
museum NW of town)
☎ 01223 355159   📄 01223 576301
e-mail: info@folkmuseum.org.uk

This timber-framed inn houses items covering the
everyday life of the people of Cambridgeshire from the
17th century to the present day. There are also
temporary exhibitions. Special exhibitions and
children's activity days take place throughout the year.
Please telephone for details.
Times: Open all year, Apr-Sep, Mon-Sat 10.30-5, Sun 2-5. Oct-Mar,
Tue-Sat 10.30-5, Sun 2-5. (Last admissions 30 mins before closing)
Closed 1 Jan, Good Fri, 24-31 Dec. **Fee:** £2.50 (ch 5-16 75p,
concessions £1.50) one free ch with every full paying adult.
Facilities: P (300 yds) (pay and display on street parking) 🕭 (braille
touch tables, tape guides & large print guides) shop 🏇 (ex guide dogs)

FITZWILLIAM MUSEUM
Trumpington St CB2 1RB (From M11 take either exit 11,
12 or 13. Museum located near city centre)
☎ 01223 332900   📄 01223 332923
e-mail: fitzwilliam-enquiries@lists.cam.ac.uk

The Fitzwilliam is the art museum of the University of
Cambridge and one of the oldest public museums in
Britain. Exhibits include ancient art and sculpture,
pottery, glass, furniture, clocks, armour, ceramics, rugs,
coins, medals and manuscripts as well as masterpieces
by painters including Picasso, Monet, Constable and
Titian. Access to the museum will be restricted during
2002; please telephone for details.
Times: Open all year Tue, Thu & Fri 10-5, Wed 10-7, Sat & Sun 12-5
plus Etr Mon, Spring & Summer BH. (Closed Good Fri, May Day & 17
Dec-4 Jan) **Fee:** Free. **Facilities:** P (400 yds) (2hr max, metered) 🕭
🕭 (Restricted access during courtyard development 2002-2004) toilets
for disabled shop 🏇 (Guide dogs only) 🍽

SCOTT POLAR RESEARCH INSTITUTE MUSEUM
Lensfield Rd CB2 1ER (1km S of City Centre)
☎ 01223 336540   📄 01223 336549
e-mail: rkh10@cam.ac.uk

An international centre for polar studies, including a
museum featuring displays of Arctic and Antarctic
expeditions, with special emphasis on those of Captain
Scott. Other exhibits include Eskimo work and other
arts of the polar regions, as well as displays on current
scientific exploration. Public lectures run from October
to December and February to April.
Times: Open all year, Mon-Fri 2.30-4. Closed some Sat, public &
university hols. **Fee:** Free. **Facilities:** P (400mtrs) 🕭 shop 🏇 (ex
guide dogs)

UNIVERSITY BOTANIC GARDEN
Cory Lodge, Bateman St CB2 1JF (1m S of city centre)
☎ 01223 336265   📄 01223 336278
e-mail: gardens@cam.ac.uk

Founded in 1762, and transferred to its present site in
1846, the Garden covers 40 acres, with collections of
trees and shrubs; botanical groups of herbaceous
perennials, and a lake. Features include a Scented
Garden and collection of native British plants, and the
Gardens hold nine National Collections.
Times: Open all year daily 10-6 (summer), 10-5 (autumn & spring),
(10-4) winter. Glasshouses 10-12.30 & 2-3.45. (Closed 25 Dec-1 Jan).
Entry by Bateman St and Station Rd gates on weekdays & by Bateman
St gate only at weekends & BH. **Fee:** £2.50 (ch & pen £2). **Facilities:**
P (0.25m) (on street parking bays-pay & display) 🕭 🕭 (scented
garden for the visually impaired) toilets for disabled shop (open Mar-
Oct) 🏇 (ex guide dogs)

UNIVERSITY MUSEUM OF ARCHAEOLOGY & ANTHROPOLOGY
Downing St CB2 3DZ (located opposite Crowne
Plaza Hotel)
☎ 01223 333516   📄 01223 333517
e-mail: cumaa@hermes.cam.ac.uk

The museum is part of the Faculty of Archaeology and
Anthropology of the University of Cambridge. It was
established in 1884 and is still housed in its 1916
building on the Downing Site in the city centre. It has
three floors displaying renowned archaeological and
anthropological collections from around the world.
Times: Open all year Tues-Sat 2-4.30. Closed 1wk Etr & 1wk Xmas.
Telephone for extended summer hours. **Fee:** Free. **Facilities:** P
(100yds) 🕭 (lift available) shop 🏇 (ex guide dogs)

🏛 DUXFORD   Map 05 TL44

IMPERIAL WAR MUSEUM DUXFORD
CB2 4QR (off M11 junct 10 on A505)
☎ 01223 835000   📄 01223 837267
e-mail: duxford@iwm.org.uk

This former Battle of Britain fighter station, with
hangars dating from WW1, is home to most of the
Imperial War Museum's collection of military aircraft,
armoured fighting vehicles, midget submarines and
other large exhibits. Also on display is the Duxford
Aviation Society's collection of civil aircraft. Flying
displays are held in summer.
Times: Open all year, mid Mar-mid Oct daily 10-6; mid Oct-mid Mar
daily 10-4. (Closed 24-26 Dec) **Fee:** £7.70 (pen £5.40 & concessions
£3.70). Ch under 16yrs free. **Facilities:** P 🕭 ✗ licensed 🕭
(wheelchair available-phone in advance) toilets for disabled shop 🏇
(ex guide dogs) 🍽

ELY — Map 05 TL58

Oliver Cromwell's House

29 St Mary's St CB7 4HF (adjacent to St Mary's church)
☎ 01353 662062 Fax 01353 668518
e-mail: elytic@compuserve.com

Times: Open all year: Apr-Sep, daily 10-5.30; Oct-Mar, Mon-Sat 10-5. Winter, Sun, 11-3. **Facilities:** P (100yds) shop (ex guide dogs) *Details not confirmed for 2002*

Ely Cathedral

CB7 4DL (A10 or A142, 15m from Cambridge)
☎ 01353 667735 Fax 01353 665658

The Octagon Tower of Ely Cathedral can be seen for miles as it rises above the surrounding flat fenland. A monastery was founded on the site by St Etheldreda in 673, but the present cathedral church dates from 1083 and is a magnificent example of Romanesque architecture.

Times: Open daily, Summer 7am-7pm, Winter 7.30-6 (5pm Sun). **Fee:** £4 (concessions £3.50). Ch free in family group. **Facilities:** P (walking distance) (no charge) licensed (touch tour for blind/partally sighted) toilets for disabled shop (ex guide dogs)

The Stained Glass Museum

The Cathedral CB7 4DN (15m N of Cambridge via A10, situated inside Ely Cathedral)
☎ 01353 660347 Fax 01223 327367
e-mail: stainedgm@lineone.net

Situated in the cathedral, this museum is the only one of its kind in the country. Case exhibits show how stained-glass windows are designed and made, and there is an exhibition of approximately 100 panels dating from the 13th century to the present day, displayed at eye level in back-lit cases. The museum is undergoing refurbishment and may be closed for one or two months. Please ring to avoid disappointment.

Times: Open daily, Mon-Fri 10.30-4.30, Sat & BH 10.30-5 & Sun 12-6. **Fee:** £3.50 (ch, students & pen £2.50). Party 10+. **Facilities:** P 400yds (Inter-active video visit) shop (ex guide dogs)

HAMERTON — Map 04 TL17

Hamerton Zoo Park

PE17 5RE (off A14 at junct with B660 signed Old Weston/Kimbolton)
☎ 01832 293362 Fax 01832 293677
e-mail: office@hamertonzoopark.com

Times: Open Summer daily 10.30-6; winter daily 10.30-4. (Closed 25 Dec) **Facilities:** P toilets for disabled shop *Details not confirmed for 2002*

LINTON — Map 05 TL54

Chilford Hall Vineyard

Chilford Hall, Balsham Rd CB1 6LE (signposted from A1307 and A11)
☎ 01223 892641 Fax 01223 894056
e-mail: simonalper@chilfordhall.co.uk

Times: Open Apr-24 Dec. **Facilities:** P toilets for disabled shop *Details not confirmed for 2002*

Linton Zoological Gardens

Hadstock Rd CB1 6NT (exit M11 at junct 9/10, situated on B1052 off A604/A1307, signposted)
☎ 01223 891308 Fax 01223 891308

The perfect place for school or family trips, this breeding centre houses many rare creatures in beautifully landscaped grounds. Wildlife includes zebras, tapirs, tigers, monkeys, parrots, snakes, tortoises and insects. Many special events, ring for details.

Times: Open daily 10-6 or dusk (ex 25 Dec). Last admission 1 hour before closing time. **Fee:** *Prices not confirmed for 2002*
Facilities: P toilets for disabled shop

LODE — Map 05 TL56

Anglesey Abbey

CB5 9EJ (6m NE of Cambridge on B1102, signposted from A14)
☎ 01223 811200 Fax 01223 811200
e-mail: aayus@smtp.ntrust.org.uk

A medieval undercroft has survived from the priory founded here in 1135, but the house dates mainly from 1600. Thomas Hobson of 'Hobson's choice' was one of the owners. A later owner was Lord Fairhaven, who amassed the huge collection of pictures, and laid out the beautiful gardens.

contd.

Times: Open House: 27 Mar-27 Oct, Wed-Sun & BH Mon 1-5. Garden: Jan-23 Mar, 27 Mar-27 Oct, 30 Oct-22 Dec, Wed-Sun & BH Mon 10.30-5.30, 4.30 Oct-Dec. Also open 3 Jul-1 Sep all wk & BH 10.30-5.30, Thur 8. Lode Mill: Jan-23 Mar, wknds 11-3; 27 Mar-27 Oct, Wed-Sun & BH Mons 1-5; 30 Oct-22 Dec wknds 11-4. **Fee:** £6.25. Garden & Mill only £3.85 (£3.25 in winter). Family & party discounts available. **Facilities:** 🅿 👕 ✗ licensed ♿ (electric buggy, wheelchairs & braille guide) toilets for disabled shop garden centre 🍴 (ex guide dogs) ⚐ ⬤

PETERBOROUGH Map 04 TL19
LONGTHORPE TOWER
PE1 1EP
☎ 01733 268482

The main attraction of this medieval fortified house are the rare wall paintings of religious and educational subjects - the finest surviving in Northern Europe. **Times:** Open Apr-Sep, daily 10-6 (Oct 10-5). Nov-Mar wknds 10-4. Closed 24-26 Dec & 1 Jan. **Fee:** £1.60 (ch 5-15 £0.80, under 5's free, con £1.80). **Facilities:** 🍴 ⚏

PETERBOROUGH CATHEDRAL
PE1 1XS (access from A1 juncts with A605 or A47)
☎ 01733 343342 ◰ 01733 52465
Times: Open all year, daily 8.30-5.15 (8pm summer) **Facilities:** 🅿 (300yds) (no parking within cathedral precincts) 👕 ✗ ♿ (touch & hearing centre, braille guide, ramps to grnd floor) shop 🍴 (ex guide dogs or in grounds) *Details not confirmed for 2002*

RAMSEY Map 04 TL28
ABBEY GATEHOUSE
Abbey School PE17 1DH (SE edge of Ramsey, at the point where Chatteris Road joins B1096)
☎ 01263 733471(Regional Off)
◰ 01263 734924

The ruins of this 15th-century gatehouse, together with the 13th-century Lady Chapel, are all that remain of the abbey. Half of the gatehouse was taken away after the Dissolution. Built in ornate late-Gothic style, it has panelled buttresses and friezes.
Times: Open Apr-Oct, daily 10-5. **Fee:** Free. **Facilities:** 🍴 ⚐

WANSFORD Map 04 TL09
NENE VALLEY RAILWAY
Wansford Station, Stibbington PE8 6LR (A1 west of Peterborough)
☎ 01780 784444 ◰ 01780 784440
Times: Open end Feb-Etr, Sun; Apr-June, Sep-end Oct, wknds; May, June & Jul, Wed; Aug, daily ex Mondays, (but inc BH Mondays). Some midweek days at other times. **Facilities:** 🅿 👕 ♿ (disabled access to trains) toilets for disabled shop *Details not confirmed for 2002* ⬤

WIMPOLE Map 05 TL35
WIMPOLE HALL
SG8 0BW (M11 junct 12, 8m SW of Cambridge off A603)
☎ 01223 207257 ◰ 01223 207838
e-mail: aweusr@smtp.ntrust.org.uk

Wimpole Hall is one of the grandest mansions in East Anglia, and has 360 acres of parkland devised and

planted by no less than four celebrated landscape designers, Charles Bridgeman, `Capability' Brown, Sanderson Miller and Humphrey Repton. The house dates back to 1640, but was altered into a large 18th-century mansion with a Georgian façade. The chapel has a painted trompe l'oeil ceiling.
Times: Open 18 Mar-22 Oct, Tue-Thu, Sat-Sun & Good Fri 1-5, BH Mon 11-5. Open Fri in Aug 1-5. 25 Oct-5 Nov, Wed, Sat & Sun 1-5. **Fee:** £5.90 (ch £2.70). Party. Joint ticket with Home Farm £7.50. Garden only £2 (ch free). **Facilities:** 🅿 👕 ✗ licensed ♿ (braille guide, battery operated vehicle, stairlift) toilets for disabled shop 🍴 (ex park only) ⚐ ⬤

WIMPOLE HOME FARM
SG8 0BW (M11 junct 12 8m SW of Cambridge off A603)
☎ 01223 208987 ◰ 01223 207838
e-mail: aweusr@smtp.ntrust.org.uk

When built in 1794, the Home Farm was one of the most advanced agricultural enterprises in the country. The Great Barn, now restored, holds a display of farm machinery and implements of the kind used at Wimpole over the past two centuries. On the farm there are rare breeds of domestic animals. Please ring for details of special events.
Times: Open 18 Mar-5 Nov, Tue-Thu & Sat-Sun 10.30-5; Jul & Aug Tue-Sun, also open Good Fri & BH Mons; 6 Nov-17 Mar Sat & Sun 11-4 (open Feb half-term week). (Closed Xmas & New Year). **Fee:** £4.70 (ch £2.70). **Facilities:** 🅿 👕 ✗ licensed ♿ (braille guide) toilets for disabled shop 🍴 (ex guide dogs) ⚐ ⬤

WISBECH Map 09 TF40
PECKOVER HOUSE & GARDEN
North Brink PE13 1JR (Leave A47 & take town centre signs, then follow brown signs.)
☎ 01945 583463 ◰ 01945 583463
e-mail: aprigx@smtp.ntrust.org.uk

Dating from 1722, Peckover House is a beautiful Georgian brick townhouse with a two-acre walled town garden, one of the finest such gardens in Britain and home to over 70 types of rose. The Victorian glasshouses include a fern house, and an orangery with 300-year-old trees that still bear fruit.
Times: Open, House, Garden & Tearoom Apr-Oct, wknds, Wed & BH Mon 12.30-5pm. Garden open: Apr-Oct, Mon & Tue & Thu 12.30-5. **Fee:** House & garden £3.80 (ch £1.50). Garden £2.50 on days when only garden is open. **Facilities:** 🅿 (400yds) 👕 ✗ licensed ♿ (Batricar available on loan) toilets for disabled shop 🍴 ⚐

WISBECH & FENLAND MUSEUM
Museum Square PE13 1ES (on A47)
☎ 01945 583817 ◰ 01945 589050
Times: Open all year, Tue-Sat 10-5 (4pm Oct-Mar). Closed Xmas. 🅿 (100 yds) shop 🍴 *Details not confirmed for 2002*

Cheshire

Bordered by Wales and the metropoli of Liverpool and Manchester, Cheshire has a rich history that can be seen in its wealth of Roman heritage, black and white buildings, and industrial waterways. The county also boasts some lovely countryside, a tradition of floral excellence, and some rather delicious cheese.

From the invasion of the Romans who made Chester one of their major garrisons, to skirmishes with Norsemen during the Dark Ages, Cheshire has been the scene of many conflicts. The area was also the base for Hugh the Wolf's violent reign in the 11th century, and the setting for the some of the fiercest battles of the Civil War, including the seige of Chester. Clearly, life is less stressful now, but the history of the county is far from forgotten.

Cheshire's canals, part of which form a ring of around 100 miles (151km) of waterways, are the ideal way to explore by foot or by boat. The county has over 200 miles (302 km) of man-made waterways – more than any other county in England – and is a centre for boating holidays. Ellesmere Port has a Boat Museum which has preserved many of the vessels used for both inland and sea travel, from a small weedcutter to a 300-ton coaster.

From a literary angle, Knutsford has a monument to Mrs Gaskell (1810-1865), a native of the town, whose novels dealt with subject matter surprisingly controversial for a female writer of her generation. Her novel, *Wives and Daughters*, was recently adapted by BBC TV.

Cheshire is full of gardens. From the acres of orangeries and Japanese gardens surrounding the stately homes, to the town parks of Crewe and Congleton, the county is a feast of flowers, lawns and landscaping. Even many private gardens are showpieces of gardening expertise.

EVENTS & FESTIVALS

May
4th Knutsford Royal May Day
15th-18th Alderley Edge Music Festival

June
18th-19th Cheshire County Show, The Showground, Tabley, nr Knutsford
tbc World Worm Charming Championship, Willaston Primary School, Willaston

July
17th-21st Royal Horticultural Society Flower Show, Tatton Park, Knutsford
tbc Macclesfield Carnival

August
18th Family Fun Day, West Park, Macclesfield
24th Poynton Show

October
Macclesfield Festival for the Performing Arts, Ryles Park High School (2 wknds of autumn half term)
tbc Chrysanthemum Show, Wilmslow Royal British Legion

Top: Eastgate Clock, Chester

⛪ BEESTON   Map 07 SJ55
BEESTON CASTLE
Tarporley CW6 9TX (on minor road off A49 or A41)
☎ 01829 260464

This ruined 13th-century stronghold was built by the
Earl Ranuf of Chester on a steep and inaccessible
hillside. The remains of the inner and outer wards can
still be seen and there is an exhibition of the castle's
history.
Times: Open all year, Apr-Sep, daily 10-6 (Oct 10-5); Nov-Mar daily
10-4. (Closed 24-26 Dec & 1 Jan). **Fee:** £2.90 (ch £1.50, under 5's free,
con £2.60). **Facilities:** 🅿 shop 🐾 (in certain areas) ♨

⛪ CAPESTHORNE   Map 07 SJ87
CAPESTHORNE HALL
SK11 9JY (On A34 between Congleton and Wilmslow)
☎ 01625 861221   🗎 01625 861619

Capesthorne has been the home of the Bromley-
Davenport family and their ancestors since Domesday
times. The present house dates from 1719 and was
designed by the Smiths of Warwick. It was
subsequently altered by Edward Blore in 1837 and after
a disastrous fire in 1861 the whole of the centre portion
was rebuilt by Anthony Salvin. Capesthorne contains a
great variety of sculptures, paintings and other contents
including a collection of American Colonial furnishings.
Times: Open Apr-Oct, Wed-Sun & BH's (Closed Xmas & New Year).
Park & Garden 12-5.30, Hall 1.30-3.30. **Fee:** Park, Garden & Chapel £4
(ch £2). Park, Gardens, Chapel & Hall £6.50 (ch £3 & pen £5.50).
Family ticket £12. Party 25+ **Facilities:** 🅿 🍽 ✗ licensed & (ramp
access to ground floor of hall & gardens) toilets for disabled 🐾 (ex
guide dogs & in gardens)

⛪ CHESTER   Map 07 SJ46
CHESHIRE MILITARY MUSEUM
The Castle CH1 2DN (follow signs to Military Museum
from town centre)
☎ 01244 327617   🗎 01244 401700

This newly refurbished military museum boasts exhibits
from the history of the Cheshire Regiment, Cheshire
Yeomanry, 5th Royal Inniskilling Dragoon Guards, and
3rd Carabiniers. Display of the work of George Jones,
Victorian battle artist, and an exhibition of life in
barracks in the 1950s. Research available by written
appointment and donation. There are special events
throughtout the year, please phone for details.
Times: Open all year, daily 10-5 (last entry 4.30pm). (Closed 22 Dec-
2 Jan). **Fee:** £2.50 (con £2). **Facilities:** 🅿 (within 400yds) & shop 🐾
(ex guide dogs)

CHESTER CATHEDRAL
Saint Werburgh St CH1 2HU (opposite the town hall)
☎ 01244 324756   🗎 01244 341110
e-mail: office@chestercathedral.org.uk

Founded as a Benedictine monastery in 1092 on the
sites of earlier churches, in 1541 it became the

cathedral of the newly created Diocese of Chester and
is a good example of a medieval monastic complex.
Restored in the 19th century, the building contains
work by Gilbert Scott, Clayton, Pugin and Kempe. There
are daily services and visitors are welcome to join in. A
summer music festival is held in July.
Times: Open daily 7.30-6.30 (subject to alteration). **Fee:** Donation of
£3 per person requested. **Facilities:** 🅿 (multi-storey) 🍽 ✗ licensed
& (induction loop, tactile model) toilets for disabled shop 🐾 (ex guide
dogs)

CHESTER VISITOR CENTRE
Vicars Ln CH1 1QX (opposite Roman Amphitheatre)
☎ 01244 402111   🗎 01244 403188
e-mail: tis@chestercc.gov.uk
Times: Open Mon-Sat 9-5.30, Sun & BHs 10-4; Nov-Apr Mon-
Sat 10-5, Sun 10-4. **Facilities:** 🅿 (200yds) (short stay visitor parking)
🍽 & (ramped access from Vicars Lane) toilets for disabled shop
Details not confirmed for 2002

CHESTER ZOO
Upton-by-Chester CH2 1LH (2m N of city centre off
A41& M53 Junct 10 southbound, Junct 12 all other
directions)
☎ 01244 380280   🗎 01244 371273
e-mail: marketing@chesterzoo.co.uk

The largest zoological gardens in the UK, with 6000
animals in 525 species. There are large outdoor islands
for chimps, orang-utans and monkeys, a children's
farm, penguin pool, and birds of prey. The Bat Cave is
the largest enclosure in the world for endangered bat
species. New features include the 'Spirit of the Jaguar',
a Komodo Dragon, a huge extension to the National
Elephant Centre, and 'Noah's Ark' children's play area.
Times: Open all year, daily from 10. Last admission varies with season
from 5.30pm high summer to 3.30pm winter. (Closed 25 Dec).
Fee: £10.50 (ch 3-15 & pen £8.50). Family ticket (2 ad+3 ch) £38. Party
15+ **Facilities:** 🅿 🍽 ✗ licensed & (electric scooters, audio guide,
induction loop) toilets for disabled shop 🐾 (ex guide & sensory dogs)
◀

DEVA ROMAN EXPERIENCE
Pierpoint Ln, (off Bridge St) CH1 1NL (city centre)
☎ 01244 343407   🗎 01244 347737

Stroll along reconstructed streets experiencing the
sights, sounds and smells of Roman Chester. From the
streets of Deva (the Roman name for Chester) you
return to the present day on an extensive archeological
'dig', where you can discover the substantial Roman,
Saxon and medieval remains beneath modern Chester.
Times: Open daily 9-5. (Closed 25-26 Dec). **Fee:** £3.95 (ch £2.25,
under 5's free, pen £3.50, student £3.50). Family ticket £11. Party.
Facilities: 🅿 (200yds) & shop 🐾 (ex guide dogs)

⛰ CHOLMONDELEY   Map 07 SJ55
CHOLMONDELEY CASTLE GARDENS
SY14 8AH (off A49/A41)
☎ 01829 720383   📠 01829 720383

Times: Open 2 Apr-28 Sep, Wed-Thu, Sun & BH 11.30-5. (Closed Good Fri). **Facilities:** 🅿 💷 ♿ (disabled car park near tearoom) toilets for disabled shop garden centre *Details not confirmed for 2002*

⛰ DISLEY   Map 07 SJ98
LYME PARK
SK12 2NX (off A6, 6.5m SE of Stockport)
☎ 01663 762023   📠 01663 765035
Times: 25 Mar-5 Nov, Wed-Sun (open BH Mon) 11.30-5 or dusk if earlier; mid Nov-mid Dec, Sat & Sun 11.30-4 (access restricted to ground floor, garden, shop and restaurant only) **Facilities:** 🅿 💷 ✗ licensed ♿ (by arrangement) toilets for disabled shop 🐕 (ex park on lead) 🐾 *Details not confirmed for 2002*

⛰ ELLESMERE PORT   Map 07 SJ47
BOAT MUSEUM
South Pier Rd CH65 4FW (M53 junct 9)
☎ 0151 355 5017   📠 0151 355 4079
e-mail: bookings@
boatmuseum.freeserve.co.uk

Occupying a historic dock complex at the junction of the Shropshire Union and Manchester Ship Canals, this museum has the world's largest collection of floating canal craft, from a small weedcutter to a 300-ton coaster. Boat trips are also available. There are indoor exhibitions on canal life and local history, together with period worker's cottages, a blacksmith's forge and working engines.
Times: Open Summer daily 10-5. Winter daily (ex Thu & Fri) 11-4. (Closed 25 & 26 Dec). **Fee:** £5.50 (ch £3.70, pen £4.30, student £4.30). Family ticket £16.50, OAP family ticket £14.50. **Facilities:** 🅿 💷 ♿ (resources pack for blind & deaf, tactile map for blind) toilets for disabled shop 🐾

⛰ GAWSWORTH   Map 07 SJ86
GAWSWORTH HALL
SK11 9RN (2.5m S of Macclesfield on A536)
☎ 01260 223456   📠 01260 223469
e-mail: gawsworth@lineone.net

This fine Tudor black-and-white manor house was the birthplace of Mary Fitton, thought by some to be the `Dark Lady' of Shakespeare's sonnets. Pictures and armour can be seen in the house, which also has a tilting ground – now thought to be a rare example of an Elizabethan pleasure garden.
Times: Open daily, 12 Apr-7 Oct, closed certain days, phone for details. **Fee:** £4.50 (ch £2.25). Party 20+ £3.50 each. **Facilities:** 🅿 💷 ✗ licensed ♿ (disabled parking in front of house) toilets for disabled shop 🐕 (guide dogs in garden only) 🐾

⛰ JODRELL BANK SCIENCE CENTRE & ARBORETUM   Map 07 SJ77
JODRELL BANK SCIENCE CENTRE, PLANETARIUM & ARBORETUM
SK11 9DL (M6 junct 18, A535 Holmes Chapel to Chelford Road)
☎ 01477 571339   📠 01477 571695
e-mail: visitorcentre@jb.man.ac.uk

The Lovell telescope is one of the largest fully-steerable radio telescopes in the world, and the Science Centre features exhibitions on space, energy, astronomy and space art. Interactive exhibits help you get to grips with
contd.

science. Outside, there are 35 acres of tree-lined walkways in the Arboretum.

Jodrell Bank Science Centre, Planetarium & Arboretum

Times: Open summer 3rd wknd in Mar-last wknd in Oct, 10.30-5.30: winter Nov-mid Mar. Tue-Sun 11-4.30. (ring for Xmas opening times) **Fee:** £4.90 (ch £2.50, pen £3.50) includes Exhibition, Planetarium, Arboretum & Environmental Discovery Centre. Family ticket £14.50. Children under 4 not admitted to the Planetarium. **Facilities:** 🅿 💷 ♿ (Audio loop, wheelchair loan, audio guide & tactile guide) toilets for disabled shop 🐾 (ex guide dogs) 🍴

🏛 KNUTSFORD   Map 07 SJ77
TABLEY HOUSE
WA16 0HB (leave M6 junct19 onto A556 S towards Chester. Entrance for cars off A5033, 2m W of Knutsford)
☎ 01565 750151 🖹 01565 653230
e-mail: inquiries@tableyhouse.co.uk

This fine Palladian house holds the first great collection of English pictures ever made, furniture by Chippendale, Gillow and Bullock, and fascinating Leicester family memorabilia. Friendly stewards are available to talk about the Leicester's 700 years at Tabley.
Times: Open Apr-end Oct, Thu-Sun & BHs, 2-5 (last entry 4.30). **Fee:** £4 (ch & students £1.50) **Facilities:** 🅿 💷 ♿ (Phone administrator in advance for help) toilets for disabled shop 🐾 (ex guide dogs)

TATTON PARK
WA16 6QN (5m from M6 junct 19, or M56 junct 7)
☎ 01625 534400 🖹 01625 534403

Tatton is one of England's most complete historic estates, with gardens and a 1000-acre country park. The centrepiece is the Georgian mansion, with gardens laid out by Humphry Repton and Sir Joseph Paxton. More recently, a Japanese garden with a Shinto temple was created. The Tudor Old Hall is the original manor house, where a guided tour is available.
Times: Open Apr-Sep, daily except Mon; Oct Sat & Sun, opening times vary telephone to check. Gardens all year daily except Mon. Park Apr-Oct daily; Nov-Mar daily except Mon. **Fee:** *Prices not confirmed for 2002* **Facilities:** 🅿 (charged) 💷 ♿ (Old Hall & areas of Farm not accessible) toilets for disabled shop garden centre 🐾 (ex in Park) 🐕 🍴

🏛 MACCLESFIELD   Map 07 SJ97
HARE HILL
SK10 4QB (4m N off B5087)
☎ 01625 828981
Times: Open Apr-Oct, Wed, Thu, Sat, Sun & BH Mons 10-5.30; 10-30 May daily 10-5.30; (Closed Nov-Mar). **Facilities:** 🅿 (charged) ♿ (wheelchair available braille guides) 🐾 (ex guide dogs) 🐕 *Details not confirmed for 2002*

MACCLESFIELD SILK MUSEUM
Heritage Centre, Roe St SK11 6UT (Turn off A523 & follow brown signs. Museum in town centre)
☎ 01625 613210 🖹 01625 617880
e-mail: postmaster@silk-macc.u-net.com

The story of silk in Macclesfield, told through a colourful audio-visual programme, exhibitions, textiles, garments, models and room settings. The Silk Museum is part of the Heritage centre, a restored Georgian Sunday school, which runs a full programme of musical and artistic events throughout the year.
Times: Open all year, Mon-Sat 11-5, Sun & BH Mon 1-5. (Closed Good Fri, 24-26 Dec & 1 Jan) **Fee:** £2.90 (concessions £2). Family ticket £7.75 Joint ticket with Paradise Mill £5.10 (concessions £2.90). Family ticket £11.15. **Facilities:** 🅿 (50m) 💷 ✕ licensed ♿ (ramps & chairlift) toilets for disabled shop 🐾 (ex guide dogs) 🍴

PARADISE MILL
Park Ln SK11 6TJ (turn off A523 'The Silk Road' & follow brown signs)
☎ 01625 618228

A working silk mill until 1981, with restored jacquard hand looms in their original location. Knowledgeable guides, many of them former silk mill workers, illustrate the silk production process with the help of demonstrations from weavers. Exhibitions and room settings give an impression of working conditions at the mill during the 1930s.
Times: Open all year, BH Mon & Tue-Sun 1-5 (1-4 in winter). (Closed Good Fri, 24 Dec-3 Jan). **Fee:** £2.90 (concessions £2). Family ticket £7.75. Joint ticket with Macclesfield Silk Museum £5.10 (concessions £2.90). Family ticket £11.15. **Facilities:** 🅿 (400 yds) ♿ (care needed on uneven floors) shop 🐾 (ex guide dogs) 🍴

🏛 MOULDSWORTH   Map 07 SJ57
MOULDSWORTH MOTOR MUSEUM
Smithy Ln CH3 8AR (6m E of Chester, off B5393, close to Delamere Forest & Oulton Park Racing Circuit, signposted)
☎ 01928 731781

Housed in an amazing 1937 large Art Deco building close to Delamere Forest, this is a superb collection of over 60 motor cars, motorcycles and bicycles. There is also a massive collection of automobilia - old signs, pumps, tools, mascots and badges, as well as old motoring toys, Dinky cars and pedal cars all complemented by a motoring art gallery, that has posters and advertising material. School parties are

contd.

encouraged for a guided tour and structured talk.
Motoring clubs visit on Sundays.
Times: Open Feb-Nov (Sun only), Etr wknd, early May BH Mon,
Spring BH Sun-Mon & Aug BH wknd; Sun, Feb-Nov; also Wed, Jul-Aug,
noon-5. **Fee:** £3 (ch £1.50, pen - reduction Wed only Jul-Aug £2.50)
Facilities: ♿ ♿ (hands on items) shop

NANTWICH   Map 07 SJ65
STAPELEY WATER GARDENS
London Rd, Stapeley CW5 7LH (off M6 junct 16, 1m S of
Nantwich on A51)
☎ 01270 623868 & 628628 ▯ 01270 624919
e-mail: stapeleywg@btinternet.com

Stapeley Water Gardens consists of three main areas.
The Palms Tropical Oasis is a glass pavilion which is
home to Koi carp, Giant Amazon water-lilies, sharks,
piranhas, parrots and exotic flowers. The two-acre
Water Garden Centre houses the National Collection of
water-lilies.
Times: Open Summer: Mon-Sat 9-6, BHs 10-6, Sun 10-4, Wed 9-8;
Winter: Mon-Sat 9-5, BHs 10-5, Sun 10-4, Wed 10-7 (Angling dept
only). The Palms Tropical Oasis open from 10am. **Fee:** The Palms
Tropical Oasis £3.85 (ch £2.15, pen £3.40). **Facilities:** ♿ ▮ ✕
licensed ♿ (free wheelchair loan service) toilets for disabled shop
garden centre ✸ (ex guide dogs) ▰

NESTON   Map 07 SJ27
**LIVERPOOL UNIVERSITY BOTANIC GARDENS
(NESS GARDENS)**
Ness Gardens CH64 4AY (off A540 near Ness-on-Wirral,
follow signs)
☎ 0151 353 0123 ▯ 0151 353 1004
e-mail: ejs@liv.ac.uk

A long association with plant collectors ensures a wide
range of plants, providing interest for academics,
horticulturists and amateurs alike. There are tree and
shrub collections, water and rock gardens, herbaceous
borders and glasshouses. A regular programme of
lectures, courses and special events take place
throughout the year for which tickets must be obtained
in advance.
Times: Open all year, Nov-Feb, daily 9.30-4; Mar-Oct, daily 9.30-5.
Closed 25 Dec. **Fee:** £4.70 (ch free admission when accompanied with
an adult, concessions £4.30) **Facilities:** ♿ ▮ ✕ licensed ♿
(wheelchair route, induction loop in lecture theatre) toilets for disabled
shop garden centre ✸ (ex guide dogs) ▰

NETHER ALDERLEY   Map 07 SJ87
NETHER ALDERLEY MILL
Congleton Rd SK10 4TW (1.5m S of Alderley Edge on E
side of A34)
☎ 01625 523012 ▯ 68045 527139
Times: Open Apr-May & Oct, Wed, Sun & BH Mon 1-4.30; Jun-Sep,
Tue-Sun & BH Mon 1-5. Parties by arrangement. **Facilities:** ♿ ✸ ♨
Details not confirmed for 2002

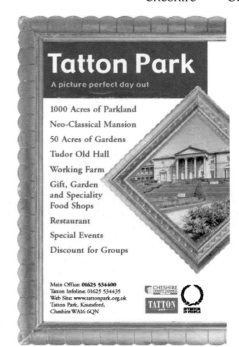

Tatton Park
A picture perfect day out

1000 Acres of Parkland
Neo-Classical Mansion
50 Acres of Gardens
Tudor Old Hall
Working Farm
Gift, Garden
and Speciality
Food Shops
Restaurant
Special Events
Discount for Groups

Main Office: 01625 534400
Tatton Infoline: 01625 534435
Web Site: www.tattonpark.org.uk
Tatton Park, Knutsford,
Cheshire WA16 6QN

NORTHWICH   Map 07 SJ67
ARLEY HALL & GARDENS
Great Budworth CW9 6NA (5m N of Northwich on
B5075. 5m NW of Knutsford A556)
☎ 01565 777353 & 777284 ▯ 01565 777465
e-mail: enquires@arleyestate.zuunet.co.uk

Owned by the same family since medieval times, the
present Arley Hall is a good example of the early
Victorian Jacobean style and contains fine furniture,
plasterwork, panelling and family portraits. The gardens
include a walled garden, unique clipped Ilex avenue,
herb garden, scented garden and a woodland garden
with rhododendrons, azaleas and exotic trees. Special
events throughout 2002, please phone for details.
Times: Open Etr-end Sep, Tue-Sun & BH 11-5. Hall open Tue & Sun
only. **Fee:** Gardens, Grounds & Chapel £4.40 (ch 6-16 £2.20, pen
£3.80) Family ticket £11 Hall £2.50 (ch 6-16 £1.60,pen £2). Party 15+.
Facilities: ♿ ▮ ✕ ♿ (ramps, parking by entrance) toilets for
disabled shop garden centre ✸ (ex in gardens on lead) ▰

SALT MUSEUM
162 London Rd CW9 8AB (on A533 0.5m S of town
centre and 0.5m N of A556. Well signposted from A556)
☎ 01606 41331 & 40394 ▯ 01606 350420
e-mail: cheshiremuseums@cheshire.gov.uk

Britain's only Salt Museum tells the fascinating story of
Cheshire's oldest industry. Models, reconstructions,

contd.

original artefacts and audio-visual programmes throw new light on something we all take for granted.
Times: Open Tue-Fri 10-5, wknds 2-5 (Sun 12-5 in Aug). Open BH & Mons in Aug 10-5. **Fee:** £2.10 (ch £1.10, con £1.85) Family ticket (2ad+2ch) £5.30. **Facilities:** 🅿 ♨ ♿ (inductory video with induction loop facilities) toilets for disabled shop 🐾 (ex guide dogs)

🏛 RUNCORN   Map 07 SJ58
NORTON PRIORY MUSEUM & GARDENS
Tudor Rd, Manor Park WA7 1SX (from M56 junct 11 in direction of Warrington, signposted)
☎ 01928 569895 📠 01928 589743
e-mail: info@nortonpriory.org

Thirty-eight acres of peaceful woodland gardens are the setting for the medieval priory remains, museum and Walled Garden. Displays tell the story of the transformation of the priory into a Tudor manor house and then into an elegant Georgian mansion. Please telephone for details of special events.
Times: Open all year, Apr-Oct, Mon-Fri 12-5; Sat, Sun & BHs 12-6; Nov-Mar daily 12-4. (Closed 24-26 Dec & 1 Jan). Walled Garden open Mar-Oct by guided walk only & when staffing permits, tel for details. **Fee:** £3.75 (ch 5-16, students, UB40's & pen £2.50) family ticket £9.80. **Facilities:** 🅿 ♨ ♿ (wheelchairs, large print & audio guides, induction loop) toilets for disabled shop garden centre (guide dogs only wall garden)

🏛 SCHOLAR GREEN   Map 07 SJ85
LITTLE MORETON HALL
Newcastle Rd CW12 4SD (4m SW of Congleton on A34)
☎ 01260 272018
Times: Open mid Mar-early Nov, Wed-Sun 11.30-5 or dusk if earlier, BH Mon 11.30-5; early Nov-mid Dec, weekends 11.30-4. **Facilities:** 🅿 (charged) ✗ licensed ♿ (wheelchair & electric vehicle available, Braille guide) toilets for disabled shop 🐾 ♨ *Details not confirmed for 2002* 💳

🏛 STYAL   Map 07 SJ88
QUARRY BANK MILL & STYAL COUNTRY PARK
Quarry Bank Mill SK9 4JQ (M56 junct 5, signposted)
☎ 01625 523012 📠 01625 539267
Times: Mill open all year, Apr-Sep daily 11-6 (last admission 4.30); Oct-Mar Tue-Sun 11-5 (last admission 3.30). Apprentice House & Garden, as Mill opening times during school hols, daily 2-4.30; Sun & Aug 11.30-6.(Closed Mon all year ex BH Mon). **Facilities:** 🅿 (charged) ♨ ✗ licensed ♿ toilets for disabled shop 🐾 (ex in Park) ♨ *Details not confirmed for 2002* 💳

🏛 WIDNES   Map 07 SJ58
CATALYST: THE MUSEUM OF THE CHEMICAL INDUSTRY
Mersey Rd WA8 0DF (signed from M62 junct 7 and M56 junct 12)
☎ 0151 420 1121 📠 0151 495 2030
e-mail: info@catalyst.org.uk

Discover a world where science and technology come alive, with over 100 interactive exhibits and hands-on displays which guarantee a fun-filled day out for all the family. Take a trip in an all-glass lift to the Observatory, 100 feet above the River Mersey. A range of special events is planned throughout the year. Please ring for details.
Times: Open all year, BH Mon, Tue-Fri daily 10-5, wknds 11-5. (Closed Mon ex BH's, 24-26 Dec & 1 Jan). **Fee:** £4.65 (ch £3.40, concessions £3.95). Family ticket £13.95. **Facilities:** 🅿 ♨ ♿ toilets for disabled shop 🐾 (ex guide dogs) 💳

Cornwall &
Isles of Scilly

Cornwall is a striking and majestic county, and also a land of contrasts. While small coastal towns like Mousehole, Mevagissey and Polperro remain largely untouched by time, the resort of Newquay is at the forefront of the European surfing scene.

Unsurprisingly, Cornwall's history is tied to the sea and seafaring, surrounded as it is by the Atlantic on three sides. For a long time the county was a centre for smuggling operations. The seclusion of its many coves and caves were ideal for the shady machinations of customs dodgers right up until the 20th century.

The isolation and ruggedness of the coastal landscape and its inhabitants has offered the perfect challenge for many religious groups and individuals. Some of Britain's earliest Christian churches and communities were started in Cornwall, including St Pirran's Church in Perranporth which was founded in the 6th century by the patron saint of tinners. Like many other missionaries of this time he came from Ireland and, local tales claim, was not the most sober of ministers. St Columba was another, perhaps more important influence on Christianity in England.

Legend has it that Cornwall was once the site of King Arthur's fabled Camelot. High on the cliffs near Tintagel is the ruined castle most strongly connected to the ancient hero, although its remains post-date Arthurian lore by some seven centuries. Some local legends state that nearby Camelford was once Camelot.

Top: Land's End

EVENTS & FESTIVALS

March
30th-1st April Falmouth Spring Flower Show

April
27th Trevithick Day, Camborne

May
1st Padstow 'Obby 'Oss celebrations
4th-5th Giant Bolster Festival, St Agnes
10th-19th Daphne du Maurier Festival, Fowey
18th-19th Re-enactment of the Battle of Stamford Hill, Bude (provisional)
tbc Calstock Festival

June
6th-8th Royal Cornwall Show, Wadebridge
8th-9th Murdoch Weekend, Redruth
20th-30th Golowan Festival, Penzance

July
15th Stithians Show, Truro
30th-9th Aug St Endellion Summer Festival, Port Isaac

August
2nd-4th Re-enactment of Arthurian Battle of Camlann, Tintagel
10th-17th Falmouth Classics & Regatta Week
24th-31st Bude Jazz Festival
25th-26th Lanlivery Vintage Rally & Country Fair
23rd-26th Wadebridge Folk Festival

September
7th Cornish Gorsedd
7th-21st St Ives Festival
tbc British & International Angling Festival, Looe

November
11th-16th Camborne Music Festival

December
23rd Tom Bawcock's Eve, Mousehole
tbc City of Lights Lantern Parade, Truro

🏛 BODMIN   Map 02 SX06
MILITARY MUSEUM
The Keep PL31 1EG (on B3268 beside steam railway)
☎ 01208 72810   🖷 01208 72810

The history of a famous County Regiment with
fascinating displays of uniforms, weapons, medals,
badges and much more.
Times: Open all year Mon-Fri, Sun during Jul & Aug 9-5. (Closed Etr &
Xmas). **Fee:** £2 (ch 50p). Parties 10+. **Facilities:** 🅿 shop

PENCARROW
Washaway PL30 3AG (4m NW, signposted off A389 &
B3266)
☎ 01208 841369   🖷 01208 841722
e-mail: pencarrow@aol.com

Still a family home, this Georgian house has a superb
collection of pictures, furniture and porcelain. The 50
acres of formal and woodland gardens include a
Victorian rockery, a lake, 700 different rhododendrons
and an acclaimed conifer collection. There is also a
craft centre and a children's play area.
Times: Open A31 Mar-Oct, Sun-Thu 1.30-4.30; 26 May-29 Aug & BH
Mon 11-4.30. Gardens open daily. **Fee:** House & Garden £5 (ch £2.50).
Gardens only £2.50 (ch free). Party 20+ **Facilities:** 🅿 🍽 ᴕ toilets for
disabled shop 🐾 (ex in gardens)

🏛 CALSTOCK   Map 02 SX46
COTEHELE
St Dominick PL12 6TA (Turn off A390, Calligan to
Tavistock rd, at St. Anne's Chapel, signposted 2.5m S of
junct)
☎ 01579 351346   🖷 01579 351222
e-mail: cctlce@smtp.ntrust.org.uk

A 15th-century house that contains tapestries,
embroideries, furniture and armour; and outside, a
beautiful garden on different levels, including a formal
Italian-style garden, medieval stewpond, dovecote, and
an 18th-century tower with lovely views. There is a
restored water mill in the valley below, and at the
Victorian riverside quay an outstation of the National
Maritime Museum.
Times: Open 27 Apr-4 Nov, House open daily (ex Fri) 11-5; (11-4.30
Oct). Mill open daily (ex Fri) 1-5.30 (4.30 Oct) - open Fri in Jul & Aug
1-6. Garden & Shop open daily 11-5 (4.30 Oct). Last admission 30
mins before closing. Nov-Mar garden & woodland open daylight hours.
Fee: House, Garden & Mill £6.20. Gardens & Mill £3.40 (ch 1/2 price,
under 5's & national trust members free) Family £15 for House,
Garden and Mill, £8.50 for Garden and Mill only. Party £5.20 each.
Facilities: 🍽 ✗ licensed ᴕ (limited access in garden, braille guide,
audio loop) toilets for disabled shop garden centre (plant sales) 🐾 (ex
guide dogs) 🐾 🍽

🏛 CAMELFORD   Map 02 SX18
BRITISH CYCLING MUSEUM
The Old Station PL32 9TZ (1m N of Camelford on B3266
at junct with B3314)
☎ 01840 212811   🖷 01840 212811

This is the nation's foremost museum of cycling history
from 1818 to the present day, with over 400 cycles;
more than 1000 cycling medals, fobs and badges; an
extensive library; displays of gas, candle, battery and oil
lighting; and many ad posters and enamel signs.
Times: Open all year, Sun-Thu 10-5. **Fee:** £2.50 (ch 5-17 £1.50)
Facilities: 🅿 ᴕ shop 🐾 (ex guide dogs)

🏛 CHYSAUSTER ANCIENT VILLAGE
Map 02 SW43
CHYSAUSTER ANCIENT VILLAGE
TR20 8XA (2.5m NW of Gulval, off B3311)
☎ 07831 757934

This fascinating ancient Celtic village, 2000 years old,
includes eight drystone houses ranged along the oldest
known village street in England.
Times: Open Apr-Oct, daily 10-6 (5pm Oct). (Reviewed Mar 2002)
Fee: £1.70 (con £1.30, ch 5-15 90p, under5's free). (Reviewed Mar
2002) **Facilities:** 🅿 🐾 🎋

🏛 DOBWALLS   Map 02 SX26
DOBWALLS FAMILY ADVENTURE PARK
PL14 6HD (0.5 N of A38)
☎ 01579 320325 & 321129
e-mail: dobwallsadpk@aol.com
Times: Open 12 Apr-10 Sep, daily 10.30-5.30 (10am in high season);
11 Sep-29 Sep, Sat-Thu; 1-22 Oct, Sat-Wed; 23-29 Oct, daily.
Facilities: 🅿 🍽 ᴕ (motorised & manual wheelchairs available) toilets
for disabled shop *Details not confirmed for 2002* 🍽

🏛 FALMOUTH   Map 02 SW83
PENDENNIS CASTLE
TR11 4LP (1m SE)
☎ 01326 316594

The well preserved granite gun fort and outer ramparts
testify to the strength of the coastal fortresses erected
in the Tudor period by Henry VIII. It was eventually
besieged and captured from the land during the Civil
War in the 17th century.
Times: Open all year, Apr-Jun & Sep, daily 10-6 (Oct 10-5); Jul-Aug,
daily 9-6; Nov-Mar, daily 10-4. Closed 24-26 Dec & 1 Jan. (Reviewed
Mar 2002) **Fee:** £3.80 (ch 5-15 £1.90, u 5 free, con £2.90). (Reviewed
Mar 2002) **Facilities:** 🅿 ᴕ shop 🐾 (in certain areas) 🎋

🏛 FOWEY   Map 02 SX15
ST CATHERINE'S CASTLE
(0.75 mile along footpath off A3082)
Times: Open all year, any reasonable time. **Facilities:** 🎋 *Details not
confirmed for 2002*

GODOLPHIN CROSS   Map 02 SW63
GODOLPHIN HOUSE
TR13 9RE (situated off A303 between Townshend and
Godolphin)
☎ 01736 763194   🗎 01736 763194
e-mail: godo@euphony.net

A romantic Tudor and Stuart mansion, begun in 1475
and considerably extended over the centuries. The
Godolphin family's taste is evident throughout the
mansion, and of particular note are examples of 16th-
and 17th-century English oak furniture and Wootton's
1731 painting, Godolphin Arabian, one of the three
Arab stallion ancestors of all British bloodstock. The
gardens are Tudor, with some areas even earlier.
Times: Open May & Jun, Thu & Sun, 2-5; Jul-Sep Thu-Fri & Sun, 2-5.
Open BH Mons. Parties by arrangement at anytime throughout the
year including Sun (refurbishment in progress, contact in advance).
Fee: £3 (ch £1). Party 20+. Prices may vary according to repair
programme & what is available for viewing. **Facilities:** 🅿 💺 ♿
(telephone prior to visit. Lift installed) toilets for disabled shop 🏮 (ex
guide dogs)

GOONHAVERN   Map 02 SW75
WORLD IN MINIATURE
Bodmin Rd TR4 9QE (Turn off A30 at Boxheater junct
onto B3285 to Perranporth)
☎ 01872 572828   🗎 01872 572829
e-mail: info@worldinminiature.co.uk

There are six major attractions for the price of one at
this theme park. Visitors can stroll amongst famous
landmarks such as the Taj Mahal and the Statue of
Liberty, all in miniature scale, set in spectacular
gardens. Then there is Tombstone, a wild-west town
complete with saloon, bank, shops, livery stable and
jail. The Adventure Dome is the original super cinema
180 direct from the USA which shows two exciting
films. The gardens are 12 acres of beautifully
landscaped grounds with over 70,000 plants and
shrubs. See Jurassic Adventure World, Super X
Simulator and children's fairground rides.
Times: Open 24 Mar-26 Oct 10-4 (Jul-Aug 10-5) **Fee:** £5 (ch under 3
free, ch 4-13 £3.50, pen £4). Family ticket (2 adults & 2 ch) £15
Facilities: 🅿 💺 ♿ toilets for disabled shop garden centre 💺

GWEEK   Map 02 SW72
NATIONAL SEAL SANCTUARY
TR12 6UG (pass RNAS Culdrose & take A3293 & then
B3291 to Gweek, the sanctuary is signposted from
village)
☎ 01326 221361 & 221874   🗎 01326 221210
Times: Open all year, daily from 9am. (Closed 25 Dec). **Facilities:** 🅿
💺 ♿ (wheelchair available) toilets for disabled shop *Details not
confirmed for 2002* 💺

HELSTON   Map 02 SW62
FLAMBARDS VILLAGE THEME PARK
Culdrose Manor TR13 0QA (0.5m SE of Helston on
A3083, Lizard road)
☎ 01326 573404   🗎 01326 573344
e-mail: info@flambards.co.uk

Three award-winning, all-weather attractions can be
visited on one site here. Flambards Victorian Village is a
recreation of streets, shops and houses from the turn of
the century, including a chemist's shop. Britain in the Blitz
is a life-size wartime street featuring shops, a pub and a
living room with Morrison shelter; and Cornwall Aero
Park covers the history of aviation. The Science Centre is a
science playground for the whole family. There are many
rides from the gentle to the daring, including the new
Thunderbolt, Hornet Rollercoaster, Flambards Family Log
Flume, Balloon Race and play areas for the very young.
Times: Open Etr-Oct 10.30-5. End Jul-Aug 10-6. Closed some Mon/Fri
in low season) **Fee:** Please ring for details. **Facilities:** 🅿 💺 ♿ (95%
accessible, free loan of wheelchairs, route guides) toilets for disabled
shop garden centre 🏮 (ex guide dogs) 💺

LANHYDROCK   Map 02 SX06
LANHYDROCK
PL30 5AD (2.5m SE of Bodmin, signposted from A30,
A38 & B3268)
☎ 01208 73320   🗎 01208 74084
e-mail: clhan@smtp.ntrust.org.uk

Part-Tudor, part-Victorian building that gives a vivid
picture of life in Victorian times. The 'below stairs'
sections have a huge kitchen, larders, dairy, bakehouse,
cellars, and servants' quarters. The long gallery has a
moulded ceiling showing Old Testament scenes, and
overlooks the formal gardens with their clipped yews and
bronze urns. The higher garden, famed for its magnolias
and rhododendrons, climbs the hillside behind the house.
Times: Open Apr-Oct: House daily (ex Mon), but open BH Mon 11-
5.30 (11-5 in Oct). Gardens daily from mid Feb, last admission half
hour before closing. Winter Gardens Nov-Feb during daylight hours.
Fee: House & Grounds £6.80 (ch £3.40). Grounds £3.70 (ch £1.85).
Family ticket £17. Party £5.80. **Facilities:** 🅿 💺 ✗ licensed ♿ (house
accessible ex 2nd floor, small lift to 1st floor) toilets for disabled shop
garden centre 🏮 (ex on lead in park) 🐾 💺

🏛 LANREATH   Map 02 SX15
LANREATH FARM & FOLK MUSEUM
Churchtown PL13 2NX (A390 from Liskeard, then
B3359 for Looe/Polperro, signposted)
☎ 01503 220321

A hands-on Countryside Museum reflecting bygone
times in Cornwall. Implements and equipment from the
farmhouse, dairy and farmyard are displayed, together
with mill workings rescued from a derelict mill house.
Demonstrations of local crafts are given on weekday
afternoons from 2-4pm. Play phones, pets, and models
to operate make it a fun place as well as educational.
Times: Open Etr-May & Oct, daily 11-5; Jun-Sep, daily 10-6. **Fee:** £2.50
(ch £1.50, under 5 free). Party. **Facilities:** 🅿 & shop

🏛 LAUNCESTON   Map 02 SX38
LAUNCESTON CASTLE
PL15 7DR
☎ 01566 772365

Dominating this old market town is the ruin of the
12th- and 13th-century castle. Built in the early years of
the Norman Conquest, it soon became a symbol of the
authority of the Earls of Cornwall.
Times: Open Apr-Sep, daily 10-6; Oct, daily 10-5; Nov-Mar, Fri-Sun 10-
1 & 2-4. (Closed 24-26 Dec & 1 Jan). (Reviewed Mar 2002) **Fee:** £1.90
(ch £1, concessions £1.40). (Reviewed Mar 2002) **Facilities:** & (outer
bailey only) 🎇 🎇

LAUNCESTON STEAM RAILWAY
St Thomas Rd PL15 8DA (turn off A30 Launceston, well
signposted)
☎ 01566 775665

The Launceston Steam Railway links the historic town
of Launceston with the hamlet of New Mills. Tickets are
valid for unlimited travel on the day of issue and you
can break your journey at various points along the
track. Launceston Station houses railway workshops, a
transport museum, gift shop and book shop.
Times: Open Good Fri: 8 days inclusive, Spring: BH Sun for 6 days,
Jun: Sun-Wed inclusive, Jul-Sep: daily ex Sat, Oct: half-term week.
Fee: £5.20 (ch £3.50, pen £4.70). Family ticket £17. Dogs 50p.
Facilities: 🅿 💺 & shop

LAWRENCE HOUSE
Castle St PL15 8BA (in centre of town, near Launceston
Castle)
☎ 01566 773277 & 774518
Times: Open Apr-early Oct, Mon-Fri 10.30-4.30. Other times by
appointment. Closed BH's.
🅿 (50yds) (public parking with small charge) & 🎇 (ex guide dogs) 🎇
Details not confirmed for 2002

🏛 LOOE   Map 02 SX25
MONKEY SANCTUARY
St Martins PL13 1NZ (signposted on B3253 at No Man's
Land between East Looe & Hessenford)
☎ 01503 262532   🖷 01503 262532
e-mail: info@monkeysanctuary.org

Visitors can see a colony of Amazonian woolly
monkeys in extensive indoor and outdoor territory.
There are also conservation gardens, children's play
area, and activity room. Vegetarian café.
Times: Open Sun-Thu 11-4.30 from the Sun before Etr-end Sep.
Fee: £4 (ch £1.50 & concession £3). **Facilities:** 🅿 💺 & toilets for
disabled shop 🎇 🎇

🏛 MADRON   Map 02 SW43
TRENGWAINTON GARDEN
Penzance TR20 8RZ (2m NW Penzance, 0.5m W of
Heamoor off Penzance - Morvah rd (B3312), 0.5m off St
Just rd (A3071))
☎ 01736 362297   🖷 01736 362297

Rhododendrons and magnolias grow in profusion at
Trengwainton, along with many plants that are difficult
to grow in Britain. The mild climate means that seed
collected on expeditions to the Far East and southern
hemisphere have flourished to produce a magnificent
display in this 20th-century garden.
Times: Open Mar-Feb, Sun-Thu also Good Fri 10-5.30. (Feb, Mar & Oct
11-5). Last admission 30 mins before closing. **Fee:** £3.60. Family ticket
£9. Party £2.90pp **Facilities:** 🅿 & (braille guide, special route, 2
w/chairs) toilets for disabled shop garden centre 🎇 🎇

🏛 MARAZION   Map 02 SW53
ST MICHAEL'S MOUNT
TR17 0HT (0.5m S of A394)
☎ 01736 710507 & 710265   🖷 01736 711544
e-mail: godolphin@manor-office.co.uk

Reached on foot by causeway at low tide, or by ferry at
high tide in the summer only, St Michael's Mount rises
dramatically from the sea, a medieval castle to which a
magnificent east wing was added in the 1870s. It is
home to Lord St Leven, whose ancestor St John Aubyn
aquired it in the 17th century.
Times: Open Apr-Oct, Mon-Fri 10.30-5.30. Last admission 4.45. The
Castle and grounds are open most weekends during the summer
season. These are special charity open days and NT members are also
asked to pay. group bookings 01736 710507. **Fee:** £4.50 (ch £2.25)
Family ticket £12. Party 20+ £4.10 each. **Facilities:** 🅿 (on mainland)
💺 🗴 licensed shop 🎇 (ex guide dogs) 🎇 🎇

🏛 MAWNAN SMITH   Map 02 SW72
GLENDURGAN
TR11 5JZ (4m SW of Falmouth. 0.5m SW of Mawnan
Smith on road to Helford Passage)
☎ 01872 862090   🖷 01872 865808
e-mail: ctlpmo@smtp.ntrust.org.uk

This delightful garden, set in a valley above the River
Helford, was started by Alfred Fox in 1820. The

contd.

informal landscape contains trees and shrubs from all over the world, including the Japanese loquat and tree ferns from New Zealand. There is a laurel maze, and a Giant's Stride which is popular with children. The house is not open.
Times: Open 16 Feb-3 Nov, Tue-Sat & BH Mon (last admission 4.30). (Closed Good Fri). **Fee:** £3.60 (ch £1.80). Family ticket £9.
Facilities: 🅿 💺 ♿ (braille guide, limited access to gardens/ground floor) toilets for disabled shop garden centre 🐾 (ex guide dogs) 🐌 ◥

TREBAH GARDEN
TR11 5JZ (signposted at Treliever Cross rdbt at junct of A39/A394 & follow brown tourist signs)
☎ 01326 250448   📠 01326 250781
e-mail: mail@trebah-garden.co.uk

A 25-acre wooded ravine garden, descending 200 feet from the 18th-century house down to a private cove on the Helford River. The cascading Water Garden has pools of Giant Koi and exotic water plants, winding through two acres of blue and white hydrangeas to the beach. There are glades of sub-tropical tree ferns and palms, as well as rhododendrons and many other trees and shrubs. The beach is open to visitors and there are children's trails and activities all year.
Times: Open daily 10.30-5 (last admission). **Fee:** Mar-Oct £4.50 (ch & disabled £2.50, ch under 5 free); Nov-Feb £2.25 (con £1.25). Party 12+ £4 each. **Facilities:** 🅿 💺 ♿ (2 powered wheelchairs & 2 wheelchair routes) shop garden centre (only on leads) ◥

🏛 NEWQUAY   Map 02 SW86
BLUE REEF AQUARIUM
Towan Promenade TR7 1DU
☎ 01637 878134   📠 01637 872578
e-mail: info@bluereefaquarium.co.uk

Offering "a spectacular visit whatever the weather", this fascinating look at the undersea world contains a massive variety of underwater life from the Cornish Coastline to a Caribbean paradise. See lobster, triggerfish, dragonets, stingrays and sharks in a mixture of open-top tanks, rock-pools and the huge coral reef ocean tank.
Times: Open all year, daily 10-last admission 5. (Closed 25 Dec)
Fee: £4.95 (ch £2.95, pen & student £3.95). Family ticket £12.95
Facilities: 🅿 5mins walk 💺 ♿ toilets for disabled shop 🐾 (ex guide dogs) ◥

DAIRY LAND FARM WORLD
Summercourt TR8 5AA (Signposted from A30 at exit for Mitchell/Summercourt)
☎ 01872 510246   📠 01872 510349
e-mail: farmworld@yahoo.com
Times: Open daily, late Mar-Oct 10.30-5. Xmas opening telephone for details. **Facilities:** 🅿 💺 ♿ (wheelchairs for loan; disabled viewing gallery - milking) toilets for disabled shop 🐾 *Details not confirmed for 2002* ◥

NEWQUAY ZOO
Trenance Gardens TR7 2LZ (off A3075)
☎ 01637 873342   📠 01637 851318
e-mail: info@newquayzoo.co.uk

Education and conservation are the key issues at this exciting Zoological Centre. Apart from attractions such as the monkey enclosures, penguin pool, tropical house and lion house, the park also boasts a Maze, an Oriental Garden, an activity Play Park, a Tarzan Trail Assault Course, and a tortoise enclosure.
Times: Open Apr-Oct, daily 9.30-6; Nov-Mar 10-5. (Closed 25 Dec)
Fee: £5.85 (ch 5-15 £3.75, ch 2-4 £1.50, pen £4).Family ticket £17.50.
Facilities: 🅿 💺 ✕ ♿ (free wheelchairs, guided tours & sensory sculptures) toilets for disabled shop 🐾 (ex guide dogs) ◥

🏛 PENTEWAN   Map 02 SX04
THE LOST GARDENS OF HELIGAN
PL26 6EN (signposted from A390 & B3273)
☎ 01726 845100   📠 01726 845101
e-mail: info@heligan.com

The largest garden reclamation project in Britain, covering 80 acres. Four walled gardens are being restored to their former glory including the re-planting of Victorian varieties of fruit and vegetables. Various events are held throughout the year including walks, horticultural events, theatre workshops and educational courses.
Times: Open daily 10-6 (last admission 4.30pm): winter 10-dusk. Closed 24-25 Dec. **Fee:** £5.50 (ch 5-15 £2.50, pen £5, ch under 5 free). Family £15. **Facilities:** 🅿 💺 ♿ (free loan of wheelchairs) toilets for disabled shop garden centre ◥

🏛 POOL   Map 02 SW64
CORNISH MINES & ENGINES
East Pool TR14 7AW (2m W of Redruth on A3047, signposted from A30, Pool exit)
☎ 01209 210900   📠 01209 210900
e-mail: info@trevithicktrust.com

Impressive relics of the tin mining industry, these great beam engines were used for pumping water from 2000ft down and for lifting men and ore from the

contd.

workings below ground. The mine at East Pool has been converted into the Cornwall Industrial Heritage Centre which includes audio visual theatre giving background to all aspects of Cornwall's industrial heritage.
Times: Open, Apr-Oct, Mon-Sat 11-5; Aug open daily 11-5. **Fee:** £5 (concessions £4.60, students £3) Family ticket £13. Party. **Facilities:** 🅿 ♿ lift to all levels, parking by arrangement toilets for disabled shop 🍴 (ex guide dogs) ♨ ☕

🏛 RESTORMEL   Map 02 SX16
RESTORMEL CASTLE
PL22 OBD (1.5m N of Lostwithiel off A390)
☎ 01208 872687

On a high mound surrounded by a deep moat, the huge circular keep of this Norman castle is remarkably well preserved and commands the Fowey Valley.
Times: Open Apr-Sep, daily 10-6(Oct 10-5). **Fee:** £1.80 (ch u5 free, ch5-15 90p, con £1.40). **Facilities:** 🅿 ♿ 🍴 ♨

🏛 ST AUSTELL   Map 02 SX05
CHARLESTOWN SHIPWRECK & HERITAGE CENTRE
Quay Rd, Charlestown PL25 3NJ (1.25m SE A3061)
☎ 01726 69897 📠 01726 68025
Times: Open Mar-Oct, daily 10-5 (later in high season). Last admission 1 hour before closing. **Facilities:** 🅿 (charged) ☕ ✕ licensed ♿ (ramps) toilets for disabled shop *Details not confirmed for 2002* ☕

THE CHINA CLAY MUSEUM - WHEAL MARTYN
Carthew PL26 8XG (2m N on B3274)
☎ 01726 850362 📠 01726 850362
e-mail: info@wheal-martyn.com

This museum tells the story of Cornwall's most important present-day industry: china clay production. The open-air site includes a complete 19th-century clayworks, with huge granite-walled settling tanks, working water-wheels and a wooden slurry pump. There is a short audio-visual programme, a working pottery, nature trails, and a children's adventure trail.
Times: Open Apr-Oct, 10-6 (last admission 5pm). **Fee:** £5 (ch & student £3, pen £4.60). **Facilities:** 🅿 ☕ ♿ shop ☕

EDEN PROJECT
Bodelva PL24 2SG (overlooking St Austell Bay signposted from A390/A30/A391)
☎ 01726 811911 📠 01726 811912

An unforgettable experience in a breathtaking location, the Eden Project is a gateway into the fascinating world of plants and human society. Space age technology meets the lost world in the biggest greenhouse ever built. Located in a 50 metre deep crater the size of 30 football pitches are two gigantic geodesic conservatories: the Humid Tropics Biodome and the Warm Temperate Biodome. This is a startling and unique day out.
Times: Open daily Mar-Oct 10-6 (last admission 5pm), Nov-Feb 10-4.30 (last admission 3pm). Closed 24-25 Dec. **Fee:** £9.50 (ch 5-15 £4, pen £7.50). Family £22 **Facilities:** 🅿 ☕ ✕ licensed ♿ (wheelchairs, car shuttle to visitor centre/biomes) toilets for disabled shop garden centre 🍴 (ex guide dogs) ☕

🏛 ST IVES   Map 02 SW54
(Park your car at Lelant Station and take advantage of the park and ride service. The fee includes parking and journeys on the train between Lelant and St Ives during the day).

BARBARA HEPWORTH MUSEUM & SCULPTURE GARDEN
Barnoon Hill TR26 1AD (M5 to Exeter, A30 onto Penzance & St Ives, in town centre)
☎ 01736 796226 📠 01736 794480

Dame Barbara Hepworth lived here from 1949 until her death in 1975, and the house is now a museum displaying sculptures and drawings, photographs, documents and other memorablia. Visitors can also visit her workshops. The garden contains a number of monumental sculptures, situated amongst semi tropical plants.
Times: Open all year daily 10-5.30 (Closed Mon Oct-Mar) **Fee:** £3.75. (concessions £3.50). **Facilities:** 🅿 (880 yds) ♿ (accessible with assistance) shop 🍴 (ex guide dogs) ☕

TATE ST IVES
Porthmeor Beach TR26 1TG (M5 to Exeter, then A30 onto Penzance & St Ives. Located on Porthmeor Beach)
☎ 01736 796226 📠 01736 794480

Tate St Ives offers a unique introduction to modern art, where many works can be seen in the surroundings and atmosphere which inspired them. The gallery presents changing displays from the Tate Gallery Collections, focusing on the post-war modern movement St Ives is so famous for. Artists represented at the gallery include Alfred Wallis, Ben Nicholson, Barbara Hepworth, Naum Gabo, Peter Lanyon, Bryan Wynter, Roger Hilton, John Wells, Patrick Heron and Terry Frost.
Times: Open all year, daily 10-5.30 (Closed Mon Oct-Mar). **Fee:** £3.95 (concessions £2.50). **Facilities:** 🅿 (800yds) ☕ ✕ licensed ♿ toilets for disabled shop 🍴 (ex guide dogs) ☕

🏛 ST MAWES   Map 02 SW83
ST MAWES CASTLE
TR2 3AA (on A3078)
☎ 01326 270526

Part of the coastal-defence system built in the reign of Henry VIII, the castle guarded the Fal estuary, together with Pendennis Castle (see Falmouth). A fine example of military architecture, it is of particular interest to military historians. Delightful gardens surrounding it.
Times: Open Apr-Sep, daily 10-6 (Oct 10-5); Nov-Mar, Fri-Tue 10-4 (closed 1-2pm). Closed 24-26 Dec & 1 Jan. **Fee:** £2.70 (ch 5-15 £1.40, ch 5 free, con £2) **Facilities:** 🅿 ♿ shop 🍴 ♨

🏛 SANCREED   Map 02 SW42
CARN EUNY ANCIENT VILLAGE
(1.25m SW, off A30)
Times: Open any reasonable time. **Facilities:** 🅿 ♨ *Details not confirmed for 2002*

⛰ TINTAGEL
Map 02 SX08

TINTAGEL CASTLE
PL34 0HE (on Tintagel Head, 0.5 mile along uneven track from Tintagel, no vehicles)
☎ 01840 770328

These romantic ruins make a dramatic sight on the edge of the towering cliffs. Associated in popular legend with King Arthur and the magician, Merlin, theories as to its origins abound: a Celtic monastery, the stronghold of Cornish Kings of the Dark Ages, the Durocornovium of the Romans? Whatever the true answer, it remains one of the most spectacular sites in Britain.
Times: Open all year, Apr-Sep, daily 10-6 (9Jul-26Aug 7pm, Oct 10-5); Nov-Mar, daily 10-4. Closed 24-26Dec & 1Jan. (Please note there is a steep climb up steps to reach the castle) **Fee:** £3 (ch 5-15 £1.50, ch u5 free, con £2.30). **Facilities:** 🅿 (in village) shop ✖ 🎫

⛰ TORPOINT
Map 02 SX45

ANTONY HOUSE
PL11 2QA (2m NW, off A374 from Trerulfoot rdbt)
☎ 01752 812191

A fine, largely unaltered mansion, built in brick and Pentewan stone for Sir William Carew between 1711 and 1721. The stable block and outhouses remain from an earlier 17th-century building. The house contains contemporary furniture and family portraits. The grounds include a dovecote and the Bath Pond House.
Times: Open 3 Apr-May & 4 Sep-1 Nov, Tue-Thu & BH Mon 1.30-5.30 (last admission 4.45). Also Sun Jun-Aug. **Fee:** House & Garden £4.20. Woodland garden £3. Combined Gardens only £3.60. Party rates available. **Facilities:** 🅿 ♿ ♿ (braille guide, access to grounds is limited) toilets for disabled shop ✖ (ex guide dogs) 🐾 🗣

⛰ TREDINNICK
Map 02 SW97

SHIRES FAMILY ADVENTURE PARK
Trelow Farm PL27 7RA (signposted off A39)
☎ 01841 540215

The Dragon Kingdom is large undercover adventure zone, with slides, ball pools, ropes and bridges. Also of interest in the Enchanted Forest: animal electronic shows with talking and singing wildlife. Train rides around the woods and lakes on the lake.
Times: Open Good Fri-Oct daily 10-5. **Fee:** £6 (ch 2-14 £5.50, pen £5) **Facilities:** 🅿 ♿ ✖ licensed ♿ (most areas are ramped) toilets for disabled shop

⛰ TRELISSICK GARDEN
Map 02 SW83

TRELISSICK GARDEN
TR3 6QL (4m S of Truro on B3289)
☎ 01872 862090 📠 01872 865808
e-mail: ctlpmo@smtp.ntrust.org.uk

Set amidst more than 500 acres of park and farmland, with panoramic views down the Carrick Roads to Falmouth and the sea. The garden is well known for its large collection of hydrangeas, camellias, rhododendrons and exotic and tender plants. The Cornish Apple Orchard contains the definitive collection of Cornish apple varieties.

Times: Open 16 Feb-3 Nov, Mon-Sat 10.30-5.30, Sun 12.30-5.30. Park & woodland walks open all year. **Fee:** £4.40 (Family ticket £11).Party rate 15+ £3.70 each. Car park charge £2 (refundable on admission). **Facilities:** 🅿 (charged) ♿ ✖ licensed ♿ braille/audio guide, wheelchairs, batricar, induction loops toilets for disabled shop (open 11-4.30) garden centre (ex in garden) 🐾 🗣

⛰ TRERICE
Map 02 SW85

TRERICE
TR8 4PG (3m SE of Newquay off A3058 at Kestle Mill)
☎ 01637 875404 📠 01637 879300
Times: Open daily 2 Apr-Oct 11-5.30 (ex Tue & Sat), Open every day from 24 Jul-9 Sep. **Facilities:** 🅿 ♿ ♿ (braille/large print guides & tape tour) toilets for disabled shop ✖ (ex guide dogs) 🐾 *Details not confirmed for 2002* 🗣

⛰ TRURO
Map 02 SW84

ROYAL CORNWALL MUSEUM
River St TR1 2SJ (follow A390 towards town centre)
☎ 01872 272205 📠 01872 240514

Interesting displays on the history of the county, a world-famous collection of minerals, and paintings and drawings, including a number of Old Masters. Other galleries house displays of archaeology, Cornish history, and Egyptian artefacts. Recently completed galleries of Cornish wildlife, fashion and textiles.
Times: Open all year, Mon-Sat 10-5. Library closes 1-2. (Closed BHs). **Fee:** £3 (unaccompanied ch 50p, pen & students £2) **Facilities:** 🅿 (200 yds) ♿ ✖ licensed ♿ (lift, ramps to main entrances) toilets for disabled shop ✖ (ex guide dogs) 🗣

⛰ WENDRON
Map 02 SW63

POLDARK MINE AND HERITAGE COMPLEX
TR13 0ER (3m from Helston on B3297 Redruth rd)
☎ 01326 573173 📠 01326 563166
e-mail: info@poldark-mine.com

This Cornish tin mine has three levels open to the public; an 18th-century village, museums and a cinema showing a film on the history of Cornish mining. On the surface there are restaurants, shops, gardens and children's amusements. The West Country's largest collection of antiquities, including a 40ft beam engine.
Times: Open Oct-Apr, 10.30-4.30 (last tour 3pm). (Closed Fri ex 1/2 term week). Please check for winter opening times. **Fee:** Free. **Facilities:** 🅿 ♿ ♿ (newly refurbished museum allowing disabled access) shop (ex grounds) 🗣

⛰ ZENNOR
Map 02 SW43

WAYSIDE FOLK MUSEUM
TR26 3DA (4m W of St Ives, on B3306)
☎ 01736 796945

Founded in 1937, this museum covers every aspect of life in Zennor and District from 3000BC to the 1930s. Over 5000 items are displayed in 14 workshops and rooms. A photographic exhibition entitled People of Past Zennor tells the story of the village.
Times: Open Apr & Oct Sun-Fri 11-5, May-Sep Sun-Fri 10.30-5.30, also Sat during Summer school & BH's. **Fee:** £2.20 (ch £1.50, over 60's £2). Party rates 10+. **Facilities:** 🅿 (50 yds) ♿ ♿ (not suitable for wheelchair users) shop ✖ (ex guide dogs) 🗣

Cumbria

The heart of Cumbria is the massive and majestic Lake District National Park, approximately 1,200 square miles of woodland, hills, lakes, mountains, rivers, and small villages. This means that a visit to Cumbria is basically a visit to some of Britain's finest landscapes.

The highest of the Lake District's peaks is Scafell Pike, which at 3,210ft (978m) is also the highest point in England. Other notable peaks include Scafell itself, Helvellyn towering above Ullswater, Skiddaw looming in the north above Bassenthwaite Lake and the impressive Langdale Pikes towering above the fertile greenery of the Great Langdale valley. In all, there are more than 60 summits above 2,500ft (762m).

At the foot of the mountains are the lakes the district takes its name from. These were scooped out millions of years ago by Ice Age glaciers, and are mostly called 'mere' (Old English) or 'water'. Derwent Water is commonly regarded as the most beautiful of these, and is a haven for wildlife. Wast Water is much more sombre, hemmed in by grim mountains and scree slopes, while long and winding Ullswater is perhaps the most spectacular. Windermere is the busiest as well as the biggest at 10.5 miles (17km) long.

It wasn't until the 18th century that the Lake District began to be appreciated, and it wasn't until the 19th century that people came in large numbers to see it. Now, those wishing to visit may want to come in the spring or autumn, as the area can get crowded in summer. Fell-walking, rock climbing, pony trekking, and fishing are major Lake District activities.

The area has inspired writers as diverse as William Wordsworth, Beatrix Potter and Arthur Ransome, who set his novel *Swallows and Amazons* largely around Coniston Water.

Top: Little Langdale

ALSTON
Map 12 NY74

SOUTH TYNEDALE RAILWAY
The Railway Station, Hexham Rd CA9 3JB (0.25m N, on A686)
☎ **01434 381696**

Running along the beautiful South Tyne valley, this narrow-gauge railway follows the route of the former Alston to Haltwhistle branch. At present the line runs between Alston and Kirkhaugh.
Times: Open Etr-Oct, wknds & BH's; Jul-Aug, daily. Please enquire for times of trains. **Fee:** Please enquire for fare details. **Facilities:** 🅿 & (railway carriage for wheelchairs-pre-booking required) toilets for disabled shop

AMBLESIDE
Map 07 NY30

ARMITT MUSEUM
Rydal Rd LA22 9BL (beyond Bridge House opposite main car park)
☎ **015394 31212**   📠 **015394 31313**
e-mail: **mail@armitttrust.fsbusiness.co.uk**

A chronicle of the Lakes from Roman times to the 20th century. Talk to John Ruskin, watch your own lantern slide show, explore Lakeland scenery with photographer Herbert Bell. Talk to Oscar Gnospelius the early seaplane pioneer and admire the treasury of Beatrix Potter's original natural history watercolours.
Times: Open all year, daily 10-5 (last entrance 4.30pm). Closed 25-26 Dec. **Fee:** £2.50 (ch, students, pen £1.80) Family ticket £5.60.
Facilities: 🅿 50 yds & (chairlift to upstairs library) toilets for disabled shop 🐾 ex guide dogs 🍴

APPLEBY-IN-WESTMORLAND
Map 12 NY62

APPLEBY CASTLE
CA16 6XH (on A66, castle is top of the main street)
☎ **017683 51402**   📠 **017683 51082**
Times: Open 4 Apr-Oct, daily 10-5 (last admission); Oct, daily 10-4.
Facilities: 🅿 🍽 ✕ & (assistance available) toilets for disabled shop garden centre 🐾 (ex on lead, guide dogs) *Details not confirmed for 2002*

BARROW-IN-FURNESS
Map 07 SD26

FURNESS ABBEY
LH13 0TJ (1.5m NE on unclass road)
☎ **01229 823420**

Founded by the wealthy Cistercian Order in the 12th century, the red sandstone abbey is an impressive ruin. Its setting is the beautiful `Glen of Deadly Nightshade' near Barrow. Fine stone carving is displayed in the site museum.
Times: Open all year, Apr-Sep, daily 10-6 (Oct 10-5); Nov-Mar, Wed-Sun 10-4. Closed 24-26 Dec & 1 Jan. **Fee:** £2.70 (ch 5-15 £1.40, under 5's free, con £2). Personal stereo tour included in admission.
Facilities: 🅿 & 🐾 (in certain areas) 🎏

BIRDOSWALD
Map 12 NY66

BIRDOSWALD ROMAN FORT
CA8 7DD (signposted off A69 between Brampton & Hexham)
☎ **016977 47602**   📠 **016977 47605**
e-mail: **birdoswald@dial.pipex.com**

This unique section of Hadrian's Wall overlooks the Irthing Gorge, and is the only point along the Wall where all the components of the Roman frontier system can be found together. Birdoswald isn't just about the Romans, though, it's also about border raids in the Middle Ages, and recent archaeological discoveries.
Times: Open Mar-Nov 10-5.30. Reduced hours in Nov. Check with site before visit. **Fee:** £2.50 (ch £1.50, pen & students £2). Family ticket £6.50 **Facilities:** 🅿 🍽 & (ramp outside, disabled parking) toilets for disabled shop (not in tea room) 🍴

BRAMPTON
Map 12 NY56

LANERCOST PRIORY
CA8 2HQ (2.5m NE)
☎ **01697 73030**

The Augustinian priory was founded around 1166. The nave of the church has survived and is now used as the local parish church, providing a striking contrast with the ruined chancel, transepts and priory buildings.
Times: Open Apr-Sep, daily 10-6 (Oct 10-5). **Fee:** £2.10 (ch 5-15 £1.10, under 5's free, con £1.60). **Facilities:** 🅿 & 🐾 🎏

BROUGH
Map 12 NY71

BROUGH CASTLE
CA17 4EJ (S of A66)
☎ **0191 261 1585**
Times: Open any reasonable time. **Facilities:** 🅿 🐾 🎏 *Details not confirmed for 2002*

BROUGHAM
Map 12 NY52

BROUGHAM CASTLE
CA10 2AA (1.5m SE of Penrith on minor road off A66)
☎ **01768 62488**

On the banks of the River Eamont lie the ruins of one of the strongest castles in the region, founded in the 13th

contd.

century and restored in the 17th by the strong-minded Lady Anne Clifford.
Times: Open Apr-Sep, daily 10-6 (Oct 10-5). **Fee:** £2.10 (ch 5-15 £1.10, under 5's free, con £1.60) **Facilities:** 🅿 ♿ (ex keep) ⛺

⛪ CARLISLE   Map 11 NY35
CARLISLE CASTLE & BORDER REGIMENTS MUSEUM
CA3 8UR (north side of city centre, close to station)
☎ 01228 591992

This medieval castle has a long history of warfare. An exhibition marks the Jacobite Rising of 1745, when Bonnie Prince Charlie took the castle. It is also the home of the museum of the King's Own Border Regiment.
Times: Open all year, daily Apr-Sep 10-6; (Oct 10-5); Nov-Mar 10-4. Closed 24-26 Dec & 1 Jan. **Fee:** £3.10 (ch 5-15 £1.60, under 5's free, con £2.30). **Facilities:** 🅿 (400 yds) ♿ (parking for disabled at Castle) shop ⛩ ⛺

CARLISLE CATHEDRAL
Castle St CA3 8TZ (M6 junct 42,43 or 44)
☎ 01228 535169   🖷 01228 547049
e-mail: office@carlislecathedral.org.uk

Founded in 1122 as a Norman Priory for Augustinian canons. The chancel roof is magnificently decorated and the cathedral features an exquisite east window.
Times: Open daily throughout the year, Mon-Sat 7.30-6.15, Sun 7.30-5, summer BHs 9.45-6.15, winter BHs, Xmas & New Year 9.45-4.
Fee: Suggested donation of £2 per adult. **Facilities:** 🅿 (5 mins walk) (2xdisabled only at establishment) ✗ licensed ♿ (disabled parking, ramped entrance, loop system) toilets for disabled shop ⛩ (ex guide dogs)

GUILDHALL MUSEUM
Green Market CA3 8JE (near town centre, opposite The Crown & Mitre Hotel)
☎ 01228 534781   🖷 01228 810249
e-mail: barbaral@carlisle-city.gov.uk
Times: Open Good Fri-Sep, Tue-Sun 1-4. Winter by arrangment.
Facilities: 🅿 (500yds) (disc parking on street, 1 hr limit) shop ⛩ (ex guide dogs) *Details not confirmed for 2002*

TULLIE HOUSE MUSEUM & ART GALLERY
Castle St CA3 8TP (M6, junct 42, 43 or 44 follow signs to city centre. Car park located in Devonshire Walk)
☎ 01228 534781   🖷 01228 810249
e-mail: barbaral@carlisle-city.gov.uk
Times: Open all year, Mon-Sat 10-5, Sun 12-5. (Closed 25-26 Dec & 1 Jan). **Facilities:** 🅿 (5mins walk) (disabled parking on site by request) ☕ ✗ licensed ♿ (chair lift) toilets for disabled shop ⛩ (ex guide dogs) *Details not confirmed for 2002* ⬤

⛪ COCKERMOUTH   Map 11 NY13
JENNINGS BREWERY TOUR
The Castle Brewery CA13 9NE
☎ 01900 821011   🖷 01900 827462
e-mail: brewery@globalnet.co.uk
Times: Tours: 16-20 Feb & 23 Mar-30 Oct, Mon-Fri 11 & 2; 13 Jul-28 Aug, extra tour at 12.30; 4 Apr-19 Sep, Sats at 11; BHs 11 & 2. (Closed Sun). **Facilities:** 🅿 shop ⛩ *Details not confirmed for 2002* ⬤

LAKELAND SHEEP & WOOL CENTRE
Egremont Rd CA13 0QX (M6 junct 40, W on A66 to rdbt at Cockermouth on A66/A586 junction)
☎ 01900 822673   🖷 01900 822673
Times: Open all year, daily 9-6 (Closed 4-14 Jan 2001). **Facilities:** 🅿 ☕ ✗ licensed ♿ (hearing loop system) toilets for disabled shop ⛩ (ex guide/hearing dogs) *Details not confirmed for 2002* ⬤

WORDSWORTH HOUSE
Main St CA13 9RX (W end of Main Street)
☎ 01900 824805   🖷 01900 824805
e-mail: rworn@smtp.ntrust.org.uk

William Wordsworth was born here on 7th April 1770, and happy memories of the house had a great effect on his work. The inside staircase, panelling and other features are original. Portraits and other items connected with the poet are displayed. Please ring for details of concerts and other events during the season.
Times: Open 2 Apr-2 Nov Mon-Fri 10.30-4.30. Also Sats in Jun, Jul & Aug. **Fee:** £3 (ch £1.50). Family ticket £7.50. Party. Ask for details of discount with Dove Cottage,the Wordsworth Museum and Rydal Mount. **Facilities:** 🅿 ☕ ♿ (braille guide) shop ⛩ 🐾

⛪ CONISTON   Map 07 SD39
BRANTWOOD
LA21 8AD (2.5m SE off B5285, unclass road. Regular ferry services from Coniston Pier)
☎ 015394 41396   🖷 015394 41263
e-mail: josie@brantwood.org.uk

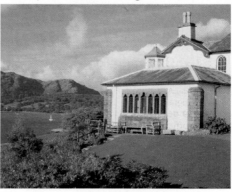

Times: Open mid Mar-mid Nov, daily 11-5.30. Winter, Wed-Sun 11-4.30. (Closed 25-26 Dec). **Facilities:** 🅿 ☕ ✗ licensed ♿ toilets for disabled shop ⛩ (ex guide dogs & on grounds) *Details not confirmed for 2002* ⬤

RUSKIN MUSEUM

The Institute, Yewdale Rd LA21 8DU (in village centre, accessed from A593, A595 & B5285)
☎ 015394 41164   ▤ 01539 441132
e-mail: museum@coniston.org.uk

John Ruskin (1819-1900) was one of Britain's most versatile and important political thinkers and artists. The museum contains many of his watercolours, drawings, letters, sketchbooks and other relics. The geology, mines and quarries of the area, Arthur Ransome's Swallows and Amazons country, and Donald Campbell's Bluebird are also explored in the Museum. **Times:** Open Apr/Etr (whichever earlier)-mid Nov, Wed-Sun 10-5.30. Phone to confirm details of winter opening. **Fee:** £3 (ch £1.75). Family ticket £8.50: Ruskin passport gives 10% discount at Brantwood, S.Y. Gondola and/or Coniston launch **Facilities:** ▣ & (audio guide) toilets for disabled shop ✼ (ex guide dogs) ◥

STEAM YACHT GONDOLA

Pier Cottage LA21 8AJ
☎ 015394 63856   ▤ 015394 35353
e-mail: rcogon@smtp.ntrust.org.uk

Launched in 1859, the graceful Gondola worked on Coniston Water until 1936. She came back into service in 1980, and visitors can once again enjoy her silent progress and old-fashioned comfort. **Times:** Open Apr-Oct to scheduled daily timetable. Trips commence 11 at Coniston Pier; 12 on Sat. Piers at Coniston, Park-a-Moor at SE end of lake & Brantwood. (Not NT). **Fee:** Ticket prices on application. **Facilities:** ▣ shop ✼ (ex guide dogs) ᭪

▥ DALEMAIN   **Map 12 NY42**

DALEMAIN

CA11 0HB (between Penrith & Ullswater on A592)
☎ 017684 86450   ▤ 017684 86223
e-mail: admin@dalemain.com
Times: Open 2 Apr-8 Oct, Sun-Thu. 10.30-5, Gardens, Medieval Hall and agricultural & countryside collections. House 11-4. **Facilities:** ▣ ♨ ✗ licensed & (ramp access at entrance, setting down & collection point) toilets for disabled shop garden centre ✼ (ex guide dogs) *Details not confirmed for 2002* ◥

▥ DALTON-IN-FURNESS   **Map 07 SD27**

SOUTH LAKES WILD ANIMAL PARK

Crossgates LA15 8JR (M6 junct 36, A590 to Dalton-in-Furness, signed)
☎ 01229 466086   ▤ 01229 466086
e-mail: office@wildanimalpark.co.uk
Times: Open all year, daily 10-6, during Winter 10-dusk. (Closed 25 Dec) **Facilities:** ▣ ♨ & (Sound system, wheelchair users may need help) toilets for disabled shop ✼ *Details not confirmed for 2002* ◥

▥ GRASMERE   **Map 11 NY30**

DOVE COTTAGE & THE WORDSWORTH MUSEUM

LA22 9SH (S, off A591, immediately before Grasmere village)
☎ 015394 35544 & 35547   ▤ 015394 35748
e-mail: enquires@wordsworth.org.uk

Dove Cottage was the inspirational home of William Wordsworth for over eight years, and it was here that he wrote some of his best-known poetry. The cottage has been open to the public since 1891, and is kept in its original condition. The museum displays manuscripts, works of art and items that belonged to the poet. **Times:** Open daily 9.30-5.30, last admission 5pm. (Closed 8 Jan-4 Feb & 24-26 Dec). **Fee:** Admission charge, discount and concessions available. Reciprocal discount offer with Rydal Mount, Ambleside & Wordsworth House, Cockermouth. **Facilities:** ▣ ♨ ✗ licensed & (ramps) toilets for disabled shop ✼ (ex guide dogs) ◥

▥ HARDKNOTT CASTLE ROMAN FORT   **Map 07 NY20**

HARDKNOTT CASTLE ROMAN FORT

(at W end of Hardknott Pass)
Times: Open any reasonable time. Access may be hazardous in winter. **Facilities:** ▣ ✿ *Details not confirmed for 2002*

▥ HAWKSHEAD   **Map 07 SD39**

BEATRIX POTTER GALLERY

Main St LA22 0NS
☎ 015394 36355   ▤ 015394 36118
e-mail: rhabpg@smtp.ntrust.org.uk

An annually changing exhibition of Beatrix Potter's original illustrations from her children's storybooks, housed in the former office of her husband, solicitor William Heelis. **Times:** Open Apr-1 Nov & Good Friday Sun-Thu 10.30-4.30 (last admission 4). Admission is by timed ticket including NT members. **Fee:** £3 (ch £1.50) Family ticket £7.50 **Facilities:** ▣ (300metres) (braille guide) shop ✼ ♿ ᭪

▥ HOLKER   **Map 07 SD37**

HOLKER HALL & GARDENS

Cark in Cartmel, Grange over Sands LA11 7PL (from M6 junct 36, on A590, signposted)
☎ 015395 58328   ▤ 015395 58776
Times: Open 2 Apr-30 Oct Sun-Fri 10-6. Last entry to grounds, hall & motor museum 4.30pm. **Facilities:** ▣ ♨ & (ramps, handrails) toilets for disabled shop ✼ (ex guide dogs & in grounds) *Details not confirmed for 2002* ◥

▥ KENDAL   **Map 07 SD59**

ABBOT HALL ART GALLERY

LA9 5AL (M6 junct 36, follow signs to Kendal. Located at S end of town centre beside church)
☎ 01539 722464   ▤ 01539 722494
e-mail: info@abbothall.org.uk

The ground floor rooms of this splendid house have been restored to their former glory, with original

contd.

carvings and fine panelling. The walls are hung with paintings by Romney, Gardner, Turner and Ruskin. The gallery has notable temporary exhibitions and a fine permanent collection of 18th- and 19th-century watercolours of the Lake District, and 20th-century British art, including works by Hepworth, Frink, Nicholson, and Sutherland.

Times: Open mid Feb-21 Dec, Mon-Sun 10.30-5 (reduced hours in Feb, Mar, Nov & Dec) please telephone for details. **Fee:** £3 (ch & students £1.50, pen £2.80). Family ticket £7.50. **Facilities:** 🅿 💺 ᕕ (chair lifts in split level galleries, large print lables) toilets for disabled shop 🐾 (ex guide dogs) 🍴

KENDAL MUSEUM

Station Rd LA9 6BT (opposite railway station)
☎ 01539 721374 ▤ 01539 737976
e-mail: enquires@kendalmuseum.org.uk

The archaeology and natural history of the Lakes is explored in this popular museum which also features a world wildlife exhibition and a display devoted to author Alfred Wainwright, who was honorary clerk to the museum.

Times: Open Feb-Dec, Mon-Sat 10.30-5. Reduced hours Feb, Mar. Nov & Dec, 10.30-4. Closed Sun. **Fee:** £3 (ch, students £1.50, pen £2.80). Family tickets £7.50. Groups 10+. Seasonal tickets available. Ticket provides reduced entry to Abbot Hall Art Gallery & Museum of Lakeland life & Industry. **Facilities:** 🅿 ᕕ toilets for disabled shop 🐾 (ex guide dogs) 🍴

MUSEUM OF LAKELAND LIFE & INDUSTRY

Abbot Hall LA9 5AL (M6 junct 36, follow signs to Kendal. Located at S end of Kendal beside Abbot Hall Art Guide)
☎ 01539 722464 ▤ 01539 722494
e-mail: info@lakelandmuseum.org.uk

The life and history of the Lake District is captured by the displays in this museum, housed in Abbot Hall's stable block. The working and social life of the area are well illustrated by a variety of exhibits including period rooms, a Victorian Cumbrian street scene and a farming display. Two of the rooms are devoted to the memory of Arthur Ransome.

Times: Open mid Feb-21 Dec, daily 10.30-5. Reduced hours Feb, Mar, Nov & Dec, please telephone for details. **Fee:** £3 (ch & students £1.50 pen £2.80). Family ticket £7.50. **Facilities:** 🅿 💺 ᕕ (listening posts, large print lables) toilets for disabled shop 🐾 (ex guide dogs) 🍴

⛰ KESWICK   Map 11 NY22
KESWICK MUSEUM & GALLERY

Fitz Park, Station Rd CA12 4NF (M6 junct 40, A66 to Keswick, follow tourist signs for Museum & Art Gallery when in Keswick)
☎ 017687 73263 ▤ 017687 80390
e-mail: keswick.museum@allerdale.gov.uk

Keswick's surprising past, from industrial mining centre to peaceful tourist town, is revealed in this fine example of a late Victorian museum. Set in the beautiful Fitz Park, the collections cover local and natural history, famous inhabitants and visitors,

including the Lake Poets, and houses the work of many artists who have been captivated by the local landscape and history.

Times: Open Good Friday-Oct, 10-4. **Fee:** £1 (ch, pen, students, UB40's & disabled 50p). Party 10+. **Facilities:** 🅿 (on road outside) (2 hour limit) ᕕ (ramp at front entrance, with handrails) shop 🐾 (ex guide & hearing dogs)

MIREHOUSE

CA12 4QE (3m N of Keswick on A591)
☎ 017687 72287 ▤ 017687 72287
e-mail: info@mireho.freeserve.co.uk

Visitors return to Mirehouse for many reasons: the spectacular setting of mountain and lake, the varied gardens, changing displays on the Poetry Walk, free childrens nature notes, four woodland playgrounds, connections with many writers and artists, live classical piano music in the house, generous Cumbrian cooking in the tearoom, and a relaxed, friendly welcome. Mirehouse was voted 'the best property for families in the UK' in the 1999 NPI Heritage Awards.

Times: Open Apr-Oct. House: Wed, Sun, (also Fri in Aug) 2-last entry 4.30. Grounds: daily 10.30-5.30. Parties by arrangement. **Fee:** House & grounds £4 (ch £2). Grounds only £2 (ch £1). Family ticket £11.75 (2 adults & up to 4 children) **Facilities:** 🅿 💺 ᕕ (notes available listing facilities) toilets for disabled 🐾 (ex guide dogs)

⛰ LAKESIDE   Map 07 SD38
AQUARIUM OF THE LAKES

LA12 8AS (M6, junct 36, take A590 to Newby Bridge. Turn rignt over bridge, follow Hawkshead Road to Lakeside. Well signposted)
☎ 015395 30153 ▤ 01539 530152
e-mail: aquariumofthelakes@reallive.co.uk

Discover the magic of the lakes at Britain's award winning freshwater aquarium. Over 30 displays, featuring the UK's largest collection of freshwater fish as well as mischievous otters and diving ducks. Walk on Windemere's re-created lakebed in the Lake District's only underwater tunnel, and come face to face with sharks and rays from around our coast in the fascinating Morecambe Bay displays.

Times: Open all year, daily from 9am. Closed 25 Dec. **Fee:** £5.50 (ch £3.75, pen £4.75). Family ticket (2ad+3ch) £16.95. **Facilities:** 🅿 (charged) 💺 ᕕ (lift to first floor) toilets for disabled shop 🐾 (ex guide dogs) 🍴

⛰ LEVENS   Map 07 SD48
LEVENS HALL

LA8 0PD (M6 junct 36. 5m S of Kendal, on A6)
☎ 015395 60321 ▤ 015395 60669
e-mail: email@levenshall.fsnet.co.uk

An Elizabethan mansion, built onto a 13th-century pele tower, with fine plasterwork and panelling. The topiary garden, laid out in 1694, has been little changed.

Times: Open: House & gardens Apr-Mid Oct, Sun-Thu. Gardens 10-5. House 12-5. Last admission 4.30. **Fee:** House & garden £6 (ch £3), garden only £4.50 (ch 2.20). **Facilities:** 🅿 💺 ᕕ (ramps within garden) toilets for disabled shop 🐾 (ex guide dogs) 🍴

MUNCASTER Map 06 SD19
MUNCASTER CASTLE, GARDENS & OWL CENTRE
CA18 1RQ (on the W coast of Cumbria, 1m S of Ravenglass on A595)
☎ 01229 717614 & 717393 (owl centre)
🖳 01229 717010
e-mail: information@muncastercastle.co.uk
Times: Open Castle; 19 Mar-5 Nov, Sun-Fri 12-5. Garden & Owl Centre, all year, daily 11-6. Parties by arrangement. **Facilities:** 🅿 💶 ✗ licensed ⅙ (wheelchair loan,induction loop,tape for partially sighted) toilets for disabled shop garden centre ✗ (ex on a lead) *Details not confirmed for 2002* 🍴

NEAR SAWREY Map 07 SD39
HILL TOP
LA22 0LF (2m S of Hawkshead. Behind The Tower Bank Arms)
☎ 015394 36269 🖳 015394 36118
e-mail: rpmhtop@smtp.ntrust.org.uk

Beatrix Potter wrote many Peter Rabbit books in this little 17th-century house, which contains her furniture and china.
Times: Open Mar-May & Sep-Oct 11-4.30, Jun-Aug 10.30-5. **Fee:** £4 (ch £2) Family ticket £7.50. **Facilities:** 🅿 (200 metres) (no parking for coaches) (braille guide,handling items,accessibility by arrangement) shop ✗ ⅜

PENRITH Map 12 NY53
WETHERIGGS COUNTRY POTTERY
Clifton Dykes CA10 2DH (approx 2m off A6, S from Penrith, signposted)
☎ 01768 892733 🖳 01768 892722
e-mail: info@wetheriggs-pottery.co.uk

Wetheriggs is the UK's only remaining steam-powered pottery. The Pots of Fun Studio is an interactive craft experience where you can throw a pot, paint a figurine, make candles or work with mosaics. There is also a newt pond and nature area.
Times: Contact establishment for details of opening times. **Fee:** Free. **Facilities:** 🅿 💶 ⅙ toilets for disabled shop ✗ (ex guide dogs & dogs on lead) 🍴

RAVENGLASS Map 06 SD09
RAVENGLASS & ESKDALE RAILWAY
CA18 1SW (close to A595)
☎ 01229 717171 🖳 01229 717011
e-mail: rer@netcomuk.co.uk

A narrow gauge steam railway, laid in the 19th century to carry iron ore from the mines at Boot. It began to carry passengers and then other freight once the mines were closed, and is now a passenger line. The railway runs through beautiful countryside for the seven mile journey from Ravenglass, along the coast, up to Dalegarth.
Times: Open: trains operate all year. Apr-Oct & between Xmas & New Year, daily; some winter weekends, please enquire. Limited service Jan & Feb except school hols. **Fee:** Return fare £7 (ch 5-15 £3.50). Family ticket £17.50. **Facilities:** 🅿 (charged) 💶 ✗ licensed ⅙ (special coaches - prior notice advisable) toilets for disabled shop 🍴

RYDAL Map 11 NY30
RYDAL MOUNT
LA22 9LU (1.5m from Ambleside on A591 to Grasmere)
☎ 015394 33002 🖳 015394 31738
e-mail: rydalmount@aol.com

The family home of William Wordsworth from 1813 until his death in 1850. The house contains important family portraits, furniture, and many of the poet's personal possessions, together with first editions of his work. In a lovely setting overlooking Windermere and Rydal Water, the gardens were designed by Wordsworth himself. Evening visits for groups can be organised.
Times: Open Mar-Oct daily 9.30-5; Nov-Feb daily (ex Tue) 10-4 (Closed 8 Jan-1 Feb). **Fee:** £3.75 (ch £1.25, pen £3.25 & student £3). Garden only £1.75. Party 10+ (pre booked groups £3.25). Reciprocal discount ticket with Dove Cottage and Wordsworth House. **Facilities:** 🅿 shop ✗ (ex guide dogs & garden) 🍴

SEDBERGH Map 07 SD69
NATIONAL PARK CENTRE
72 Main St LA10 5AS
☎ 015396 20125 🖳 015396 21732
Times: Open Apr-Oct, daily 10-5. Nov-Mar open 2 days a week. **Facilities:** 🅿 (charged) ⅙ (accessible with help Radar key scheme) toilets for disabled shop *Details not confirmed for 2002*

SELLAFIELD Map 06 NY00
THE SELLAFIELD VISITORS CENTRE
CA20 1PG (off A595, signposted)
☎ 019467 27027 🖳 019467 27021

Enter the Sellafield Visitors Centre, and computerised technology takes you into the future. Designed to inform and entertain the whole family, it features 'hands-on' interactive scientific experiments, intriguing shows and fascinating displays of technology.
Times: Open all year, Apr-Oct, 10-5; Nov-Mar daily 10-4. (Closed 25 Dec). **Fee:** Free. **Facilities:** 🅿 💶 ⅙ (induction loop) toilets for disabled shop ✗ (ex guide dogs)

SHAP Map 12 NY51
SHAP ABBEY
CA10 3NB (1.5m W on bank of River Lowther)
Times: Open any reasonable time. **Facilities:** 🅿 ⅙ ⚑ *Details not confirmed for 2002*

🏛 SIZERGH   Map 07 SD48
SIZERGH CASTLE & GARDEN
LA8 8AE (3.5m S of Kendal)
☎ 015395 60070 📠 015395 61621
e-mail: ntrust@sizerghcastle.fsnet.co.uk

The castle has a 60-foot high pele tower, built in the
14th century, but most of the castle dates from the 15th
to the 18th centuries. There are panelled rooms with
fine carved overmantles and adze-hewn floors, and the
gardens, laid out in the 18th century, contain the
National Trust's largest limestone rock garden.
Times: Open 28 May-Oct, Sun-Thu 1.30-5.30; Garden open 23 Apr-
Oct, 12.30. Last admission 5pm. **Fee:** £4.60 (ch £2.30). Family ticket
£11.50, Garden £2.30, Party 15+. **Facilities:** 🅿 💺 ♿ (wheelchair and
powered buggy for use, braille guide etc) toilets for disabled shop 🍴 🐾

🏛 SKELTON   Map 12 NY43
HUTTON-IN-THE-FOREST
CA11 9TH (6m NW of Penrith on B5305 to Wigton, 2.5m
from M6 junct 41)
☎ 017684 84449 📠 017684 84571
e-mail: hutton-in-the-forest@talk21.com

Times: Open, House; 12.30-4 12 Apr-30 Sep, Thu, Fri, Sun,& BH Mons.
Grounds daily (ex Sat) 11-5. Groups any day booked in advance from
Apr-Oct. **Facilities:** 🅿 💺 ♿ (electric wheelchair available) shop 🍴
(ex in grounds on leads) *Details not confirmed for 2002*

🏛 TEMPLE SOWERBY   Map 12 NY62
ACORN BANK GARDEN
CA10 1SP (6m E of Penrith on A66)
☎ 017683 61893 📠 017683 61467
e-mail: racon@smtp.ntrust.org.uk

A delightful garden of some two and a half acres, which
is used to grow an extensive collection of over 180
varieties of medicinal and culinary herbs. Scented
plants are grown in the small greenhouse, and a
circular walk runs beside the Crowdundle Beck. Please
ring for details of special events.
Times: Open 31 Mar-4 Nov, daily 10-5 (last admission 5pm).
Fee: £2.50 (ch £1.20). Family ticket £6.20. Party 15+ £1.80. **Facilities:**
🅿 💺 ♿ (braille guide) toilets for disabled shop 🍴 (ex on lead on
woodland walk) 🐾

🏛 TROUTBECK   Map 07 NY40
TOWNEND
LA23 1LB (3m SE of Ambleside at S end of village)
☎ 015394 32628
e-mail: rtown@smtp.ntrust.org.uk

The house is one of the finest examples of a
`statesman' (wealthy yeoman) farmer's house in
Cumbria, built in 1626 for George Browne, whose
descendents lived here until 1943. Inside is the original
home-made carved furniture, with domestic utensils,
letters and papers of the farm.
Times: Open 2 Apr-Oct, Tue-Fri, Sun & BH Mon 1-5 or dusk if earlier.
Last admission 4.30pm. **Fee:** £3 (ch £1.50). Family ticket £7.50.
Facilities: 🅿 (braille guide) 🍴 🐾

🏛 WINDERMERE   Map 07 SD49
LAKE DISTRICT VISITOR CENTRE AT
BROKHOLE
LA23 1LJ (on A591, between Windermere and
Ambleside)
☎ 015394 46601 & 01539 73126(minicom)
📠 015394 45555
e-mail: infodesk@lake-district.gov.uk

Times: Open Etr-Oct, 10-5 daily. Grounds & gardens open all year.
Facilities: 🅿 (charged) 💺 ✕ licensed ♿ (wheelchairs with
accessible trails & routes, lifts) toilets for disabled shop *Details not
confirmed for 2002* 🌊

WINDERMERE STEAMBOAT CENTRE
Rayrigg Rd LA23 1BN (0.5m N of Bowness-on-
Windermere on the A592)
☎ 015394 45565 📠 015394 48769

A unique collection of Victorian and Edwardian
steamboats and vintage motorboats, including the
oldest steamboat in the world - the S L Dolly of 1850.
Displays tell the social and commercial history of
England's largest lake, and there are steamboat trips
daily, weather permitting.
Times: Open 16 Mar-27 Oct daily, 10-5. Steamboat trips subject to
availability & weather. **Fee:** £3.40 (ch £2). Family ticket £8.50.
Facilities: 🅿 💺 ♿ toilets for disabled shop 🌊

Derbyshire

The natural features of this central English county range from the modest heights of the Peak District National Park, where Kinder Scout stands at 2,088 ft (636 m), to the depths of its remarkable underground caverns, floodlit to reveal exquisite Blue John stone.

These underground explorations may extend as far as a mile by boat at Speedwell Cavern, or half a mile by foot at Peak Cavern. Walkers and cyclists will enjoy the High Peak Trail which extends from the Derwent Valley to the limestone plateau near Buxton.

The county is well endowed with stately homes. Most notably Chatsworth, the home of the Duke and Duchess of Devonshire, with its outstanding collections of paintings, statuary and art. Other gems include Haddon Hall, a well preserved medieval house, the Elizabethan Hardwick Hall, and Kedleston Hall, created by the Scottish designer Robert Adam.

The spa town of Matlock is the county's administrative centre. Other major towns are Derby, home of Royal Crown Derby china, and the old coal mining town of Chesterfield, with its crooked spire. Bargain hunters will enjoy a browse around the huge open air market in Chesterfield on a Monday, Friday and Saturday, or the Flea Market on a Thursday.

Around the villages of Derbyshire, look out for the ancient tradition of well dressing, the decorating of springs and wells – the precious sources of life-sustaining water – with pictures formed from flowers.

The county also has links with angling. Izaak Walton, the 17th-century "Father of Angling" and his friend Charles Cotton together wrote *The Compleat Angler*, based on their fishing experiences in Derbyshire.

Top: Monsal Dale

EVENTS & FESTIVALS

February
Pancake Races, Winster

May-September
Well dressings throughout the county

April
26th-27th & 4th May Buxton Music, Speech & Drama Festival
tbc Flagg Races, Flagg Moor
tbc Steam Into Spring, Peak Rail, Rowsley South Station

May
11th-12th Chatsworth Horse Trials, Chatsworth
tbc Derbyshire County Show, Alvaston

July
11th-21st Buxton Opera Festival, Buxton (provisional)
21st Ashbourne Highland Gathering

August
7th-8th Bakewell Show, Bakewell
17th Ashbourne Show
26th Chesterfield Evening Fireworks
31st-1st Sep Chatsworth Country Fair

September
31st August-1st Chatsworth Country Fair
tbc Buxton Country Music Festival, Buxton
tbc Wirksworth Festival

October
16th Ilkeston Charter Fair

November
3rd Dovedale Dash, Thorpe

BOLSOVER
Map 08 SK47
BOLSOVER CASTLE
Castle St S44 6PR (on A632)
☎ 01246 822844

An enchanting and romantic spectacle, situated high on a wooded hilltop dominating the surrounding landscape, this 17th-century mansion was built on the site of a Norman castle. The keep displays elaborate fireplaces, panelling and wall paintings and there is also an impressive indoor Riding School.
Times: Open all year, Apr-Sep, daily 10-6 (Oct 10-5); Nov-Mar, Wed-Sun 10-4. Closed 24-26 Dec & 1 Jan. **Fee:** £5 (ch 5-15 £2.50, under 5's free, con £3.80). Personal stereo tour included in admission.
Facilities: 🅿 ♿ (keep not accessible) shop ✕ ✿

BUXTON
Map 07 SK07
POOLE'S CAVERN (BUXTON COUNTRY PARK)
Green Ln SK17 9DH (from A6 or A515 follow signs)
☎ 01298 26978   🖷 01298 73563
e-mail: info@poolescavern.co.uk
Times: Open Mar-Oct, daily 10-5. (Open in winter for groups only).
Facilities: 🅿 ♨ ♿ toilets for disabled shop ✕ (ex in woodland)
Details not confirmed for 2002 ♥

CALKE
Map 08 SK32
CALKE ABBEY
DE73 1LE (9m S of Derby, on A514)
☎ 01332 863822   🖷 01332 865272
e-mail: eckxxx@smtp.ntrust.org.uk

A fine baroque mansion standing in extensive parkland with walled flower garden. A large natural history collection is among many treasures here.
Times: Open 27 Mar-1 Nov Sat-Wed (incl BH Mon); House & church 1-5.30 Gardens from 11am. Last admission 5pm. Park open all year, Apr-Oct closes 9pm or dusk if earlier. House, church & garden closed one Sat Aug. **Fee:** £5.40 (ch £2.70) Family ticket £13.50. Garden only £3. **Facilities:** 🅿 ✕ licensed ♿ (braille guide, hearing system, buggy/wheelchair available) toilets for disabled shop ✕ (ex guide dogs) ♥ *Details not confirmed for 2002*

CASTLETON
Map 07 SK18
BLUE-JOHN CAVERN & MINE
Buxton Rd S33 8WP (follow brown "Blue-John Cavern" signs from Castleton)
☎ 01433 620638 & 620642   🖷 01433 621586
e-mail: lesley@bluejohn.gemsoft.co.uk

A remarkable example of a water-worn cave, over a third of a mile long, with chambers 200ft high. It contains 8 of the 14 veins of Blue John stone, and has been the major source of this unique form of fluorspar for nearly 300 years.
Times: Open all year daily 9.30-6 (or dusk). Guided tours of approx 1hr every 10 mins tour. **Fee:** £6 (ch £3, pen & student £4) Family ticket £16. Party rates on request. **Facilities:** 🅿 ♨ (not suitable for disabled visitors) shop ♥

PEAK CAVERN
S33 8WS (on A6187, in centre of Castleton)
☎ 01433 620285   🖷 01433 623229
e-mail: info@peakcavern.co.uk

One of the most spectacular natural limestone caves in the Peak District, with an electrically-lit underground walk of about half a mile. Ropes have been made for over 500 years in the 'Grand Entrance Hall', and traces of a row of cottages can be seen. Rope-making demonstrations are included on every tour.
Times: Open Etr-Oct, daily 10-5. Nov-Etr wknds only 10-5 **Fee:** £5 (ch £3, other concessions £4). Family ticket £14. **Facilities:** 🅿 (charged) shop ♥

PEVERIL CASTLE
Market Place SW33 8WQ (on S side of Castleton)
☎ 01433 620613

William Peveril, one of William the Conqueror's trusted knights, guarded the King's manors in the Peak from this natural vantage point which commands spectacular views of the Hope Valley. The area is designated a Site of Special Scientific Interest.
Times: Open all year, Apr-Sep, daily 10-6 (Oct 10-5); Nov-Mar, Wed-Sun 10-4. Closed 24-26 Dec & 1 Jan. **Fee:** £2.30 (ch 5-15 £1.20, under 5's free, con £1.70) **Facilities:** shop ✕ ✿

SPEEDWELL CAVERN
Winnats Pass S33 8WA (off A625, (A625 becomes A6187 at Hathersage) 0.5m W of Castleton)
☎ 01433 620512   🖷 01433 621888
e-mail: info@speedwellcavern.co.uk

Descend 105 steps to a boat that takes you on a 1 mile underground exploration of the floodlit cavern.
Times: Open all year, Etr-Oct daily 9.30-6, Nov-Etr 10-5. (Closed 25 Dec). Phone to check Winter opening times due to weather.
Fee: £5.50 (ch £3.50) **Facilities:** 🅿 (charged) shop ♥

TREAK CLIFF CAVERN
S33 8WP (0.75m W of Castleton on A6187)
☎ 01433 620571   🖷 01433 620519

An underground world of stalactites, stalagmites, flowstone, rock and cave formations, minerals and fossils. There are rich deposits of the rare and beautiful Blue John stone, and the show caves include the Witch's Cave, Aladdin's Cave and Fairyland Grotto.
Times: Open all year, Mar-Oct daily 9.30-last tour 4.45. Nov-Feb daily 10-last tour at 3.20. All tours are guided & last about 40 mins.
Fee: Adults £5.50 (ch 5-15 £3). Family ticket (2ad+2ch) £15.
Facilities: 🅿 ♨ (establishment can only cater for walking disabled) shop ♥

🏛 CHATSWORTH   Map 08 SK27
CHATSWORTH
DE45 1PP (8m N of Matlock on B6012)
☎ 01246 582204   📠 01246 583536
e-mail: visit@chatsworth-house.co.uk
Times: Open 15 Mar-29 Oct, House & garden 11-4.30, Farmyard
10.30-4.30. **Facilities:** 🅿 (charged) 🍽 ✕ licensed 🦽 (3 electric
wheelchairs available for garden) toilets for disabled shop garden
centre 🐾 (ex park & gardens on lead) *Details not confirmed for 2002*

🏛 CRESWELL   Map 08 SK57
CRESWELL CRAGS VISITOR CENTRE
Crags Rd, Welbeck S80 3LH (1m E off B6042)
☎ 01909 720378

Times: Open all year, Feb-Oct, daily, 10.30-4.30; Nov-Jan, Sun only
10.30-4.30. **Facilities:** 🅿 🦽 (wheelchair loan) toilets for disabled shop
Details not confirmed for 2002

🏛 CRICH   Map 08 SK35
NATIONAL TRAMWAY MUSEUM
DE4 5DP (off B5035)
☎ 01773 852565   📠 01773 852326
e-mail: info@tramway.co.uk

A mile-long scenic journey through a Period Street to
open countryside with panoramic views. You can enjoy
unlimited vintage tram rides, and the exhibition hall
houses the largest collection of vintage electric trams in
Britain. Ring for details of special events.
Times: Open Apr-Oct, daily 10-5.30 (6.30pm wknds Jun-Aug & BH
wknds). Winter, open Sun & Mon, 10.30-4. **Fee:** £7 (ch 4-15 £3.50, pen
£6). Family ticket (2ad+3ch) £19. **Facilities:** 🅿 🍽 🦽 🐦 (Braille
guidebooks, converted tram, talktype facility) toilets for disabled shop

🏛 CROMFORD   Map 08 SK25
ARKWRIGHT'S CROMFORD MILL
Mill Ln DE4 3RQ (off A6, 3m S of Matlock)
☎ 01629 824297   📠 01629 823256
e-mail: info@cromfordmill.co.uk

Sir Richard Arkwright established the world's first
successful water-powered cotton spinning mill at
Cromford in 1771. The Arkwright Society are involved

in a major restoration to create a lasting monument to
an extraordinary genius. Guided tours are available.
A programme of lectures and visits - ring for details.
Times: Open all year, daily 9-5 (Closed 25 Dec). **Fee:** Guided tour &
exhibitions £2 (ch & pen £1.50). Mill site Free. **Facilities:** 🅿 ✕ 🦽
toilets for disabled shop 🐦

🏛 DENBY   Map 08 SK34
DENBY POTTERY VISITOR CENTRE
Derby Rd DE5 8NX (8m N of Derby, on B6179)
☎ 01773 740799   📠 01773 740749

Tours of the factory take place daily and include lots of
hands-on activities like painting a plate and making a
tray. Cookery demonstrations take place alongside the
extensive Cookery Emporium, and a huge range of
discounted seconds are available in the Denby Factory
Shop.
Times: Open all year. Full factory tours, Mon-Thu 10.30 & 1. Craftroom
tour only, daily 10-3.15. Visitors Centre Mon-Sat 9.30-5, Sun 10-5.
Fee: Free. **Facilities:** 🅿 🍽 ✕ licensed 🦽 (lift) toilets for disabled
shop garden centre 🐾 (ex guide dogs) 🐦

⚏ DERBY   Map 08 SK33

DERBY MUSEUM & ART GALLERY
The Strand DE1 1BS (in city centre)
☎ 01332 716659 ▤ 01332 716670
e-mail: enquire@derbymuseum.freeserve.co.uk

The museum has a wide range of displays, notably of Derby porcelain, and paintings by the local artist Joseph Wright (1734-97). Also antiquities, natural history and militaria, as well as many temporary exhibitions. **Times:** Open all year, Mon 11-5, Tue-Sat 10-5, Sun & BHs 2-5. (Closed Xmas, telephone for details). **Fee:** Free. **Facilities:** P (50yds) ዹ (lift to all floors, portable mini-loop, large print labels) toilets for disabled shop ✙ (ex guide dogs)

INDUSTRIAL MUSEUM
The Silk Mill, Silk Mill Ln, off Full St DE1 3AR (From Derby inner ring road, head for Cathedral & Assembly Rooms car park. 5 mins walk from here)
☎ 01332 255308 ▤ 01332 716670

The museum is set in an early 18th-century silk mill and adjacent flour mill. Displays cover local mining, quarrying and industries, and include a major collection of Rolls Royce aero-engines from 1915. There is also a section on railway engineering in Derby. **Times:** Open all year, Mon 11-5, Tue-Sat 10-5, Sun & BHs 2-5. (Closed Xmas telephone for details). **Fee:** Free. **Facilities:** P ዹ (lift to all floors) toilets for disabled shop ✙ (ex guide dogs) ◥

PICKFORD'S HOUSE MUSEUM OF GEORGIAN LIFE & COSTUME
41 Friar Gate DE1 1DA (from A38 into Derby, follow signs to city centre)
☎ 01332 255363 ▤ 01332 255527

The house was built in 1770 by the architect Joseph Pickford as a combined workplace and family home. It now shows domestic life at different periods, with Georgian reception rooms and service areas and a 1930s bathroom. Other galleries are devoted to temporary exhibitions. There is also a display on the growth of Georgian Derby, and on Pickford's contribution to Midlands architecture. **Times:** Open all year, Mon 11-5, Tue-Sat 10-5, Sun & BHs 2-5. (Closed Xmas, telephone for details). **Fee:** Free. **Facilities:** P ዹ (tape guides, video with sign language subtitles) shop ✙ (ex guide dogs)

ROYAL CROWN DERBY VISITOR CENTRE
194 Osmaston Rd DE23 8JZ (10 mins walk from bus & rail stations & Derby city centre)
☎ 01332 712800 & 712841 (tours)
▤ 01332 712863
e-mail: sjbirks@royal-doulton.com
Times: Open all year, daily. Factory tours twice daily, booking strongly advised. **Facilities:** P ♥ ✗ licensed ዹ (visitor entry accessible but not factory tour) toilets for disabled shop ✙ (ex guide dogs) *Details not confirmed for 2002* ◥

⚏ EYAM   Map 08 SK27

EYAM HALL
S32 5QW (in village centre)
☎ 01433 631976 ▤ 01433 631603
e-mail: nicwri@eyamhall.co.uk

An intimate 17th-century manor house in the heart of the famous "plague village". Home to the Wright family since 1671, the Hall offers a glimpse of domestic history through the eyes of one family in portraits, furniture, tapestries, costumes and memorabilia. Converted farm buildings house the Eyam Hall Craft Centre. Musical and theatrical events throughout the season. **Times:** House 27 May-2 Sep Tue-Thu, Sun & BH Mon 11-4. Craft Centre open Mar-Xmas Tue-Sun 10.30-5. **Fee:** House £4.25 (ch £3.25, pen £3.75). Family ticket £13.50. Party. Craft centre free admission. **Facilities:** P ♥ ✗ licensed ዹ (disabled entrance via special gate, ramps) toilets for disabled shop ✙ (ex guide & dogs in grounds) ◥

⚏ HADDON HALL   Map 08 SK26

HADDON HALL
DE45 1LA (1.5m S of Bakewell off A6)
☎ 01629 812855 ▤ 01629 814379
e-mail: info@haddonhall.co.uk

Originally held by the illegitimate son of William the Conqueror, Haddon has been owned by the Manners family since the 16th century. Little has been added since the reign of Henry VIII, and, despite its time-worn steps, few medieval houses have so successfully withstood the ravages of time. **Times:** Open Etr-Sep, 10.30-5, Oct, Mon-Thu 10.30-4.30. **Fee:** £5.90 (ch £3 & pen £5). Family ticket £15. Party 15+. **Facilities:** P (charged) ✗ licensed ዹ (access is impossible for those in wheelchairs) toilets for disabled shop ✙ (ex guide dogs) ◥

⚏ HARDWICK HALL   Map 08 SK46

HARDWICK OLD HALL
Doe Lea S44 5QJ (2m S M1 junct 29)
☎ 01246 850431 ▤ 01246 854200
e-mail: hwxxx@smtp.ntrust.org.uk

Hardwick Hall is celebrated as the creation of Bess of Hardwick, who began the building at 70, after the death

contd.

of her husband, the Earl of Shrewsbury. The house has a vast area of windows, which become taller from the ground floor up. The High Great Chamber and the long gallery are hung with tapestries and Cavendish portraits. Some of the needlework is by Mary, Queen of Scots, who was a prisoner here for 15 years.
Times: Open 27 Mar-27 Oct, Wed-Thu, Sat & Sun; BH Mon & Good fri 12.30-5 (Oct 12.30-4) Last admission 30 mins before closing. Garden daily except Tue 11-5.30. **Fee:** £6.40 (ch £3.20) Family ticket £16. Garden only £3.40 (ch £1.70) Family ticket £8.50 **Facilities:** 🅿 ✗ licensed ⅖ (hearing scheme, wheelchair if prebooked, braille guides) toilets for disabled shop ✹ (ex in park on leads) ❧

⛏ ILKESTON   Map 08 SK44
AMERICAN ADVENTURE THEME PARK
DE7 5SX (off M1 junct 26, signposted, take A610 to A608 then A6007)
☎ 01773 531521 (switchboard)
535301 (bookings) 📠 01773 716140
e-mail: sales@americanadventure.co.uk

This is one of Britain's few fully themed parks, based on the legend of a whole continent. The experiences here are widely varied, from the Missile Rollercoaster in Spaceport USA, to the wet and wild excitement of the Rocky Mountain Rapids ride and the Nightmare Niagara log flume. Fort Adventure is an action packed challenge and the driving school is great for kids. There's also a Mississippi paddle steamer, a horse-show in Silver City, glamorous Lazy Lil's Saloon Show and, Skycoaster, a 200ft free fall.
Times: Open Etr-end Oct, daily from 10. **Fee:** Prices not confirmed for 2002 **Facilities:** 🅿 ➦ ✗ licensed ⅖ (free wheelchair hire, must pre book, call 01773 531521) toilets for disabled shop ✹ (ex guide dogs) ➦

⛏ KEDLESTON HALL   Map 08 SK34
KEDLESTON HALL
DE22 5JH (5m NW of Derby)
☎ 01332 842191 📠 01332 841972
e-mail: ekdxxx@smtp.ntrust.org.uk

Derbyshire home of the Curzon Family for eight centuries. In 1760 Robert Adam built the south front and designed most of the interior, including the marble hall.
Times: Open - House; 23 Mar-3 Nov, Sat-Wed 12-4.30, last admission 5 (closed Good fri). Garden open same as house 10-6. Park open all year, Mar-Nov daily 10-6; Nov-Mar 10-4. Closed Xmas & New Year.
Fee: £5.30 (ch £2.60) Family ticket £13.20. **Facilities:** 🅿 ✗ licensed ⅖ (braille guide, wheelchair, self-drive vehicle) toilets for disabled shop ✹ (ex in park, must be on leads) ❧ Details not confirmed for 2002

⛏ MATLOCK BATH   Map 08 SK25
THE HEIGHTS OF ABRAHAM COUNTRY PARK & CAVERNS
DE4 3PD (on A6, signposted from M1 junct 28 & A6. Base station next to Matlock Bath railway station)
☎ 01629 582365 📠 01629 581128
e-mail: info@h-of-a.co.uk

Visitors here can ride high above the Derwent Valley in cable cars to the Heights of Abraham, with their spectacular views. Included in the ticket are underground tours in two famous show caverns, Explorer's Challenge, High Falls Rocks, a fossils shop, and picnic and play areas.

The Heights of Abraham Country Park & Caverns

Times: Open daily Etr-Oct 10-5 (later in high season) for Autumn & Winter opening telephone for details. **Fee:** £6.80 (ch £4.80, pen £5.80). Under 5's free - one per adult. **Facilities:** 🅿 (300m) ➦ ✗ licensed ⅖ (please ring for details) toilets for disabled shop ✹ (ex in grounds & cable car) ➦

PEAK DISTRICT MINING MUSEUM
The Pavilion DE4 3NR (On A6)
☎ 01629 583834
e-mail: mail@peakmines.co.uk

A large display explains the history of the Derbyshire lead industry from Roman times to the present day. The geology of the area, mining and smelting processes, the quarrying and the people who worked in the industry, are illustrated by a series of static and moving exhibits. The museum also features an early 19th-century water pressure pumping engine.
Times: Open all year, daily 11-4 (later in summer season). (Closed 25 Dec). **Fee:** Museum & Mine: £4 (ch, students, disabled & pen £2.50). Family £9. Museum only or mine only £2.50 (ch, students, disabled £1.50). Family £6. Party rates. **Facilities:** 🅿 (charged) ➦ ⅖ (Chair lift to Mezanine) shop

TEMPLE MINE
Temple Rd DE4 3NR (off A6)
☎ 01629 583834

In the process of being restored to how it was in the 1920s and 1930s, this old lead and fluorspar workings makes interesting viewing. A self-guided tour illustrates the geology, mineralisation and mining techniques.
Times: Open all year, Summer 10-5, Winter timed visits during afternoon. **Fee:** Museum & Mine: £4 (ch, pen, disabled £2.50). Family ticket £9. Museum only or mine only: £2.50 (ch, pen, disabled £1.50). Family £6. Party rates. **Facilities:** 🅿 (100mtrs) shop ✹ (ex guide dogs)

🏛 MELBOURNE
Map 08 SK32

MELBOURNE HALL & GARDENS

DE73 1EN (9m S of Derby on A514)

☎ 01332 862502 📠 01332 862263

Sir John Coke (Charles I's Secretary of State) bought the lease of Melbourne Hall in 1628 and the house has been home to two Prime Ministers: Lord Melbourne and Lord Palmerston. The glorious formal gardens are among the finest in Britain.

Times: Open, house daily throughout Aug only (ex first three Mons) 2-5 (last admission 4.15). Prebooked parties by appointment in Aug. Gardens Apr-Sep, Wed, Sat, Sun & BH Mon 1.30-5.30. **Fee:** House Tue-Sat (guided tour) £3 (ch £1.50, pen £2.50), Sun & BH Mon (no guided tour) £2.50 (ch £1, pen £2). House & Garden (Aug only) £5 (ch £3, pen £4). Garden only £3 (pen £2). Family £8. **Facilities:** 🅿 (200yds) 🖤 🖕 (ramp at garden entrance) shop 🗙 (ex guide dogs)

🏛 MIDDLETON BY WIRKSWORTH
Map 08 SK25

MIDDLETON TOP ENGINE HOUSE

Middleton Top Visitor Centre DE4 4LS (Signed off A6 in Cromford then, 0.5m S from B5036 Cromford/Wirksworth road)

☎ 01629 823204 📠 01629 825336

A beam engine built in 1829 for the Cromford and High Peak Railway, and its octagonal engine house. The engine's job was to haul wagons up the Middleton Incline, and its last trip was in 1963 after 134 years' work.

Times: Open: Information Centre, daily, wknds only winter. Engine House Etr-Oct 1st wknd in month (engine in motion). **Fee:** Static Engine 60p (ch 30p). Working Engine £1.20 (ch 60p). **Facilities:** 🅿 (charged) 🖕 (ex Engine house) toilets for disabled shop 🖤

🏛 OLD WHITTINGTON
Map 08 SK37

REVOLUTION HOUSE

High St S41 9LA (3m N of Chesterfield town centre, on B6052 off A61, signposted)

☎ 01246 453554 & 345727 📠 01246 345720

Originally the Cock and Pynot alehouse, this 17th-century cottage was the scene of a meeting between local noblemen to plan their part in the Revolution of 1688. The house is now furnished in 17th-century style. A video relates the story of the Revolution and there is a small exhibition room.

Times: Open 29 Mar-end Sep, daily 10-4. Xmas opening 16-24 Dec & 27 Dec-1 Jan, daily 10-4. **Fee:** Free. **Facilities:** 🅿 (100yds) 🖕 (signing available by prior arrangement) shop 🗙 (ex guide dogs)

🏛 RIPLEY
Map 08 SK35

MIDLAND RAILWAY CENTRE

Butterley Station DE5 3QZ (1m N of Ripley on B6179, signposted from A38)

☎ 01773 747674 & 749788 📠 01773 570721

e-mail: info@midlandrailwaycentre.co.uk

A regular steam-train passenger service runs here, to the centre where the aim is to depict every aspect of the golden days of the Midland Railway and its

successors. Exhibits range from the steam locomotives of 1866 to an electric locomotive. There is also a large section of rolling stock spanning the last 100 years.

Times: Open Apr-Oct, every wknd, Wed & most school holidays. **Fee:** £7.95 (ch 5-16 £4, pen £6.50) children under 5 free. Party 15+. **Facilities:** 🅿 🖤 🖕 (special accommodation on trains) toilets for disabled shop 🖤

🏛 SUDBURY
Map 07 SK13

SUDBURY HALL

DE6 5HT (6m E of Uttoxeter)

☎ 01283 585305 📠 01283 585139

e-mail: esuxxx@smtp.ntrust.org.uk

A 17th-century country house with a rich interior. The Great Staircase is one of the finest of its kind in an English house.

Times: Open 16 Mar-3 Nov, Wed-Sun & BH Mon & Good Fri 1-5.30pm or sunset if earlier. Last admissions 30 mins before closing. Gardens open 10-5. **Fees:** £3.90 (ch £2) Family £9.80. Joint ticket £6.30. Family joint ticket £15.60. **Facilities:** 🅿 🖤 🖕 (wheelchair available, braille guide & hearing system) toilets for disabled shop 🗙 (ex in grounds) 🐾 *Details not confirmed for 2002*

🏛 WIRKSWORTH
Map 08 SK25

WIRKSWORTH HERITAGE CENTRE

Crown Yard DE4 4ET (on B5023 off A6)

☎ 01629 825225

e-mail: heritage@crownyard.fsnet.co.uk

The Centre has been created in an old silk and velvet mill. The three floors of the mill have interpretative displays of the town's past history as a prosperous lead-mining centre. Each floor offers many features of interest including a computer game called `Rescue the injured lead-miner', a mock-up of a natural cavern, and a Quarryman's House. During Spring Bank Holiday, you can also see the famous Well Dressings.

Times: Open mid Feb-Etr & Nov Wed-Sat 11-4, Sun 1-4; Etr-mid Jul & mid Sep-Oct Tue-Sat 10.30-4.30, Sun 1-4.30; mid Jul-mid Sep daily 10-5. Also BH Sun & Mon. Last admission 40 mins before closing. **Fee:** £2 (ch & pen £1) Family (2ad+3ch) £5. Party 20+. **Facilities:** 🅿 (80yds) (pay & display) 🖤 🗙 licensed shop 🗙 (ex guide dogs)

Devon

A county of great contrasts, Devon encompasses wild moorland terrain and rolling farming country dotted with delightful villages. Exmoor extends to the spectacular northern coastline with England's highest cliffs, where there are excellent walks on the hills and coastal footpath.

In the south, stretching from Dartmoor to the seaside resort of Torbay, is the area alluringly dubbed the 'English Riviera'. Other major resorts are Torquay, Paignton and Teignmouth on the south coast, and Ilfracombe on the north. Perhaps more interesting to explore however, are the estuaries of Kingsbridge and Dartmouth, Sidmouth with its elegant seafront, and Salcombe with its flotilla of yachts.

Both Dartmoor and Exmoor have National Park status which preserves them from encroachment. Exmoor is home to the hardy little Exmoor pony and is the only remaining habitat in England for the native red deer. Dartmoor is the largest expanse of untamed country in Southern England, with Dartmoor Forest at its heart.

Devon's main cities are Exeter and Plymouth. The former was badly damaged in World War II, but the cathedral survives. Plymouth has been closely associated with naval history since Sir Francis Drake played his legendary game of bowls before facing the Spanish Armada, but as a centre for shipbuilding and a military base, it was also doomed to devastation by Luftwaffe bombing.

One of Devon's most famous natives is Agatha Christie (1890-1976). The queen of the mystery novel was born in Torquay and the town has a special walk and many plaques to commemorate the prolific novelist.

Local products to look out for while visiting Devon are seafood, cider, clotted cream, Honiton lace and Dartington glass.

EVENTS & FESTIVALS

May
16th-18th Devon County Show, Westpoint, Clyst St Mary
tbc Brixham Heritage Festival (music, dance, street theatre & fireworks)

June
28th-14th July Exeter Festival (various venues)

July
28th June-14th Exeter Festival
15th-21st Okehampton Arts Music Festival

August
2nd-9th Sidmouth International Festival (various venues, folk music, dance & song)
15th Okehampton Agricultural Show
22nd Chagford Agricultural Show
23rd-25th West Country Hot Air Balloon Festival, Tavistock (provisional)
9th-11th Dartmoor Folk Festival

September
10th Widecombe Fair, Widecombe-in-the-Moor

November
tbc Plymouth American Thanksgiving Festival (various venues), Plymouth

Top: Dartmoor

🏛 APPLEDORE   Map 02 SS43
NORTH DEVON MARITIME MUSEUM
Odun House, Odun Rd EX39 1PT
☎ 01237 422064
Times: Open Etr-Oct, daily 2-5; also May-Sep, Mon-Fri 11-1.
Facilities: P (opposite) & (hands-on items for visually impaired)
toilets for disabled shop ✗ (ex guide dogs) *Details not confirmed for
2002*

🏛 ARLINGTON   Map 02 SS64
ARLINGTON COURT
EX31 4LP (7m NE of Barnstaple, on A39)
☎ 01271 850296 🗎 01271 850711

Arlington Court was built in 1822 and is situated in the
thickly wooded Yeo valley. The centrepiece is the
Victorian mansion, surrounded by formal and informal
gardens. Also open to visitors is the working stable
yard, housing a collection of carriages and horsedrawn
vehicles. The extensive parkland around the house is
grazed by Shetland ponies and Jacob sheep.
Times: Open daily (ex 23 Mar-3 Nov) 10.30-5.30. Last admission 4.30.
Grounds open Nov-Mar during daylight hours. **Fee:** House & grounds
£5.40 (ch £2.70). Grounds only £2.70. Parties 15+ £4.60 each.
Facilities: P 🍴 & (wh.chrs available, ramps at house, batricar, braille
guide) toilets for disabled shop ✗ (ex in grounds on lead) 🍴 🍴

🏛 BARNSTAPLE   Map 02 SS53
MARWOOD HILL GARDENS
EX31 4EB (signposted off A361)
☎ 01271 342528

The gardens with their three small lakes cover 18 acres
and have many rare trees and shrubs. There is a large
bog garden and a walled garden, collections of
clematis, camellias and eucalyptus. Alpine plants are
also a feature, and there are plants for sale.
Times: Open daily, dawn to dusk. **Fee:** £3 (ch under 12 free, if
accompanied). **Facilities:** P 🍴 & garden centre

🏛 BEER   Map 03 SY28
PECORAMA PLEASURE GARDENS
Underleys EX12 3NA (from A3052 take B3174, Beer
road, signed)
☎ 01297 21542 🗎 01297 20229

The gardens are high on a hillside, overlooking Beer. A
miniature steam and diesel passenger line offers
visitors a stunning view of Lyme Bay as it runs through
the Pleasure Gardens. Attractions include an aviary,
crazy golf, children's activity area and the Peco
Millennium Garden. The main building houses an
exhibition of railway modelling in various small
gauges. There are souvenir and railway model shops,
plus full catering facilities.
Times: Open Etr-Sep (plus Autumn Half Term), Mon-Fri 10-5.30, Sat
10-1. Also Sun at Etr & 26 May-1 Sep 2002 **Fee:** £4.50 (ch 4-14 £2.95,
pen £4, over 80's, under 4's & disabled helpers free). **Facilities:** P 🍴
✗ licensed & (access with helper, wl.chr available. some of garden
steep) toilets for disabled shop ✗ (ex guide dogs) 🍴

🏛 BICKLEIGH   Map 03 SS90
BICKLEIGH CASTLE
EX16 8RP (off A396 follow signs from Bickleigh Bridge)
☎ 01884 855363
Times: Open Etr wk (Sun-Fri), then Wed, Sun & BH to late May BH,
then daily (ex Sat) to 1st Sun in Oct. **Facilities:** P 🍴 & (specially
arranged tours with experienced guide) shop garden centre ✗ (ex
guide dogs) *Details not confirmed for 2002*

🏛 BICTON   Map 03 SY08
BICTON PARK BOTANICAL GARDENS
East Budleigh EX9 7BJ (2m N of Budleigh Salterton on
B3178, leave M5 at junct 30 & follow brown tourism
signs)
☎ 01395 568465 🗎 01395 568374
e-mail: info@bictongardens.co.uk

Fifty acres of gardens, woodland, lakes, ponds and
fountains, with an Italian garden and a restored palm
house where bananas and other exotica flourish. There
are also fuchsia, geranium and temperate houses. A
countryside museum contains farm tools, wagons and
a cider press, and there's also an adventure playground
and Bicton Woodland Railway.
Times: Open Winter 10-5, Summer 10-6. (Closed 25 Dec) **Fee:** £4.75
(ch £2.75, concessions £3.75). Family ticket £12.75. **Facilities:** P 🍴
✗ licensed & (adapted carriage on woodland railway, wheelchairs)
toilets for disabled shop garden centre 🍴

🏛 BLACKMOOR GATE   Map 03 SS64
EXMOOR ZOOLOGICAL PARK
South Stowford, Bratton Fleming EX31 4SG (off A399)
☎ 01598 763352 🗎 01598 763352
e-mail: exmoorzoo@fsb.dial.co.uk

These natural and landscaped gardens cover an area of
12.5 acres with a waterfall, streams and a lake with
penguins, swans and other water birds, all roaming
free. There are enclosures with over two hundred
species of animals, birds, insects and reptiles on display
from all over the world, including lemurs, marmosets,
capybara and many, many more. The zoo specializes in

contd.

close encounters, handling sessions, and keepers' talks.
Times: Open daily, Apr-Oct 10-6; Nov-Mar 10-4. (Closed 16 Nov-4 Feb) **Fee:** £4.95 (ch 3-16 £3.50, under 3 free, pen £4.45), Family £15.
Facilities: 🅿 🍴 ⚬ toilets for disabled shop ✻ (ex guide dogs) 🍸

🏛 BUCKFASTLEIGH   Map 03 SX76
BUCKFAST ABBEY
TQ11 0EE (off A38 on A384 Dartbridge turn off, follow tourist signs for 0.5m)
☎ 01364 645530   🖷 01364 645533
Times: Open all year daily 5.30am-9.30pm. (visitor facilities 9-5 (summer) 10-4.30 (winter) **Facilities:** 🅿 🍴 ✗ licensed ⚬ (level site, braille plan, wheelchair available) toilets for disabled shop ✻ (ex guide dogs) *Details not confirmed for 2002*

BUCKFAST BUTTERFLY FARM & DARTMOOR OTTER SANCTUARY
TQ11 0DZ (off A38, at Dart Bridge junct, follow tourist signs)
☎ 01364 642916   🖷 01364 642916
e-mail: info@ottersandbutterflies.co.uk

Visitors can wander around a specially designed, undercover tropical garden, where free-flying butterflies and moths from around the world can be seen. The otter sanctuary has large enclosures with underwater viewing areas. Three types of otters can be seen including the native British otter along with Asian and North American otters.
Times: Open Good Fri-end Oct, daily 10-5.30 or dusk (if earlier).
Fee: £4.95 (ch £3.50, pen £4.50). Family ticket £15. **Facilities:** 🅿 🍴 ⚬ (wheelchair ramps) shop ✻ (ex guide dogs) 🍸

🏛 BUCKLAND ABBEY   Map 02 SX46
BUCKLAND ABBEY
PL20 6EY (off A386 0.25m S of Yelverton, signed)
☎ 01822 853607   🖷 01822 855448
e-mail: dbamex@smtp.ntrust.org.uk

Originally a prosperous 13th-century Cistercian Abbey, and then home of the Grenville family, Buckland Abbey was sold to Sir Francis Drake in 1581, who lived there until his death in 1596. Several restored buildings house a fascinating exhibition about the abbey's history. Among the exhibits is Drake's drum, which is said to give warning of danger to England. A new Elizabethan garden is now open.
Times: Open Apr-Oct, daily (ex Thu) 10.30-5.30. Nov-end Mar, Sat & Sun 2-5. Closed Xmas to mid-Feb. Last admissions 45mins before closing. **Fee:** Abbey & grounds £4.60. Grounds only £2.40. Party 15+. (Car park charge fundable against purchase of admission ticket).
Facilities: 🅿 (charged) ✗ licensed ⚬ (wheelchairs & motorised buggy available) toilets for disabled shop ✻ (ex guide dogs) 🐾

🏛 CHITTLEHAMPTON   Map 03 SS62
COBBATON COMBAT COLLECTION
Cobbaton EX37 9RZ (signed from A361 & A377)
☎ 01769 540740   🖷 01769 540141
e-mail: info@cobbatoncombat.co.uk

World War II British and Canadian military vehicles, war documents and military equipment can be seen in this private collection. There are over fifty vehicles including tanks, one a Gulf War Centurian, and a recent Warsaw Pact section. There is also a section on `Mum's War' and the home front. The children's play area includes a Sherman tank.
Times: Open Apr-Oct, daily 10-6. Winter, most weekdays, phone for details. **Fee:** £4 (ch £2.75, pen £3.50) **Facilities:** 🅿 🍴 ⚬ (most areas accessible) toilets for disabled shop ✻ (ex guide dogs) 🍸

🏛 CHUDLEIGH   Map 03 SX87
CANONTEIGN FALLS
EX6 7NT (off A38 at Chudleigh/Teign Valley junction onto B3193 and follow tourist signs for 3m)
☎ 01647 252434   🖷 01647 52617
e-mail: canonteignfalls@lineone.net

A magical combination of waterfalls, woodlands and lakes.
Times: Open all year, mid Mar-mid Nov, daily 10-5.30; Feb Half Term & Winter, Sun only 11-4. **Fee:** £4.50 (ch £3 & pen £4). Family ticket £14. Party 12+. **Facilities:** 🅿 🍴 ✗ licensed (grounds partly accessible) shop 🍸

🏛 CHURSTON FERRERS   Map 03 SX95
GREENWAY GARDEN
TQ5 0ES (follow NT brown acorn signs)
☎ 01803 842382   🖷 01803 661900
e-mail: dgwrtb@smtp.ntrust.org.uk

Greenway Garden is on the east bank of the River Dart, with south facing slopes. A woody valley with open areas in which many half-hardy trees and shrubs thrive. Managed in a natural state, Greenway boasts a superb plant collection with many rarities from all over the world, but chiefly from the southern hemisphere. The garden has a mysterious, wild character with stunning native flora.
Times: Open Mar-Sep, Wed-Sat **Fee:** £3.50 (ch £1.75) **Facilities:** 🅿 🍴 ⚬ toilets for disabled shop ✻ (ex guide dogs & in Parkland) 🐾

🏛 CLOVELLY   Map 02 SS32
THE MILKY WAY ADVENTURE PARK
EX39 5RY (on A39, 2m from Clovelly)
☎ 01237 431255   🖷 01237 431735
e-mail: info@themilkyway.co.uk

One of the West Country's leading attractions for the biggest rides and the best shows. Attractions include Clone Zone - Europe's first interactive adventure ride featuring a suspended roller coaster; Time Warp indoor adventure play area; daily displays from the North Devon Bird of Prey Centre; archery centre; golf driving nets; railway; pets corner and more. A new attraction 'Droid

contd.

Destroyers' has been added which invites pilots to save the Earth from the Vega Asteroid.
Times: Open Etr-Oct, daily 10.30-6. Telephone for winter opening times. **Fee:** £6.50 (ch £5.50). Family ticket (2 ad+2 ch) £21-extra ch £4 each. **Facilities:** 🅿 💺 ♿ (ramps) toilets for disabled shop 🍴 (ex if they are no leads) 🏊

🏛 CLYST ST MARY　　　　Map 03 SX99
CREALY ADVENTURE PARK
Sidmouth Rd EX5 1DR (leave M5 junct 30 onto A3052 Exeter to Sidmouth road)
☎ 01395 233200　📠 01395 233211
e-mail: fun@crealy.co.uk

Crealy Adventure Park offers indoor adventures including the River Raiders' Challenge and the Children's Magical Kingdom. Go-karts, bumper boats and train rides, plus lots of friendly animals.
Times: Open Apr-Oct, daily 10-6; Nov-Feb 10-5. (Closed winter term time Mon, 24-26 Dec & 1 Jan). **Fee:** £6.25 (pen £4.89, under 3's free). 4+ £5.99, Party 20+ £4.89. Annual ticket £24.99. **Facilities:** 🅿 💺 ✗ licensed ♿ (Carers admitted free) toilets for disabled shop 🏊

🏛 COMBE MARTIN　　　　Map 02 SS54
THE COMBE MARTIN MOTORCYCLE COLLECTION
Cross St EX34 0DH (adjacent to the main car park, behind beach)
☎ 01271 882346
e-mail: combemartin@motorcycle-collection.co.uk
Times: Open Etr then 20 May-29 Oct, daily 10-5. **Facilities:** 🅿 (adjacent to site) (public car parks have charges) ♿ toilets for disabled shop *Details not confirmed for 2002*

COMBE MARTIN WILDLIFE PARK & DINOSAUR PARK
EX34 0NG (M5 junct 7 then A361 towards Barnstaple and turn right onto A399)
☎ 01271 882486　📠 01271 882486
Times: Open Etr-1 Nov, daily 10-4 (last admission) **Facilities:** 🅿 💺 shop 🍴 (ex guide dogs) *Details not confirmed for 2002*

🏛 COMPTON　　　　Map 03 SX86
COMPTON CASTLE
TQ3 1TA (off A381 Newton Abbot road. 4m W of Torquay)
☎ 01803 875740　📠 01803 875740
e-mail: dpaset@smtp.ntrust.org.uk

A fortified house of the 14th to 16th centuries, Compton has been the home of the Gilbert family for 600 years. The Great Kitchen still has its bread ovens and knife-sharpening marks, and the withdrawing room has squints through which occupants could watch services in the chapel. Defensive measures were added in the 16th century, when there were French raids in the area.
Times: Open 2 Apr-Oct, Mon, Wed & Thu 10-12.15 & 2-5. **Fee:** Castle & garden £2.90 (ch £1.40) Party 15+. **Facilities:** 🅿 🍴 (ex guide dogs) 🐾

🏛 DARTMOUTH　　　　Map 03 SX85
BAYARD'S COVE FORT
TQ6 9AT (on riverfront)
Times: Open at all reasonable times. **Facilities:** 🅿 🍴 (in certain areas) ⚏ *Details not confirmed for 2002*

DARTMOUTH CASTLE
Castle Rd TQ6 0JN (1m SE off B3205, narrow approach road)
☎ 01803 833588

The castle dates from 1481 and was one of the first to be designed for artillery. It faces Kingswear Castle on the other side of the Dart estuary, and a chain could be drawn between the two in times of war.
Times: Open all year, Apr-Sep, daily 10-6 daily (Oct 10-5); Nov-Mar, daily 10-4. Closed 24-26 Dec & 1 Jan. (Review Mar 2002) **Fee:** £3.20 (con £2.40, ch 5-15 £1.60, under 5's free). (Review Mar 2002) **Facilities:** 🅿 shop 🍴 ⚏

WOODLANDS LEISURE PARK
Blackawton TQ9 7DQ (W, off A3122)
☎ 01803 712598　📠 01803 712680
e-mail: fun@woodlands-leisure-park

All weather fun with an outstanding range of indoor and outdoor attractions. Experience the biggest indoor venture centre in the UK. Enjoy 60 acres of outoor attractions for all the family including three watercoasters, a 500m toboggan run, Arctic Gliders, Mystic Maze and 15 massive play zones. There is an indoor falconry centre with flying displays, and a wide selection of animals and birds.
Times: Open 26 Mar-5 Nov daily, also wknds & school holidays. **Fee:** £6.10 Family ticket (2ad+2ch) £22.95. **Facilities:** 🅿 💺 ♿ (ramps) toilets for disabled shop 🍴 (ex guide dogs) 🐾

🏛 DREWSTEIGNTON　　　　Map 03 SX79
CASTLE DROGO
EX6 6PB (4m S of A30)
☎ 01647 433306　📠 01647 433186
e-mail: dcdpjj@smtp.ntrust.org.uk

India tea baron Julius Drewe's dream house. This granite castle, built between 1910 and 1930, is one of

contd.

the most remarkable works of Sir Edward Lutyens, and combines the grandeur of a medieval castle with the comfort of the 20th century. A great country house with terraced formal garden, woodland spring garden, huge circular croquet lawn and colourful herbaceous borders. Standing at more than 900ft overlooking the wooded gorge of the River Teign with stunning views of Dartmoor and delightful walks.

Times: Open Apr-Oct, daily (ex Fri but open Good Fri) 11-5.30. Garden open all year, daily 10.30-5.30 (or dusk if earlier). **Fee:** Castle £5.60. Garden & grounds only £2.80. Ch half price, under 5's free. Family ticket £14 **Facilities:** ⊡ ☻ ✕ licensed ஃ (wheelchairs available, lift to lower ground floor) toilets for disabled shop garden centre ⅍ (ex guide/hearing dogs) ✖ ➳

⌂ EXETER   Map 03 SX99
GUILDHALL
High St EX4 3EB (city centre)
☎ 01392 665500
e-mail: guildhall@exeter.gov.uk

This is one of the oldest municipal buildings still in use. It was built in 1330 and then altered in 1446, and the arches and façade were added in 1592-5. The roof timbers rest on bosses of bears holding staves, and there are portraits of Exeter dignitaries, guild crests, civic silver and regalia.

Times: Open when there are no mayoral functions. Times are posted outside weekly. Special opening by arrangement. **Fee:** Free.
Facilities: ⅊ (200yds) ஃ toilets for disabled ⅍ (ex guide dogs)

ST NICHOLAS' PRIORY
Mint Ln, off Fore St EX4 3AT
☎ 01392 665858 ▯ 01392 421252
e-mail: ramm-events@exeter.gov.uk
Times: Open Etr-Oct, Mon, Wed & Sat 3-4.30pm **Facilities:** ⅊ (200yds) shop ⅍ (ex guide dogs) *Details not confirmed for 2002*

⌂ EXMOUTH   Map 03 SY08
THE WORLD OF COUNTRY LIFE
Sandy Bay EX8 5BU (M5 junct 30, take A376 to Exmouth. Follow signs to Sandy Bay)
☎ 01395 274533 ▯ 01392 273457
Times: Open Etr-Oct, daily 10-5. **Facilities:** ⊡ ☻ ✕ ஃ (all parts accessible ex 'safari train') toilets for disabled shop ⅍ (ex guide dogs) *Details not confirmed for 2002* ➳

⌂ GREAT TORRINGTON   Map 02 SS41
DARTINGTON CRYSTAL
EX38 7AN (Turn off A386 in centre of Great Torrington down School Lane (opposite church). Dartington Crystal is 200mtrs on left)
☎ 01805 626262 ▯ 01805 626263
e-mail: enquiries@dartington.co.uk

Dartington Crystal has won many international design awards in recognition of its excellence. The factory tour allows visitors watch the glassware being crafted, from the safety of elevated viewing galleries. All age groups are encouraged to have fun in the glass activity area

and to discover the fascinating story of glass and the history of Dartington in the Visitor Centre.

Times: Open all year. (Closed Xmas & Etr Sun). Glass centre: Mon-Sat 9.30-4; Sun 10-4. Factory tour: Mon-Fri 9.30-3.15 (closed wkend & public holidays). Factory shops & restaurant: Mon-Sat 9.30-5; Sun 10.30-4.30. **Fee:** £3.95 (ch 6-16 £1.50, pen £2.95). Family ticket £10. Party on application. **Facilities:** ⊡ ☻ ✕ licensed ஃ (special tours available, book in advance) toilets for disabled shop ⅍ (ex guide dogs) ➳

RHS GARDEN ROSEMOOR
EX38 8PH (1m SE of town on A3124)
☎ 01805 624067 ▯ 01805 624717
e-mail: annet@rhs.org.uk

Rosemoor is the Royal Horticultural Society's first Regional Garden and Centre, second only to Wisley. The Formal Garden includes 200 varieties of rose, and there is a herb garden, potager, cottage garden, winter garden, alpine terrace and extensive herbaceous borders.

Times: Open: Gardens all year; Visitor Centre Apr-Sep 10-6, Oct-Mar 10-5. (Closed Xmas day) **Fee:** £4.50 (ch under 6 free; 6-16 £1). Party 10+ **Facilities:** ⊡ ☻ ✕ licensed ஃ (Herb garden for disabled) toilets for disabled shop garden centre ⅍ (ex guide dogs) ➳

⌂ HONITON   Map 03 ST10
ALLHALLOWS MUSEUM
High St EX14 1PG (next to parish church of St Paul)
☎ 01404 44966 & 42996 ▯ 01404 46591
e-mail: dyateshoniton@msn.com

The museum has a wonderful display of Honiton lace, and there are lace demonstrations from June to August. The town's history is also illustrated, and the museum is interesting for its setting in a chapel built in about 1200.

Times: Open Mon before Easter to end of Sep, Mon-Fri 10-5 & Sat 10-1.30. Oct, Mon-Fri 10-4, Sat 10-1.30. Winter opening by special arrangement. **Fee:** £2 (ch 50p, pen £1.50) **Facilities:** ⅊ (400 yds) ஃ (stair lift between floors) shop ⅍ (ex guide dogs)

⌂ ILFRACOMBE   Map 02 SS54
ILFRACOMBE MUSEUM
Runnymede Gardens, Wilder Rd EX34 8AF (Situated next to the Landmark Theatre & TIC on seafront)
☎ 01271 863541
e-mail: ilfracombe@devonmuseums.net

Ilfracombe was an important trading port from the 14th to the 16th centuries and during the Napoleonic Wars became a popular resort. The history, archaeology, geology, natural history and maritime traditions of the area are illustrated here, along with Victoriana, costumes, photographs and china.

Times: Open all year, Apr-Oct, daily 10-5; Nov-Mar Mon-Fri 10-12.30. **Fee:** £1.50 (ch 50p con £1). ch u5, Disabled & booked school groups free. **Facilities:** ⅊ (10yds) ஃ (ramp to front door, wide aisles) shop ⅍ (ex guide dogs)

WATERMOUTH CASTLE

EX34 9SL (3m NE off A399, midway between
Ilfracombe & Combe Martin)
☎ 01271 863879 🖷 01271 865864
e-mail: enquiries@watermouthcastle.com

Overlooking a beautiful bay, this 19th-century castle is
one of North Devon's finest. It caters enthusiastically
for the public, offering such unique experiences as a
mechanical musical demonstration and the
Watermouth Water Fountains. Other attractions include
a tube slide, carousel and Gnomeland.
Times: Open Apr-Oct, closed Sat & Fri in off season. Ring for further
details. **Fee:** £6 (ch & pen £5) **Facilities:** 🅿 ♨ & (special wheelchair
route) toilets for disabled shop ⅋ (ex guide dogs) ◥

🏛 KILLERTON HOUSE   Map 03 SS90
& GARDEN

EX5 3LE (off B3181)
☎ 01392 881345

Elegant 18th-century house set in an 18-acre garden
with sloping lawns and herbaceous borders. A majestic
avenue of beech trees runs up the hillside, past an
arboretum of rhododendrons and conifers. The garden
has an ice house and rustic summer house where the
family pet bear was once kept.
Times: Open: House, daily (ex Tue), Mar & Oct, Wed-Sun, Aug daily
11-5. Gardens open all year, daily from 10.30. House will close Sept
2002 until Etr 2003 for essential maintenance work. Gardens will
remain open. **Fee:** House & grounds £5.20. Grounds only £3.70.
Facilities: 🅿 ♨ ✕ licensed & (wheelchairs & motorised buggy
available) toilets for disabled shop garden centre ⅋ (ex in park &
guide dogs) ◥

🏛 KINGSBRIDGE   Map 03 SX74
COOKWORTHY MUSEUM OF RURAL LIFE

The Old Grammar School, 108 Fore St TQ7 1AW
☎ 01548 853235
e-mail: wcookworthy@talk21.com
Times: Open all year, Apr-Sep Mon-Sat 10-5; Oct Mon-Fri 10.30-4.
Nov-Mar groups by arrangement. Local history room Tue-Thu 10-12 &
Wed also 2-4, other times by appointment. **Facilities:** 🅿 (100mtrs) &
(Braille labels on selected exhibits) toilets for disabled shop ⅋ (ex
guide dogs) *Details not confirmed for 2002*

🏛 KINGSWEAR   Map 03 SX85
COLETON FISHACRE HOUSE & GARDEN

Brownstone Rd TQ6 0EQ (3m from Kingswear. Take
Ferry Road and turn off at Toll House)
☎ 01803 752466 🖷 01803 753017
e-mail: dcfdmx@smtp.ntrust.org.uk

The house, set in a stream fed valley on a beautiful
stretch of South Devon coastline, was designed in the
1920s for Rupert and Lady D'Oyly Carte (of Gilbert &
Sullivan fame) reflecting the Arts & Crafts tradition, but
with refreshingly modern interiors. A luxuriant garden

was created around it, and has year round interest with
a wide variety of rare and exotic plants.
Times: Garden open 3-17 Mar, Sat & Sun only 11-5; 23 Mar-3 Nov,
Wed-Sun & BH Mon 10.30-5.30. House open 23 Mar-3 Nov, Wed-Sun
& BH Mon 11-4.30. **Fee:** £4.80 (ch £2.40). Family ticket £12.
Facilities: 🅿 ♨ & (wheelchair available, braille guides) toilets for
disabled shop garden centre ⅋ (ex guide dogs) ◥ ◥

🏛 KNIGHTSHAYES COURT   Map 03 SS91
KNIGHTSHAYES COURT

EX16 7RQ (2m N of Tiverton off A396)
☎ 01884 254665 & 257381 🖷 01884 243050

This fine Victorian mansion, a rare example of William
Burges' work, offers much of interest to all ages. The
garden is one of the most beautiful in Devon, with
formal terraces, amusing topiary, a pool garden and
woodland walks.
Times: House & garden open 23 Mar-Sep, daily ex Fri 11-5.30. Oct-
early Nov, daily ex Thu & Fri. **Fee:** House & garden £5.40 (ch £2.70).
Party. **Facilities:** 🅿 ♨ ✕ licensed & (wheelchairs available, lift, braille
& audio guide) toilets for disabled shop garden centre ⅋ (ex guide
dogs & in park/woods ◥ ◥

🏛 LYDFORD   Map 02 SX58
LYDFORD CASTLE

EX20 4BH (off A386)
Times: Open all reasonable times. **Facilities:** 🅿 ♨ *Details not
confirmed for 2002*

LYDFORD GORGE

EX20 4BH (off A386, between Okehampton &
Tavistock)
☎ 01822 820320 & 820441 🖷 01822 822000
e-mail: dlybhx@smpt.ntrust.org.uk

The spectacular gorge has been formed by the River
Lyd, which has cut into the rock and caused swirling
boulders to scoop out potholes in the stream bed. This
has created some dramatic features, notably the Devil's
Cauldron close to Lydford Bridge. At the end of the
gorge is the 90ft-high White Lady Waterfall.
Times: Open Apr-Sep, daily 10-5.30; Oct, daily 10-4. (Nov-Mar,
waterfall entrance only, daily 10.30-3). **Fee:** £3.60 (ch £1.80) Party
£3.50 (ch £1.75). **Facilities:** 🅿 ♨ (easy access path above gorge,
audio tapes) shop ◥

🏛 MORWELLHAM   Map 02 SX47
MORWELLHAM QUAY

PL19 8JL (4m W of Tavistock, off A390. Midway
between Gunnislake & Tavisock). Signed)
☎ 01822 832766 & 833808 🖷 01822 833808

Morwellham was the greatest copper port in Queen
Victoria's empire. Once the mines were exhausted the
port area disintegrated into wasteland, until 1970,
when a charitable trust was set up for its restoration.
Visitors can ride by electric tramway underground into
a copper mine, last worked in 1869. Staff wear

Victorian costume, and visitors can try on replica costumes in the Limeburner's Cottage.

Morwellham Quay

Times: Open all year (ex Xmas wk) 10-5.30. (4.30 Nov-Etr). Last admission 3.30 (2.30 Nov-Etr). **Fee:** £8.60 (ch 5-16 £6.20, pen & students £7.80). **Facilities:** 🅿 💺 ✗ licensed ♿ (smooth paths, but difficult areas in Victorian village) toilets for disabled shop 🕊 (ex on lead) 🍴

🏛 NEWTON ABBOT　　　Map 03 SX87
Bradley Manor
TQ12 6BN (SW of Newton Abbot on A381 Totnes rd. 1m from town centre)
☎ 01626 354513

A National Trust property of 70 acres, the 15th-century house and chapel are surrounded by woodland. The River Lemon and a millstream flow through the estate. **Times:** Open Apr-Sep, Wed & Thu, 2-5. **Fee:** £2.80 **Facilities:** 🅿 🕊 🚗 ♨

Hedgehog Hospital at Prickly Ball Farm
Denbury Rd, East Ogwell TQ12 6BZ (1.5m from Newton Abbot on A381 towards Totnes, follow brown tourist signs)
☎ 01626 362319 & 330685 📄 01626 330685
e-mail: hedgehog@hedgehog.org.uk
Times: Open 26 Mar-Sep, 10-5. Last admission 1hr before closing. **Facilities:** 🅿 💺 ♿ (large print menu, use of wheelchair, Braille menu) toilets for disabled shop 🕊 (ex guide dogs) *Details not confirmed for 2002* 🍴

Tuckers Maltings
Teign Rd TQ12 4AA (follow brown tourist signs from Newton Abbot railway station)
☎ 01626 334734 📄 01626 330153

The only working malthouse in England open to the public, producing malt from barley for over 30 West Country breweries. Learn all about the process of malting - and taste the end product at the in-house brewery. Guided tours last an hour.
Times: Open Good Fri-end Oct, Mon-Sat (Closed Sun ex in Jul & Aug). Speciality bottled beer shop open throughout the year. **Fee:** £4.35 (ch 5-15 £2.75, 16-17 £3.50, pen £3.95). Family ticket £12.25. **Facilities:** 🅿 ♿ toilets for disabled shop (open all year) 🍴

🏛 OKEHAMPTON　　　Map 02 SX59
Museum of Dartmoor Life
3 West St EX20 1HQ
☎ 01837 52295 📄 01837 659330
e-mail: dartmoormuseum@eclipse.co.uk

The Tourist Information Centre and working craft studios are in the courtyard of this three storey mill. There is a display of Victorian life, and reconstructions of local tin and copper mines are complemented by a geological display of the moor. Local history, prehistory, domestic life, industry and environmental issues are explored. A shop sells crafts and books and an exhibition gallery changes its displays regularly.
Times: Open Etr-Oct, Mon-Sat 10-5 (also Sun, Jun-Sep). Winter opening times, telephone for details. **Fee:** £2 (ch 5-16 & students £1, pen £1.80). Family ticket £5.60. Party 10+. **Facilities:** 🅿 💺 ♿ toilets for disabled

Okehampton Castle
Castle Lodge EX20 1JB (1m SW of town centre)
☎ 01837 52844

The chapel, keep and hall date from the 11th to 14th centuries and stand on the northern fringe of Dartmoor National Park.
Times: Open all year, Apr-Sep, daily 10-6 (Oct 10-5). (Reviewed Mar 2002) **Fee:** £2.50 (ch 5-15 £1.30, ch u5 free, con £1.90). Personal stereo tours included in admission. (Reviewed Mar 2002) **Facilities:** 🅿 ♨

🏛 OTTERTON　　　Map 03 SY08
Otterton Mill Centre
EX9 7HG (between North Poppleford & Budleigh Salterton on A3572)
☎ 01395 568521 📄 01395 568521
e-mail: ottertonmill@ukonline.co.uk

Mentioned in the Domesday Book, this water-powered mill grinds wholemeal flour used in the baking of bread and cakes sold on the premises. A gallery houses exhibitions through the summer and autumn, and there are sculpture, pottery, weaving, basket-making and spinning studios. There is a co-operative craft shop, and an annual exibition of furniture from West Country workshops.
Times: Open all year, daily, summer 10.30-5.30; winter 11-4. **Fee:** £2 (ch 75p). Party £1 (ch 60p) each. **Facilities:** 🅿 ✗ licensed ♿ (free entry to ground floor) shop garden centre 🍴

🏛 OTTERY ST MARY   Map 03 SY19
CADHAY
EX11 1QT (1m NW of Ottery St Mary, near junct of A30 & B3167)
☎ 01404 812432   🖥 01404 812432

A beautiful Tudor and Georgian house, which stands around a courtyard and dates from 1550.
Times: Open Jul-Aug Tue, Wed & Thu. Also Sun & Mon of late spring & late summer BH's. 2-5.30. **Fee:** £4 (ch £2). Party 20+ by appointment. **Facilities:** 🅿 🕭 ✻ (ex guide dogs)

🏛 PAIGNTON   Map 03 SX86
PAIGNTON & DARTMOUTH STEAM RAILWAY
Queens Park Station, Torbay Rd TQ4 6AF (from Paignton follow brown tourist signs)
☎ 01803 555872   🖥 01803 664313

Steam trains run for seven miles from Paignton to Kingswear on the former Great Western line, stopping at Goodrington Sands, Churston, and Kingswear, connecting with the ferry crossing to Dartmouth. Combined river excursions available. Ring for details of special events.
Times: Open Jun-Sep daily 9-5.30 & selected days Oct & Apr-May. **Fee:** Paignton to Kingswear £6.40 (ch £4.40, pen £5.80). Family £20. Paignton to Dartmouth (including ferry) £7.50 (ch £5, pen £6.90). Family £23. **Facilities:** 🅿 (5mins walk) 🍽 🕭 (wheelchair ramp for boarding train) toilets for disabled shop

PAIGNTON ZOO ENVIRONMENTAL PARK
Totnes Rd TQ4 7EU (1m from Paignton town centre on A3022 Totnes road)
☎ 01803 697500   🖥 01803 523457
e-mail: info@paigntonzoo.org.uk

Paignton is one of Britain's biggest zoos, set in a beautiful and secluded woodland valley, where new enclosures are spacious and naturalistic. A tour will take you through some of the world's threatened habitats, Forest, Savannah, Wetland and Desert, with hundreds of species, many of them endangered and part of conservation breeding programmes. There are regular keeper talks and a children's play area, and special events include an annual Easter Egg Safari.
Times: Open all year, daily 10-6 (5pm in winter). Last admission 5pm (4pm in winter). (Closed 25 Dec). **Fee:** £7.70 (ch 3-15 £5.50, stu & pen £6.20). Family ticket £23.70 (2ad+2ch). Party 15+. **Facilities:** 🅿 🍽 ✗ licensed 🕭 (some steep hills, wheelchair loan-booking essential) toilets for disabled shop ✻ (ex guide dogs) 🍴

🏛 PLYMOUTH   Map 02 SX45
CITY MUSEUM & ART GALLERY
Drake Circus PL4 8AJ (turn off A38 onto A374, follow signs to city centre, museum on NW of city centre, opposite university)
☎ 01752 304774   🖥 01752 304775
e-mail: museum@plymouth.gov.uk

The City Museum and Art Gallery is home to a Fine and Decorative Art Collection of paintings, prints and Reynolds family portraits, silver and Plymouth China, and the Cottonian Collection of Drawings, Sculpture and Books. There is a lively programme of art exhibitions, as well as archaeology, local and natural history displays, and the Discovery Centre with a 'hands-on' section for children.
Times: Open all year, Tue-Fri 10-5.30, Sat 10-5, BH Mon 10-5. (Closed Good Fri & 25-26 Dec). **Fee:** Free. **Facilities:** 🅿 200yds 🕭 (wheelchair available) toilets for disabled shop ✻ ex guide dogs

MERCHANT'S HOUSE MUSEUM
33 St Andrews St PL1 2AX (Turn off A38 onto A374, follow signs to city centre, house located behind St Andrew's Church).
☎ 01752 304774   🖥 01752 304775
e-mail: museum@plymouth.gov.uk

The largest and finest 16th-century house surviving in Plymouth. Inside visitors can discover various aspects of Plymouth's past, including a reconstructed Victorian pharmacy, life during World War II, and a Victorian schoolroom which is available for group bookings.
Times: Open Apr-Sep, Tue-Fri 10-5.30, Sat 10-5, BH Mon 10-5 (summer), (closed 1-2) **Fee:** 90p (ch 30p), half price last hour of opening, children under 7 free **Facilities:** 🅿 (400 yds) 🕭 shop ✻

PLYMOUTH DOME
The Hoe PL1 2NZ
☎ 01752 603300 & 600608 (recorded message) 🖥 01752 256361
Times: Open all year, daily, 4 Apr-24 May 9-6; 25 May-13 Sept 9-7.30; 14 Sep-1 Nov 9-6; 3 Nov-Mar 9-5.30. (Closed 25 Dec). Last admission one hour before closing. **Facilities:** 🅿 (200 yds) 🍽 🕭 (audio descriptions, induction loop, wheelchairs available) toilets for disabled shop ✻ ex guide dogs *Details not confirmed for 2002* 🍴

ROYAL CITADEL
PL1 2PD (at the end of Plymouth Hoe)
☎ 01752 775841
Times: Open for guided tours only May-Sep, daily. For security reasons tours may be suspended at short notice. **Facilities:** ✻ ⚏
Details not confirmed for 2002

⚜ PLYMPTON
Map 02 SX55

SALTRAM
PL7 1UH (2m W between A38 & A379)
☎ 01752 333500 01752 333503
🖥 01752 336474

This magnificent George II house still has its original contents. The collection of paintings was begun at the suggestion of Reynolds and includes many of his portraits. The saloon and dining room were designed by Robert Adam and have superb decorative plasterwork and period furniture.
Times: Open House: 24 Mar-3 Nov, Sat-Thu 12.30-4.30. Garden open all year, Mar-Nov 10.30-5.30, Nov-Feb 11-4. **Fee:** £6. Gardens only £3.
Facilities: 🅿 (charged) ☕ ✗ licensed & (wheelchairs available, lift, braille & audio guides) toilets for disabled shop 🐾 (ex in park on leads) 🍴 🍃

⚜ POWDERHAM
Map 03 SX98

POWDERHAM CASTLE
EX6 8JQ (signposted off A379 Exeter/Dawlish road)
☎ 01626 890243 🖥 01626 890729
e-mail: castle@powderham.co.uk

Built between 1390 and 1420, this ancestral home of the Earls of Devon was damaged in the Civil War. The house was restored and altered in later times and is set in beautiful rose gardens with views over the deer park to the Exe Estuary. Ring for details of special events.
Times: Open Apr-28 Oct, 10-5.30 (last admission 5pm). Closed Sat.
Fee: £5.85 (ch £2.95, pen £5.35). Family ticket £14.65. Party.
Facilities: 🅿 ☕ ✗ licensed & (ramps) toilets for disabled shop garden centre 🍃

⚜ SALCOMBE
Map 03 SX73

OVERBECKS MUSEUM & GARDEN
Sharpitor TQ8 8LW (2.5m SW of Salcombe and 2m S of Malborough)
☎ 01548 842893 🖥 01548 845020
e-mail: dovrcx@smtp.ntrust.org.uk

The garden is on the most southerly tip of Devon, and allows many exotic plants to flourish. The Edwardian house displays toys, dolls and a natural history collection, and there is a `secret room' for children in which they can search for Fred the friendly ghost.
Times: Open Apr-Jul Sun-Fri 11-5.30; Aug daily 11-5.30; Sep Sun-Fri 11-5.30; Oct Sun-Thu 11-5. Gardens open all year, 11-5 (or sunset if earlier). **Fee:** Museum & gardens £4.10. Gardens only £2.90. Family ticket £10.20 (2ad+3ch). **Facilities:** 🅿 (charged) ☕ & (ramp from garden, braille guide) shop 🐾 🗒 🍴 🍃

⚜ SOUTH MOLTON
Map 03 SS72

QUINCE HONEY FARM
EX36 3AZ (3.5m W of A361, on N edge of South Molton)
☎ 01769 572401 🖥 01769 574704
e-mail: info@quincehoney.co.uk

Follow the story of honey and beeswax from flower to table. The exhibition allows you to see the world of bees up close in complete safety; hives open at the press of a button revealing the honeybees' secret life. After viewing the bees at work, sample the fruits of their labour in the café or shop.
Times: Open daily, Apr-Sep 9-6; Oct 9-5; Shop only Nov-Etr 9-5. (Closed 25 Dec-4 Jan). **Fee:** £3.20 (ch 5-16 £1.80, pen £2.60)
Facilities: 🅿 ☕ & toilets for disabled shop 🐾 (ex guide dogs) 🍃

⚜ STICKLEPATH
Map 03 SX69

FINCH FOUNDRY
EX20 2NW (Turn off A30 at Okehampton junct, follow brown signs to Finch Foundry. Located in main street of village. Approx. 7m from Okehampton).
☎ 01837 840046 🖥 01837 840046

Finch Foundry was, in the 19th century, a water-powered factory for making sickles, scythes, shovels and other hand tools. Although no longer in production, three waterwheels can still be seen driving huge hammers, shears, grindstone and other machinery, with daily working demonstrations. These demonstrations explain the key role the foundry played in the local community.
Times: Open Apr-Nov, daily ex Tue, 11-5.30. **Fee:** £2.90 (ch £1.40).
Facilities: 🅿 ☕ & (access to shop/tea room, view main foundry via shop) shop 🍃

⚜ TIVERTON
Map 03 SS91

TIVERTON CASTLE
EX16 6RP (M5 junct 27, then 7m on A361 towards Tiverton to roundabout where Castle is signposted)
☎ 01884 253200 & 255200 🖥 01884 254200
e-mail: tiverton.castle@unf.net

The original castle, built in 1106 by order of Henry I, was rebuilt late 13th/early 14th century. It resisted General Fairfax during the Civil War but fell to him when a lucky shot hit the drawbridge chain. Now a private house, the gardens are lovely and there's a fine Civil War armoury.
Times: Open Etr-Jun & Sep, Sun,Thu & BH Mon's only 2.30-5.30; Jul & Aug, Sun-Thu 2.30-5.30. **Fee:** £3.50 (ch 7-16 £2, under 7 free). Disabled half price if accessing ground floor only. **Facilities:** 🅿 & toilets for disabled shop 🐾 (ex guide dogs)

TIVERTON MUSEUM
Saint Andrew St EX16 6PH
☎ 01884 256295
e-mail: su7711@eclipse.co.uk

This large and comprehensive museum consists of eight galleries and is housed in a restored 19th-century school. The numerous local exhibits include a Heathcote Lace Gallery featuring items from the local lacemaking industry. There is also an agricultural section with a collection of farm wagons and implements. Other large exhibits include two waterwheels and a railway gallery.
Times: Open: Mon-Sat 10.30-4.30 **Fee:** Admission Charged
Facilities: 🅿 (100 yds) & shop 🐾

🏛 TORQUAY   Map 03 SX96
BABBACOMBE MODEL VILLAGE
Hampton Av, Babbacombe TQ1 3LA (follow brown tourist signs from outskirts of town)
☎ 01803 328669 & 315315 📠 01803 315173
e-mail: ss@babbacombemodelvillage.co.uk
Times: Open all year, Good Fri-Jun, 9.30-10; Jul-Aug, 9-10; Sep, 9.30-10; Oct, 9.30-9; Nov-Good Fri, 10-dusk. Closed25 Dec. **Facilities:** 🅿 (charged) 🍽 ♿ (push button audio information) toilets for disabled shop *Details not confirmed for 2002* 🍽

'BYGONES'
Fore St, St Marychurch TQ1 4PR (follow tourist signs into Torquay and St Marychurch)
☎ 01803 326108 📠 01803 326108

Step back in time in this life-size Victorian exhibition street of over 20 shops including a forge, a pub and period display rooms, housed in a former cinema. Exhibits include a large model railway layout, illuminated fantasyland, railwayana and military exhibits including a walk-through World War I trench. At Christmas the street is turned into a winter wonderland. A new set-piece features Babbacombe's John Lee ('the man they couldn't hang') in his cell. There is something here for all the family.
Times: Open all year, Summer 10am-1pm, (Fri-Sun 10-6); Spring & Autumn 10-6; Winter 10-4, Wkends & school hols 10-5. **Fee:** £3.95 (ch 4-14 £3, pen £3.50). Family ticket £12. Prices may change, contact in advance. **Facilities:** 🅿 (50 yds) 🍽 shop 🐕 (ex guide dogs)

KENTS CAVERN
Cavern House, 91 Ilsham Rd, Wellswood TQ1 2JF (1.25m NE off B3199, follow brown tourist signs. 1m from Torquay Harbour)
☎ 01803 215136 📠 01803 211034
e-mail: mail@kents-cavern.co.uk

Probably the most important Palaeolithic site in Britain and recognised as one of the most significant archaeological areas. This is not only a world of spectacular natural beauty, but also a priceless record of past times, where a multitude of secrets of mankind, animals and nature have become trapped and preserved over the last 350,000 years. 175 years after the first excavations and with over 70,000 remains already unearthed, modern research is still discovering new clues to our past.
Times: Open daily (ex 25 Dec). Oct-Mar 10-last tour 4pm; Apr-Jun & Sep 10-last tour 4.30pm; Jul-Aug 9.30-last tour 5pm. Evenings: Jul-Aug (Mon-Thu) 6-9.30. **Fee:** Daytime: £5.50 (ch 4-15 £3.50) Family £16. Ghost evening tour: £5.50 (ch £3.50) Family £16. **Facilities:** 🅿 🍽 ♿ toilets for disabled shop 🐕 (ex guide dogs) 🍽

TORRE ABBEY HISTORIC HOUSE & GALLERY
The Kings Dr TQ2 5JE (on Torquay seafront, next to Riviera Centre)
☎ 01803 293593 📠 01803 215948
e-mail: michael.rhodes@torbay.gov.uk
Times: Open daily Apr-1 Nov, 9.30-6. (Last admission 5pm).
Facilities: 🅿 (100 yds) 🍽 ♿ shop 🐕 (ex guide dogs) *Details not confirmed for 2002*

🏛 TOTNES   Map 03 SX86
BOWDEN HOUSE GHOSTLY TALES & THE BRITISH PHOTOGRAPHIC MUSEUM
TQ9 7PW (off A381 from Totnes)
☎ 01803 863664

Parts of the house date back as far as the 12th century, but most of it was built in 1510 by John Giles, supposedly the wealthiest man in Devon. The Grand Hall is decorated in neo-Classical Baroque style, and the Great Hall is adorned with 18th-and 19th-century weaponry. The museum has a large collection of vintage cameras, a replica Victorian studio, Edwardian darkroom, shops, and the Les Allen movie pioneer display. Ghostly Tales Tours are at 2, 3 and 4 o'clock.
Times: Open 27 May-27 Sep from noon. Bowden House & Museum Mon-Fri. **Fee:** £4.95 (ch 9-13 £3.40, ch 6-8 £2.20, ch 2-5 £1).
Facilities: 🅿 🍽 ♿ (museum only suitable) toilets for disabled shop 🐕 (ex guide/hearing dogs)

GUILDHALL
Rampart Walk, off High St TQ9 5QH (behind St Mary's Church on the main street)
☎ 01803 862147 📠 01803 864275
e-mail: totnestowncouncil@btinternet.com

Originally the refectory, kitchens, brewery and bakery for the Benedictine Priory of Totnes (1088-1536), the building was established as the Guildhall in 1553 during the reign of Edward VI. A magistrates' court and a prison opened in 1624, and the council chamber is still used today.
Times: Open Apr-Oct, Mon-Fri 10.30-1 & 2-4; Other times by appointment. **Fee:** £1 (ch 25p, con 50p). **Facilities:** 🅿 (50yds) shop

TOTNES CASTLE
TQ9 5NU (on hill overlooking town)
☎ 01803 864406

A classic example of the Norman motte-and-bailey castle, Totnes dates from the 11th, 13th and 14th centuries. The circular shell-keep, protected by a curtain wall, gives marvellous views.
Times: Open all year, Apr-Sep, daily 10-6 (Oct 10-5); Nov-Mar, Wed-Sun 10-4, (closed 1-2). Closed 24-26 Dec & 1 Jan. **Fee:** £1.60 (ch 5-15 80p, under 5' free, con £1.20). **Facilities:** 🅿 (70yds) ⚇

TOTNES MUSEUM
70 Fore St TQ9 5RU (town centre)
☎ 01803 863821
Times: Open Etr-30 Oct, Mon-Fri & BHs 10.30-5, Sat group bookings only. **Facilities:** 🅿 (440yds) ♿ Personal guided tours available shop 🐕 (ex small dogs) *Details not confirmed for 2002*

♨ UFFCULME
Map 03 ST01

COLDHARBOUR MILL WORKING WOOL MUSEUM

Coldharbour Mill EX15 3EE (2m from M5 junct 27, off B3181. Follow signs to Willand, then brown signs to Working Wool Museum)
☎ 01884 840960 🖹 01884 840858
e-mail: info@coldharbourmill.org.uk

Originally an important centre for the wool trade, the Culm Valley now has only one working woollen mill. This was built as a grist mill in 1753, but was converted to a wool mill in 1797 by a Somerset woollen manufacturer, Thomas Fox. The mill closed in 1981 but was reopened as a Working Wool Museum. There are displays of machinery and artefacts connected with the wool trade, plus a weaver's cottage, dye and carpenters' workshops and a display on New World tapestry.

Times: Open Apr-Oct, daily 10.30-5. Last tour 4pm. Nov-Mar, Mon-Fri (please telephone for times). **Fee:** £5.50 (ch 5-16 £2.50). Family ticket £15. Party 20+. **Facilities:** 🅿 ✗ licensed ♿ (helpful guides & lift) toilets for disabled shop 🐾 (ex guide dogs) ⬛

♨ YEALMPTON
Map 02 SX55

NATIONAL SHIRE HORSE CENTRE

PL8 2EL (On A379, Plymouth to Kingsbridge)
☎ 01752 880268 🖹 01752 881014
Times: Open 1 May-31 Sep. **Facilities:** 🅿 🍽 ✗ licensed ♿ toilets for disabled shop *Details not confirmed for 2002* ⬛

♨ YELVERTON
Map 02 SX56

YELVERTON PAPERWEIGHT CENTRE

4 Buckland Ter, Leg O'Mutton PL20 6AD (off A386, Plymouth to Tavistock road)
☎ 01822 854250 🖹 01822 854250
e-mail: paperweightcentre@btinternet.com
Times: Open Apr-Oct, daily 10-5; 1-24 Dec, daily; Nov & Jan-Mar wknds only or by appointment. **Facilities:** 🅿 (100yds) ♿ (ramp on request) shop *Details not confirmed for 2002* ⬛

Dorset

EVENTS & FESTIVALS

January
1st Annual Bath Race, Poole

May
tbc Trawler Race & Water Carnival, Weymouth
tbc Weymouth International Beach Kite Festival

June
7th-9th Wimborne Folk Festival, Wimborne
15th Dorchester Carnival (provisional)
tbc Annual Military & Veterans Festival, Weymouth
tbc Teddy Bears' Picnic, Dorchester

July
21st Tolpuddle Martyrs Memorial Rally & Festival, Tolpuddle
27th July-4th Lyme Regis Lifeboat Week, Lyme Regis
tbc International Maritime Modelling Festival, Weymouth

August
27th July-4th Lyme Regis Lifeboat Week
28th-1st Sept Great Dorset Steam Fair, Tarrant Hinton
tbc Weymouth Carnival

September
7th-8th Dorchester Show

October
tbc Weymouth Beach Motocross Championship

November
tbc Weymouth Guy Fawkes, The Beach

One of England's most picturesque counties, Dorset has such a wealth of history, stunning scenery and coastal attractions on offer that one is spoilt for choice when writing about it, and it seems a shame that so many people simply drive through it on their way somewhere else.

Possibly the county's most famous landmark is the Cerne Abbas giant, a 180-foot high depiction of a naked man with a club, visible for miles around. However, those visiting this important remnant of Dorset's distant past shouldn't pass by Cerne Abbas itself, which contains a centuries-old church, and the remains of a 10th-century Abbey.

Rural Dorset has retained a great deal of the charm and tranquility of England before the Industrial Revolution. All of the market towns in this area (Gillingham, Blandford Forum, Stalbridge, Shaftesbury and Sturminster Newton) are well worth seeing. Shaftesbury is one of England's oldest towns and is the site of an abbey founded by Alfred The Great. The area around these towns, – known as 'Hardy Country', after Thomas Hardy, the 19th-century novelist, – has been designated an Area of Outstanding Natural Beauty, and includes Cranborne Chase, Blackmore Vale and the Dorset Downs.

The major coast resorts, – Weymouth, Poole and Bournemouth – offer a wide range of activities, combined with some beautiful scenery, and yet more of historic interest. The best example of the latter is probably Corfe Castle, which stands on the Isle of Purbeck. The keep was built by the Normans, and the whole thing was completed by 1300. Unfortunately for future generations, the castle was ruined during a Civil War siege. Local legend has it that a lone woman betrayed the castle to Cromwell, and that her headless ghost can be seen by the gate of the ruined structure.

Top: Corfe Castle

ABBOTSBURY
Map 03 SY58

ABBOTSBURY SWANNERY
New Barn Rd DT3 4JG (9m from Weymouth on B3157 coastal road to Bridport)
☎ 01305 871858 ▣ 01305 871092
e-mail: info@abbotsbury-tourism.co.uk

Abbotsbury is the breeding ground of the only managed colonial herd of mute swans. The swans can be seen safely at close quarters, and the site is also home or stopping point for many wild birds. The highlight of the year is the cygnet season, end of May to the end of June, when there may be over 100 nests on site.
Times: Open mid Mar-Oct, daily 10-6, last admission 5pm. **Fee:** £5.20 (ch £3.70 & pen £4.90). **Facilities:** ▣ ▼ ✕ licensed ᵺ (wheelchair loan, herb garden for blind) toilets for disabled shop ✻ ➳

ATHELHAMPTON
Map 03 SY79

ATHELHAMPTON HOUSE & GARDENS
DT2 7LG (off A35 Northbrook junct, follow brown tourist signs towards Puddletown, at traffic lights turn left, Athelhampton is approx 1m on left)
☎ 01305 848363 ▣ 01305 848135
e-mail: pcooke@athelhampton.co.uk

Athelhampton, one of the finest 15th-century houses in England, contains magnificently furnished rooms including The Great Hall of 1485 and the library. The glorious Grade I Listed gardens contain the world-famous topiary pyramids, fountains, and collections of tulips, magnolias, roses, clematis and lilies in season.
Times: Open Mar-Nov, daily 10.30-5. Also Sun in winter (ex Xmas). (Closed Sat). **Fee:** House & Garden £5.50 (ch free, pen £5.20, student & disabled £3.50). Garden only £3.90 (ch free). **Facilities:** ▣ ▼ ✕ licensed ᵺ toilets for disabled shop ✻ (ex assistance dogs) ➳

BEAMINSTER
Map 03 ST40

MAPPERTON GARDENS
DT8 3NR (2m SE off A356 & B3163)
☎ 01308 862645 ▣ 01308 863348
e-mail: office@mapperton.com

Several acres of terraced valley gardens, with specimen trees and shrubs and formal borders surround a manor house dating back to the 16th-century. There are also fountains, grottoes, stone fishponds and an orangery, and the garden offers good views and walks. The Mapperton Courtyard Fair is held annually (in August) with craft demonstrations, stalls, house tours and local displays.
Times: Open Mar-Oct, daily 2-6 (Wed, Thu & Sat 1-6). **Fee:** Gardens £3.50 (ch 5-18 £1.50, under 5 free). **Facilities:** ▣ ▼ ᵺ ramp from parking area to garden toilets for disabled shop ✻ (ex guide dogs) ➳

BLANDFORD FORUM
Map 03 ST80

ROYAL SIGNALS MUSEUM
Blandford Camp DT11 8RH (signposted off B3082 Blandford/Wimborne rd & A354 Salisbury rd)
☎ 01258 482248 ▣ 01258 482084
e-mail: royalsignalsmuseum@army.mod.uk

The Royal Signals Museum depicts the history of military communications, science and technology from the Crimea to the Gulf. As well as displays on all major conflicts involving British forces, there are the stories of the ATS, the Long Range Desert Group, Air Support, Airborne, Para and SAS Signals. For children there are trails and interactive exhibits.
Times: Open all year, daily 10-5, Sat-Sun 10-4. Closed 10 days over Xmas & New Year **Fee:** £4.50 (ch £2.50, pen £3.50). Family £10 **Facilities:** ▣ ▼ ᵺ (ramps & chair lift) toilets for disabled shop ✻ (ex guide dogs) ➳

BOURNEMOUTH
Map 04 SZ09

OCEANARIUM
Pier Approach BH2 5AA (from A338 Wessex Way, follow Oceanarium tourist signs)
☎ 01202 311993 ▣ 01202 311990
e-mail: oceanarium@reallive.co.uk
Times: Open all year, daily from 10am. (Closed 25 Dec). **Facilities:** ▣ (100mtrs) ▼ ᵺ (wheelchair for hire) toilets for disabled shop ✻ (ex guide dogs) *Details not confirmed for 2002* ➳

BOVINGTON CAMP
Map 03 SY88

CLOUDS HILL
BH20 7NQ (4m SW of Bere Regis)
☎ 01929 405616
Times: Open 2 Apr-29 Oct, Wed-Fri & Sun, also BH Mon, 12-5, or dusk if earlier. **Facilities:** (Braille guide) ✻ ⚐ ❦ *Details not confirmed for 2002*

THE TANK MUSEUM
BH20 6JG (off A352 or A35, follow brown tank signs from Bere Regis & Wool)
☎ 01929 405096 ▣ 01929 405360
e-mail: admin@tankmuseum.co.uk

The Tank Museum houses the world's finest international collection of Armoured Fighting Vehicles. Tanks in Action displays are held every Thursday at noon during July-September and every Tuesday from 24th July to 28th August. Armoured vehicle rides are available throughout the summer, and various special events take place - please telephone for details.
Times: Open all year, daily 10-5 (Closed from 17-26 Dec). **Fee:** £7 (ch £5, pen £6). Family saver (2ad+2ch) £21 (1ad+2ch) £17. Group rates available. **Facilities:** ▣ ✕ licensed ᵺ (wheelchairs available, Braille & audio tours) toilets for disabled shop ✻ (ex guide dogs) ➳

BROWNSEA ISLAND
Map 03 SZ08

BROWNSEA ISLAND
BH15 7EE (located in Poole Harbour)
☎ 01202 707744 ▣ 01202 701635
Times: Open Apr-1 Oct, daily 10-5 (10-6 Jul & Aug) **Facilities:** ▼ ✕ ᵺ (Braille guide, 2 selfdrive vehicles- booking advisable) toilets for disabled shop ✻ ❦ *Details not confirmed for 2002*

🏛 CANFORD CLIFFS   Map 04 SZ08
COMPTON ACRES GARDENS
Canford Cliffs Rd BH13 7ES (on B3065, follow brown tourist signs)
☎ 01202 700778 🖷 01202 707537
e-mail: sales@comptonacres.co.uk

The ten acres of Compton Acres incorporate Japanese, Roman and Italian gardens, rock and water gardens, and heather gardens. There are fine views over Poole Harbour and the Purbeck Hills, and a collection of bronze and marble statuary. Two of the gardens have recently been themed to create an Egyptian Court Garden and a Spanish Water Garden.
Times: Open Apr-Dec 10-6 (last entry 5.15) **Fee:** £5.75 (ch £2.95, pen £5.25). Party 15+ **Facilities:** 🅿 ⬛ ✗ licensed ♿ (level paths and ramps into shops and cafe) toilets for disabled shop garden centre 🍴 (ex guide & hearing dogs) 🍽

🏛 CHRISTCHURCH   Map 04 SZ19
CHRISTCHURCH CASTLE & NORMAN HOUSE
(near Christchurch Priory)
Times: Open any reasonable time. **Facilities:** 🔀 Details not confirmed for 2002

RED HOUSE MUSEUM & GARDENS
Quay Rd BH23 1BU (follow brown tourist signs from Christchurch, Red House is on the corner of Quay Rd)
☎ 01202 482860 🖷 01202 481924

A museum with plenty of variety, featuring local history, archaeology, and natural history, displayed in a beautiful Georgian house. There's an excellent costume collection, some Arthur Romney-Green furniture and gardens with a woodland walk and herb garden. Temporary exhibitions include contemporary art and change regularly.
Times: Open all year, Tue-Sat 10-5 Sun 2-5 (Closed Mon ex BH). Last admission 4pm. **Fee:** £1.50 (con 80p). Family ticket £3.50.
Facilities: 🅿 (200yds) ⬛ ♿ shop 🍴 (ex guide & hearing dogs)

🏛 CORFE CASTLE   Map 03 SY98
CORFE CASTLE
BH20 5EZ (on A351)
☎ 01929 481294 🖷 01929 481294
e-mail: wcfgen@smpt.ntrust.org.uk

Built in Norman times, the castle was added to by King John. It was defended during the Civil War by Lady Bankes, who surrendered after a stout resistance. Parliament ordered the demolition of the castle, and today it is one of the most impressive ruins in England. Ring for details of special events.
Times: Open daily: 5-25 Mar 10-4.30; 26 Mar-29 Oct 10-5.30; 30 Oct-3 Mar 11-3.30. (Closed 25-26 Dec & 2 days end of Jan). **Fee:** £4 (ch £2). Family ticket £10 (2 adults & 3 ch) or £6 (1 adult & 3 ch). Party.
Facilities: 🅿 ⬛ ✗ licensed (Braille guide & menu) shop 🐾

CORFE CASTLE MUSEUM
West St BH20 5HE
☎ 01929 480415
Times: Open all year, Apr-Oct, daily 9.30-6; Nov-Mar, wknds and Xmas holidays 10-5. **Facilities:** 🅿 (200 yds) ♿ toilets for disabled 🍴 Details not confirmed for 2002

🏛 DORCHESTER   Map 03 SY69
DINOSAUR MUSEUM
Icen Way DT1 1EW (In town centre, just off main street, High East St)
☎ 01305 269880 🖷 01305 268885

Britain's only museum devoted to dinosaurs has an appealing mixture of fossils, skeletons, life-size reconstructions and interactive displays such as the 'feelies'. There are audio-visual presentations, and the idea is to provide an all-round family attraction with new displays each year.
Times: Open all year, daily 9.30-5.30 (10-4.30 Nov-Mar). (Closed 24-26 Dec). **Fee:** £4.75 (ch £2.95, pen & student £3.75, under 4's free). Family ticket £13.75. **Facilities:** 🅿 (50yds) ♿ (Many low level displays) shop 🍽

DORSET COUNTY MUSEUM
High West St DT1 1XA (turn off A354 signposted Dorchester, attraction on right half way up main street)
☎ 01305 262735 🖷 01305 257180
e-mail: dorsetcountymuseum@dor-mus.demon.co.uk

Displays cover prehistoric and Roman times, including sites such as Maiden Castle, and there's a gallery on Dorset writers with sections on the poet William Barnes, Thomas Hardy (with a reconstruction of his study), and 20th-century writers. Also geology, local wildlife and social history are explored in the museum.
Times: Open May-Oct, Mon-Sat, 10-5. Also open Sun during May-Oct. (Closed 25 Dec). **Fee:** £3.50 (concessions £2.35, ch £1.70) . Family ticket £8.70. **Facilities:** 🅿 (150 yds) ♿ (Free entry for disabled visitors) shop

DORSET TEDDY BEAR MUSEUM
Antelope Walk, Cornhill DT1 1BE (in town centre near Tourist Information Centre)
☎ 01305 263200 🖷 01305 268885

A visit to the museum begins with the home of Edward Bear and his extended family of human-sized teddy bears. Then, in a more traditional museum setting, view hundreds of teddy bears from throughout the last century in atmospheric and evocative displays.
Times: Open daily 9.30-5. (Closed 25-26 Dec) **Fee:** £2.95 (ch £1.50, under 4's free). Family £7.95. **Facilities:** 🅿 (500 metres) shop 🍴 (ex guide dogs) 🍽

HARDY'S COTTAGE
Higher Bockhampton DT2 8QJ (3m NE of Dorchester, 0.5m S of A35)
☎ 01305 262366
Times: Open 2 Apr-Oct daily execpt Fri & Sat, 11-5 or dusk if earlier. Open Good Fri. **Facilities:** 🅿 ᵶ (car parking by arrangement with custodian) ⅀ ⅀ *Details not confirmed for 2002*

MAIDEN CASTLE
DT1 9PR (2m S, access off A354, N of bypass)
Times: Open any reasonable time. **Facilities:** 🅿 ⊞ *Details not confirmed for 2002*

THE MILITARY MUSEUM OF DEVON & DORSET
The Keep, Birdport Rd DT1 1RN (situated near the top of High West St)
☎ 01305 264066 ᐧ 01305 250373
Times: Open all year, Mon-Sat 9-5 (also in Jul & Aug Sun 10-4). (Closed Xmas & New Year). **Facilities:** 🅿 ⅀ ᵶ (lift avalible to 3 floors) toilets for disabled shop ⅀ (ex guide dogs) *Details not confirmed for 2002*

TUTANKHAMUN EXHIBITION
High West St DT1 1UW (In town centre)
☎ 01305 269571 ᐧ 01305 268885

The exhibition recreates the excitement of one of the world's greatest discoveries of ancient treasure. A reconstruction of the tomb and facsimiles of its contents are displayed. The superbly preserved mummified body of the boy king can be seen, wonderfully recreated in every detail. Special exhibitions include `The Jewels of Tutankhamun', `The Discovery of the Tomb of Tutankhamun' and `The Curse of Tutankhamun'.
Times: Open daily, 9.30-5.30; Nov-Mar 9.30-5, wknds 10-4.30. (Closed 24-26 Dec). **Fee:** £4.75 (ch £2.95, pen & student £3.75, under 5's free). Family ticket £13.75. **Facilities:** 🅿 (200yds) ᵶ shop ⅀ (ex guide dogs)

🏛 MINTERNE MAGNA　　　Map 03 ST60
MINTERNE GARDENS
DT2 7AU (2m N of Cerne Abbas on A352 Dorchester-Sherborne road)
☎ 01300 341370 ᐧ 01300 341747

Lakes, cascades, streams and many fine and rare trees will be found in these lovely landscaped gardens. The 18th-century design is a superb setting for the spring shows of rhododendrons, azaleas and spring bulbs, and the autumn colour.
Times: Open Mar-10 Nov, daily 10-7. **Fee:** £3 (accompanied ch free). **Facilities:** 🅿

🏛 POOLE　　　Map 03 SZ09
POOLE POTTERY
The Quay BH15 1RF (towards Poole town centre, follow signs for Poole Quay, situated on the front)
☎ 01202 666200 ᐧ 01202 682894
Times: Open all year factory tours, daily 10-4. (Closed 22 Dec-2 Jan). Shop open 9-5 (out of season), 9-5.30 & later (in season). Telephone for details. **Facilities:** 🅿 (100 yds) ⅀ ✗ licensed ᵶ (wheelchairs available, ask a member of staff) toilets for disabled shop ⅀ (ex guide dogs) *Details not confirmed for 2002*

WATERFRONT MUSEUM & SCAPLEN'S COURT
4 High St BH15 1BW (off Poole Quay)
☎ 01202 262600 ᐧ 01202 262622
e-mail: c.fisher@poole.gov.uk

The museum tells the story of Poole's seafaring past. Learn of the Roman occupation and see material raised from the Studland Bay wreck. Scaplen's Court, just a few yards from the museum, is a beautifully restored domestic building dating from the medieval period. There is a Victorian school room, a kitchen and scullery.
Times: Museum: open Apr-Oct, Mon-Sat 10-5, Sun noon-5; Nov-Mar, Mon-Sat 10-3, Sun noon-3. Scaplen's Court: Aug, Mon-Sat 10-5, Sun noon-5. **Fee:** Museum: £2-£4 (ch £1.35-2.85, pen & student £1.70-£3.40). Family Ticket £6.30-£11.50. **Facilities:** 🅿 (250meters) ᵶ (ex Town Cellars & Scaplen's Court) toilets for disabled ⅀ (ex guide dogs)

🏛 PORTLAND　　　Map 03 SY67
PORTLAND CASTLE
Castleton DT5 1AZ (overlooking Portland harbour)
☎ 01305 820539

One of the best preserved of Henry VIII's coastal forts, built of white Portland stone and originally intended to thwart attack by the Spanish and French. The castle was much fought over in the Civil War.
Times: Open Apr-Sep, daily 10-6 (Oct 10-5). Nov-Mar Fri-Sun 10-4 (Closed 24-26 Dec & 1 Jan). (Reviewed Mar 2002) **Fee:** £3 (ch 5-15 £1.50, u 5 free, con £2.30). Personal stereo tour included in admission. (Reviewed Mar 2002) **Facilities:** 🅿 ᵶ shop ⅀ ⊞

PORTLAND MUSEUM
217 Wakeham DT5 1HS (A354, through Fortuneswell to Portland Heights Hotel, then English Heritage signs)
☎ 01305 821804 ᐧ 01305 761654
e-mail: tourism@weymouth.gov.uk

Avice's cottage in Thomas Hardy's book `The Well-Beloved', this building is now a museum of local and historical interest, with varied displays. Regular temporary exhibitions are held. The adjoining Marie Stopes cottage houses the shop and a display of maritime history.
Times: Open Etr-Oct, Fri-Tue (ex school holidays open daily), 10.30-5 (Closed 1-1.30 daily). **Fee:** £2 (pen £1). **Facilities:** 🅿 50yds (coach parking on roadside) ᵶ shop

SHAFTESBURY
SHAFTESBURY ABBEY MUSEUM & GARDEN
Park Walk SP7 8JR
☎ 01747 852910 ▤ 01747 852910

Map 03 ST82

The Abbey at Shaftesbury was part of a nunnery
founded by King Alfred in 888. It became one of the
wealthiest in the country but was destroyed during the
Dissolution in 1539. The excavated ruins show the
foundations of the abbey church. A museum displays
artefacts found during the excavations and information
panels tell the story of the life of the Abbey.
Times: Open Apr-Oct, daily, 10am-5pm. **Fee:** £1.50 (ch 60p, pen &
concessions £1). **Facilities:** ℙ (250yds) ঠ (large print guides, audio
tour) toilets for disabled shop

SHERBORNE
SHERBORNE CASTLE
New Rd DT9 5NR (off A30, 0.5m E of Sherborne)
☎ 01935 813182 ▤ 01935 816727
e-mail: enquiries@sherbornecastle.com

Map 03 ST61

Built by Sir Walter Raleigh in 1594, Sherborne Castle
has been the home of the Digby family since 1617.
Prince William of Orange was entertained here in 1688,
and George III visited in 1789. Splendid collections of
art, furniture and porcelain are on show in the Castle.
Lancelot 'Capability' Brown created the lake in 1753.
Times: Open Apr-Oct. Tue-Thu, Sun & BH Mon 11-4.30. Castle opens
from 2.30 on Sat. Last admission 4.30. **Fee:** £5.75 (seniors £5.25).
Gardens only £3. Ch under 15 free (max of 4 ch accompanied by an
adult) Party 15+. **Facilities:** ℙ ▆ shop ✱ (ex guide dogs & in
garden) ➤

SHERBORNE MUSEUM
Abbey Gate House, Church Ln DT9 3BP (Turn off A303
to B3145 to Sherborne)
☎ 01935 812252
e-mail: admin@shermus.fsnet.co.uk

The museum features a model of Sherborne's original
Norman castle, as well as a fine Victorian doll's house
and other domestic and agricultural bygones. There are

also items of local geological, natural history and
archaeological interest, including Roman material.
Times: Open Apr-Oct, Tue-Sat 10.30-4.30, Sun 2.30-4.30; BH Mon
2.30-4.30 **Fee:** £1 (ch & students free) **Facilities:** ℙ (200yds) ঠ
toilets for disabled shop ✱ (ex guide dogs)

SHERBORNE OLD CASTLE
Castleton D19 3SA (0.5 mile E off B3145)
☎ 01935 812730

The 12th-century castle was built by Roger, Bishop of
Salisbury. In Elizabethan times it belonged to Sir Walter
Raleigh, but was largely destroyed by Cromwell in the
Civil War. The ruined Norman buildings remain.
Times: Open Apr-Sep, daily 10-6 (Oct 10-5); Nov-Mar, Wed-Sun 10-4,
(closed 1-2pm Winter). **Fee:** £1.80 (ch 5-15 90p, ch u5 free, con £1.40)
Facilities: ℙ ঠ ✱ ♯

SWANAGE
SWANAGE RAILWAY
Station House BH19 1HB (signed from A351)
☎ 01929 425800 ▤ 01929 426680

Map 03 SZ07

Times: Open every weekend throughout the year, daily Apr-Oct.
Facilities: ℙ ▆ ✗ licensed ঠ (special disabled persons coach)
toilets for disabled shop (shop at Swanage Station) *Details not
confirmed for 2002*

TOLPUDDLE
TOLPUDDLE MARTYRS MUSEUM
DT2 7EH (on A35, 7m E of Dorchester)
☎ 01305 848237 ▤ 01305 848237
e-mail: jpickering@tuc.org.uk

Map 03 SY79

Tolpuddle was made famous by the agricultural
workers from the village who united to improve their
wages and conditions of employment. They were
arrested and transported in 1834 and became known as
the Tolpuddle Martyrs. In the 1930s the TUC built a
museum and six cottages named after them. The
museum tells the story of the martyrs, and the

contd.

Tolpuddle Martyrs Rally is held on the third Sunday of July each year, 12.30-4pm.
Times: Open all year, Apr-Oct, Tue-Sat 10-5.30, Sun 11-5.30; Nov-Mar, Tue-Sat 10-4, Sun 11-4. Open BH Mon. (Closed 20 Dec-2 Jan).
Fee: Free. **Facilities:** P (outside museum) & (interactive computers at wheelchair height) toilets for disabled shop ✱ (ex guide dogs)

🏛 WEST LULWORTH   Map 03 SY88
LULWORTH CASTLE
BH20 5QS (from Wareham, W on A352 for 1m, left onto B3070 to E Lulworth, follow tourist signs)
☎ 01929 400352   🖨 01929 400563
e-mail: estate.office@lulworth.com

Glimpse life below stairs in the restored kitchen, and enjoy beautiful views from the top of the tower of this historic castle set in beautiful parkland. The 18th-century chapel is reputed to be the first Catholic chapel built in England after the Reformation. Children will enjoy the animal farm, play area, indoor activity room and pitch and putt.
Times: Open 27 Mar-26 Oct, 10.30-6; 27 Oct-23 Dec 10.30-4.30, daily (ex Sat). Closed 24-16 Feb. Lulworth Castle House open 30 May-26 Sep, Wed 2-5. **Fee:** Free. **Facilities:** P ☕ & (limited in castle due to grade one listing) toilets for disabled shop 🍴

LULWORTH COVE HERITAGE CENTRE
Lulworth Cove BH20 5RQ (From A352 to Wool, then onto B3071 and follow brown signs)
☎ 01929 400587
Times: Open daily Nov-Mar 10-4; Apr-Oct 10-6 (Closed 25 Dec)
Facilities: P (charged) & toilets for disabled shop ✱ *Details not confirmed for 2002* 🍴

🏛 WEYMOUTH   Map 03 SY67
DEEP SEA ADVENTURE & SHARKY'S PLAY ZONE
9 Custom House Quay, Old Harbour DT4 8BG
☎ 01305 760690   🖨 01305 760690
e-mail: deepsea_adventure.co.uk

A fascinating attraction telling the story of underwater exploration and marine exploits. Discover the history of Weymouth's Old Harbour, compelling tales of shipwreck survival, explore the Black Hole and search for Ollie the Oyster. Also a unique display telling the gripping tale of the *Titanic* disaster. Sharky's Play Area is four floors of fun-packed adventure. Separate toddler area for the under fives.
Times: Open all year, daily 9.30-7 (high season 9.30-8). (Closed 25 & 26 Dec & 1 Jan). **Fee:** Sharky's Play Area: Adults free (ch £3). Deep Sea Adventure: £3.75 (ch 5-15 £2.75, pen/student £3.25). Family ticket £11.95. Combined ticket for both attractions, ch £4.75. **Facilities:** P (100yds) ✕ licensed & (lift & sign language for deaf) toilets for disabled shop ✱ (ex guide dogs) 🍴

RSPB NATURE RESERVE RADIPOLE LAKE
The Swannery Car Park DT4 7TZ (within the town, close to seafront & railway station)
☎ 01305 778313   🖨 01305 778313
Times: Open daily 9-5. **Facilities:** P (concessions for members from centre) & shop *Details not confirmed for 2002* 🍴

SEA LIFE PARK
Lodmoor Country Park DT4 7SX (on A353)
☎ 01305 788255   🖨 01305 760165
Times: Open all year, daily from 10am. (Closed 25 Dec). **Facilities:** P (charged) ☕ & toilets for disabled shop ✱ *Details not confirmed for 2002*

🏛 WIMBORNE   Map 03 SZ09
KINGSTON LACY HOUSE, GARDEN & PARK
BH21 4EA (1.5m W of Wimborne, B3082)
☎ 01202 883402 (Mon-Fri) & 842913 (wknds)
🖨 01202 882402
Times: Garden & Park; Apr-29 Oct daily ex 18 Aug 11-6; Nov & Dec open Fri-Sun 11-4. House; Apr-29 Oct daily ex Thu & Fri 12-5.30. Last admission 4.30pm. **Facilities:** P ✕ licensed & (parking by arrangement) toilets for disabled shop ✱ (ex on leads in park & wood) ♨ *Details not confirmed for 2002*

KNOLL GARDENS & NURSERY
Stapehill Rd, Hampreston BH21 7ND (3m E between Wimborne and Ferndown off A31, at Canford Bottom rdbt, into B3073 Ham Lane).
☎ 01202 873931   🖨 01202 870842
e-mail: enquiries@knollgardens.co.uk

Over 6000 plant species from all over the world thrive here, within a six-acre site. There are water gardens with waterfalls, pools and a stream, herbaceous borders, and many other features. The nursery offers a wide range of plants; best known for its range of Ornamental Grasses and 'plants for the modern lifestyle'.
Times: Open all year, Sun-Thu 10-5 (or dusk if earlier). Closed Xmas & New Year hols. **Fee:** £4 (ch 5-15 £2, student £3, pen £3.50). Party 15+.
Facilities: P ☕ ✕ licensed & (wheelchairs available) toilets for disabled shop garden centre ✱ (ex guide dogs) 🍴

PRIEST'S HOUSE MUSEUM AND GARDEN
23-27 High St BH21 1HR
☎ 01202 882533   🖨 01202 882533
Times: Open Apr-Oct, Mon-Sat, 10.30-5. Also every Sun 2-5 Jun-Sep. Special Christmas season. **Facilities:** P (200 yds) ☕ & (hands on archæology gallery, audio tapes) shop ✱ *Details not confirmed for 2002*

STAPEHILL ABBEY
Wimborne Rd West BH21 2EB (2.5m E, off A31)
☎ 01202 861686   🖨 01202 894589

This early 19th-century abbey, home for nearly 200 years to Cistercian nuns, is now a busy working crafts centre with many attractions under cover. There are award-winning landscaped gardens, parkland and picnic spots, and the Power to the Land exhibition. Telephone for details of special events.
Times: Open daily 10-5; Oct-Etr Wed-Sun 10-4. (Closed 22 Dec-2 Feb). **Fee:** £7 (ch 4-16 £4.50, students & pen £6.50). Family ticket (2 adults & 2 ch) £18.50. **Facilities:** P ☕ & toilets for disabled shop garden centre ✱ (ex guide dogs) 🍴

County Durham

EVENTS & FESTIVALS

May
19th Morgan Car Meet, Beamish, North of England Open Air Museum (provisional)
tbc Teesdale Thrash, Bernard Castle

June
7th-8th Durham Regatta, River Wear, Durham (provisional)

July
6th-7th Summer Festival, Durham city centre
13th Durham Miners Gala - miners paraded through Durham (provisional)
tbc Durham County Show, Lambton Park

August
10th-17th Billingham International Folklore Festival, Stockton-on-Tees
24th-25th Weardale Agricultural Show, St John's Chapel
25th-26th Durham Light Infantry Vehicle Rally, (provisional)

September
7th-8th Wolsingham & Wear Valley Agricultural Show, Wolsingham (provisional)
14th-15th Stanhope Agricultural Show & Country Fair, Stanhope (provisional)
tbc Classic Car Day, Beamish

December
7th-8th Victorian Christmas Festival, Durham city centre (provisional)

The Durham Dales lie between the Northumberland National Park and the Yorkshire Dales, and form around a third of the county's area. This huge expanse of waterfalls, meadows, heath and river valleys contains some beautiful scenery.

There are two record-holding geographic features in the area. The road from Killhope to Nenthead in Cumbria rises to over 2,000 feet, and is the highest classified road in England. The waterfall at High Force, where the River Tees falls 70 feet, is the highest waterfall in England.

The history of the area is as rich as the scenery. In the middle ages the Prince Bishops ruled the County Palatine with a blend of political and ecclesiastic power. This power extended into Northumberland and Yorkshire, and was the first line of defence against the marauding Scots. These unusual figures maintained their own armies, had their own courts and nobility, and minted their own coins. Essentially they were the rulers of virtually independent states. The best expression of this dual worldly and heavenly power is Durham's cathedral, once described as "Half Church of God, half Castle 'gainst the Scot."

In the 19th century the area around Weardale was the centre of the lead-mining industry. The industry has long since disappeared, and the 34-foot waterwheel and mine at the Killhope Lead Mining Centre are among the few reminders that this work ever took place.

More recently Co. Durham was the birthplace of pop singer and organist, Alan Price. Born in Fatfield he was a member of 60s band The Animals, and then a solo artist whose down-to-earth music encapsulated many of the area's political and social concerns.

Top: Durham Cathedral

⛪ BARNARD CASTLE   Map 12 NZ01
BARNARD CASTLE
DL12 8NP
☎ 01833 638212

The town's name comes from Bernard Baliol, who built the castle in 1125. The impressive ruins cling to the steep banks of the River Tees. **Times:** Open all year, Apr-Sep 10-6 (Oct 10-5); Nov-Mar, Wed-Sun 10-4. Closed 1-2pm & 24-26 Dec & 1 Jan) **Fee:** £2.40 (ch £1.20, under 5's free, con £1.80) **Facilities:** P & shop ▦

THE BOWES MUSEUM
DL12 8NP (on outskirts of town)
☎ 01833 690606   ▤ 01833 637163

Times: Open daily 11-5. **Facilities:** P ♥ & (lift, ramped entrance, reserved parking) toilets for disabled shop ✕ (ex guide dogs) *Details not confirmed for 2002* ◥

EGGLESTONE ABBEY
DL12 8QN (1m S on minor road off B6277)
Times: Open any reasonable time. **Facilities:** P & ▦ *Details not confirmed for 2002*

⛪ BEAMISH   Map 12 NZ25
BEAMISH, THE NORTH OF ENGLAND OPEN-AIR MUSEUM
DH9 0RG (off A693 & A6076 signposted off A1(M) junct 63)
☎ 0191 370 4000   ▤ 0191 370 4001
e-mail: museum@beamish.org.uk

Set in 200 acres of countryside, award winning Beamish recreates life in the early 1800s and 1900s. Costumed staff welcome visitors to a 1913 town street, colliery village, farm and railway station; a display of how people lived and worked. Ride on early electric tramcars, take a ride on a replica of an 1825 steam railway and visit Pockerley Manor where a yeoman farmer and his family would have lived. **Times:** Open all year Summer, Apr-end Oct, daily from 10am. Winter visits centred on The Town & tramway, other areas closed, Nov-Mar from 10am but closed Mon & Fri. Closing times vary according to season it is advisable to check. Also check for Xmas & New Year times. **Fee:** Summer £12 (ch £6, over 60's £9). Winter £4 (ch £4, over 60's £4). **Facilities:** P & & (free admission for essential helpers) & free leaflet toilets for disabled shop ◥

⛪ BISHOP AUCKLAND   Map 08 NZ22
AUCKLAND CASTLE
DL14 7NR
☎ 01388 601627   ▤ 01388 605264
e-mail: auckland.castle@zetnet.co.uk
Times: Open May-16 Jul & Sep, Fri, Sun & BH Mon 2-5; 17 Jul-Aug daily ex Sat, 2-5. **Facilities:** P & toilets for disabled shop ✕ (ex guide dogs) *Details not confirmed for 2002*

⛪ BOWES   Map 12 NY91
BOWES CASTLE
DL12 9LD (on A66)
Times: Open any reasonable time. **Facilities:** ⌂ ▦ *Details not confirmed for 2002*

⛪ COWSHILL   Map 12 NY84
KILLHOPE LEAD MINING MUSEUM
DL13 1AR (beside A689 midway between Stanhope & Alston)
☎ 01388 537505   ▤ 01388 537617
e-mail: killhope@durham.gov.uk

Equipped with hard hats and lamps, you can descend into the depths of the earth and explore the working conditions of lead miners. The lead mine and 19th-century crushing mill have been restored to look as they would have done in the 1870s, and the 34ft water wheel has been restored to working order. There's also a visitor centre and exhibition based on the life of miners and their families. **Times:** Open Apr-Sep, daily, Oct wknds & 1/2 term week 10.30-5. Last entry 4.30pm. **Fee:** £3.40 (ch, disabled, & UB40 £1.70, pen £2.40). Additional charge for mine visit £1.60(ch, disabled, UB40 80p) **Facilities:** P ♥ & toilets for disabled shop ◥

⛪ DARLINGTON   Map 08 NZ21
DARLINGTON RAILWAY CENTRE & MUSEUM
North Rd Station DL3 6ST (0.75m N, off A167)
☎ 01325 460532

Housed in the carefully restored North Road Station, this museum's prize exhibit is *Locomotion*, which pulled the first passenger train and was built by Robert Stephenson & Co in 1825. Several other steam locomotives are also shown, together with models and other exhibits relating to the Stockton and Darlington and the North Eastern Railway companies. Live steam days throughout the year. **Times:** Open daily 10-5; Last admission 4.30pm. May be subject to amendment. **Fee:** £2.10 (ch £1.05, OAP £1.50). Parties 10+. **Facilities:** P ♥ & (guide tape for visually handicapped) toilets for disabled shop ✕ (ex guide dogs) ◥

🏛 DURHAM   Map 12 NZ24
DURHAM CATHEDRAL

DH1 3EH (A1(M) to Durham, turn off at A690 into city
take turn into market place & follow signs)
☎ 0191 386 4266 ▤ 0191 386 4267
e-mail: enquiries@durhamcathedral.co.uk

Founded in 1093 as a shrine to St Cuthbert, whose
bones still rest in the Feretory. The cathedral is a
remarkable example of Norman architecture, set in an
impressive position high above the River Wear. A full
programme of concerts throughout the year. St
Cuthbert's Day Procession (phone for details).
Times: Open daily, 9.30-6.15, 21Jun-8 Sep 9.30-8. (Sun 12.30-5).
Cathedral is closed to visitors during evening recitals & concerts.
Fee: £3 Donation requested. **Facilities:** P (in city centre) (very poor
parking) ✗ licensed & (braille guide touch/hearing centre,
stairclimber) toilets for disabled shop ⊀ (ex guide dogs)

DURHAM LIGHT INFANTRY MUSEUM & DURHAM ART GALLERY

Aykley Heads DH1 5TU (0.5m NW, turn right off A691)
☎ 0191 384 2214 ▤ 0191 386 1770
e-mail: dli@durham.gov.uk

The history of the Regiment is told in displays of
artefacts, medals, uniforms and vehicles. The Art
Gallery has a continuous programme of temporary
exhibitions, and holds regular lectures and concerts.
Times: Open all year, Apr-Oct, daily 10-5; Nov-Mar, daily 10-4 (closed
25 Dec). **Fee:** £2.50 (£1.25 concessions). family ticket £6.25
Facilities: P ➥ & (wheelchair available, lift, ramps) toilets for
disabled shop ⊀ (ex guide dogs) ➥

FINCHALE PRIORY

Brasside, Newton Hall DH1 5SH (3m NE)
☎ 0191 386 3828

This lovely setting was the refuge chosen by St Godric
in 1110 for his years of solitary meditation, and the
priory, used by monks from Durham Cathedral, was
founded in 1180. Remains of the 13th-century church
can be seen.
Times: Open Apr-Sep, daily 10-6 (Oct 10-5). **Fee:** £1.40 (ch 5-15 70p,
under 5's free, con £1.10) **Facilities:** P (charged) & ⊀ ⊞

ORIENTAL MUSEUM

University of Durham, Elvet Hill DH1 3TH (signposted
from A167 & A177)
☎ 0191 374 7911 ▤ 0191 374 7911
e-mail: oriental.museum@durham.ac.uk

The March of China gallery opened in 2000 and
introduces the visitor to contemporary China, its history
and decorative arts. Other displays cover the Islamic
World, Buddhism, Chinese archaeology, the story of
writing, and there is a Javanese gamelan.
Times: Open Mon-Fri 10-5, wknds 12-5. (Closed Xmas-New Year).
Fee: £1.50 (ch, pen & students 75p) **Facilities:** P ➥ & (lifts to all
floors) toilets for disabled shop ⊀ ➥

🏛 HARTLEPOOL   Map 08 NZ53
HARTLEPOOL HISTORIC QUAY

Maritime Av TS24 0XZ (from A19 take A179 and follow
signs for marina then historic quay)
☎ 01429 860077 ▤ 01429 867332
Times: Open daily 10-5 (10-7 in summer). Closed 25 Dec & 1 Jan.
Facilities: P ➥ ✗ licensed & (all areas ramped or lift access) toilets
for disabled shop ⊀ Details not confirmed for 2002 ➥

HMS TRINCOMALEE

Jackson Dock TS24 0SQ (From A19 take A689 or A179,
follow signs for Hartlepool Historic Quay)
☎ 01429 223193 ▤ 01429 864385
e-mail: office@hms-trincomalee.co.uk
Times: Open all year, Summer: 10-4, Winter: 11-3. Closed Fri in winter,
Xmas & New Year. **Facilities:** P ⊀ Details not confirmed for 2002
➥

MUSEUM OF HARTLEPOOL

Jackson Dock, Maritime Av TS24 0XZ (Historic Quay &
Museum towards the Marina)
☎ 01429 860077 ▤ 01429 523477
Times: Open all year, daily (closed 25-26 Dec & 1 Jan). **Facilities:** P
➥ & toilets for disabled shop ⊀ (ex guide dogs) Details not
confirmed for 2002

🏛 STAINDROP   Map 12 NZ12
RABY CASTLE

DL2 3AH (on A688, Barnard Castle to Bishop Auckland
rd, 1m N of Staindrop, 8m NE of Barnard Castle)
☎ 01833 660202 ▤ 01833 660169
e-mail: admin@rabycastle.com

The castle was built during Saxon times but is
predominantly 14th-century, with many later additions.
It has an impressive gateway; nine towers; a vast
medieval hall; and a splendid restored Victorian
octagonal drawing-room which has re-emerged as one
of the most striking interiors from the 19th century. The
castle contains fine pictures, interesting furniture and
ceramics, and a carriage collection.
Times: Open May & Sep, Wed & Sun only. Jun-Aug, Sun-Fri. Castle
open 1-5. Park & gardens 11-5.30, (last admission 4.30pm). Open BH
wknds Sat-Wed. **Fee:** Castle, Park & Gardens £5 (ch £2 & pen £4).
Family ticket (2 adults & 3 ch) £12. Park, Park & Gardens £3 (ch & pen
£2). Party 20+. **Facilities:** P ➥ & (most of ground floor accessible)
toilets for disabled shop ⊀ (ex in Park) ➥

🏛 TANFIELD   Map 12 NZ15
TANFIELD RAILWAY

Old Marley Hill NE16 5ET (on A6076 1m S of Sunniside)
☎ 0191 388 7545 ▤ 0191 387 4784
e-mail: tanfield@ingsoc.demon.co.uk
Times: Open all year, summer daily 10-5; winter daily 10-4. Trains: Sun
& Summer BH's wknds; also Thu & Sat mid Jul-Aug. Santa's Specials
Sat & Sun in Dec (booking essential). Mince pie specials Boxing Day.
Facilities: P ➥ & (all trains carry ramps for wheelchair access)
toilets for disabled shop Details not confirmed for 2002

Essex

Essex and its inhabitants have for some time been the butt of jokes that imply financial acuity but a lack of taste, discernment and sophistication. This might be due to the county's proximity to London, which has led to the development of commuter towns and changed the nature of a once rural area.

However, moving northeast into East Anglia there are some fine country towns and villages, and, approaching the Suffolk border, all the scenic delights of Constable country around the Stour Valley.

The big resorts of Southend and Clacton are the best known on the Essex coast, but by contrast there are pretty places on the Tendring Peninsula, the sailing centres of Burnham-on-Crouch and Maldon, the marshy headland of the Naze, and the birdlife of Maplin Sands.

From medieval times to the 18th century, Saffron Walden was the centre of the saffron crocus industry. It was saffron wealth that bought the town the largest parish church in Essex, and the streets around the church reflect this historic prosperity.

Colchester lays claim to being England's oldest town, and is a fascinating place to visit. There is evidence of a settlement from the fifth century BC, and the town was King Cymbeline's capital in the first century AD. The Romans also made it their capital in 43 AD and the town prospered despite being burned by Boudicca/Boadicea in 60 AD. The Roman walls are largely intact, and the remains of the Norman castle are there to be seen.

Famous natives of Essex include Noel Edmonds, Lee Evans, Helen Mirren, two members of The Prodigy, Samuel Pepys, Dick Turpin and Matthew Hopkins, Witchfynder General.

EVENTS & FESTIVALS

May
19th Essex Young Farmers Show, Great Leighs
tbc Southend Air Show (Europe's largest free show)
tbc Tour de Tendring Cycle Ride, Tendring area

June
23rd Essex History Fair, Cressing Temple, nr Braintree
tbc Concert in the Park, Southend (Royal Philharmonic with grand fireworks finale)
tbc Essex County Show, Essex County Showground, Great Leighs
tbc Thaxted Morris Ring Meet (various venues), annual meeting of morris men

July
tbc Classic Car Rally London-Southend
tbc Tendring Hundred Show, Lawford

August
22nd-26th Clacton Jazz Festival
tbc Clacton Air Show, Clacton Seafront
tbc Clacton Carnival
tbc Southend Carnival, Chalkwell Park
tbc Southend Jazz Festival

September
tbc Maldon Town Regatta
tbc Old Leigh Regatta

Top: Beach Huts, Walton-on-the-Naze

🏛 AUDLEY END   Map 05 TL53
AUDLEY END HOUSE & GARDENS
CB11 4JF (1m W of Saffron Walden on B1383)
☎ 01799 522399

Built on a grandiose scale by Thomas Howard, Earl of
Suffolk, to entertain King James I, Audley End House
was gradually reduced in size over the next century, but
what we see today is still impressive in scale and the 30
rooms open to the public display a stunning collection
of art, as well as period furnishings. Gardens and a
landscaped park surround the mansion.
Times: Open Parks & Gardens: Apr-Sep, Wed-Sun & BH's 11-6 (or
dusk if earlier). 3-31Oct: Wed-Fri, 11-4, Sat/Sun 11-5 (Last admission 1
hr before closing). House: Apr-Sep Wed-Sun & Bhs 12-5. 3-31Oct Wed-
Sun 11-4 (Last admission 1hr before closing). **Fee:** House & Grounds:
£6.75 (ch 5-15 £3.40, con £5.10). Grounds £4 (ch £2, ch u5 free, con
£3) **Facilities:** 🅿 (charged) ♨ ዿ shop ⊀ ⌗

🏛 BRAINTREE   Map 05 TL72
THE WORKING SILK MILL
New Mills, South St CM7 3GB (follow brown tourist
signs)
☎ 01376 553393   ▤ 01376 330642
Times: Open Mon-Fri, 10-12.30 & 1.30-5. Last admission to mill 12
noon and 4pm. **Facilities:** 🅿ዿ (ramps) toilets for disabled shop ⊀
(ex guide dogs) *Details not confirmed for 2002* ♨

🏛 CASTLE HEDINGHAM   Map 05 TL73
COLNE VALLEY RAILWAY & MUSEUM
Castle Hedingham Station CO9 3DZ (4m NW of
Halstead on A1017)
☎ 01787 461174

The old Colne Valley and Halstead railway buildings
have been rebuilt here. Stock includes seven steam
locomotives plus 60 other engines, carriages and
wagons, in steam from Easter to December. Visitors
can dine in style in restored Pullman carriages while
travelling along the line. Please telephone for a free
timetable and details of the many special events.
Times: Open all year, daily 10-dusk. Steam days, rides from 12-4.
(Closed 23 Dec-1 Feb). Steam days every Sun and BH from Mothering
Sunday to end Oct, Tue-Thu of school summer holidays & special
events. Phone 01787 461174 for timetable information. **Fee:** Steam
days £6 (ch £3 pen £5); Family ticket £16. Non-steam days (to view
static exhibits only) £3 (ch £1.50); Family ticket £7.50. **Facilities:** 🅿 ♨
✗ licensed ዿ (ramps for wheelchairs to get onto carriages) shop ⊀
(ex guide dogs) ♨

HEDINGHAM CASTLE
CO9 3DJ (on B1058, 1m off A1017
Colchester/Cambridge. Follow brown tourist signs to
Hedingham Castle)
☎ 01787 460261   ▤ 01787 461473
e-mail: hedinghamcastle@aspects.net

This impressive Norman castle was built in 1140. It was
besieged by King John, and visited by Henry VII, Henry
VIII and Elizabeth I, and was home to the de Veres,
Earls of Oxford, for over 500 years. Please telephone for

details of civil ceremony weddings, corporate hire and
special events.

Hedingham Castle

Times: Open wk before Etr-Oct, daily 10-5. **Fee:** £4 (ch £3,
concessions £3.50). Family ticket £11.50. **Facilities:** 🅿 ♨ shop ⊀ (ex
in grounds) ♨

🏛 COGGESHALL   Map 05 TL82
PAYCOCKE'S
West St CO6 1NS (Signposted from A120, on S side of
West Street)
☎ 01376 561305

This timber-framed house is a fine example of a
medieval merchant's home. It was completed in about
1505 and has interesting carvings on the outside
timbers, including the Paycocke trade sign. Inside there
are further elaborate carvings and linenfold panelling.
Behind the house is a pretty garden.
Times: Open 2 Apr-15 Oct Tue, Thu, Sun & BH Mon 2-5.30.
Fee: £2.20, joint ticket with Coggeshall Grange Barn £3. **Facilities:** 🅿
(400yds) ዿ ⊀ (ex guide dogs) ⅍

🏛 COLCHESTER   Map 05 TL92
BETH CHATTO GARDENS
Elmstead Market CO7 7DB (5m E of Colchester on
A133)
☎ 01206 822007   ▤ 01206 825933
e-mail: info@bethchatto.fsnet.co.uk

Begun almost 40 years ago, when Beth Chatto and her
late husband began working on acres of wasteland.
Today the wasteland has become a garden of three
distinctive areas. The south-west facing dry garden is
on gravel, and has plants such as yucca and pineapple
broom. It faces a group of oaks which shade the second
area, with woodland and other shade-loving plants.
Lastly, there is the wetland garden, with five large pools
filled with fish and surrounded by swathes of bog
plants.
Times: Open all year, Mar-Oct, Mon-Sat 9-5; Nov-Feb, Mon-Fri 9-4.
(Closed BHs & Sun). **Fee:** £3 (accompanied ch under 14 free)
Facilities: 🅿 ♨ ዿ (access to parts of garden may be difficult) toilets
for disabled garden centre ⊀ (ex guide dogs) ♨

COLCHESTER CASTLE MUSEUM
Castle Park, High St CO1 1TJ (at E end of High St)
☎ 01206 282931   📠 01206 282925

The largest Norman castle keep in Europe - built over the remains of the magnificent Roman Temple of Claudius which was destroyed by Boudicca in AD60. Colchester was the first capital of Roman Britain, and the archaeological collections are among the finest in the country. Please telephone for details of a range of events held in the school holidays.
Times: Open all year, Mon-Sat 10-5, Sun 11-5. **Fee:** £3.90 (ch u5's free, ch & concessions £2.60). Family ticket £10.50 (2 ad+2ch or 1ad+ 3 ch). **Facilities:** 🅿 (town centre) ♿ (ramps to all areas & lift) toilets for disabled shop ✸ 🍽

COLCHESTER ZOO
Stanway, Maldon Rd CO3 5SL (turn off A12 onto A1124 and follow elephant signs)
☎ 01206 331292   📠 01206 331392
e-mail: colchester.zoo@btinternet.com

One of England's finest zoos, Colchester Zoo has over 200 types of animals. Visitors can meet the elephants, handle a snake, and see parrots, seals, penguins and birds of prey all appearing in informative daily displays. New enclosures include Spirit of Africa, Elephant Kingdom, Penguin Shores, the Wilds of Asia for orangutans, and Chimp World. There is also an undercover soft play complex, road train, four adventure play areas, eating places and gift shops, all set in 40 acres of gardens.
Times: Open all year, daily from 9.30. Last admission 5.30pm (1hr before dusk out of season). (Closed 25 Dec). **Fee:** £8.80 (ch 3-14 & pen £5.60, disabled £4). **Facilities:** 🅿 🍽 ✕ licensed ♿ (easy route developed) toilets for disabled shop garden centre ✸ 🍽

🏛 HADLEIGH   Map 05 TQ88
HADLEIGH CASTLE
(0.75m S of A13)
☎ 01536 402840
Times: Open any reasonable time. **Facilities:** ⚏ *Details not confirmed for 2002*

🏛 HARLOW   Map 05 TL41
HARLOW MUSEUM
Passmores House, Third Av CM18 6YL
☎ 01279 454959   📠 01279 626094
Times: Open all year, Tue-Fri 9.30-4.30 & Sat 10-12.30 & 1.30-4.30. Last admission 4.15pm. **Facilities:** 🅿 ♿ shop ✸ *Details not confirmed for 2002*

🏛 HARWICH   Map 05 TM23
HARWICH REDOUBT FORT
CO12 3TE (behind 29 Main Rd)
☎ 01255 503429   📠 01255 503429
e-mail: theharwichsociety@quista.net

The 180ft-diameter circular fort was built in 1808 in case of invasion by Napoleon. It has a dry moat and 8ft-thick walls, with 18 rooms for stores, ammunition and quarters for 300 men. The Redoubt is being restored by the Harwich Society, and contains three small museums. Ten guns can be seen on the battlements.
Times: Open May-Aug, daily 10-5; Sep-Apr, Sun only 10-5. **Fee:** £1 (accompanied ch free). **Facilities:** 🅿 (200yds) shop

🏛 LAYER MARNEY   Map 05 TL91
LAYER MARNEY TOWER
CO5 9US (off B1022 Colchester to Maldon road, signposted)
☎ 01206 330784   📠 01206 330784
e-mail: nicholas@layermarney.demon.co.uk

The tallest Tudor gatehouse in the country, intended to be the entrance to a courtyard which would have rivalled Hampton Court Palace. The death of Henry, 1st Lord Marney in 1523, and of his son in 1525, meant that the building work ceased before completion. The beautiful parish church lies within the grounds and a wildlife walk offers the chance to see a large herd of red deer, among other livestock.
Times: Open Apr-Sep, Mon-Fri 12-5, Sun 12-5 & BHs 11-5. **Fee:** £3.50 (ch £2). Family ticket £10. Guided tour £4.75. Party 20+. **Facilities:** 🅿 🍽 ✕ licensed ♿ (ramps in garden and farm) toilets for disabled shop ✸ (ex guide dogs) 🍽

🏛 MISTLEY   Map 05 TM13
MISTLEY TOWERS
CO11 1NJ (on B1352, 1.5m E of A137 at Lawford)
Times: Open all reasonable times. Key available from Mistley Quay Workshops & Teashop. **Facilities:** ♿ (exterior only) ✸ (in certain areas) ⚏ *Details not confirmed for 2002*

🏛 NEWPORT   Map 05 TL53
MOLE HALL WILDLIFE PARK
Widdington CB11 3SS (situated between Stansted & Saffron Walden, off B1383)
☎ 01799 540400   📠 01799 540400
e-mail: enquires@molehall.co.uk
Times: Open all year, daily 10.30-6 (or dusk). (Closed 25 Dec). Butterfly House open mid Mar-Oct. **Facilities:** 🅿 🍽 ♿ (Difficult in wet weather for wheelchairs) toilets for disabled shop garden centre ✸ (ex guide dogs) *Details not confirmed for 2002*

🏛 SAFFRON WALDEN   Map 05 TL53
SAFFRON WALDEN MUSEUM
Museum St CB10 1JL (take B184 & follow signs to Saffron Walden)
☎ 01799 510333   📠 01799 510334
e-mail: museum@uttesford.gov.uk

Built in 1834, this friendly museum lies near the castle ruins in the centre of town. Its collections include local archaeology, natural history, ceramics, glass, costume, furniture, toys, an ancient Egyptian room, a new

contd.

natural history gallery and Discovery Centre. This museum has won awards for disabled access.
Times: Open all year, Mar-Oct, Mon-Sat 10-5, Sun & BHs 2-5; Nov-Feb, Mon-Sat, 10-4.30, Sun & BHs 2-4.30. (Closed 24 & 25 Dec). **Fee:** £1 (concessions 50p & ch under 18 free). **Facilities:** P ♿ (ramped entrance,spare wheelchairs,stairlift to upper floor) toilets for disabled shop (ex guide dogs)

SOUTHEND-ON-SEA Map 05 TQ88

SOUTHEND MUSEUM, PLANETARIUM & DISCOVERY CENTRE

Victoria Av SS2 6EW (take A127 or A13 towards town centre. Museum is adjacent to Southend Victoria Railway Station)
☎ 01702 434449 & 215131 Fax 01702 349806

A fine Edwardian building housing displays of archaeology, natural history and local history, telling the story of man in the south-east Essex area. Also the only planetarium in the South East outside London. Ring for details of special events.
Times: Open Central Museum: Tue-Sat 10-5 (Closed Sun-Mon & BH); Planetarium: Wed-Sat, shows at 11, 2 & 4. **Fee:** Central Museum free. Planetarium £2.25 (ch & pen £1.60). Family tickets £7. Party rates on request. **Facilities:** P (50m) (disabled only behind museum) ♿ (planetarium not accessible, disabled access to centre) shop (ex guide dogs)

STANSTED Map 05 TL52

HOUSE ON THE HILL MUSEUM ADVENTURE

CM24 8SP (off B1383)
☎ 01279 813237 Fax 01279 816391
e-mail: gold@enta.net

A large, privately-owned toy museum, housed on two floors covering 7,000 sq. ft. A huge variety of toys, books and games from the late Victorian period up to the 1970s. There is a train room, space display, Teddy Bears' picnic, Action Men, Sindy, Barbie, military displays and much more. Additional displays of film, theatre and television memorabilia are on show.
Times: Open daily, 10-5; (closed for a few days over the Xmas period) **Fee:** £3.80 (ch under 14's £2.80, pen £3.50). Party 15+. **Facilities:** P (charged) shop (ex guide dogs)

MOUNTFITCHET CASTLE & NORMAN VILLAGE

CM24 8SP (off B1383, in centre of village)
☎ 01279 813237 Fax 01279 816391
e-mail: gold@enta.net

Norman motte and bailey castle and village reconstructed as it was in Norman England of 1066, on its original historic site. A vivid illustration of village life in Domesday England, complete with houses, church, seige tower, seige weapons, and many types of animals roaming freely. Animated wax figures in all the buildings give historical information to visitors.
Times: Open daily, 11 Mar-11 Nov, 10-5. **Fee:** £4.80 (ch under 14's £3.80, pen £4). Party 15+. **Facilities:** P (charged) ☕ ♿ (laser commentaries) toilets for disabled shop (ex guide dogs)

TILBURY Map 05 TQ67

TILBURY FORT

No 2 Office Block, The Fort RM18 7NR (0.5 mile E off A126)
☎ 01375 858489

The largest English example of 17th-century military engineering, the fort originally dates from the earlier Tudor period, and is most famous for Queen Elizabeth I's review of her troops before the defeat of the Spanish Armada. It defended the country again in the 17th century against the Dutch and the French.
Times: Open all year, Apr-Sep, daily 10-6 (Oct 10-5); Nov-Mar, Wed-Sun 10-4. (Closed 24-26 Dec & 1 Jan). **Fee:** £2.75 (ch 5-15 £1.40, under 5's free, con £2.10). Personal stereo tours included in admission price.
♿ shop (in certain areas)

WALTHAM ABBEY Map 05 TL30

LEE VALLEY PARK FARMS

Stubbings Hall Ln, Crooked Mile EN9 2EG (off B194)
☎ 01992 892781 & 892291 Fax 01992 893113
Times: Open all year, Mon-Fri 10-4.30, wknds & BH 10-5.30pm. **Facilities:** P ☕ ♿ (graded concrete paths, signed routes) toilets for disabled shop *Details not confirmed for 2002*

WALTHAM ABBEY GATEHOUSE, BRIDGE & ENTRANCE TO CLOISTERS

Times: Open any reasonable time. **Facilities:** *Details not confirmed for 2002*

Gloucestershire

Most of the Cotswolds lie in the county of Gloucestershire; limestone hills dotted with picturesque villages built from the local stone, varying in hue from honey gold to silver grey. The large churches and substantial manor houses are a legacy of the wealthy medieval wool trade.

The bits of Gloucestershire outside the Cotswolds include the county town of Gloucester, the Regency spa town of Cheltenham and the countryside around the Severn estuary, the site of the Slimbridge wildfowl reserve. The county's other major natural feature is the Forest of Dean, a mining area exploited from Roman times until the 20th century.

Gloucester has plenty to see and do. The Victorian docks now house offices, shops, and cafés, while the canal is busy with pleasure craft.

Nearby Cheltenham is more upmarket, with Regency architecture and exclusive boutiques. The mineral spring was discovered in 1715 through the observation of pigeons coming and going. Pigeons are incorporated into the town's crest to this day, though Cheltenham is probably better known for horse-racing.

South of Cheltenham is the charming and rather less self-conscious Cirencester, the 'capital of the Cotswolds'. It was once an immensely powerful town known as Corinium by the Romans, and in those days was second only to Londinium. Little of its Roman heritage remains, although some replicas of ancient mosaics have been made.

Laurie Lee (1914-1997), a native of Slad near Stroud, wrote the classic novel *Cider With Rosie*, which explored his childhood in the 1920s among the rolling Cotswold hills. His carefree writing captures the spirit of the area.

EVENTS & FESTIVALS

February
8th-10th Sixth Cheltenham Folk Festival

April
5th-7th Cheltenham Festival of Literature Spring Weekend

May
1st-5th Cheltenham International Jazz Festival
6th Cheese Roll, Brockworth
21st-27th First Cheltenham Science Festival
31st Robert Dover's Cotswold Olimpick Games, Chipping Coopers Hill

June
14th-20th July Longborough Festival Opera
15th-17th Three Counties Show, Malvern

July
6th-7th The Cotswold Country Fair, Cirencester
6th-21st Cheltenham International Festival of Music
19th-21st Tewkesbury Water Festival (provisional)
20th-21st Royal International Air Tattoo, RAF Fairford
27th-28th International Kite Festival, Tewkesbury

September
7th Moreton Show
28th-29th Malvern Show

October
11th-20th Cheltenham Festival of Literature

Top: Owlpen Manor

🏛 BARNSLEY
Map 04 SP00

BARNSLEY HOUSE GARDEN

GL7 5EE (3m NE of Cirencester on B4425, on right on entering village)

☎ 01285 740561 📠 01285 740628

e-mail: cverey@barnsleyhouse.freeserve.co.uk

Home of renowned plantswoman, gardener and author Rosemary Verey. A lovely garden, with herb and knot garden, and a vegetable garden planted as a potager; here small paths form a chequerboard around fruit trees trained as pyramids, ornamental brassicas and other decorative kitchen plants. Other features include a laburnum walk and a lime walk.

Times: Open all year, Mon, Wed, Thu & Sat 10-5.30; Parties & guided tours by appointment only. (Closed Xmas-end Jan). House not open. **Fee:** £3.75 (ch free, pen £3). **Facilities:** 🅿 ♿ shop garden centre 🎏 ➰

🏛 BERKELEY
Map 03 ST69

BERKELEY CASTLE

GL13 9BQ (on B4509, 1.5m W of A38)

☎ 01453 810332

Home of the Berkeleys for almost 850 years, the castle is a rambling great place surrounded by 14ft thick walls, with a Norman keep, a great hall, medieval kitchens, and the dungeon where Edward II was murdered gruesomely. Outside there are Elizabethan terraced gardens and an extensive park.

Times: Open: Tue-Sun, 2-5 Apr-May. Tue-Sat 11-5, Sun 2-5, Jun & Sep. Mon-Sat 11-5, Sun 2-5 Jul & Aug. Sun only 2-5 Oct. BH Mon 11-5. **Fee:** Castle & Gardens: £5.50 (ch £3, pen £4.50). Gardens only £2 (ch £1). Party 25+ **Facilities:** 🅿 🍽 shop 🎏 (ex guide dogs) ➰

JENNER MUSEUM

Church Ln, High St GL13 9BH (follow tourist signs from A38 to town centre, turn left into High St & left again into Church Ln)

☎ 01453 810631 📠 01453 811690

e-mail: manager@jennermuseum.com

This beautiful Georgian house was the home of Edward Jenner, the discoverer of vaccination against smallpox. The house and the garden, with its Temple of Vaccinia, are much as they were in Jenner's day. The displays record Jenner's life as an 18th-century country doctor, his work on vaccination and his interest in natural history.

Times: Open Apr-Sep, Tue-Sat 12.30-5.30, Sun 1-5.30. Oct, Sun 1-5.30. (Closed Mon, ex BH Mon 12.30-5.30). **Fee:** £2.80 (ch £1.25, students & pen £2). Family ticket £7. Party 20+. **Facilities:** 🅿 ♿ (level wide access, hand rails) toilets for disabled shop 🎏 (ex guide dogs)

🏛 BOURTON-ON-THE-WATER
Map 04 SP12

BIRDLAND PARK & GARDENS

Risssington Rd GL54 2BN (on A429)

☎ 01451 820480 📠 01451 822398

e-mail: sb.birdland@virgin.net

Times: Open all year, Apr-Oct, daily 10-6; Nov-Mar, daily 10-4. Last admission 1hr before closing. (Closed 25 Dec). **Facilities:** 🅿 (adjacent) 🍽 ♿ toilets for disabled shop *Details not confirmed for 2002*

MODEL VILLAGE

Old New Inn GL54 2AF

☎ 01451 820467 📠 01451 810236

e-mail: old_new_inn@compuserve.com

The model is built of Cotswold stone to a scale of one-ninth, and is a perfect replica of the village. It includes a miniature River Windrush, a working model waterwheel, churches and shops, with tiny trees, shrubs and alpine plants.

Times: Open all year 9-5.45 (summer), 10-dusk (winter). (Closed 25 Dec). **Fee:** £2.75 (ch £2, pen £2.25) party 20+ **Facilities:** 🅿 🍽 ✕ licensed shop

🏛 CHEDWORTH
Map 04 SP01

CHEDWORTH ROMAN VILLA

Yanworth GL54 3LJ (3m NW of Fossebridge on A429)

☎ 01242 890256 📠 01242 890544

e-mail: chedworth@smtp.ntrust.org.uk

Times: Open 2 May-Sep, Tue-Sun & BH Mon 10-5; Mar-Apr & 4 Oct-mid Nov, Wed-Sun & Etr Mon 11-4. **Facilities:** 🅿 ♿ (Braile guide & audio tour) toilets for disabled shop 🎏 🐾 *Details not confirmed for 2002*

🏛 CHELTENHAM
Map 03 SO92

CHELTENHAM ART GALLERY & MUSEUM

Clarence St GL50 3JT (close to town centre and bus station)

☎ 01242 237431 📠 01242 262334

e-mail: artgallery@cheltenham.gov.uk

The museum has an outstanding collection relating to the Arts and Crafts Movement, including fine furniture and exquisite metalwork. The Art Gallery contains Dutch and British paintings from the 17th century to the present day. The Oriental Gallery features pottery, costumes and treasures from the Ming Dynasty to the reign of the last Chinese Emperor. There is also a display about Edward Wilson who journeyed with Captain Scott in 1911-12, together with the history of Britain's most complete Regency town and archaeological treasures from the neighbouring Cotswolds. Special exhibitions are held throughout the year.

Times: Open all year, Mon-Sat 10-5.20, Sun 2-4.20. (Closed BHs & Etr Sun). **Fee:** Free. **Facilities:** 🅿 (500 metres) 🍽 ♿ (handling tables; speech reinforcement system) toilets for disabled shop 🎏 (ex guide dogs)

HOLST BIRTHPLACE MUSEUM
4 Clarence Rd, Pittville GL52 2AY (just off Evesham Rd, opposite gateway of Pittville Park)
☎ 01242 524846 580182 🖷 01242 580182
e-mail: holstmuseum@btconnect.com

Times: Open Tue-Sat 10-4 (Closed Mon) open some BH, please enquire. **Facilities:** P (100 yds) shop ✘ (ex guide dogs) *Details not confirmed for 2002*

🏛 CIRENCESTER   Map 04 SP00
CORINIUM MUSEUM
Park St GL7 2BX (in town centre)
☎ 01285 655611 🖷 01285 643286
e-mail: simone.clark@cotswold.gov.uk

Cirencester was the second largest town in Roman Britain and the Corinium Museum brings the period to life with full-scale reconstructions. There's a Cotswold Prehistory gallery, a Medieval Cotswolds gallery, and galleries on Roman military history, the Roman town of Corinium, and the Civil War in the Cotswolds.
Times: Open all year, Mon-Sat 10-5, Sun 2-5. Also open BHs. (Closed Xmas & New Year). **Fee:** £2.50 (ch £1, students £1, pen £2). Family ticket £5. Party. Fri after 3.30pm free admission. **Facilities:** P (440yds town centre) 🍴 ✘ licensed 🚻 (large print & braille guide for exhibits) toilets for disabled shop 🍴

🏛 CLEARWELL   Map 03 SO50
CLEARWELL CAVES ANCIENT IRON MINES
GL16 8JR (1.5m S of Coleford town centre, off B4228 follow brown tourist signs)
☎ 01594 832535 🖷 01594 833362
e-mail: jw@clearwellcaves.com

The mines have been worked since the Iron Age, and the industry grew under the Romans. Over half a million tons of ore were extracted in the 19th century, and mining continues today. Nine large caverns can be explored, with deeper trips for the more adventurous. There are engine rooms, a blacksmith's shop, and exhibits of local mining and geology.
Times: Open Mar-Oct daily 10-5. Jan-Feb Sat-Sun 10-5. Christmas Fantasy 1-24 Dec, daily 10-5. **Fee:** £3.50 (ch £2.20, concessions £3) **Facilities:** P 🍴 🚻 ("Hands-on" exhibits, contact in advance) toilets for disabled shop ✘ (ex guide & hearing dogs) 🍴

🏛 CRANHAM   Map 03 SO81
PRINKNASH ABBEY AND POTTERY
GL4 8EX (on A46 between Cheltenham & Stroud)
☎ 01452 812066 🖷 01452 812529
e-mail: bjnicholls@prinknash.fsnet.co.uk
Times: Open all year. Abbey Church: daily 5am-8pm. Pottery: Mon-Sat 11-4.30 (Sun pm). Pottery shop & tearoom 9-5.30. (Closed Good Fri, 25 & 26 Dec). **Facilities:** P 🍴 🚻 toilets for disabled shop *Details not confirmed for 2002*

PRINKNASH BIRD & DEER PARK
GL4 8EX (M5 junct 11a, A417 Cirencester. Take 1st exit signposted A46 Stroud. Follow brown tourist signs)
☎ 01452 812727
Times: Open all year, daily 10-5 (4pm in winter). Park closes at 6pm (5pm in winter). (Closed 25-26 Dec, 1 Jan & Good Fri). **Facilities:** P 🍴 shop ✘ *Details not confirmed for 2002*

🏛 DEERHURST   Map 03 SO82
ODDA'S CHAPEL
(off B4213 near River Severn at Abbots Court SW of parish church)
Times: Open any reasonable time. **Facilities:** ♿ *Details not confirmed for 2002*

🏛 DYRHAM   Map 03 ST77
DYRHAM PARK
SN14 8ER (8m N of Bath, 2m from M4 junct 18)
☎ 0117 937 2501
e-mail: wdycjc@smtp.ntrust.org.uk

Dyrham Park is a splendid William and Mary house, with interiors which have hardly altered since the late 17th century. It has contemporary Dutch-style furnishings, Dutch pictures and blue-and-white Delft ware. Around the house is an ancient park with fallow deer.
Times: Open House: Apr-29 Oct; daily ex Wed & Thu, 12-5.30. Garden open same as house except 11-5.30 or dusk if earlier. Park open all year daily 12-5.30 or dusk if earlier, opens 11 when garden opens. Winter: domestic rooms open 4 Nov-17 Dec, Sat & Sun 12-4. Closed 25 Dec. Property closed 7, 8 & 9 Jul for concerts. **Fee:** £7.50 (ch £3.70) Family £18.50. Grounds only £2.60 (ch £1.20) Family £6.50. Park only ticket on days when house & gardens closed: £1.80 (ch 90p). Winter: park & domestic rooms £3.80 (£1.90 ch). Party **Facilities:** P 🍴 ✘ licensed 🚻 (Braille & audio guides, stairclimber, free bus from carpark toilets for disabled shop ✘ (ex in dog walk area). 🦮

🏛 GLOUCESTER   Map 03 SO81
CITY MUSEUM & ART GALLERY
Brunswick Rd GL1 1HP
☎ 01452 396131 🖷 01452 410898
e-mail: city.museum@gloucester.gov.uk

This museum contains a range of exhibits showing the early life and natural history of the city. These include dinosaur displays, unusual Roman remains and the
contd.

amazing Birdlip mirror. Artists on display at the gallery include Turner and Gainsborough.
Times: Open all year, Mon-Sat 10-5. (Also Jul-Sep, Sun 10-4). **Fee:** £2 (concessions £1). Free for Gloucester City residents and under 18's. **Facilities:** P (adjacent) & (lift suitable only for manual wheelchairs) toilets for disabled shop ✱ ◥

FOLK MUSEUM
99-103 Westgate St GL1 2PG
☎ **01452 526467**   🖷 **01452 330495**
e-mail: **irenez@gloscity.gov.uk**
Times: Open all year, Mon-Sat 10-5. (Also Jul-Sep, Sun 10-4). Open BH Mon. **Facilities:** P (200yds) & (parking on request, ramps) shop ✱ (ex guide dogs) *Details not confirmed for 2002* ◥

NATIONAL WATERWAYS MUSEUM
Llanthony Warehouse, The Docks GL1 2EH (follow signs for historic docks off M5, situated to S of city)
☎ **01452 318054**   🖷 **01452 318066**
e-mail: **info@nwm.demon.co.uk**
Times: Open all year, daily 10-5 (Closed 25 Dec). **Facilities:** P (charged) ♥ & (wheelchair, lifts, limited access to floating exhibits) toilets for disabled shop ✱ (ex guide dogs) *Details not confirmed for 2002* ◥

NATURE IN ART
Wallsworth Hall, Tewkesbury Rd, Twigworth GL2 9PA (on A38, from village follow tourist signs)
☎ **01452 731422**   🖷 **01452 730937**
e-mail: **ninart@globalnet.co.uk**

Times: Open all year, Tue-Sun & BH's 10-5. Mon by arrangement. (Closed 24-26 Dec). **Facilities:** P ♥ & (lift & ramps at entrance) toilets for disabled shop ✱ (ex guide dogs) *Details not confirmed for 2002*

ROBERT OPIE COLLECTION-MUSEUM OF ADVERTISING & PACKAGING
Albert Warehouse, Gloucester Docks GL1 2EH (follow signs for Gloucester 'Historic Docks')
☎ **01452 302309**   🖷 **01452 308507**
e-mail: **sales@robertopie.telme.com**
Times: Open all year, daily, 10-6; winter Tue-Fri 10-5, Sat & Sun 10-6. (Closed 25-26 Dec). **Facilities:** P (charged) ♥ & shop ✱ (ex guide dogs) *Details not confirmed for 2002*

⛫ GREAT WITCOMBE   Map 03 SO91
WITCOMBE ROMAN VILLA
(off A417, 0.5m S of reservoir in Witcombe Park)
Times: Open any reasonable time. Guided tours may be available contact 01451 862000. **Facilities:** P ✚ *Details not confirmed for 2002*

⛫ GUITING POWER   Map 04 SP02
COTSWOLD FARM PARK
GL54 5UG (signposted off B4077 from M5 Junct 9)
☎ **01451 850307**   🖷 **01451 850423**
e-mail: **info@cotswoldfarmpark.co.uk**

At the Cotswold Farm Park there are nearly 50 breeding herds and flocks of the rarest British breeds of sheep, cattle, pigs, goats, horses, poultry and waterfowl. Set on the very top of the Cotswold Hills, this is the perfect opportunity to get to know a Bagot goat, cuddle a Cotswold lamb, stroke a mighty Longhorn ox, and admire generations of our living agricultural heritage. New born lambs and goat kids can be seen from April to May, spring calves in May, foals and sheep shearing in June and piglets throughout the year.
Times: Open Apr-1 Oct, daily 10.30-5. **Fee:** £4.50 (ch £2.50, pen £4). Family ticket £13. **Facilities:** P ♥ & (ramps, wheelchair to let) toilets for disabled shop ✱ (only guide dogs inside) ◥

⛫ HAILES   Map 04 SP02
HAILES ABBEY
GL54 5PB (2m NE of Winchcombe off B4632)
☎ **01242 602398**

This Cistercian abbey was, in the Middle Ages, one of the main centres of pilgrimage in England because it possessed a phial reputed to contain some of Christ's blood. Good medieval sculpture and floor tiles are displayed in the museum.
Times: Open Apr-Sep, daily 10-6; Oct, daily 10-5; Nov-Mar, Sat & Sun 10-4. (Closed 24-26 Dec & 1 Jan). (Reviewed Mar 2002) **Fee:** £2.60 (ch u5 free, ch £1.30 & con £2). (Reviewed Mar 2002) **Facilities:** P & shop ✱ ✚ ⚘

⛫ LITTLEDEAN   Map 03 SO61
LITTLEDEAN HALL
GL14 3NR
☎ **01594 824213**   🖷 **01594 824213**
e-mail: **sheila@lttledean.com**

The largest known Roman temple in rural Britain was unearthed here in 1984 and the manor itself is Norman. The house has always been lived in, and has been relatively untouched since the 19th century. Inside there are interpretive displays and the grounds offer beautiful walks. There are fish pools in the walled garden, and, of course, the Roman excavations.
Times: Open - House, Grounds & Archaeological site, Apr-Oct, daily 11-5. **Fee:** £3.50 (ch £1.50, pen £2.50) **Facilities:** P ✱ (ex in grounds)

🏛 LYDNEY   Map 03 SO60
DEAN FOREST RAILWAY

Norchard Railway Centre, New Mills, Forest Rd GL15
4ET (1m N of Lydney-Parkend Rd, on B4234, signed
from A48)

☎ **01594 845840 & (843423 recorded info)**
🖨 **01594 845840**
e-mail: **mike@cornick.8.freeserve.co.uk**

Times: Open all year, daily for static displays. Steam days: Sun from
Etr-Oct; Wed & Sat, Jun-Aug (Aug also open Tue & Thu). Lydney Road
& Rail show 3rd Sun in Oct. Santa special Dec (Additional days &
school holidays telephone 01594 843423 for details). **Facilities:** 🅿 ▼
& (specially adapted coach for wheelchairs) toilets for disabled shop
Details not confirmed for 2002 ▼

🏛 MICKLETON   Map 04 SP14
HIDCOTE MANOR GARDEN

Chipping Campden GL55 6LR (1m E of B4632)
☎ **01386 438333**   🖨 **01386 438817**
Times: Open, Gardens only Apr-Sep, daily (ex Tue & Fri) 11-7; also
open Tue in Jun & Jul only 11-7; Oct-1 Nov, daily (ex Tue & Fri) 11-6.
Last admission 1hr before closing. **Facilities:** 🅿 ▼ ✗ licensed &
(limited due to stone paths) toilets for disabled shop garden centre 🐾
🐾 *Details not confirmed for 2002*

KIFTSGATE COURT GARDEN

Mickleton GL55 6LN (0.5m S off A46, adjacent Hidcote
NT garden)
☎ **01386 438777**   🖨 **01386 438777**
e-mail: **kiftsgte@aol.com**

Kiftsgate Garden is spectacularly set on the edge of the
Cotswold Escarpment, with views over the Vale of
Evesham. It contains many rare plants collected by
three generations of women gardeners, including the
largest rose in England, the R. Filipes Kiftsgate.
Times: Open Apr-May & Aug-Sep; Wed, Thu, Sun & BH Mon 2-6. Jun-
Jul Wed, Thu, Sat & Sun 12-6. **Fee:** (ch £1). **Facilities:** 🅿 ▼
garden centre 🐾 (ex guide dogs)

🏛 MORETON-IN-MARSH   Map 04 SP23
BATSFORD ARBORETUM

Admissions Centre, Batsford Park GL56 9QB (1.5m NW,
off A44 from Moreton-in-Marsh)
☎ **01386 701441**   🖨 **01386 701827**
e-mail: **batsarb@batsfound.freeserve.co.uk**

Batsford Arboretum has one of the largest private
collections of trees in Great Britain and wonderful
views across the Vale of Evenlode. Visitors can stroll
amongst the spring flowers that cascade down the
hillside, and see many rare and unusual trees. There is

an impressive display of colour during autumn, and
peace and tranquillity are ever present.

Batsford Arboretum

Times: Open Feb (wknds only); Mar-mid Nov daily, 10-5. **Fee:** £4 (ch
under 4-15 (inc) £1, con £3). Party 12+. **Facilities:** 🅿 ▼ & (some
steep & slippery paths not suited to wheelchairs) toilets for disabled
shop garden centre

COTSWOLD FALCONRY CENTRE

Batsford Park GL56 9QB (1m W of Moreton-in-Marsh
on A44)
☎ **01386 701043**
e-mail: **geoffdalton@yahoo.co.uk**

Conveniently located by the Batsford Park Arboretum,
the Cotswold Falconry gives daily demonstrations in
the art of falconry. The emphasis here is on breeding
and conservation, and eagles, hawks, owls and falcons
can be seen.
Times: Open mid Feb-mid Nov, 10.30-5.30. (Last admission 5pm).
Fee: £4 (ch 4-15 £2, con £3). Joint ticket with Batsford Arboretum
£6.50 (ch 4-15 £3, con £6). **Facilities:** 🅿 & (no steps, wide doorways)
toilets for disabled shop garden centre 🐾 (ex on leads in car park)
▼

SEZINCOTE

GL56 9AW (1.5m out of Moreton-in-Marsh on A44,
Evesham road)

The Indian-style house at Sezincote was the inspiration
for Brighton Pavilion; its charming water garden adds
to its exotic aura and features trees of unusual size.
Times: Open: House, May-Jul & Sep, Thu & Fri 2.30-6. Garden only, all
year (ex Dec) Thu, Fri & BH Mon 2-6 or dusk if earlier. **Fee:** House &
garden £5. Garden only £3.50 (ch £1 under 5 free). Children not
allowed in the House. Groups by appointment only. **Facilities:** 🅿 🐾
(ex guide dogs in garden)

⛫ NEWENT
Map 03 SO72

THE NATIONAL BIRDS OF PREY CENTRE
GL18 1JJ (follow A40, right onto B4219 towards
Newent. Follow brown tourist signs from Newent)
☎ 0870 9901992 📠 01531 821389
e-mail: jpj@nbpc.demon.co.uk

Trained birds can be seen at close quarters in the Hawk
Walk and the Owl Courtyard and there are also
breeding aviaries, a gift shop, bookshop, picnic areas,
coffee shop and children's play area. Birds are flown
three times daily in summer and winter, giving an
exciting and educational display. There are over 110
aviaries on view with 85 species. The centre leads the
world in the field of captive breeding.
Times: Open Feb-Nov, daily 10.30-5.30 or dusk if earlier. Also open in
Dec for evening events. **Fee:** £5.75 (ch £3.50). Family ticket £16.50.
Party 12+. **Facilities:** 🅿 ☕ ♿ (special tours available, pre-booking
required) toilets for disabled shop 🐾 (inc guide dogs) 🐚

THE SHAMBLES
Church St GL18 1PP (close to town centre near church)
☎ 01531 822144 📠 01531 821120

Cobbled streets, alleyways, cottages and houses set in
over an acre with display shops and trades, even a tin
chapel and cottage garden all helping to recreate the
feel and atmosphere of a small Victorian town.
Times: Open 15 Mar-Xmas, Tue-Sun & BH's 10-5 (or dusk). **Fee:** £3.50
(ch £1.95, pen £2.95). **Facilities:** 🅿 (100yds) ☕ ♿ toilets for disabled
shop 🐚

⛫ NORTHLEACH
Map 04 SP11

COTSWOLD HERITAGE CENTRE
Fosseway GL54 3JH (12m E of Cheltenham on A429 at
Northleach crossroads)
☎ 01451 860715 📠 01451 860091
e-mail: simone.clark@cotswold.gov.uk

The story of everyday rural life in the Cotswolds is told
here, in the remaining buildings of the Northleach
House of Correction. There's a unique collection of
Gloucestershire harvest-wagons; a `below stairs'
gallery showing a dairy, kitchen and laundry; and the
work of local craftsmen and artists is promoted through
exhibitions, workshops and demonstrations.
Times: Open Apr-Oct, Mon-Sat 10-5, Sun 2-5 & BHs 10-5. Open at
other times by prior arrangement. **Fee:** £2.50 (ch £1, pen £2 & student
£1). Family ticket £5. Party. **Facilities:** 🅿 ☕ ♿ (wheelchair, special
parking, photos of unaccessable areas) toilets for disabled shop 🐚

KEITH HARDING'S WORLD OF MECHANICAL MUSIC
Oak House, High St GL54 3ET (at crossroads of A40 &
A429)
☎ 01451 860181 📠 01451 861133
e-mail: keith@mechanicalmusic.co.uk
Times: Open all year, daily 10-6. Closed 25-26 Dec. **Facilities:** 🅿 ♿
toilets for disabled shop 🐾 (ex guide dogs) *Details not confirmed for*
2002 🐚

⛫ OWLPEN
Map 03 ST79

OWLPEN MANOR
GL11 5BZ (3m E of Dursley off B4066, follow brown
tourist signs)
☎ 01453 860261 📠 01453 860819
e-mail: sales@owlpen.com
Times: Open Apr-15 Oct, Tue-Sun & BH Mon, 2-5. **Facilities:** 🅿 ☕ ✗
licensed 🐾 *Details not confirmed for 2002* 🐚

⛫ PAINSWICK
Map 03 SO80

PAINSWICK ROCOCO GARDEN
GL6 6TH (on B4073 0.5m NW of Painswick)
☎ 01452 813204 📠 01452 814888
e-mail: info@rococogarden.co.uk

This beautiful Rococo garden (a compromise between
formality and informality) is the only one of its period
to survive complete. There are ponds, woodland walks,
a maze, kitchen garden and herbacious borders, all set
in a Cotswold valley famous for snowdrops in the early
spring. Ring for details of special events.
Times: Open Jan-Nov, Wed-Sun, 11-5; May-Sep, daily. **Fee:** £3.30 (ch
£1.75, pen £3) **Facilities:** 🅿 ☕ ✗ licensed shop garden centre 🐚

⛫ SLIMBRIDGE
Map 03 SO70

WWT SLIMBRIDGE
GL2 7BT (off A38, signed from M5 junct 13 & 14)
☎ 01453 890333 📠 01453 890827
e-mail: slimbridge@wwt.org.uk

Slimbridge is home to the world's largest collection of
exotic wildfowl - and the only place in Europe where all
six types of flamingo can be seen. Up to 8,000 wild
birds winter on the 800-acre reserve of flat fields,
marsh and mudflats on the River Severn.
Times: Open all year, daily from 9.30-5.30 (winter 4pm). (Closed 25
Dec). **Fee:** £6 (ch £3.60, pen £4.80). Family ticket £15. Party 10+.
Facilities: 🅿 ☕ ✗ licensed ♿ (wheelchair loan, tapes for blind,
hearing pads & loops) toilets for disabled shop 🐾 (ex guide/hearing
dogs) 🐚

⛫ SNOWSHILL
Map 04 SP03

SNOWSHILL MANOR
WR12 7JU (3m SW of Broadway, off A44)
☎ 01386 852410   🖹 01386 852410
e-mail: snowshill@smtp.ntrust.org.uk
Times: Open Apr-29 Oct, Wed-Sun & BH Mon (also Mon in Jul-Aug).
Gardens 11-5.30; Manor 12-5. Last admission to manor 45 mins before
closing. **Facilities:** 🅿 ✕ ♿ (Braille guides) toilets for disabled shop ⚲
(ex guide dgos) ♨ *Details not confirmed for 2002* ⬱

⛫ SOUDLEY
Map 03 SO61

DEAN HERITAGE CENTRE
Camp Mill GL14 2UB (on B4227, in Forest of Dean)
☎ 01594 822170   🖹 01594 823711
e-mail: deanmuse@btinternet.com

The Centre tells the story of this unique area with
museum displays which include a reconstructed
cottage, coal mine and waterwheel. There are also
nature trails (one of which is level), and picnic areas.
Charcoal burning takes place twice a year.
Times: Open all year, daily, Apr-Sep 10-6, last admission 5.30, Oct-Mar
10-4. (Closed 24-26 Dec). **Fee:** £3.50 (ch £2, pen & con £3). Family
ticket £10. Under 5's free. **Facilities:** 🅿 ☕ ♿ (help from
establishment staff) toilets for disabled shop ⚲ (ex guide dogs) ⬱

⛫ TETBURY
Map 03 ST89

CHAVENAGE HOUSE
GL8 8XP (2m NW of Tetbury signposted off B4014. 1m
SE of Stroud off A46)
☎ 01666 502329 & 01453 832700
🖹 01453 836778
e-mail: info@chavenage.com

Built in 1576, this unspoilt Elizabethan house contains
stained glass from the 16th-century and earlier, and some
good furniture and tapestries. The owner during the Civil
War was a Parliamentarian, and the house contains
Cromwellian relics. In more recent years, the house has
been the location for `Grace and Favour`, `Poirot`, `The
House of Elliot`, `Berkeley Square`, `Casualty` and `Cider with
Rosie`. Tours of the house are 'enlivened' by ghost stories.
Times: Open May-Sep, Thu, Sun & BHs 2-5. Also Etr Sun & Mon.
Other days by appointment only. **Fee:** £4 (ch £2). **Facilities:** 🅿 ♿ ⚲
(ex guide dogs)

⛫ ULEY
Map 03 ST79

ULEY TUMULUS
(3.5m NE of Dursley on B4066)
Times: Open any reasonable time. **Facilities:** ⛿ *Details not
confirmed for 2002*

⛫ WESTBURY ON SEVERN
Map 03 SO71

WESTBURY COURT GARDEN
GL14 1PD (9m SW of Gloucester on A48)
☎ 01452 760461
e-mail: westbury@smtp.ntrust.org.uk
Times: Open Apr-Oct, Wed-Sun & BH Mon 11-6. Other months by
appointment only. **Facilities:** 🅿 ♿ (braille guide, wheelchair available)
toilets for disabled shop ⚲ (ex guide dogs) ♨ *Details not confirmed
for 2002*

SUDELEY 🐉 CASTLE
& GARDENS

- Former home of Queen Katherine Parr, Henry
  VIII's last wife
- Garrison headquarters of Charles I's nephew,
  Prince Rupert, during the Civil War
- Surrounded by magnificent award winning gardens
- Licensed Restaurant • Gift Shop • Plant Centre
- Exhibition of the Life and Times of Emma Dent
- Fort Sudeley Adventure Playground
- Picnic Area

*Open 2nd March-27th October 10.30am-5.30pm
(Castle opens 23rd March)*

ENQUIRIES -
Sudeley Castle, Winchcombe, Cheltenham
Gloucestershire GL54 5JD   Tel: 01242 602308
email: marketing@sudeley.org.uk
www.stratford.co.uk/sudeley

⛫ WESTONBIRT
Map 03 ST88

WESTONBIRT ARBORETUM
GL8 8QS (3m S Tetbury on A433)
☎ 01666 880220   🖹 01666 880559
Times: Open all year, daily 10-8 or sunset. Visitor centre & shop all
year. (Closed Xmas & New Year) **Facilities:** 🅿 ☕ ♿ (electric &
manual wheelchair for loan, telephone to book) toilets for disabled
shop garden centre *Details not confirmed for 2002*

⛫ WINCHCOMBE
Map 04 SP02

SUDELEY CASTLE & GARDENS
GL54 5JD (B4632 to Winchcombe, Castle is signposted
from town)
☎ 01242 602308   🖹 01242 602959
e-mail: marketing@sudeley.org.uk

Sudeley Castle was home to Katherine Parr, who is
buried in the Chapel. Henry VIII, Anne Boleyn, Lady
Jane Grey and Elizabeth I all stayed or visited here; and
it was the headquarters of Prince Rupert during the
Civil War. The Queen's Garden is famous for its rose
collection, and there is an exhibition centre, and a
children's adventure playground.
Times: Open daily 3 Mar-28 Oct, Grounds, Gardens, exhibition, shop
& plant centre 10.30-5.30. Apr-28 Oct, Castle apartments & Church &
restaurant 11-5. **Fee:** Castle & Gardens £6.20 (ch £3.20 & concessions
£5.20). Gardens only £4.70 (ch £2.50 & concessions £3.70). Family
ticket £17. Party 20+ **Facilities:** 🅿 ✕ licensed ♿ (partial access to
disabled) toilets for disabled shop garden centre ⚲ (by request on
arrival) ⬱

Greater Manchester

A conurbation in the northwest of England, Greater Manchester incorporates the towns of Bolton, Oldham, Rochdale, Salford, Stockport and Wigan, with the vibrant city of Manchester as its administrative headquarters.

Manchester was founded in Roman times, and developed during the 17th century as a textile town, becoming the centre of the English cotton industry. Magnificent Victorian Gothic public buildings are reminders of Manchester's prosperous heyday. These include the town hall designed by Alfred Waterhouse which takes up one side of Albert Square. Also look out for the recently restored Royal Exchange, – damaged in the IRA bombing of 1996 – the Athenaeum, The Theatre Royal, and the Free Trade Hall. The Castlefield area, 15 minutes' walk southwest of the town hall, has been redeveloped in recent times to include a reconstruction of the Roman fort that once stood on the site. This area is also home to the world's most famous soap opera – Coronation Street.

Another feature is the Manchester Ship Canal, completed in 1894, linking the Mersey with the sea and bringing ocean-going vessels into Manchester and enabling the city to compete with its rival, Liverpool.

The city of Manchester is alive with a vibrant youth culture (it has England's largest student population), a flourishing club scene, and a whole range of multi-cultural festivals and events. Musical groups from Manchester include Magazine, Oasis, New Order and James. To take in the atmosphere, take a stroll around Britain's biggest Chinatown (between Charlotte Street and Princess Street), or wander down to Rusholme to take in the tempting aromas of curry houses and browse among the sari shops, Asian grocers, and Indian sweet shops.

Top: Albert Square

🏛 ALTRINCHAM
Map 07 SJ78

DUNHAM MASSEY
WA14 4SJ (3m SW of Altrincham (off A56), off M6 junct
19 or off M56 junct 7, then follow brown signs)
☎ 0161 941 1025 📠 0161 929 7508
e-mail: mdmjxf@smtp.ntrust.org.uk
Times: Open: Park open all year. House open Apr-end Oct, 12-5 (11
Sun & BH Mon, closes at 4 during Oct). Garden Apr-end Oct, 11-5.30
(closes 4.30 in Oct). Last entry to house & Gardens 30mins before
closing time. **Facilities:** 🅿 (charged) ✖ licensed & (loan of
batricar/wheelchairs, lift, braille guide, parking) toilets for disabled shop
🐾 (ex on lead in Park) 🐾 *Details not confirmed for 2002* 🍵

🏛 ASHTON-UNDER-LYNE
Map 07 SJ99

CENTRAL ART GALLERY
Central Library Building, Old St OL6 7SG
☎ 0161 342 2650
e-mail: portland.basin@mail.gov.uk

Set in a fine Victorian Gothic building, the Central Art
Gallery has three areas, each of which offers a varied
programme of temporary exhibitions. The range covers
painting, sculpture and textiles.
Times: Open all year, Tue, Wed & Fri 10-5; Thu 1-7.30 & Sat 9-4.
Fee: Free. **Facilities:** 🅿 & toilets for disabled shop 🐾 (ex guide dogs)

MUSEUM OF THE MANCHESTER REGIMENT
The Town Hall, Market Place OL6 6DL (in town centre,
follow signs for museum)
☎ 0161 342 3078 & 0161 342 3710
📠 0161 343 2869
e-mail: portland.basin@mail.tameside.gov.uk

The social and regimental history of the Manchesters is
explored at this museum, tracing the story back to its
origins in the 18th century. The Manchesters fought in
both World Wars, the Boer War, and the Crimea.
Times: Open all year, Mon-Sat, 10-4. (Closed Sun). **Fee:** Free.
Facilities: 🅿 (50yds) (pay & display) & toilets for disabled shop 🐾
(ex guide dogs)

PORTLAND BASIN MUSEUM
Portland Place OL7 0QA (off A635)
☎ 0161 343 2878 📠 0161 343 2869
e-mail: portland.basin@mail.gov.uk

Exploring the social and industrial history of Tameside,
this museum is part of the recently rebuilt Ashton Canal
Warehouse, built in 1834. Visitors can walk around a
1920s street, dress up in old hats and gloves, steer a
virtual canal boat, and see the original canal powered
waterwheel that once drove the warehouse machinery.
Times: Open all year, Tue-Sun 10-5. (Closed Mon, ex BH's) **Fee:** Free.
Facilities: 🅿 & toilets for disabled shop 🐾 (ex guide dogs)

🏛 BRAMHALL
Map 07 SJ88

BRAMALL HALL & PARK
SK7 3NX (from A6 turn right at Blossoms public house
through Davenport village then turn right - signposted)
☎ 0161 485 3708 📠 0161 486 6959
Times: Open all year, Good Fri-Sep Mon-Sat 1-5, Sun 11-5; Oct-New
Year's Day Tue-Sat 1-4, Sun 11-4; 2 Jan-Good Fri Sat & Sun 12-4.
Closed 25-26 Dec. **Facilities:** 🅿 (charged) 🍵 & (access for
wheelchair users) toilets for disabled shop 🐾 (ex guide dogs) *Details
not confirmed for 2002* 🍵

🏛 MANCHESTER
Map 07 SJ89

CITY ART GALLERY
Mosley St/Princess St M2 3JL
☎ 0161 234 1456 📠 0161 236 7369
e-mail: cityart@mcrl.poptel.org.uk
Times: Whole gallery closed until Mar 2002 for major expansion
scheme. Telephone for details. *Details not confirmed for 2002*

GALLERY OF COSTUME
Platt Hall, Rusholme M14 5LL (in Platt Fields Park,
access from Wilmslow Rd. 2m S of city centre)
☎ 0161 224 5217 📠 0161 256 3278
Times: Open all year, daily 10-5.30 (Nov-Feb 10-4). **Facilities:** 🅿 &
shop 🐾 (ex guide dogs) *Details not confirmed for 2002*

JOHN RYLANDS LIBRARY
150 Deansgate M3 3EH (on Deangate, a main
thoroughfare in city centre, A56. Situated next to the
Manchester Evening News Building)
☎ 0161 834 5343 📠 0161 834 5574

Founded as a memorial to Manchester cotton-magnate
and millionaire John Rylands, this is the Special
Collections Division of the John Rylands University
Library of Manchester. Internationally renowned, it
extends to two million books, manuscripts and archival
items representing some 50 cultures and ranging in
date from the third millennium BC to the present day.
Times: Open all year, Mon-Fri 10-5.30, Sat 10-1. (Closed BH & Xmas-
New Year). **Fee:** Free. **Facilities:** 🅿 (400yds) shop 🐾 (ex guide dogs
by arrangement)

MANCHESTER MUSEUM
The University, Oxford Rd M13 9PL (S of city centre on
B5117)
☎ 0161 275 2634 📠 0161 275 2676
e-mail: dot.fenton@man.ac.uk/museum
Times: Open all year, Mon-Sat 10-5, Sun & BHs 11-4. Phase 2 of a
major refurbishment is due to be completed by Jun 2002. **Fee:** Free.
Facilities: 🅿 (350m) & (Provision for disabled telephone in advance)
shop 🐾 (ex guide dogs)

MANCHESTER UNITED MUSEUM & TOUR CENTRE

Sir Matt Busby Way, Old Trafford M16 0RA (2m from city centre, off A56)
☎ 0161 868 8631 🗎 0161 868 8861
e-mail: tours@manutd.co.uk

This museum was opened in 1986 and is the first purpose-built British football museum. It covers the history of Manchester United in words, pictures, sound and vision, from its inception in 1878 to the present day.
Times: Open daily 9.30-5 (open until 1/2hr before kick off on Match Days). (Closed some days over Xmas & New Year) **Fee:** Stadium tour & Museum: £8.50 (ch & pen £5.75) Family ticket £23.50. Museum only: £5.50 (ch & pen £3.75) Family ticket £15.50. **Facilities:** 🅿 💺 ✗ licensed 🔥 (wheelchair,audio visual scrips,part of tour not accessible) toilets for disabled shop 🐾 (ex dogs only) 🍴

THE MUSEUM OF SCIENCE AND INDUSTRY IN MANCHESTER

Liverpool Rd, Castlefield M3 4FP (follow brown tourist signs from city centre)
☎ 0161 832 2244 0161 832 1830
🗎 0161 833 1471
e-mail: marketing@msim.org.uk

This museum is housed in the buildings of the world's oldest passenger railway station. Colourful galleries packed full of fascinating facts and amazing artefacts bring the past to life. Walk away from your own shadow in Xperiment! The mind bending science centre, see wheels of industry turning in the Power Hall, and the planes that made flying history in the Air and Space Hall. A programme of changing exhibitions.
Times: Open all year, daily 10-5. Last admission 4.30. (Closed 24-26 Dec). **Fee:** Free. **Facilities:** 🅿 (charged) ✗ licensed 🔥 (lifts, wheelchair loan service) toilets for disabled shop 🐾 (ex guide dogs) 🍴

MUSEUM OF TRANSPORT

Boyle St, Cheetham M8 8UW
☎ 0161 205 2122 🗎 0161 205 2122
e-mail: Gmts.enquire@btinternet.com

This museum is a must-see for fans of public transport! Among the many interesting exhibits are more than 80 beautifully restored buses and coaches from the region – the biggest collection in the UK. Displays of old photographs, tickets and other memorabilia complement the vehicles, some of which date back to 1890. Please telephone for details of special events.
Times: Open all year, Wed, Sat, Sun & BH 10-5 ex Xmas. **Fee:** £3 (ch u5 free, ch 5-15 & pen £1.75, registered disabled, UB40 free). Family ticket (2ad+3ch) £9. Adult season ticket (unlimited visits for 6 months) £8, ch & pen season ticket £6, family season ticket £20. **Facilities:** 🅿 💺 🔥 toilets for disabled shop 🍴

THE WHITWORTH ART GALLERY

The University of Manchester, Oxford Rd M15 6ER (follow brown tourist signs)
☎ 0161 275 7450 🗎 0161 275 7451
e-mail: whitworth@man.ac.uk

The gallery houses an impressive range of modern and historic drawings, prints, paintings and sculpture, as well as the largest collection of textiles and wallpapers outside London and an internationally famous collection of British watercolours.
Times: Open Mon-Sat 10-5, Sun 2-5. (Closed Good Fri & Xmas-New Year). **Fee:** Free. **Facilities:** 🅿 ✗ licensed 🔥 (wheelchair available, induction loop, Braille lift buttons) toilets for disabled shop 🐾 (ex guide dogs)

🏛 PRESTWICH   Map 07 SD80
HEATON HALL

Heaton Park M25 2SW
☎ 0161 773 1231 or 0161 234 1456
🗎 0161 236 2880
Times: Open Etr-end Oct, but phone for time details on 0161-234 1456. **Facilities:** 🅿 (charged) 🔥 (occasional 'touch tours'. Phone for details) toilets for disabled shop 🐾 (ex guide dogs) *Details not confirmed for 2002*

🏛 SALFORD   Map 07 SJ89
THE LOWRY

Pier Eight, Salford Quays M5 2AZ
☎ 0161 876 2000 🗎 0161 876 2001
e-mail: info@thelowry.com

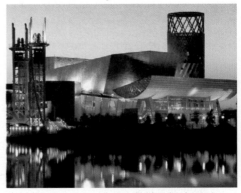

Times: Open from 28 Apr, daily 9.30-midnight. (Closed 25 Dec). **Facilities:** 🅿 (charged) 💺 ✗ licensed 🔥 toilets for disabled shop 🐾 (ex guide dogs) *Details not confirmed for 2002* 🍴

SALFORD MUSEUM & ART GALLERY

Peel Park, Crescent M5 4WU (from N leave M60 junct 13, A666. From S follow signs from end of M602. Museum on A6)

☎ 0161 736 2649 🖳 0161 745 9490

e-mail: salford.museum@salford.gov.uk

The museum features a reconstruction of a 19th-20th century northern street with original shop fronts. Upstairs in the galleries there are temporary exhibitions, Victorian paintings and decorative arts, and displays featuring local scenes by LS Lowry, and Royal Lancastrian pottery.

Times: Open all year, Mon-Fri 10-4.45, Sat & Sun 1-5. (Closed Good Fri, Etr Sat, 25 & 26 Dec, 1 Jan). **Fee:** Free. **Facilities:** 🅿 🖳 ᴭ (Braille & large print labels & visitor packs, hearing loop) toilets for disabled shop 🛪 (guide dogs) 🦮

STALYBRIDGE   Map 07 SJ99

ASTLEY CHEETHAM ART GALLERY

Trinity St

☎ 0161 338 2708

e-mail: portland.basin@mail.tameside.uk

Built as a gift to the town in 1901 by mill owner John Frederick Cheetham, this one-time lecture hall has been an art gallery since 1932 when Cheetham left his collection to the town. Among the works are Italian paintings from the Renaissance, British masters such as Cox and Burne-Jones, and more recent gifts such as works by Turner and local artist Harry Rutherford.

Times: Open all year, Mon-Tue, Wed & Fri 1-7.30; Sat 9-4. **Fee:** Free. **Facilities:** 🅿 shop 🛪 (ex guide dogs)

UPPERMILL   Map 07 SD90

SADDLEWORTH MUSEUM & ART GALLERY

High St OL3 6HS (From M62 E exit at junct 22 or from M62 W exit at junct 21. On A670)

☎ 01457 874093 & 870336

Based in an old mill building next to the Huddersfield canal, the museum explores the history of the Saddleworth area. Wool weaving is the traditional industry, displayed in the 18th-century Weaver's Cottage and the Victoria Mill Gallery. The textile machinery is run regularly by arrangement. The Art Gallery has regular exhibitions.

Times: Open all year, Nov-late Mar, daily 1-4; late Mar-Oct, Mon-Sat 10-5, Sun 12-5. **Fee:** £2 (concessions £1) Family ticket £4.

Facilities: 🅿 ᴭ (stairlift, ramps, braille & large print guides, wheelchair) toilets for disabled shop 🛪 (ex guide dogs) 🦮

WIGAN   Map 07 SD50

WIGAN PIER

Trencherfield Mill WN3 4EF (follow brown tourist signs from motorway)

☎ 01942 323666 🖳 01942 701927

e-mail: wigan.pier@wiganmbc.gov.uk

Part museum, part theatre, Wigan Pier is a mixture of entertainment and education. The professional actors of the Wigan Pier Theatre Company perform plays and Victorian music hall shows. Opie's Museum of Memories ensures a memorable day for all ages, based on the domestic lifestyle collection of the social historian Robert Opie.

Times: Open all year, Mon-Thu 10-5; Sat & Sun 11-5. (Closed 25-26 Dec, 1 Jan & Fri (ex Good Fri). **Fee:** £6.95 (concessions £5.25). Family ticket (2ad+3ch) £19.95. **Facilities:** 🅿 🖳 ✕ licensed ᴭ toilets for disabled shop 🛪 (ex guide dogs) 🦮

Hampshire

Hampshire is mainly rural with a gentle landscape and coastal cities – Portsmouth and Southampton – that enjoy a proud maritime history.

EVENTS & FESTIVALS

February
11th-16th Children's Festival, The Tower, Winchester

June
5th-7th Hat Fair, Winchester
5th-7th Southampton Balloon & Flower Festival, Southampton
tbc Butser Festival of Flight, Portsmouth
tbc Southsea Spectacular, Southsea Common

July
5th-14th Winchester Festival (multi arts festival)
22nd-28th Farnborough International Airshow
26th-28th Steam Engine Rally, Southampton

August
tbc Cutty Sark Tall Ships Race, Portsmouth
Portsmouth & Southsea Show, Southsea Common

September
13th-22nd Southampton International Boat Show, Southampton
14th Romsey Show, Romsey
tbc Great South Run, Southsea Seafront

November
tbc Bonfire Night Firework Spectacular, Cosham
tbc Winchester Grand Firework Display

Portsmouth has been an important naval base since the 12th century, and Southampton has long been associated with the romance of the ocean liner. Both cities were badly bombed in World War II, though areas of interest remain for the visitor.

A more attractive destination is the charming town of Lyndhurst at the heart of the glorious New Forest. Recently celebrating its 900th anniversary, the Forest is a huge expanse of woodland, heath and hills set aside as a royal hunting ground by William the Conqueror in 1079, and covers some 93,000 acres. Now millions visit every year. 'Forest' can seem a bit of a misnomer as large areas are quite open and covered only by heather and gorse. Wildlife flourishes, and walkers can see red, fallow, roe and muntjac deer, as well as badgers, adders, and the famous ponies. Lyndhurst was home to Alice Hargreaves, (née Liddell) the inspiration for Alice in Lewis Carroll's world-famous books. She is buried in the graveyard of St Michael and All Angels Church.

Winchester is a town with a historic atmosphere and a vibrant present. The cathedral dominates the town once used as Alfred the Great's capital. William the Conqueror claimed his crown here, and Jane Austen is buried in the nave. The town is well known for street entertainment.

Hampshire has many picturesque villages. Alresford has the Watercress Line, Silchester has nearby Roman remains including an amphitheatre, and Old Basing has the delightful River Loddon and the remains of Basing House, once the largest private house in England.

Top: Deer in the New Forest

🏛 ALDERSHOT   Map 04 SU85

AIRBORNE FORCES MUSEUM

Browning Barracks, Queens Av GU11 2BU (from M3
take A325 to Aldershot then take next left)
☎ 01252 349619 📄 01252 349203
e-mail: airborneforcesmuseum@
army.mod.uk.net

The museum traces the history of the Parachute
Regiment and British Airborne Forces since 1940. Using
weapons, equipment, dioramas and briefing models it
depicts the story of airborne actions such as the early
raids, D-Day, Arnham, the Rhine Crossing, and post-
war campaigns such as Suez, the Falklands and
Kosovo.
Times: Open all year, Mon-Fri 10-4.30 (last admission 3.45), Sat-Sun &
BH 10-4. (Closed Xmas). **Fee:** £3 (ch, pen & former members of the
Regiment £1) **Facilities:** 🅿 ♿ (wheelchair ramps) shop ✹ (ex guide
dogs) ☕

ALDERSHOT MILITARY MUSEUM

Evelyn Woods Rd, Queens Av GU11 2LG (from A331
take exit for 'Aldershot Military Town (North)',
attraction near to North Camp)
☎ 01252 314598 📄 01252 342942
e-mail: musmim@hants.gov.uk

A look behind the scenes at the daily life of soldiers and
civilians as Aldershot and Farnborough grew up around
the military camps to become the home of the British
Army.
Times: Open Mar-Oct, daily 10-5; Nov-Feb, daily 10-4.30. **Fee:** £2 (ch,
pen & unemployed £1) **Facilities:** 🅿 ♿ shop

🏛 ALRESFORD   Map 04 SU53

WATERCRESS LINE

The Railway Station SO24 9JG (stations at Alton &
Alresford signposted off A31)
☎ 01962 733810 📄 01962 735448
e-mail: watercressline@compuserve.com

The Watercress Line runs through ten miles of rolling
scenic countryside between Alton and Alresford. All
four stations are `dressed' in period style, and there's a
locomotive yard and picnic area at Ropley.
Times: Open Aug daily; Sep, Tue-Thu & wknds; May & Jul, Mon-Wed &
wknds; Jun, Wed-Fri & wknds; Apr, Etr, Oct & Dec, wknds only.
Fee: Unlimited travel for the day, £9 (ch £2, pen £8). Family ticket £20.
Facilities: 🅿 (charged) ☕ ✗ licensed ♿ (ramp access to trains) shop
(at Alresford, Alton & Ropley stations) ☕

🏛 AMPFIELD   Map 04 SU42

THE SIR HAROLD HILLIER GARDENS & ARBORETUM

Jermyns Ln SO51 0QA (3m NE of Romsey, signposted
off A3090 & B3057)
☎ 01794 368787 📄 01794 368027
Times: Open all year, Apr-Oct wkdays 10.30-6, wknds & BHs 9.30-6.
Nov-Mar daily 10.30-5 or dusk if earlier (closed Xmas). **Facilities:** 🅿 ✗
licensed ♿ (all ability path) toilets for disabled garden centre ✹ (ex
guide dogs) *Details not confirmed for 2002*

🏛 ANDOVER   Map 04 SU34

FINKLEY DOWN FARM PARK

SP11 6NF (signposted from A303 & A343)
☎ 01264 352195 📄 01264 363172
e-mail: a1finkley@aol.com

A wide range of farm animals and poultry can be seen
here, including some rare breeds. The pets corner has
tame, hand-reared animals that can be stroked and
petted. There are also a Countryside Museum, housed
in a barn, Romany caravans and rural bygones to see,
an adventure playground and a large picnic area.
Times: Open 18 Mar-4 Nov, daily 10-6. Last admission 5pm.
Fee: £4.25 (ch £3.25, pen £3.75). Family ticket £14. **Facilities:** 🅿 ☕
♿ toilets for disabled shop ✹ (ex guide dogs) ☕

🏛 ASHURST   Map 04 SU31

LONGDOWN DAIRY FARM

Longdown SO40 4UH (off A35 between Lyndhurst &
Southampton)
☎ 023 8029 3326 📄 023 8029 3376
e-mail: annette@longdown.uk.com

A wonderful opportunity to get close to lots of friendly
farm animals. Watch the afternoon milking from the
viewing gallery and learn about modern farming
methods. Visitors can try their hand at being a farmer
for a day. Also home to the National Dairy Council
Museum Collection.
Times: Open Etr-Oct, daily. **Fee:** £4.30 (ch 3-14 £3, pen £3.50). Saver
ticket £14 (2 adults + 2 children) £9.75 (1 adult + 2 children).
Facilities: 🅿 ♿ toilets for disabled shop ✹ (kennels provided) ☕

🏛 BASINGSTOKE   Map 04 SU65

MILESTONES - HAMPSHIRE'S LIVING HISTORY MUSEUM

Basingstoke Leisure Park, Churchill Way West
RG21 6YR (M3 junct 6, clockwise around ringroad to
Town Centre West rdbt, follow Leisure Park signs)
☎ 01256 477766 📄 01256 477784
e-mail: linda.owen@hants.gov.uk

Milestones brings Hampshire's recent past to life
through stunning period street scenes and exciting
interactive areas, all under one roof. Nationally
important collections of transport, technology and
everyday life are presented in an entertaining way. Staff
in period costumes, mannequins and sounds will bring
the streets to life.
Times: Open Tue-Fri 10-5, Sat-Sun 10-6; Etr, May BH's & Aug BH 10-6.
(Closed 24-26 & 31 Dec). **Fee:** £5.95 (ch 5-16 £2.95, concessions
£4.75). Family £14.90. **Facilities:** 🅿 ☕ ♿ (induction loops & audio
trails) toilets for disabled shop ✹ (ex guide dogs) ☕
See advert on p93

⚏ BEAULIEU   Map 04 SU30
BEAULIEU : NATIONAL MOTOR MUSEUM
SO42 7ZN (M27 junct 2, A326, B3054, then follow tourist signs)
☎ 01590 612345   ▤ 01590 612624
e-mail: info@beaulieu.co.uk

Set in the heart of William the Conqueror's New Forest, on the banks of the Beaulieu River, stands this 16th-century house. It has become most famous as the home of the National Motor Museum. The site also contains the picturesque abbey building ruins, which have an exhibition on life in the middle ages, and various family treasures and memorabilia.
Times: Open all year - Palace House & Gardens, National Motor Museum, Beaulieu Abbey & Exhibition of Monastic Life, May-Sep 10-6; Oct-Apr 10-5. (Closed 25 Dec) **Fee:** £9.50 (ch £6.75, pen £8.50). Family £29.95. **Facilities:** ▣ ☛ ♿ (ramp access to most areas) toilets for disabled shop ☜

⚏ BISHOP'S WALTHAM   Map 04 SU51
BISHOP'S WALTHAM PALACE
SO32 1DH (on A333)
☎ 01489 892460

Bishop's Waltham Palace was once among the greatest stately homes of the medieval period. Although mostly destroyed in the Civil War, remains are still impressive.
Times: Open Apr-Oct, daily 10-6 (Oct 10-5). **Fee:** £2.10 (ch 5-15 £1.10, under 5's free, con £1.60). **Facilities:** ▣ ♿ ☜ (in certain areas) ✠

⚏ BOLDRE   Map 04 SZ39
SPINNERS
School Ln SO41 5QE (off A337, between Brockenhurst & Lymington)
☎ 01590 673347

The garden has been entirely created by the owners since 1960. It has azaleas, rhododendrons, camellias and magnolias, interspersed with primulas, blue poppies and other woodland and ground cover plants. The nursery is famed for its rare trees, shrubs and plants.
Times: Open Apr-14 Sep daily 10-5. Other times on application. Nursery and part of garden open all year, but garden and nursery both closed on Sun & Mon. **Fee:** £2 (accompanied ch under 6 free). **Facilities:** ▣ garden centre ☜ (ex guide dogs)

⚏ BREAMORE   Map 04 SU11
BREAMORE HOUSE & COUNTRYSIDE
SP6 2DF (turn off A338, between Salisbury & Fordingbridge and follow signs for 1m)
☎ 01725 512468   ▤ 01725 512858
e-mail: breamore@estate.fsnet.co.uk

The handsome manor house was completed in around 1583 and has a fine collection of paintings, china and tapestries. The museum has good examples of steam engines, and uses reconstructed workshops and other displays to show how people lived and worked a century or so ago. There is also a children's playground.
Times: Open Apr, Tue, Wed, Sun & Etr, May-Jul & Sep, Tue-Thu & Sat, Sun & all BH, Aug, daily 2-5.30 (Countryside Museum 1pm).
Fee: Combined tickets £5 (ch £3.50). Party £4.50 each. **Facilities:** ▣ ☛ ♿ (ramps, parking by house) toilets for disabled shop ☜ (ex guide dogs)

⚏ BUCKLER'S HARD   Map 04 SU40
BUCKLER'S HARD VILLAGE & MARITIME MUSEUM
SO42 7XB (M27 junct 2, A326, B3054 then follow tourist signs to Beaulieu then follow tourist signs to Bucklers Hard)
☎ 01590 616203   ▤ 01590 612624
e-mail: info@bucklershard.co.uk

Wooden warships, including some of Nelson's fleet, were built here, using New Forest oak, and the wide main street was used for rolling great logs to the 'hard' where the ships were built. The 18th-century homes of a shipwright and labourer, and a master shipbuilder's office can be seen.
Times: Open all year, Etr-Sep 10.30-5, winter 11-4. (Closed 25 Dec). **Fee:** £3.50 (ch £1.50, pen £2.50). **Facilities:** ▣ ☛ ✗ licensed ♿ shop ☜

⚏ BURGHCLERE   Map 04 SU46
SANDHAM MEMORIAL CHAPEL
RG20 9JT (4m S of Newbury, off A34)
☎ 01635 278394   ▤ 01635 278394
Times: Open Apr-Oct, Wed-Sun, 11.30-5 & BH Mon. Nov & Mar, Sat & Sun 11.30-4. Dec-Feb by appointment only. **Facilities:** ▣ ♿ (Braille guide) ☜ (ex on leads in grounds) ☙ *Details not confirmed for 2002*

CHAWTON
Map 04 SU73
JANE AUSTEN'S HOUSE
GU34 1SD (1m SW of Alton, in centre of village)
☎ 01420 83262 ▤ 01420 83262
e-mail: museum@janeausten.demon.co.uk

Jane Austen lived and wrote here from 1809 to 1817.
Restored to look as it would have done in the early
1800s, with items such as the author's donkey cart and
writing table to be seen. **Times:** Open daily Mar-1 Jan, also Feb half term. Jan & Feb wknds
only. (Closed 25 & 26 Dec). **Fee:** £3 (ch 8-18, 50p, pen & students
£2.50). Party £2.50pp. **Facilities:** ℙ (300yds) ᬗ (wheelchair ramp)
toilets for disabled shop ✻ (ex guide dogs & service dogs) ➡

EXBURY
Map 04 SU40
EXBURY GARDENS
Exbury Estate Office SO45 1AZ (from M27 junct 2. 3m
from Beaulieu, off B3054)
☎ 023 8089 1203 ▤ 023 8089 9940

A 200-acre landscaped woodland garden on the east
bank of the Beaulieu River, with one of the finest
collections of rhododendrons, azaleas, camellias and
magnolias in the world - as well as many rare and
beautiful shrubs and trees. A labyrinth of tracks and
paths enable you to explore the beautiful gardens and
walks. A steam railway is new for 2002 along with the
creation of the new railway garden.
Times: Open daily 24 Feb-25 Nov 10-5.30 or dusk if earlier. **Fee:** 24th
Feb-mid Mar £3.50 (ch 10-15 £2.50, OAP £3). Mid Mar-mid Jun £5 (ch
£4, OAP £4.50. Mid Jun-25 Nov £3.50 (ch £2.50, OAP £3) OAP £4
Tues-Thur. Under 10's free. **Facilities:** ℙ ᬗ (wheelchair loans &
routes designed for them, buggy tours) toilets for disabled shop
garden centre ➡

FAREHAM
Map 04 SU50
ROYAL ARMOURIES FORT NELSON
Downend Rd PO17 6AN (from M27 junct 11, follow
brown tourist signs for Royal Armouries)
☎ 01329 233734 ▤ 01329 822092
e-mail: fnenquiries@armouries.org.uk

Built as part of a protective ring around Portsmouth
harbour during the 1860s, this restored artillery fort has
19 acres with grass ramparts, underground magazines,
tunnels and the Royal Armouries National Collection of
Artillery. This collection has over 350 pieces and
displays the history of artillery from Roman times to the
present. Annual summer Grand Military Tattoo.
Times: Open all year: Apr-Oct daily 10-5, Nov-Mar daily 10.30-4.
Fee: £4.25 (ch u17/pen free) **Facilities:** ℙ ᬗ (access guide on
request, ramps) toilets for disabled shop ✻ (ex guide/hearing dogs)
➡

GOSPORT
Map 04 SZ69
EXPLOSION! MUSUEM OF NAVAL FIREPOWER
Priddy's Hard PO12 4LE (from A32 and follow signs)
☎ 023 9250 5600 ▤ 023 9250 5605
e-mail: info@explosion.org.uk

Set in the former Royal Navy armaments depot that has
been a state secret for 200 years, this multi-million
pound interactive museum tells the story of naval
firepower from the 18th century to the present day. A
unique collection includes the Red Beard atom bomb,
the Schwartzkopf torpedo, and the Sea Slug. State-of-
the-art audio-visuals tell the story of the guns and their
ammunition from manufacture to firing.
Times: Open all year, Apr-Oct, daily 10-5.30; Nov-Mar, daily 10-4.30.
(Closed 25-26 Dec & 1 Jan) **Fee:** £5 (ch £3, pen £4). Family ticket £13
Facilities: ℙ ᬗ toilets for disabled shop ✻ (ex guide dogs) ➡

ROYAL NAVY SUBMARINE MUSEUM & HMS ALLIANCE
Haslar Jetty Rd PO12 2AS (M27 junct 11, follow signs
for Submarine Museum)
☎ 023 9252 9217 & 9251 0354
▤ 023 9251 1349
e-mail: rnsubs@rnsubmus.co.uk

The great attraction of this museum is the chance to see
inside a submarine, and there are guided tours of *HMS
Alliance*, as well as displays exploring the development of
submarines. Two periscopes from *HMS Conqueror* can be
seen in the reconstruction of a nuclear submarine
control room, giving panoramic views of Portsmouth
Harbour. A new gallery shows the development of
submarine weapons from the tiny torpedo to the huge
polaris nuclear missile. Navy's first submarine is back on
display in a new gallery and exhibition space.
Times: Open all year, Apr-Oct 10-5.30; Nov-Mar 10-4.30. (Closed 24
Dec-1 Jan). Allow 3 hrs for visit. Last tour 1 hour before closing.
Fee: £4 (ch & pen £2.75). Family ticket (2 adults & 4 ch) £11. Party
12+. Discounted entry scheme "Follow the Drum", in association with
Southern Military Museums. **Facilities:** ℙ ᬗ (information in
Braille, lift to upper gallery) toilets for disabled shop ✻ ➡

HARTLEY WINTNEY
Map 04 SU75
WEST GREEN HOUSE GARDENS
West Green RG27 8JB (off A30, at Phoenix Green follow sign
to West Green, along Thackhams Lane. House last left)
☎ 01252 844611 ▤ 01252 844611
Times: Open May-Aug, Wed-Sun 11-4. **Facilities:** ℙ ᬗ (most
areas accessible) toilets for disabled ✻ (ex guide dogs) *Details not
confirmed for 2002*

HAVANT
Map 04 SU70
STAUNTON COUNTRY PARK
Middle Park Way PO9 5HB (off B2149, between Havant
& Horndean)
☎ 023 9245 3405 ▤ 023 9249 8156
e-mail: ccgsrc@hants.gov.uk

This colourful Victorian park offers a wonderful range
of attractions for all age groups. Meet and feed the

contd.

animals at the Ornamental Farm where there is a broad range of animals from llama and shirehorses to pigs and pigmy goats. Explore the Victorian tropical glasshouses with exotic flowers from around the world, including the giant Amazonian waterlily.
Times: Open 10-5 (4pm winter) **Fee:** £3.60 (ch £2.60, pen £3.20). Family £10.50. **Facilities:** 🅿 ☕ & (wheelchair for visitors) toilets for disabled shop garden centre 🎋 (dogs in parkland only) 🍴

⛪ HIGHCLERE
Map 04 SU45

HIGHCLERE CASTLE & GARDENS
RG20 9RN (4.5m S of Newbury, off A34)
☎ 01635 253210 🖹 01635 255315
e-mail: theoffice@highclerecastle.co.uk

This splendid early Victorian mansion stands in beautiful parkland. It has sumptuous interiors and numerous Old Master pictures. Also shown are early finds by the 5th Earl of Carnarvon, one of the discoverers of Tutankhamun's tomb.
Times: Open Jul-Aug (may occasionally be subject to closure during this period), Mon-Fri & Sun 11-5 (last admission 4pm); Sat 11-3.30 (last admission 2.30pm) **Fee:** £6.50 (ch £3, pen £5). Grounds & gardens only £3 (ch £1.50). Family ticket £15. Party 15+. **Facilities:** 🅿 ☕ ✕ licensed & (wheelchair available) toilets for disabled shop 🎋 (ex guide dogs) 🍴

⛪ HINTON AMPNER
Map 04 SU62

HINTON AMPNER
SO24 0LA (off A272, 1m W of Bramdean)
☎ 01962 771305 🖹 01962 793101
e-mail: shigen@smtp.ntrust.org.uk

Set in superb Hampshire countryside, this delightful garden combines formality of design with informality of planting. Full of scent and colour, the walks open up into unexpected vistas. The house, restored after a fire in 1960, displays a fine collection of Regency furniture and Italian paintings.
Times: Open Garden: Apr-Sep, Tue-Wed, Sat-Sun & BH Mon, 1.30-5.30. Last admission 5pm. House: Apr-end Jul & Sep, Tue & Wed only. Tue-Wed, Sat-Sun in Aug 1.30-5.30. **Fee:** House and Garden £5, garden only £4. **Facilities:** 🅿 ☕ & (Braille guides, special parking) toilets for disabled 🎋 🐑

⛪ HURST CASTLE
Map 04 SZ38

HURST CASTLE
SO4 0FF (on Pebble Spit S of Keyhaven)
☎ 01590 642344

Built by Henry VIII, Hurst Castle was the pride of Tudor England's coastal defences. Crouched menacingly on a shingle spit, the castle has a fascinating history, including involvement in the smuggling trade in the 17th and 18th centuries.
Times: Open Apr-Oct, daily 10-5 or dawn till dusk **Fee:** £2.70 (ch £1.50 & con £2.20). **Facilities:** ☕ 🎋 (in certain areas) 🔱

JANE AUSTEN'S HOUSE
CHAWTON, ALTON, HANTS
Telephone: 01420 83262

17th-century house where Jane Austen lived from 1809 to 1817

OPEN 11 – 4.00pm
1st Mar–30 Nov: daily
Dec, Jan and Feb: Sats and Suns only,
and 27 Dec- 2 Jan
(Closed Christmas Day and Boxing Day)
Adult £4, Child 50p
Groups and Concessions £3.50

Refreshments available in village   Bookshop

⛪ LIPHOOK
Map 04 SU83

BOHUNT MANOR
GU30 7DL (on old A3)
☎ 01428 722208
Times: Open all year, daily, until 5pm. **Facilities:** 🅿 🎋 *Details not confirmed for 2002*

HOLLYCOMBE STEAM COLLECTION
Iron Hill, Midhurst Rd GU30 7LP (1.5m SE Liphook on Midhurst rd, follow brown tourist signs)
☎ 01428 724900 🖹 01428 723682
e-mail: hooker-chris@hotmail.com

A comprehensive collection of working steam-power, including a large Edwardian fairground, three railways, including one with spectacular views of the South Downs, traction engine hauled rides, steam agricultural machinery, pets corner, sawmill and even a paddle steamer engine.
Times: Open Apr-14 Oct, Sun & BH's; 22 Jul-27 Aug, daily 12-5. Rides open from 1. **Fee:** £6.50 (ch & pen £5). Saver ticket (2ad+2ch) £20. Party 15+. **Facilities:** 🅿 ☕ & shop 🎋 (guide dogs on request) 🍴

🏛 LYMINGTON   Map 04 SZ39
BRAXTON GARDENS
Braxton Courtyard, Lymore Ln SO41 0TX (leave A337 at
Everton onto B3058 then turn left into Lymore Ln,
Braxton Courtyard on left)
☎ 01590 642008

Beautiful gardens set around attractive Victorian farm
buildings. A courtyard with raised lily pool leads into a
walled garden, which overflows with aromatic plants
during the summer. A converted barn is available for
private hire.
Times: Open daily 10-5. Shorter opening hours in winter, please
telephone for details. **Fee:** Free. **Facilities:** 🅿 ♨ ♿ shop garden
centre ✗ (ex guide dogs) ♨

🏛 LYNDHURST   Map 04 SU30
NEW FOREST MUSEUM & VISITOR CENTRE
Main Car Park, High St SO43 7NY (leave M27 at
Cadnam & follow A337 to Lyndhurst. Museum
signposted)
☎ 023 8028 3914   📠 023 8028 4236
e-mail: nfmuseum@lineone.net
Times: Open all year, daily from 10am (Closed 25 Dec) **Facilities:** 🅿
♿ toilets for disabled shop *Details not confirmed for 2002* ♨

🏛 MARWELL   Map 04 SU52
MARWELL ZOOLOGICAL PARK
Colden Common SO21 1JH (M3 junct 11 or M27 junct 5.
Zoo located on B2177)
☎ 01962 777407   📠 01962 777511
e-mail: marwell@marwell.org.uk

Devoted to the conservation and breeding of rare wild
animals, Marwell has a worldwide reputation. There is
an encounter village where animals can be approached
and stroked by children. Covering 100 acres of
parkland, the collection includes over 1000 animals,
and some of the species here no longer exist in the
wild. There is also a gift shop and many attractions for

younger children, including a children's farmyard,
Tropical World, Penguin World and road trains.
Times: Open all year, daily (ex 25 Dec), 10-6 (in summer), 10-4 (in
winter). Last admission 90 min before closing. **Fee:** £9 (ch 3-14 £6.50,
pen £8). Family ticket £29.50. **Facilities:** 🅿 ♨ ✗ licensed ♿ (tours
for visually impaired/disabled groups by arrangement) toilets for
disabled shop ✗ (inc guide dogs) ♨

🏛 MIDDLE WALLOP   Map 04 SU23
MUSEUM OF ARMY FLYING
SO20 8DY (on A343, between Andover & Salisbury)
☎ 01980 674421   📠 01264 781694
e-mail: et@flyingmuseum.org.uk

One of the country's finest historical collections of
military kites, gliders, aeroplanes and helicopters.
Imaginative dioramas and displays trace the
development of Army flying from before the First World
War to more recent conflicts in Ireland, the Falklands
and the Gulf. Sit at the controls of a real Scout
helicopter and test your skills on the helicopter flight
simulator, plus children's interactive science and
education centre.
Times: Open all year, daily 10-4.30. Closed week prior to Xmas.
Evening visits by special arrangement. **Fee:** £4.80 (ch £3.20, pen &
student £3.80) Family £13. Party 10+. **Facilities:** 🅿 ♨ ✗ licensed ♿
(lifts to upper levels) toilets for disabled shop ✗ (ex guide dogs or in
grounds) ♨

🏛 MINSTEAD   Map 04 SU21
FURZEY GARDENS
SO43 7GL (1m S of junct A31/M3 Cadnam off A31 or
A337 near Lyndhurst)
☎ 023 8081 2464 & 8081 2297
📠 023 8081 2297
e-mail: mtp@milestonenet.co.uk

A large thatched gallery is the venue for refreshments
and displays of local arts and crafts, and the eight acres
of peaceful glades which surround it include winter and
summer heathers, rare flowering trees and shrubs and
a mass of spring bulbs. There is a 16th-century cottage,
lake, and the nursery, run by the Minstead Training
Project for Young People with Learning Disabilities,
sells a wide range of produce.
Times: Gardens open daily 10-5 (or dusk if earlier). (Closed Xmas).
Gallery Open: Mar-Oct, 10-5. **Fee:** Mar-Oct: £3.50 (ch £1.50, OAP
£2.80) Family £9. Nov-Feb: £1.50 (ch 50p, OAP £1) Family £3. Party
10+. **Facilities:** 🅿 ♨ ♿ (garden access for wheelchair visitors with
assistance) toilets for disabled shop garden centre ✗ (guide dogs)

🏛 MOTTISFONT   Map 04 SU32
MOTTISFONT ABBEY GARDEN
SO51 0LP (4.5m NW Romsey, 1m W of A3057)
☎ 01794 340757   📠 01794 341492
e-mail: smogen@smtp.ntrust.org.uk

In a picturesque setting by the River Test, Mottisfont
Abbey is an 18th-century house adapted from a 12th-
century priory. The north front shows its medieval
church origins quite clearly, and the garden has
splendid old trees and a walled garden planted with the

national collection of old-fashioned roses. The estate includes Mottisfont village and surrounding farmland and woods.
Times: Open Garden & Grounds: 17 Mar-4 Nov, Sat-Wed 11-6 (or dusk if earlier). 9-24 June special opening daily from 11-8.30. Last admission to grounds 1hr before closing. House: 1-5. Derek Hill Picture Collection: Sun-Tue 1-5. **Fee:** £6 (ch £3) Family ticket £15.
Facilities: ◨ ☕ ✕ licensed ⅏ (Braille guide,wheelchair available,volunteer driven buggy) toilets for disabled shop garden centre ✻ ⅖ ☜

⌂ NETLEY   Map 04 SU40
NETLEY ABBEY
SO31 5FB (4m SE of Southampton, facing Southampton Water)
☎ 023 80453076
Times: Open any reasonable time. **Facilities:** ◨ ⅏ ✻ ✿ *Details not confirmed for 2002*

⌂ NEW MILTON   Map 04 SZ29
SAMMY MILLER MOTORCYCLE MUSEUM
Bashley Cross Rd BH25 5SZ (signposted off A35)
☎ 01425 620777   🖷 01425 619696
e-mail: info@sammymiller.co.uk
Times: Open all year, daily 10-4.30. **Facilities:** ◨ ☕ ⅏ toilets for disabled shop ✻ *Details not confirmed for 2002* ☜

⌂ OLD BASING   Map 04 SU65
BASING HOUSE
Redbridge Ln RG24 7HB (signed from Basingstoke Ring Road)
☎ 01256 467294   🖷 01256 326283

The largest house of Tudor England, almost entirely destroyed by Parliament during a two-year siege ending in 1645. Built on the site of a Norman castle in 1530, the ruins include a 300ft.long tunnel. There is a re-creation of a garden of 1600 and exhibitions showing the history of the house. A fine 16th-century tithe barn stands nearby.
Times: Open Apr-Sep, Wed-Sun & BH 2-6. **Fee:** £1.50 (ch & pen 70p). Registered disabled free. **Facilities:** ◨ ⅏ (disabled parking by prior arangement) toilets for disabled shop

⌂ OWER   Map 04 SU31
PAULTONS PARK
SO51 6AL (exit M27 junct 2, near junct A31 & A36)
☎ 023 8081 4455 & 8081 4442
🖷 023 8081 3025

Paultons Park offers a great day out for all the family with over forty different attractions. Many fun activities include Stinger Roller coaster, bumper boats, 6-lane astroglide, teacup ride and raging river ride log flume. Attractions for younger children include Kid's Kingdom, Tiny Tots Town, Rabbit Ride, the Magic Forest where nursery rhymes come to life, Wonderful World of Wind in the Willows and the Ladybird ride. Pirate Ship Swingboat, Dragon Ride Roundabout and Viking Boats Water Ride are all new rides for 2002. In a beautiful parkland setting with extensive `Capability' Brown

gardens landscaped with ponds and aviaries for exotic birds; lake and hedge maze.
Times: Open mid Mar-end Oct, daily 10-6, earlier closing at certain times of the year - daily info on hotline. Nov & Dec, wknds only until Xmas. **Fee:** £10.50 (ch under 14 & pen £9.50). Children under 1m tall enter for free. Range of Family Supersavers. **Facilities:** ◨ ☕ ✕ ⅏ (Pre-booked wheelchair hire - some rides unsuitable) toilets for disabled shop ✻ (ex guide dogs) ☜

⌂ PETERSFIELD   Map 04 SU72
BEAR MUSEUM & STEIFF CLUB STORE
38 Dragon St GU31 4JJ (100yds from bottom of the High Street, signed)
☎ 01730 265108

This was the world's first Teddy Bear Museum, and children were allowed to cuddle and play with some of the exhibits. A variety of bears are displayed in the Victorian-style nursery while downstairs is the `Teddy Bear's Picnic'. The centenary of the Teddy Bear in 2002 is a milestone for bear lovers.
Times: Open Tue-Sat 10-4.30. **Fee:** Free entry. Contributions welcomed. **Facilities:** ℗ (200yds) shop ✻ (ex guide dogs) ⅗

⌂ PORTCHESTER   Map 04 SU60
PORTCHESTER CASTLE
Castel St PO16 9QW (off A27)
☎ 01705 378291

Built on the site of a Roman fort, the castle has witnessed many famous events of English history. From here Henry V embarked for France and the Battle of Agincourt; here Henry VIII courted Anne Boleyn, and later still the castle was 'home' to prisoners during the Napoleonic wars. The castle has the most complete Roman walls in Europe; remains of the church and other medieval buildings can also be seen.
Times: Open all year, Apr-Oct, daily 10-6 (Oct 10-5); Nov-Mar, daily 10-4. Closed 24-26 Dec & 1 Jan. **Fee:** £3 (ch 5-15 £1.50, under 5's free, con £2.30). **Facilities:** ◨ ⅏ shop ✻ (in certain areas) ✿

⌂ PORTSMOUTH   Map 04 SZ69
CHARLES DICKENS' BIRTHPLACE MUSEUM
393 Old Commercial Rd PO1 4QL (accessible from M27)
☎ 023 9282 7261   🖷 023 9287 5276
e-mail: cspendlove@portsmouthcc.gov.uk

A small terraced house built in 1805 which became the birthplace and early home of the famous novelist, born in 1812. On display are items pertaining to Dickens' work, portraits of the Dickens' family, and the couch on which he died. Dickens readings are given in the exhibition room on the first Sunday of each month.
Times: Open Mar-Oct, daily 10-5.30 (last admission 5pm). **Fee:** £2.50 (ch & student £1.50, accompanied ch 13 free, pen £1.80). Family ticket £6.50. **Facilities:** ℗ (150mtrs) shop ✻ (ex guide & helper dogs) ☜

CITY MUSEUM & RECORDS OFFICE
Museum Rd PO1 2LJ (M27/M275 into Portsmouth, follow museum signs)
☎ 023 9282 7261 ▌ 023 9287 5276
e-mail: cspendlove@portsmouthcc.gov.uk

Dedicated to local history, time and decorative art, 'The Story of Portsmouth' displays room settings showing life here from the 17th century to the 1950s. The 'Portsmouth at Play' exhibition features leisure pursuits from the Victorian period to the 1970s. Temporary exhibitions are also held.
Times: Open all year, Apr-Oct daily 10-5.30; Nov-Mar daily 10-5. Closed 24-26 Dec and Record Office closed on public holidays. **Fee:** Free.
Facilities: ▣ ⬤ ⓖ (induction loops, lift & wheelchairs available, parking) toilets for disabled shop ✟ (ex guide & helper dogs) ⬤

D-DAY MUSEUM & OVERLORD EMBROIDERY
Clarence Esplanade PO5 3NT (M27/M275 into Portsmouth follow D Day Museum sign)
☎ 023 9282 7261 ▌ 023 9287 5276
e-mail: cspendlove@portsmouthcc.gov.uk

Portsmouth's D-Day Museum tells the dramatic story of the Allied landings in Normandy in 1944. Centrepiece is the magnificent 'Overlord Embroidery', 34 individual panels and 83 metres in length. Experience the world's largest ever seaborne invasion, and step back in time to scenes of wartime Britain. Military equipment, vehicles, landing craft and personal memories complete this special story.
Times: Open all year, Apr-Oct daily 10-5.30. Nov-Mar, 10-5. **Fee:** £5 (ch £3, pen £3.75). Family ticket £13. **Facilities:** ▣ (charged) ⬤ ⓖ (induction loops,sound aids for blind,wheelchairs available) toilets for disabled shop ✟ (ex guide & helper dogs) ⬤

EASTNEY BEAM ENGINE HOUSE
Henderson Rd, Eastney PO4 9JF (accessible from A3(M), A27 & A2030, first left at Bransbury Park traffic lights)
☎ 023 9282 7261 ▌ 023 9287 5276
e-mail: cspendlove@portsmouthcc.gov.uk

The main attraction here is a magnificent pair of James Watt Beam Engines still housed in their original High-Victorian engine house opened in 1887. One of these engines is in steam when the museum is open. A variety of other pumping engines, many in running order are also on display.
Times: Open all year, last (whole) weekend of every month Apr-Oct 1-5.30, Nov-Mar 1-5 (last admission 30 minutes before closing).
Fee: £2.50 (ch & student £1.50, accompanied ch under 13 free & pen £1.80). Family ticket £6.50. **Facilities:** ▣ (adjacent or 300m) ✟ (ex guide & helper dogs)

FLAGSHIP PORTSMOUTH
HM Naval Base PO1 3LJ (follow brown historic ships sign from M27/M275)
☎ 023 9287 0999 ▌ 023 9229 5252
e-mail: enquiries@flagship.org.uk
Times: Open all year, Apr-Oct, daily 10-5.30; Nov-Mar, daily 10-5. (Closed 25 Dec). **Facilities:** ▣ (charged) ⬤ ✗ ⓖ toilets for disabled shop ✟ (ex on leads) *Details not confirmed for 2002* ⬤

NATURAL HISTORY MUSEUM & BUTTERFLY HOUSE
Cumberland House, Eastern Pde PO4 9RF (accessible from via A3(M), A27 or A2030, follow signs to seafront)
☎ 023 9282 7261 ▌ 023 9282 5276
e-mail: cspendlove@portsmouthcc.gov.uk

Focusing on the natural history and geology of the area, with wildlife dioramas including a riverbank scene with fresh water aquarium. During the summer British and European butterflies fly free in the Butterfly House.
Times: Open daily, Apr-Oct 10-5.30. **Fee:** £2.50 (ch £1.50, accompanied ch under 13 free & pen £1.80). Family ticket £6.50.
Facilities: ▣ (200mtrs) shop ✟ (ex guide & helper dogs) ⬤

THE ROYAL MARINES MUSEUM
Southsea PO4 9PX (signposted from seafront)
☎ 023 9281 9385 ▌ 023 9283 8420
e-mail: info@royalmarinesmuseum.co.uk

Telling the story of the 330-year history of the Marines through dramatic displays, exciting films and videos, state of the art interactives and there's even a live snake and scorpion! Also a world famous medal collection, portraits and silverware.
Times: Open all year, Spring BH-Aug daily 10-5; Sep-May daily 10-4.30. (Closed 3 days Xmas) **Fee:** £4 (ch £2.25, pen £3) Family ticket £12. **Facilities:** ▣ ⬤ ✗ licensed ⓖ (wheelchairs, hearing loops, special tours-prior notice) toilets for disabled shop ✟ (ex guide dogs or in grounds) ⬤

SOUTHSEA CASTLE
Clarence Esplanade PO5 3PA (accessible from M27, A27, A3M, A2030, follow castle signposts)
☎ 023 9282 7261 ▌ 023 9287 5276
e-mail: cspendlove@portsmouthcc.gov.uk

Part of Henry VIII's national coastal defences, this fort was built in 1544. In the 'Time Tunnel' experience, the ghost of the castle's first master gunner guides you through the dramatic scenes from the castle's eventful history. Audio-visual presentation, underground passages, Tudor military history displays, artillery, and panoramic views of the Solent and Isle of Wight.
Times: Open all year, Apr-Sep, daily 10-5.30. **Fee:** £2.50 (ch & students £1.50, ch accompanied 13 free, pen £1.80). Family ticket £6.50. **Facilities:** ▣ (charged) ⓖ (wheelchair available) shop ✟ (ex guide & helper dogs) ⬤

SPITBANK FORT
(ferries depart from HM Naval Base Portsmouth, Portsmouth Hard & Gosport Ferry Pontoon)
☎ 01329 664286 & 07977 066560
Times: Open May-Sep, Tue-Sun. (Weather permitting). **Facilities:** ▣
⬤ *Details not confirmed for 2002*

⛏ RINGWOOD   Map 04 SU10
MOORS VALLEY COUNTRY PARK
Horton Rd, Ashley Heath BH24 2ET (1.5m from Ashley
Heath rdbt on A31 near Three Legged Cross)
☎ 01425 470721   📠 01425 471656
e-mail: mvalley@eastdorsetdc.gov.uk

Fifteen hundred acres of forest, woodland, heathland,
lakes, river and meadows provide a home for a wide
variety of plants and animals, and there's a Visitor
Centre, Adventure Playground, picnic area, Moors
Valley Railway, and Tree Top Trail. Cycle hire is also
available.
Times: Open all year (ex 25 Dec), 8-dusk. Visitor centre open 9.30-
4.30 (later in summer). **Fee:** No admission charge but parking up to
£4 per day. **Facilities:** 🅿 (charged) 🍽 ♿ (visitor centre & park mostly
accessible, wheelchairs) toilets for disabled shop 🐾 (ex in park on
lead)

⛏ ROCKBOURNE   Map 04 SU11
ROCKBOURNE ROMAN VILLA
SP6 3PG (from Salisbury exit A338 at Fordingbridge,
take B3078 W through Sandleheath & follow signs. Or
turn off A354 Salisbury to Blandford road, W of Coombe
Bissett)
☎ 01725 518541

Discovered in 1942, the site features the remains of a
40-room Roman villa and is the largest in the area.
Displays include mosaics and a very rare hypocaust
system. The museum displays the many artefacts found
on the site during excavations. Roman re-enactments
are performed - please ring for details.
Times: Open Apr-Sep, daily 10.30-6. Last admission 5.30pm.
Fee: £1.75 (concessions 95p). **Facilities:** 🅿 🍽 ♿ (ramps in & out of
museum) toilets for disabled shop 🐾 (ex guide/hearing dogs)

⛏ ROMSEY   Map 04 SU32
BROADLANDS
SO51 9ZD (main entrance on A3090 Romsey by-pass)
☎ 01794 505010   📠 01794 505040
e-mail: admin@broadlands.net

Famous as the home of the late Lord Mountbatten,
Broadlands is now home to his grandson Lord Romsey.
An elegant Palladian mansion in a beautiful landscaped
setting on the banks of the River Test, Broadlands was
also the country residence of Lord Palmerston, the
great Victorian statesman.
Times: Open daily, 11 Jun-2 Sep, 12-5.30. Last admission 4pm.
Fee: £5.50 (ch 12-16 £3.80, pen/stu/disabled £4.70). Party 15+.
Facilities: 🅿 🍽 ♿ toilets for disabled shop 🐾 (ex guide dogs)

⛏ SELBORNE   Map 04 SU73
GILBERT WHITE'S HOUSE & THE OATES
MUSEUM
The Wakes, High St GU34 3JH (on village High St)
☎ 01420 511275   📠 01420 511040

Charming 18th-century house, home of famous
naturalist, the Rev. Gilbert White, author of *The Natural
History and Antiquities of Selborne*. There are also

exhibitions on two famous members of the Oates
family - Captain Oates who accompanied Scott to the
South Pole, and Frank Oates, a Victorian explorer.
Special events include an Unusual Plants Fair in June.

Gilbert White's House & The Oates Museum

Times: Open daily Jan-24 Dec, 11-5. **Fee:** £4 (ch £1, pen £3.50).
Facilities: 🅿 (200yds) 🍽 ♿ shop 🐾 (ex guide dogs) 🍽

⛏ SHERBORNE ST JOHN   Map 04 SU65
THE VYNE
RG24 9HL (4m N of Basingstoke, off A340, signposted)
☎ 01256 881337   📠 01256 881720
Times: Open House Apr-29 Oct daily ex Mon & Fri 1-5. Grounds open
wknds in Feb & Mar, 11-4; Apr-29 Oct daily ex Mon & Fri, 11-6. Open
Good Fri & BH Mons. **Facilities:** 🅿 🍽 ✗ licensed ♿ (Braille guide)
shop 🐾 (ex guide & hearing dogs) 🦯 *Details not confirmed for 2002*

⛏ SILCHESTER   Map 04 SU66
CALLEVA MUSEUM
Bramley Rd RG7 2LU (between Basingstoke & Reading.
Accessed from A340)

Little remains of the Roman town of Calleva Atrebatum
except the 1.5 miles of city wall, still an impressive
sight, and the amphitheatre. This small museum shows
what life may have been like in a Roman town, while
the main artefacts from the site can be seen in the
Silchester Gallery at Reading Museum.
Times: Open daily 9am-sunset. Closed 25 Dec. **Fee:** Free.
Facilities: 🅿

⛏ SOUTHAMPTON   Map 04 SU41
MUSEUM OF ARCHAEOLOGY
God's House Tower, Winkle St SO14 2NY (near
waterfront, near Queen's Park and Town Quay)
☎ 023 8063 5904 & 8083 2768
📠 023 8033 9601
e-mail: historic.sites@southampton.gov.uk
Times: Open Tue-Fri 10-12 & 1-5; Sat 10-12 & 1-4; Sun 2-5. Also open
BH Mon. **Facilities:** 🅿 (400 yds) (designated areas only, parking
charges) shop 🐾 (ex guide dogs) *Details not confirmed for 2002*

SOUTHAMPTON CITY ART GALLERY
Civic Centre, Commercial Rd SO14 7LP (on Watts Park side of the Civic Centre, a short walk from station)
☎ 023 8063 2601   📄 023 8083 2153
e-mail: artgallery@southampton.gov.uk
Times: Open all year, Tue, Wed & Fri 10-5, Thu 10-5, Sat 10-5, Sun 1-4. (Closed 25-27 & 31 Dec). **Facilities:** P (250yds) ☕ & toilets for disabled shop 🎁 *Details not confirmed for 2002*

SOUTHAMPTON HALL OF AVIATION
Albert Rd South SO1 1FR
☎ 023 8063 5830
Times: Open all year, Tue-Sat 10-5, Sun 12-5. Also BH Mon & School Holidays. (Closed Xmas). **Facilities:** P (150 yds) (roadside parking on meter) & (lift to all levels) toilets for disabled shop 🎁 *Details not confirmed for 2002*

SOUTHAMPTON MARITIME MUSEUM
The Wool House, Town Quay SO14 2AR (on waterfront, near Town Quay)
☎ 023 8022 3941 & 8063 5904
📄 023 8033 9601
e-mail: historic.sites@southampton.gov.uk
Times: Open all year, Tue-Fri 10-12 & 1-5, Sat 10-12 & 1-4, Sun 2-5. Also open BH Mon. **Facilities:** P (400 yds) (metered parking adjacent) & shop 🎁 (ex guide dogs) *Details not confirmed for 2002*

TUDOR HOUSE MUSEUM
St Michael's Square, Bugle St SO14 2AD (follow signs for Old Town & Waterfront. 500yds from Wool House)
☎ 023 8033 2513 & 8063 5904
📄 023 8033 9601
e-mail: historic.sites@southampton.gov.uk
Times: Open Tue-Fri 10-5 (closed between 12-1), Sat 10-4 (closed between 12-1), Sun 2-5. Open BH Mon. **Facilities:** P (20yds) (metered & disabled parking opposite) & toilets for disabled shop 🎁 (ex guide dogs) *Details not confirmed for 2002*

🏛 STRATFIELD SAYE   Map 04 SU66
STRATFIELD SAYE HOUSE
RG7 2BZ (off A33 between Reading & Basingstoke)
☎ 01256 882882   📄 01256 882882
Times: Open Sat & Sun in May and BH Mon; Daily ex Fri Jun-Aug; Sat & Sun in Sep. Groups by prior booking during week. **Facilities:** P ✕ licensed & toilets for disabled shop 🎁 (ex in grounds) *Details not confirmed for 2002*

WELLINGTON COUNTRY PARK
RG7 1SP
☎ 0118 932 6444   📄 0118 932 6445
(For full entry see Riseley, Berkshire)

🏛 TITCHFIELD   Map 04 SU50
TITCHFIELD ABBEY
PO15 5RA (0.5m N off A27)
☎ 023 9252 7667
Times: Open Apr-Sep, daily 10-6; Oct, daily 10-5; Nov-Mar, daily 10-4. **Facilities:** P & 🎁 ⚡ *Details not confirmed for 2002*

🏛 WEYHILL   Map 04 SU34
THE HAWK CONSERVANCY AND COUNTRY PARK
SP11 8DY (3m W of Andover, signposted from A303)
☎ 01264 772252   📄 01264 773772
e-mail: info@hawk-conservancy.org

This is the largest centre in the south for birds of prey from all over the world including eagles, hawks, falcons, owls, vultures and kites. Exciting birds of prey demonstrations are held daily at noon, 2pm, and 3.30pm, including the 'Valley of the Eagles' at 2pm. Different birds are flown at these times and visitors may have the opportunity to hold a bird and adults can fly a Harris hawk.
Times: Open mid Feb-first Sun in Oct, daily from 10.30 (last admission 4pm). **Fee:** £5.95 (ch £3.50, pen £5.45). Family ticket £17.50.
Facilities: P ☕ & (Wheelchair area in flying grounds) toilets for disabled shop 🎁 ⚡

🏛 WHITCHURCH   Map 04 SU44
WHITCHURCH SILK MILL
28 Winchester St RG28 7AL
☎ 01256 892065

The Mill was built on an island on the River Test nearly 200 years ago, and still weaves high quality silks today. The noisy Victorian machinery is powered by a water wheel. Phone for details of exhibitions and events.
Times: Open Tue-Sun & BH Mon 10.30-5. Closed 24 Dec-1 Jan.
Fee: £3 (ch £1.50, pen £2.50) **Facilities:** P ☕ & toilets for disabled shop 🎁 (ex guide dogs) ⚡

🏛 WINCHESTER   Map 04 SU42
GURKHA MUSEUM
Peninsula Barracks, Romsey Rd SO23 8TS (Exit M3 junct 9 to Winchester, follow one-way system into High St, 1st left after Westgate)
☎ 01962 842832   📄 01962 877597
e-mail: curator@thegurkhamuseum.co.uk

This museum tells the fascinating story of the Gurkha's involvement with the British Army. Travel from Nepal to the North-West Frontier and beyond, with the help of life-sized dioramas, interactive exhibits and sound displays.
Times: Open all year, BH Mon, Tue-Sat 10-5, Sun 12-4. Telephone for Xmas opening times. (Closed 25-26 Dec, 1 Jan and Tue following BH Mon) **Fee:** £1.50 (pen 75p). Party 15+. **Facilities:** P & (lift & chair lift) toilets for disabled shop 🎁 (ex guide dogs)

HOSPITAL OF ST CROSS
St Cross SO23 9SD (1.5m S of city, on A3335)
☎ 01962 851375   📄 01962 878221

Founded in 1132 for the benefit of 13 poor men, and still functioning as an almshouse. Throughout the Middle Ages the hospital handed out the Dole - bread and beer - to travellers, and this is still done. The Church of St Cross, Brethrens Hall and medieval

kitchen, and the walled Master's Garden are all worthy of note.
Times: Open all year, Apr-Oct, Mon-Sat 9.30-5; Nov-Mar 10.30-3.30. (Closed Sun, Good Fri & 25 Dec). **Fee:** £2 (ch 50p, students & pen £1.25). **Facilities:** P (200 yds) (2 hrs) 🍽 ﻝ (A resident Brother can act as guide and assistant) toilets for disabled shop 🐾 (ex guide dogs) 🍵

THE KING'S ROYAL HUSSARS REGIMENTAL MUSEUM

Peninsula Barracks, Romsey Rd SO23 8TS (exit M3 junct 9/10 follow signs for city centre, then hospital A&E red signs to Romsey rd. Vehicle access is from Romsey rd. A3090/B3040 towards Royal Hampshire Hospital)
☎ 01962 828539 🖹 01962 828538
e-mail: beresford@krhmuseum.freeserve.co.uk

The Royal Hussars were formed by the amalgamation of two regiments raised at the time of the Jacobite Rebellion in 1715. The museum was formed by the amalgamation in 1992 of the Royal Hussars and the 14th/20th King's Hussars. This museum tells their story.
Times: Open 5 Jan-18 Dec, Tue-Fri 10-4, Sat, Sun, BH's & 1/2 term Mon - 12-4. **Fee:** Free. **Facilities:** 🅿 ﻝ (lift to first floor) toilets for disabled shop 🐾 (ex guide dogs)

ROYAL HAMPSHIRE REGIMENT MUSEUM & MEMORIAL GARDEN

Serle's House, Southgate St SO23 9EG (near city centre, 150mtrs from traffic lights in high street)
☎ 01962 863658 🖹 01962 888302

Regimental Museum of the Royal Hampshire Regiment 1702-1992, set in an 18th-century house by the regiment's Memorial Garden. The museum tells the history of the regiment, its regulars, militia, volunteers and Territorials.
Times: Open all year (ex 2 wks Xmas & New Year), Mon-Fri 10-12.30 & 2-4; Apr-Oct wknds & BH noon-4. **Fee:** Free. **Facilities:** P (800mtrs) ﻝ shop 🐾 (ex guide dogs)

THE GREAT HALL

Castel Av SO23 8PJ
☎ 01962 846476 🖹 01962 841326

The only surviving part of Winchester Castle, once home to the Domesday Book, this 13th-century hall was the centre of court and government life. The round table, closely associated with the legendary King Arthur, has hung here for over 600 years. A visitor centre and the Winch Castle exhibition add to the displays to be seen.
Times: Open all year, Mar-Oct daily 10-5; Nov-Feb, daily 10-5, wknds 10-4. (Closed 25-26 Dec). **Fee:** Free. **Facilities:** P (200yds) ﻝ toilets for disabled shop 🐾 (ex guide/hearing dogs) 🍵

WINCHESTER CATHEDRAL

SO23 9LS (in city centre - follow city heritage signs)
☎ 01962 857200 & 866854 🖹 01962 857201
e-mail: cathedral.office@winchester-cathedral.org.uk

The longest medieval church in Europe, founded in 1079 on a site where Christian worship had already been offered for over 400 years. Among its treasures are the 12th-century illuminated Winchester Bible, the font, medieval wall paintings and Triforium Gallery Museum.
Times: Open all year, daily 8.30-6.30. Subject to services and special events. **Fee:** Free. **Facilities:** P 500m 🍽 ✗ licensed ﻝ (chair lift to east end of Cathedral, touch & hearing model) toilets for disabled shop 🐾 (ex guide dogs)

WINCHESTER CITY MILL

Bridge St SO23 8EJ (by city bridge between King Alfred's statue & Chesil St)
☎ 01962 870057 🖹 01962 870057
e-mail: swigen@smtp.ntrust.org.uk
Times: Open Apr-Oct, Wed-Sun & BH Mons 11-4.45; Mar wknds only. Last admission 15 mins before closing. **Facilities:** P (200 yds) shop 🥕 *Details not confirmed for 2002* 🍵

WINCHESTER CITY MUSEUM

The Square SO23 9ES
☎ 01962 848269 🖹 01962 848299
Times: Open all year, Mon-Sat 10-5, Sun 2-5 (Closed Mon Oct-Mar, Good Fri, Xmas & 1 Jan). **Facilities:** ﻝ shop 🐾 *Details not confirmed for 2002*

WINCHESTER COLLEGE

College St SO23 9NA (S of Cathedral Close, beyond Kingsgate arch)
☎ 01962 621209 🖹 01962 621166
e-mail: enterprises@wincoll.ac.uk

Founded in 1382, Winchester College is believed to be the oldest continuously running school in England. The college has greatly expanded over the years but the original buildings remain intact. Visitors can follow in the footsteps of John Keats, and see the college's many historic buildings, including a schoolhouse thought to have been designed by Christopher Wren.
Times: Open all year for unbooked guided tours, 10.45, 12, 2.15, 3.30. (ex Tue & Thu 10.45, 12 & Sun 2.15, 3.30). Groups 10+ by arrangement only. **Fee:** Booked tours £3 (pen & students 18 £2.50), unbooked tours £2.50 (pen & students £2). **Facilities:** P (250yds) (Street parking 1hr) ﻝ toilets for disabled shop 🐾 (ex guide dogs)

Herefordshire

Herefordshire is split in two by the River Wye which meanders through the county on its way to the Severn and the sea. The entire county is largely rural, with Hereford, Leominster and Ross-on-Wye the only towns or cities of any size.

EVENTS & FESTIVALS

May
4th-5th Bromyard Spring Festival
7th-9th Hereford May Fair
31st-9th June Hay-on-Wye Festival of Literature
31st-9th June Leominster Festival (mixed arts, various venues)

June
31st May-9th Hay-on-Wye Festival of Literature
31st May-9th Leominster Festival (mixed arts, various venues)
28th-30th Music Festival, Dore Abbey, Abbeydore

July
4th-14th Ledbury Poetry Festival
13th-21st Madley Festival

August
15th-26th Ross-on-Wye International Festival
tbc Eardisland Annual Duck Races

September
tbc Bromyard Folk Festival

October
tbc Big Apple Weekend, Much Marcle, nr Ledbury

October/November
tbc Herefordshire Photography Festival

The countryside and ancient villages of Herefordshire are probably the county's major asset, and visitors can take advantage of a number of trails which will guide them through much of interest. These are set out on leaflets available from Tourist Information Centres. Those especially interested in villages should try the Black and White Village Trail, which takes the motorist on a 35 - mile drive around timber-framed villages in the northwest of the county from Leominster to Weobley, (established in the 7th century and known as a centre of witchcraft in the 18th), Kinnersley Castle, Eardisley (where the Church of St Mary Magdalene boasts a early 12th-century carved font), Great Oak, Kington (one of the five market towns of Herefordshire), Pembridge, and others.

Other trails include the Mortimer Trail; – a 30 - mile walk through unspoilt countryside between Ludlow and Kington – the Hop Trail; – which goes from Bromyard to Ledbury through fields which display the varying stages of hop growing – and the Hidden Highway, which begins at Ross-on-Wye and ends in Chester, taking in much of the area's dramatic countryside and many secret places on the way.

Hereford has a glorious 11th-century cathedral situated on the River Wye. It contains a 13th-century Mappa Mundi, and the world's largest chained library that dates from the 8th century.

Top: Abbey Dore

🏛 ASHTON
Map 03 SO56

BERRINGTON HALL
Berrington HR6 0DW (3m N of Leominster, on A49)
☎ 01568 615721 ▤ 01568 613263
e-mail: berrington@smtp.ntrust.org.uk
Times: Open Apr-Oct, Sat-Wed & Good Fri 1.30-5.30 (4.30pm in Oct). Last admission 30min before closing. Garden open 12.30-6 (5pm in Oct). Park walk open Jul-Oct, same times as house. **Facilities:** 🅿 ✗ licensed ⚒ (by arrangement, Braille guide, 2 wheelchairs) toilets for disabled shop 🐾 (ex guide dogs) 🐾 *Details not confirmed for 2002*

🏛 BROCKHAMPTON
Map 03 SO65

LOWER BROCKHAMPTON
WR6 5UH (2m E of Bromyard on A44)
☎ 01885 488099 & 482077 ▤ 01885 482151
Times: Open: Medieval hall, Parlour, Minstrel gallery, Information room, gatehouse & chapel 29 Mar-Sep, Wed-Sun & BH Mon 10-5. Oct, Wed-Sun 10-4. **Facilities:** 🅿 ▣ ⚒ (special parking for disabled) toilets for disabled 🐾 🐾 *Details not confirmed for 2002*

🏛 CROFT
Map 03 SO46

CROFT CASTLE
HR6 9PW (off B4362)
☎ 01568 780246 ▤ 01568 780462
e-mail: croft@smtp.ntrust.org.uk
Times: Open Etr Sat & Sun; Apr Sat, Sun & BH Mon 1.30-4.30; Oct-1 Nov Sat & Sun. 1.30-4.30; May-Sep, Wed-Sun & BH Mon 1.30-5.30. Last admission to house half hour before closing. Parkland open all year. (Closed Good Fri). **Facilities:** 🅿 (charged) ▣ ⚒ (parking available, braille guide) 🐾 (ex in parkland) 🐾 *Details not confirmed for 2002*

🏛 GOODRICH
Map 03 SO51

GOODRICH CASTLE
HR9 6HY (5m S of Ross-on-Wye, off A40)
☎ 01600 890538

Goodrich Castle dominates an ancient crossing of the River Wye. Its huge towers, graceful arches and chapel are well worth the visit, and there is a maze of rooms, passages and a gloomy dungeon to be explored. It was besieged in the Civil War, and the locally made canon used to bombard it, and nicknamed 'Roaring Meg', is on display in Hereford Cathedral.
Times: Open all year, Apr-Sep, daily 10-6 (Oct 10-5); Nov-Mar 10-4. Closed 24-26 Dec & 1 Jan. **Fee:** £3.60 (ch 5-15 £1.80, under 5's free, con £2.70) **Facilities:** 🅿 🐾 ▦

🏛 HEREFORD
Map 03 SO53

CHURCHILL HOUSE MUSEUM & HATTON ART GALLERY
3 Venn's Ln HR1 1DE
☎ 01432 267409 & 260693 ▤ 01432 342492
Times: Open 2-5 Apr-Sep, Wed-Sun, inc BH Mons. **Facilities:** 🅿 ⚒ (access guide & tape,braille guides & plans) shop 🐾 *Details not confirmed for 2002*

CIDER MUSEUM & KING OFFA DISTILLERY
21 Ryelands St HR4 0LW (off A438 Hereford to Brecon road)
☎ 01432 354207 ▤ 01432 371641

Explore the fascinating history of cider making - old cidermaking equipment, the cooper's workshop and Vat house with hydraulic presses and bottling machinery.
Times: Open all year, Apr-Oct, daily 10-5.30; Nov-Dec, daily 11-3. Jan-Mar, Tue-Sun 11-3. Pre-booked groups at anytime. **Fee:** £2.50 (concessions £2). Party 15+. **Facilities:** 🅿 ▣ ⚒ (audiotapes, large print guidesheets shop 🐾 (ex guide dogs)

HEREFORD CATHEDRAL
HR1 2NG (A49 to Hereford, signed from city inner ring roads)
☎ 01432 374200 ▤ 01432 374220
e-mail: office@herefordcathedral.co.uk

The first bishop was appointed to the See of Hereford in 676AD. The cathedral is mainly Norman with a 13th-century Lady Chapel. Hereford's two outstanding treasures are exhibited together in the museum building at the West front. The Mappa Mundi - drawn in 1289, and the famous Chained Library - containing over 1400 chained books and 227 manuscripts dating from the 8th century.
Times: Cathedral open daily for visitors 9.30-5; Mappa Mundi & Chained Library Exhibition Summer: Mon-Sat 10-4.15, Sun 11-3.15. Winter: Mon-Sat 11-3.15 (closed Sun). **Fee:** Cathedral admission free (donation invited). Mappa Mundi & Chained Library Exhibition £4 (concessions £3.50). Family £10. Party 10+. **Facilities:** 🅿 (0.25m) ▣ ⚒ (touch facility for blind, braille & large print info) toilets for disabled shop 🐾 (ex guide dogs) 🍴

OLD HOUSE
High Town HR1 2AA (in centre of High Town)
☎ 01432 260694

The Old House is a fine Jacobean building dating from around 1621, and was once in a row of similar houses. Its rooms are furnished in 17th-century style and give visitors the chance to learn what life was like in Cromwell's time.
Times: Open Apr-Sep, Tue-Sat 10-5, Sun & BH Mon 10-4. **Fee:** Free. **Facilities:** 🅿 ⚒ shop 🐾 (ex guide dogs)

⛫ KINGTON   Map 03 SO25
HERGEST CROFT GARDENS
HR5 3EG (turn off A44 W of Kington and follow signs)
☎ 01544 230160 🖷 01544 230160
e-mail: banks@hergest.kc3.co.uk

From spring bulbs to autumn colour, this is a garden for
all seasons. A fine collection of trees and shrubs
surrounds the Edwardian house. There's an old
fashioned kitchen garden with spring and summer
borders, and Park Wood, a hidden valley with splendid
rhododendrons.

Times: Open 30 Mar-Oct, 1.30-6. (May & Jun noon-6). **Fee:** £4 (ch
under 16 free). Party 20+ **Facilities:** 🅿 🍽 ﴾ (portable ramp &
wheelchair available) toilets for disabled shop garden centre ✲ (ex on
lead) 🍴

⛫ LEDBURY   Map 03 SO73
EASTNOR CASTLE
Eastnor HR8 1RL (2.5m E of Ledbury on A438
Tewkesbury road)
☎ 01531 633160 🖷 01531 631776
e-mail: eastnorcastle@eastnorcastle.com

A magnificent Georgian castle in a lovely setting, with a
deer park, arboretum and lake. Inside are tapestries,
fine art and armour, and the Italianate and Gothic
interiors have been beautifully restored. There's an
adventure playground, nature trails and lakeside walks.
Times: Open Etr-7 Oct, Sun & BH Mon; Jul & Aug, Sun-Fri 11-5. Last
admission 4.30pm. **Fee:** Castle & grounds £5 (ch £3) Family £13.
Grounds £3 (ch £2). **Facilities:** 🅿 🍽 ✕ & shop garden centre 🍴

⛫ SWAINSHILL   Map 03 SO44
THE WEIR GARDENS
HR4 8BS (5m W of Hereford, on A438)
☎ 01981 590509 (info line)
e-mail: sevinfo@smtp.ntrust.org.uk
Times: Open 14 Feb-Oct, Wed-Sun & BH Mon 11-6. **Facilities:** 🅿 ✲
🚐 🦽 *Details not confirmed for 2002*

Hertfordshire

Southeastern county of England, close to London, making its county town of Hertford and the towns of Hemel Hempstead, Watford and Harpenden a haven for commuters to the capital.

St Albans, less than 19 miles (30km) from London, has retained its distinctive character, along with many historic remains. The Roman city of Verulamiun is situated in a nearby park, and excavations have revealed an amphitheatre, a temple, parts of the city walls and the foundations of houses. Some spectacular mosaic pavements are displayed in the Verulamium Museum.

The abbey church at St Albans is built on the site where St Alban, the first British Christian martyr, was executed in the 3rd century. The abbey was founded in 793 by King Offa of Mercia, and contains his shrine, made of Purbeck marble. Lost for years, it was discovered in the 19th century, in pieces, and restored by Sir Giles Gilbert Scott. Rebuilt by the Normans, the abbey contains some wonderful medieval wall paintings.

Nicholas Breakspear was born in St Albans, the son of an abbey tenant. In 1154 he took the name Adrian IV, and became the first, and so far only, English pope.

Another famous historic son of Hertfordshire was Sir Francis Bacon, Elizabethan scholar and Lord High Chancellor, who some believe was the real author of Shakespeare's plays. He was born at Gorhambury House near Hemel Hempstead in 1561.

The county has also produced some famous daughters, namely two of the world famous Spice Girls: Geri Halliwell (now solo) and Victoria Beckham.

EVENTS & FESTIVALS

May
25th-26th Herts County Show, Herts County Showground, Redbourn
tbc Herts Garden Show, Knebworth House
tbc Luton Carnival

June
22nd-23rd Festival of Gardening, Hatfield House
tbc Hertford Carnival

July
tbc Fireworks & Laser Concert, Knebworth House
tbc St Albans Festival

August
26th St Albans Carnival

September
14th Hoddeson Carnival
14th-15th Discover St Albans Festival

October
tbc Apple Day Fair & Market, city centre St Albans

November
tbc Firework display, Verulamium Park, St Albans

Top: Rose, Chiswellgreen

🏛 AYOT ST LAWRENCE   Map 04 TL11
SHAW'S CORNER
AL6 9BX (A1(M) junct 4 or M1 junct 10. Follow B653
signed Wheathampstead & follow signs to Luton and
The Ayots. Turn right, and establishment is signed)
☎ 01438 820307   📄 01438 820307
e-mail: tscgen@smtp.ntrust.org.uk

George Bernard Shaw lived here from 1906 until his
death in 1950. He gave the house to the National Trust
in 1946, and the contents are much as they were in his
time. Among the displays are his hats, including a soft
homburg he wore for 60 years, his bicycle exercise
machine, fountain pens, spectacles and several
pictures.
Times: Open Apr-4 Nov **Fee:** £3.50. Family ticket £8.75 **Facilities:** 🅿
♿ (braille guide to house, scented plants, items to touch) 🐕 (ex on
lead in car park) 🛝

🏛 BERKHAMSTED   Map 04 SP90
BERKHAMSTED CASTLE
HP4 1HF
☎ 01536 402840
Times: Open all year, daily 10-4. Keykeeper. **Facilities:** 🅿 ♿ 🚻
Details not confirmed for 2002

🏛 HATFIELD   Map 04 TL20
HATFIELD HOUSE
AL9 5NQ (2m from junct 4 A1(M) on A1000, 7m from
M25 junct 23. House is opposite Hatfield railway
station)
☎ 01707 287010   📄 01707 287033
e-mail: curator@hatfield-house.demon.co.uk

Home of the Cecil family for 400 years, this celebrated
Jacobean house is steeped in Elizabethan and Victorian
political history and is famous for its exquisite furniture,
tapestries and paintings. The extensive formal gardens
reflect their historic origins, were designed and
developed by Lady Salisbury and are managed entirely

organically. A children's play area and nature trails are
also open to the public.
Times: Open 30 Mar-Sep. House: daily 12-4, guided tours only on
weekdays. Park & gardens: daily 11-5.30. **Fee:** House Park & Gardens:
£7 (ch £3.50). Park only £2 (ch £1). Park & gardens: £4.50 (ch 3.50).
Park only £2 (ch £1). Mon & Fri (Connoisseurs' Days), £10.50 (no
concessions) **Facilities:** 🅿 ✕ licensed ♿ toilets for disabled shop
garden centre 🐕 (ex guide dogs) 🍴

🏛 KNEBWORTH   Map 04 TL22
**KNEBWORTH HOUSE, GARDENS & COUNTRY
PARK**
SG3 6PY (direct access from A1(M) junct 7 at
Stevenage)
☎ 01438 812661   📄 01438 811908
e-mail: info@knebworthhouse.com

The original Tudor manor was transformed in 1843 by
the spectacular high Gothic decoration of Victorian
novelist Sir Edward Bulwer Lytton. The formal gardens,
laid out by Lutyens in 1908, include a Jekyll herb
garden, a maze, recently restored walled garden and
wilderness walks. The 250-acre park includes a
miniature railway, an adventure playground, and a deer
park.
Times: Open 28 Apr-20 May, 9 Jun-1 July, 8-30 Sep wknds & BHs
only. Daily 7-22 Apr, 26 May-3 Jun. 7 Jul-4 Sep. Park, gardens,
playground & railway 11-5.30. House & Indian Raj display noon-5 (last
admission 4.15). **Fee:** £7 (ch4-16 & pen £6.50); Park, Playground &
Gardens only: £5.50. Family ticket £23.50/£19. Party 20+. **Facilities:** 🅿
🍴 ♿ (with prior notice visitors can be driven to front door) toilets for
disabled shop (2 shops) garden centre 🐕 (ex guide dogs & in park)
🍴

🏛 LETCHWORTH   Map 04 TL23
MUSEUM & ART GALLERY
Broadway SG6 3PF (next to Public Library, in the town
centre, near Broadway Cinema)
☎ 01462 685647   📄 01462 481879
e-mail: letchworth.museum@nhdc.gov.uk

Opened in 1914 to house the collections of the
Letchworth Naturalists' Society, this local museum has
exhibits on local wildlife, geology, arts and crafts, and

contd.

archæology. Also a museum shop and a regular
programme of workshops.
Times: Open Mon-Tue, Thu-Sat from 4 Jun. (Closed BHs) **Fee:** Free.
Facilities: P (100 yds) & (special provisions on request) shop ✱ (ex
guide dogs)

🏛 LONDON COLNEY   Map 04 TL10
DE HAVILLAND AIRCRAFT HERITAGE CENTRE
Salisbury Hall AL2 1EX (signposted from M25 junct 22.
Follow signs for 'Mosquito Aircraft Museum')
☎ 01727 822051 & 826400   🖹 01727 826400

The oldest aircraft museum in Britain, opened in 1959
to preserve and display the de Havilland Mosquito
prototype on the site of its conception. A working
museum with displays of 20 de Havilland aircraft and
sections together with a comprehensive collection of de
Havilland engines and memorabilia. Selective cockpits
are open to enter.
Times: Open Mar-Oct, Sun & BH Mons 10.30-5.30, Tue, Thu & Sat 2-
5.30. **Fee:** £5 (ch u5 free, ch & pen £3) Family ticket (2ad+2ch) £13.
Facilities: 🅿 ♨ & (wheelchairs available) toilets for disabled shop
(not accessible for disabled) ✱ (ex on lead & under control) ⬤

🏛 ST ALBANS   Map 04 TL10
CLOCK TOWER
Market Place AL3 3DR (City centre, junct of High St
(A1081) & Market Place)
☎ 01727 855843

This early 15th-century curfew tower, which faces the
High Street, provides fine views over the city (especially
of the abbey) and the surrounding countryside. This is
one of the only two medieval curfew towers in the
country. It has a bell, older than the tower itself, which
strikes on the hour.
Times: Open Good Fri-mid Sep, Sat, Sun & BH 10.30-5. **Fee:** 30p (ch
5-11 15p, accompanied ch under 5 free) **Facilities:** P (400yds) shop
✱

Knebworth
HOUSE, GARDENS & PARK

Home of the Lytton family for over 500 years, where
Elizabeth I visited, Charles Dickens acted and
Winston Churchill painted. Extensive Gardens, Maze,
Indian Raj Display (1st floor), Adventure Playground,
Miniature Railway, Gift Shop and Tea Room.

*FULL PROGRAMME OF EXCITING EVENTS IN THE
PARK, FROM APRIL TO SEPTEMBER - PLEASE
TELEPHONE FOR DETAILS.*

So much to see – So much to do!
For further information, please contact:
**The Estate Office, Knebworth Park,
Near Stevenage, Herts SG3 6PY**
Tel: 01438 812661 www.knebworthhouse.com
Direct access at Junction 7 - A1(M), 15 miles from M25 (J23). Ample free parking.

GARDENS OF THE ROSE (ROYAL NATIONAL ROSE SOCIETY)
Chiswell Green Ln AL2 3NR (2m S off B4630 Watford Rd)
☎ 01727 850461   🖹 01727 850360
e-mail: mail@rnrs.org.uk

The gardens of the Royal National Rose Society, which
include the International Trial Ground for new roses.
The gardens contain over 30,000 plants in 1,650
different varieties. These include old-fashioned roses,

contd.

modern roses and the roses of the future. The National Miniature Rose Show takes place during July.
Times: Open 2 Jun-Sep, Mon-Sat 9-5 (Sun & BH Mon 10-6). **Fee:** £4 (ch 5-15 £1.50, pen & UB40 £3.50) Party 20+ £3.50 each.
Facilities: 🅿 ☕ ♿ (ramps where necessary) toilets for disabled shop 🐾

GORHAMBURY
AL3 6AH (entry via lodge gates on A414)
☎ 01727 855000   🖥 01727 843675
Times: Open May-Sep, Thu 2-5. **Facilities:** 🅿 shop 🐾 *Details not confirmed for 2002*

MUSEUM OF ST ALBANS
Hatfield Rd AL1 3RR (in city centre on A1057 Hatfield road)
☎ 01727 819340   🖥 01727 837472
e-mail: a.wheeler@stalbans.gov.uk

Exhibits include the Salaman collection of craft tools, and reconstructed workshops. The history of St Albans is traced from the departure of the Romans up to the present day. There is a special exhibition gallery with a surprising variety of exhibitions and a wildlife garden with picnic area.
Times: Open all year, daily 10-5, Sun 2-5. Closed 25 & 26 Dec.
Fee: Free. **Facilities:** 🅿 ♿ toilets for disabled shop 🐾 (ex guide dogs) 🐾

ROMAN THEATRE OF VERULAMIUM
St Michaels AL3 6AH (off A4147)
☎ 01727 835035   🖥 01727 843675
Times: Open all year, daily 10-5 (4 in winter). Closed 25-26 Dec. 1 Jan by appointment only. **Facilities:** 🅿 ♿ shop *Details not confirmed for 2002*

ST ALBANS CATHEDRAL
Sumpter Yard AL1 1BY (exit M25 junct 22a, in city centre)
☎ 01727 860780   🖥 01727 850944
e-mail: admin@stalbanscathedal.org.uk

An imposing Norman abbey church built on the site of the execution of St Alban, Britain's first martyr (c250AD). The cathedral is constructed from recycled Roman brick taken from nearby Verulamium.
Times: Open daily, 9-5.45 **Fee:** Free. **Facilities:** 🅿 (200mtrs) ♿ (touch & hearing centre, braille guides) toilets for disabled shop 🐾 (ex guide dogs)

VERULAMIUM MUSEUM
St Michaels AL3 4SW (follow signs for St Albans, museum signposted)
☎ 01727 751810   🖥 01727 859919
e-mail: a.coles@stalbans.gov.uk

Verulamium was one of the largest and most important Roman towns in Britain - by the 1st century AD it was declared a 'municipium', giving its inhabitants the rights of Roman citizenship, the only British city granted this honour. A mosaic and underfloor heating system can be seen, and the museum has wall

paintings, jewellery, pottery and other domestic items. On the second weekend of every month legionaries occupy the galleries and describe the tactics and equipment of the Roman Imperial Army and the life of a legionary.
Times: Open all year wkdys 10-5.30, Sun 2-5.30. (Closed 25-26 Dec).
Fee: £3.20 (ch, pen & students £1.85). Family ticket £8.05. Subject to change. **Facilities:** 🅿 (charged) ♿ (ramp access to main entrance) toilets for disabled shop 🐾 (ex guide dogs) 🐾

🏛 TRING   Map 04 SP91
THE WALTER ROTHSCHILD ZOOLOGICAL MUSEUM
Akeman St HP23 6AP (signposted from A41)
☎ 020 7942 6171   🖥 020 7942 6150
e-mail: tring-enquiries@nhm.ac.uk

An unusual museum, founded in the 1890s by Lionel Walter, 2nd Baron Rothschild, scientist, eccentric and natural history enthusiast. Now part of the Natural History Museum, it houses more than 4000 specimens from whales to fleas, and humming birds to tigers.
Times: Open all year, Mon-Sat 10-5, Sun 2-5. (Closed 24-26 Dec).
Fee: Free. **Facilities:** 🅿 ☕ ♿ (ramps to shop & cafe, disabled parking space) toilets for disabled shop 🐾 (ex guide dogs) 🐾

🏛 WARE   Map 05 TL31
SCOTT'S GROTTO
Scott's Rd SG12 9JQ (off A119)
☎ 01920 464131

Scott's Grotto, built in the 1760s by the Quaker poet John Scott, has been described by English Heritage as 'one of the finest in England'. Recently restored by the Ware Society, it consists of underground passages and chambers decorated with flints, shells, minerals and stones, and extends 67ft into the side of the hill. Please wear flat shoes and bring a torch.
Times: Open Apr-end Sep, Sat & BH Mon 2-4.30. Other times by appointment only. **Fee:** Free. **Facilities:** 🅿 (on street) 🐾

Kent

Often called the 'garden of England', Kent is renowned for its fruit production in the agricultural area of the Weald, and its hop growing for the brewing industry. Historically, hops were picked by itinerant workers, many from London, who moved in for the season.

For many years, Londoners have flocked to the seaside resorts of the Isle of Thanet, Margate, Broadstairs and Ramsgate. Of these, Broadstairs retains a quiet charm, and is probably best known as Charles Dickens' resort of choice, where he lived overlooking the bay in a rather forbidding residence since known as Bleak House. More popular yet with visitors from all over the world is the ancient city of Canterbury, the metropolis of the Anglican church since Augustine's mission to England in 597, and site of a magnificent cathedral.

The Channel Tunnel and the Channel ports of Dover, Folkestone and Ramsgate ensure good transport links into the county. The administrative centre is Maidstone, and other main towns are: Chatham, home of the historic Royal Naval Dockyard, part of which has become a film set used in films such as *The Mummy* and *Tomorrow Never Dies*; Rochester with its lovely cathedral; and the elegant spa town of Royal Tunbridge Wells.

Kent is blessed with some fine castles, houses and gardens. Chief among these are Leeds Castle, east of Maidstone; Hever Castle, birthplace of Anne Boleyn; Knole, England's largest house with 365 rooms; Churchill's house, Chartwell, near Westerham; Penshurst Place, a 14th-century house with a splendid hall and long gallery; and the inspirational Sissinghurst Garden created by Vita Sackville-West.

Top: Lullingstone viaduct

EVENTS & FESTIVALS

May
tbc Art & Soul Festival, Dover, Deal and Sandwich
tbc Ramsgate Spring Festival
tbc Sellindge Steam Festival, Ashford
tbc Tonbridge Carnival

June
2nd-4th Kent Garden Show
15th-23rd Broadstairs Dickens Festival
Golden Jubilee Celebrations throughout June in Dover, Deal and Sandwich
tbc Tamboo Bamboo Pageant, Sandwich

July
11th-13th Kent County Show, Maidstone
tbc Deal Carnival & Regatta
tbc Deal Summer Music Festival
tbc Dover Carnival

August
9th-16th Broadstairs Folk Week
11th Broadstairs & St Peters Carnival
26th Sandwich Festival
tbc Broadstairs Water Gala
tbc Dover Regatta
tbc Margate Summer Carnival
tbc Sedan Chair Race, Tunbridge Wells

September
tbc Sandwich Carnival

December
tbc Winter Street Festival, Tunbridge Wells

⛫ AYLESFORD
Map 05 TQ75
AYLESFORD PRIORY
The Friars ME20 7BX (M20 junct 6, M2 junct 3, signposted)
☎ 01622 717272 🖺 01622 715575
e-mail: friarsevents@hotmail.com

Built in the 13th and 14th centuries, the Priory has been restored and is now a house of prayer, guesthouse, conference centre and a place of pilgrimage and retreat. It has fine cloisters, and displays sculpture and ceramics by modern artists.
Times: Open all year, daily 9-dusk. Gift & book shop May-Sep, 10-5; Oct-Apr, 10-4 (Sun 11am). Guided tours of the priory by arrangement. **Fee:** Donations. £2 for annual fund-raising day. **Facilities:** 🅿 ☕ ໕ (wheelchairs available, ramps) toilets for disabled shop 🎫 (ex guide & hearing dogs) ➳

⛫ BEKESBOURNE
Map 05 TR15
HOWLETTS WILD ANIMAL PARK
CT4 5EL (off A2, 3m S of Canterbury, follow brown tourist signs)
☎ 01227 721286 🖺 01227 721853
e-mail: karenw@howletts.net

Howletts is a wild animal park founded by John Aspinall and has the world's largest breeding gorilla colony in captivity. It also has tigers, small cats, free-running deer and antelope, snow leopards, bison, honey badgers, African elephants, and many endangered species of monkey.
Times: Open all year, daily 10-5, (3.30pm in winter). Closed 25 Dec. **Fee:** £9.80 (ch 4-14 & pen £7.80) family ticket £28 **Facilities:** 🅿 ☕ ✕ licensed ໕ toilets for disabled shop 🎫 ➳

⛫ BELTRING
Map 05 TQ64
HOP FARM & COUNTRY PARK
TN12 6PY (on A228 at Paddock Wood)
☎ 01622 872068 🖺 01622 872630
e-mail: enquiry@thehopfarm.co.uk

The largest group of Victorian oast houses and galleried barns in the country, with features including the Hop Story Exhibition, Shire Horse Centre and pottery workshop.
Times: Open all year from 10am (Closed 25-26 & 31 Dec) **Fee:** £6.50 (ch 4-15 & pen £4.50). Family ticket £18 (2 adults & 2 children) under 4's free. **Facilities:** 🅿 ☕ ✕ licensed ໕ toilets for disabled shop ➳

⛫ BIDDENDEN
Map 05 TQ83
BIDDENDEN VINEYARDS & CIDER WORKS
Little Whatmans, Gribble Bridge Ln TN27 8DH (0.5m S off A262, between Biddenden & Tenterden)
☎ 01580 291726 🖺 01580 291933
e-mail: info@biddendenvineyards.co.uk

The present vineyard was established in 1969 and now covers 22 acres. Visitors are welcome to stroll around the vineyard and to taste wines, ciders and apple juice available at the shop.
Times: Open all year, Shop: Mon-Fri 10-5, Sat 10-5, Sun &BH 11-5. Closed noon 24 Dec-2 Jan & Sun in Jan & Feb. **Fee:** Non-guided groups and individuals free. Pre-booked guided tours (minimum 15 adults) £3 (ch 10-18 £1, ch under 12 free). **Facilities:** 🅿 ☕ ໕ shop ➳

⛫ BOROUGH GREEN
Map 05 TQ65
GREAT COMP GARDEN
TN15 8QS (2m E off B2016)
☎ 01732 882669 & 886154

A beautiful seven-acre garden created since 1957 by Mr and Mrs R Cameron for low maintenance and year-round interest. There is a plantsmans' collection of trees, shrubs, heathers and herbaceous plants in a setting of fine lawns and grass paths. The 17th-century house is not open. Chamber music, classical concerts and other events are organised by the Great Comp Society, details from the Secretary, Great Comp Society at the above address.
Times: Open Apr-Oct, daily 11-6. **Fee:** £3.50 (ch £1). Annual ticket £10 (pen £7). **Facilities:** 🅿 ☕ ✕ ໕ (wheelchair for hire) toilets for disabled garden centre 🎫 (ex guide dogs)

⛫ BRASTED
Map 05 TQ45
EMMETTS GARDEN
Ide Hill TN14 6AY (1m S of A25, Sundridge-Ide Hill road)
☎ 01732 868381 (Chartwell office)
🖺 01732 868193
e-mail: kchxxx@smpt.ntrust.org.uk

Emmetts is a charming hillside shrub garden, with bluebells, azaleas and rhododendrons in spring and fine autumn colours. It has magnificent views over Bough Beech Reservoir and the Weald. Emmetts Blues Concert in August.
Times: Open Apr & May, Wed-Sun & BH; Jun-Oct, Wed & wknds 11-5.30 (last admission 4.30). Special arrangement for pre-booked parties at other times. BH Mons late opening until 7 (last admission 6.30) **Fee:** £3.40 (ch £1.70). Family ticket £8.50. **Facilities:** 🅿 ☕ ໕ (wheelchairs & buggy service from car park to garden) toilets for disabled shop 🎫 (must be on lead) 🐾

⛫ BROADSTAIRS
Map 05 TR36
BLEAK HOUSE DICKENS MARITIME & SMUGGLING
Fort Rd CT10 1EY (off Eastern Esplanade, near Viking Bay)
☎ 01843 862224
Times: Open mid Feb-mid Dec, daily; Jan-mid Feb wknds only. **Facilities:** 🅿 (100 yds) ໕ (provisions made for blind) shop *Details not confirmed for 2002*

DICKENS HOUSE MUSEUM
Victoria Pde CT10 1QS (on the seafront)
☎ 01843 863453 🖹 01843 863453
e-mail: aleeault@aol.com

The house was immortalised by Charles Dickens in 'David Copperfield' as the home of the hero's aunt, Betsy Trotwood, whom Dickens based on owner Miss Mary Pearson Strong. Dickens' letters and possessions are shown, with local and Dickensian prints, costumes and general Victoriana.
Times: Open Apr-mid Oct, daily 2-5, also Sat-Sun during summer 10.30-5. **Fee:** £2 (ch 50p). **Facilities:** P (400yds) (play & display) shop 🏃 (ex guide dogs)

🏛 CANTERBURY   Map 05 TR15
CANTERBURY HERITAGE MUSEUM
Stour St CT1 2RA (in the Medieval Poor Priest's Hospital, just off St Margaret's St)
☎ 01227 452747 🖹 01227 455047

An award-winning museum in a lovely medieval building beside the river. The tour starts in Roman times and continues up to the present day. Some of the most exciting of the city's treasures are shown - the Canterbury Cross, Anglo-Saxon gold, and Viking finds. The displays include a reconstruction of Becket's tomb; a medieval street with a pilgrim badge shop; the city in the Civil War; and Stephenson's locomotive `Invicta'. There is a Rupert Bear Gallery and a collection of Joseph Conrad memorabilia.
Times: Open all year, Mon-Sat 10.30-5 & Sun (Jun-Oct) 1.30-5 (last admission 4pm). (Closed Good Fri & Xmas period). **Fee:** £1.90 (ch 5-18, disabled & pen & students £1.20). Family ticket £5. **Facilities:** P & shop 🏃

CANTERBURY ROMAN MUSEUM
Butchery Ln, Longmarket CT1 2RA
☎ 01227 785575 🖹 01227 455047

Underground, at the level of the Roman town, you will find this famous Roman house with its mosaic floors. There is a fascinating reconstruction of some Roman buildings, including a market place with stallholders' wares. Displays reveal a wealth of Roman artefacts. A computer-generated reconstruction video guides you on the tour.
Times: Open all year, Mon-Sat 10-5 & Sun (Jun-Oct) 1.30-5. Last admission 4pm. (Closed Good Fri & Xmas period). **Fee:** £2.50 (ch 5-18, disabled, pen & students £1.60). Family ticket £6.50. **Facilities:** P (500mtrs) & (lift) toilets for disabled shop 🏃

CANTERBURY ROYAL MUSEUM, ART GALLERY & BUFFS REGIMENTAL MUSEUM
High St CT1 2RA
☎ 01227 452747 🖹 01227 455047

The city's picture collection including the T S Cooper Gallery - England's leading Victorian animal painter; and the Canterbury and Europe Gallery which displays the fine archaeological objects and decorative arts resulting from close links over the centuries. Regular art events are held in the Special Exhibitions Gallery. Also housed here is the Buffs Regimental Museum, telling the story of one of England's oldest infantry regiments.
Times: Open all year, Mon-Sat 10-5. (Closed Good Fri and Xmas period). **Fee:** Free. **Facilities:** P 500 mtrs shop 🏃

CANTERBURY TALES VISITOR ATTRACTION
Saint Margaret's St CT1 2TG (city centre, follow finger signs)
☎ 01227 479227 🖹 01227 765584
e-mail: thecanterburytales@hotmail.com

Step back in time to experience the sights sounds and smells of the Middle Ages in this reconstruction of 14th-century England. Travel from the Tabard Inn in London to St. Thomas Becket's Shrine in Canterbury with Chaucer's colourful pilgrims. Their tales of chivalry, romance and intrigue are vividly brought to life for you along your journey.
Times: Open all year. Jan-mid Feb, 10-4.30; mid Feb-end Jun, 10-5; Jul-early Sep, 9.30-5.30; early Sep-end Oct, 10-5; end Oct-end Dec, 10-4 (closed 25 Dec). **Fee:** £5.90 (ch 5-16, pen & student £4.90) Family ticket (1ad+2ch) £15 (2ad+2ch) £18.50. **Facilities:** P (200 mtrs) 💺 & (notice required for wheelchairs) toilets for disabled shop 🏃 (except guide dogs) 🐕

CANTERBURY WEST GATE MUSEUM
St Peter's St CT1 2AT (at end of main street, entrance under main arch)
☎ 01227 452747 🖹 01227 455047

The last of the city's fortified gatehouses sits astride the London road with the river as a moat. Rebuilt in around 1380 by Archbishop Sudbury, it was used as a prison for many years. The battlements give a splendid panoramic view of the city and are a good vantage point for photographs. Arms and armour can be seen in the guardroom, and there are cells in the towers.
Times: Open all year (ex Good Fri & Xmas period), Mon-Sat; 11-12.30 & 1.30-3.30. Last admission 15 mins before closure **Fee:** £1 (ch, disabled, pen, students & UB40 65p). Family ticket £2.50. Party 10+. **Facilities:** P (100 yds) shop 🏃

DRUIDSTONE WILDLIFE & ART PARK

Honey Hill, Blean CT2 9JR (3m NW on A290)
☎ 01227 765168   🖷 01227 768860

Enjoy the company of the animals and birds in a relaxing country setting. Make friends with the animals in the farmyard, meet the parrots, walk through the gardens, which are home to the owls and wallaby, or along the woodland trail to see giant toadstools and the dragon sleeping. An extra attraction of sculptures by famous artists has been added to the park.
Times: Open Etr-Nov, daily, 10-5.30. **Fee:** £3.90 (ch £2.60 & concessions £3.50). Family ticket £11. **Facilities:** 🅿 ☕ ♿ toilets for disabled shop 🐾 (ex guide dogs)

ST AUGUSTINE'S ABBEY

Longport CT1 1TF (off A28)
☎ 01227 767345

The abbey, founded by St Augustine in 598, when he brought Christianity from Rome to England, is one of the oldest monastic sites in the country. Its long and fascinating history can be traced in the ruins.
Times: Open all year, Apr-Oct, daily 10-6 (Oct 10-5); Nov-Mar, daily 10-4. Closed 24-26 Dec & 1 Jan. **Fee:** £2.60 (ch 5-15 £1.30, under 5's free, con £2). **Facilities:** 🅿 ♿ shop ♨

▥ CHARTWELL   Map 05 TQ45

CHARTWELL
TN16 1PS (2m S of Westerham, off B2026)
☎ 01732 866368 (info line) & 868381
🖷 01732 868193
e-mail: kchxxx@smpt.ntrust.org.uk

The former home of Sir Winston Churchill is filled with reminders of the great statesman, from his hats and uniforms to gifts presented by Stalin and Roosevelt. There are paintings of Churchill and other works by notable artists, and also many paintings by Churchill himself.
Times: Open Apr-4 Nov, house, garden & studio, Wed-Sun 11-5, BH Mon 11-7. Open BH Mons & Tue in Jul/Aug. Last admission 4.15pm (5.30pm BH) **Fee:** House, Garden & studio £5.60 (ch £2.80). Gardens and studio only £2.80 (ch £1.40). Family ticket £14. **Facilities:** 🅿 ✗ licensed ♿ (2 steps to lift, grounds partially accessible, parking) toilets for disabled shop 🐾 (ex in garden on lead) 🐾 ☕

▥ CHATHAM   Map 05 TQ76

FORT AMHERST
Dock Rd ME4 4UB (adjacent to A231 dock road, 0.5m from Chatham Dockyard)
☎ 01634 847747   🖷 01634 847747
e-mail: enquires@fortamherst.org.uk

A fine Georgian fortress set in over 15 acres of attractive parkland. A fascinating collection of caves, tunnels, gun-batteries and barracks gives visitors an insight into the life of the Napoleonic soldier. Please telephone for details of special events, including historic re-enactments.
Times: Open daily 10-5 **Fee:** £4 (ch, pen & students £2) Family tickets £10. **Facilities:** 🅿 ☕ ♿ (wheelchair provided, road access up to fort) toilets for disabled shop 🐾 (ex guide dogs) ☕

THE HISTORIC DOCKYARD

ME4 4TZ (short distance from M25. Signposted as 'Historic Dockyard' from junct 1, 3 & 4 of M2)
☎ 01634 823800   🖷 01634 823801
e-mail: info@chdt.org.uk

The Historic Dockyard celebrates over 400 years of naval history in one 80-acre site. Exhibits include Battle Ships with WWII destroyer *HMS Cavalier* and the spy sub *Ocelot*. Lifeboat with a display of 15 full size boats, archive film and artefacts; and Wooden Walls which looks at the life of a carpenter's apprentice in the 18th century. The navel architecture is spectacular.
Times: Open Apr-Oct, daily 10-5; Feb, Mar & Nov, Wed, Sat & Sun 10-4. **Fee:** £8.50 (ch 5-16 £5.50, student & pen £6.50). Family ticket (2 adults & 4 ch) £22.50. **Facilities:** 🅿 ☕ ✗ licensed ♿ (wheelchair available, Braille guides) toilets for disabled shop ☕

▥ CHIDDINGSTONE   Map 05 TQ54

CHIDDINGSTONE CASTLE
TN8 7AD (off B2027, at Bough Beech)
☎ 01892 870347

The `castle' is a 17th-century house, almost completely rebuilt in the castle style c1800 by William Atkinson. It contains Stewart and Jacobite paintings and other relics, Egyptian and Oriental antiquities, and a fine collection of Japanese lacquer and swords. The interior has recently been refurbished with extra rooms open to visitors. The grounds are now undergoing restoration.
Times: Open Apr-May, Oct, Easter & Public Holidays, Jun-Sep, Wed-Fri & Sun. Weekdays 2-5.30; Sun & BH 11.30-5.30. **Fee:** £4, (ch 5-15 £2). Party 20+ by prior arrangement. **Facilities:** 🅿 ☕ ♿ shop 🐾 (ex guide dogs on lead)

▥ DEAL   Map 05 TR35

DEAL CASTLE
Victoria Rd CT14 7BA (SW of town centre)
☎ 01304 372762

This huge, austere structure, shaped like a Tudor rose, was an important part of the coastal defences built by Henry VIII. Its unrelenting walls are rounded to deflect cannon shot and inside, the dark passages tell the reality of garrison life.
Times: Open all year, Apr-Oct, daily 10-6 (Oct 10-5); Nov-Mar, Wed-Sun 10-4. Closed 24-26 Dec & 1 Jan. **Fee:** £3.10 (ch 5-15 £1.60, ch u5 free, con £2.30). Personal stereo tour included in admission price. **Facilities:** ♿ shop ♨

WALMER CASTLE

Walmer, Kingsdown Rd CT14 7LJ (1m S on coast, off A258)
☎ 01304 364288

Of similar design to Deal Castle, Walmer was also part of the defences of Tudor England. It is the official residence of the Lord Warden of the Cinque Ports (Dover, Sandwich, Hythe, Romney and Hastings were
contd.

the original five), an honorary post now held by Queen Elizabeth the Queen Mother.
Times: Open all year, Apr-Oct, daily 10-6 (Oct 10-5); Nov-28 Mar, Wed-Sun 10-4 (wknds only Jan-Feb). Closed 24-26 Dec, 1 Jan & when Lord Warden in residence Jan & Feb. **Fee:** £4.80 (ch 5-15 £2.40, under 5's free, con £3.60). Personal stereo tour included in admission price, also available for the partially sighted, those with learning difficulties. P ♿ shop (in certain areas)

DOVER — Map 05 TR34

Crabble Corn Mill

Lower Rd CT17 0UY (Exit M20 onto A20 into Dover. Follow brown tourist signs)
☎ 01304 823292
e-mail: mill@ccmt.freeserve.co.uk

Visit this beautifully restored working Kentish water mill dating from 1812. Regular demonstrations of waterwheel working and making stoneground wholemeal flour from Kentish organic wheat. Flour for sale, also home-baked produce in café. Exhibition space displays work of local artists and craftspeople.
Times: Open all year, Etr-Jun & Sep, Sat & Sun 11-5; Jul-Aug, Wed-Sun 11-5; Winter Sun 11-5. **Fee:** £2 (ch 15 £1, students & pen £1.50). Family ticket £5. **Facilities:** P shop (ex guide/hearing dogs)

Dover Castle & Secret Wartime Tunnels

CT16 1HU
☎ 01304 201628

A giant among England's castles, set high on the famous white cliffs, Dover Castle traces its history back to the Iron Age, and many relics of its different periods remain. The underground tunnel system, nicknamed Hellfire Corner, was originally built in medieval times.
Times: Open all year, Apr-Sep, daily 10-6 (Oct 10-5); Nov-Mar, daily 10-4. Closed 24-26 Dec & 1 Jan. **Fee:** £7 (ch 5-15 £3.50, under 5's free, con £5.30). **Facilities:** P ✕ ♿ shop (in certain areas)

Old Town Gaol

Dover Town Hall, Biggin St CT16 1DL (Follow brown tourist signs from town centre)
☎ 01304 201200 01304 201200
Times: Open all year, Tue-Sat 10-4.30, Sun 2-4.30. (Closed Mon & Tue, Oct-May). Telephone 01304 202723 for further information.
Facilities: P (charged) ♿ shop (ex guide dogs) *Details not confirmed for 2002*

Roman Painted House

New St CT17 9AJ (follow A20 to York St bypass, located in town centre)
☎ 01304 203279

Visit five rooms of a Roman hotel built 1800 years ago, famous for its unique, well-preserved Bacchic frescos. The Roman underfloor heating system and part of a late-Roman defensive wall are also on view. There are extensive displays on Roman Dover, and special events are held throughout the year.
Times: Open Apr-Sep, Tue-Sun 10-5, also BH Mon & Mon Jul & Aug. **Fee:** £2 (ch & pen 80p) **Facilities:** P ♿ (touch table, glass panels on gallery for wheelchairs) shop

DUNGENESS — 05 TR01

Dungeness Power Stations' Visitor Centre

Map TN29 9PP (follow A259 to New Romney, right turn signposted B2075 to Lydd, power station signposted)
☎ 01797 321815 01797 321844
Times: Open Mar-Oct, daily, 10-4. Regular Tours of A & B power stations available. No children under 5 allowed on tour. Nov-Feb by appointment only. **Facilities:** P ♿ (information centre only/shortened tour by appointment) toilets for disabled shop (ex guide dogs)
Details not confirmed for 2002

DYMCHURCH — Map 05 TR12

Martello Tower

TN29 0NU (access from High St not seafront)
Times: Telephone 01304 211067 for opening details. **Facilities:**
Details not confirmed for 2002

EYNSFORD — Map 05 TQ56

Eynsford Castle

(off A225)
Times: Open all year, Mar-Sep, daily 10-6; Oct-Feb, daily 10-4.
Facilities: P ♿ *Details not confirmed for 2002*

Lullingstone Castle

DA4 0JA (1m SW of Eynsford via A225 & Lullingstone Roman villa)
☎ 01322 862114 01322 862115

The house was altered extensively in Queen Anne's time, and has fine state rooms and beautiful grounds. The 15th-century gate tower was one of the first gatehouses in England to be made entirely of bricks,

and there is a church with family monuments. Please telephone for details of special events.
Times: Open, House May-Aug, Sat, Sun & BH 2-6. Parties by arrangement. **Fee:** House & Gardens £5 (ch £2 & pen £4) family £10. **Facilities:** ⓟ & shop ⚹

LULLINGSTONE ROMAN VILLA
DA4 0JA (0.5m SW off A225)
☎ 01322 863467

The excavation of this Roman villa in 1939 uncovered one of the most exciting archaeological finds of that century. These remarkable villa remains include wonderful mosaic floors, wall paintings and one of the earliest Christian chapels.
Times: Open all year, Apr-Sep, daily 10-6 (Oct 10-5); Nov-28 Mar, daily 10-4. Closed 24-26 Dec & 1 Jan. **Fee:** £2.60 (ch 5-15 £1.30, ch u5 free, con £2). Personal stereo tour included in admission price.
Facilities: ⓟ ⚹ ♨

🏛 FAVERSHAM — Map 05 TR06
FLEUR DE LIS HERITAGE CENTRE
10-13 Preston St ME13 8NS (3 minutes' drive from M2 junct 6)
☎ 01795 534542
e-mail: faversham@btinternet.com

Recently expanded and updated, and housed in 16th-century premises, the Centre features colourful displays and room settings that vividly evoke the 2000-year history of Faversham. Special features include the 'Gunpowder Experience' and a working old-style village telephone exchange, one of only two remaining in Britain. In July, during the Faversham Open House Scheme, over 20 historic properties in the town are opened to the public.
Times: Open all year, Mon-Sat, 10-4; Sun 10-1. **Fee:** £2 (ch & pen £1) **Facilities:** ⓟ (200 yds) & toilets for disabled shop

🏛 FOLKESTONE — Map 05 TR23
RUSSIAN SUBMARINE
South Quay, Folkestone Harbour CT20 1QH (adjacent to Hoverspeed Seacat Terminal)
☎ 01303 240400
e-mail: info@sovietsub.co.uk

The fascinating history of U475 (known as The Black Widow) is shrouded in secrecy. Only the select few, the Chiefs of Staff of the former Soviet Navy, know the full history. Was it part of their plan for the U475 to patrol the waters off Cuba after the successful deployment of missiles on the island in 1963? A mysterious and sometimes chilling day out.
Times: Open all year, Mon-Fri 10-dusk, wknds 10-6. Closed 25 Dec. **Fee:** £3.95 (ch £2.50 con £3.50). Family ticket £10. Party. **Facilities:** ⓟ (20mtrs) shop ⚹ 🍴

🏛 FORDWICH — Map 05 TR15
TOWN HALL
The Square CT2 0DW (off A28)
☎ 01227 710756 🖷 01227 713773
Times: Open Etr, Jun-Sep, Sun 2-4 & Wed in Aug 2-4. **Facilities:** ⓟ
Details not confirmed for 2002

🏛 GILLINGHAM — Map 05 TQ76
ROYAL ENGINEERS MUSEUM
Prince Arthur Rd ME4 4UG (follow brown signs from Gillingham & Chatham town centres)
☎ 01634 406397 🖷 01634 822371
e-mail: remuseum.rhqre@gtnet.gov.uk

The museum covers the diverse and sometimes surprising work of the Royal Engineers. Learn about the first military divers, photographers, aviators and surveyors; see memorabilia relating to General Gordon and Field Marshal Lord Kitchener, Wellington's battle map from Waterloo and a Harrier jump-jet. The superb medal displays include 25 Victoria Crosses.
Times: Open all year, Mon-Thu 10-5, Sat-Sun & BH Mon 11.30-5. (Closed Good Fri, 25-26 Dec & 1 Jan). Friday by appointment only. **Fee:** £3.50 (ch, pen & UB40s £2). Family ticket £9. Guided tour £5. Party 15+ £2.50 & £1.50. School groups £1 per child. **Facilities:** ⓟ & (help available if required, chair lift to upper level) toilets for disabled shop ⚹ (ex guide dogs) 🍴

🏛 GOUDHURST — Map 05 TQ73
FINCHCOCKS
TN17 1HH (off A262)
☎ 01580 211702 🖷 01580 211007
Times: Open Etr-Sep, Sun & BH Mon 2-6; Aug, Wed, Wed, Thu & Sun only 2-6. Private groups on other days by appointment Apr-Oct.
Facilities: ⓟ 🍽 ✗ licensed & shop garden centre ⚹ (ex guide dogs)
Details not confirmed for 2002

🏛 GROOMBRIDGE PLACE — Map 05 TQ53
GROOMBRIDGE PLACE GARDENS & ENCHANTED FOREST
TN3 9QG (turn off A264 onto B2110, 0.5m from Langton Green. Follow signs to Groombridge. Entrance at bottom of Groombridge Hill)
☎ 01892 861444 (office) & 863999 (info line)
🖷 01892 863996
e-mail: office@groombridge.co.uk

Groombridge Place is surrounded by magnificent parkland and has stunning 17th-century walled gardens with extensive herbaceous borders flanking a moat. Above the walled gardens and estate vineyard is the Enchanted Forest, where there is much to entertain

contd.

children and teenagers. Adventure and themed playgrounds, gardens, and canal boat rides offer something for everyone.
Times: Open 29 Mar-27 Oct, daily 9-6. **Fee:** £7.50 (ch 3-12 & pen £6.50) Family ticket (2ad + 2ch 3-12) £25. Groups 20+. Prices subject to change on event days. **Facilities:** ▣ ▆ Ġ (ramps, canal boat) toilets for disabled shop ✱ (ex guide/hearing dogs) ▅

⛫ HAWKINGE
Map 05 TR23
KENT BATTLE OF BRITAIN MUSEUM
Aerodrome Rd CT18 7AG (off A260, 1m along Aerodrome road)
☎ 01303 893140
Times: Open Etr-Sep, daily 10-5; Oct, daily 11-4. Closed Nov-Etr. Last admission 1 hour before closing. **Facilities:** ▣ Ġ shop ✱ (ex guide dogs) *Details not confirmed for 2002*

⛫ HEVER
Map 05 TQ44
HEVER CASTLE & GARDENS
TN8 7NG (M25 junct 5 or 6, 3m SE of Edenbridge, off B2026)
☎ 01732 865224 🖹 01732 866796
e-mail: mail@hevercastle.co.uk
Times: Open Mar-Nov, daily. Castle 12-6, Gardens 11-6. Last admission 5pm. (Closes 4pm Mar & Nov). **Facilities:** ▣ ▆ ✕ licensed Ġ (wheelchairs available, book in advance) toilets for disabled shop garden centre ✱ (ex on leads in grounds) *Details not confirmed for 2002* ▅

⛫ HYTHE
Map 05 TR13
ROMNEY, HYTHE & DYMCHURCH RAILWAY
TN28 8PL (off M20 junct 11, off A259 signed New Romney)
☎ 01797 362353 & 363256 🖹 01797 363591
e-mail: 106104.245@compuserve.com

Times: Open daily Etr-Sep, also wknds in Mar & Oct. For times apply to: The Manager, RH & DR, New Romney, Kent. **Facilities:** ▣ (charged) ▆ Ġ (stairlift to Toy & Model Museum) toilets for disabled shop (Dymchurch & Dungeness high season only) *Details not confirmed for 2002*

⛫ IGHTHAM
Map 05 TQ55
IGHTHAM MOTE
TN15 0NT (2.5m S off A227, 6m E of Sevenoaks)
☎ 01732 810378 & 811145 (info line)
🖹 01732 811029
e-mail: kimxxx@smtp.ntrust.org.uk

This moated manor house, nestling in a sunken valley, dates from 1340. The main features of the house span many centuries and include the Great Hall, old chapel and crypt, Tudor chapel with painted ceiling, drawing room with Jacobean fireplace, frieze and 18th-century handpainted Chinese wallpaper and the billiards room. There is an extensive garden and interesting walks in the surrounding woodland.
Times: Open Apr-Nov, daily ex Tue & Sat, 11-5.30. Pre-booked parties wkday am only. Open Good Fri. Last admission 4.30pm. **Fee:** £5 (ch £2.50). Family ticket £12.50. **Facilities:** ▣ ▆ Ġ (wheelchairs available, special parking ask at ticket office) toilets for disabled shop ✱ ✖

⛫ LAMBERHURST
Map 05 TQ63
BAYHAM ABBEY
TN3 8DE (off B2169, 2m W in East Sussex)
☎ 01892 890381

Set in the wooded Teise Valley, these ruins date back to the 13th century and include parts of the old church, cloisters and gatehouse.
Times: Open Apr-Sep, daily 10-6 (Oct 10-5). Nov-28Mar, wknds 10-4. Closed 24-26 Dec & 1 Jan **Fee:** £2.20 (ch 5-15 £1.10 ch u5 free, con £1.70). **Facilities:** ▣ Ġ ✿

SCOTNEY CASTLE GARDEN
TN3 8JN (1m S, of Lamberhurst on A21)
☎ 01892 891081 🖹 01892 890110
e-mail: kscxxx@smtp.ntrust.org.uk

The beautiful gardens at Scotney were planned in the 19th century around the remains of the old, moated Scotney Castle. There is something to see at every time of year, with spring flowers followed by rhododendrons, azaleas and a mass of roses, and then superb autumn colours.
Times: Open Garden: Apr-end Oct. Old Castle open May-mid Sep, Wed-Sun, 11-6 or sunset if earlier. BH Mon 11-6. (Closed Good Fri). Last admission 1hr before closing. **Fee:** Telephone for details. **Facilities:** ▣ Ġ (wheelchair available) toilets for disabled shop ✱ (ex guide & hearing dogs) ✖ ▅

⛫ LEEDS
For Leeds Castle see Maidstone

⛫ LYDD
Map 05 TR02
RSPB NATURE RESERVE
Boulderwall Farm, Dungeness Rd TN29 9PN (off Lydd to Dungeness road, 1m SE of Lydd)
☎ 01797 320588 🖹 01797 321962
e-mail: dungeness@rspb.org.uk

This coastal reserve comprises 2,106 acres of shingle beach and flooded pits. An excellent place to watch

contd.

breeding terns, gulls and other water birds. Wheatears, great crested and little grebes also nest here, and outside the breeding season there are large flocks of teals, shovelers, and goldeneyes, goosanders, smews and both Slavonian and red-necked grebes.
Times: Open daily 9am-9pm (or sunset if earlier). Visitor Centre daily 10-5 Mar-Oct, 10-4 Nov-Feb. (Closed 25 & 26 Dec). **Fee:** £3 (ch £1, concessions £2). Family ticket £6. **Facilities:** ▣ ໕ (access by car to some hides) toilets for disabled shop 🐾 (ex guide dogs) 🍴

🏛 LYMPNE   Map 05 TR13
PORT LYMPNE WILD ANIMAL PARK, MANSION & GARDEN
CT21 4PD (off M20 junct 11, follow brown tourist signs)
☎ 01303 264647   📠 01303 264944
e-mail: karenw@howletts.net

The late John Aspinall's 300-acre wild animal park houses hundreds of rare animals: Indian elephants, rhinos, wolves, bison, black and snow leopards, Siberian and Indian tigers, gorillas and monkeys. The mansion designed by Sir Herbert Baker is surrounded by 15 acres of spectacular gardens. Inside, the most notable features include the recently restored Rex Whistler Tent Room, Moroccan Patio and hexagonal library where the Treaty of Paris was signed after World War I.
Times: Open all year, daily fr 10am, last admission 5pm summer, 3.30pm winter. (Closed 25 Dec). **Fee:** £9.80 (ch 4-14 & pen £7.80). Family ticket £28. **Facilities:** ▣ 🍴 ✗ licensed ໕ (very limited access for disabled) toilets for disabled shop 🐾 🍴

🏛 MAIDSTONE   Map 05 TQ75
LEEDS CASTLE
ME17 1PL (7m E of Maidstone at junct 8 of M20/A20)
☎ 01622 765400   📠 01622 735616
e-mail: enquires@leeds-castle.co.uk

Set on two islands in the centre of a lake, Leeds Castle has been called the 'loveliest castle in the world', and was home to six medieval Queens of England, as well as being Henry VIII's Royal Palace. Among the

treasures inside are many paintings, tapestries and furnishings.
Times: Open all year daily, Mar-Oct 10-5 (Castle 11-5.30). Nov-Feb 10-3 (Castle 10.15-3.30). **Fee:** Castle, Park & Gardens £10 (ch 4-15 £6.50, students & pen £8.50); Park & gardens £8.50 (ch 4-15 £5.20, students & pen £7). Family ticket £29, Park & gardens only £24. Party 15+.
Facilities: ▣ 🍴 ✗ licensed ໕ (Braille information, induction loops & wheelchair, lift) toilets for disabled shop garden centre 🐾 (ex guide dogs) 🍴

MAIDSTONE MUSEUM & BENTLIF ART GALLERY
Saint Faith's St ME14 1LH (close to County Hall & Maidstone East railway station)
☎ 01622 754497   📠 01622 685022

Set in an Elizabethan manor house which has been much extended over the years, this museum houses an outstanding collection of fine and applied arts, including watercolours, furniture, ceramics, and a collection of Japanese art and artefacts. The museum of the Queen's Own Royal West Kent Regiment is also housed here. Please apply for details of temporary exhibitions, workshops etc.
Times: Open all year, Mon-Sat 10-5.15, Sun & BH Mon 11-4. (Closed 25-26 Dec). **Fee:** Free. **Facilities:** ▣ (50 yds) 🍴 ໕ shop 🐾 (ex guide dogs)

MUSEUM OF KENT LIFE
Lock Ln, Sandling ME14 3AU (from A229, follow signs for Aylesford. From M20 junct 6 onto A229 Maidstone road)
☎ 01622 763936   📠 01622 662024
e-mail: enquiries@museum-kentlife.co.uk

Kent's award-winning open air museum is home to an outstanding collection of historic buildings which house exhibitions on life in Kent over the last 100 years. An early 20th-century village hall and reconstruction of cottages from the 17th & 20th-centuries are more recent buildings to be viewed.
Times: Open Mar-end Oct, daily 10-5.30. **Fee:** £4.70 (concessions £3.20). Family ticket £14. **Facilities:** ▣ 🍴 ✗ licensed ໕ (wheelchairs available, ramps) toilets for disabled shop 🍴

Tyrwhitt Drake Museum of Carriages

The Archbishop's Stables, Mill St ME15 6YE (close to River Medway & Archbishop's Palace, just off A229 in town centre)

☎ 01622 754497 ▤ 01622 682451

A wide array of horse-drawn carriages and vehicles is displayed in these late-medieval stables, which are interesting in themselves. The exhibits include state, official and private carriages, and some are on loan from royal collections.
Times: Open all year, Apr-Oct daily 10.30-4.30. Last admission 3.45.
Fee: £1.60 (ch & pen £1.05). **Facilities:** P (50 yds) & shop ✻ (ex guide dogs)

⛪ MINSTER-IN-THANET
Minster Abbey

Map 05 TR36

CT12 4HF (turn off A253 at Minster rdbt. Downhill through village. Turn left at St. Mary's Church)

☎ 01843 821254

One of the first nunneries in England was built on this site in the 7th century. Rebuilt in later centuries, it is still home to a religious community, run by Benedictine nuns. The ruins of the old abbey and the cloisters are open to the public. One wing dates back to 1027, and there is a 12th-century carving of Christ.
Times: Open all year, May-Sep, Mon-Fri 11-12 & 2.30-4, Sat 11-12; Oct-Apr, Mon-Sat 11-12. **Fee:** Free. **Facilities:** P & toilets for disabled shop (ex guide dogs)

⛪ PENSHURST
Penshurst Place & Gardens

Map 05 TQ54

TN11 8DG (from M25 junct 5 take A21 Hastings road then exit at Hildenborough, then follow signs)

☎ 01892 870307 ▤ 01892 870866
e-mail: enquiries@penshurstplace.com

Built between 1340 and 1345, the original house is perfectly preserved. Enlarged by successive owners during the 15th, 16th and 17th centuries, the great variety of architectural styles creates a dramatic backdrop for the extensive collections of English, French and Italian furniture, tapestries and paintings. The chestnut-beamed Baron's Hall is the oldest and finest in the country, and the house is set in magnificent formal gardens. There is a toy museum, venture playground, woodland trail and 10 acres of walled formal gardens.
Times: Open: House Apr-Oct daily. Gardens, Grounds & venture playground open 10.30-6 and also wknds from 4 Mar. **Fee:** House & Grounds £6 (ch 5-16 £4, pen & students £5.50) Family (2 adults & 2 ch) £16. Grounds only £4.50 (ch 5-16 £3.50, pen & students £4) Family (2 adults & 2 ch) £13. Party 20+. Garden season ticket £25.
Facilities: P ✕ licensed & (ramp into Barons Hall, Braille room guides) toilets for disabled shop garden centre ✻ (ex guide dogs) ☜

⛪ RAMSGATE
Maritime Museum

Map 05 TR36

Clock House, Pier Yard, Royal Harbour CT11 8LS (follow Harbour signs)

☎ 01843 587765 & 570622 ▤ 01843 582359
e-mail: museum@ekmt.fsnet.co.uk

The Maritime Museum Ramsgate is housed in the early 19th-century Clock House, and contains four galleries depicting various aspects of the maritime heritage of the East Kent area. The adjacent restored dry dock and floating exhibits from the museum's historic ship collection include the steam tug *Cervia* and the Dunkirk little ship, motor yacht *Sundowner*.
Times: Open Mar-Sep 10am-5pm. Oct-Mar 4 days a week 9.30am-4.30pm. (Closed Mons ex during school holidays). **Fee:** Combined ticket for museum & steam tug £1.50. (ch & pen 75p). Family £4.
Facilities: P (charged) & (restricted) shop ✻

⛪ RECULVER
Reculver Towers & Roman Fort

Map 05 TR26

CT6 6SU (3m E of Herne Bay)

☎ 01227 740676
Times: Open any reasonable time. **Facilities:** P & ✻ ⛃ *Details not confirmed for 2002*

⛪ RICHBOROUGH
Richborough Castle

Map 05 TR36

CT13 9JW (1.5m N of Sandwich off A257)

☎ 01304 612013

Now landlocked in the Kent countryside, Richborough Castle once stood on the coast, the bridgehead from which the Romans launched their invasion of Britain in AD43. The foundations of the great monumental archway can still be seen, and the remains of the massive wall and defensive ditches vividly convey the power of the ancient Roman empire.
Times: Open Apr-Oct, daily 10-6 (Oct 10-5); Nov-Mar, 10-4 Wed-Sun (wkends only Dec-Feb). **Fee:** £2.70 (ch 5-15 £1.40, under 5's free, con £2). **Facilities:** P & ✻ (in certain areas) ⛃

⛪ ROCHESTER
Charles Dickens Centre

Map 05 TQ76

Eastgate House, High St ME1 1EW

☎ 01634 844176 ▤ 01634 827980
Times: Open all year, daily 10-5.30. (Closed Xmas). Last admission 4.45pm. **Facilities:** P (250 yds) shop ✻ *Details not confirmed for 2002* ☜

GUILDHALL MUSEUM
High St ME1 1PY (Follow signs from A2 to Rochester city centre, museum is at N end of High St)
☎ 01634 848717 ▤ 01634 832919

Housed in two adjacent buildings, one dating from 1687 and the other from 1909. The collections are arranged chronologically from Prehistory to the Victorian and Edwardian periods. They cover local history and archæology, fine and decorative art. There is a gallery devoted to the prison hulks of the River Medway. A programme of temporary exhibitions.
Times: Open all year, daily 10-4.30. Last admissions 4 (Closed Xmas & New Year). **Fee:** Free. **Facilities:** ℙ (250 yds) & shop ⍩ (ex guide & hearing dogs)

ROCHESTER CASTLE
ME1 1SX (by Rochester Bridge, A2, M2 junct 1)
☎ 01634 402276
Times: Open all year, Apr-Sep, daily 10-6; Oct, daily 10-5; Nov-Mar, daily 10-4. (Closed 24-26 Dec & 1 Jan). **Facilities:** shop ▦ *Details not confirmed for 2002*

⛫ ROLVENDEN   Map 05 TQ83
C M BOOTH COLLECTION OF HISTORIC VEHICLES
Falstaff Antiques, 63 High St TN17 4LP (on A28)
☎ 01580 241234

Not just vehicles, but various other items of interest connected with transport. There is a unique collection of three-wheel Morgan cars, dating from 1913, and the only known Humber tri-car of 1904, as well as a 1929 Morris van, a 1936 Bampton caravan, motorcycles and bicycles. There is also a toy and model car display.
Times: Open all year, Mon-Sat 10-6. (Closed 25-26 Dec). **Fee:** £1.50 (ch 75p) **Facilities:** ℙ (roadside) shop ▰

⛫ SEVENOAKS   Map 05 TQ55
KNOLE
TN15 0RP (S end of Sevenoaks, E of A225)
☎ 01732 462100 & 450608 (info line)
▤ 01732 465528
e-mail: kknxxx@smtp.ntrust.org.uk

In the 15th-century Thomas Bourchier, Archbishop of Canterbury, transformed Knole from a simple medieval manor house into a palace. A century later Henry VIII extended it to even grander proportions. In the middle of the 16th century Elizabeth I gave it to Thomas Sackville and the Sackvilles kept the house for ten generations.
Times: Open Apr-Oct, telephone for details. **Fee:** £5 (ch £2.50). Garden £1 (ch 50p). Deer Park free to pedestrians. Family ticket £12.50. Parking £2.50 per car. **Facilities:** ℙ (charged) ▰ & toilets for disabled shop ⍩ (ex in park on lead) ⛫ ▰

⛫ SISSINGHURST   Map 05 TQ73
SISSINGHURST CASTLE GARDEN
TN17 2AB (1m E of Sissinghurst village on A262)
☎ 01580 710700 ▤ 01580 710702
e-mail: ksixxx@smtp.ntrust.org.uk

The Tudor mansion of Sissinghurst Castle was bought in a neglected state in 1930 by Sir Harold Nicolson and his wife, the writer Vita Sackville-West. They set about restoring house and gardens and the gardens now rank among the most attractive and popular in England.
Times: Open: Gardens Apr-14 Oct, Tue-Fri 1-6.30; Sat, Sun & Good Fri 10-6.30 (last admission 5.30) Closed Mon incl BH Mon. Limited capacity timed tickets in operation so visitors may have to wait for admission, garden may be closed when its capacity has been reached. Garden is least crowded in Apr, Sep & Oct. **Fee:** £6.50 **Facilities:** ℙ ✕ licensed & (Admission restricted to 2 wheelchairs at any one time) toilets for disabled shop ⍩ (ex guide dogs) ⛫ ▰

⛫ SITTINGBOURNE   Map 05 TQ96
DOLPHIN SAILING BARGE MUSEUM
Crown Quay Ln ME10 3SN (N on A2, signed)
☎ 01795 423215

The museum presents the history of the Thames spritsail sailing barge; many were built along the banks of Milton Creek. Tools of the trade, photographs and associated artefacts can be seen at the barge yard along with the sailing barge *Cambria*. Privately owned barges are repaired here.
Times: Open Etr-Oct, Sun & BHs 11-5. Other times by arrangement. **Fee:** £1.50 (concession £1). **Facilities:** ℙ & toilets for disabled shop

⛫ SMALLHYTHE   Map 05 TQ83
SMALLHYTHE PLACE
TN30 7NG (2m S of Tenterden, on E of B2082)
☎ 01580 762334 ▤ 01580 762334
e-mail: ksmxxx@smtp.ntrust.org.uk

Once a Tudor harbour master's house, this half-timbered, 16th-century building was Dame Ellen Terry's last home, and is now a museum of Ellen Terry memorabilia. The barn is now a theatre and is open most days courtesy of the Barn Theatre Society.
Times: Open Apr-Oct, Sat-Wed 1.30-6 or dusk if earlier, also Good Fri. Last admission 30 mins before closing. The Barn Theatre may be closed some days at short notice. **Fee:** £3.20 (ch £1.60). Family ticket £8. **Facilities:** ℙ & (album of descriptions & photos of upstairs) ⍩ (ex guide dogs) ⛫

⛫ SWINGFIELD MINNIS   Map 05 TR24
THE BUTTERFLY CENTRE
McFarlanes Garden Centre CT15 7HX (on A260 by junction with Elham-Lydden road)
☎ 01303 844244

A tropical greenhouse garden with scores of colourful free-flying butterflies from all over the world among exotic plants such as bougainvillea, oleander and banana. The temperate section houses British butterflies and some rarer varieties.
Times: Open Apr-1 Oct, daily 10-5. Closed Easter Sunday. **Fee:** £2 (ch £1.25 & pen £1.50). Family ticket (2ad+2ch) £5.50. **Facilities:** ℙ ▰ & shop garden centre ⍩ (ex guide dogs) ▰

⛪ TUNBRIDGE WELLS   Map 05 TQ53

A DAY AT THE WELLS
The Corn Exchange, The Pantiles TN2 5QJ (accessible from A26/A21/A267).
☎ 01892 546545   📠 01892 513857

The legacy of the Georgians surrounds the visitor to Royal Tunbridge Wells. This is a journey to discover the essence of life in this most English of Georgian towns. Experience the sights, sounds and smells of a summer's day on the Pantiles in the 1740s.
Times: Open daily, Apr-Oct 10-5, Nov-Mar 10-4. Closed 25 Dec. **Fee:** £5.50 (ch & pen/student £4.50). **Facilities:** 🅿 (charged) 🍽 & (specially designed flat route) toilets for disabled shop 🐾 (ex guide dogs) 🍴

TUNBRIDGE WELLS MUSEUM AND ART GALLERY
Civic Centre, Mount Pleasant TN1 1JN (adjacent to Town Hall, off A264)
☎ 01892 554171 & 526121   📠 01892 534227

The museum displays local history, along with Tunbridge ware, archæology, toys and dolls, and domestic and agricultural bygones. The art gallery has regularly changing art and craft exhibitions and touring displays from British and European museums.
Times: Open all year, daily 9.30-5. (Closed Sun, BH's & Etr Sat). **Fee:** Free. **Facilities:** 🅿 (200 yds) & shop 🐾 (ex guide dogs)

⛪ UPNOR   Map 05 TQ77

UPNOR CASTLE
ME2 4XG (on unclass road off A228)
☎ 01634 718742
Times: Open Apr-Sep, daily 10-6. **Facilities:** 🅿 & 🐾 (in certain areas) 🎫 *Details not confirmed for 2002*

⛪ WESTERHAM   Map 05 TQ45

QUEBEC HOUSE
TN16 1TD (at E end of village on N side of A25 facing junct with B2026 Edenbridge Road.)
☎ 01892 890651   📠 01892 890110

Westerham was the birthplace of General Wolfe, who spent his childhood in this multi-gabled, square brick house, now renamed Quebec House. The house probably dates from the 16th century and was extended and altered in the 17th century. An exhibition on Wolfe and the Quebec campaign.
Times: Open Apr-Oct, Tue & Sun only 2-6 (last admission 5.30pm). Parties by written arrangement. **Fee:** Telephone 0870 458 4000 for prices. **Facilities:** 🅿 (150m) & toilets for disabled 🐾 🐾

SQUERRYES COURT MANOR HOUSE & GARDENS
TN16 1SJ (0.5m W of town centre, signed off A25)
☎ 01959 562345 & 563118   📠 01959 565949
e-mail: squerryescourt@squerryes.co.uk

This beautiful manor house, built in 1681, has been the home of the Wardes since 1731. It contains a fine collection of pictures, furniture, porcelain and tapestries. The lovely garden was landscaped in the 18th century and has a lake and woodland walks.
Times: Open Apr-Sep any day for pre-booked parties 20+. **Fee:** House & grounds £4.20 (ch 14 £2.50 & pen £3.80). Grounds £2.50 (ch 14 £1.50 & pen £2.20) **Facilities:** 🅿 🍽 ✗ licensed & (telephone in advance, part of grounds accessible) shop 🐾 (ex on leads in grounds)

⛪ WEST MALLING   Map 05 TQ65

ST LEONARD'S TOWER
ME19 6PE (on unclass road W of A228)
Times: Open any reasonable time for exterior viewing. Contact West Malling Parish Council for interior viewing - 01732 870872.
& 🎫 *Details not confirmed for 2002*

Lancashire

Lancashire was at the centre of the British cotton industry in the 19th century, which lead to the urbanisation of great tracts of the area. The cotton boom came and went, but the industrial profile remains.

These days Preston is the county's administrative headquarters, and is part of the Central Lancashire New Town, along with Fulwood, Bamber Bridge, Leyland and Chorley. Preston was also the birthplace of Oscar-winning animator Nick Park, creator of Wallace and Gromit.

The former county town, Lancaster, boasts one of the younger English universities, dating from 1964. Other towns, built up to accommodate the mill-workers with back-to-back terraced houses, are Burnley, Blackburn, Rochdale and Accrington. The last of these is home to Accrington Stanley FC one of the original members of the Football League.

Lancashire's resorts, Blackpool, Southport and Morecambe Bay, were developed to meet the leisure needs of the cotton mill town workers. Blackpool is the biggest and brashest, celebrated for its tower, miles of promenade, and the coloured light 'illuminations'. Amusements are taken very seriously here, day and night, though sadly the beach has suffered pollution in recent times.

Famous names from Lancashire include actor David Thewlis, Paul Heaton of The Beautiful South, and Gracie Fields, singer and actress of the 30s and 40s.

To get out of town, you can head for the Pennines, the 'backbone of England', a series of hills stretching from the Peak District National Park to the Scottish borders. To the north of the county is the Forest of Bowland, which despite its name is fairly open country, high up, with magnificent views.

Top: Forest of Bowland

🏛 BLACKPOOL   Map 07 SD33
BLACKPOOL ZOO PARK
East Park Dr FY3 8PP (signed off M55 junct 4)
☎ 01253 765027 📄 01253 798884

This modern zoo, built in 1972, houses over four
hundred animals within its 32 acres of landscaped
gardens. There is a miniature railway, the chance to
ride with dolphins in the 'Swimulator', a children's play
area, animal feeding times and keeper talks throughout
the day.
Times: Open all year daily, summer 10-6; winter 10-5 or dusk. (Closed
25 Dec). **Fee:** £6.50 (con £5 ch £4.50). Family (2ad & 3ch) £22.
Facilities: 🅿 💺 ✗ licensed ⧖ (wheelchair loan, braille factsheets,
sensory experiences) toilets for disabled shop 🎠 💬

🏛 CHARNOCK RICHARD   Map 07 SD51
CAMELOT THEME PARK
PR7 5LP (from M6 junct 27/28, or M61 junct 8 follow
brown tourist signs)
☎ 01257 453044 📄 01257 452320
e-mail: kingarthur@camelotthemepark.co.uk

Camelot Theme Park is based on the legend of King
Arthur and provides a full day out packed with
entertainment for all ages. The park has new
attractions for 2001, and a variety of live shows,
alongside the existing rides.
Times: Open Apr-Oct. Telephone for further details. **Fee:** £12 (ch over
1 metre £12, under 1metre free, pen & disabled £9) **Facilities:** 🅿 💺
⧖ (disabled car parking) toilets for disabled shop 🎠 (ex guide dogs)
💬

🏛 CHORLEY   Map 07 SD51
ASTLEY HALL MUSEUM & ART GALLERY
Astley Park PR7 1NP (2m W of Chorley off A581
Southport road)
☎ 01257 515555 📄 01257 515556
e-mail: astleyhall@lineone.net

A charming Tudor/Stuart building set in beautiful
parkland, this lovely Hall retains a comfortable `lived-

in' atmosphere. There are pictures and pottery to see,
as well as fine furniture and rare plasterwork ceilings.
Times: Open Apr-Oct, Tue-Sun 12-5; Nov-Mar Sat-Sun 12-4.
Fee: £2.95 (concessions £1.95). Family ticket £7.50. Party 10+.
Facilities: 🅿 (200 yds) ⧖ (video of upper floors, print/braille guide,
CD audio guide) shop 🎠 (ex guide dogs) 💬

🏛 CLITHEROE   Map 07 SD74
CLITHEROE CASTLE MUSEUM
Castle Gate, Castle St BB7 1BA (follow Clitheroe signs
from A59 by-pass. In town centre)
☎ 01200 424635

The museum has a good collection of carboniferous
fossils, and items of local interest. Displays include
local history and the industrial archaeology of the
Ribble Valley, while special features include the
restored Hacking ferry boat, printer's and clogger's
shops and Edwardian kitchen. The area is renowned
for its early 17th-century witches, and the museum has
a small display on witchcraft.
Times: Mar-Etr, Sat-Wed; Etr-Oct, daily inc BH; Nov, Dec & Feb, wknds
& school half terms. **Fee:** £1.60 (ch 25p, pen 75p). Family ticket £3.40
Facilities: 🅿 (500yds) (disabled only parking at establishment) ⧖
shop 🎠 (ex guide dogs)

🏛 LANCASTER   Map 07 SD46
CITY MUSEUM (ALSO 15 CASTLE HILL)
Market Sq LA1 1HT (In city centre, just off A6)
☎ 01524 64637 📄 01524 841692

The fine Georgian town hall is the setting for the
museum, which explores the history and archaeology
of the city from prehistoric and Roman times onwards.
Also housed here is the museum of the King's Own
Royal Lancaster Regiment. The Cottage Museum,
furnished in the style of an artisan's house of around
1820, faces Lancaster Castle.
Times: Open all year, Mon-Sat 10-5, (Closed 25 Dec-1 Jan). 15 Castle
Hill, Etr-Sep, daily 2-5. **Fee:** City Museum free. 15 Castle Hill 75p
(concessions 25p). **Facilities:** 🅿 (5 mins walk) ⧖ (ramp to
entrance/ground floor, 2 stairlifts) shop 🎠 (ex guide dogs)

LANCASTER MARITIME MUSEUM
St George's Quay LA1 1RB (close to M6, junct 33 & 34.
From A6 follow signs to Lancaster town centre)
☎ 01524 64637 📄 01524 841692
Times: Open all year, daily, Etr-Oct 11am-5pm; Nov-Etr 12.30-4pm.
Facilities: 🅿 💺 ⧖ (ramped access, lift to all floors, ground floor
entry) toilets for disabled shop 🎠 (ex guide dogs) *Details not
confirmed for 2002*

SHIRE HALL
Lancaster Castle, Castle Pde LA1 1YJ (follow brown tourist signs from M6 junct 33/34)
☎ 01524 64998 ▤ 01524 847914
e-mail: christine.goodier@
property.lancscc.gov.uk

Founded on the site of three Roman forts, Lancaster Castle dominates Castle Hill, above the River Lune. The Norman keep was built in about 1170 and King John added a curtain wall and Hadrian's Tower. The Shire Hall, noted for its Gothic revival design, contains a splendid display of heraldry. The Crown Court was notorious as having handed out the greatest number of death sentences of any court in the land.
Times: Open 17 Mar-15 Dec, daily 10.30 (1st tour)-4 (last tour). Court sittings permitting -it is advisable to telephone before visiting except in August or at weekends. **Fee:** £4 (ch, pen & students £2.50).
Facilities: ℙ (100m) (voucher system) & shop ✗ (ex guide dogs) ✑

⛫ LEIGHTON HALL   Map 07 SD47
LEIGHTON HALL
LA5 9ST (M6 junct 35 onto A6 & follow signs)
☎ 01524 734474 ▤ 01524 720357
e-mail: leightonhall@yahoo.co.uk

Early Gillow furniture is displayed among other treasures in the fine interior of this neo-Gothic mansion. Outside a large collection of birds of prey can be seen, and flying displays are given each afternoon. There are also fine gardens, a maze and a woodland walk.
Times: Open May-Sep, Sun, Tue-Fri & BH Mon from 2pm. For Aug only open from 12.30. (Last admission 4.30pm). **Fee:** £4 (ch 5-16 £2.70, pen £3.50). Family ticket £12. **Facilities:** ℙ ✑ & shop garden centre ✗ (ex guide dogs & in park)

⛫ LEYLAND   Map 07 SD52
BRITISH COMMERCIAL VEHICLE MUSEUM
King St PR5 1LE (0.75m from M6 junct 28)
☎ 01772 451011 ▤ 01772 623404
Times: Open 2 Apr-Sep, Sun, Tue & BH (Oct Sun only). **Facilities:** ℙ ✑ & (ramps to decked viewing area) toilets for disabled shop ✗ (ex guide dogs) *Details not confirmed for 2002*

⛫ LYTHAM ST ANNES   Map 07 SD32
TOY & TEDDY BEAR MUSEUM
373 Clifton Dr North FY8 2PA (350yds from town centre, on A584 towards Blackpool)
☎ 01253 713705

This museum has a collection of old toys arranged in five large rooms and the Toytown Arcade. Charming displays include: Teddy Bears' Picnic and Bears at the Seaside. Other attractions include a Mini Motor Museum, a collection of more than 200 dolls, 35 dolls' houses, toy trains, working layouts, Dinky cars, aeroplanes, meccano, books and games.
Times: Open all BHs & school holidays, daily 1-5; Jul-Aug, daily (ex Tue) 1-5. Winter open for groups & schools daily by appointment.
Fee: £2.95 (ch & pen £2.25) **Facilities:** ℙ & shop

⛫ MARTIN MERE   Map 07 SD41
WWT MARTIN MERE
L40 0TA (signposted from M61, M58 &M6, 6m from Ormskirk, off A59)
☎ 01704 895181 ▤ 01704 892343
e-mail: info@martinmere.co.uk

One of Britain's most important wetland sites, where you can get really close to a variety of ducks, geese and swans from all over the world as well as two flocks of flamingos. Thousands of wildfowl, including Pink-footed geese, Bewick's and Whooper swans, winter here. Other features include a children's adventure playground, exhibition gallery, craft area and an educational centre.
Times: Open all year, daily 9.30-5.30 (4pm in winter). (Closed 25 Dec). **Fee:** £5.25 (ch £3.25, pen £4.25). **Facilities:** ℙ ✑ & (wheelchair loan, Braille trail, heated hide) toilets for disabled shop garden centre ✗ (ex guide dogs) ✑

⛫ MORECAMBE   Map 07 SD46
FRONTIERLAND - FAMILY PARK
The Promenade LA4 4DG (from M6 take junct 34 northbound and junct 35 southbound)
☎ 01524 410024 ▤ 01524 831399
Times: Open 8 Apr-3 Sep, days & times vary, telephone for details.
Facilities: ℙ (charged) ✑ & toilets for disabled shop ✗ *Details not confirmed for 2002* ✑

⛫ PADIHAM   Map 07 SD73
GAWTHORPE HALL
BB12 8UA (off A671)
☎ 01282 771004 ▤ 01282 770178
e-mail: rpmgaw@smtp.ntrust.org.uk

An early 17th-century manor house, built around Britain's most southerly pele tower, restored in 1850. A collection of portraits from the National Portrait Gallery and the Kay Shuttleworth Collections of costume, embroidery and lace are on show in the expanded exhibition areas.
Times: Open 31 Mar-Oct, Garden: daily 10-6. Hall: Tue-Thu, Sat & Sun 1-5. Also open BH Mon & Good Fri. (Last admission 4.30). **Fee:** House: £3 (ch & con £1.50). Family ticket £8. Garden free. Party 15+.
Facilities: ℙ ✑ & toilets for disabled shop ✗ (ex in grounds) 🐾

⛫ PRESTON   Map 07 SD52
HARRIS MUSEUM & ART GALLERY
Market Square PR1 2PP (exit M6 at junct 31, follow signs for Preston town centre)
☎ 01772 258248 ▤ 01772 886764
e-mail: harris.museum@preston.gov.uk

An impressive Greek Revival building containing extensive collections of fine and decorative art including a gallery of Clothes and Fashion. The Story of Preston covers the town's history and the lively exhibition programmes of contemporary art and social history are accompanied by events and activities throughout the year.
Times: Open all year, Mon-Sat 10-5. (Closed Sun & BHs). **Fee:** Free.
Facilities: ℙ (5 mins walk) (blue badge disabled parking only) ✑ & (Wheelchair available. Chair lift mezzanine galleries) toilets for disabled shop ✗ (ex guide/assistance dogs)

🏛 ROSSENDALE   Map 07 SD72
WHITAKER PARK & ROSSENDALE MUSEUM
Whitaker Park, Haslingden Rd, Rawtenstall BB4 6RE
(off A681, 0.25m W of Rawtenstall centre)
☎ 01706 244682   ▤ 01706 250037

Former mill owner's house, built in 1840 and set in the delightful Whitaker Park. Displays include fine and decorative arts, a Victorian drawing room, natural history, costume, local and social history.
Times: Open Mon-Fri, 1-5; Sat 10-5 (Apr-Oct), 10-4 (Nov-Mar); Sun noon-5 (Apr-Oct), noon-4 (Nov-Mar). BH's 1-5. Closed 24-26 Dec & 1 Jan). **Fee:** Free. **Facilities:** ▣ ᕱ (large print, audio guides, induction loop) toilets for disabled ⚲ (ex guide dogs)

🏛 RUFFORD   Map 07 SD41
RUFFORD OLD HALL
L40 1SG (off A59, 7m North of Ormskirk)
☎ 01704 821254   ▤ 01704 821254

There is a story that William Shakespeare performed here for the owner Sir Thomas Hesketh in the magnificent Great Hall. Built in 1530, it was the Hesketh family seat for the next 250 years. The Carolean Wing, altered in 1821, features fine collections of 16th and 17th century oak furniture, arms, armour and tapestries.
Times: Open 31 Mar-4 Nov, Sat-Wed, (but open 31 May, 2, 9, 16, 23 Aug). Hall 1-5 (Last admission 4.30pm); Garden & shop 12-5.30.
Fee: £3.80 (ch £1.90). Family ticket £9.50. Booked parties £2.60 each. Garden only £2. **Facilities:** ▣ ✖ ᕱ (braille guide, wheelchairs, adapted cutlery etc) shop ⚲ (ex in grounds) ⛺

🏛 SAMLESBURY   Map 07 SD53
SAMLESBURY HALL
Preston New Rd PR5 0UP (M6 junct 31, A677 for 3m)
☎ 01254 812010 & 812229   ▤ 01254 812174

A well restored half-timbered manor house, built during the 14th and 15th centuries, and set in five acres of beautiful grounds. Sales of antiques and collector's items, craft shows and temporary exhibitions are held all year round.
Times: Open all year ex last wk Dec & 1st 2 wks Jan, Tue-Sun 11-4.30. Historical part of hall closed Sat for weddings, newer part of hall open Sat for antiques sales. **Fee:** £2.50 (ch 4-16 £1). **Facilities:** ▣ ✖ licensed ᕱ toilets for disabled ⚲ (ex guide dogs)

🏛 SILVERDALE   Map 07 SD47
RSPB NATURE RESERVE
Myers Farm LA5 0SW (M6 junct 35, then N along A6 for several miles, follow brown tourist signs)
☎ 01524 701601   ▤ 01524 701601

A large reed swamp with meres with willow and alder scrub in a valley with woodland on its limestone slopes. The reserve covers 321 acres, and is home to one of Britain's largest concentration of bitterns, together with bearded tits, reed, sedge and grasshopper warblers, shovelers, pochards, tufted ducks and marsh harriers. Black terns and ospreys regularly pass through in spring and greenshanks and various sandpipers in

† Lancaster Castle †

Owned by HM The Queen in right of her Duchy of Lancaster

Used as a Court and a Prison – *see*
Lancashire County Council
• where the Lancashire Witches were tried, convicted and condemned to die
• the Shire Hall, with its display of heraldic shields
• the dungeons, 'Drop Room' and 'Hanging Corner'
• the court from which convicts were transported to Australia
• the Grand Jury Room where Queen Victoria dined

Open daily mid-March to mid-December
Tours every half-hour from 10.30am-4pm (Court sittings permitting)
Check by telephoning (01524) 64998
http://www.lancashire.gov.uk/resources/ps/castle/index.htm

the autumn. Wintering wildfowl include large flocks of mallards, teals, wigeons, and shovelers.
Times: Open daily 9am-9pm (or sunset if earlier). Visitor Centre daily 10-5. (closed Xmas Day). **Fee:** £4 (ch £1, concessions £2.50) Family £8.
Facilities: ▣ ⬤ ᕱ (chair lift to 1st floor, ramp access to 4 hides) toilets for disabled shop ⚲ (ex guide dogs) ⬛

🏛 TURTON BOTTOMS   Map 07 SD71
TURTON TOWER
BL7 0HG (on B6391, off A666 or A676)
☎ 01204 852203   ▤ 01204 853759
Times: Open May-Sep, Mon-Thu 10-12 & 1-5. Wknds 1-5; Mar, Apr & Oct Sat-Wed, 1-4; Nov & Feb, Sun 1-4. Other times by prior arrangement. **Facilities:** ▣ ⬤ ᕱ toilets for disabled shop ⚲ (ex in grounds) *Details not confirmed for 2002*

🏛 WHALLEY   Map 07 SD73
WHALLEY ABBEY
BB7 9SS (Just off A59, 4m S of Clitheroe)
☎ 01254 828400   ▤ 01254 828401

The ruins of a 14th-century Cistercian abbey, set in the delightful gardens of the Blackburn Diocesan Retreat and Conference House, a 17th-century manor house with gardens reaching down to the River Calder. The remains include two gateways, a chapter house and the abbot's lodgings and kitchen.
Times: Grounds open all year; coffee shop, shop & exhibition area, Jan-Dec daily 11-5. (Closed Xmas & New Year). **Fee:** £2 (ch 50p, pen £1.25). **Facilities:** ▣ ⬤ ✖ licensed ᕱ (chair lifts, ramps) toilets for disabled shop ⚲ (ex guide dogs)

EVENTS & FESTIVALS

February
tbc Comedy Festival, Leicester

March
tbc Festival of Jewish Arts & Music, Leicester
tbc Leicester Jazz Festival

April
tbc Leicester Short Film Festival

May
5th-6th Leicestershire County Show, Loughborough
11th Heart Link Street Organ Festival, Leicester
25th-15th June Leicester Early Music Festival

June
3rd Melton Show, Melton Mowbray
25th May-15th Leicester Early Music Festival
tbc International Music Festival, Leicester

July
tbc Belgrave Mela, Leicester
tbc Mardi Gras, Leicester

August
tbc Abbey Park Festival, Leicester
tbc Caribbean Carnival, Leicester

October
tbc Literature Festival, Leicester

November
tbc Bonfire & Fireworks, Leicester
tbc Diwali Celebrations, Leicester

Leicestershire

Leicestershire is divided between the large country estates of its eastern side and the industrial towns of the East Midlands to its west.

Coal mining was an important part of the county's industrial development in the 19th and early 20th centuries, and this is reflected in its heritage, including a reclaimed mine near Coalville, now divided between a nature reserve and Snibston Discovery Park, where children can find out about the mining industry.

Agricultural areas are concentrated around the pleasant market towns of Market Harborough and Market Bosworth. The latter was the site of the Battle of Bosworth Field, the final engagement of the War of the Roses in 1485, where Richard III, the Yorkist king was defeated and killed by Henry of Richmond, who was then crowned Henry VII, the first of the Tudors.

The administrative centre is the city of Leicester, and other major towns are Loughborough, which includes bell-founding among its many industries, and Melton Mowbray, home of Stilton cheese and a particularly English item, the pork pie.

Around Melton Mowbray is serious fox-hunting country for the Belvoir, Cottesmore and Quorn hunts. Northeast of Melton Mowbray is the lovely Vale of Belvoir, beneath which are large deposits of coal.

Charnwood Forest, with fewer trees than one would expect, provides a wild and rugged landscape conveniently situated for escape from the city. It lies to the northwest of Leicester extending to Loughborough and Coalville, with some interruptions.

Top: Beacon Hill

⛪ ASHBY-DE-LA-ZOUCH   Map 08 SK31
ASHBY-DE-LA-ZOUCH CASTLE
LE65 1BR
☎ 01530 413343
Times: Open Apr-Sep, daily 10-6; Oct, daily 10-5; Nov-Mar, daily 10-4.
(Closed 24-26 Dec & 1 Jan). **Facilities:** 🅿 ♿ 🅧 ⚌ *Details not confirmed for 2002*

⛪ BELVOIR   Map 08 SK83
BELVOIR CASTLE
NG32 1PD (between A52 & A607, follow the brown
heritage signs from A1, A52, A607 & A46)
☎ 01476 870262   📠 01476 870443
e-mail: info@belvoircastle.com

Although Belvoir Castle has been the home of the
Dukes of Rutland for many centuries, the turrets,
battlements, towers and pinnacles of the house are a
19th-century fantasy. Amongst the many treasures to
be seen inside are paintings by Murillo, Holbein and
other famous artists. Also here is the museum of the
Queens Royal Lancers. Lovingly restored gardens are
also open to visitors. Special events planned every
weekend throughout the season.
Times: Etr wknd-Sep daily 11-5 & Sun in Oct **Fee:** £6 (ch £3.50 pen
£5.50). **Facilities:** 🅿 🍽 🅧 licensed ♿ (permitted to be driven/drive
right up to castle entrance) toilets for disabled shop 🦮 (ex guide dogs)
🛥

⛪ CASTLE DONINGTON   Map 08 SK42
DONINGTON GRAND PRIX COLLECTION
Donington Park DE74 2RP (adjacent to Racing Circuit,
2m from M1 junct 23a/24 & M42/A42)
☎ 01332 811027   📠 01332 812829
e-mail: donington@zoom.co.uk
Times: Open daily 10-5 (last admission 4pm). Open later on race
days. (Closed over Xmas period - telephone to confirm opening times
over this period). **Facilities:** 🅿 🍽 🅧 licensed ♿ shop 🦮 (ex guide
dogs) *Details not confirmed for 2002* 🛥

⛪ COALVILLE   Map 08 SK41
SNIBSTON DISCOVERY PARK
County Hall LE3 8TB (4.5m from M1 junct 22/2m or
from A42/M42 junct 13 on A511 on the west side of
Coalville)
☎ 01530 278444   📠 01530 813301
e-mail: snibston@leics.gov.uk

At Leicestershire's all-weather science and industry
museum, visitors can try to solve over 50 hands-on
experiments, or explore our rich heritage in the
Transport, Extractive, Engineering and Textile and
Fashion Galleries. Ex-miners give tours of Snibston's
colliery buildings, and kids can let off steam in the
outdoor science and water playgrounds.
Times: Open all year, 10-5 (Closed 25-26 Dec). **Fee:** £4.75 (ch £2.95,
concessions £3.25). Family ticket £13.50. Party. **Facilities:** 🅿 🍽 ♿
(Braille labels, touch tables, parking available) toilets for disabled shop
🦮 (ex guide dogs) 🛥

⛪ DONINGTON-LE-HEATH   Map 08 SK41
DONINGTON-LE-HEATH MANOR HOUSE
Manor Rd LE67 2FW (S of Coalville)
☎ 01530 831259   📠 01530 831259
e-mail: museum@leics.gov.uk

This is a rare example of a medieval manor house,
tracing its history back to about 1280. It has now been
restored as a period house, with fine oak furnishings.
The surrounding grounds include period gardens, and
the adjoining stone barn houses a restaurant.
Times: Open all year: Apr-Sep, 11-5; Oct-Mar, 11-3. **Fee:** Free.
Facilities: 🅿 🍽 🅧 ♿ shop 🦮 (ex guide dogs)

⛪ KIRBY MUXLOE   Map 04 SK50
KIRBY MUXLOE CASTLE
Oakcroft St LE9 9MD (off B5380)
☎ 0116 238 6886

When Lord Hastings drew up designs for his castle in
the late 15th century, he first had to obtain 'licence to
crenellate', but his moated, fortified manor was never
completed, as he was executed only a few years after
the work was begun. It stands as a ruin in his memory.
Times: Open Apr-Oct, wknds & BH's 12-5. **Fee:** £2 (ch 5-15 £1, under
5's free, con £1.50) **Facilities:** 🅿 ♿ ⚌

⛪ LEICESTER   Map 04 SK50
ABBEY PUMPING STATION
Corporation Rd, Abbey Ln LE4 5PX (off A6, 1m N from
city centre)
☎ 0116 299 5111   📠 0116 299 5125
Times: Open Apr-Oct, Mon-Sat 10-5, Sun 2-5; Nov-Mar, Mon-Sat 10-
4.30, Sun 2-4.30 (Closed 24-26 & 31 Dec & 1 Jan). Subject to change.
Facilities: 🅿 ♿ (loan of wheelchairs) toilets for disabled shop 🦮 (ex
guide dogs) *Details not confirmed for 2002*

BELGRAVE HALL & GARDENS
Church Rd, off Thurcaston Rd, Belgrave LE4 5PE (off
Belgrave/Loughborough road, 1m from city centre)
☎ 0116 266 6590   📠 0116 261 3063
Times: Open all year, Apr-Oct, Mon-Sat 10-5, Sun 2-5; Nov-Mar, Mon-
Sat 10-4.30, Sun 2-4.30. Closed 24-26 Dec/New Year. Opening times
subject to change, ring Hall for details. **Facilities:** 🅿 ♿ (loan of
wheelchair) toilets for disabled shop 🦮 *Details not confirmed for 2002*

JEWRY WALL MUSEUM & SITE
St Nicholas Circle LE1 4LB (opposite The Holiday Inn)
☎ 0116 247 3021   📠 0116 251 2257
Times: Open Apr-Oct, Mon-Sat 10-5, Sun 2-5; Nov-Mar, Mon-Sat 10-
4.30, Sun 2-4.30 (Closed 31 Dec & 1 Jan). Subject to change. 🅿
(300yds) (limited on-street parking) ♿ toilets for disabled shop 🦮 (ex
guide dogs) *Details not confirmed for 2002* 🛥

LEICESTERSHIRE MUSEUM & ART GALLERY
53 New Walk LE1 7EA
☎ 0116 255 4100   📠 0116 247 3005
Times: Open all year, Apr-Oct, Mon-Sat 10-5, Sun 2-5. Nov-Mar, Mon-
Sat 10-4.30, Sun 2-4.30. Closed 24-26 Dec/New Year. **Facilities:** 🅿 🍽
♿ (wheelchair for loan) toilets for disabled shop 🦮 (ex guide dog)
Details not confirmed for 2002 🛥

NATIONAL SPACE CENTRE

Exploration Dr LE4 5NS (off A6, 2m N of city centre)
☎ 0116 261 0261 📠 0116 258 2100
e-mail: info@spacecentre.co.uk

Offering five themed galleries, cutting-edge audio-visual technology and glimpses into genuine space research, the National Space Centre is a unique experience. Learn about the planets, astronaut life, weather forecasting, space-stations and satellites. Visit the Space Theatre and the Newsdesk, and take a look at the scientists and astronomers undertaking genuine research in the Space Science Research Unit.
Times: Open all year, Tue-Fri 9.30-last entry 4pm, Sat-Sun 9.30-4.30. School holidays, Mon 12-4.30 & Tue-Sun 9.30-4.30. **Fee:** £7.50 (ch 5-14 & concessions £5.50). Family ticket £22-£27 **Facilities:** 🅿 (charged) 💺 ✗ licensed ♿ toilets for disabled shop 🐾 (ex guide dogs) 🍴

NEWARKE HOUSES

The Newarke LE2 7BY
☎ 0116 247 3222 📠 0116 247 0403
Times: Telephone Newarke Houses Museum on 0116 247 3222 for details of opening hours. 🅿 (200 yds) shop 🐾 *Details not confirmed for 2002*

THE RECORD OFFICE FOR LEICESTERSHIRE, LEICESTER & RUTLAND

Long St, Wigston Magna LE18 2AH (Old A50, S of Leicester City)
☎ 0116 257 1080 📠 0116 257 1120
e-mail: museums@leics.gov.uk

Housed in a converted 19th-century school in Wigston, the Record Office holds photographs, electoral registers and archive film, files of local newspapers, history tapes and sound recordings, all of which can be studied.
Times: Open all year, Mon, Tue & Thu 9.15-5, Wed 9.15-7.30, Fri 9.15-4.45, Sat 9.15-12.15. (Closed Sun & BH wknds Sat-Tue). **Fee:** Free. **Facilities:** 🅿 ♿ toilets for disabled 🐾

UNIVERSITY OF LEICESTER HAROLD MARTIN BOTANIC GARDEN

Beaumont Hall, Stoughton Dr South, Oadby LE2 2NA (3m SE A6, entrance at 'The Knoll', Glebe Rd, Oadby)
☎ 0116 271 7725

The grounds of four houses, now used as student residences and not open to the public, make up this 16-acre garden. A great variety of plants in different settings provide a delightful place to walk, including rock, water and sunken gardens, trees, borders, heathers and glasshouses.
Times: Open Mon-Fri 10-4 (ex 25-26 Dec & 1 Jan), Sat & Sun 10-4 (from 3rd weekend in Mar to 2nd weekend in Nov inclusive).
Fee: Free. **Facilities:** 🅿 ♿ toilets for disabled 🐾 (ex guide dogs)

WYGSTON'S HOUSE MUSEUM OF COSTUME

12 Applegate, St Nicholas Circle LE1 5LD
☎ 0116 247 3056 📠 0116 262 0964
Times: Open Apr-Oct, Mon-Sat 10-5, Sun 2-5; Nov-Mar, Mon-Sat, 10-4.30, Sun 2-4.30 (Closed Good Fri & 25-26 & 31 Dec & 1 Jan).
Facilities: 🅿 (150 yds) ♿ shop 🐾 *Details not confirmed for 2002*

🏛 LOUGHBOROUGH   Map 08 SK51

GREAT CENTRAL RAILWAY

Great Central Rd LE11 1RW (signposted from A6)
☎ 01509 230726 📠 01509 239791
e-mail: booking_office@gcrailway.co.uk

This private steam railway runs over eight miles from Loughborough Central to Leicester North, with all trains calling at Quorn & Woodhouse and Rothley. The locomotive depot and museum are at Loughborough Central. A buffet car runs on most trains.
Times: Open Sat, Sun & BH Mon & midweek Jun-Sep. **Fee:** Runabout (all day unlimited travel) £9.80 (ch & pen £6.50). Family ticket £20. **Facilities:** 🅿 💺 ✗ licensed ♿ (Disabled coach available on most trains, check beforehand) toilets for disabled shop 🍴

🏛 MARKET BOSWORTH   Map 04 SK40

BATTLEFIELD STEAM RAILWAY LINE

Shackerstone Station, Shackerstone, Nuneaton CV13 6NW (from A444/A447 take B585 to Market Bosworth follow signs for Congerstone/Shackerstone. Follow brown tourist signs from M42 junct 11).
☎ 01827 880754 📠 01827 881050

Together with a regular railway service (mainly steam) from Shackerstone to Shenton, there is an extensive railway museum featuring a collection of rolling stock and many other relics from the age of steam.
Times: Open all year, Station & Museum, Sat & Sun, 10.30-5.30. Passenger steam train service operates Etr-Oct, Sat, Sun & BH Mon. Diesel trains operate Jun-Sep, Wed & Sat only. **Fee:** Shackerstone station: £1 (ch 5-15 free). Return train fare £5 (ch £2.50). Family ticket £14. **Facilities:** 🅿 💺 ✗ ♿ toilets for disabled shop 🍴

BOSWORTH BATTLEFIELD VISITOR CENTRE & COUNTRY PARK

Ambion Hill, Sutton Cheney CV13 0AD (follow brown tourist signs from A447, A444 & A5)
☎ 01455 290429 📠 01455 292841

Times: Open all year - Country Park & Battle trails all year during daylight hours. Visitor Centre Apr-Oct, Mon-Sat 11-5. Sun & BH, 11-6. Parties all year by arrangement. **Facilities:** 🅿 (charged) 💺 ♿ wheelchair hire,trail accessible with help,tactile exhibits toilets for disabled shop *Details not confirmed for 2002* 🍴

🏛 MOIRA
Map 08 SK31

HEART OF THE NATIONAL FOREST VISITOR CENTRE

Enterprise Glade, Bath Ln DE12 6BD (on B500)

☎ 01283 216633 📠 01283 210321

Times: Open daily, summer 10-6, winter 10-5. Closed 25-26 Dec &1 Jan. **Facilities:** 🅿 ☕ ✗ licensed ♿ (multi access walks & trails accessible to wheelchairs) toilets for disabled shop garden centre 🐾 (ex guide dogs) *Details not confirmed for 2002* ⚑

🏛 SWINFORD
Map 04 SP57

STANFORD HALL

LE17 6DH (7.5m NE of Rugby, 1.5m from Swinford. 2m from M1, M6, A14 junct)

☎ 01788 860250 📠 01788 860870

e-mail: enquiries@stanfordhall.co.uk

A beautiful William and Mary house, built in 1697 by Sir Roger Cave, ancestor of the present owner. The house contains antique furniture, paintings (including the Stuart Collection) and family costumes. Special events include car and motorcycle owners' club rallies.

Times: Open Etr Sat-end Sep, Sat, Sun, BH Mon & Tue following 1.30-5.30; noon on BH & Event Days (House 1.30). Last admission 5pm. Motorcycle Museum: Sun & BH Mons only, 1.30-5. **Fee:** House & Grounds £4.20 (ch £2); Grounds only £2.50 (ch £1); Motorcycle Museum £1 (ch 35p). Party 20+. **Facilities:** 🅿 ☕ ♿ (museum also accessible) toilets for disabled shop 🐾 (ex guide dogs & in park)

🏛 TWYCROSS
Map 04 SK30

TWYCROSS ZOO PARK

CV9 3PX (M42 junct 11, on A444)

☎ 01827 880250 📠 01827 880700

Set in 50 acres of parkland, the zoo is home to around 1000 animals, most are endangered species. Twycross is the only zoo in Britain to house Bonobos - humans' closest living relative. Various other animals include lions, tigers, elephants and giraffes, and a pets' corner for younger children. There's also a penguin pool with underwater viewing and a children's adventure Playground.

Times: Open all year, daily 10-6 (4pm in winter). (Closed 25 Dec). **Fee:** Please telephone for prices. **Facilities:** 🅿 ☕ ♿ toilets for disabled shop 🐾 (ex guide dogs) ⚑

Lincolnshire

Lincolnshire is an east coast county with an agricultural economy, attractive seaside resorts, some lovely countryside, and quintessentially English market towns.

EVENTS & FESTIVALS

May
4th-6th Spalding Flower Festival & Springfields Country Fair
15th-18th Tallington Beer Festival (real ale & live music)
tbc Beer Festival, Cleethorpes
tbc Folk Festival, Cleethorpes

June
29th-30th Royal Air Force Waddington International Air Show, RAF Waddington

July
27th-28th Heckington Show, Estate Showground, Heckington
tbc International Dance & Music Festival, Belton House, Park & Gardens, Belton

July/August
tbc Cleethorpes Carnival Parade

August
24th-25th Lincolnshire Steam & Vintage Rally, Lincolnshire Showground, Grange-de-Lings, Lincoln

November
tbc Bonfire night celebrations, Cleethorpes

Top: Flower Festival at Spalding

Much of the fenland around the Wash has been drained of its marshes and reclaimed as highly productive farmland. Further north, the coastline, with its sandy beaches, has been developed to accommodate the holiday industry, with caravans, campsites and the usual seaside paraphernalia. The main resorts are Skegness, Mablethorpe, Cleethorpes and Ingoldmells. Inland, the chalky margin of the Lincolnshire Wolds offers an undulating landscape of hills and valleys, designated as an Area of Outstanding Natural Beauty.

Lincoln, the county town, is dominated by its magnificent cathedral. Most of interest in the city is in the uphill area, Steep Hill, ascending from the River Witham; the Bailgate spanned by the Newport Arch, and the Minster Yard with its medieval and Georgian architecture. During World War II the county was the base for Bomber Command, and it was from Scampton that the famous Dambuster mission of May 1943 took off.

Boston, on the banks of the Witham, was England's second biggest seaport in the 13th and 14th centuries, when the wool trade was at its height. The town is distinguished by the Boston Stump, the 272-ft (83m) tower on the church of St Boltoph, which can be seen for miles around.

There are market towns all over the county still holding weekly markets, including Barton-upon-Humber, Boston, Bourne, Brigg, Crowland, Gainsborough, Grantham, Great Grimsby, Holbeach, Horncastle, Long Sutton, Louth, Market Rasen, Scunthorpe, Sleaford, Spalding (the centre of the flower industry), and the elegant Edwardian spa resort of Woodhall Spa.

🏛 ALFORD
Map 09 TF47

MANOR HOUSE MUSEUM
West St LN13 9DJ (on the A1104, in town centre)
☎ 01507 463073

This thatched 17th-century manor house is now a folk museum with local history displays: a chemist's shop, shoemaker's shop, school room, wash house and garden, photographic display, veterinary display and a nursery and maid's bedroom. There are also displays of agricultural and craft tools, sweet-making equipment, a kitchen and even a police cell.
Times: Open Etr-Sep daily, Mon-Sat 10-5, Sun 12-4. **Fee:** £1.50 (accompanied ch 50p) **Facilities:** 🅿 💺 shop 🐾 (ex guide dogs)

🏛 BELTON
Map 08 SK93

BELTON HOUSE PARK & GARDENS
NG32 2LS (3m NE Grantham on A607)
☎ 01476 566116 📠 01476 579071
e-mail: ebahah@smtp.ntrust.org.uk

The house contains an exceptional interior, as well as important collections of furniture and art. Surrounded by formal gardens and landscaped park
Times: Open 23 Mar-3 Nov, Wed-Sun & BH Mon (Closed Good Fri). House open 12.30-5 (last admission 4.30pm). Grounds open 11-5.30. **Fee:** £5.60 (ch £2.80) Family ticket £14. **Facilities:** 🅿 ✗ licensed ⚅ (braille guide, hearing scheme) toilets for disabled shop 🐾 (ex in grounds)

🏛 CLEETHORPES
Map 08 TA30

PLEASURE ISLAND THEME PARK
Kings Rd DN35 0PL (From A46, follow signs to Cleethorpes, then brown tourist signs)
☎ 01472 211511 📠 01472 211087
e-mail: pleasureisland@btinternet.com

Pleasure Island is packed with over 70 rides and attractions, including the new tower ride, the Hyper Blaster.
Times: Open from Apr-Oct, daily. **Fee:** £10 (ch under 4 free, pen £6). Family ticket £34. **Facilities:** 🅿 💺 ✗ ⚅ toilets for disabled shop 💺

🏛 CONINGSBY
Map 08 TF25

BATTLE OF BRITAIN MEMORIAL FLIGHT VISITOR CENTRE
LN4 4SY (on A153)
☎ 01526 344041 📠 01526 342330
e-mail: bbmf@lincolnshire.gov.uk

View the aircraft of the Battle of Britain Memorial Flight, comprising the only flying Lancaster in Europe, five Spitfires, two Hurricanes, a Dakota and two Chipmunks. Because of operational commitments, specific aircraft may not be available. Ring for information before planning a visit.
Times: Open all year, Mon-Fri, conducted tours 10-3.30. (Closed 2 wks Xmas). (Phone prior to visiting to check security situation) **Fee:** £3.50 (ch £1.50, pen £2, u5's free). **Facilities:** 🅿 💺 ⚅ (electric wheelchairs not allowed in hangers) toilets for disabled shop 🐾 💺

🏛 EPWORTH
Map 08 SE70

OLD RECTORY
1 Rectory St DN9 1HX (on A161, 3m S of M180 junct 2)
☎ 01427 872268
e-mail: epworth@oldrectory63.freeserve.co.uk
Times: Open daily Mar-Oct, Mon-Sat 10-12 & 2-4, Sun 2-4 (only in Mar, Apr & Oct) May-Sep Mon-Sat 10-4.30. Sun 2-4.30. Other times by prior arrangement. **Facilities:** 🅿 💺 ✗ ⚅ shop 🐾 (ex guide dogs) Details not confirmed for 2002 💺

🏛 GAINSBOROUGH
Map 08 SK88

OLD HALL
Parnell St DN21 2NB (A1 onto A57 to Gainsborough. Follow brown heritage signs in city centre. Old hall is adjacent to town centre)
☎ 01427 612669 📠 01427 612779
e-mail: crawleyg@lincolnshire.gov.uk

A complete medieval manor house dating back to 1460-80 and containing a remarkable Great Hall and original kitchen with a variety of room settings. Richard III, Henry VIII, the Mayflower Pilgrims and John Wesley all visited the Old Hall.
Times: Open all year, Mon-Sat 10-5; Etr-Oct, Sun 2-5.30. Closed 25-26 Dec, 1 Jan & Good Fri. **Fee:** £2.50 (ch £1, pen £1.50). **Facilities:** 🅿 (100 yds) (unrestricted parking 100yds from Hall) 💺 ⚅ (audio tour, induction loop, wheelchair for visitors use) shop 🐾 (ex guide dogs)

🏛 GRANTHAM
See Belvoir, Leicestershire

🏛 GRIMSBY
Map 08 TA20

NATIONAL FISHING HERITAGE CENTRE
Alexandra Dock DN31 1UZ (follow signs off M180)
☎ 01472 323345 📠 01472 323555

Sign on as a crew member for a journey of discovery, and experience the harsh reality of life on board a deep sea trawler built inside the Centre. Through interactive games and displays, your challenge is to navigate the icy waters of the Arctic in search of the catch.
Times: Open Apr-Sep, Mon-Thu 10-4, Sat-Sun 11-5 (10.30-5.30 Jul-Sep). **Fee:** £4.95 (concessions £3.85). Family ticket £16.50. Prices subject to change. **Facilities:** 🅿 💺 ⚅ (easy access route) toilets for disabled shop 🐾 (ex guide dogs) 💺

🏛 GRIMSTHORPE
Map 08 TF02

GRIMSTHORPE CASTLE
PE10 0NB (on A151, 8m E of Colsterworth rbt on A1)
☎ 01778 591205 📠 01778 591259
e-mail: ray@grimsthorpe.co.uk
Times: Open 22 Apr-Sep, Sun, Thu & BH's. Daily in Aug ex Fri & Sat. Park & Gardens 11-6, Castle 1-6 (last admission 4.30). **Facilities:** 🅿 💺 ✗ licensed ⚅ toilets for disabled shop Details not confirmed for 2002

⚒ HECKINGTON   Map 08 TF14
THE PEAROOM
Station Yard NG34 9JJ (4m E of Sleaford, off A17)
☎ 01529 460765 📠 01529 460948
Times: Open all year, Mon-Sat & BHs 10-5, Sun 12-5. **Facilities:** 🅿
♿ ♿ toilets for disabled shop ✸ (ex guide dogs) *Details not confirmed for 2002*

⚒ LINCOLN   Map 08 SK97
MUSEUM OF LINCOLNSHIRE LIFE
Burton Rd LN1 3LY (100mtr walk from Lincoln Castle)
☎ 01522 528448 📠 01522 521264
e-mail: finchj@lincolnshire.gov.uk

A large and varied social history museum, where two centuries of Lincolnshire life are illustrated by enthralling displays of domestic implements, industrial machinery, agricultural tools and a collection of horse-drawn vehicles. The exciting and interactive Royal Lincolnshire Regiment Museum contains videos, an audio tour, and touch screen computers.
Times: Open all year, May-Sep, daily 10-5.30; Oct-Apr, Mon-Sat 10-5.30, Sun 2-5.30. **Fee:** £2 (ch 60p). Family (2ad+3ch) £4.50.
Facilities: 🅿 ♿ ♿ (wheelchair available, parking space) toilets for disabled shop ✸

USHER GALLERY
Lindum Rd LN2 1NN (in city centre, signed)
☎ 01522 527980 📠 01522 560165
e-mail: usher.gallery@lincolnshire.gov.uk

Built as the result of a bequest by Lincoln jeweller James Ward Usher, the Gallery houses his magnificent collection of watches, porcelain and miniatures, as well as topographical works, watercolours by Peter de Wint, Tennyson memorabilia and coins.
Times: Open all year, Tue-Sat 10-5.30 (last entry 4.30pm), Sun 2.30-5. (Closed 25/26 Dec & 1 Jan). Open BHs. **Fee:** £2 (ch, pen & students 50p). Free day Friday. **Facilities:** 🅿 (150yds) ♿ ♿ (large print exhibition guides) toilets for disabled shop ✸ (ex guide dogs) ⚑

⚒ SCUNTHORPE   Map 08 SE81
NORMANBY HALL COUNTRY PARK
Normanby DN15 9HU (4m N of Scunthorpe off B1430)
☎ 01724 720588 📠 01724 721248
Times: Open, Park all year, daily 9am-dusk. Walled garden: daily 11-5 (4pm winter). Hall & Farming Museum: Apr-Sep daily 1-5.
Facilities: 🅿 (charged) ♿ ✕ licensed ♿ (audio tour & sensory bed in walled garden) toilets for disabled shop ✸ (ex guide dogs & park on lead) *Details not confirmed for 2002*

⚒ SKEGNESS   Map 09 TF56
CHURCH FARM MUSEUM
Church Rd South PE25 2HF (follow brown Museum signs on entering Skegness)
☎ 01754 766658 📠 01754 898243
e-mail: walkerr@lincolnshire.gov.uk

A farmhouse and outbuildings, restored to show the way of life on a Lincolnshire farm at the end of the 19th century, with farm implements and machinery plus household equipment on display. Temporary exhibitions are held in the barn with special events throughout the season. A timber framed mud & stud cottage is restored on site.
Times: Open Apr-Oct, daily 10.30-5.30 **Fee:** £1 (ch 50p).
Facilities: 🅿 ♿ ♿ (wheelchair available, grounds accessible with care) toilets for disabled shop ✸ (ex guide dogs)

SKEGNESS NATURELAND SEAL SANCTUARY
North Pde PE25 1DB (north end of seafront)
☎ 01754 764345 📠 01754 764345
e-mail: natureland@fsbdial.co.uk

Natureland houses seals, penguins, tropical birds, aquarium, reptiles, pets' corner etc. Also free-flight tropical butterflies (May-Oct). Natureland is well known for its rescue of abandoned seal pups, and has successfully reared and returned to the wild a large number of them. The hospital unit incorporates a public viewing area, and a large seascape seal pool (with underwater viewing).
Times: Open all year, daily at 10am. Closing times vary according to season. (Closed 25-26 Dec & 1 Jan). **Fee:** £4.25 (ch u3 free, ch £2.80, pen £3.45). Family ticket £12.20. **Facilities:** 🅿 (100 yds) ♿ ♿ toilets for disabled shop ⚑

⚒ SPALDING   Map 08 TF22
BUTTERFLY & FALCONRY PARK
Long Sutton PE12 9LE (off A17 at Long Sutton)
☎ 01406 363833 & 363209 📠 01406 363182
e-mail: butterflypark@hotmail.com

The Park contains one of Britain's largest walk-through tropical houses, in which hundreds of butterflies and birds from all over the world fly freely. Outside are 15 acres of butterfly and bee gardens, wildflower meadows, nature trail, farm animals, a pets' corner and a large adventure playground. At the Falconry Centre, there are daily birds of prey displays. See also a farm museum and an iguana den and an ant room where visitors can observe leaf-cutting ants in their natural habitat. New to the park is Reptile Land, home to crocodiles and snakes.
Times: Open end Mar-end Oct, daily 10-5. (Sep & Oct 10-4).
Fee: £4.90 (ch 3-16 £3.50, pen £4.50). Family ticket £16-£18. Party rates on application. **Facilities:** 🅿 ✕ licensed ♿ (wheelchairs available) toilets for disabled shop ✸ (ex guide dogs) ⚑

SPALDING TROPICAL FOREST

Glenside North, Pinchbeck PE11 3SD (signposted approach to Pinchbeck)

☎ 01775 710822   ▤ 01775 710882

e-mail: mike@rosecottagewgc.co.uk

Times: Open daily summer 10-5.30, winter 10-4. Closed 25 Dec-2 Jan.
Facilities: 🅿 💺 ⚟ (disabled parking close to establishment) toilets for disabled shop garden centre ✹ *Details not confirmed for 2002* ➤

SPRINGFIELDS GARDENS

Camelgate PE12 6ET (1m E on A151, signposted from the Spalding by-pass)

☎ 01775 724843 & 713253   ▤ 01755 711209

e-mail: brianwillonghby@springfields.net

Times: Open 10 Mar-7 May, daily 10-6 (last admission 5pm)
Facilities: 🅿 💺 ✗ licensed ⚟ (free wheelchair hire) toilets for disabled shop garden centre ✹ (guide dogs) *Details not confirmed for 2002*

⛫ STAMFORD   Map 04 TF00

BURGHLEY HOUSE

PE9 3JY (1.5m off A1 at Stamford)

☎ 01780 752451   ▤ 01780 480125

e-mail: burghley@dial.pipex.com

Times: Open Apr-8 Oct, daily, 11-4.30. (Closed 2 Sep). **Facilities:** 🅿 💺 ✗ licensed ⚟ (chairlift access to restaurant and staterooms) toilets for disabled shop ✹ (guide dogs) *Details not confirmed for 2002* ➤

STAMFORD MUSEUM

Broad St PE9 1PJ (from A1 follow town centre signs from any Stamford exit)

☎ 01780 766317   ▤ 01780 480363

e-mail: crawleyt@lincolnshire.gov.uk

The museum illustrates the history and archaeology of Stamford. Perhaps the most unusual exhibits are the clothes of Daniel Lambert (1770-1809), who died in Stamford, one of only three men in Britain recorded as weighing over 50 stone (317kg). These are displayed with the clothes of American midget, General Tom Thumb, who was 3ft 4in (102cm) when he died.
Times: Open all year, Apr-Sep, Mon-Sat 10-5, Sun 2-5; Oct-Mar Mon-Sat 10-5. (Closed 24-26 & 31 Dec & 1 Jan). **Fee:** Free. **Facilities:** 🅿 (200 yds) (on street parking is limited waiting) ⚟ (info on 1st floor gallery available) shop ✹ (ex guide dogs)

STAMFORD SHAKESPEARE COMPANY

Rutland Open Air Theatre, Tolethorpe Hall, Little Casterton PE9 4BH (off A6121, follow heritage signs to Tolethorpe Hall)

☎ 01780 54381   ▤ 01780 481954

Times: Open daily 10-4, May-Sep. Rutland Open Air Theatre performances Jun-29 Aug. **Facilities:** 🅿 💺 ⚟ toilets for disabled shop ✹ *Details not confirmed for 2002*

⛫ TATTERSHALL   Map 08 TF25

TATTERSHALL CASTLE

LN4 4LR (S of A153)

☎ 01526 342543   ▤ 01526 342543

e-mail: etcxxx@smtp.ntrust.org.uk

Large 15th-century fortified house on each of the four storeys are fine heraldic chimney pieces.
Times: Open 23 Mar-3 Nov, Sat-Wed, 11-5.30pm; Oct until 4; also open in Aug; 9 Nov-15 Dec Sat & Sun only 12-4. **Facilities:** 🅿 ⚟ toilets for disabled shop ✹ ♨

⛫ THORNTON   Map 08 TA11

THORNTON ABBEY

DN39 6TU

☎ 01469 40357

Times: Open Apr-Sep, 1st & 3rd Sun of month 12-6; Oct-Mar, 3rd Sun of month 12-4. Grounds open any reasonable time. **Facilities:** 🅿 ⚟ ✹ (in certain areas) ✢ *Details not confirmed for 2002*

⛫ WOOLSTHORPE   Map 08 SK92

WOOLSTHORPE MANOR

23 Newton Way NG33 5NR (7m S of Grantham, 1m W of A1)

☎ 01476 860338

e-mail: ewmxxx@smtp.ntrust.org.uk

A small 17th-century manor house, the birthplace and family home of Sir Isaac Newton.
Times: Open 23 Mar-29 Sep, Wed-Sun & BH Mon 1-5pm; Jul & Aug 1-6; early Oct-early Nov, Sat & Sun 1-5, Wed-Sun during half term.
Fee: £3.50 (ch £1.70) Family £8.70. **Facilities:** 🅿 ✹ ♨

London

The capital of England and the United Kingdom, London is the largest city in Europe with a population of nearly seven million people.

Londinium was established in 43 AD, at the lowest crossing point of the River Thames. In the second century the city walls were built, but London soon grew beyond them to merge with Westminster and, by the 11th century, was the main city in England and the home of William the Conqueror.

London continued to flourish until the plague of 1665 and the Great Fire of London in 1666. Much of the city was rebuilt at this time under the direction of Sir Christopher Wren. During WWII the Blitz did immense damage to the city, razing whole streets and destroying domestic and public buildings alike. Post-war architecture introduced modern structures of concrete and glass. Ancient sights include the Tower of London, built by William the Conqueror on a Roman site; the 15th-century Guildhall; and the Monument, designed by Wren to commemorate the Great Fire. Most of the public buildings are 18th-century or Victorian.

London's role as a port has declined, with most activity now outside the metropolitan area. The East End docks have been redeveloped to provide housing, offices, factories and the Docklands Light Railway. London is a major financial centre, and the focus of the national media, including film and publishing.

London has been a cosmopolitan city for centuries, and much of the excitement of the city's life is derived from its cultural diversity. The foods, dress, languages, art and music of every continent can be experienced on its streets.

Top: London Eye

W1
APSLEY HOUSE, THE WELLINGTON MUSEUM
Hyde Park Corner WIJ 7NT (Underground - Hyde Park Corner, exit 1 overlooking rdbt)
☎ 020 7499 5676 ▤ 020 7493 6576

Number One, London, is the popular name for one of the Capital's finest private residences, 19th-century home of the first Duke of Wellington. Built in the 1770s, its rich interiors have been returned to their former glory, and house the Duke's magnificent collection of paintings, silver, porcelain, sculpture and furniture.
Times: Open Tue-Sun 11-5. (Closed Mon ex BH Mon, Good Fri, May Day BH, 24-26 Dec & 1 Jan). Last admission 4.30pm. **Fee:** £4.50 (ch under 18 & pen free, disabled & UB40 £3). Includes the use of a soundguide. **Facilities:** P (NCP 10mins walk) & lift, learning disabilities shop 🛪 (ex guide dogs) ◥

EC2
BANK OF ENGLAND MUSEUM
Threadneedle St EC2R 8AH (museum housed in Bank of London, entrance in Bartholomew Lane)
☎ 020 7601 5545 ▤ 020 7601 5808
e-mail: museum@bankofengland.co.uk

Located in the heart of The City, this museum traces the history of the Bank from its foundation in 1694, and includes a collection of gold bars, old and new. New interactive programme.
Times: Open all year, Mon-Fri 10-5. (Closed wknds & BH's). Open on the day of the Lord Major's Show and Open House Weekend.
Fee: Free. **Facilities:** P (10 mins walk) & (advance notice helpful) toilets for disabled shop

SW1
BANQUETING HOUSE AT WHITEHALL PALACE
Whitehall SW1A 2ER (Underground - Westminster, Charing Cross or Embankment)
☎ 020 7930 4179 ▤ 020 7930 8268

Designed by Inigo Jones, this is the only surviving building of the vast Whitehall Palace, destroyed by fire 300 years ago. The Palace has seen many significant royal events, including the execution of Charles I in 1649. The Banqueting House's Rubens ceiling paintings are stunning examples of the larger works of the Flemish Master and its classical Palladian style set the fashion for much of London's later architecture.
Times: Open all year, Mon-Sat 10-5. (Closed Good Fri, 24 Dec-1 Jan & BH's). Liable to close at short notice for Government functions.
Fee: £3.90 (ch 16 £2.30 (under 5 free) students & pen £3.10).
Facilities: P (no parking in Whitehall) & toilets for disabled shop 🛪 (ex guide dogs) ◥

E2
BETHNAL GREEN MUSEUM OF CHILDHOOD
Cambridge Heath Rd E2 9PA (Underground - Bethnal Green)
☎ 020 8980 2415 ▤ 020 8983 5225

The National Museum of Childhood houses a multitude of childhood delights. Toys, dolls and dolls' houses,

model soldiers, puppets, games, model theatres, children's costume and nursery antiques are all included in its well planned displays. There are Saturday workshops and Sunday soft play sessions for children, and activities in the holidays.
Times: Open all year, Mon-Thu & Sat-Sun 10-5.50 (Closed Fri, 24-26 Dec & 1 Jan). **Fee:** Free. **Facilities:** P (Metered parking) ▼ & (disabled parking by arrangment) toilets for disabled shop 🛪

W1
BBC EXPERIENCE
Broadcasting House W1A 1AA (Underground - Oxford Circus, Great Portland St)
☎ 0870 6030304
Times: Open all year, daily 9.30-5.30 (last tour commences). Closed 25 Dec. **Facilities:** P ▼ & toilets for disabled shop *Details not confirmed for 2002* ◥

WC1
BRITISH MUSEUM
Great Russell St WC1B 3DG (Underground - Russell Sq, Tottenham Court Rd, Holborn)
☎ 020 7323 8000 ▤ 020 7323 8616
e-mail: information@thebritishmuseum.ac.uk

Behind its imposing Neo-Classical façade the British Museum displays the rich and varied treasures which make it one of the great museums of the world. Founded in 1753, displays cover the works of humanity from pre-historic to modern times. The galleries are the responsibility of ten departments, which include Egyptian, Greek and Roman, Japanese, Medieval and later, Prints and Drawings, and Ethnography. Among the treasures to be seen are the Egyptian mummies, the sculptures from the Parthenon, the Anglo-Saxon treasure from the Sutton Hoo ship burial and the Vindolanda Tablets from Hadrian's Wall. There is a regular programme of gallery talks, guided tours and lectures, and young visitors can enjoy special children's trails.
Times: Open all year, Gallery: Mon-Sat 10-5.30 & Thu-Fri 10-8.30. Great Court: Mon 9-6, Tue-Wed & Sun 9-9, Thu-Sat 9am-11pm. (Closed Good Fri, 24-26 Dec & 1 Jan). **Fee:** Free. **Facilities:** P (5 mins walk) ▼ ✗ licensed & (parking by arrangement) toilets for disabled shop 🛪 (ex guide/companion dogs) ◥

SW1
BUCKINGHAM PALACE
Buckingham Palace Rd SW1 1AA (Underground - Victoria, Green Park)
☎ 020 7839 1377 ▤ 020 7930 9625
e-mail: buckinghampalace@ royalcollection.org.uk

The official London residence of Her Majesty The Queen, whose personal standard flies when Her Majesty is in residence. Each August and September the State Rooms are open to visitors. These principle rooms now include the Ballroom, the largest room in the Palace. The rooms occupy the main west front overlooking the garden and are all opulently decorated
contd.

with the finest pictures and works of art from the Royal Collection.

Times: Open 4 Aug-Sep 9.30-4.30 (provisional dates) **Fee:** £11 (ch under 17 £5.50, pen £9) Family ticket (2 adults & 2 ch) £27.50. Tickets bought in advance £12, no concessions. **Facilities:** P (200yds) (very limited, driving not recommended) & (ex gardens, pre-booking essential) toilets for disabled shop 🛪 (ex guide dogs) 🍽

SW1
CABINET WAR ROOMS
Clive Steps, King Charles St SW1A 2AQ (Underground - Westminster or St James Park)
☎ 020 7930 6961 📄 020 7839 5897
e-mail: cwr@iwm.org.uk

The underground emergency accommodation used to protect the Prime Minister, Winston Churchill, his War Cabinet and the Chiefs of Staff during WWII provides a fascinating insight into those tense days and nights. Among the 21 rooms are the Cabinet Room, the Map Room (where information about operations on all fronts was collected) and the Prime Minister's room, all carefully preserved since the end of the war. There is a changing exhibition of war documents.

Times: Open all year, daily 9.30-6. (10-6 Oct-Mar) last admission 5.15 (Closed 24-26 Dec). **Fee:** £5.40 (ch under 16 free, students & pen £3.90). Party 10+. **Facilities:** P (10 mins walk) & (education service, object handling session) toilets for disabled shop 🛪 🍽

SW3
CARLYLE'S HOUSE
24 Cheyne Row SW3 5HL (Underground - Sloane Square. Off Cheyne Walk between Bettersea & Albert Bridges)
☎ 020 7352 7087 📄 020 7352 5108

`The Sage of Chelsea' - distinguished essayist and writer of historical works, Thomas Carlyle - lived in this 18th-century town house from 1834 until his death in 1881. His soundproofed study and the kitchen, where such literary notables as Tennyson, Thackeray and Browning were entertained have been preserved exactly as the Carlyles knew them.

Times: Open Apr-Oct, Wed-Sun & BH Mons 11-5. Last admission 4.30. (Closed Good Fri). **Fee:** £3.50 (ch £1.75). **Facilities:** P (street metered) 🛪 🚻 🐾

SW3
CHELSEA PHYSIC GARDEN
66 Royal Hospital Rd, (entrance in Swan Walk) SW3 4HS (Underground - Sloane Square)
☎ 020 7352 5646 📄 020 7376 3910

Begun in 1673 for the study of plants used by the Society of Apothecaries. This garden is one of Europe's oldest botanic gardens and is the only one to retain the title 'Physic' after the old name for the healing arts. The garden is still used for botanical and medicinal

research, and offers displays of many fascinating plants in lovely surroundings.

Chelsea Psysic Garden

Times: Open Apr-Oct, Wed 12-5, Sun 2-6. Additional opening during Chelsea Flower Show week, late May & Chelsea Festival week late Jun. Groups at other times by appointment. **Fee:** £4 (ch 5-15, students & unemployed £2). **Facilities:** P (0.5m) (west end of Battersea Park) 🍽 & (disabled parking) toilets for disabled shop garden centre 🛪 (ex guide dogs)

W4
CHISWICK HOUSE
Burlington Ln, Chiswick W4 2RD (Underground - Gunnersbury)
☎ 020 8995 0508

Built by Lord Burlington in the 1720s, Chiswick House is inspired by the architecture of ancient Rome. The interior has a fine collection of art and the Italianate gardens delight visitors with their statues, temples, urns and obelisks.

Times: Open all year, Apr-Sep, daily 10-6 (Oct 10-5); Nov-Mar, Wed-Sun 10-4. Closed 24-26Dec & 1-18Jan. **Fee:** £3.50 (ch 5-15 £1.70, under 5's free con £2.50). Personal stereo tour included in admission, also available for the partially sighted, those with learning difficulties, and in French & German **Facilities:** P & shop 🛪 (in certain areas) 🎏

W8
COMMONWEALTH INSTITUTE
Kensington High St W8 6NQ (Underground - High Street Kensington)
☎ 020 7603 4535 📄 020 7602 7374
e-mail: info@commonwealth.org.uk

Times: Commonwealth Institute is being redeveloped please ring 020 7603 4535 for details. **Facilities:** P (500yds) 🍽 & (lift from car park, intercom at Holland Park gate) toilets for disabled shop 🛪 *Details not confirmed for 2002* 🍽

WC2
COURTAULD GALLERY
Somerset House, Strand WC2R 0RN (Underground - Temple, Embankment)
☎ 020 7848 2526   📠 020 7848 2589
e-mail: galleryinfo@courtauld.ac.uk

The Galleries contain the superb collection of paintings begun by Samuel Courtauld in the 1920s and 1930s and presented to the University of London in memory of his wife. This is the most important collection of Impressionist and post-Impressionist works in Britain and includes paintings by Monet, Renoir, Degas, Cézanne, Van Gogh and Gauguin. There are also works by Michelangelo, Rubens, Goya, and other notable Masters, as well as early Italian paintings.
Times: Open Mon-Sat 10-6, Sun & BH's 12-6. **Fee:** £4 (concessions £3). **Facilities:** P (NCP Drury Lane) ♨ ♿ (parking arranged, lift) toilets for disabled shop 🐾 (ex guide dogs) 🍴

SE17
CUMING MUSEUM
155-157 Walworth Rd SE17 1RS (Underground - Elephant & Castle, North line exit follow signs for the shopping centre)
☎ 020 7701 1342   📠 020 7703 7415
Times: Open all year, Tue-Sat 10-5. (Closed BH's & Sat of BH wknd). **Facilities:** P (20 yds) (on street pay & display meters) shop 🐾 (ex guide dogs) *Details not confirmed for 2002*

SE10
CUTTY SARK CLIPPER SHIP
King William Walk, Greenwich SE10 9HT (situated in dry dock beside Greenwich Pier)
☎ 020 8858 3445 & 020 8858 2698
📠 020 8853 3589
e-mail: info@cuttysark.org.uk

The fastest tea clipper ever, built in 1869, she once sailed 363 miles in a single day. Preserved in dry dock since 1957, her graceful lines dominate the riverside at Greenwich. Exhibitions and a video presentation the story of the ship, and restoration work can be seen.
Times: Open all year, daily 10-5 (Closed 24-26 Dec). Last ticket 30 mins before closing. **Fee:** £3.50 (concessions £2.50). Family ticket £8.50. Party 10+ 20% reduction. **Facilities:** P car park 500 metres (100 yds metered) ♿ shop 🐾 (ex guide dogs) 🍴

SE1
DALI UNIVERSE
County Hall, Riverside Building SE1 7PB
☎ 020 7450 7600   📠 020 7620 3120
e-mail: info@daliuniverse.com

Salvador Dali (1904-1989) was one of the 20th century's most important artistic forces. Born in Spain, he joined the Surrealist movement in Paris in 1928. His interest in subjects such as Catholicism, Freudianism and dreams led to some of the most unusual, disturbing and technically well-executed work of any 20th-century artist. This wide-ranging exhibition contains over 500 of his works including paintings, sculpture, furniture and bizarre objects such as the well-known Mae West Lips sofa.
Times: Open daily (ex 25 Dec) **Fee:** £8.50 (children under 5 free, ch 5-16 £5, concessions £7) **Facilities:** P ♿ shop 🐾 🍴

SE1
DESIGN MUSEUM
Butler's Wharf, 28 Shad Thames SE1 2YD (Underground - London Bridge & Tower Hill)
☎ 020 7403 6933   📠 020 7378 6540
Times: Open all year: wkdys 11.30-6; wknds 10.30-6. (last entry 5.30) closed 25-26 Dec only. **Facilities:** P (3 mins walk) (NCP car park is chargeable) 🍴 ✗ licensed ♿ (ramped entrance, wheelchair & lift, Audio guides.) toilets for disabled shop 🐾 (ex guide dogs) *Details not confirmed for 2002* 🍴

WC1
THE DICKENS HOUSE MUSEUM
48 Doughty St WC1N 2LX (Underground - Russell Square or Chancery Lane)
☎ 020 7405 2127   📠 020 7831 5175
e-mail: dhmuseum@rmplc.co.uk

Charles Dickens lived in Doughty Street in his twenties and it was here he worked on his first full-length novel, *The Pickwick Papers*, and later *Oliver Twist* and *Nicholas Nickelby*. Pages of the original manuscripts are on display, together with valuable first editions, his marriage licence and many other personal mementoes.
Times: Open all year, Mon-Sat 10-5. **Fee:** £4 (ch under 16 £2, concession £3). Family ticket £9. **Facilities:** P (in street) (metered, 2 hrs max) ♿ shop 🐾 🍴

EC4
DR JOHNSON'S HOUSE
17 Gough Square EC4A 3DE (Underground - Temple, Blackfriars, Chancery Lane)
☎ 020 7353 3745   📠 020 7353 3745
e-mail: curator@drjh.dircon.co.uk

The celebrated literary figure, Dr Samuel Johnson, lived here between 1748 and 1759. He wrote his English Dictionary here, and a facsimile first edition is on display at the house. The dictionary took nine and a half years to complete and contained 40,000 words.

contd.

Johnson then undertook the formidable task of editing the complete works of Shakespeare. The house is a handsome example of early 18th-century architecture, and includes a collection of prints, letters and other Johnson memorabilia.

Times: Open all year, May-Sep, daily 11-5.30; Oct-Apr 11-5. (Closed Sun, BH's, Good Fri & 24 Dec). **Fee:** £4 (ch £1, under 10 free, students & pen £3). Family £9. **Facilities:** P (500 yards) (limited meters) (Large print info sheets, handrails, seating) shop ✱

SE21
DULWICH PICTURE GALLERY
Gallery Rd, Dulwich SE21 7AD (off South Circular A205 follow signs to Dulwich village)
☎ 020 8693 5254 📠 020 8299 8700
Times: Open all year, Tue-Fri 10-5, wknds & BH Mon 11-5. (Closed Mon). **Facilities:** P ✗ licensed & (wheelchair available) toilets for disabled shop ✱ (ex guide dogs) *Details not confirmed for 2002* ▼

SE9
ELTHAM PALACE HOUSE & GARDENS
Court Yard SE9 5QE
☎ 020 8294 2548

Stephen and Virginia Courtauld's stunning country house in 1930s art-deco style, incorporating a medieval Great Hall. One of its most charming features is the old bridge, spanning the moat.
Times: Open all year, Apr-Sep, Wed-Fri & Sun 10-6 (Oct 10-5); Nov-Mar, Wed-Fri & Sun 10-4. Also open BH's. Closed 24-26 Dec & 1 Jan.
Fee: House & Gardens: £6 (ch 5-15 £3, ch u5 free, con £4.50); Gardens only:£3.60 (ch 5-15 £1.80, under 5's free, con £2.70)
Facilities: ✱ 🐾 ✿

NW3
FENTON HOUSE
Windmill Hill NW3 6RT (Underground - Hampstead)
☎ 020 7435 3471 📠 020 7435 3471
e-mail: tfehse@smtp.ntrust.org.uk

A William and Mary mansion built about 1693 and set in a walled garden, Fenton House is now owned by the National Trust. It contains a display of furniture and some notable pieces of Oriental and European porcelain as well as the Benton Fletcher collection of early keyboard instruments.
Times: Open Mar, Sat & Sun 2-5; Apr-Oct, Sat-Sun & BH Mon 11-5pm, Wed-Fri 2-5pm. Last admission 30mins before closing. Closed Good Fri. **Fee:** £4.30 (ch £2.15). Family ticket £10.50, Group 15+
Facilities: & (photographs of upper floors which are not accessible) ✱ 🐾

SE18
FIREPOWER
Royal Arsenal, Woolwich SE18 6ST (A205, turn R at Woolwich ferry onto A206, Firepower is signposted from there)
☎ 020 8855 7755 📠 020 8855 7100
e-mail: info@firepower.org.uk

'Firepower', a new interactive attraction at the Royal Arsenal, tells the story of artillery from Roman catapults to guided missile systems. The centrepiece is a vivid re-creation of a 20th-century battlefield. Multimedia displays explain the science and technology of artillery and tell the stories of the people who served in battle.
Times: Open daily 10-5, (Closed Xmas Day). **Fee:** £6.50 (ch 4.50, con £5.50) Family tickets & group discounts (10+) available. **Facilities:** P (charged) & (wheelchairs available) shop ✱ (ex guide dogs) ▼

SE1
FLORENCE NIGHTINGALE MUSEUM
Gassiot House, 2 Lambeth Palace Rd SE1 7EW (Underground - Westminster, Waterloo. On the site of St Thomas' Hospital)
☎ 020 7620 0374 📠 020 7928 1760
e-mail: curator@florence-nightingale.co.uk

Florence Nightingale needs no introduction, but this museum shows clearly that she was more than 'The Lady with the Lamp'. Beautifully designed, the museum creates a personal setting in which are displayed some of Florence's possessions, a lamp from the Crimean War, and nursing artefacts. There are audio and visual displays and a life-size reconstruction of a Crimean ward scene.
Times: Open all year, Mon-Fri 10-5; wknds & BH's 11.30-4.30. (last admission 1hr before closing). (Closed 24 Dec-2 Jan, Good Fri & Etr Sun). **Fee:** £4.80 (concessions £3.60) Family ticket (2 adults & 2 ch) £10. **Facilities:** P (charged) & toilets for disabled shop ✱ (ex guide dogs) ▼

NW3
FREUD MUSEUM
20 Maresfield Gardens, Hampstead NW3 5SX (Underground - Finchley Road)
☎ 020 7435 2002 & 7435 5167
📠 020 7431 5452
e-mail: freud@gn.apc.org
Times: Open all year, Wed-Sun 12-5 (Closed BH's, telephone for Xmas Holiday times). **Facilities:** P & (personal tours can be arranged if booked in advance) shop ✱ *Details not confirmed for 2002* ▼

E2
GEFFRYE MUSEUM
Kingsland Rd E2 8EA (Underground - Old Street or Liverpool Street)
☎ 020 7739 9893 📠 020 7729 5647
e-mail: info@geffrye-museum.org.uk

The only museum in the UK to specialise in the domestic interiors and furniture of the urban middle classes. Displays span the 400 years from 1600 to the present day, forming a sequence of period rooms which capture the nature of English interior style. The museum is set in elegant, 18th-century buildings, surrounded by delightful gardens including an award-winning walled herb garden and a series of historical gardens which highlight changes in urban middle-class gardens from the 17th to 20th centuries. One of the

contd.

museum's historic almshouses will shortly be restored, furnished and opened to the public.
Times: Open all year, Tue-Sat 10-5, Sun & BH Mons 12-5 (Closed Mon, Good Fri, Xmas & New Year). **Fee:** Free. Prices for special lectures on request. **Facilities:** P (150yds) (meter parking) ✗ licensed & (wheelchair available) toilets for disabled shop ✖ (ex guide dogs)

WC2
GILBERT COLLECTION
Somerset House, Strand WC2R 1LN (Underground - Temple, Covent Garden)
☎ 020 7240 9400 ▤ 020 7240 4060
e-mail: info@gilbert-collection.org.uk
Times: Open Mon-Sat 10-6, Sun & BH Mon's noon-6pm. Last admission 5.15pm. **Facilities:** P (400 metres) ▦ ✗ & toilets for disabled shop ✖ (ex guide dogs) *Details not confirmed for 2002* ▦

SE1
GOLDEN HINDE EDUCATIONAL MUSEUM
St Mary Overie Dock, Cathedral St SE1 9DE (On the Thames path between Southwark Cathedral and Globe Theatre)
☎ 020 7403 0123 ▤ 020 7407 5908
e-mail: info@goldenhinde.co.uk

A full size replica of Sir Francis Drake's famous 16th century galleon. Just like the original, this *Golden Hinde* has circumnavigated the globe. You can explore the five decks, and costumed crew add to the atmosphere. Special events include Living History re-enactments. There are holiday workshops for children and the ship is also available for private hire.
Times: Open all year, 9.30-5.30. Visitors are advised to check opening times as they may vary due to closures for functions. **Fee:** £2.50 (ch 4-13 £1.75, under 4's free, concessions £2.10) **Facilities:** P (on street parking) ▦ shop (ex guide dogs) ▦

EC2
THE GUILDHALL
Gresham Steet EC2V 5AE (Underground - Bank, St Paul's)
☎ 020 7606 3030 ▤ 020 7260 1119
Times: Open all year, May-Sep, daily 10-5; Oct-Apr, Mon-Sat 10-5. (Closed Xmas, New Year, Good Fri, Etr Mon & infrequently for Civic occasions). **Facilities:** & shop ✖ *Details not confirmed for 2002*

N6
HIGHGATE CEMETERY
Swains Ln N6 6PJ (Underground - Archway, see directions posted at exit)
☎ 020 8340 1834
Times: Open all year. Eastern Cemetery: daily 10 (11 wknds)-5 (4 in winter). Western Cemetery by guided tour only: Sat & Sun 11-4 (3 in winter); midweek tours 12, 2 & 4 (12, 2 & 3 in winter). No weekday tours in Dec, Jan & Feb. Special tours by arrangement. (Closed 25-26 Dec & during funerals). **Facilities:** ▣ shop ✖ *Details not confirmed for 2002*

SE1
HMS BELFAST
Morgans Ln, Tooley St SE1 2JH (Underground - London Bridge/Tower Hill/Monument. Rail: London Bridge)
☎ 020 7940 6300 ▤ 020 7403 0719
e-mail: hmsbelfast@iwm.org.uk

Europe's last surviving big gun armoured warship from WWII, *HMS Belfast* was launched in 1938 and served in the North Atlantic and Arctic with the Home Fleet. She led the Allied naval bombardment of German positions on D-Day, and was saved for the nation in 1971. A tour of the ship will take you from the Captain's Bridge through nine decks to the massive Boiler and Engine Rooms. You can visit the cramped Messdecks, Officers' Cabins, Galley, Sick Bay, Dentist and Laundry.
Times: Open all year, daily. Mar-Oct 10-6, last admission 5.15; Nov-28 Feb 10-5, last admission 4.15. **Fee:** £5.40 (ch under 16 free, concessions £4.40). Party. **Facilities:** P (150yds) ▦ & (wheelchair lift for access on board) toilets for disabled shop ✖ (ex guide dogs) ▦

W4
HOGARTH HOUSE
Hogarth Ln, Great West Rd W4 2QN (50yds W of Hogarth rdbt on Great West Road A4)
☎ 020 8994 6757 ▤ 020 8583 4595

This 18th-century house was the country home of artist William Hogarth (1697-1764) during the last 15 years of his life. The house contains displays on the artist's life, and many of his satirical engravings.
Times: Open Apr-Oct, Tue-Fri 1-5, Sat-Sun 1-6; Nov-Mar, Tue-Fri 1-4, Sat-Sun 1-5. (Closed Mon (ex BH's), Jan, 25-26 Dec, Good Fri).
Fee: Free. **Facilities:** P (25 & 50yds) (spaces marked in Axis Centre car park) & toilets for disabled shop ✖ (ex guide dogs)

SE23
THE HORNIMAN MUSEUM & GARDENS
London Rd, Forest Hill SE23 3PQ (situated on A205)
☎ 020 8699 2339 (rec info) 020 8699 1872
▤ 020 8291 5506
e-mail: marketing@horniman.ac.uko.uk
Times: Open all year, Mon-Sat 10.30-5.30, Sun 2-5.30 (Closed 24-26 Dec). Gardens close at sunset.
Facilities: P (opposite museum) ▦ & (chair lift to parts of upper floor) toilets for disabled shop (closed until 2001) ✖ (ex guide dogs or in gardens) *Details not confirmed for 2002*

SW1
HOUSES OF PARLIAMENT
Westminster SW1A 0AA (Underground - Westminster)
☎ 020 7219 4272 ▤ 020 7219 5839
e-mail: poi@parliament.uk
Times: Telephone well in advance for information on how to go about arranging permits for a tour of the building, or to listen to debates from the Strangers Gallery. Tours must be arranged through a Member of Parliament. **Facilities:** P (250yds) & (by arrangement) toilets for disabled shop ✖ ▦ *Details not confirmed for 2002*

SE1
IMPERIAL WAR MUSEUM
Lambeth Rd SE1 6HZ (Underground - Lambeth North, Elephant & Castle or Waterloo)
☎ 020 7416 5000 ▤ 020 7416 5374
e-mail: mail@iwm.org.uk

Founded in 1917, this museum illustrates and records all aspects of the two World Wars and other military operations involving Britain and the Commonwealth since 1914. There are always special exhibitions and the programme of events includes film shows and lectures. The museum has a wealth of military reference material, although some reference departments are open to the public by appointment only.
Times: Open all year, daily 10-6. (Closed 24-26 Dec). **Fee:** £6.50 (ch & pen free, concessions £5.50). Free admission after 4.30 daily. Reduced rates for disabled & group bookings. **Facilities:** ℙ (on street 100 mtr) (metered Mon-Fri) ▆ ☉ (disabled parking, wheelchair hire & access, study room) toilets for disabled shop ⅄ (ex guide dogs) ▅

N3
THE JEWISH MUSEUM
The Sternberg Centre, 80 East End Rd, Finchley N3 2SY (Underground - Finchley Central, 10 mins walk via Station Rd & Manor View)
☎ 020 8349 1143 ▤ 020 8343 2162
e-mail: jml.finchley@btinternet.com
Times: Open all year, Sun 10.30-4.30, Mon-Thu 10.30-5. Closed Jewish festivals, public holidays & 24 Dec-4 Jan. Also closed Sun in Aug & BH wknds. **Facilities:** ℙ (50m) (on street parking) ▆ ☉ toilets for disabled shop ⅄ *Details not confirmed for 2002*

NW1
THE JEWISH MUSEUM
Raymond Burton House, 129-131 Albert St, Camden Town NW1 7NB (Underground - Camden Town, 3 mins walk from station)
☎ 020 7284 1997 ▤ 020 7267 9008
e-mail: admin@jmus.org.uk

The museum explores the history and religious life of the Jewish community in Britain and beyond. The History Gallery traces Jewish roots in Britain from the Norman Conquest until recent times, and the Ceremonial Art Gallery illustrates Jewish religious life. There are social history displays and re-constructions, and, at a different address, a moving exhibition on a British-born Holocaust survivor.
Times: Open Mon-Thu, 10-4, Sun 10-5. Closed Jewish Festivals & public holidays. **Fee:** £3.50 (ch, students, disabled & UB40 £1.50, pen £2.50) Family ticket £8. **Facilities:** ℙ (outside museum) (pay & display parking) ☉ (induction loop in lecture room linked to audio-visual unit) toilets for disabled shop ⅄ (ex guide dogs) ▅

NW3
KEATS HOUSE
Keats Grove, Hampstead NW3 2RR (Underground - Hampstead, about 15mins walk from station)
☎ 020 7435 2062 ▤ 020 7431 9293
e-mail: keatshouse@corpoflondon.gov.uk

The poet John Keats lived in this house from 1818-1820 and wrote some of his most famous poems, including 'Ode to a Nightingale' here. His fiancée, Fanny Brawne, lived next door, and they often walked together on nearby Hampstead Heath. The house contains many of his personal items including inkstand, engagement ring, paintings, jewellery and manuscripts.
Times: Open 23 Apr-10 Dec, Tue-Sat 12-5. Tue-Sat between 10-12 guided tours, schools & visits by appointment take place. Wed between 5-8 a programme of tours & lectures are available. Sun & BH'S 12-5. **Fee:** £3 (under 16's free, concessions £1.50) Party 10+. Garden free. **Facilities:** ℙ (500yds) (residents parking in operation) ☉ shop ⅄ (ex guide dogs)

W8
KENSINGTON PALACE STATE APARTMENTS & ROYAL CEREMONIAL DRESS COLLECTION
Kensington Gardens W8 4PX (Underground - High Street Kensington or Notting Hill Gate)
☎ 020 7937 9561 ▤ 020 7376 0198

Highlights of a visit to Kensington include the recently restored Kings Apartments with a fine collection of Old Masters; Tintoretto and Van Dyke amongst them. The Royal Ceremonial Dress Collection includes a selection of HM The Queen's dresses, representations of tailor's and dressmaker's workshops, and a display of dresses that belonged to Diana, Princess of Wales.
Times: Open 10-4, from Mar-Winter season daily 10-5, Open Wed-Sun 10-4 during Winter. **Fee:** £8.80 (ch £6.30, concessions £6.90) Family ticket £26.80. Prices subject to change. **Facilities:** ℙ (500yds) ▆ ☉ (cafeteria has wheelchair access ramp) toilets for disabled shop ⅄ (ex guide dogs) ▅

NW3
KENWOOD
Hampstead Ln NW3 7JR (Underground - Hampstead)
☎ 020 8348 1286 ▤ 020 8348 7325
Times: Open all year, Apr-Oct, daily 10-6 (Sun 10-8 in Aug); Oct, daily 10-5; Nov-Mar, daily 10-4. (Closed 24-25 Dec & 1 Jan). **Facilities:** ℙ ▆ ✕ licensed ☉ toilets for disabled shop ⅄ (ex grounds) ⧓ *Details not confirmed for 2002*

W14
LEIGHTON HOUSE MUSEUM & ART GALLERY
12 Holland Park Rd W14 8LZ (Underground - High Street Kensington)
☎ 020 7602 3316 ▤ 020 7371 2467
Times: Open all year, daily 11-5.30. Garden open Apr-Sep 11-5. (Closed Tue). Open Spring & Summer BH's. **Facilities:** ✝ *Details not confirmed for 2002*

W8
LINLEY SAMBOURNE HOUSE
18 Stafford Ter W8 7BH (Underground - High Street Kensington)
☎ 020 7602 3316 ▤ 020 7602 3316

The home of Linley Sambourne (1844-1910), chief political cartoonist at *Punch* magazine, has had its magnificent artistic interior preserved, almost unchanged, since the late 19th century. Also displayed are many of Sambourne's own drawings and photographs.
Times: Closed until 2002, telephone for details. **Fee:** Admission charged **Facilities:** ℙ (metered parking) shop ✝

SE1
LONDON AQUARIUM
County Hall, Riverside Building, Westminster Bridge Rd SE1 7PB (Underground-Waterloo & Westminster. On south bank next to Westminster Bridge, nr Big Ben & London Eye)
☎ 020 7967 8000 ▤ 020 7967 8029
e-mail: info@londonaquarium.co.uk

One of Europe's largest displays of global aquatic life. Explore the waters of the world and witness breathtakingly beautiful and dramatic underwater scenes, featuring thousands of living specimens from rivers, oceans and seas across our planet.
Times: Open all year, daily 10-6. Last admission 1hr before closing. Closed 25 Dec. **Fee:** £8.75 (ch 3-14 £5.25, pen & students £6.50, ch under 3yrs free, registered disabled £3.50). Family ticket (2 adults, 2 children) £25. **Facilities:** ℙ (600m) ☕ ♿ (wheelchairs available) toilets for disabled shop ✝ (ex guide & hearing dogs) ◗

N1
THE LONDON CANAL MUSEUM
12/13 New Wharf Rd N1 9RT (Underground - Kings Cross)
☎ 020 7713 0836
e-mail: info@canalmuseum.org.uk

The museum covers the development of London's canals (particularly Regent's Canal), canal vessels and trade, and the way of life of the canal people. Housed in a former ice warehouse and stables, it also illustrates horse transport and the unusual trade of importing ice from Norway; there are two large ice wells under the floor. Facilities include temporary moorings, so you can arrive by boat if you want. There are regular special exhibitions.
Times: Open all year, Tue-Sun & BH Mon 10-4.30 (last admission 4). Closed 24-26 & 31 Dec. **Fee:** £2.50 (ch, students, pen & UB40s £1.25, under 8's free). Groups 10+ **Facilities:** ℙ (metered parking Mon-Fri before 6.30pm) ♿ (Large print guides) toilets for disabled shop ✝ (ex guide dogs) ◗

SE1
LONDON DUNGEON
28-34 Tooley St SE1 2SZ (Next to London Bridge Stn)
☎ 0870 8460666 ▤ 020 7378 1529
e-mail: londondungeon@
merlin-entertinments.com

A modest entrance off a street near London Bridge station will lead you through a series of vaults where the seamy side of life in past centuries is re-created. Not recommended for the faint-hearted. Entry includes the `Jack the Ripper' show, which presents a 15-minute tour through Victorian Whitechapel and `Great Fire of London'.
Times: Open all year, daily, Apr-Sep 10-5.30; Oct-Mar 10.30-5. Late night opening in the Summer. Telephone for exact times. **Fee:** £10.95 (ch 14 & pen £6.95, students £9.50). **Facilities:** ℙ (NCP 200yds) ☕ ♿ toilets for disabled shop ✝ (ex guide dogs) ◗

NW1
LONDON PLANETARIUM
Marylebone Rd NW1 5LR (Underground - Baker Street)
☎ 020 7935 6861 ▤ 020 7465 0862
e-mail: firstname.lastname@
madame-tussauds.com
Times: Open daily (ex 25 Dec), star shows from 12.20, every 40 mins (10.20am wknds & holidays). **Facilities:** ℙ (200 mtrs) ♿ (induction loop) toilets for disabled shop ✝ (ex guide dogs) *Details not confirmed for 2002* ◗

WC2
LONDON TRANSPORT MUSEUM
The Piazza, Covent Garden WC2E 7BB (Underground - Covent Garden, Leicester Sq or Holburn)
☎ 020 7379 6344 & 020 7565 7299
▤ 020 7565 7250
e-mail: contact@ltmuseum.co.uk

Covent Garden's original Victorian flower market is home to this excellent museum which explores the colourful story of London and its famous transport system from 1800 to the present day. There are buses, trams, tube trains, and posters, as well as touch-screen displays, videos, working models and tube simulators to bring the story to life.
Times: Open all year, daily 10-6, Fri 11-6. Last admission 5.15pm. (Closed 24-26 Dec). **Fee:** £5.95 (con £3.95, under 16 free). Family ticket £13.95. Family season ticket £24.95) Party. **Facilities:** ℙ (5 mins walk) (parking meters) ☕ ♿ (lift & ramps, touch & sign tours) toilets for disabled shop ✝ (ex guide dogs) ◗

NW1
London Zoo

Regents Park NW1 4RY (Underground - Camden Town or Regents Park)
☎ 020 7722 3333 🖷 020 7586 5743
e-mail: marketing@zsl.org

London Zoo is home to over 12,000 animals, insects, reptiles and fish. First opened in 1828, the Zoo can claim the world's first aquarium, insect and reptile house. Daily events such as Animals in Action, feeding times and Animal Encounters give an insight into animal behaviour. Exhibits include the Aquarium, Reptile House, and the Moonlight World where day and night are reversed. The 'Web of Life' exhibition introduces the amazing range of life forms found in Earth's major habitats, through live animal exhibits and interactive displays.

Times: Open all year, daily from 10am. (Closed 25 Dec). **Fee:** £10 (ch 3-15 £7, concessions £8.50). Family £30. **Facilities:** P (charged) ☕ ✕ licensed ♿ (wheelchairs & booster scooter available) toilets for disabled shop

NW8
Lord's Tour & M.C.C. Museum

Lord's Ground NW8 8QN (Underground - St John's Wood)
☎ 020 7432 1033 🖷 020 7266 3825
e-mail: tours@mcc.org.uk

Established in 1787, Lord's is the home of the MCC and cricket. Guided tours take you behind the scenes, and highlights include the Long Room and the MCC Museum, where the Ashes and a large collection of paintings and memorabilia are displayed. The Museum is open on match days for spectators.

Times: Open all year, Oct-Mar tours at 12 & 2pm. Apr-Sep 10am, 12 & 2pm (restrictions on some match days). Telephone for details & bookings. **Fee:** Guided tour £6.50 (ch £4.50, students & pen £5). Family ticket (2 adults & 2 ch) £19. Party 25+. Museum only £2.50 (concessions £1) plus ground admission (match days only). **Facilities:** P ✕ licensed ♿ (by arrangment) toilets for disabled shop (ex guide dogs)

NW1
Madame Tussaud's

Marylebone Rd NW1 5LR (Underground - Baker Street)
☎ 020 7935 6861 🖷 020 7465 0862
e-mail: firstname.lastname@madame-tussauds.com

Times: Open all year 10-5.30 (9.30am wknds, 9am summer). (Closed 25 Dec). **Facilities:** P (200 mtrs) ☕ ♿ (All parts accessible except Spirit of London ride) toilets for disabled shop (ex guide dogs) *Details not confirmed for 2002*

SW1
Mall Galleries

The Mall SW1Y 5BD (Underground - Charing Cross)
☎ 020 7930 6844 🖷 020 7839 7830

Times: Open all year, daily 10-5. **Facilities:** P (50 yds) (no parking at the Mall) ♿ (chairlift to galleries) *Details not confirmed for 2002*

EC4
Middle Temple Hall

The Temple EC4Y 9AT (Underground - Temple, Blackfriars. Turn left at the embankment & left into Middle Temple Lane. Hall half way up on left)
☎ 020 7427 4800 🖷 020 7427 4801
e-mail: library@middletemple.org.uk

Between Fleet Street and the Thames are the Middle and Inner Temples, separate Inns of Court, so named because of the Knights Templar who occupied the site from about 1160. Middle Temple Hall is a fine example of Tudor architecture and was completed in about 1570. The hall has a double hammerbeam roof and beautiful stained glass. The 29ft-long high table was made from a single oak tree from Windsor Forest. Sir Francis Drake was a visitor to and friend of the Middle Temple, and a table made from timbers from the *Golden Hind* - the ship in which he sailed around the world - is shown.

Times: Open all year, Mon-Fri 10-12 & 3-4 (Closed BH & legal vacations). **Fee:** Free. **Facilities:** ♿

EC3
The Monument

Monument St EC3R 8AH (Underground - Monument)
☎ 020 7626 2717 🖷 020 7403 4477

Designed by Wren and Hooke and erected in 1671-7, the Monument commemorates the Great Fire of 1666 which is reputed to have started in nearby Pudding Lane. The fire destroyed nearly 90 churches and about 13,000 houses. This fluted Doric column stands 202ft high (Pudding Lane is exactly 202ft from its base) and you can climb the 311 steps to a platform at the summit, and receive a certificate as proof of your athletic abilities.

Times: Open Mon-Sun, 10-6. Last admission 5.40pm. **Fee:** £1.50 (ch under 16 50p). **Facilities:**

SE1
Museum of Garden History

Lambeth Palace Rd SE1 7LB (Underground - Waterloo/Lambeth North, next to Lambeth Palace)
☎ 020 7401 8865 🖷 020 7401 8869
e-mail: info@museumgardenhistory.org

Adjacent to the south gateway of Lambeth Palace is the former church of St Mary-at-Lambeth, now the Museum of Garden History. There is a permanent exhibition on the history of gardens and a collection of ancient tools. The shop sells souvenirs, gifts and seeds from the plant collection. Admiral Bligh of the *Bounty* is buried in the garden.

Times: Open daily 10.30-5, tel for winter opening. **Fee:** Free. **Facilities:** P (100yds) (metered) ☕ ♿ shop (ex guide dogs)

EC2
MUSEUM OF LONDON
150 London Wall EC2Y 5HN (Underground - St Paul's, Barbican)
☎ 020 7600 3699 ▤ 020 7600 1058
e-mail: info@museumoflondon.org.uk

Dedicated to the story of London and its people, the Museum of London exists to inspire a passion for London in all who visit it. As well as the permanent collection, the Museum has a varied exhibition programme with three major temporary exhibitions and six topical displays each year. There are also smaller exhibitions in the newly-developed foyer gallery. A wide programme of lectures and activities are provided. **Times:** Open all year, Mon-Sat 10-5.50, Sun 12-5.50 (closed 24-26 Dec & 1 Jan). **Fee:** £5 (concessions £3, under 16 free). An annual ticket, 1 year from date of purchase. **Facilities:** ▣ ▣ ♿ (wheelchairs available, lifts & induction loops, parking) toilets for disabled shop ✖ (ex guide dogs) ▼

EC1
MUSEUM OF THE ORDER OF ST JOHN
St John's Gate, St John's Ln EC1M 4DA (Underground - Farringdon, Barbican)
☎ 020 7253 6644 ▤ 020 7336 0587
Times: Open all year, Mon-Sat 10-5, Sat 10-4 (Closed Etr, Xmas wk & BH wknds). Guided tours 11 & 2.30 Tue, Fri & Sat. **Facilities:** ▣ (meters/ NCP 300yds) ♿ toilets for disabled shop ✖ (ex guide dogs) *Details not confirmed for 2002*

WC2
MUSEUMS OF THE ROYAL COLLEGE OF SURGEONS
35-43 Lincoln's Inn Fields WC2A 3PN (Underground - Holborn)
☎ 020 7869 6560 ▤ 020 7869 6564
e-mail: museums@rcseng.ac.uk

Two museums are housed here - the Hunterian Museum contains the anatomical and pathological specimens collected by John Hunter FRS (1728-1793), a renowned surgeon and teacher of anatomy, and displays relating to the work of Sir Joseph Lister, pioneer of antiseptic surgery. The Odontological Museum contains an extensive collection of human and animal skulls and teeth as well as dental instruments. **Times:** Currently under refurbishment, (Closed for 18 months from Nov 2001) **Fee:** Free. **Facilities:** ▣ (25 metres) (pay & display 8-6pm) ♿ (prior notice required) shop ✖ (ex guide dogs)

SW3
NATIONAL ARMY MUSEUM
Royal Hospital Rd, Chelsea SW3 4HT (Underground - Sloane Square)
☎ 020 7730 0717 ▤ 020 7823 6573
e-mail: info@national-army-museum.ac.uk
Times: Open all year, daily 10-5.30. (Closed Good Fri, May Day, 24-26 Dec & 1 Jan). **Facilities:** ▣ ▣ ♿ (wheelchair lift to access lower ground floor) toilets for disabled shop ✖ (ex guide dogs) *Details not confirmed for 2002*

LORD'S TOUR
Lord's Cricket Ground
London, NW8 8QN
Telephone 020 7432 1033

Expert guided tours of Lord's include:

- **PAVILION** – visit the Long Room, Players' Dressing Room and Presentation Balcony.
- **MCC MUSEUM** – the fascinating history of cricket bought to life with hundreds of exhibits including the Ashes.
- **REAL TENNIS COURT** – the ancient game of Henry VIII lives on at Lord's.
- **MOUND STAND** – uniquely designed with magnificent views of the ground.
- **NURSERY END** – home to the Indoor School, Practice Ground and futuristic NatWest Media Centre.
- **LORD'S SHOP** – souvenirs from a tee shirt to a tea towel, a mug to a cap.

OPEN THROUGHOUT THE YEAR
(*except major matches and preparation days*).
ADMISSION CHARGE
Group rates and family tickets available.
Tours normally at 12 noon and 2pm (also 10am April to September) – *telephone for more details and bookings.*

WC2
NATIONAL GALLERY
Trafalgar Square WC2N 5DN (Underground - Charing Cross, Leicester Square, Embankment & Piccadilly Circus. Rail: Charing Cross. Located on N side of Trafalgar Sq)
☎ 020 7747 2885 ▤ 020 7747 2423
e-mail: information@ng-london.org.uk

All the great periods of Western European painting from 1260-1900 are represented here, although most of the national collection of British works is housed at the Tate. The gallery's particular treasures include Velazquez's *Toilet of Venus,* Leonardo da Vinci's cartoon *(the Virgin and Child with Saints Anne and John the Baptist)*, Rembrandt's *Belshazzar's Feast*, Van Gogh's *Sunflowers*, and Titian's *Bacchus and Ariadne*. The British paintings include Gainsborough's *Mr and Mrs Andrews* and Constable's *Haywain*. **Times:** Open all year, daily 10-6, (Wed until 9pm). Special major charging exhibitions open normal gallery times. Closed Good Fri, 24-26 Dec & 1 Jan. **Fee:** Free. **Facilities:** ▣ (100yds) ▣ ✖ licensed ♿ (wheelchair,induction loop,lift,deaf/blind visitor tours) toilets for disabled shop ✖ (ex guide & hearing dogs) ▼

SE10
NATIONAL MARITIME MUSEUM
Romney Rd SE10 9NF (central Greenwich)
☎ 020 8858 4422 & 8312 6565 info line
🖷 020 8312 6632
Times: Open all year, daily 10-5. (Closed 24-26 Dec & 1 Jan)
Facilities: P (50 yds) (parking in Greenwich limited) ✗ licensed & (wheelchairs, advisory service for hearing/sight impaired) toilets for disabled shop 🦮 *Details not confirmed for 2002* ☜

WC2
NATIONAL PORTRAIT GALLERY
St Martin's Place WC2H 0HE (Underground - Charing Cross, Leicester Square)
☎ 020 7306 0055 🖷 020 7306 0056

The aim of the gallery is to illustrate British history through a collection of portraits of famous, and infamous, men and women. The portraits are arranged in chronological order from the top floor, and as well as paintings, there are sculptures, miniatures, engravings, photographs and cartoons among the displays.
Times: Open all year, Mon-Wed & Sat-Sun 10-6, Thu-Fri 10-9. (Closed Good Fri, 24-26 Dec & 1 Jan). **Fee:** Free. **Facilities:** P (200yds) ☕ ✗ licensed & (stair climber, touch tours, audio guide, large print captions) toilets for disabled shop 🦮 (ex guide dogs) ☜

SW7
THE NATURAL HISTORY MUSEUM
Cromwell Rd SW7 5BD (Underground - South Kensington)
☎ 020 7942 5000 🖷 020 7942 5536
e-mail: marketing@nhm.ac.uk
Times: Open all year, Mon-Sat 10-5.50, Sun 11-5.50 (last admission 5.30) **Facilities:** P (metered 180yds) limited parking, public transport advised ☕ ✗ licensed & (ex top floor & one gallery, wheelchairs available) toilets for disabled shop (4 giftshops) 🦮 (ex guide dogs) *Details not confirmed for 2002* ☜

SE10
OLD ROYAL OBSERVATORY
Greenwich Park, Greenwich SE10 9NF (off A2)
☎ 020 8858 4422 & 8312 6565 recording
🖷 020 8312 6632
Times: Open all year, daily 10-5 (Closed 24-26 Dec & 1 Jan)
Facilities: P & toilets for disabled shop 🦮 *Details not confirmed for 2002* ☜

WC1
PETRIE MUSEUM OF EGYPTIAN ARCHAEOLOGY
Malet Place, Univerity College London WC1E 6BT (on 1st floor of the D M S Watson building, in Malet Place, off Torrington Place)
☎ 020 7504 2884 🖷 020 7504 2886
e-mail: petrie.museum@ucl.ac.uk
Times: Open all year, Tue-Fri 1-5, Sat 10-1. Closed for 1 wk at Xmas/Etr. **Facilities:** ☕ ✗ & shop 🦮 (ex guide dogs) *Details not confirmed for 2002*

W1
POLLOCK'S TOY MUSEUM
1 Scala St W1P 1LT (Underground - Goodge Street)
☎ 020 7636 3452
e-mail: toymuseum@hotmail.com
Times: Open all year, Mon-Sat 10-5. (Closed Sun & Xmas).
Facilities: P (100 yds) (Central London restrictions) & shop *Details not confirmed for 2002* ☜

SW1
THE QUEEN'S GALLERY
Buckingham Palace, Buckingham Palace Rd SW1A 1AA (Underground - Victoria/Green Park/St. James' Park)
☎ 020 7839 1377 🖷 020 7930 9625
e-mail: buckinghampalace@royalcollection.org.uk

The Queen's Gallery at Buckingham Palace was first opened to the public in 1962 to display paintings, drawings, furniture and other works of art in the Royal Collection.
Times: Closed for major refurbishment, due to re-open 2002, the year of The Queen's Golden Jubilee. **Fee:** *Prices not confirmed for 2002*
Facilities: P (200yds) & shop 🦮 (ex guide dogs)

SE10
THE QUEENS HOUSE
Romney Rd SE10 9NF (central Greenwich)
☎ 020 8858 4422 & 8312 6565 info line
🖷 020 8312 6632
Times: Open from Dec-24 Sep. **Facilities:** P (50 yds) ✗ licensed & (Blind kit/stairclimber/wheelchairs) toilets for disabled shop 🦮 *Details not confirmed for 2002* ☜

SE3
RANGERS HOUSE
Chesterfield Walk SE10 8QY
☎ 020 8853 0035
Times: Open all year, Apr-Sep, daily 10-6 (Oct 10-5); Nov-Mar, Wed-Sun 10-4. (Closed 24-25 Dec & 1 Jan). Telephone for further details.
Facilities: P & toilets for disabled 🦮 (in certain areas) ⚎ *Details not confirmed for 2002*

W1
ROCK CIRCUS
London Pavilion, Piccadilly Circus W1V 9LA (Underground - Piccadilly Circus)
☎ 020 7734 7203 🖷 020 7734 8023
Times: Open all year, Mar-Sep, Sun-Mon & Wed-Thu 10-8, Tue 11-8, Fri & Sat 10-9; Oct-Feb, Sun-Mon & Wed-Thu 10-6, Tue 11-6, Fri & Sat 10-7. **Facilities:** P (200yds) & (lift to all floors with member of staff) toilets for disabled shop 🦮 *Details not confirmed for 2002* ☜

W1
ROYAL ACADEMY OF ARTS
Burlington House, Piccadilly W1V 0DS (Underground - Piccadilly Circus)
☎ 020 7300 8000   & 0171 439 4996/7
🖹 020 7300 8001
Times: Open all year, daily 10-6. (Closed 25 Dec & Good Fri).
Facilities: 💶 ✖ licensed & toilets for disabled shop 🎁 🚻 *Details not confirmed for 2002* 🥢

NW9
ROYAL AIR FORCE MUSEUM
Grahame Park Way, Hendon NW9 5LL (Underground - Colindale)
☎ 020 8205 2266   🖹 020 8358 4981
e-mail: groupbusiness@rafmuseum.com

Seventy full-size original aeroplanes and other exhibits, all under cover, tell the story of flight through the ages. Of particular note is our spectacular sensory, sound and light show "Our Finest Hour" telling the story of the Battle of Britain. Visitors can try the interactive gallery, thrill on the simulator ride, take control of the cockpit trainer and walk through the mighty Sunderland flying boat.
Times: Open daily 10-6. (Closed 24-26 Dec & 1 Jan). **Fee:** £7.50 (accompanied ch, pen & disabled free. Unaccompanied ch, students & reg unemployed £4.90). Party 20+. **Facilities:** 🅿 💶 ✖ licensed & (lifts, ramps & wheelchairs available) toilets for disabled shop 🎁 (ex guide dogs) 🥢

SW1
THE ROYAL MEWS
Buckingham Palace, Buckingham Palace Rd SW1W 0QH (Underground - Green Park, St. James' Park)
☎ 020 7839 1377   (info line)
🖹 020 7930 9625
e-mail: buckinghampalace@ royalcollection.org.uk

Designed by John Nash and completed in 1825, the Royal Mews houses the State Coaches, horse drawn carriages and motor cars used for coronations, state visits, royal weddings and the State Opening of Parliament. These include the Gold State Coach, made in 1762, with panels painted by the Florentine artist Cipriani. As one of the finest working stables in existence, the Royal Mews provides a unique opportunity for you to see a working department of the Royal Household.
Times: Open Oct-Jul, Mon-Thu, 12-4; Aug-Sep, Mon-Thu, 10.30-4.30.
Fee: £4.60 (ch 5-17 £2.60, under5's free, pen £3.60) Family ticket (2 adults & 2 ch) £10.80. **Facilities:** 🅿 (200yds) & toilets for disabled shop 🎁 (ex guide dogs) 🥢

SE10
ROYAL NAVAL COLLEGE
Greenwich SE10 9NN (In centre of Greenwich, off the one-way system, college approach, located on the Thames next to the Cutty Sark)
☎ 020 8269 4791   🖹 020 8269 4786
e-mail: info@greenwichfoundation.org.uk

The Grade I listed Old Royal Navy College buildings are now in the care of the Greenwich Foundation. They occupy the site of the Tudor palace where Henry VIII and Elizabeth I were born. The former Greenwich Hospital buildings incorporate a painted hall by Thornhill and a chapel by James Stuart. Also open to the public are the beautiful grounds of the estate, and a visitor centre featuring an exhibition on its Tudor origins and on the world heritage site of maritime Greenwich.
Times: Open all year (Painted Hall and Chapel only), daily 10-5 (last admission 4.15). **Fee:** Gate Centre: free admission. Painted Hall & Chapel: £3 (ch free & con £2), admission free after 3.30 & all day Sun.
Facilities: 🅿 (200m) (all local streets: yellow line roads) 💶 ✖ licensed (can be given access if prior notice given) shop 🎁 (ex guide dogs) 🥢

SW7
SCIENCE MUSEUM
Exhibition Rd, South Kensington SW7 2DD (Underground - South Kensington, signposted from tube station)
☎ 020 7942 4000   🖹 020 7942 4421
e-mail: sciencemuseum@nmsi.ac.uk

Ideal for children and adults too, the displays feature many working models with knobs to press, handles to turn and buttons to push to various different effects: exhibits are set in motion, light up, rotate and make noises. The collections cover science, technology, engineering and industry through the ages; there are galleries dealing with printing, chemistry, nuclear physics, navigation, photography, electricity, communications and medicine. The new Wellcome Wing includes an IMAX cinema, six new galleries and a restaurant.
Times: Open all year, daily 10-6. (Closed 24-26 Dec). **Fee:** £7.95 (concessions £4.95, under 16's free). Admission is free after 4.30pm.
Facilities: 💶 ✖ licensed & (personal 2hr tour of museum) toilets for disabled shop 🎁 (ex guide dogs) 🥢

SE1
SHAKESPEARE'S GLOBE EXHIBITION
New Globe Walk, Bankside SE1 9DT (Underground - London Bridge, walk along Bankside. Mansion House, walk across Southwark Bridge)
☎ 020 7902 1500 🖹 020 7902 1515

Guides help to bring England's theatrical heritage to life at the 'unparalleled and astonishing' recreation of this famous theatre. Discover what an Elizabethan audience would have been like, find out about the rivalry between the bankside theatres, the bear baiting and the stews, hear about the penny stinkards and find out what a bodger is.
Times: Open all year; Sep-May, daily 10-5 (ex 24-25 Dec). May-Sep (theatre season), opening times restricted, phone for details.
Fee: *Prices not confirmed for 2002* **Facilities:** P (10 mins walk) ☕ ✗ licensed ♿ toilets for disabled shop ✸ (ex guide dogs) 🐕

WC2
SIR JOHN SOANE'S MUSEUM
13 Lincoln's Inn Fields WC2A 3BP (Underground - Holborn)
☎ 020 7405 2107 🖹 020 7831 3957

Sir John Soane was responsible for some of the most splendid architecture in London, and his house, built in 1812, contains his collections of antiquities, sculpture, paintings, drawings and books. Amongst his treasures are the *Rake's Progess* and *Election* series of paintings by Hogarth.
Times: Open all year, Tue-Sat 10-5. Also first Tue of month 6-9pm. (Closed BH). Lecture tour Sat 2.30 (limited no of tickets sold from 2pm) **Fee:** Free. **Facilities:** P (200yds) (metered parking) ♿ (w/chair available, phone for details of accessibility) shop ✸ (ex guide dogs) 🐕

SE5
SOUTH LONDON GALLERY
65 Peckham Rd SE5 8UH
☎ 020 7703 6120 7703 9799-taped info
🖹 020 7252 4730
e-mail: mail@southlondonart.com
Times: Open only when exhibitions are in progress, Tue-Fri 11-6, Thu 11-7, wknds 2-6 (Closed Mon). **Facilities:** P (50yds) ✸ *Details not confirmed for 2002*

E9
SUTTON HOUSE
2 & 4 Homerton High St E9 6JQ (Hackney Central train station)
☎ 020 8986 2264
e-mail: tshtan@smtp.ntrust.org.uk
Times: Open 7 Feb-Nov, Wed, Sun & BH Mon 11.30-5.30. Last admission 5pm. (Closed Good Fri). **Facilities:** P (on street parking) (meters) ☕ ♿ (induction loop braille guide) toilets for disabled shop ✸ ✿ *Details not confirmed for 2002*

SW1
TATE BRITAIN
Millbank SW1P 4RG (Underground - Pimlico)
☎ 020 7887 8000 & rec info 020 7887 8008
e-mail: information@tate.org.uk
Times: Open daily 10-5.50. (Closed 24-26 Dec). **Facilities:** P ☕ ✗ licensed ♿ (wheelchairs on request, parking by prior arrangement). toilets for disabled shop ✸ (ex guide & hearing dogs) *Details not confirmed for 2002* 🐕

SE1
TATE MODERN
Bankside SE1 9TG
☎ 020 7887 8008 (info) & 020 7887 8888
🖹 020 7401 5052
e-mail: information@tate.org.uk
Times: Open all year, Sun-Thu 10-6, Fri & Sat 10am-10pm. (Closed 24-26 Dec). **Facilities:** P (limited) ☕ ✗ licensed ♿ (parking available) toilets for disabled shop ✸ (ex guide dogs) *Details not confirmed for 2002* 🐕

SE18
THAMES BARRIER VISITORS CENTRE
Unity Way SE18 5NJ
☎ 020 8305 4188 🖹 020 8855 2146
e-mail: jane.finch@environment-agency.gov.uk
Times: Open all year, telephone for opening times. (Closed Xmas - telephone for details). **Facilities:** 🅿 (charged) ☕ ♿ (lift from river pier approach) toilets for disabled shop ✸ *Details not confirmed for 2002* 🐕

WC2
THEATRE MUSEUM
Russell St, Covent Gardent WC2E 7PA (Underground - Covent Garden, Leicester Sq)
☎ 020 7943 4700 🖹 020 7943 4777
e-mail: tmmailing@vam.ac.uk

Major developments, events and personalities from the performing arts, including stage models, costumes, prints, drawings, posters, puppets, props and a variety of other theatre memorabilia. There are guided tours, demonstrations on the art of stage make-up, and you can dress up in costumes from National Theatre companies. Groups are advised to book in advance.
Times: Open all year, Tue-Sun 10-6. (closed 25 Dec & other public hols) **Fee:** Free. **Facilities:** P (meters, NCP 250yds) ♿ toilets for disabled shop ✸ (ex guide dogs) 🐕

SE1
THE TOWER BRIDGE EXPERIENCE
SE1 2UP (Underground - Tower Hill or London Bridge)
☎ 020 7940 3985 🖹 020 7357 7935
e-mail: enquires@towerbridge.org.uk

One of the capital's most famous landmarks, its glass-covered walkways stand 142ft above the Thames, affording panoramic views of the river. Much of the original machinery for working the bridge can be seen in the engine rooms. The exhibition, The Tower Bridge Experience, uses state-of-the-art effects to present the

contd.

Shakespeare's Globe Exhibition and Theatre Tour

Shakespeare's Globe Exhibition
- **ALL THE WORLD'S A STAGE** - is the most exciting place in which to explore Shakespeare's theatre and the London in which he lived and worked. In the vast UnderGlobe beneath the theatre every aspect of Shakespeare's work is brought imaginatively to life using a

combination of modern technology and traditional crafts. Against the background of Elizabethan Bankside - the city of London's playground in Shakespeare's time - the role of actor, musician and audience is explored. Elizabethan special effects are brought to life on touch screens and the secrets of period costume designs revealed. A visit to the Exhibition includes a tour into today's working theatre, where modern play-acting is informing our understanding of original practice.

OPENING TIMES
Open daily October-April 10am to 5pm. May-September (theatre season) 9am to 12 midday, exhibition and guided tour into the theatre. 12:30 to 4pm exhibition and 'virtual tour' of the theatre. Only closed 24 & 25 December.

Group rates available on request; advanced booking essential.

Telephone 020 7902 1500.

Fax 020 7902 1515

Theatre Box Office
Tel: (+44) (0) 20 7401 9919

Globe Education
Tel: (+44) (0) 20 7902 1433

story of the bridge in a dramatic and exciting fashion.
Times: Open all year, Apr-Oct, 10-6.30; Nov-Mar 9.30-6 (last ticket sold 75 mins before closing). (Closed 24-25 Dec, 16 Jan). **Fee:** £6.25 (ch 5+, Pen, Student £4.25) Family ticket £18.50. Party 10+.
Facilities: P (100yds) & toilets for disabled shop 🍴 🍷

EC3
TOWER OF LONDON
Tower Hill EC3N 4AB (Underground - Tower Hill)
☎ 020 7709 0765

Perhaps the most famous castle in the world, the Tower of London has played a central part in British history. The White Tower, built by William the Conqueror as a show of strength to the people of London, remains one of the most outstanding examples of Norman military architecture in Europe. For hundreds of years the Tower was used, among other things, as the State Prison. It was here that Henry VIII had two of his wives executed, here that Lady Jane Grey died and here that Sir Walter Raleigh was imprisoned. The Yeoman Warders, or `Beefeaters' play an important role in the protection of the Tower - home of the Crown Jewels - and are informative and entertaining. Look out for the ravens, whose continued residence is said to ensure that the Kingdom does not fall. The Crowns and Diamonds exhibition features a number of crowns never displayed to the public before and more than 12,000 rough and polished diamonds. Also open to the public are the Royal Armouries, which received their first recorded visitor as long ago as 1489. The displays include an extensive range of arms and armour dating from the Norman ages, a collection of Spanish arms and the Line of Kings.
Times: Open all year, Mar-Oct, Mon-Sat 9-6, Sun 10-6 (last admission 5pm); Nov-Feb, Tue-Sat 9-5, Sun 10-5 (last admission 4pm). (Closed 24-26 Dec & 1 Jan). **Fee:** £11.30 (ch £7.50, concessions £8.50). Family ticket £34. **Facilities:** P (100yds) (NCP Lower Thames St) 🍷 & (access guide can be obtained in advance call 020 7488 5694) toilets for disabled shop 🍴 (ex guide dogs) 🍷

SW7
VICTORIA AND ALBERT MUSEUM
Cromwell Rd, South Kensington SW7 2RL
(Underground - South Kensington)
☎ 020 7942 2000 ▤ 020 7942 2266
e-mail: infodome@vam.ac.uk

The world's finest museum of the decorative arts, with collections spanning 2000 years, and comprising sculpture, furniture, fashion and textiles, paintings, silver, glass, ceramics, jewellery, books, prints, and photographs from Britain and all over the world. Highlights include the national collection of watercolours, the Dress Court showing fashion from 1500 to the present day, a superb Asian collection, the Jewellery Gallery including the Russian Crown Jewels, and the 20th Century Gallery, devoted to contemporary art and design. Special exhibitions for 2002 include: Radical Fashion (18 Oct 2001 - 6 Jan 2002), Out of Japan (17 Sep 2001 - 3 Feb 2002), Italian Sculpture (14 Mar - 7 Jul 2002). The British Galleries recently re-opened after refurbishment; they tell the story of British design from 1500 to 1900.
Times: Open all year, Mon-Sun 10-5.45. (Closed 24-26 Dec). Wed & last Fri of month open late, 10-10. **Fee:** Free. **Facilities:** P (500yds) 🍷 ✗ licensed & (braille guide, tour tape. for further info, please phone) toilets for disabled shop 🍴 (ex guide dogs) 🍷

SE1
VINOPOLIS, CITY OF WINE
1 Bank End SE1 9BU (Underground-London Bridge. Borough High Street West exit, R into Stoney St, then L into Park St)
☎ 0870 241 4040 ▤ 020 7403 7093
e-mail: sales@vinopolis.co.uk
Times: Open all year, Mon-Fri 10-5.30 (last admission 3.30pm); Sat-Mon from 10 (last admisssion 6pm). Closed 25 Dec & 1 Jan.
Facilities: P (5-10 min walk) (NCP parking) 🍷 ✗ licensed & (lifts & ramps) toilets for disabled shop 🍴 (ex guide dogs) *Details not confirmed for 2002* 🍷

W1
WALLACE COLLECTION
Hertford House, Manchester Square W1U 3BN
(Underground - Bond Street, Baker Street)
☎ 020 7935 0687 ▤ 020 7224 2155
e-mail: admin@wallcoll.demon.co.uk
Times: Open all year, Mon-Sat 10-5, Sun 11-5 (Closed Good Fri, May Day, 24-26 Dec & 1 Jan). **Facilities:** P (NCP & meters) & (ramp wheelchair available upon request) shop 🍴 *Details not confirmed for 2002* 🍷

EC1
WESLEY'S CHAPEL, HOUSE & MUSEUM OF METHODISM
49 City Rd EC1Y 1AU (Underground - Old Street- exit number 4)
☎ 020 7253 2262 ▤ 020 7608 3825

Wesley's Chapel has been the Mother Church of World Methodism since its construction in 1778. The crypt

contd.

houses a museum which traces the development of Methodism from the 18th century to the present day. Wesley's house - built by him in 1779 - was his home when not touring and preaching. Special events are held on May 24 (the anniversary of Wesley's conversion), and November 1st (the anniversary of the Chapel's opening). **Times:** Open all year, Mon-Sat & BH 10-4 (Closed BH's, 25 & 26 Dec). Main service 11am Sun followed by an opportunity to tour the museum and house. **Fee:** House & museum £4 (ch, students, UB40's & pen £2) Party 20+ **Facilities:** P (NCP at Finsbury Square) & (lift to the crypt of the chapel) toilets for disabled shop 𝕏 (ex guide dogs)

SW1
WESTMINSTER ABBEY
Broad Sanctuary SW1P 3PA (Underground - Westminster, St James's Park)
☎ 020 7222 5152 🖷 020 7233 2072
e-mail: jackiepope@westminster-abbey.org

Westminster Abbey was originally a Benedictine monastery. In the 11th century, it was re-founded by St. Edward the Confessor. The great Romanesque abbey Edward built next to his royal palace became his burial place shortly after it was completed. Over the centuries that followed, many more kings and queens have been buried, and many great figures commemorated, in the abbey. The abbey has been the setting for nearly every coronation since that of William the Conqueror in 1066, and for numerous other royal occasions. The present building, begun by Henry III in 1245, is one of the most visited churches in the world. **Times:** Open all year. Abbey: Mon-Fri 9.30-4.45, Sat 9-2.45. Last admission 60 mins before closing. Cloister daily 8-6. No tourist visiting on Sundays, however visitors are welcome at services. The Abbey may at short notice be closed for special services & other events. **Fee:** £6 (ch 11-15 £3, under11's free, pen & students £3). Family ticket (2 adults & 2 ch) £12. **Facilities:** 🍽 & (areas accessible induction loop) shop 𝕏 (ex guide dogs) 🥄

SW1
WESTMINSTER CATHEDRAL
Victoria St SW1P 1QW (300yds from Victoria Station)
☎ 020 7798 9055 🖷 020 7798 9090
e-mail: bpalmer@westminstercathedral.org.uk

Westminster Cathedral is a fascinating example of Victorian architecture. Designed in the Early Christian Byzantine style by John Francis Bentley, its strongly oriental appearance makes it very distinctive. The foundation stone was laid in 1895 but the interior was never completed. The Campanile Bell Tower is 273ft high and has a four-sided viewing gallery with magnificent views over London. The lift is open daily 9am-5pm Mar-Nov but shut Mon-Wed from Dec-Feb. **Times:** Open all year, daily 7-7. **Fee:** Free. **Facilities:** P (0.25m) (2hr metered parking) 🍽 & (all parts accessible except side chapels) shop 𝕏 (ex guide dogs)

If you visit only one museum in London ...

Where else will you find over seven miles of gallery space devoted to 5000 years of sculpture, painting, photography, fashion, glass, furniture and more? The world's most exciting collection of the decorative arts is waiting to be discovered.

make it the V&A.

Victoria and Albert Museum
The National Museum of Art and Design
⊖ South Kensington
For info, call 0870 442 0808
or visit www.vam.ac.uk

SW1
WESTMINSTER HALL
Westminster SW1A 0AA (Underground - Westminster Hall)
☎ 020 7219 4272
Times: Westminster Hall can only be viewed by those on a tour of the Houses of Parliament, which must be arranged by an MP or Peer. **Facilities:** & toilets for disabled shop 𝕏 *Details not confirmed for 2002*

SW13
THE WETLAND CENTRE
Queen Elizabeth Walk SW13 9WT (Underground - Hammersmith)
☎ 020 8409 4400 🖷 020 8409 4401
e-mail: info@wetlandcentre.org.uk

Twenty-five minutes from the heart of London, the Wetland Centre is unique in being the first created wetland habitat on such a huge scale (105 acres) to have been developed in any capital city in the world. Built on the site of the former Barn Elms reservoirs and waterworks, the site has a Discovery Centre, an observatory, an audio-visual theatre, an art gallery, and a restaurant. **Times:** Open all year, Summer, daily 9.30-6 (last admission 5); Winter, daily 9.30-5 (last admission 4). (Closed Xmas Day). **Fee:** £6.75 (ch £4 & pen £5.50). Family ticket £17.50. Groups 10+ **Facilities:** P (charged) 🍽 ✗ licensed & (99% accessible, ramps, lifts) toilets for disabled shop 𝕏 (ex guide dogs) 🥄

E17
WILLIAM MORRIS GALLERY
Lloyd Park, Forest Rd E17 4PP (Underground - Walthamstow Central)
☎ 020 8527 3782 📄 020 8527 7070

Victorian artist, craftsman, poet and free thinker William Morris lived here from 1848 to 1856, and the house has been devoted to his life and work. Displays include fabrics, stained glass, wallpaper and furniture, as well as Pre-Raphaelite paintings, sculpture by Rodin, ceramics and a collection of pictures by Frank Brangwyn, who worked briefly for Morris.
Times: Open all year, Tue-Sat and 1st Sun in each month 10-1 & 2-5. (Closed Mon & BH's). Telephone for Xmas/New Year opening times.
Fee: Free. **Facilities:** 🅿 ♿ shop ✗ ➦

SW19
WIMBLEDON LAWN TENNIS MUSEUM
Centre Court, Church Rd SW19 5AE (Underground - Southfields, 15mins walk)
☎ 020 8946 6131 📄 020 8944 6497
e-mail: alex.keane@AECTC.com

Pictures, displays and memorabilia trace the development of the game over the last century. See the world famous Championship's trophies, as well as film and video footage of great players in action from the 1920s to the present day. There is also the chance to go for a behind-the-scenes guided tour of Centre Court, No.1 Court, and the BBC studios.
Times: Open daily all year, 10.30-5. (Closed middle Sun of Championships, Mon immediately following the Championships, 24-26 Dec & 1 Jan). **Fee:** £5 (ch u5 free, ch £3.50, con £4.25). Party 15+.
Facilities: 🅿 ➦ ✗ licensed ♿ (lift, stairlift to cafe) toilets for disabled shop ✗ (ex guide dogs) ➦

SE1
WINSTON CHURCHILL'S BRITAIN AT WAR EXPERIENCE
64/66 Tooley St SE1 2TF (between London Bridge & Tower Bridge. 2min walk from London Bridge Stn)
☎ 020 7403 3171 📄 020 7403 5104
e-mail: britainatwar@dial.pipex.com

How did it feel to be a British citizen during WWII? Journey back in time and take the lift to the London Underground and shelter from the air raids. Crouch in an Anderson Shelter and hear enemy aircraft overhead. The special effects recreate the sights, sounds and smells of the London Blitz.
Times: Open all year, Apr-Sep 10-5.30pm; Oct-Mar 10-4.30. (Closed 24-26 Dec)
Fee: £5.95 (ch 16 £2.95, student, pen & UB40 £3.95). Family ticket £14.
Facilities: 🅿 (100mtrs) ♿ shop ✗ (ex guide dogs) ➦

🏛 BARNET Map 04 TQ29
MUSEUM OF DOMESTIC DESIGN & ARCHITECTURE
Middlesex University, Cat Hill EN4 8HT (from M25 junct 24 signposted A111 Cockfosters to Cat Hill)
☎ 020 8411 5244 📄 020 8411 6639
e-mail: moda@mdx.ac.uk

Located on Middlesex University's Cat Hill campus, the MoDA houses one of the most comprehensive collections of late 19th and 20th century decorative design for the home. A wide ranging exhibition programme is offered throughout the year, alongside the permanent exhibit, Exploring Interiors: Decoration of the Home 1900-1960.
Times: Open Tue-Sat 10-5, Sun 2-5. (Closed Mon, 22 Dec-1 Jan & Etr).
Fee: Free. **Facilities:** 🅿 ♿ toilets for disabled shop ✗ (ex guide dogs)

🏛 BEXLEY Map 05 TQ47
HALL PLACE
Bourne Rd DA5 1PQ (near junct of A2 & A233)
☎ 01322 526574 📄 01322 522921

Hall Place is an attractive Grade I listed mansion of chequered flint and brick, with wonderful gardens. There is topiary in the form of the `Queen's Beasts'; rose, rock, peat and water gardens; and a herb garden with a fascinating range of plants (labelled in braille) for medicine and cooking. There is also a conservatory, a local studies centre and museum. Please telephone for details of the programme of temporary exhibitions, lectures and concerts in the museum and Great Hall.
Times: Open all year, House: Mon-Sat 10-5, Sun & BHs 11-5 (summer); Tue-Sat 10-4.15 (winter). Gardens: Mon-Fri 7.30-dusk, Sat & Sun 9-dusk. **Fee:** Free. **Facilities:** 🅿 ➦ ✗ licensed ♿ toilets for disabled shop garden centre ✗ (ex guide/hearing dogs)

🏛 BRENTFORD Map 04 TQ17
KEW BRIDGE STEAM MUSEUM
Green Dragon Ln TW8 0EN (Underground - Kew Gardens, district line then 391 bus. Museum 100yds from the N side of Kew Bridge. From M4 junct 2 follow A4 to Chiswick rdbt, take A315 to Kew Bridge, Green Dragon Ln is 1st right after lights)
☎ 020 8568 4757 📄 020 8569 9978
e-mail: info@kbsm.org

This Victorian pumping station has steam engines and six beam engines, of which five are working and one is the largest in the world. A forge, diesel house, waterwheel and old workshops can also be seen along with London's only steam narrow-gauge railway which operates on the second and last weekend of each month (Mar-Nov). The Water for Life Gallery tells the story of London's water supply from Pre-Roman times.
Times: Open all year, daily 11-5. In steam wknds & BHs. (Closed Good Fri & Xmas wk). **Fee:** Weekdays: £3 (ch 5-15 £1, OAP/students £2) Family ticket £7. Weekends: £4 (ch £2, OAP/students £3) Family ticket £10.50. **Facilities:** 🅿 ➦ ♿ (tours for partially sighted, whchair loan, large print guide) toilets for disabled shop ➦

MUSICAL MUSEUM
368 High St TW8 0BD (Underground - Gunnersbury, nr Kew Bridge)
☎ 020 8560 8108

This museum will take you back to a bygone age to hear and see a marvellous working collection of automatic musical instruments from small music boxes to a mighty Wurlitzer theatre organ. Working demonstrations.
Times: Open Apr-Oct, Sat & Sun 2-5. Also Jul-Aug, Wed 2-4.
Fee: £3.20 (ch & pen £2.50). Family ticket £10. 🅿 (200 yds) ♿ shop ✶ (guide dogs)

⛿ CHESSINGTON   Map 04 TQ16
CHESSINGTON WORLD OF ADVENTURES
KT9 2NE (M25 junct 9/10, on A243)
☎ 01372 729560 0870 444 7777
🖥 01372 725050

A new attraction is 'Trail of Kings' - a jungle themed animal experience with giant viewing windows enabling visitors to get nose to nose with one of the biggest gorilla families in Europe and some of the rarest and most endangered big cats. Toytown has new surprises including Berry Bouncers and Toadies Crazy Cars; cartoon fans will love to chortle on the new Bash Street Bus ride in Beanoland. More intrepid explorers will revel in the Mystic East where the mighty Samurai and Dragon Falls await and Rameses seeks revenge!
Times: Open Apr-end Oct, daily. (closed some dates in Sep-Oct). Late opening until 9pm during Jul & Aug. **Fee:** £19.95 (ch u4 free 4-13 £16). Family ticket (2ad+2ch) £63. Annual pass £70 each. **Facilities:** 🅿 💺 ✕ licensed ♿ (some rides not accessible, disabled guide available) toilets for disabled shop ✶ (ex guide dogs & hearing dogs) 🦻

⛿ CHISLEHURST   Map 05 TQ47
CHISLEHURST CAVES
Old Hill BR7 5NB (off A222 nr Chislehurst railway stn)
☎ 020 8467 3264 🖥 020 8295 0407
e-mail: enquiries@chislehurstcaves.co.uk

Miles of mysterious caverns and passages hewn out of the chalk over some 4,000 years can be explored with experienced guides to tell the history and legends of the caves.
Times: Open all year, daily during school hols (incl half terms). All other times Wed-Sun, 10-4. Closed Xmas. **Fee:** £3 (ch & pen £1.50); longer tours: Sun & BH's only £5 (ch & pen £2.50). **Facilities:** 🅿 💺 ✕ licensed ♿ (ramps) toilets for disabled shop ✶ (ex guide dogs)

⛿ DOWNE   Map 05 TQ46
DOWN HOUSE - HOME OF CHARLES DARWIN
Luxted Rd BR6 7JT (Off A233, signposted)
☎ 01689 859119

The home of Charles Darwin for forty years. The drawing room and Old Study are furnished as they were when he was working on his famous book *On the Origin of Species by means of Natural Selection*. The Museum includes memorabilia from his voyage on HMS *Beagle*. The garden is also maintained, including

Take a lamplit guided tour lasting approximately 45 minutes through the miles of darkness beneath Chislehurst. Only 20 minutes by rail from London Bridge, a short walk from Chislehurst mainline station.

Telephone (020) 8467 3264 for further details

OLD HILL · CHISLEHURST
KENT BR7 5NB (off the A222)

* Open 7 days a week during school holidays – Wednesday-Sunday the rest of the year * Guided tours hourly from 10am-4pm * All children must be accompanied by an adult * Reduced rates for school or group bookings *

GIFT SHOP – CAFE
FREE CAR PARK

OPEN ALL YEAR

the famous Sand Walk or thinking path, along which he took his daily walk.
Times: Open all year, Apr-Sep, Wed-Sun 10-6 (last admission 5.30)(Oct); Nov-Mar, Wed-Sun 10-4. Also BH Mon. (Closed 24 Dec-7 Feb). **Fee:** £5.50 (ch 5-15 £2.80, under 5's free, con £4.10). Visits must be booked in advance. **Facilities:** 🅿 ♿ shop ✶

⛿ ENFIELD   Map 04 TQ39
FORTY HALL MUSEUM
Forty Hill EN2 9HA (M25 junct 25 onto A10, turn right into Bullsmoor Lane)
☎ 020 8363 8196 & 020 8363 4046
🖥 020 8367 9098
Times: Open all year, Thu-Sun 11-5 & BH's. **Facilities:** 🅿 💺 ♿ (Disabled parking in main carpark & 3 near house) toilets for disabled shop ✶ (ex guide dogs) *Details not confirmed for 2002*

⛿ ESHER   Map 04 TQ16
CLAREMONT LANDSCAPE GARDEN
Portsmouth Rd KT10 9JG (E of A307)
☎ 01372 467806 🖥 01372 464394
e-mail: sclgen@smtp.ntrust.org.uk

Laid out by Vanbrugh and Bridgeman before 1720, extended and naturalised by Kent, this is the earliest surviving example of an English landscaped garden. Its 50 acres include a lake with an island pavilion, a grotto

contd.

and a turf amphitheatre. Telephone 01372 451596 for details of events.

Times: Open all year Apr-end of Oct daily, Nov-end Dec & Jan-end Mar daily (ex Mon). Apr-Oct Mon-Fri 10-6, Sat-Sun & BH Mon 10-7 (closed all day 10 & 11 Jul closes 2pm 12-15 Jul); Nov-Mar 10-5 or sunset if earlier. Closed 25 Dec and 1 Jan. House open Feb-Nov, 1st wknd of month 2-3 (ex 1st Sat in Jul). House not National Trust. **Fee:** £3.50 (ch £1.75). Family ticket £8.75 **Facilities:** 🅿 💷 ♿ (wheelchairs available, Braille guide) toilets for disabled shop 🐾 (ex on leads, Nov-Mar only) 💐

🏛 HAM   Map 04 TQ17
Ham House
TW10 7RS (W of A307, between Kingston & Richmond)
☎ 020 8940 1950   🖺 020 8332 6903

Times: Open gardens: all year, Sat-Wed 10.30-6 or dusk if earlier. (Closed 25-26 Dec & 1 Jan). House: Apr-29 Oct, Sat-Wed 1-5. Last admission 4.30. 🅿 (500 yds) 💷 ♿ (Braille guide, wheelchairs & stairclimber, lift access) toilets for disabled shop 🐾 (ex guide/hearing dogs) 💐 *Details not confirmed for 2002*

🏛 HAMPTON COURT   Map 04 TQ16
Hampton Court Palace
KT8 9AU (on A308, close to A3, M3 & M25 exits. Train from Waterloo - Hampton Court, 2mins walk from station)
☎ 020 8781 9500 & 8781 9501
🖺 020 8781 9669

With over 500 years of royal history Hampton Court Palace has something to offer everyone, from the magnificent State Apartments to the domestic reality of the Tudor Kitchens. Costumed guides and audio tours bring the palace to life and provide an insight into how life in the palace would have been in the time of Henry VIII and William III.

Times: Open all year, mid Mar-Oct, Mon 10.15-6, Tue-Sun 9.30-6 (4.30pm Nov-mid Mar). (Closed 24-26 Dec). **Fee:** £10.80 (ch 5-16 £7.20, pen, students £8.30). Family £32.20. **Facilities:** 🅿 (charged) 💷 ✗ licensed ♿ (lifts, buggies for gardens, wheelchairs, wardens to assist) toilets for disabled shop (4 shops on site) 🐾 (ex in gardens) 💐

🏛 ISLEWORTH   Map 04 TQ17
Syon House
TW8 8JF (A310 Twickenham road into Park Rd)
☎ 020 8560 0882   020 8560 0883
🖺 020 8568 0936
e-mail: info@syonpark.co.uk

Set in 200 acres of parkland, Syon House is the London home of the Duke of Northumberland, whose family have lived here since the late 16th century. During the second half of the 18th century the first Duke of Northumberland engaged Robert Adam to remodel the interior and `Capability' Brown to landscape the grounds. Adam was also responsible for the furniture and decorations, and the result is particularly spectacular in the superbly coloured Ante-Room and Long Gallery.

Times: Open 15 Mar-Oct, Wed-Thu, Sun & BH 11-5 (last ticket 4.15pm). **Fee:** Combined ticket for house and gardens £6.25 (concessions £5.25). Family ticket £15. **Facilities:** 🅿 💷 ♿ (Only accessible if visitor can walk 5 stairs to entrance) toilets for disabled shop garden centre 🐾 💐

Syon Park
TW8 8JF (A310 Twickenham road into Park Rd)
☎ 020 8560 0881   🖺 020 8568 0936
e-mail: info@syonpark.co.uk

Contained within the 40 acres that make up Syon Park Gardens is one of the inspirations for the Crystal Palace at the Great Exhibition of 1851: a vast crescent of metal and glass, the first construction of its kind in the world and known as the Great Conservatory. Although the horticultural reputation of Syon Park goes back to the 16th century, its beauty today is thanks to the master of landscape design, `Capability' Brown.

Times: Open all year, daily 10-5.30 or dusk if earlier. (Closed 25 & 26 Dec). **Fee:** £3 (concessions £2.50). Combined ticket for house & gardens £6.25 (concessions £5.25). Family ticket £15. **Facilities:** 🅿 💷 ♿ toilets for disabled shop garden centre 🐾 (ex guide dogs) 💐

🏛 KEW   Map 04 TQ17
Kew Gardens (Royal Botanic Gardens)
TW9 3AB (Underground - Kew Gdns)
☎ 020 8940 1171   🖺 020 8332 5197
e-mail: info@kew.org

Times: Open all year, Gardens daily 9.30-between 4 & 6.30pm on weekdays, between 4-7.30pm Suns & BH's, depending on the time of sunset.(Closed 25 Dec & 1 Jan)

Facilities: 🅿 (charged) 💷 ✗ licensed ♿ (16 seat bus tour: enquiries ring 020 8332 5623) toilets for disabled shop 🐾 (ex guide dogs) *Details not confirmed for 2002* 💐

Kew Palace
Royal Botanic Gardens TW9 3AB (Underground - Kew Bridge)
☎ 020 8781 9540

A favourite country residence during the reign of the first three Hanoverian Kings, Kew was the site of several royal houses. A fairly modest red-brick building,

contd.

built in the Dutch style with gables, Kew Palace was built in 1631 and used for nearly a century until 1818 when Queen Charlotte died. Family paintings, furniture and tapestries are on display, and a charming 17th-century garden has been recreated. **Times:** Closed for refurbishment until 2003. **Fee:** *Prices not confirmed for 2002*

PUBLIC RECORD OFFICE MUSEUM
Ruskin Av TW9 4DU (Underground - Kew Gardens)
☎ 020 8392 5202 020 8392 5323
▤ 020 8392 5345
e-mail: events@pro.gov.uk

The Public Record Office houses one of the finest, most complete archives in Europe, comprising the records of the central government and law courts from the Norman Conquest to the present century. It is a mine of information and some of the most interesting material including Domesday Book is on display. **Times:** Open Mon, Wed & Fri, 9-5; Tue, 10-7; Thu, 9-7 (closed 1st wk in Dec, Sun & public holiday wkends). **Fee:** Free. **Facilities:** ▣ ▩ & (hearing loops & large print text in museum) toilets for disabled shop ⚑

QUEEN CHARLOTTE'S COTTAGE
Royal Botanic Gardens TW9 3AB (Underground - Kew Bridge)
☎ 020 8332 5189

Typical of the fashionable rustic style popular with the gentry in the 18th century, the cottage was built for George III and Queen Charlotte as a home for their menagerie of exotic pets, as well as a picnic spot and summer house. **Times:** Open weekends only between May & Sep. **Fee:** Free. shop ⚑

⛪ OSTERLEY   Map 04 TQ17
OSTERLEY PARK HOUSE
TW7 4RB (Underground - Osterley)
☎ 020 8560 7714 ▤ 020 8568 7714
e-mail: tsogen@smtp.ntrust.org.uk
Times: Open all year: Park & pleasure grounds, daily 9-7.30 or sunset if earlier. House: Apr-1 Nov, Wed-Sun 2-5, BH Sun & Mon 1-5. Last admission 4.30. (Closed Good Fri & 25-26 Dec). **Facilities:** ▣ (charged) ▩ & toilets for disabled shop ⚑ (ex on lead in park) ✾ *Details not confirmed for 2002*

⛪ TWICKENHAM   Map 04 TQ17
MARBLE HILL HOUSE
Richmond Rd TW1 1NL
☎ 020 8892 5115

An example of the English Palladian school of architecture, Marble Hill House was built in the 18th century for a mistress of George II. The perfectly proportioned Thames-side villa, contains a notable collection of paintings and furniture, as well as the Lazenby Chinoiserie Bequest. **Times:** Open all year, daily, Apr-Sep 10-6 (Oct, 10-5); Nov-Mar, Wed-Sun 10-4. (Closed 24-25 Dec & 1-18 Jan). **Fee:** £3.30 (ch 5-15 £1.70, under 5's free, con £2.50) **Facilities:** ▣ ▩ ✕ licensed & toilets for disabled shop ⚑ (ex in grounds) ⚏

MUSEUM OF RUGBY & TWICKENHAM STADIUM TOURS
Rugby Football Union, Rugby Rd TW1 1DZ (M3 into London, A316 follow signs to museum)
☎ 020 8892 8877 ▤ 020 8892 2817
e-mail: **museum@rfu.com**

Located beneath the East Stand of the Twickenham Stadium, home of the England team and headquarters of the Rugby Football Union, the museum uses interactive displays, period set pieces and video footage to bring the history of the game to life. The tour includes a visit to the England dressing room, and magnificent views of the stadium from the top of the north stand. **Times:** Museum: open Tue-Sat 10-5, Sun 2-5. Last admission 4.30pm. Tours: 10.30am, noon, 1.30pm, & 3pm; Sun 3pm. No tours on match days. Museum open on match days for ticket holders only. Ground closed Mon (ex BH), 24-26 Dec, Good Fri & the Sunday after a match. **Fee:** Museum: £4 (ch, pen, student £3). Twickenham Stadium Tour: £4 (ch, pen, students £3). Joint ticket for Museum and Tour £6 (ch, pen, students £4). Family ticket £19. **Facilities:** ▣ ▩ ✕ licensed & (special tours and lifts to all floors) toilets for disabled shop ⚑ (ex guide dogs) ▰

ORLEANS HOUSE GALLERY
Riverside TW1 3DJ (From Twickenham along Richmond rd (A305), Orleans Rd on right just past Orleans Park School)
☎ 020 8892 0221 ▤ 020 8744 0501
e-mail: **m.denovellis@richmond.gov.uk**

Stroll beside the Thames and through the woodland gardens of Orleans House, where you will find stunning 18th century interior design and an excellent public art gallery. Visitors of all ages can try out their own artistic talents in pre-booked workshops, and wide-ranging temporary exhibitions are held throughout the year - please telephone for details. **Times:** Open Oct-Mar, Tue-Sat 1-4.30; Sun & BH 2-4.30; Apr-Sep Tue-Sat 1-5.30, Sun & BH 2-5.30. **Fee:** Free. **Facilities:** ▣ & (handling objects & large print labels for some exhibitions) toilets for disabled shop ⚑ (ex guide dogs)

Merseyside

Northwestern metropolitan county on the River Mersey, with Liverpool as its administrative centre, Merseyside incorporates the towns of Bootle, Birkenhead, St Helens, Wallasey, and Southport.

The fortunes of the city have declined since the 19th century when Liverpool was England's second greatest port, and the area has been dogged by urban deprivation and unemployment. However, Merseyside is now on the upturn, due in part to that indomitable Scouse spirit.

When the port of Chester silted up in medieval times, Liverpool took up the slack. The first dock was built in 1715 and the port came to prominence with the slave trade. Following abolition, the port grew to a seven-mile stretch of docks, busy with freight cargoes of cotton, tobacco and sugar and the huge wave of emigration from Europe to the New World in the 19th and early 20th centuries. In its turn, immigration brought an influx of people to Merseyside to join its expanding population, including many from Ireland fleeing the potato famine of 1845.

In the second half of the 20th century, accessible air travel brought to an end the era of the ocean-going liners. At the same time, trade with Europe was picked up by the southeastern ports. Merseyside waned and its population dwindled, although it remains one of Britain's most vibrant and interesting areas.

Liverpool's shipping heritage is part of its attraction today, in the museums and galleries of the redeveloped Albert Dock, and in the impressive architecture reflecting the city's civic pride. Look out for the Royal Liver Building and the Cunard Building on the waterfront, and the architecture around St George's Hall, Dale Street, Water Street and William Brown Street.

Top: The Liver Building overlooking the Mersey

🏛 BIRKENHEAD Map 07 SJ38

BIRKENHEAD PRIORY
Priory St CH41 5JH
☎ 0151 666 1249
Times: Open all year, Sat & Sun 1-5 (in summer), 12-4 (in winter) &
Tue-Sun 1-5 (school holidays), 12-4 (Oct & Feb half term). Telephone
to confirm. **Facilities:** 🅿 ♿ toilets for disabled shop ✱ (ex guide
dogs) *Details not confirmed for 2002*

HISTORIC WARSHIPS
East Float, Dock Rd CH41 1DJ (end of M53 'All docks'
turn off; follow tourist signs; from Liverpool Wallasey
tunnel 1st exit after toll & follow brown heritage signs)
☎ 0151 650 1573 📠 0151 650 1473
e-mail: manager@warships.freeserve.co.uk

HMS *Onyx* served in the Falklands and is the only
submarine afloat in the UK that visitors can explore.
HMS *Plymouth*, an anti-submarine frigate also served in
the Falklands. The U534 is the only WWII German
U-Boat to be raised from the sea bed. Pre-booking
required, adults only admitted to U-Boat.
Times: Open all year, Sep-Mar daily 10-4, Apr-Aug daily 10-5. (Closed
24-26 Dec). **Fee:** £5 (ch £3, pen £4). Family ticket £14. Combined
ships & U-Boat £12.50 (adults only). U-Boat £7.50. **Facilities:** 🅿 ♨ ♿
museum only shop ✱ (ex guide dogs) ♨

WILLIAMSON ART GALLERY & MUSEUM
Slatey Rd CH43 4UE
☎ 0151 652 4177 📠 0151 670 0253
e-mail: wag@museum-service.freeserve.co.uk
Times: Open all year, Tue-Sun & BHs 1-5, (Closed Xmas & Good Fri).
Facilities: 🅿 ♿ toilets for disabled shop ✱ *Details not confirmed for
2002*

🏛 LIVERPOOL Map 07 SJ39

THE BEATLES STORY
Britannia Pavilion, Albert Dock L3 4AA
☎ 0151 709 1963 📠 0151 708 0039

Relive the story of the four lads from Liverpool who
took the world by storm and changed the face of
popular music for ever.
Times: Open Apr-Oct daily 10-6, Nov-Mar daily 10-5 (last admission
always 1hr before close). **Fee:** £7.95 (concessions £4.95). Family ticket
£19. **Facilities:** 🅿 ♿ toilets for disabled shop ✱ (ex guide dogs) ♨

CENTRAL LIBRARY
William Brown St L3 8EW (Adjacent to St. George's
Hall, which is opposite Lime St. Station. Between
museum and art gallery)
☎ 0151 233 5858 📠 0151 233 5824
e-mail: refham.central.library@liverpool.gov.uk

The Picton, Hornby and Brown buildings, situated in
the Victorian grandeur of William Brown Street, house
Liverpool's collection of over one million books,
forming one of Britain's largest and oldest public
libraries. The Liverpool Record Office is one of the

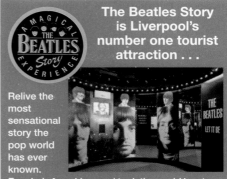

country's largest and most significant County Record
offices.
Times: Open all year, Mon-Thu 9-7.30, Fri 9-5, Sat 10-4 & Sun 12-4)
Closed BHs. **Fee:** Free. **Facilities:** 🅿 (50 yds) (pay & display parking
only) ♿ (lift, text magnification, reading machine) toilets for disabled
✱ (ex guide dogs)

CROXTETH HALL & COUNTRY PARK
Muirhead Av East L12 0HB (5m NE of city centre, near
M57 junct 4)
☎ 0151 228 5311 📠 0151 228 2817
Times: Open, all facilities daily 11-5 in season (phone for details);
Some facilities remain open through winter, hours on request.
Facilities: 🅿 ♨ ♿ (permit parking next to the Hall) toilets for
disabled shop ✱ (ex in park & grounds) *Details not confirmed for
2002*

HM CUSTOMS & EXCISE NATIONAL MUSEUM
Merseyside Maritime Museum, Albert Dock L3 4AQ
☎ 0151 478 4499 📠 0151 478 4590
Times: Open all year, daily 10-5. Last admission 4. (Closed 23-26 Dec
& 1 Jan) **Facilities:** 🅿 ♨ ✕ licensed ♿ (restricted wheelchair access,
no access to basement) toilets for disabled shop ✱ (ex guide dogs)
Details not confirmed for 2002 ♨

LIVERPOOL FOOTBALL CLUB VISITORS CENTRE TOUR
Anfield Rd L4 0TH
☎ 0151 260 6677 ▤ 0151 264 0149
e-mail: done.lfcmuseum@btinternet.com

See all the first team kit set out for a match day, listen to a recorded 'team talk' from Gerard Houllier, and then touch the famous 'This is Anfield' sign to the sound of 45,000 cheering fans - a marvellous experience for any Liverpool fan!
Times: Open: Museum daily 10-5 last admission 4pm. (Closed 25-26 Dec). Match days 9am until last admission- 1hr before kick off. Museum & Tour - tours are run subject to daily demand. Advance booking is essential to avoid disappointment. **Fee:** Museum only £5 (ch under 6 & pen £3) Family £13. Museum & Tour £8.50 (ch under 16 & pen £5.50) Family £23. **Facilities:** ▤ ▣ & (lifts to all areas for wheelchairs) toilets for disabled shop ⅋ (ex guide dogs) ▰

MERSEYSIDE MARITIME MUSEUM
Albert Dock L3 4AA (The Albert Dock is near Liverpool's historic waterfront. Entry into the dock is from the strand)
☎ 0151 478 4499 ▤ 0151 478 4590

A large museum in restored 19th-century docklands, which includes a Cooperage and the Albert Dock Warehouse, containing varied displays about the Port of Liverpool. There are floating craft, outdoor exhibits and demonstrations.
Times: Open all year, daily 10-5 (Closed 23-26 Dec & 1 Jan). **Fee:** £3 (con £1.50, ch & pen free) Admission charge is for a 12 month ticket with unlimited return visits. **Facilities:** ▤ ▣ ✗ licensed & (lifts, wheelchairs, ramps, ex pilot boat & basement) toilets for disabled shop ⅋ (ex guide dogs) ▰

METROPOLITAN CATHEDRAL OF CHRIST THE KING
Mount Pleasant L3 5TQ (5 mins walk from either Liverpool Lime Street or Liverpool Central Railway Station. 'Smart' buses stop outside)
☎ 0151 709 9222 ▤ 0151 708 7274
e-mail: met.cathedral@cwcom.net

A modern Roman Catholic cathedral which provides a focal point on the Liverpool skyline. The imposing structure of curving concrete ribs and stained glass was designed by Sir Frederick Gibberd and consecrated in 1967.
Times: Open daily 8-6 (Sun 5pm in winter). **Fee:** Free. **Facilities:** ▤ & (lift, loop system, no access to Crypt) toilets for disabled shop ⅋ (ex guide dogs)

MUSEUM OF LIVERPOOL LIFE
Pier Head L3 4AA (follow signs for Albert Dock, museum on Pier Head side)
☎ 0151 478 4080 ▤ 0151 478 4090

This museum explores the history of Liverpool, its people and their contribution to national life. Displays focus on three main themes: Mersey Culture, Making a Living and Demanding a Voice.
Times: Open all year, daily 10-5. (Closed 23-26 Dec & 1 Jan). **Fee:** Free. **Facilities:** ▤ (charged) & (wheelchairs, audio handsets, subtitles on video terminals) toilets for disabled shop ⅋ (ex guide/hearing dogs) ▰

NATIONAL WILDFLOWER CENTRE
Court Hey Park L16 3NA (M62 junct 5, take B5080 to rdbt. Exit into Roby Rd, entrance 0.5 mile on left)
☎ 0151 737 1819 ▤ 0151 737 1820
e-mail: info@nwc.org.uk

Times: Open Etr Sat-Oct, Wed-Sun 11-5; Nov-Good Fri, Thu-Sun 10.30-4. Telephone for confirmation as times may vary. **Facilities:** ▤ ▣ & toilets for disabled shop garden centre ⅋ (ex guide dogs & in park) *Details not confirmed for 2002* ▰

TATE LIVERPOOL
Albert Dock L3 4BB (within walking distance of Liverpool Lime Street railway station)
☎ 0151 702 7400 & 0151 702 7402
▤ 0151 702 7401
e-mail: liverpoolinfo@tate.org.uk

Times: Open Tue-Sun 10-5.30. (Closed Mon ex BH Mon, 24-26 Dec, 1 Jan & Good Fri). **Facilities:** ▤ ▣ & (wheelchairs available, leaflets in braille, hearing loop) toilets for disabled shop ⅋ *Details not confirmed for 2002* ▰

Norfolk

A fertile agricultural county in the east of the country, sparsely populated, with plenty of fresh air and wide open spaces.

Norfolk is the northern bit of East Anglia, en route to nowhere, and too far from London to be colonised. Its coastline encompasses fenland round the Wash, the wonderfully unspoilt seaside towns of the north coast, and two of the country's most important nature reserves at Blakeney Point and the Cley marshes. Common features of the countryside are windmills, and attractive houses built of Norfolk flint with Dutch gables, a relic of the area's historical trade links with the Low Countries.

The Norfolk Broads are the county's main tourist attraction. The 'broads' are waterways set in marshy fenland, which came about from extensive peat cutting and subsequent flooding in the 13th and 14th centuries. Reed cutting for local thatching helped to keep the waterways clear. The Broads now has National Park status, to help protect the important wetland site from the demands of tourism and agriculture. The best way to see the Broads is to hire a boat, and there is plenty of opportunity for this at boatyards in Wroxham and Hoveton.

The county town is the city of Norwich, the largest in East Anglia, with a fine cathedral, a Norman keep, a huge market place and an attractive medieval centre. Norwich came to prominence in the 17th century as a centre for the textile industry. Today it is most famously associated with Coleman's, the mustard company.

Famous Norfolk natives include Horatio Nelson, Edith Cavell, Anna Sewell (author of *Black Beauty*), and Delia Smith, the TV celebrity cook who is also a director on the board of Norwich City Football Club.

Top: Hickling Broad in the Norfolk Broads

EVENTS & FESTIVALS

May
1st King's Lynn May Garland Procession, town centre, King's Lynn
1st-12th Norfolk & Norwich Festival (music and the arts)
tbc Norfolk Visual Arts Festival (various venues)

June
2nd Norwich Bike Ride, 50/100-mile ride around Norfolk (provisional)
26th-27th Royal Norfolk Show, The Showground, Dereham Road, New Costessey, Norwich

July
6th-7th Morris & Folk Festival, Sheringham
12th-14th Norwich Music Festival
13th Lord Mayor's Celebrations, Norwich
14th Theatre in the Park, Norwich (various parks and open spaces in the city)

August
4th-10th Mundesley Festival, Mundesley
17th-24th Cromer Carnival Week, Cromer
26th Aylsham Show, Aylsham

October
tbc CAMRA Norwich Beer Festival

⛪ BACONSTHORPE   Map 09 TG13
BACONSTHORPE CASTLE
NR25 6LN (0.75m N off unclass road)
Times: Open all year, daily 10-4. **Facilities:** 🅿 ♿ *Details not confirmed for 2002*

⛪ BANHAM   Map 05 TM08
BANHAM ZOO
The Grove NR16 2HE (on B1113)
☎ 01953 887771 & 887773 📄 01953 887445
Times: Open all year, daily from 10am. (Closed 25-26 Dec).
Facilities: 🅿 ♨ ✗ licensed ♿ (3 wheelchairs for hire) toilets for disabled shop ✗ *Details not confirmed for 2002* ⚑

⛪ BLICKLING   Map 09 TG12
BLICKLING HALL
NR11 6NF (on B1354, 1.5m NW of Aylsham, signposted off A140 Norwich to Cromer road)
☎ 01263 738030 📄 01263 731660
e-mail: abgusr@smtp.ntrust.org.uk

Flanked by dark yew hedges and topped by pinnacles, the warm red brick front of Blickling is a memorable sight. The grounds include woodland and a lake, a formal parterre, and a dry moat filled with roses, camellias and other plants.
Times: Hall open 31 Mar-28 Oct, Wed-Sun & BH, 1-4.30 (1-3.30 Oct). Also open Tue in Aug. Garden, shop & restaurant same days as hall 10.15-5.15. **Fee:** £6.70 (ch £3.35). **Facilities:** 🅿 ♨ ✗ licensed ♿ (wheelchairs & batricars) Braille guide, lift, parking) toilets for disabled shop garden centre ✗ (ex guide dogs) ⚘ ⚑

⛪ BRESSINGHAM   Map 05 TM08
BRESSINGHAM STEAM MUSEUM & GARDENS
IP22 2AB (on A1066 2.5 miles W of Diss)
☎ 01379 686900 📄 01379 688085
e-mail: info@bressingham.co.uk

Alan Bloom is an internationally recognised nurseryman and a steam enthusiast, and has combined his interests to great effect at Bressingham. There are three miniature steam-hauled trains, including a 15in gauge running through two and a half miles of the wooded Waveney Valley. The Dell Garden has 5000 species of perennials and alpines; Foggy Bottom has wide vistas, pathways, trees, shrubs, conifers and winter colour (restricted opening). A steam roundabout is another attraction, and the Norfolk fire museum is housed here. Various events are held, including Friends of Thomas the Tank Engine, please telephone for details.
Times: Open - Steam Museum, Dad's Army collection, Foggy Bottom & Dell Garden Apr-Oct, daily 10.30-5.30 (10.30-4.30 Oct). Museum & collections open all year ex 24 Dec-8 Jan. **Fee:** 7 (ch £5, pen £6).
Facilities: 🅿 ♨ ✗ licensed ♿ (wheelchairs can be taken onto Nursery & Waveney lines) toilets for disabled shop garden centre ✗ (ex guide dogs) ⚑

⛪ BURGH CASTLE   Map 05 TG40
BERNEY ARMS WINDMILL
NR30 1SB
☎ 01493 700605
Times: Open Apr-Oct, daily 9-1 & 2-5. **Facilities:** ✗ ♿ *Details not confirmed for 2002*

THE CASTLE
NR31 9PZ (off A143)
Times: Open any reasonable time. **Facilities:** ♿ *Details not confirmed for 2002*

⛪ CAISTER-ON-SEA   Map 09 TG51
ROMAN TOWN
Times: Open any reasonable time. **Facilities:** ♿ *Details not confirmed for 2002*

⛪ CASTLE ACRE   Map 09 TF81
CASTLE ACRE PRIORY & CASTLE
Stocks Green PE32 2XD
☎ 01760 755394

The priory was built for the Cluniac order in the Norman period. After the Dissolution under Henry VIII, the priory fell into ruin, but its extensive remains are dominated by the glorious, arcaded west front of the priory church, a reminder of past splendour. The chapel and 15th-century gatehouse also remain, and there are impressive ruins of a great castle which also stood nearby.
Times: Open all year, Apr-Sep, daily 10-6 (Oct 10-5); Nov-Mar, Wed-Sun 10-4. Closed 24-26Dec & 1Jan. **Fee:** £3.50 (ch 5-15 £1.80, under 5's free, con £2.60). Personal stereo tour included in admission.
Facilities: 🅿 ♿ shop ✗ (in certain areas) ♿

⛪ CASTLE RISING   Map 09 TF62
CASTLE RISING CASTLE
PE31 6AH (off A149)
☎ 01553 631330
Times: Open all year, Apr-Sep, daily 10-6; Oct, daily 10-5; Nov-Mar, Wed-Sun 10-4. (Closed 24-26 Dec & 1 Jan). **Facilities:** 🅿 ♿ (exterior only) toilets for disabled shop ✗ ♿ *Details not confirmed for 2002*

⛪ CROMER   Map 09 TG24
CROMER MUSEUM
East Cottages, Tucker St NR27 9HB (in town centre)
☎ 01263 513543 📄 01263 511651
e-mail: cromer.museum@norfolk.gov.uk

The museum is housed in five 19th-century fishermen's cottages, one of which has period furnishings. There are pictures and exhibits from Victorian Cromer, with collections illustrating local natural history, archaeology, social history and geology.
Times: Open all year, Mon-Sat 10-5, Sun 2-5. Closed Mon 1-2. (Closed Good Fri, Xmas period & 1 Jan). **Fee:** £1.80 (ch 90p, con £1.40).
Facilities: 🅿 (200yds) shop ✗

HENRY BLOGG MUSEUM
No 2 Boathouse, The Promenade NR27 9HE (at the bottom of East Gangway)
☎ 01263 511294   🖷 01263 513018
e-mail: rfmuirhead@csma-netlink.co.uk

A lifeboat has been stationed at the Cromer since 1804, and the museum in No 2 boat house at the bottom of The Gangway covers local lifeboat history and the RNLI in general. The main exhibit is the WWII Watson Class lifeboat "H F Bailey", the boat Henry Blogg coxed. In ten years he helped to save over 500 lives.
Times: Open Etr-Oct daily 10-4. Or by appointment with the Curator. **Fee:** Donations welcome. **Facilities:** 🅿 (pay & display in town) & shop

🏛 ERPINGHAM   Map 09 TG13
WOLTERTON PARK
NR11 7LY (signposted from A140 Norwich to Cromer)
☎ 01263 584175   🖷 01263 761214

Covering some 800 hectares this huge estate contains managed conservation areas, 18th-century landscaped gardens, a Heritage rose garden, lakes, a scented garden, a ruined church, horses graves, and Wolverton Hall, built in the 1720s. Special events include gardening demonstrations, concerts, craft fairs, guided walks and history lectures.
Times: Open - Park daily; Hall, late Apr-Oct, Fri 2-5 (last entry 4). **Fee:** £5 **Facilities:** 🅿 & toilets for disabled shop 🛉 (ex on lead & guide dogs)

🏛 FAKENHAM   Map 09 TF93
PENSTHORPE WATERFOWL PARK & NATURE RESERVE
Pensthorpe NR21 0LN (signed off A1067 Norwich to Fakenham road)
☎ 01328 851465   🖷 01328 855905

Covering 200 acres of beautiful Norfolk countryside, with five lakes which are home to the largest collection of waterfowl and waders in Europe. Spacious walk-through enclosures and a network of hard-surfaced pathways ensures close contact with birds at the water's edge.
Times: Open all year, daily 10-5 mid Mar-end of year. **Fee:** £4.90 (ch £2.40, pen £4.30) **Facilities:** 🅿 🍽 ✕ licensed & (network of hard surfaced pathways ensures access to shore) toilets for disabled shop 🛉 (ex guide dogs) 🐾

🏛 FELBRIGG   Map 09 TG23
FELBRIGG HALL
NR11 8PR (off B1436 betweeen A148 Cromer to King's Lynn & A1404 Cromer to Norwich)
☎ 01263 837444   🖷 01263 837032
e-mail: afgusr@smtp.ntrust.org.uk

Felbrigg is a 17th-century house built on the site of an existing medieval hall. It contains a superb collection of 18th-century furniture and pictures and an outstanding library. A 550-acre wood shelters the house from the North Sea and contains waymarked walks and a working dovecot.
Times: Open house and garden: late Mar-early Nov, Sat-Wed, house 1-5, garden 11-5.30. BH Sun & BH Mon 11-5. Park walks available daily dawn-dusk. **Fee:** House & garden £5.80 (ch £2.90). Family ticket £14.20. Garden only £2.20. Party. **Facilities:** 🅿 (charged) 🍽 ✕ licensed & (battery operated wheelchair for garden, braille guide) toilets for disabled shop 🛉 (ex guide or on lead in park) 🐾 🐾

🏛 FILBY   Map 09 TG41
THRIGBY HALL WILDLIFE GARDENS
NR29 3DR (on unclass road off A1064, between Acle & Caister-on-Sea)
☎ 01493 369477   🖷 01493 368256
e-mail: thrigby@globalnet.co.uk

The 250-year-old park of Thrigby Hall is now the home of animals and birds from Asia, and the lake has ornamental wildfowl. There are tropical bird houses, a unique blue, willow-pattern garden and tree walk and a summer house as old as the park. The enormous jungled swamp hall has special features such as underwater viewing of large crocodiles.
Times: Open all year, daily from 10. **Fee:** £5.90 (ch 4-14 £3.90, pen £4.90). **Facilities:** 🅿 🍽 & (wheelchairs available) toilets for disabled shop 🛉 (ex guide dogs) 🐾

🏛 FLEGGBURGH   Map 09 TG41
THE VILLAGE
Burgh St. Margaret NR29 3AF (7m from Great Yarmouth, on A1064 between Acle and Caister-on-Sea)
☎ 01493 369770   🖷 01493 369318

The Village Experience is set in over 30 acres of woodland. Working steam and traditional fairground rides, exploratorium, live shows including a puppet show and a cinema-organ concert. Other attractions include a fairground, a children's drawing studio, a soft play area and a maze. Recent additions are the Haunted Conservatory, the Swinging Chairs and the Wareham Bears Collection.
Times: Open 24 Mar-end Oct, daily 10-5. Other times not confirmed. Saturday is grounds only day (admission reduced accordingly) **Fee:** £5.95 (ch £3.95 pen £5.45). Grounds only Sat £2.75. **Facilities:** 🅿 🍽 ✕ licensed & toilets for disabled shop 🛉 (ex guide dogs) 🐾

🏛 GREAT BIRCHAM   Map 09 TF73
BIRCHAM WINDMILL
PE31 6SJ (0.5m W off unclassified Snettisham road)
☎ 01485 578393
e-mail: birchamwindmill@btinternet.com

This windmill is one of the last remaining in Norfolk. Sails turn on windy days, and the adjacent tea room serves home-made cakes, light lunches and cream teas. There is also a bakery shop and cycle hire.
Times: Open Etr-Sep 10-5 **Fee:** £2.75 (ch £1.50, pen £2.50) **Facilities:** 🅿 🍽 & toilets for disabled shop

🏛 GREAT YARMOUTH   Map 05 TG50
ELIZABETHAN HOUSE MUSEUM
4 South Quay NR30 2QH
☎ 01493 855746

A rich merchant built this house in 1596. It has been completely re-displayed to show a wealthy household through time from the 16th to 19th centuries. Visitors can see a Victorian kitchen, scullery and parlour, a Tudor bedroom and dining room, a Stuart (Civil War) 'conspiracy' room and a children's toy room.
Times: Open 2 Apr-26 Oct Mon-Fri 10-5; Sat & Sun 1.15-5 **Fee:** £2 (ch £1, concessions £1.50). Family ticket £4.70. **Facilities:** P (100yds) & shop ✝

MARITIME MUSEUM
Marine Pde NR30 2EN
☎ 01493 842267

The sea and the fishing industry have played an enormous part in East Anglia's history and this museum has exhibits on the herring fishery, the wherry, life-saving and the most recent industry - oil and gas in the North Sea.
Times: Open 28 May-28 Sep Mon-Fri 10-5; Sat & Sun 1.15-5. **Fee:** £1.10 (ch 70p, concessions 90p). **Facilities:** P shop ✝

MERRIVALE MODEL VILLAGE
Wellington Pier Gardens, Marine Pde NR30 3JG
☎ 01493 842097

Set in attractive landscaped gardens, this comprehensive miniature village is built on a scale of 1:12. The layout includes a two and a half inch gauge model railway, radio-controlled boats, and over 200 models set in an acre of landscaped gardens. There are additional amusements and remote-controlled cars and boats.
Times: Open Etr 9.30-6, Jun-Oct 9.30-10. **Fee:** £3 (ch 3-14 £1.50, pen £2.50) **Facilities:** P (opposite) ♨ & shop ✝ (ex on leads)

OLD MERCHANT'S HOUSE
Row 111, Greyfriar's Cloister NR30 2RQ (follow signs to dock and south quay)
☎ 01493 857900

Two 17th-century Row Houses, a type of building unique to Great Yarmouth, contain original fixtures and display items salvaged from the bombing raids of the Second World War. Nearby are the remains of a Franciscan friary, with a rare vaulted cloister, accidentally discovered during bomb-damage repairs.
Times: Open Apr-Sep 10-6. Oct 10-5 (closed 1-2). **Fee:** £2.40 (ch 5-15 £1.20, under 5's free. con £1.80) **Facilities:** ✝ ✿

TOLHOUSE MUSEUM
Tolhouse St NR30 2SH
☎ 01493 858900   ▤ 01493 745459

This late 13th-century building was once the town's court house and gaol and has dungeons which can be visited. The rooms above contain exhibits on local history. The museum has become a brass rubbing

centre and has a wide range of replica brasses from which rubbings can be made. Prices start at 50p and include materials and instructions.
Times: Open 28 May-28 Sep, Mon-Fri 10-5; Sat & Sun 1.15-5.
Fee: £1.10 (ch 70p, concessions 90p). **Facilities:** P (100yds) (lift to ground & 2nd floor) shop ✝

🏛 GRESSENHALL   Map 09 TF91
NORFOLK RURAL LIFE MUSEUM & UNION FARM
Beech House NR20 4DR (A47, B1110 through East Dereham towards Holt, onto B1146 to Fakenham, museum is 1.5m on right)
☎ 01362 860563   ▤ 01362 860385
e-mail: gressenhall.museum@norfolk.gov.uk

Housed in a former workhouse, the museum reflects the rural history of the county over the past 200 years. Displays include Cherry Tree Cottage and garden, a typical farm labourer's home of the early 20th century, as well as reconstructed craftsmen's workshops. Union Farm is a working farm, which is worked with heavy horses and stocked with rare breeds of sheep, cattle, pigs and poultry. Farm trail, woodland and riverside walk, osier beds. Special events and demonstrations throughout the season.
Times: Open daily Apr-Nov 10-5. **Fee:** £4.70 (ch £3.30, con £4). Family ticket £13. **Facilities:** P ♨ & (sound guide & wheelchair loan) toilets for disabled shop ✝ ♨

🏛 GRIMES GRAVES   Map 05 TL88
GRIMES GRAVES
Lynford IP26 5DE (7m NW of Thetford off A134)
☎ 01842 810656

Grimes Graves is the largest known group of Neolithic flint mines in Britain. It consists of a network of hundreds of pits, the oldest dating from about 3000BC. Vertical shafts lead through the flint seams to galleries. Visitors can descend 10 metres (30 feet) into an excavated shaft and there are regular demonstrations of the craft of flint-knapping.
Times: Open all year, Apr-Sep, daily 10-6 (Oct 10-5); Nov-Mar, Wed-Sun 10-4. Closed 1-2pm. Last visit to pit 20 minutes before closing).
Fee: £2.10 (ch 5-15 £1.10 under 5's free, con £1.60). A torch is useful.
Facilities: P & (exhibition area, grounds only; access track rough) shop ✝ (in certain areas) ✿

🏛 HEACHAM   Map 09 TF63
NORFOLK LAVENDER
Caley Mill PE31 7JE (on A149 at junct with B1454)
☎ 01485 570384   ▤ 01485 571176
e-mail: admin@norfolk-lavender.co.uk

This is the largest lavender-growing and distilling operation in Britain. Different coloured lavenders are grown in strips and harvested in July and August. There

contd.

are also rose and herb gardens and a fragrant Plant Centre, and guided tours of the distillery and gardens.

Times: Open all year, daily 10-5. (Closed 25-26 Dec & 1 Jan). **Fee:** Admission to grounds free. Guided tours £1.75 (May-Sep). Trip to Lavender Field £3.95, mid Jun-mid Aug. **Facilities:** 🅿 ☙ ✗ licensed ♿ (wheelchairs for loan) toilets for disabled shop garden centre

⚏ HOLKHAM   Map 09 TF84
HOLKHAM HALL & BYGONES MUSEUM
NR23 1AB (off A149, 2m W of Wells-next-the-Sea)
☎ 01328 710227   🖷 01328 711707

This classic Palladian mansion was built between 1734 and 1764 by Thomas Coke, 1st Earl of Leicester, and is home to his descendants. It has a magnificent alabaster entrance hall and the sumptuous state rooms house Greek and Roman statues, fine furniture and paintings by Rubens, Van Dyck, Gainsborough and others. The Bygones Museum, housed in the stable block, has over 5,000 items on display - from gramophones to fire engines.

Times: Open 26 May-Sep, Sun-Thu 1-5; Etr, May & Summer BHs, Sun & Mon 11.30-5. **Fee:** Hall £5 (ch £2.50). Bygones £5 (ch £2.50). Combined ticket Hall & Bygones: £8 (ch £4) **Facilities:** 🅿 ✗ licensed ♿ (wheelchair ramps at all entrances) toilets for disabled shop garden centre ✗ (ex guide & on lead in park) 🖝

⚏ HORSEY   Map 09 TG42
HORSEY WINDPUMP
NR29 4EF (2.5m NE of Potter Heigham)
☎ 01493 393904

The windpump mill was built 200 years ago to drain the area, and then rebuilt in 1912 by Dan England, a noted Norfolk millwright. It has been restored since being struck by lightning in 1943, and overlooks Horsey Mere and marshes, noted for their wild birds and insects.

Times: Open Apr-Oct, daily 11-5. (Closed Good Fri). **Fee:** £1.30 (national trust members free entry & parking). Mooring fees payable to the horsey estate (inc NT members). **Facilities:** 🅿 (charged) ☙ (easy route to viewpoint overlooking Horsey Mere) shop ✗ (ex guide dogs) ✤ 🖝

⚏ HORSHAM ST FAITH   Map 09 TG21
CITY OF NORWICH AVIATION MUSEUM
Old Norwich Rd NR10 3JF (follow brown tourist signs from A140 Norwich to Cromer Road)
☎ 01603 893080
e-mail: derek.waters@virgin.net

A massive Avro Vulcan bomber, veteran of the Falklands War, dominates the collection of military and civilian aircraft at this museum. There are several displays relating to the aeronautical history of Norfolk, including some on the role played by Norfolk-based RAF and USAF planes during World War II, and a section dedicated to the operations of RAF Bomber Command's 100 group.

Times: Open all year, Apr-Oct Tue-Sat, 10-5. Sun 12-5. Nov-Mar, Wed & Sat 10-4. Sun 12-4. **Fee:** £2.50 (ch & concessions £1.50, pen £2) Family ticket (2 adults & 2 ch) £7. **Facilities:** 🅿 ☙ ♿ (assistance available) shop ✗ (ex guide dogs)

⚏ HOUGHTON   Map 09 TF72
HOUGHTON HALL
PE31 6UE (1.25m off A148)
☎ 01485 528569   🖷 01485 528167
e-mail: administrator@houghtonhall.com

This splendid Palladian house in beautiful parkland was built for Sir Robert Walpole. The state rooms have decorations and furniture by William Kent. There is a model soldier collection.

Times: Open Etr Sun-last Sun Sep, Thu, Sun & BH's 1-5.30. House open Etr Sun-last Sun Sep, Thu, Thu & BH's2-5.30. Last admission 5pm. **Fee:** £6 (ch 5-16 £3, ch under 5 free). Excluding house £3.50 (ch 5-16 £2) **Facilities:** 🅿 ☙ ♿ toilets for disabled shop ✗

⚏ HUNSTANTON   Map 09 TF64
SEA LIFE AQUARIUM & MARINE SANCTUARY
Southern Promenade PE36 5BH
☎ 01485 533576   🖷 01485 533531

With over 30 fascinating displays of marine life, this fascinating aquarium offers close encounters with starfish, sharks, octopus, eels and many other underwater wonders. Feeding demonstrations, talks and special presentations. Latest addition: Otters.

Times: Open all year, daily from 10. (Closed 25 Dec) **Fee:** £4.99 (ch £3.50 & pen £3.95) **Facilities:** 🅿 (charged) ☙ ✗ ♿ toilets for disabled shop ✗ (ex guide dogs) 🖝

⚏ KING'S LYNN   Map 09 TF62
AFRICAN VIOLET CENTRE
Terrington St Clement PE34 4PL (4m W of King's Lynn, on A17)
☎ 01553 828374   🖷 01553 828376
Times: Open daily Mon-Sat 9-5, Sun 10-5. (Closed Xmas & New Year). **Facilities:** 🅿 ☙ ♿ (ramps to reach tea room & outside sales areas) toilets for disabled shop garden centre ✗ (ex guide dogs) *Details not confirmed for 2002*

KING'S LYNN ARTS CENTRE
27-29 Kings St PE30 1HA (located just off Tuesday Market Place in Kings Street, next to Globe Hotel)
☎ 01553 765565   01553 764864
🖷 01553 762141
e-mail: marketing.section@dialpipex.com

Although it has been used for many purposes, the theatrical associations of this 15th-century Guildhall are strongest: Shakespeare himself is said to have performed here. The annual King's Lynn Festival takes place towards the end of July.

Times: Open Mon-Fri 10-2. Closed show days, Sun & BHs. **Fee:** Free. **Facilities:** 🅿 ☙ ✗ ♿ (hearing loop, ramp) toilets for disabled ✗ ✤

LYNN MUSEUM
Market St PE30 1NL (town centre)
☎ 01553 775001   🖷 01553 775001
e-mail: lynn.museum@norfolk.gov.uk

Once it was a walled city of considerable importance; its two great churches, two marketplaces and two Guildhalls testify to its size. King's Lynn was also a

contd.

noted port and a stop on the Pilgrim's Way to Walsingham. The geology, archaeology and natural history of the area are the main collections in the local museum. Objects in the archaeology gallery include Bronze Age weapons and the skeleton of a Saxon warrior. Relics from the medieval town of Lynn include an important collection of pilgrim badges. Also see the Snarling Tiger, the Medieval Stonemason, the Victorian Ironmonger's Shop and the beautiful 19th-century fairground roundabout horses of Frederick Savage. **Times:** Open all year, Tue-Sat, 10-5. **Fee:** £1 (ch 60p, concessions 80p). **Facilities:** P (500yds) & shop ⅋

⛪ LITTLE WALSINGHAM Map 09 TF93
WALSINGHAM ABBEY GROUNDS & SHIREHALL MUSEUM
NR22 6BP (take B1105 from Fakenham)
☎ 01328 820259 🖷 01328 820098
e-mail: walsingham.museum@farmline.com

In the grounds of the Abbey are the ruins of the original Augustinian priory built in the 1100s. The priory was built over the shrine of Our Lady of Walsingham which had been established in 1061. Shirehall Museum consists of an original Georgian Courthouse, displays on the history of Walsingham and local artifacts. **Times:** Open Apr-late Oct, daily 10-4.30; Oct-Dec, wknds only 10-4; late Jan-late Feb, daily 10-4. Other times through Estate office Mon-Fri 9-5. **Fee:** not confirmed **Facilities:** P (100 yds) & toilets for disabled shop garden centre

⛪ NORTH CREAKE Map 09 TF83
CREAKE ABBEY
NR21 9LF (1m N off B1355)
Times: Open any reasonable time. **Facilities:** ☒ *Details not confirmed for 2002*

⛪ NORWICH Map 05 TG20
BRIDEWELL MUSEUM
Bridewell Alley NR2 1AQ (in city centre)
☎ 01603 667228 🖷 01603 765651
e-mail: museums@norfolk.gov.uk

Built in the late 14th century, this flint-faced merchant's house was used as a prison from 1583 to 1828. It now houses displays illustrating the trades and industries of Norwich during the past 200 years, including a large collection of locally made boots and shoes. There are also reconstructions of a 1920s pharmacy, a 1930s pawnbroker's shop and a blacksmith's smithy. Special for children: "Hunt the Animals" quiz trail. **Times:** Open all year Mon-Sat 10-5 (Closed Sun, 25-26 Dec & 1 Jan). **Fee:** £2 (ch £1, con £1.50) Family ticket £5. **Facilities:** P 5min walk shop ⅋

NORWICH CASTLE MUSEUM
Castle Meadow NR1 3JU (in city centre)
☎ 01603 493625 🖷 01603 493623
e-mail: museums@norfolk.gov.uk

The Castle keep was built in the 12th century, and the museum houses displays of art, archaeology, natural history, Lowestoft porcelain, Norwich silver, a large collection of paintings (with special emphasis on the Norwich School of Painters) and British ceramic teapots. There are also guided tours of the dungeons and battlements. A programme of exhibitions, children's events, gallery and evening talks takes place throughout the year. Please ring for details. **Times:** Open all year, Mon-Sat 10.30-5, Sun 2-5; School holidays: Etr & half terms Mon-Sat 10.30-6, Sun 12-5; Summer Mon-Sat 10-7, Sun 12-5. (Closed Good Fri, Xmas period & New Year). **Fee:** Castle Keep & Archaeology or Exhibitions & Art Galleries: £2.90 (ch £2.25, con £2.55) Family ticket £8.95. Whole museum: £4.70 (ch £3.50, con £4.10) Family ticket £13.95. **Facilities:** P (200mtrs) ⬤ & (lift to first floor, special parking by prior arrangement) toilets for disabled shop ⅋

NORWICH CATHEDRAL
The Close NR1 4DH (A47, A11 to city centre, inner ring rd to Barrack St rdbt, take road towards city centre to Tombland)
☎ 01603 764385 & 767617 (weekends)
🖷 01603 766032
e-mail: vis&profficer@cathedral.org.uk

The cathedral was founded in 1096 as part of a Benedictine priory; it possesses the largest monastic cloisters in England and is of great artistic and architectural interest, being one of the finest complete Romanesque buildings in Europe. Of particular note are: the Saxon Bishop's throne, medieval nave bosses depicting Biblical scenes, and the 14th-century Despenser reredos. **Times:** Open daily, 7.30-7 (6pm mid Sep-mid May). **Fee:** Free. **Facilities:** P (440yds) (parking at Cathedral for services only) ✗ licensed & (parking on site, touch & hearing centre) toilets for disabled shop ⅋ (ex guide dogs)

ROYAL NORFOLK REGIMENTAL MUSEUM
Shirehall, Market Av NR1 3JQ (adjacent to Norwich Castle Museum)
☎ 01603 493649 🖷 01603 765651

Museum displays deal with the social as well as military history of the county regiment from 1685, including the daily life of a soldier. Audio-visual displays and graphics complement the collection and there's a programme of temporary exhibitions. **Times:** Open all year, Mon-Sat 10-5, Sun 2-5. (Closed Good Fri, Xmas period & 1 Jan). **Fee:** £1.80 (ch 90p, con £1.40). Joint ticket with Castle Museum available. **Facilities:** P (400yds) & (stair lift available, ring for details) shop ⅋ (ex guide dogs)

SAINSBURY CENTRE FOR VISUAL ARTS
University of East Anglia NR4 7TJ
☎ 01603 456060 & 593199 🖷 01603 259401
e-mail: scva@uea.ac.uk
Times: Open Tue-Sun 11-5. (Closed Mon & University closure at Xmas). **Facilities:** P ⬤ ✗ licensed & (parking at main entrance, wheelchair available on loan) toilets for disabled shop ⅋ (guide dogs by arrangement) *Details not confirmed for 2002* 🐾

⛪ OXBOROUGH
Map 05 TF70

OXBURGH HALL
PE33 9PS (7m SW of Swaffham. Signposted from A134 at Stoke Ferry & Swaffham)
☎ 01366 328258 📠 01366 328066
e-mail: aohusr@smtp.ntrust.org.uk

The outstanding feature of this 15th-century moated building is the 80ft high Tudor gatehouse which has remained unaltered throughout the centuries. Henry VII lodged in the King's Room in 1487. A parterre garden of French design stands outside the moat, and rare needlework by Mary, Queen of Scots and Bess of Hardwick is on display.
Times: Open House: 23 Mar-3 Nov daily (ex Thu & Fri) 1-5, BH Mon 11-5, last admission 4.30. Garden: 2-17 Mar Sat & Sun, 11-4; 23 Mar-3 Nov daily, 11-5.30 (ex Thu & Fri); Aug open daily. Shop & Restaurant: open same as garden & every wknd between 9 Nov-22 Dec 11-4.
Fee: House & Garden £5.50 (ch £2.80) Family ticket £14.50. Garden & Estate £2.80 (ch £1.40). Party 15+ £4.50 each (ex on BH's).
Facilities: 🅿 ✖ licensed ♿ (braille guide, w/chairs available, touch tour - pre-book) toilets for disabled shop ⧔ (ex guide dogs) 🐾 🍽

⛪ REEDHAM
Map 05 TG40

PETTITTS ANIMAL ADVENTURE PARK
NR13 3UA (off A47 at Acle)
☎ 01493 700094 & 701403 📠 01493 700933
Times: Open Etr Sun-Oct, daily 10-5.30. (Closed Sat). **Facilities:** 🅿 🍽 ✖ ♿ (ramps to all areas) toilets for disabled shop *Details not confirmed for 2002* 🍽

⛪ ST OLAVES
Map 05 TM49

ST OLAVES PRIORY
(5.5m SW of Great Yarmouth on A143)
Times: Open any reasonable time. **Facilities:** ⊞ *Details not confirmed for 2002*

⛪ SANDRINGHAM
Map 09 TF62

SANDRINGHAM HOUSE, GROUNDS, MUSEUM & COUNTRY PARK
PE35 6EN (off A148)
☎ 01553 772675 📠 01485 541571
e-mail: enquiries@sandringhamestate.co.uk

The private country retreat of Her Majesty The Queen,

this neo-Jacobean house was built in 1870 for King Edward VII. The main rooms used by the Royal Family when in residence are all open to the public. Sixty acres of glorious grounds surround the House and offer beauty and colour throughout the season. Sandringham Museum contains fascinating displays of Royal memorabilia.
Times: Open Etr Sat-mid Jul & early Aug-Oct. House open 11-4.45, Museum 11-5 & Grounds 10.30-5. **Fee:** House, Museum & Grounds: £6 (ch £3.50, pen £4.50). Family ticket £15.50. Grounds & Museum £5 (ch £3, pen £4). Family ticket £13. **Facilities:** 🅿 🍽 ✖ licensed ♿ (wheelchair loan, free transport in grounds, braille guide) toilets for disabled shop garden centre ⧔ (ex guide dogs) 🍽

⛪ SAXTHORPE
Map 09 TG13

MANNINGTON GARDENS & COUNTRYSIDE
Mannington Hall NR11 7BB (signposted from Corpusty/Saxthorpe on B1149 Norwich-Holt road. Follow brown signs)
☎ 01263 584175 📠 01263 761214

The moated manor house, built in 1460 and still a family home, forms a centrepiece for the pretty gardens which surround it. Enjoy the roses, the chief feature of the gardens, and lovely countryside walks.
Times: Open: Gardens Jun-Aug, Wed-Fri 11-5; also Sun noon-5; 30 Apr-1 Oct. Walks open every day from 9am. Hall open by prior appointment only. **Fee:** Garden £3 (accompanied ch 16 free, students & pen £2.50). Walks free (car park for walkers £1). **Facilities:** 🅿 🍽 ♿ (boardwalk across meadow, wheelchair ramps) toilets for disabled shop garden centre ⧔ (ex guide dogs)

⛪ SHERINGHAM
Map 09 TG14

NORTH NORFOLK RAILWAY
Sheringham Station, Station Approach NR26 8RA (from A148 take A1082. Next to large car park by rdbt in town centre)
☎ 01263 820800 📠 01263 820801

A steam railway with trains operating on most days (Apr-Sep), with extra days as the season progresses and a daily service in the summer. On Sundays, lunch is served on the train. At Weybourne Station there is a collection of steam locomotives and rolling stock, some of which are undergoing or awaiting restoration. There is also a museum of railway memorabilia.
Times: Open Apr-Sep; daily during summer season; Dec (Santa specials). Telephone for details of other running days. **Fee:** Return £7.50 (ch £4, pen £6.50). Family ticket £21. **Facilities:** 🅿 🍽 ♿ (ramps to trains, carriage converted for wheelchair access) shop 🍽

⛪ SNETTISHAM
Map 09 TF63

PARK FARM
PE31 7NQ (signposted on A149, Park Farm is close to the church)
☎ 01485 542425 📠 01485 543503
e-mail: parkfarm@supanet.com

You can see farming in action here with lambing in the spring, sheep shearing in May and deer calving in June and July. Sheep, goats, lambs, rabbits, turkeys, ducks, *contd.*

chickens, ponies, piglets etc can be seen in the paddocks, and the sheep centre has over 40 different breeds. Other attractions include a large adventure playground, horse and pony rides, 2.5 miles of farm trails, visitor centre and craft workshops, including pottery studio and leather worker.
Times: Open all year, Spring, Summer & Autumn, daily 10-5; Winter, Fri-Mon, 10-dusk. Closed 25 Dec. **Fee:** £4.25 (ch £3.25, pen £3.50). Family ticket £14. **Facilities:** P ⬤ & (gravel paths, ramps where needed) toilets for disabled shop ✻ (ex on farm trails) ⬤

🏛 SOUTH WALSHAM   Map 09 TG31
FAIRHAVEN WOODLAND & WATER GARDEN
School Rd NR13 6DZ (follow brown tourist signs from A47 onto B1140 to South Walsham. Through village towards Gt Yarmouth. Turn left into School Road, 100yds past South Walsham Hall)
☎ 01603 270449 ▤ 01603 270449
e-mail: fairhavengardens@norfolkbroads.com

These delightful woodland and water gardens offer a combination of cultivated and wild flowers. In spring there are masses of primroses and bluebells, with azaleas and rhododendrons in several areas. Candelabra primulas and some unusual plants grow near the waterways, and in summer the wild flowers provide a habitat for butterflies, bees and dragonflies.
Times: Open daily 10-5, extended opening until 9pm Wed & Thu, May-Aug. (Closed 25 Dec). **Fee:** £3.50 (ch £1.25, under 5 free, pen & con £3). Single membership tickets £12.50. Family membership ticket £30. **Facilities:** P ⬤ & (ramp, grab rail) toilets for disabled shop garden centre (on leads) ⬤

🏛 THETFORD   Map 05 TL88
ANCIENT HOUSE MUSEUM
White Hart St IP24 1AA (in town centre)
☎ 01842 752599
e-mail: ancient.house.museum@norfolk.gov.uk

An early Tudor timber-framed house with beautifully carved beamed ceilings, it now houses an exhibition on Thetford and Breckland life. This has been traced back to very early times, and there are examples from local Neolithic settlements. Brass rubbing facilities are

available and there is a small period garden recreated in the rear courtyard.
Times: Open all year, Mon-Sat, 10-5 (Closed Mon 12.30-1); Jun-Aug also Sun 2-5. (Closed Good Fri, Xmas period & New Year's Day). **Fee:** Free (ex Jul & Aug £1, ch £60p, stu & con 80p). **Facilities:** P (20yds) shop ✻

THETFORD PRIORY
(on W side of Thetford near station)
Times: Open any reasonable time. **Facilities:** ✻ ✢ *Details not confirmed for 2002*

WARREN LODGE
(2m NW, on B1107)
Times: Open any reasonable time. **Facilities:** ✢ *Details not confirmed for 2002*

🏛 THURSFORD GREEN   Map 09 TF93
THURSFORD COLLECTION
NR21 0AS (1m off A148)
☎ 01328 878477 ▤ 01328 878415
e-mail: admin@thursfordcollection.co.uk

This exciting collection specialises in organs, with a Wurlitzer cinema organ, fairground organs, barrel organs and street organs among its treasures. There are live musical shows every day. The collection also includes showmen's engines, ploughing engines and farm machinery. There is a children's play area and a breathtaking `Venetian gondola' switchback ride.
Times: Open Apr-Oct, daily noon-5. **Fee:** £4.80 (ch u4 free, ch 4-14 £2.30, pen £4.50, ch under 4 free, students £4.05). Party 15+ £4.05 each. **Facilities:** P ⬤ ✗ & toilets for disabled shop ✻ (ex guide dogs) ⬤

🏛 TITCHWELL   Map 09 TF74
RSPB NATURE RESERVE
PE31 8BB (6m E of Hunstanton on A149, signposted entrance)
☎ 01485 210779 ▤ 01485 210779
e-mail: titchwell@rspb.org.uk

A firm path takes you to three hides and on to the beach where a platform overlooking the sea is suitable for wheelchairs. A colony of avocets nest on the enclosed marsh with gadwalls, tufted ducks, shovelers and black-headed gulls. During the season many migrants visit the marsh including wigeon, black-tailed godwits, curlews, and sandpipers.
Times: Open at all times. Visitor Centre daily 10-5 (4pm Nov-Mar). **Fee:** Free. **Facilities:** P (charged) ⬤ & (ramps to hides, wheelchair bays in hides) toilets for disabled shop ⬤

🏛 WEETING   Map 05 TL78
WEETING CASTLE
IP27 0RQ (2m N of Brandon off B1106)
Times: Open any reasonable time. **Facilities:** ✢ *Details not confirmed for 2002*

🏛 WELLS-NEXT-THE-SEA   Map 09 TF94
WELLS & WALSINGHAM LIGHT RAILWAY
NR23 1QB (A149 Cromer road)
☎ 01328 710631

The railway covers the four miles between Wells and Walsingham, and is the longest ten and a quarter inch gauge track in the world. The line passes through some very attractive countryside, particularly noted for its wild flowers and butterflies. This is the home of the unique Garratt Steam Locomotive specially built for this line.
Times: Open daily Etr-Oct. **Fee:** £5.50 return (ch £4 return).
Facilities: 🅿 ♨ & shop

🏛 WELNEY   Map 05 TL59
WWT WELNEY
Hundred Foot Bank PE14 9TN (off A1101, N of Ely)
☎ 01353 860711   📠 01353 860711
e-mail: welney@wwt.org.uk

This important wetland site on the beautiful Ouse Washes is famed for the breathtaking spectacle of wild ducks, geese and swans which spend the winter here. Impressive observation facilities, including hides, towers and an observatory, offer outstanding views of the huge numbers of wildfowl which include Bewick's and Whooper swans, wigeon, teal and shoveler. Floodlit evening swan feeds take place between November and February. There are two hides for wheelchair users.
Times: Open all year, daily 10-5. (Closed 25 Dec). **Fee:** £4.90 (ch £2.90, pen £3.90). **Facilities:** 🅿 ♨ & (wheelchair access to major parts of reserve) toilets for disabled shop 🍴 (ex guide dogs) 🥤

🏛 WEST RUNTON   Map 09 TG14
NORFOLK SHIRE HORSE CENTRE
West Runton Stables NR27 9QH (off A149)
☎ 01263 837339   📠 01263 837132
e-mail: bakewell@
norfolkshirehorse.fsnet.co.uk
Times: Open 9 Apr-Oct, Sun-Fri; also Sats Jul-Aug & BHs.
Facilities: 🅿 ♨ ✗ licensed & toilets for disabled shop 🍴 (ex on lead) *Details not confirmed for 2002* 🥤

🏛 WEYBOURNE   Map 09 TG14
THE MUCKLEBURGH COLLECTION
Weybourne Military Camp NR25 7EG (on A149, coast road, 3m W of Sheringham)
☎ 01263 588210 & 588608   📠 01263 588425
e-mail: info@muckleburgh.co.uk

The largest privately-owned military collection of its kind in the country, which incorporates the Museum of the Suffolk and Norfolk Yeomanry. Exhibits include restored and working tanks, armoured cars, trucks and artillery of WWII, and equipment and weapons from the Falklands and the Gulf War. Live tank demonstrations are run daily (except Saturdays) during school holidays.
Times: Open 18 Feb-28 Oct, daily 10-5. **Fee:** £4.95 (ch £2.50 & pen £4). Family ticket £12.50. **Facilities:** 🅿 ♨ ✗ & (ramped access, wheelchairs available) toilets for disabled shop 🍴 (ex guide dogs) 🥤

Northamptonshire

Northamptonshire is a mainly rural county of gentle beauty, with farmland, forest and great country estates. Rivers, canals and watermeadows are all part of the tranquil scene, providing a haven for wildlife.

EVENTS & FESTIVALS

May
1st-3rd British Waterways
Annual Boat Show, Crick
12th-19th Moulton village
Festival
tbc Daventry & District Arts
Festival (various venues)

July
6th-7th Hollowell Steam &
Heavy Horse Show, Hollowell
nr Northampton
tbc Northampton Town
Show, Abington Park,
Northampton

August
tbc Northampton Hot Air
Balloon Festival,
Northampton Racecourse,
Northampton

Northamptonshire is ideal country for touring, walking and exploring lovely villages of stone and thatch, and visiting some particularly impressive churches. Among the most interesting of these are the Saxon churches at Brixworth and Earls Barton.

In the main square of the pretty village of Geddington stands one of the three surviving Eleanor Crosses. Edward I, grief-stricken at the death of his queen, erected a series of these crosses to mark the resting place of her body, each night, on its journey south from Leicestershire to London. Another such cross can be seen on the southern outskirts of Northampton at Hardingstone. In recent times, Althorp, home of the Spencer family and last resting place of Diana Princess of Wales, has put the county firmly on the tourist map, in quite a similar way.

Northampton is the county town, and along with Kettering, has long been associated with the production of footwear. Kettering was the second largest town until it was overtaken by the rapid development of Corby as a major centre of the steel industry. With the decline of the steel industry, Corby, has fought back as an enterprise zone to provide a home for a variety of modern industries.

Jane Austen's novel *Mansfield Park* is set in Northamptonshire, although it seems that Austen never actually visited the county. Other famous connections include the poet John Dryden, King Richard III and George Washington, whose family came from Sulgrave Manor.

Top: Stoke Park,
Stoke Bruerne

🏛 ALTHORP
Map 04 SP66

ALTHORP
NN7 4HQ (M1 junct 16 and follow signs to Althorp)
☎ 01604 770107 ▤ 01604 770042
e-mail: mail@althorp.com

Althorp House has been the home of the Spencer family since 1508. The house was built in the 16th century, but has been changed since, most notably by Henry Holland in the 18th century. Recently restored by the present Earl, the house is carefully maintained and in immaculate condition. The award-winning exhibition 'Diana, A Celebration' is located in six rooms and depicts the life and work of Diana, Princess of Wales.
Times: Open Jul-Aug, daily 9-5. **Fee:** £11 (ch £5 & pen £9). Family ticket £27. Tickets discounted if pre-booked. **Facilities:** ▣ ⬤ & toilets for disabled shop ✷ (ex guide dogs) ◥

🏛 CANONS ASHBY
Map 04 SP55

CANONS ASHBY HOUSE
NN11 3SD (easy access from either M40 junct 11 or M1 junct 16)
☎ 01327 860044 ▤ 01327 860168
e-mail: ecaxxx@smtp.ntrust.org.uk

An exceptionally small 16th-century manor house with Elizabethan wall paintings and Jacobean plasterwork. There is also a formal garden, an orchard featuring varieties of fruit trees from the 16th-century and remains of an Augustinian priory.
Times: Open 23 Mar-3 Nov, Sat-Wed & BH Mon (closed Good Fri) 1-5.30 or dusk if earlier, Oct-Nov, 12-4.30. **Fee:** £5.20 (ch £2.60) Family ticket £13. **Facilities:** ▣ ⬤ & (hearing scheme taped guide wheelchair available) toilets for disabled shop ✷ (ex on lead in home paddock) ⬥

🏛 DEENE
Map 04 SP99

DEENE PARK
NN17 3EW (0.5m off A43, between Kettering & Stamford)
☎ 01780 450278 ▤ 01780 450282

A mainly 16th-century house of great architectural importance, and home of the Brudenell family since 1514 (including the 7th Earl of Cardigan who led the Charge of the Light Brigade). There's a large lake and park, and extensive gardens with old-fashioned roses, rare trees and shrubs. Phone for details of garden openings and any other special events.
Times: Open 2-5 BH's (Sun & Mon) Etr, May, Spring & Aug; Jun-Aug, Sun. Party 20+ by prior arrangement with House Keeper. **Fee:** House & Gardens: £5 (ch 10-14 £2.50). Gardens only: £3 (ch £1.50). Children under 10 free admission with accompanying adult. **Facilities:** ▣ ⬤ & (ramps to cafeteria and gardens) toilets for disabled ✷ (ex guide dogs in garden only) ⬥

KIRBY HALL
NN17 5EN (on unclass road off A43, 4m NE of Corby)
☎ 01536 203230

A beautiful Elizabethan manor house boasting an unusual richness and variety of architectural detail in the Renaissance style. The extensive gardens were among the finest in England at their peak during the 17th century.
Times: Open all year, Apr-Sep, daily 10-6 (Oct 10-5); Nov-Mar, wkends 10-4. Closed 24-26 Dec & 1 Jan & leading up to event on 11/12Aug. **Fee:** £3 (ch 5-15 £1.50, under 5's free, con £2.30). Personal stereo tours included in admission. **Facilities:** ▣ & shop ✷ (in certain areas) ▦

🏛 HOLDENBY
Map 04 SP66

HOLDENBY HOUSE, GARDENS & FALCONRY CENTRE
NN6 8DJ (7m NW of Northampton, off A5199 or A428)
☎ 01604 770074 ▤ 01604 770962

Just across the fields from Althorp, this former palace and prison of Charles I provides a stately backdrop to a beautiful garden and host of attractions. Falconry, 17th-century farmstead, children's amusements, shop and tearoom.
Times: Open; Gardens & Falconry Centre Apr-end Sep, Sun 1-5. Jul & Aug open daily 1-5 (ex Sat). House open Etr, Whitson & Aug BH. Contact for details of additional Falconry Centre opening days.
Fee: Gardens & Falconry Centre £3 (ch £1.75, pen £2.50). House, Gardens & Falconry Centre £5 (ch £3, pen £4.50). **Facilities:** ▣ ⬤ & (gravel paths with ramps) toilets for disabled shop (on leads)

🏛 KETTERING
Map 04 SP87

ALFRED EAST GALLERY
Sheep St NN16 0AN (A43, A6, in town centre)
☎ 01536 534274 ▤ 01536 534370
e-mail: kettering.museum@excite.co.uk

The Gallery has a new permanent exhibition space showing work by Sir Alfred East, Thomas Cooper Gotch and other local artists, as well as selections from the Gallery's contemporary collection, including Sir Howard Hodgkin and John Bevan. Two further display spaces are dedicated to monthly changing sales exhibitions of art, craft and photography.
Times: Open all year, Mon-Sat 9.30-5 (ex Wed closed until 10am & closed BHs) **Fee:** Free. **Facilities:** ℙ (300yds) & shop ✷ (ex guide dogs)

🏛 LYVEDEN NEW BIELD
Map 04 SP98

LYVEDEN NEW BIELD
PE8 5AT (4m SW Oundle via A427)
☎ 01832 205358
e-mail: elnbxxx@smtp.ntrust.org.uk

An incomplete Elizabethan garden house and moated garden. Designed by Sir Thomas Tresham to symbolise the Catholic faith.
Times: Open 23 Mar-3 Nov Wed-Sun, 10.30-5. 4 Nov-22 Mar, Sat & Sun 10.30-4. **Facilities:** ℙ (0.5 m along track) ✷ (ex on leads) ◉ ⬥

NASSINGTON   Map 04 TL09
PREBENDAL MANOR HOUSE
PE8 6QG
☎ 01780 782575
e-mail: info@prebendal-manor.demon.co.uk

Dating from the early 13th century, this is the oldest manor in Northamptonshire. There's a 15th-century dovecote and tithe barn museum, and the largest re-created medieval garden in Europe, boasting fishponds, herbers, arbours, turf seats, trellised herbers, medieval vegetable garden and vineyard.
Times: Open May-Jun & Sep Sun & Wed 1-5.30; Jul & Aug Sun, Wed & Thu 1-5.30. BH Mon (Closed Xmas) **Fee:** House & garden £4 (ch £1.20) Party 20+; Garden only £3.50. **Facilities:** 🅿 💺 ♿ (ramps) shop ✸ (guide dogs)

NORTHAMPTON   Map 04 SP76
CENTRAL MUSEUM & ART GALLERY
Guildhall Rd NN1 1DP (in town centre)
☎ 01604 238548 🖷 01604 238720
e-mail: museums@northhampton.gov.uk

Reflecting Northampton's proud standing as Britain's boot and shoe capital, the museum houses a collection of boots and shoes which is considered one of the finest in the world. Other displays include the History of Northampton, Decorative Arts, the Art Gallery, and special temporary exhibitions.
Times: Open all year, Mon-Sat 10-5, Sun 2-5. **Fee:** Free. **Facilities:** 🅿 (200 yds) ♿ (wheelchairs available, large print catalogues) toilets for disabled shop ✸ (ex guide/assistance dogs) 💺

ROCKINGHAM   Map 04 SP89
ROCKINGHAM CASTLE
LE16 8TH (2m N of Corby, off A6003)
☎ 01536 770240 🖷 01536 771692
e-mail: michaeltebbutt@lineone.net
Times: Open Apr-Sep, Thu, Sun, BH Mon & following Tue (also Tues in Aug) 1-5. Grounds open at 11.30 on Sun & BH Mon.
Facilities: 🅿 💺 ♿ (may alight at entrance, ramped) shop *Details not confirmed for 2002* 💺

RUSHTON   Map 04 SP88
TRIANGULAR LODGE
NN14 1RP
☎ 01536 710761

Almost every detail of the lodge built by Sir Thomas Tresham in 1593 has a meaning. The building was designed as an expression of his staunch Roman Catholic faith; intriguing symbols of the Trinity and the Mass abound.
Times: Open Apr-Sep, daily 10-6; Oct, daily 10-5. **Fee:** £1.75 (ch 90p, ch u5 free, con £1.30). **Facilities:** ♿ ✸ ⌗

STOKE BRUERNE   Map 04 SP74
CANAL MUSEUM
NN12 7SE (A508, 4m S of M1 junct 5)
☎ 01604 862229 🖷 01604 864199
e-mail: britishwaterways@sosb.globalnet.co.uk

Housed on three floors of an old cornmill, the colourful collection vividly portrays the many aspects of inland waterways from their origins to the present day, complementing the flight of locks and long canal tunnel outside.
Times: Open Etr-Oct daily, 10-5; Nov-Etr Tue-Sun, 10-4. Closed 25-26 Dec. Last admission 30 mins before closing time. **Fee:** £3 (ch, pen & student £2). Family ticket (2 adults & 2 ch) £8. **Facilities:** 🅿 (charged) ♿ toilets for disabled shop ✸ (ex guide dogs) 💺

SULGRAVE   Map 04 SP54
SULGRAVE MANOR
Manor Rd OX17 2SD (off B4525 Banbury to Northampton rd. 6m from M40 junct 11, 15m from M1 junct 15a)
☎ 01295 760205 🖷 01295 768056
e-mail: sulgrave-manor@talk21.com

Home to George Washington's ancestors until 1656 when his great-grandfather, John, emigrated to Virginia. Inside the house there are many relics of George Washington. Though much of the house is a 20th-century restoration, original parts include the porch (with a carving of the original American flag), a screens passage, the great hall and the great chamber.
Times: Open Apr-Oct, Mon-Fri (ex Wed) 2-5.30, Sat, Sun & BH 10.30-1 & 2-5.30; Dec, Sat & Sun only 10.30-1 & 2-4.30; Other times by appointment. (Closed 25-26 Dec & Jan). **Fee:** £4.50 (ch £2.25). Party 12+. Special event days £5 (ch £2.50). Family ticket £14. Party 12+.
Facilities: 🅿 💺 ✗ licensed ♿ (induction loop available in shop or ticket office) toilets for disabled shop garden centre ✸ (ex guide & outside on leads) 💺

Northumberland

Northumberland is a county of wide open spaces taking in the Northumberland National Park to the northwest, with miles of moorland around Hadrian's Wall rising to the Cheviot Hills on the Scottish border, and incorporating great swathes of Forestry Commission planted conifers.

The Pennine Way walking trail runs through the park from Hadrian's Wall to The Cheviot, the National Park's highest peak at 2,674 feet/815 metres, and crosses the border into Scotland. Towards the east, the park changes character in the gentle valleys of the rivers Coquet, Redesdale and North Tyne.

Hadrian's Wall, the Roman astonishing feat of engineering and an enduring legacy, runs for 73 miles across northern England, and there are several well preserved forts, including Housestead's, one of the most popular sites on the wall.

The long, low lying coastline of Northumberland, designated an Area of Outstanding Natural Beauty, is dotted with a series of magnificent castles, Warworth, Alnick, Bamburgh, plus the remains of the 12th-century castle at Berwick-upon-Tweed and the impressive Elizabethan ramparts. Berwick is England's northernmost town, held alternately by the Scottish and English over centuries of bitter struggle.

The county town is Morpeth, which is the administrative centre, though this is disputed to some extent by Alnick, the seat of the Duke of Northumberland. The attractive market town of Hexham warrants some exploration, with its Abbey, Moot Hall and other medieval remains, and also makes a good base for visiting Hadrian's Wall.

Top: Holy Island

EVENTS & FESTIVALS

April
5th-7th Morpeth Northumbrian Gathering

May
1st Riding the Bounds, Berwick-upon-Tweed
tbc Border Marches, Berwick-upon-Tweed
tbc Northumberland County Show, Corbridge

June
1st Allendale Fair
15th Ovingham Goose Fair, Packhorse Bridge, Ovingham
23rd-29th Alnwick Fair

July
6th-7th Amble Sea Fair, Amble
12th Rothbury Traditional Music Festival
28th Alnwick Castle Tournament, Alnwick

August
3rd Powburn Show & Sheepdog Trials, Powburn
3rd-9th Alnwick International Music Festival, Alnwick (provisional)
10th Slaley Show, Slaley

September
7th Alnwick District Horticultural Show
tbc Military Tattoo, Barracks, Berwick-upon-Tweed

November
2nd Northumbrian Gathering

⛪ ALNWICK Map 12 NU11
ALNWICK CASTLE
NE66 1NQ (off A1 on outskirts of town)
☎ 01665 510777 📠 01665 510876
e-mail: enquiries@alnwickcastle.com

Alnwick Castle is the main seat of the Duke of
Northumberland whose family have lived here since
1309. The stern, medieval exterior belies the treasure
house within, furnished in Renaissance style, with
paintings by Titian, Van Dyck and Canaletto, and an
exquisite collection of Meissen china. The Regiment
Museum of Royal Northumberland Fusiliers is housed
in the Abbot's Tower of the Castle. Refurbished towers
include museums of local archaeology and the Percy
Tenantry volunteers.
Times: Open Apr-26 Oct, daily 11-5 (last admission 4.15). **Fee:** £6.75
(ch £3.50, concessions £5.75). Family ticket £15.50. Party 14+.
Facilities: 🅿 ♨ ♿ (Castle lift for those able to walk a little) toilets for
disabled shop ✘ (ex guide dogs) ➶

⛪ BAMBURGH Map 12 NU13
BAMBURGH CASTLE
NE69 7DF (A1 Belford by-pass, E on B1342 to
Bamburgh)
☎ 01668 214515 & 214208 📠 01668 214060
Times: Open Apr-Oct, daily 11-5 (last admission 4.30pm). Other times
by prior arrangement. **Facilities:** 🅿 (charged) ♨ ♿ shop ✘ (ex
guide dogs) *Details not confirmed for 2002*

GRACE DARLING MUSEUM
Radcliffe Rd NE69 7AE (follow A1, turn off at Bamburgh
& follow signs to Northumbria Coastal route, museum
on right)
☎ 01668 214465 📠 01668 214465

Pictures, documents and other reminders of the heroine
are on display, including the boat in which Grace
Darling and her father, keeper of Longstone
Lighthouse, Farne Islands, rescued nine survivors from
the wrecked `SS Forfarshire' in 1838.
Times: Open Etr-Oct, daily 10-5 (Sun 12-5). **Fee:** Free. **Facilities:** 🅿
(400yds) ♿ (ramps) shop ✘ (ex guide dogs)

⛪ BARDON MILL Map 12 NY76
VINDOLANDA (CHESTERHOLM)
Vindolanda Trust NE47 7JN (signposted from A69 or
B6318)
☎ 01434 344277 📠 01434 344060
e-mail: vindolandatrust@btinternet.com
Times: Open daily from 10am, all facilities mid Feb-mid Nov.
Facilities: 🅿 ♨ ♿ toilets for disabled shop ✘ (ex guide dogs)
Details not confirmed for 2002 ➶

⛪ BELSAY Map 12 NZ07
BELSAY HALL, CASTLE AND GARDENS
NE20 0DX (on A696)
☎ 01661 881636

Belsay Castle, with its splendid turrets and battlements,
dates from 1370 and was the home of the Middleton
family, until they built the Jacobean manor house

beside it, and then the magnificent Grecian-style Hall.
There are also wonderful gardens.
Times: Open all year, daily Apr-Sep 10-6 (Oct 10-5); Nov-Mar, daily 10-
4. Closed 24-26 Dec & 1 Jan. **Fee:** £3.90 (ch 5-15 £2, under 5's free,
con £2.90). **Facilities:** 🅿 ✘ ♿ toilets for disabled shop ✘ (in certain
areas) ♨

⛪ BERWICK-UPON-TWEED Map 12 NT95
BERWICK BARRACKS, MUSEUM & ART
GALLERY
TD15 1DF (on the Parade, off Church St, in town centre)
☎ 01289 304493

Enclosed by its Elizabethan ramparts, Berwick is an
outstanding example of a fortified town, and the
barracks have changed little since 1721. The museum
covers 200 years of military and regimental history, and
the Art Gallery houses the important Burrell Collection.
Times: Open all year, Apr-Oct daily 10-6 (Oct 10-5); Nov-Mar Wed-
Sun 10-4. Closed 24-26 Dec & 1 Jan. **Fee:** £2.70 (ch 5-15 £1.40, under
5's free, con £2). **Facilities:** 🅿 ♿ shop ✘ ♨

PAXTON HOUSE
TD15 1SZ (3m from A1 Berwick-upon-Tweed bypass on
B6461 Kelso road)
☎ 01289 386291 📠 01289 386660
e-mail: info@paxtonhouse.com

Built in 1758 for the Laird of Wedderburn, the house is
a fine example of neo-Palladian architecture. Much of
the house is furnished by Chippendale and there is a
large picture gallery. The house is set in 80 acres beside
the River Tweed, and the grounds include an adventure
playground.
Times: Open daily from Apr-Oct, House & gallery 11-5 (last tour of
house 4.15pm). Grounds 10-sunset. **Fee:** House & Grounds: £5 (ch
£2.50, adult concessions £4.50) Family ticket £14. Grounds only: £2.50
(ch £1, adult concessions £2) Family ticket £6. **Facilities:** 🅿 ♨ ✘
licensed ♿ (lifts to main areas of house, parking close to reception)
toilets for disabled shop ✘ (ex guide/on lead in grounds) ➶

⛪ CAMBO Map 12 NZ08
WALLINGTON HOUSE WALLED GARDEN &
GROUNDS
NE61 4AR (6m NW of Belsay)
☎ 01670 773600 📠 01670 774420
e-mail: nwaplr@smtp.ntrust.org.uk

The house is set in a great moorland estate of over
12,000 acres. It features delicate plasterwork,
'Capability' Brown gardens and William Bell Scott
murals. In the 19th century Ruskin and other writers
and artists came here as guests. Special events include
open air concerts and theatre productions.
Times: Open: House Apr-Sep, daily (ex Tue) 1-5.30, Oct daily (ex Tue)
1-4.30. Last admission half hour before closing. Walled garden Apr-
Oct, daily 10-7 or dusk; Nov-Mar, 10-4 or dusk if earlier. Grounds open
all year. **Fee:** House, walled garden & grounds: £5.50, family ticket
£13.75. Walled gardens & grounds only: £4. Party £5 each.
Facilities: 🅿 ♨ ✘ ♿ (Vessa Ventura scooter, braille guide) toilets for
disabled shop garden centre ♨ ➶

🏛 CARRAWBROUGH   Map 12 NY87
ROMAN WALL (MITHRAIC TEMPLE)
(on B6318)
Times: Open any reasonable time. **Facilities:** 🅿 ♯ *Details not confirmed for 2002*

🏛 CHILLINGHAM   Map 12 NU02
CHILLINGHAM CASTLE
NE66 5NJ (signposted from A1 & A697)
☎ 01668 215359   ▤ 01668 215463
e-mail: enquiries@chillingham.castle.com

This remarkable castle with its alarming dungeons and torture chamber is now undergoing restoration. Romantic grounds laid out by Sir Jeffry Wyatville command views over the Cheviots and include topiary gardens and woodland walks. Weddings, private functions and meals can be arranged, and fishing is available. Please ring for details of special events.
Times: Open Etr wknd & May-Sep, daily (ex closed Tue in May, Jun & Sep) 12-5 (Last admission 4.30pm). Other times by prior arrangement.
Fee: £4.80 (ch free with paying adult max 5, pen £3.80). Party 10+.
Facilities: 🅿 ♨ ✕ licensed ♿ shop ⛵

CHILLINGHAM WILD CATTLE PARK
NE66 5NP (off B6348, follow brown tourist signs off A1 and A697)
☎ 01668 215250   ▤ 01668 215250

The park, a registred charity, at Chillingham boasts an extraordinary survival: a herd of wild white cattle descended from animals trapped in the park when the wall was built in the 13th century; they are the sole surviving pure-bred examples of their breed in the world. Binoculars are recommended for a close view. Visitors are accompanied into the park by the Warden.
Times: Open Apr-Oct, daily 10-12 & 2-5, Sun 2-5. (Closed Tue).
Fee: £3 (ch £1 & pen £2.50). **Facilities:** 🅿 (tour via warden's Range Rover – ring in advance) shop ⛵

🏛 CORBRIDGE   Map 12 NY96
CORBRIDGE ROMAN STATION
NE45 5NT (0.5m NW on minor road - signposted)
☎ 01434 632349

The remains of Roman `Corstopitum', built around AD210, include granaries, portico columns and the probable site of legionary headquarters.
Times: Open all year, Apr-Sep, daily 10-6 (or dusk if earlier in Oct); Nov-Mar, Wed-Sun 10-4. Closed 24-26 Dec & 1 Jan. **Fee:** £2.90 (ch 5-15 £1.50, under 5's free, con £2.20). **Facilities:** 🅿 ♿ ⛵ (in certain areas) ♯

🏛 EMBLETON   Map 12 NU22
DUNSTANBURGH CASTLE
Craster NE66 2RD (1.5m E on footpaths from Craster or Embleton)
☎ 01665 576231

The skeletal ruins of the huge castle, partly built by John of Gaunt, stand on cliffs 100ft above the North Sea. Already a ruin by Tudor times, its setting has inspired many paintings, including three by Turner.
Times: Open all year, Apr-Sep, daily 10-6 (Oct 10-5); Nov-Mar, Wed-Sun 10-4. Closed 24-26 Dec & 1Jan. **Fee:** £1.90 (ch 5-15 £1, under 5's free, con £1.40) **Facilities:** 🅿 (charged) ♯

🏛 FORD   Map 12 NT93
LADY WATERFORD HALL
TD15 2QA (approx 1.5m E of A697)
☎ 01890 820338   ▤ 01890 820384
Times: Open Mar-Nov, daily 10.30-12.30 & 1.30-5.30. Open by appointment in winter. **Facilities:** 🅿 ♿ shop *Details not confirmed for 2002*

🏛 HOLY ISLAND (LINDISFARNE)
Map 12 NU14
LINDISFARNE CASTLE
TD15 2SH (8m S Berwick from A1 on Holy Island)
☎ 01289 389244

The 16th-century castle was restored by Sir Edwin Lutyens in 1903 for the owner of *Country Life* magazine. The austere outside walls belie the Edwardian comfort within, and there is a little garden designed by Gertrude Jekyll.
Times: Open Apr-Oct, daily (closed Fri ex Good Fri) as Lindisfarne is a tidal island, the Castle will open 4.5hrs which will always include 12-3 and then either earlier opening or later closing as the tide allows.
Fee: £4.20 (ch £2.10) Family ticket £10.50. **Facilities:** 🅿 (1m in village) ⛵ ♨

LINDISFARNE PRIORY
TD15 2RX (Can only be reached at low tide across a causeway. Tide tables posted at each end of the causeway)
☎ 01289 389200

St Aidan and monks from Iona founded the first monastery on the island in the 7th century, and from here preached the gospel to much of Northern England, also producing the illuminated Lindisfarne Gospels, now in the British Library. The priory ruins date from the 11th century and the island can be reached by a causeway at low tide (tide tables are displayed), or phone the custodian for details.
Times: Open all year, Apr-Sep, daily 10-6 (Oct 10-5); Nov-Mar, daily 10-4. Subject to tides. Closed 24-26 Dec & 1 Jan. **Fee:** £2.90 (ch 5-15 £1.50, under 5's free, con £2.20) **Facilities:** shop ⛵ (in certain areas) ♯

🏛 HOUSESTEADS   Map 12 NY76
HOUSESTEADS ROMAN FORT
Bardon Mills NE47 6NN (2.5m NE of Bardon Mill on B6318)
☎ 01434 344363
Times: Open all year, Apr-Sep, daily 10-6 (Oct 10-5); Nov-Mar, daily 10-4. Closed 24-26 Dec & 1 Jan. **Facilities:** 🅿 (0.25m from fort) shop ⛵ ♯ ♨ *Details not confirmed for 2002*

🏛 LONGFRAMLINGTON   Map 12 NU10
BRINKBURN PRIORY
NE65 8AR (off B6344)
☎ 01665 570628

The priory was founded in 1135 for Augustinian canons, and stands on a bend of the River Coquet. After the Dissolution of the Monasteries it fell into disrepair, but was restored in 1858.
Times: Open Apr-Oct, daily 10-6, (Oct 10-5). **Fee:** £1.70 (ch 5-15 90p, under 5's free, con £1.35) **Facilities:** 🅿 ☓ (in certain areas) ⊞

🏛 MORPETH   Map 12 NZ28
MORPETH CHANTRY BAGPIPE MUSEUM
Bridge St NE61 1PJ (off A1)
☎ 01670 519466   ▤ 01670 511326
Times: Open all year, Mon-Sat 10-5. (Closed 25-26 Dec, 1 Jan & Etr Mon). **Facilities:** 🅿 (100 metres) ♿ (induction loop, not suitable for wheelchairs) shop *Details not confirmed for 2002* 🍴

🏛 NORHAM   Map 12 NT94
CASTLE
TD15 2JY
☎ 01289 382329
Times: Open Apr-Oct, 10-6 (Oct 10-5). **Facilities:** 🅿 ♿ ☓ ⊞ *Details not confirmed for 2002*

🏛 PRUDHOE   Map 12 NZ06
PRUDHOE CASTLE
NE42 6NA (on minor road off A695)
☎ 01661 833459

Standing on the River Tyne, this medieval castle was the stronghold of the d'Umfravelles and Percys. The keep stands in the inner bailey and a notable gatehouse guards the outer bailey. Access is to the Pele Yard only.
Times: Open Apr-Oct, daily 10-6 (Oct 10-5). **Fee:** £1.90 (ch 5-15 £1, under 5's free, con £1.40). **Facilities:** 🅿 shop ☓ (in certain areas) ⊞

🏛 ROTHBURY   Map 12 NU00
CRAGSIDE HOUSE, GARDEN & ESTATE
Cragside House NE65 7PX (1m NW of Morpeth on A697, L onto B6341, entrance 1m N of Rothbury)
☎ 01669 620333 & 620150   ▤ 01669 620066

This Victorian mansion was the first building in the world to be lit by hydro-electricity. In the 1880s the house had hot and cold running water, central heating, telephones and a passenger lift. There is a vast forest garden to explore containing one of Europe's largest rock gardens, formal gardens, lakes and an adventure play area.
Times: Open, Estate & Gardens: 31 Mar-4 Nov, Tue-Sun & BH Mons 10.30-7; 7 Nov-16 Dec, Wed-Sun 11-4. House: Tue-Sun & BH Mon's 1-5.30. Last admission 4.30pm. **Fee:** House, Estate & Gardens £6.70 (ch £3.40) Family (2ad+3ch) £16.80. Party 15+. Estate & Gardens £4.20 (ch2.10) Family (2ad+3ch) £10.50. Party 15+ **Facilities:** 🅿 ✗ licensed ♿ (braille guide, wheelchair path, lift) toilets for disabled shop ☓ (ex in grounds on lead) 🐾 🍴

🏛 WALWICK   Map 12 NY97
CHESTERS ROMAN FORT & MUSEUM
Chollerford NE46 4EP (0.5m W of Chollerford on B6318)
☎ 01434 681379

One of the Roman forts on Hadrian's Wall is now in the park of Chesters, an 18th-century mansion. The fort named *Cilurnum* housed 500 soldiers and covered nearly 6 acres. Excavations have shown that it was destroyed and rebuilt three times. Evidence of an aqueduct and substantial remains of a bath house show that the standard of living was high.
Times: Open all year, Apr-Sep, daily 9.30-6; Oct, daily 10-5; Nov-Mar, daily 10-4. Closed 24-26Dec & 1Jan. **Fee:** £2.90 (ch 5-15 £1.50, under 5's free, con £2.20) **Facilities:** 🅿 ☕ ♿ shop ☓ (in certain areas) ⊞

🏛 WARKWORTH   Map 12 NU20
WARKWORTH CASTLE
NE66 0UJ
☎ 01665 711423
Times: Open all year, Apr-Oct, daily 10-6 (Oct 10-5); Nov-Mar, daily 10-4 (or dusk if earlier, closed 1-2pm). Closed 24-26 Dec & 1 Jan.
Facilities: 🅿 ♿ ☓ (in certain areas) ⊞ *Details not confirmed for 2002*

WARKWORTH HERMITAGE
NE65 0UJ
☎ 01665 711423

Upstream from Warkworth Castle is the Hermitage, a refuge dug into the rockface by a 14th-century hermit. It consists of a chapel and two living chambers. Nearby is Coquet Island, which was also the home of hermit monks.
Times: Open Apr-Sep, daily 10-6, (Oct 10-5); Nov-Mar, daily 10-4. Closed 24-26 Dec & 1 Jan. **Fee:** £1.70 (ch 5-15 90p, under 5's free, con £1.30) **Facilities:** 🅿 ♿ ☓ ⊞

Nottinghamshire

The inland county of Nottinghamshire in eastern England is strongly associated with the legend of Robin Hood, though Robin's territory, the former royal hunting ground of Sherwood Forest, has been somewhat tamed since his outlaw days.

The county is divided between the old coalfields north of the city of Nottingham, the commuter belt of the Wolds to the south, and the area of most interest, that of Sherwood Forest and the great country estates known as the 'Dukeries'. One of these, Clumber Park, was formerly home to the Dukes of Newcastle, and is now owned by the National Trust.

The traditional industry of Nottinghamshire, alongside agriculture, was coal mining, though this has declined in recent years. It is also an oil producing area, and during World War II produced the only oil out of reach of the German U-Boats.

D H Lawrence was a Nottinghamshire man, the son of a miner and former schoolteacher. He grew up in poverty, and his book *Sons and Lovers* reflects the experiences of his early years. There is a D H Lawrence commemorative walk from his home at Eastwood to Old Brinsley Colliery.

Other Nottinghamshire notables include Thomas Cranmer, the first Protestant Archbishop; Jesse Boot, founder of the Boots pharmaceutical company; Henry Ireton, the man who signed Charles I's death warrant; Torvill & Dean, Olympic skaters; and Paul Smith, fashion designer.

Other towns of note are the river port and market town of Newark, which hosts a major antiques fair six times a year, and Southwell, known for the medieval minster with exquisite carvings of Sherwood Forest.

Top: Nottingham Council House

EVENTS & FESTIVALS

February
tbc Youth Arts Festival, Nottingham (various venues)

May
11th-12th Nottingham County Show, Winthorpe
tbc Parklife, Woollaton Park, Nottingham

June
tbc Motor Show, Nottingham

July/August
tbc Annual Robin Hood Festival, Edwinstowe
tbc Newstead Summer Stage, Nottingham (open air theatre at Newstead Abbey)

August
tbc Caribbean Carnival, Nottingham
tbc City in the Park, Woollaton Park
tbc Eid Mela, Nottingham (Muslim festival)
tbc Riverside Festival, Nottingham

September
29th Robin Hood Marathon, Nottingham (from Victoria Embankment)

October
2nd-6th Goose Fair, Nottingham
tbc Dusshera Mela, Nottingham (Hindu festival)

October/November
tbc Now Festival, Nottingham

November
1st-3rd Robin Hood Pageant, Nottingham

⚏ EASTWOOD   Map 08 SK44
DURBAN HOUSE HERITAGE CENTRE
Mansfield Rd NG16 3DZ (signed on A610)
☎ 01773 717353   🖷 01773 713509
Times: Open all year, Apr-Oct, daily 10-5; Nov-Mar, daily 10-4. Closed 24 Dec-1 Jan. **Facilities:** 🅿 💺 ✕ ♿ (lift to exhibition) toilets for disabled shop ✻ (ex guide dogs) *Details not confirmed for 2002* ◥

⚏ EDWINSTOWE   Map 08 SK66
SHERWOOD FOREST COUNTRY PARK & VISITOR CENTRE
NG21 9HN (on B6034 N of village between A6075 and A616)
☎ 01623 823202   & 824490   🖷 01623 823202
e-mail: marilynlouden@nottscc.gov.uk

At the heart of the Robin Hood legend is Sherwood Forest. Today it is a country park and visitor centre with 450 acres of ancient oaks and shimmering silver birches. Waymarked pathways guide you through the forest. A year round programme of events includes the spectacular Robin Hood Festival.

Times: Country Park: open daily dawn to dusk. Visitor Centre: open daily 10.30-5 (4.30pm Nov-Mar) **Fee:** *Prices not confirmed for 2002* **Facilities:** 🅿 (charged) 💺 ♿ toilets for disabled shop (ex guide dogs)

⚏ FARNSFIELD   Map 08 SK65
WHITE POST MODERN FARM CENTRE
NG22 8HL (12m N of Nottingham on A614)
☎ 01623 882977 & 882026   🖷 01623 883499
e-mail: tim@whitepostfarmcentre.co.uk

This award-winning working farm gives an introduction to a variety of modern farming methods. It explains how farms work, with exhibits such as llamas, deer, pigs, cows, snails, quails, snakes and fish. There's lots to see indoors, including the incubator room, mousetown and a reptile house.

Times: Open all year, Mon-Fri 10-5. Wknds & BH's 10-6. **Fee:** £4.95 (ch 3-16 £3.95, under 3 free, pen & people with special needs £3.95). Party 10+. **Facilities:** 🅿 💺 ♿ (sign language, free hire wheelchairs, book if more than 6) toilets for disabled shop ✻ (ex guide dogs) ◥

⚏ HAUGHTON   Map 08 SK67
WORLD OF ROBIN HOOD
Haughton Farm DN22 8DZ (on B6387 just outside Walesby, signposted off A1)
☎ 01623 860210   🖷 01623 836003
e-mail: worldofrobinhood@talk21.com
Times: Open 10.30-4. Telephone for winter opening times.
Facilities: 🅿 💺 ✕ licensed ♿ toilets for disabled shop ✻ (outside areas only) *Details not confirmed for 2002* ◥

⚏ NEWARK-ON-TRENT   Map 08 SK75
MILLGATE MUSEUM
48 Millgate NG24 4TS (easy access from A1 & A46)
☎ 01636 655730   🖷 01636 655735
e-mail: museums@newark-sherwooddc.gov.uk

Fascinating exhibitions - recreated streets, shops and houses in period settings. The museum displays illustrate the working and domestic life of local people, from Victorian times to 1950. The mezzanine gallery, home to a number of temporary exhibitions showing the work of local artists, designers and photographers.

Times: Open all year, Mon-Fri 10-5, Sat & Sun & BH 1-5. Last admission 4.30. **Fee:** Free. **Facilities:** 🅿 (250yds) 💺 ♿ toilets for disabled shop ✻ (ex aid dogs)

NEWARK AIR MUSEUM
The Airfield, Winthorpe NG24 2NY (easy access from A1, A46, A17, follow tourist signs)
☎ 01636 707170   🖷 01636 707170
e-mail: newarkair@lineone.net

A diverse collection of transport, training and reconnaisance aircraft, jet fighters, bombers and helicopters, now numbering more than fifty. An Undercover Aircraft Display Hall and an Engine Hall make the museum an all-weather attraction. Everything is displayed around a WWII airfield.

Times: Open all year, Mar-Sep daily 10-5; Oct-Feb, daily 10-4. (Closed 24-26 Dec). Other times by appointment. **Fee:** £4 (ch £2.50, pen £3.50). Family ticket £11. Party 10+. **Facilities:** 🅿 💺 ♿ toilets for disabled shop ◥

VINA COOKE MUSEUM OF DOLLS & BYGONE CHILDHOOD
The Old Rectory, Cromwell NG23 6JE (5m N of Newark off A1)
☎ 01636 821364

All kinds of childhood memorabilia are displayed in this 17th-century house: prams, toys, dolls' houses, costumes and a large collection of Victorian and Edwardian dolls including Vina Cooke hand-made character dolls.

Times: Open all year, Tue-Thu 10.30-12 & 2-5. Sat, Sun & BH Mon 10.30-5. Mon, Fri & other times open by appointment. **Fee:** £2.50 (ch £1.50, pen £2). **Facilities:** 🅿 💺 ♿ shop

⬛ NEWSTEAD
Map 08 SK55

NEWSTEAD ABBEY
Newstead Abbey Park NG15 8GE (off A60, between
Nottingham & Mansfield)
☎ 01623 455900 📄 01623 455904

This beautiful house is best known as the home of poet
Lord Byron. Visitors can see Byron's own rooms, his
mementoes and other splendidly decorated rooms. The
grounds of over 300 acres include waterfalls, ponds,
water gardens and Japanese gardens. Special events
include outdoor theatre and opera, Christmas events
and Ghost Tours.

Times: Open: Grounds all year, daily 9-dusk (ex last Fri in Nov);
House Apr-Sep, daily 12-5. Last admission 4pm **Fee:** House & Grounds
£4 (ch £1.50, concessions £2) Family ticket (2 adults & 3 ch) £10.
Grounds only £2 (ch & concessions £1.50) Family ticket £6. Subject to
change. **Facilities:** 🅿 🍷 ✗ licensed ♿ (audio tour, mobility car &
wheelchair for loan Apr-Sep) toilets for disabled shop (open Apr-Sep)
🐾 (ex guide or garden on lead)

⬛ NOTTINGHAM
Map 08 SK53

BREWHOUSE YARD MUSEUM
Castle Boulevard NG7 1FB
☎ 0115 915 3600 & 0115 915 3640
📄 0115 915 3601

Housed in 17th-century cottages, the museum depicts
everyday life in Nottingham over the past 300 years.
Locally made or used objects are shown in a mixture of
period rooms, re-created shops and displays. Caves
behind the houses are also part of the museum.

Times: Open all year 10-4.30. (Closed Fri Nov-Mar & 25-26 Dec).
Fee: Free Mon-Fri but donations appreciated. Weekends & BH's £1.50
(con 80p). Family ticket £3.80. **Facilities:** 🅿 (100yds) ♿ toilets for
disabled shop 🐾 (ex guide dogs)

CASTLE MUSEUM
NG1 6EL
☎ 0115 915 3700 📄 0115 915 3653

This 17th-century building is both museum and art
gallery, with major temporary exhibitions as well as the
permanent collections. There is a 'Story of Nottingham'
exhibition, and the 'Meet you at the Lions' exhibition,
which celebrates the diversity of people living in
Nottingham today. Guided tour of the underground
passages most afternoons.

Times: Open all year, daily 10-5. (ex Fri Nov-Feb) Grounds 8-dusk.
(Closed 25 & 26 Dec). **Fee:** Mon-Fri free, wknds & BH's £2 (ch &
concessions £1). Family ticket £5. **Facilities:** 🅿 (400yds) 🍷 ♿ (chair
lift, mobility car available) toilets for disabled shop 🐾 (ex guide dogs)

THE CAVES OF NOTTINGHAM
Upper Level, Broadmarsh Shopping Centre NG1 7LS
(within Broadmarsh Shopping Centre, on first floor)
☎ 0115 924 1424 📄 0115 924 1430
e-mail: info@cavesofnottingham.co.uk

A unique 750-year-old cave system situated beneath a
modern day shopping centre. A digital audio tour
guides you through the only remaining underground

medieval tannery in England, beer cellars, an air raid
shelter and the remains of Drury Hill, one of the oldest
streets in Nottingham.

Times: Open daily 10-5, Sun 11-5 (last admission 4.15pm, Sun 4pm).
(Closed 24-26 Dec, 1 Jan & Etr Sun). **Fee:** £3.75 (con £2.75). Family
ticket £11.50. **Facilities:** 🅿 (charged) ♿ (non-accessible to
wheelchairs,induction loop,textual guide) shop 🐾 (ex guide dogs)

GALLERIES OF JUSTICE
The Shire Hall, High Pavement, Lace Market NG1 1HN
(follow signs to city centre, brown tourist signs to Lace
Market & Galleries of Justice)
☎ 0115 952 0555 📄 0115 993 9828
e-mail: info@galleriesofjustice.org.uk

The Galleries of Justice are located on the site of an
original Court and County Gaol. Visitors can take a tour
through the Crime and Punishment Experience and see
a trial re-created in the authentic Victorian courtroom
before being 'sent down' to the original cells and
medieval caves. In the genuine Edwardian police
station, an interactive forensic science display allows
visitors to 'crack the case'.

Times: Open all year, Tue-Sun & BH Mon's 10-5. Last admission one
hour before closing. (Closed 31 Dec-2 Jan). **Fee:** £6.95 (ch £5.25, con
£5.95). Family ticket £19.95 (2ad+2ch). Ticket vaild for one visit to
three exhibitions for 12 months from date of purchase. **Facilities:** 🅿
(5 mins walk) 🍷 ♿ (braille control lifts, induction loop, large print
lables) toilets for disabled shop 🐾 (ex guide dogs)

THE LACE CENTRE
Severns Building, Castle Rd NG1 6AA (follow signs for
the Castle; opposite Robin Hood statue)
☎ 0115 941 3539 📄 0115 941 3539
Times: Open all year, Jan-Mar, daily 10-4; Apr-Nov, 10-5. Every Sun
11am-4pm. (Closed Xmas & New Year) **Facilities:** 🅿 (100yds)
(metered street parking) ♿ shop *Details not confirmed for 2002*

MUSEUM OF COSTUME & TEXTILES
43-51 Castle Gate NG1 6AF (close to city centre, near
Robin Hood statue, Nottingham Castle Museum & Art
Gallery)
☎ 0115 915 3500 📄 0115 915 3653

Costume from 1730 to 1960 is displayed in appropriate
room settings. Other rooms contain embroidery, dress
accessories, the Lord Middleton Collection and map
tapestries. Knitted, woven and printed textiles are also on
show, together with embroidery from Europe and Asia.

Times: Open all year, Wed-Sun & BHs 10-4. **Fee:** Free. **Facilities:** 🅿
(200yds) ♿ shop 🐾 (ex guide dogs)

MUSEUM OF NOTTINGHAM LACE
3-5 High Pavement, The Lace Market NG1 1HF (Follow
signs for Lace Market. Parking in city centre)
☎ 0115 989 7365 📄 0115 989 7301
e-mail: info@nottinghamlace.org

'Nottingham Lace and its People' is a free exhibition
that includes four archive videos, a photographic story

contd.

and hand-lace and machine-lace demonstrations. The Lace Market Trail, which takes about an hour, guides you to all the points of interest around this historical part of the city.
Times: Open daily 10-5 (Closed Xmas). **Fee:** Free. **Facilities:** P (100yds) ♥ ♿ (counters at lower level, lift, audio & written tour) shop ✘ (ex guide dogs)

NATURAL HISTORY MUSEUM
Wollaton Hall, Wollaton NG8 2AE (3m W, off A52 & A6514)
☎ 0115 915 3911   ⓘ 0115 915 3932

Standing in a large deer park, this imposing Elizabethan mansion houses a wide variety of displays, including birds, mammals, fossils and minerals.
Times: Open all year, daily 11-5 (Closed Fri Nov-Mar & 25-26 Dec). **Fee:** Weekdays free, wknds & BH £1.50 (concessions 80p) Family £3.80. **Facilities:** P (charged) ♿ toilets for disabled shop ✘

NOTTINGHAM INDUSTRIAL MUSEUM
Courtyard Buildings, Wollaton Park NG8 2AE (4m from city centre, off A6514)
☎ 0115 915 3910   ⓘ 0115 915 3941

Nottingham's industrial history is on display in this 18th-century stable block. Lace, hosiery, pharmaceuticals (Nottingham was the home of the founder of Boots the Chemists), tobacco and much else are among the exhibits. There is a beam engine, and other steam engines, regularly in steam.
Times: Open Apr-Sep, daily 11-5; Oct-Mar only open on steaming days, contact for details. **Fee:** Mon-Fri free. Sat, Sun & BH's £1.50 (ch 80p). **Facilities:** P (charged) ♿ (hand & powered wheelchairs available) toilets for disabled shop ✘ (ex guide dogs)

TALES OF ROBIN HOOD
30-38 Maid Marian Way NG1 6GF (in city centre, follow brown signs. Near Nottingham Castle)
☎ 0115 948 3284   ⓘ 0115 950 1536
e-mail: robinhoodcentre@mail.com

Special effects and adventure cars transport the visitor back to medieval Nottingham and Sherwood Forest, legendary home of Robin Hood. There is commentary in seven languages via portable CD players. Medieval banquets and other events take place throughout the year.
Times: Open all year, daily 10-6 (last admission 4.30pm). (Closed 25-26 Dec). **Fee:** £5.95 (ch £3.95, pen & students £4.95) Family ticket £17.75 (2ad+2ch), £19.95 (2ad+3ch). Party. **Facilities:** P (NCP 200 yds) ♥ ♿ (specially adapted 'car') toilets for disabled shop ✘ (ex guide dogs) ♥

☷ OLLERTON   Map 08 SK66
RUFFORD ABBEY AND COUNTRY PARK
NG22 9DF (2m S of Ollerton, adjacent to A614)
☎ 01623 822944   ⓘ 01623 825919
e-mail: marilyn.louden@nottscc.gov.uk

At the heart of the wooded country park stand the remains of a 12th-century Cistercian Abbey, housing an exhibition on the life of a monk at Rufford. Many species of wildlife can be seen on the lake, and there are lovely formal gardens, with sculptures and Britain's first centre for studio ceramics.
Times: Open all year 10.30-5.30 (closes 4pm Jan & feb). For further details of opening times telephone establishment. **Fee:** *Prices not confirmed for 2002* **Facilities:** P (charged) ♥ ✘ licensed ♿ (lift to craft centre gallery, free parking,wheelchair loan) toilets for disabled shop garden centre ✘ (ex park)

☷ RAMPTON   Map 08 SK77
SUNDOWN KIDDIES ADVENTURELAND
(Sundown Pets Garden), Treswell Rd DN22 0HX (3m off A57 at Dunham crossroads)
☎ 01777 248274   ⓘ 01777 248967

The children's story book theme park, is especially designed for the under 10's. This is a land where wonderful stories spring magically to life. The Village houses Santa's All Year Sleigh Ride, the Mouses' Tales Walkthrough, Musical Pet Shop, Witches' Cauldron and the Animated Market. Other attractions include; The Smugglers Cove with Boozey Barrel Boatride, Shotgun City, Rocky Mountain Railroad and Indoor Jungle (Height Restriction), Story Book Village, Captain Sandy's play area and Animated Farm.
Times: Open all year, daily from 10am. (Closed 25-26 Dec & wkdys in Jan & 1st wk in Feb). **Fee:** £5.25 (ch under 2 free). **Facilities:** P ♥ ♿ (some assistance to rides) toilets for disabled shop ✘ (ex guide dogs) ♥

☷ SUTTON-CUM-LOUND   Map 08 SK68
WETLANDS WATERFOWL RESERVE & EXOTIC BIRD PARK
Off Loundlow Rd DN22 8SB (Signed on A638)
☎ 01777 818099

The Reserve is a 32-acre site for both wild and exotic waterfowl. Visitors can see a collection of birds of prey, parrots, geese, ducks, and wigeon among others. There are also many small mammals, farm and wild animals, including llamas, wallabies, emus, monkeys and red squirrels.
Times: Open all year, daily 10-5.30 (or dusk whichever is earlier). (Closed 25 Dec). **Fee:** £2 (ch & pen £1.25). **Facilities:** P ♥ ♿ (wheelchair available) shop ✘ (ex guide dogs)

☷ WORKSOP   Map 08 SK57
CLUMBER PARK
The Estate Office, Clumber Park S80 3AZ (4.5m SE of Worksop, signed from A1)
☎ 01909 476592   ⓘ 01909 500721
Times: Open all year, daily during daylight hours. Walled Garden, Victorian Apiary, Fig House, Vineries & Garden Tools exhibition Apr-Sep Wed & Thu, Sat, Sun & BH Mon 10.30-5.30. Conservation centre open throughout summer contact Warden, Estate Office. Chapel: Apr-Sep, daily 10.30-5.30 (until 6 Sat & Sun). **Facilities:** P (charged) ♥ ✘ licensed ♿ (powered self-drive vehicle available if booked) toilets for disabled shop garden centre ✿ *Details not confirmed for 2002*

Oxfordshire

The city of Oxford, situated on the River Thames (known locally as the Isis), is renowned for its ancient buildings and 'dreaming spires'. It is home to Britain's oldest university, established during the 12th century, with a collegiate system dating from the 13th.

Other well-known towns include Banbury, though the Banbury Cross of nursery rhyme fame was destroyed in 1602 by the Puritans, only to be replaced in 1858. Henley-on-Thames is home to the Royal Regatta, an amateur rowing competition of world renown and a highlight of the social calendar. Witney is a blanket-making town, using two important local resources, wool, and power from the River Windrush.

The Cotswold Hills extend over the border from Gloucestershire into the east of Oxfordshire, dotted with pretty towns and villages built of mellow Cotswold stone hewn from the hillsides. These settlements prospered from the sheep who grazed the hills, producing wool for the flourishing medieval wool trade. Great churches are a feature of the area, an enduring symbol of medieval wool wealth.

To the southeast of the county are the Chiltern Hills, chalk downlands excellent for walking. The Chilterns range from the Berkshire Downs to the East Anglian Ridge, passing through Oxfordshire and reaching their highest point at Coombe Hill, near Wendover in Buckinghamshire, at 852 ft (260m).

Southwest of Oxford is the Vale of the White Horse, a prehistoric figure, 374 ft (114m) long, carved into the chalk, some 18 miles (29km) from the city.

Top: Thame

🏛 BANBURY
BANBURY MUSEUM
Spiceball Park Rd OX16 2PG (M40 Junct 11 straight across at first rdbt into Hennef Way, left at next rdbt into Concord Ave, right at next rdbt & left at next rdbt, Castle Quay Shopping Centre & Museum on right)
☎ 01295 259855   🖹 01295 270556
e-mail: banburymuseum@cherwell-dc.gov.uk

This museum, housed in the old boardroom of the Poor Law Guardians, overlooks Banbury Cross and tells the story of the town's history. There is an exciting programme of temporary exhibitions. Holiday sessions and special events are regularly organised for children and there is a separate programme of exhibitions and displays by local artists. There is also a small herb garden.
Times: Open Mon-Sat 10-5, (tel. for Sun details). **Fee:** Free.
Facilities: P (500yds) ✗ & toilets for disabled shop ✻ (ex guide dogs)

🏛 BROUGHTON
Map 04 SP43
BROUGHTON CASTLE
OX15 5EB (2m W of Banbury Cross on B4035 Shipston-on-Stour)
☎ 01295 276070 & 01869 337126
🖹 01869 337126 & 01295 276070
Times: Open Etr & 19 May-12 Sep, Wed & Sun (also Thu in Jul & Aug) & BH Sun & Mon 2-5. **Facilities:** P 🍴 & shop ✻ (ex in grounds on leads) *Details not confirmed for 2002*

🏛 BURFORD
Map 04 SP21
COTSWOLD WILDLIFE PARK
OX18 4JW (2m S of Burford on A361)
☎ 01993 823006   🖹 01993 823807

This 180-acre landscaped zoological park, surrounds a listed Gothic-style manor house. There is a varied collection of animals from all over the world, many of which are endangered species such as Asiatic Leopards, White Rhinos and Red Pandas. There's an adventure playground, a children's farmyard, and train rides during the summer.
Times: Open all year, daily (ex 25 Dec) from 10am, last admission 5pm Mar-Sep, 4pm Oct, 3.30pm Nov-Feb. **Fee:** £6.50 (ch 3-16 & pen £4). Party: £5.50 (ch £3 pen £3.50) **Facilities:** P 🍴 ✗ licensed & (parking, free hire of wheelchairs) toilets for disabled shop 🍴

🏛 BUSCOT
Map 04 SU29
BUSCOT PARK
SN7 8BU (on A417 between Faringdon & Lechdale)
☎ 01367 240786 & 0845 3453387
🖹 01367 241794
e-mail: estbuscot@aol.com

A highlight of this 18th-century house is the Faringdon Collection which includes work by Reynolds, Gainsborough, Rembrandt, Murillo, several of the Pre-Raphaelites, and some 20th-century artists. The charming formal water gardens were laid out by Harold Peto in the early 20th century. There is also an attractively planted kitchen garden, with unusual concentric walls.
Times: House & grounds Apr-29 Sep (incl Good Fri, Etr Sat & Sun) Wed-Fri 2-6. Also every 2nd & 4th wknd in each month 2-6 (last admission to house 5.30pm). Grounds as House but also Mon & Tue 2-6. **Fee:** House & Gardens £4.40 Grounds only £3.30. **Facilities:** P 🍴✻🐾

🏛 DEDDINGTON
Map 04 SP43
DEDDINGTON CASTLE
OX5 4TE (S of B4031 on E side of Deddington)
Times: Open any reasonable time. **Facilities:** ⊞ *Details not confirmed for 2002*

🏛 DIDCOT
Map 04 SU58
DIDCOT RAILWAY CENTRE
OX11 7NJ (on A4130 at Didcot Parkway Station)
☎ 01235 817200   🖹 01235 510621
e-mail: didrlyc@globalnet.co.uk

Based around the original GWR engine shed, the Centre is home to the biggest collection anywhere of Great Western Railway steam locomotives, carriages and wagons. A typical GWR station has been re-created and a section of Brunel's original broad gauge track relaid.
Times: Open all year, Sat & Sun; 23 Mar-29 Sep daily, 10-5; Nov-Feb daily, 10-4. Steam days first & last Sun each month from Mar, BHs, all Sun in Jul-Aug, Wed 17 Jul-27 Aug & Sat in Aug. **Fee:** £4-£8 depending on event (ch £3-£7.50, over 60's £3.50-£6.50). **Facilities:** P (100yds) 🍴 & (advance notice recommended, some awkward steps) toilets for disabled shop 🍴

🏛 GREAT COXWELL — Map 04 SU29
GREAT COXWELL BARN
(2m SW of Faringdon between A420 & B4019)
☎ 01793 762209
e-mail: tbcjaw@smtp.ntrust.org.uk
Times: Open all reasonable times. For details please contact Estate Office. **Facilities:** 🅿 ✝ (ex on leads) ✖ *Details not confirmed for 2002*

🏛 HENLEY-ON-THAMES — Map 04 SU78
GREYS COURT
Rotherfield Greys RG9 4PG (M4 junct 8 or 9, take A404 (M) to Henley-on-Thames. From Nettlebed mini rdbt on A4130 take B481. Property is signed 3m on left. Or from Henley follow signs to Peppard/Greys for 3m)
☎ 01491 628529
e-mail: tgrgen@smtp.ntrust.org.uk

This appealing house has evolved over hundreds of years. The present gabled building has a pre-medieval kitchen but dates mainly from the 16th century. Additions were made in the 18th century and there are some fine decorations and furniture. Also of great interest is the wheelhouse with its huge wheel, once turned by a donkey to bring water up from the well.
Times: Open: House: part of ground floor only, 4 Apr-Sep Wed-Fri & BH Mons (closed Good Fri). Garden 3 Apr-Sep daily ex Sun & Mon (closed Good Fri, open BH Mons). **Fee:** House & Garden £4.60. Family ticket £11.50. Garden only £3.20 Family ticket £8. **Facilities:** 🅿 ✝ & shop (bookshop) ✝ (ex on lead in car park) ✖

RIVER & ROWING MUSEUM
Mill Meadows RG9 1BF (off A4130, signed to Mill Meadows)
☎ 01491 415600 🖥 01491 415601
e-mail: museum@rrm.co.uk

The award-winning River and Rowing Museum is the only museum in the world with galleries dedicated to rowing and the 'Quest for Speed', from the Greek Trireme to Modern Olympic rowing boats; the River Thames from source to sea with its rich history and varied wildlife. See the boat that won gold in Sydney and the riverside town of Henley featuring the Royal Regatta.
Times: Open Summer: May-Aug 10-5.30. Winter: Sep-Apr 10-5. (museum closed 24-25 & 31 Dec & 1 Jan). **Fee:** £4.95 (concessions £3.75). Family ticket from £13.95. Party 10+. **Facilities:** 🅿 ✝ ✖ licensed & toilets for disabled shop ✝ (ex guide dogs) 🠗

🏛 LONG WITTENHAM — Map 04 SU59
PENDON MUSEUM
OX14 4QD (follow brown signs from A4130 Didcot-Wallingford or A415 Abingdon-Wallingford road)
☎ 01865 407365

This charming exhibition shows highly detailed and historically accurate model railway and village scenes transporting the visitor back into 1930s country landscapes. Skilled modellers can often be seen at work on the exhibits.
Times: Open Sat & Sun 2-5, BH wknds 11-5 also Wed in Jul & Aug 2-5. (Closed Dec). **Fee:** £4 (ch £2, pen £3.50, ch u6 free). **Facilities:** 🅿 ✝ & (phone in advance, special seating with handrails) toilets for disabled shop ✝ (ex guide dogs) 🠗

🏛 MAPLEDURHAM — Map 04 SU67
MAPLEDURHAM HOUSE & WATERMILL
RG4 7TR (off A4074, follow tourist signs)
☎ 0118 972 3350 🖥 0118 972 4016
e-mail: mtrust1997@aol.com

The small community at Mapledurham includes the house, a watermill and a church. The fine Elizabethan mansion, surrounded by quiet parkland which runs down to the River Thames, was built by the Blount family in the 16th century. The estate has literary connections with the poet Alexander Pope, with Galsworthy's *Forsyte Saga* and Kenneth Graham's *Wind in the Willows*, and was a location for the film *The Eagle has Landed*.
Times: Open Etr-Sep, Sat, Sun & BH's 2-5.30. Picnic area 2-5.30. Last admission 5pm. Group visits midweek by arrangement. **Fee:** Combined house, watermill & grounds £6 (ch £3). House & grounds £4 (ch £2). Watermill & grounds £3 (ch £1.50). **Facilities:** 🅿 ✝ & shop ✝ (ex park area) 🠗

MAPLEDURHAM WATERMILL
RG4 7TR (off A4074)
☎ 0118 972 3350 🖥 0118 972 4016
e-mail: mtrust1997@aol.com

Close to Mapledurham House stands the last working corn and grist mill on the Thames, still using traditional wooden machinery and producing flour for local bakers and shops. The watermill's products can be purchased in the shop. When Mapledurham House is open the mill can be reached by river launch.
Times: Open Etr-Sep, Sat, Sun & BHs 2-5.30. Picnic area 2-5.30. Last admission 5. Groups midweek by arrangement. **Fee:** Watermill & grounds £3 (ch £1.50) **Facilities:** 🅿 ✝ & shop ✝ (ex in country park) 🠗

🏛 MINSTER LOVELL   Map 04 SP31
MINSTER LOVELL HALL & DOVECOT
OX8 5RN (adjacent to Minster Lovell church, 3m W of Witney off A40)
☎ 01993 775315
Times: Open any reasonable time. **Facilities:** 🅿 (ex Dovecot) 🏋 ♯
Details not confirmed for 2002

🏛 NORTH LEIGH   Map 04 SP31
NORTH LEIGH ROMAN VILLA
OX8 6QB (2m N)
Times: Open, grounds all year. No access to mosaic. Pedestrian access only from the main road - 600 yds. **Facilities:** 🏋 ♯ *Details not confirmed for 2002*

🏛 OXFORD   Map 04 SP50
ASHMOLEAN MUSEUM OF ART & ARCHAEOLOGY
Beaumont St OX1 2PH (city centre, opposite The Randolph Hotel)
☎ 01865 278000   📠 01865 278018

The oldest museum in the country, opened in 1683, the Ashmolean contains Oxford University's priceless collections. Many important historical art pieces and artefacts are on display, including work from Ancient Greece through to the 20th century.
Times: Open all year, Tue-Sat 10-5, Sun & BH Mons 2-5. (Closed Etr & during St.Giles Fair in early Sep, Xmas & 1 Jan). **Fee:** Free. Guided tours by arrangement. **Facilities:** 🅿 (100-200metres) (pay & display) 💷 ✗ licensed ♿ (entry ramp from Beaumont St. Tel. before visit) toilets for disabled shop 🏋 🍽

HARCOURT ARBORETUM
Nuneham Courtenay OX44 9PX (400yds S of Nuneham Courtenay on A4074)
☎ 01865 343501   📠 01865 341828
e-mail: piers.newth@botanic-garden.ox.ac.uk

The gardens consist of 75 acres of mixed woodland, meadow, pond, rhododendron walks and fine specimen trees.
Times: Open May-Oct, daily 10-5; Nov-Apr, Mon-Fri 10-4.30. Closed 22 Dec-4 Jan & Good Fri-Etr Mon. **Fee:** Free. **Facilities:** 🅿 (charged) ♿ 🏋 (ex guide dogs)

MUSEUM OF OXFORD
St Aldate's OX1 1DZ
☎ 01865 252761   📠 01865 252254
Times: Open all year, Tue-Fri 10-4, Sat 10-5 & Sun 12-4. (Closed 25-26 Dec, Good Fri & Etr Sun). shop 🏋 *Details not confirmed for 2002* 🍽

MUSEUM OF THE HISTORY OF SCIENCE
Old Ashmolean Building, Broad St OX1 3AZ (Next to Sheldonian Theatre in city centre)
☎ 01865 277280   📠 01865 277288
e-mail: museum@mhs.ox.ac.uk

The first purpose-built museum in Britain, containing the world's finest collection of early scientific instruments used in astronomy, navigation, surveying, physics and chemistry.
Times: Open Tue-Sat 12-4 (closed Xmas wk) **Fee:** Free. **Facilities:** 🅿 (300 metres) (limited street parking, meters) ♿ toilets for disabled shop 🏋 (ex guide dogs) 🍽

THE OXFORD STORY EXHIBITION
6 Broad St OX1 3AJ (city centre, follow signs)
☎ 01865 728822   📠 01865 791716
e-mail: info@oxfordstory.co.uk

Capture the essence of Oxford University's fascinating 900-year history as you travel through the exhibition's re-created scenes of a bygone era. Learn about the University's early beginnings, the interesting facts behind its record breaking discoveries and come face to face with some of the famous people who have studied there.
Times: Open every day (ex Xmas Day): Jan-Jul & Sep-Dec, Mon-Sat 10-4.30 & Sun 11-4.30. Jul & Aug daily 9.30-5. **Fee:** £6.10 (ch, pen & stu £4.90) Family Ticket £18.50 (4 people), Family ticket £15 (1ad+2ch). **Facilities:** 🅿 (300 metres) (Park & Ride all round city) ♿ (advisable to phone in advance) toilets for disabled shop 🏋 (ex guide dogs) 🍽

OXFORD UNIVERSITY MUSEUM OF NATURAL HISTORY
Parks Rd OX1 3PW (opposite Keble College)
☎ 01865 272950   📠 01865 272970
e-mail: info@oum.ox.ac.uk

Built between 1855 and 1860, this museum of "the natural sciences" was intended to satisfy a growing interest in biology, botany, archaeology, zoology, entomology and so on. The museum concentrates on Oxford University's position as a 19th-century centre of learning, with displays of early dinosaur discoveries, Darwinian evolution and Elias Ashmole's collection of preserved animals. Although visitors to the Pitt-Rivers Museum must pass through the University Museum, the two should not be confused.
Times: Open daily 12-5. Times vary at Xmas & Etr. **Fee:** Free. **Facilities:** 🅿 (meter parking at 100yds) ♿ toilets for disabled shop 🏋

PITT RIVERS MUSEUM
South Parks Rd OX1 3PP
☎ 01865 270927 📠 01865 270943
e-mail: prm@prm.ox.ac.uk

The museum is one of the city's most popular attractions, it is part of the University of Oxford and was founded in 1884. The collections held at the museum are internationally acclaimed, and contain many objects from different cultures of the world and from various periods, all grouped by type, or purpose. Special exhibitions during 2002 include 'Transformations: The Art of Recycling'.
Times: Open Mon-Sat 1-4.30 & Sun 2-4.30. (Closed Xmas & Etr, open BH's) **Fee:** Free. **Facilities:** ⅃ (audio guide) toilets for disabled shop ⁒ (ex guide dogs)

ST EDMUND HALL
College of Oxford University OX1 4AR (Queen's Lane, near High Street).
☎ 01865 279000 📠 01865 279090

This is the only surviving medieval academic hall and has a Norman crypt, 17th-century dining hall, chapel and quadrangle. Other buildings are of the 18th and 20th centuries.
Times: Open all year. (Closed 23 Dec-3 Jan, 9-17 Apr & 28-31 Aug). **Fee:** Free. 🍽 ⅃ toilets for disabled shop ⁒ 🍴

UNIVERSITY OF OXFORD BOTANIC GARDEN
High St OX1 4AZ (E end of High St on banks of river Cherwell).
☎ 01865 286690 📠 01865 286693
e-mail: postmaster@botanic-garden.ox.ac.uk

Founded in 1621, these botanic gardens are the oldest in the country and are of great interest. There is a collection of over 8000 species of plants from all over the world.
Times: Open all year, daily 9-4.45 (9-4.30 Oct-Mar), Greenhouses, daily 10-4.30. Last admission 4.15. (Closed Good Fri & 25 Dec). **Fee:** Apr-Aug £2. otherwise free. Accompanied ch under 12 free. **Facilities:** 🅿 (0.5 mile) ⅃ toilets for disabled ⁒ (ex guide dogs)

🏛 ROUSHAM   Map 04 SP42
ROUSHAM HOUSE
OX25 4QX (1m E of A4260. 0.5m S of B4030)
☎ 01869 347110

This attractive mansion was built by Sir Robert Dormer in 1635. During the Civil War it was a Royalist garrison. The house contains over 150 portraits and other pictures, and also much fine contemporary furniture. The gardens are a masterpiece by William Kent, and are his only work to survive unspoiled.
Times: Open all year, garden only, daily 10-4.30. House, Apr-Sep, Wed, Sun & BH Mon 2-4.30 (last entry). **Fee:** House £3, Garden £3. Groups by arrangement. No children under 15. **Facilities:** 🅿 ⅃ ⁒ (ex guide dogs)

🏛 RYCOTE   Map 04 SP60
RYCOTE CHAPEL
OX9 2PE (off B4013)

This small private chapel was founded in 1449 by Richard Quatremayne. It has its original font, and a particularly fine 17th-century interior. The chapel was visited by both Elizabeth I and Charles I.
Times: Open Apr-Sep, Fri-Sun & BH's 2-6. **Fee:** £1.70 (ch 5-15 90p, under 5's free, con £1.30) **Facilities:** 🅿 ⅃ (if assisted) ⁒ 🍴

🏛 STONOR   Map 04 SU78
STONOR HOUSE & PARK
RG9 6HF (M40 junct 6, through Watlington left onto B480)
☎ 01491 638587 📠 01491 639348
e-mail: lisa@stonor.com

The house dates back to 1190 but features a Tudor façade. It has a medieval Catholic chapel which is still in use today, and shows some of the earliest domestic architecture in Oxfordshire. Its treasures include rare furniture, paintings, sculptures and tapestries from Britain, Europe and America. The house is set in beautiful gardens commanding views of the surrounding deer park.
Times: Open Apr-Sep, Sun 2-5.30; Jul & Aug, Sun & Wed 2-5.30; BH Mons. Parties by appointment Tue-Thu Apr-Sep. **Fee:** £4.50 (ch 14 accompanied free). Gardens only £2.50. Party 12+ £4. Private guided tours £5 each. **Facilities:** 🅿 🍽 ⅃ shop ⁒ (ex in grounds on lead)

🏛 UFFINGTON   Map 04 SU38
CASTLE, WHITE HORSE & DRAGON HILL
(S of B4507)
Times: Open - accessible any reasonable time. **Facilities:** 🅿 ⁒
Details not confirmed for 2002

🏛 WATERPERRY   Map 04 SP60
WATERPERRY GARDENS
OX33 1JZ (2.5m from A40, turn off at Wheatley)
☎ 01844 339226 & 339254 📠 01844 339883
Times: Open all year, Gardens (ex Xmas & New Year & during "Art in Action" 15-18 Jul). Apr-Oct 9-5.30, Nov-Mar 9-5 daily. **Facilities:** 🅿 🍽 ✗ licensed ⅃ (grounds mostly accessible) shop garden centre ⁒ (ex on leads) *Details not confirmed for 2002* 🍴

🏛 WITNEY   Map 04 SP31
COGGES MANOR FARM MUSEUM
Church Ln, Cogges OX28 3LA (0.5m SE off A4022)
☎ 01993 772602 📠 01993 703056

The museum includes the Manor, dairy and walled garden, and has breeds of animals typical of the Victorian period. The first floor of the manor contains period rooms. Special events take place through the season.
Times: Open Apr-Nov, Tue-Fri & BH Mon 10.30-5.30, Sat & Sun 12-5.30. Early closing Oct. (Closed Good Fri). **Fee:** £4.20 (ch £2.10, pen, students & UB40 £2.65). Family ticket (2ad+2ch £11.55. **Facilities:** 🅿 🍽 ⅃ (wheelchair available,commentary/history file for 1st floor) toilets for disabled shop 🍴

🏛 WOODSTOCK
Map 04 SP41

BLENHEIM PALACE
OX20 1PX (M40 junct 9, follow signs to Blenheim, on
A44 8m N of Oxford)
☎ 01993 811091 & 811325 (information line)
📄 01993 813527
e-mail: admin@blenheimpalace.com

Home of the 11th Duke of Marlborough and birthplace
of Sir Winston Churchill, Blenheim Palace is an English
Baroque masterpiece. Fine furniture, sculpture,
paintings and tapestries are set in magnificent gilded
staterooms that overlook sweeping lawns and formal
gardens. 'Capability' Brown landscaped the 2,100-acre
grounds, which are open to visitors for pleasant walks
and beautiful views.

Times: Open: Palace & Gardens mid Mar-Oct, daily 10.30-5.30 (last
admission 4.45pm). Park all year. **Fee:** £9.50 (ch £4.80, pen & students
£7.30). Family ticket £25. Group rates for coach parties. **Facilities:** 🅿
💺 ✗ licensed ♿ (ramps to front door, disabled parking) toilets for
disabled shop 🐾 (ex in park on leads) 🍴

OXFORDSHIRE MUSEUM
Fletcher's House OX20 1SN (A44 Stratford-upon-Avon
road from Oxford)
☎ 01993 811456 📄 01993 813239
e-mail: oxon.museum@oxfordshire.go.uk

Situated in the heart of the historic town, Fletcher's
House has undergone an award-winning
redevelopment. The new museum presents
Oxfordshire's heritage, environmental diversity and
contemporary innovation.

Times: Open all year, Tue-Sat 10-5. Last admission 4.45. Sun 2-5 last
admission 4.45. (Closed Good Fri, 25 & 26 Dec & 1 Jan). Galleries are
closed on Mon. **Fee:** £2.50 (ch 50p, con £1) Family £4.50. Charges
made for some temporary exhibitions. **Facilities:** 🅿 (outside
entrance) (3hr free, no return within 1hr) 💺 ♿ (chair lifts to all
galleries) 🐾 🍴

Rutland

A mere twenty miles across, the county of Rutland was reinstated in 1997 due to public demand from Rutlanders who had fiercely maintained their identity through twenty years as part of Leicestershire. The county motto is "Multum in Parvo", which is Latin for 'much in little'.

Oakham is the only town of any size in the county, and as Rutland only has a population of around 35,000 it's not hard to imagine what kind of size that is! Those who don't live there inhabit one of the fifty or so villages, or the other two towns, Uppingham and Stamford.

Many of these villages have their own little oddities which are so tantalising to students of eccentric England. For example, Wing has a strange ancient turf maze, the story of the fools who tried to fence a cuckoo in, and the Wise Woman of Wing.

Some famous connections with Rutland are John Clare, the 18th-century pastoral poet; the Gunpowder Plotters (who are said to have met at Stoke Dry); Thomas Barker, a pioneer of modern weather forecasting, and more recently the TV production of George Eliot's *Middlemarch*, which was filmed at Stamford.

Apart from its small attractions, Rutland also has a large one. Rutland Water is, at 5,000 acres, the largest man-made reservoir in Europe. As well as a mass of wildlife and water pursuits such as windsurfing and sailing, Rutland Water has its own church, Normanton Church, which sits on an outcrop that juts out onto the Water itself.

Top: Normanton Church at Rutland Water

🏛 LYDDINGTON
Map 04 SP89

BEDE HOUSE
Blue Coat Ln LE15 9LZ
☎ 01572 822438

Built in the late 15th century as the episcopal residence of the Bishops of Lincoln, Bede House was the administrative centre of their vast diocese. Later it became an almshouse. Beautiful wooden ceilings, painted glass and a grand fireplace bear witness to its former life as a palace.

Times: Open Apr-Sep, daily 10-6 (Oct 10-5). **Fee:** £2.75 (ch 5-15 £1.40, under 5's free, con £2.10). **Facilities:** ♿ ✦ ♨

🏛 OAKHAM
Map 04 SK80

OAKHAM CASTLE
off Market Place (in town centre)
☎ 01572 758440 🖷 01572 758445

An exceptionally fine Norman Great Hall of a 12th-century fortified manor house. Earthworks, walls and remains of an earlier motte can be seen, along with medieval sculptures and unique presentation horseshoes forfeited by peers of the realm and royalty to the Lord of the Manor. Licensed for Civil Marriages. Please enquire for details of the Oakham Festival.

Times: Open all year, late Mar-late Oct, Mon-Sat, 10-5, closed between 1-1.30 & Sun 1-5; late Oct-late Mar Castle closes at 4. Closed Good Fri & Xmas. **Fee:** Free. **Facilities:** P (400 yds) (disabled parking only by notification) ♿ shop ✦ (ex guide dogs)

RUTLAND COUNTY MUSEUM
Catmos St LE15 6HW (on A6003, S of town centre)
☎ 01572 758440 🖷 01572 758445

The Museum of Rutland Life has displays of farming equipment, machinery and wagons, rural tradesmen's tools, domestic collections and local archaeology, all housed in a splendid late 18th-century cavalry riding school. There is a special gallery on the Volunteer Soldier in Leicestershire and Rutland.

Times: Open all year, Mon-Sat 10-5. (Also open Sun 2-5 Apr-Oct & 2-4 Nov-Mar). Closed Good Fri & Xmas. **Fee:** Free. **Facilities:** P (adjacent) (pay & display) ♿ (induction loop in meeting room) toilets for disabled shop ✦ (ex guide dogs)

Shropshire

Shropshire is a mainly agricultural county in the west of England, on the Welsh border. Home to beautiful rivers and lakes, as well as spectacular walking opportunities, the county is sparsely populated and has some fine market towns.

Britain's longest river, the Severn, flows from northwest to southeast. Other natural features are the 'Shropshire Lakes' at Ellesmere in the northwest, and the Clee Hills in the south, between Ludlow and Kidderminster, rising to 1,800 ft (610m). The two ridges, Wenlock Edge and the Long Mynd, running either side of Church Stretton, are much favoured by walkers. This part of the country was immortalised in A E Houseman's poem, *A Shropshire Lad*, published in 1896.

The two largest centres of population in a sparsely populated county are Shrewsbury, the county town, situated on a hilly site in a loop of the River Severn, and Telford New Town, named after the engineer, Thomas Telford. In the 5th century, Shrewsbury was the capital of the kingdom of Powys, with the name Pengwern (later part of Mercia). A rich legacy of half-timbered Tudor buildings and red brick Georgian buildings remains, along with the castle, which has Norman origins.

Telford was created about 30 years ago, and is home to some of the Far East's most successful electronics firms, as well as monuments to British engineering of the 19th century, such as Abraham Darby's Ironbridge.

There are some fine market towns, well worth a visit. Chief among these are Ludlow, capital of the Marches, and widely held to be one of the most beautiful of British towns, with its intricately decorated black and white buildings; Bishop's Castle, retaining much of its medieval character, and the dramatically located hilltop town of Bridgnorth.

EVENTS & FESTIVALS

May
5th-6th Shropshire Game Fair, Chetwynd Park, Telford

June
15th Shrewsbury Carnival & Show, Quarry Park
21st-22nd Shropshire & West Midlands Show, Showground, Berwick Road, Shrewsbury
22nd-7th July Ludlow Festival in the ruins of Ludlow Castle
29th-30th International Kite & Boomerang Festival, Shrewsbury
tbc Much Wenlock Festival

July
22nd June-7th Ludlow Festival in the ruins of Ludlow Castle

August
3rd Oswestry Show, Oswestry
9th-10th Shrewsbury Flower Show
16th-17th Shrewsbury Flower Festival
23rd-25th Bridgnorth Folk Festival
tbc County of Salop Steam Rally

September
tbc Shrewsbury Real Ale Festival

December
tbc Music Hall Pantomime, Shrewsbury

Top: Ironbridge

⛫ ACTON BURNELL   Map 07 SJ50
ACTON BURNELL CASTLE
SY5 7PE (on unclass road 8m S of Shrewsbury)
Times: Open at all reasonable times. **Facilities:** ꕔ ✿ *Details not confirmed for 2002*

⛫ ACTON SCOTT   Map 07 SO48
ACTON SCOTT HISTORIC WORKING FARM
Wenlock Lodge SY6 6QN (follow tourist signs off A49)
☎ 01694 781306 & 781307 🖹 01694 781569
Times: Open 28 Mar-29 Oct, Tue-Sun 10-5; BH Mon 10-5.
Facilities: 🄿 ꕤ ꕔ (Braille guide, wheelchairs available) toilets for disabled shop 🐾 (ex guide dogs) *Details not confirmed for 2002*

⛫ ATCHAM   Map 07 SJ50
ATTINGHAM PARK
SY4 4TP (4m SE of Shrewsbury on B4380)
☎ 01743 708123 🖹 01743 708175
e-mail: matsec@smtp.ntrust.org.uk
Times: House open mid Mar-Oct, Fri-Tue 1.30-5, BH Mon 11-5. Deer park & grounds daily Mar-Oct 9am-8pm, Nov-Feb 9am-5pm.
Facilities: 🄿 ꕤ ꕔ (2 electric self drive buggies) toilets for disabled shop 🐾 (ex guide & hearing dogs) 🦌 *Details not confirmed for 2002*

⛫ BENTHALL   Map 07 SJ60
BENTHALL HALL
TF12 5RX (on B4375)
☎ 01952 882159
Times: Open Apr-Sep, Wed, Sun & BH Mon 1.30-5.30. Last admission 5pm. Other days by appointment only. **Facilities:** 🄿 ꕔ 🐾 🦌 *Details not confirmed for 2002* ꕥ

⛫ BOSCOBEL   Map 07 SJ80
BOSCOBEL HOUSE AND THE ROYAL OAK
Brewood ST19 9AR (on unclass road between A41 and A5)
☎ 01902 850244

The house was built around 1600 by John Giffard, a Roman Catholic, and includes a number of secret hiding places. One of them was used by King Charles II after his defeat at the Battle of Worcester in 1651.
Times: Open all year, Apr-Sep, daily 10-6 (Oct 10-5); Nov-Mar, Wed-Sun 10-4, last admission 45 minutes before closing. Closed 24-26 Dec & all Jan. **Fee:** £4.40 (ch 5-15 £2.20, under 5's free, con £3.30).
Facilities: 🄿 ꕤ ꕔ shop 🐾 ✿

WHITELADIES PRIORY (ST LEONARDS PRIORY)
Times: Open any reasonable time. ✿ *Details not confirmed for 2002*

⛫ BUILDWAS   Map 07 SJ60
BUILDWAS ABBEY
TF8 7BW (on S bank of River Severn on B4378)
☎ 01952 433274

The beautiful, ruined, Cistercian abbey was founded in 1135, and stands in a picturesque setting. The church with its stout round pillars is roofless but otherwise almost complete.
Times: Open Apr-Sep, daily 11-5. **Fee:** £2 (ch £1, ch u5 free, con £1.50) **Facilities:** ꕔ ✿

⛫ BURFORD   Map 03 SO56
BURFORD HOUSE GARDENS
WR15 8HQ (off A456, 1m W of Tenbury Wells, 8m from Ludlow)
☎ 01584 810777 🖹 01584 810673
e-mail: treasures@burford.co.uk

The beauty of Burford House Gardens is a tribute to the late John Treasure who, since the early 1950's, transformed the setting of this early Georgian house into a garden of quiet serenity and fascination. The garden is famous for its range of unusual plants, and the National Clematis Collection. Ring for details of special events.
Times: Open all year 10-5 or dusk if earlier. **Fee:** £3.50 (ch £1). Party 10+£3. **Facilities:** 🄿 ꕤ ✕ licensed ꕔ (ramp into gardens, sloping paths) toilets for disabled shop garden centre 🐾 (ex in Plant Centre) ꕥ

⛫ COSFORD   Map 07 SJ70
ROYAL AIR FORCE MUSEUM
TF11 8UP (on A41, 1m S of M54 junct 3. From S M6 junct 10a, from N M6 junct 12 then follow A5 W)
☎ 01902 376200 🖹 01902 376211
e-mail: cosford@rafmuseum.com

This is one of the largest aviation collections in the UK. Exhibits include the Victor and Vulcan bombers, the Hastings, York and British Airways airliners, the Belfast freighter and the last airworthy Britannia. The research and development collection includes the notable TSR2, Fairey Delta, Bristol 188 and many other important aircraft.
Times: Open all year daily, 10-6 (last admission 4). Closed 24-26 Dec & 1 Jan. **Fee:** £5.90 (students 16+ & UB40 £3.75) All other categories free. **Facilities:** 🄿 ✕ licensed ꕔ (limited amount of wheelchairs on request) toilets for disabled shop 🐾 (ex guide dogs) ꕥ

⛫ CRAVEN ARMS   Map 07 SO48
SHROPSHIRE HILLS DISCOVERY CENTRE
School Rd SY7 9RS (on A49, on southern edge of Craven Arms)
☎ 01588 676000 🖹 01588 676030
e-mail: hope.alderson@shropshire-cc.gov.uk

This brand new attraction explores the history, nature and geography of the Shropshire Hills through a series of interactive displays and simulations. These include: Landscape of Contrasts, Ancient Landscape, a simulated Balloon Flight, and Land of Inspiration. There is also a shop, a restaurant and a visitors' information centre.
Times: Open all year, daily from 10am. **Fee:** £4.25 (ch £2.75 & pen £3.75). Family ticket £12.20. Groups 20+ **Facilities:** 🄿 ꕤ ✕ licensed ꕔ (Wheelchair available) toilets for disabled shop 🐾 (ex assistance dogs) ꕥ

HAUGHMOND ABBEY
Map 07 SJ51

HAUGHMOND ABBEY
Upton Magna SY4 4RW (off B5062)
☎ 01743 709661

The ruined abbey was founded for Augustinian canons around 1135, and partly converted into a house during the Dissolution. The chapter house has a fine Norman doorway, and the abbot's lodging and the kitchens are well preserved.
Times: Open Apr-Oct, daily 10-6 (5pm Oct) **Fee:** £2 (ch 5-15 £1, under 5's free, con £1.50). **Facilities:** 🅿 ♿ ⍟ ⊞

HODNET
Map 07 SJ62

HODNET HALL GARDENS
TF9 3NN (M6 junct 12/15 or M54 junct 3. Hodnet is on A442, Telford-Whitchurch road and A53 Shrewsbury-Market Drayton road)
☎ 01630 685202 📠 01630 685853

Sixty acres of landscaped gardens offer tranquillity among pools, lush plants and trees. Big game trophies adorn the 17th-century tearooms, and plants are usually for sale in the kitchen gardens. The house, rebuilt in Victorian-Elizabethan style, is not open.
Times: Open Apr-Sep, Tue-Sun & BH Mon 12-5. **Fee:** £3.25 (ch £1.20, pen £2.75). Party £2.75. **Facilities:** 🅿 ⍩ ♿ (2 wheelchairs available) toilets for disabled shop garden centre

IRONBRIDGE
Map 07 SJ60

IRONBRIDGE GORGE MUSEUMS
TF8 7AW (M54 junct 4, signposted)
☎ 01952 433522 & 0800 590258
📠 01952 432204
e-mail: info@ironbridge.org.uk
Times: Open all year, 10-5. Some small sites closed Nov-Mar. Telephone or write for exact winter details. **Facilities:** 🅿 ⍩ ✗ licensed ♿ (wheelchairs,potters wheel,braille guide,lifts,hearing loop) toilets for disabled shop ✟ (ex Blists Hill & guide dogs) *Details not confirmed for 2002* 🍴

LILLESHALL
Map 07 SJ71

LILLESHALL ABBEY
TF10 9HW (1.5m SW off A518 on unclass road)
Times: Open Apr-Oct, any reasonable time. (Closed Nov-Mar).
Facilities: 🅿 ✟ ⊞ *Details not confirmed for 2002*

LUDLOW
Map 07 SO57

LUDLOW CASTLE
Castle Square SY8 1AY (A49, to town centre)
☎ 01584 873355

Ludlow Castle dates from about 1086. In 1473, Edward IV sent the Prince of Wales and his brother - who were later to become the Princes in the Tower - to live here, and Ludlow Castle became a seat of government. John Milton's *Comus* was first performed at Ludlow Castle in 1634; today, contemporary performances of Shakespeare's plays, together with concerts, are put on in the castle grounds during the Ludlow Festival (2 weeks, end June-early July).

Times: Open all year, Jan Sat-Sun 10-4; Feb-Mar daily 10-4; Apr-Jul daily 10-5; Aug daily 10-7; Sep daily 10-5; Oct-Dec daily 10-4 (last admission 30 minutes before closing). **Fee:** £3 (ch under 6 free, ch 6+ £1.50, pen £2.50). Family ticket £8.50. **Facilities:** 🅿 (100 yds) ♿ toilets for disabled shop 🍴

LYDBURY NORTH
Map 07 SO38

WALCOT HALL
SY7 8AZ (3m E of Bishops Castle, on B4385, beside the Powls Arms)
☎ 01568 610693 📠 01568 615851
e-mail: lesley@walcothall.com

Re-designed by Sir William Chambers for Lord Clive of India in 1763. The Georgian House possesses a free-standing and recently restored Ballroom, stableyard with matching clock towers and extensive walled garden. There is an Arboretum, noted for its rhododendrons and azaleas, specimen trees, pools and a lake. The Ballroom is available for hire and the Hall holds a licence for civil weddings.
Times: Open 2-4 Jun. Other times, by appointment. Arboretum & gardens open Mon & Fri-Sun in Apr-Oct 12-4.30. **Fee:** £3 (ch under 15 free) **Facilities:** 🅿 ♿ (lift to 1st floor)

MORETON CORBET
Map 07 SJ52

CASTLE
Times: Open all reasonable times. **Facilities:** 🅿 ♿ ⊞ *Details not confirmed for 2002*

MUCH WENLOCK
Map 07 SO69

MUCH WENLOCK PRIORY
TA3 6HS
☎ 01952 727466

The original priory, founded here as a convent in the 7th century, was destroyed by the Danes but was rebuilt and the ruins date from the 11th century and later periods.
Times: Open all year, Apr-Oct, daily 10-6 (Oct 10-5); Nov-Mar, Wed-Sun 10-4. Closed 24-26 Dec & 1 Jan. **Fee:** £2.85 (ch £1.40, under 5's free, con £2.10). Personal stereo tour included in price, also available for the partially sighted, those with learning difficulties and in French & German. **Facilities:** 🅿 ⊞

OSWESTRY
Map 07 SJ22

OLD OSWESTRY HILL FORT
(1m N, accessible from unclass road off A483)
Times: Open any reasonable time. **Facilities:** ⊞ *Details not confirmed for 2002*

🏛 QUATT
Map 07 SO78
DUDMASTON
WV15 6QN (4m SE of Bridgnorth on A442)
☎ 01746 780866 ▤ 01746 780744
e-mail: mouefe@smtp.ntrust.org.uk
Times: Open Apr-Sep, Teu, Wed & Sun & BH Mons, 2-5.30. Garden
noon-6. Closed Good Fri. **Facilities:** 🅿 💺 & (Braille guides, taped
tours) toilets for disabled shop ✝ (ex in grounds) 🐾 *Details not
confirmed for 2002* 🏷

🏛 SHREWSBURY
Map 07 SJ41
**SHREWSBURY CASTLE AND SHROPSHIRE
REGIMENTAL MUSEUM**
The Castle, Castle St SY1 2AT (in town centre, adjacent
to railway station)
☎ 01743 358516 ▤ 01743 354811
e-mail: shropsrm@zoom.co.uk

The museum of The King's Shropshire Light Infantry
and The Shropshire Yeomanry is housed in the main
surviving building of Shrewsbury Castle, which once
dominated the town. The grounds contain the medieval
'motte' and the romantic 'Laura's Tower'.
Times: Open Tue-Sat 10-4.30, also Sun from Etr-1 Oct & BH Mon.
Closed Dec & Jan. Telephone for winter opening times. Castle grounds
open Mon-Sat & Sun as above, 9-5 **Fee:** £2 (£1 concessions). All local
residents, ch under 18 or in full time education free. **Facilities:** 🅿 (3
mins NCP) (on street parking by voucher only) & (please ask staff for
assistance) toilets for disabled shop ✝ (ex guide dogs)

SHREWSBURY QUEST
193 Abbey Foregate SY2 6AH (opposite Shrewsbury
Abbey)
☎ 01743 243324 ▤ 01743 244342
Times: Open Apr-Oct 10-5 (last admission); Nov-Mar 10-4 (last
admission). Closed 25-26 Dec & 1 Jan. **Facilities:** 🅿 (charged) ✗
licensed & (Braille maps, lift) toilets for disabled shop ✝ (ex assistance
dogs) *Details not confirmed for 2002* 🏷

🏛 STOKESAY
Map 07 SO48
STOKESAY CASTLE
SY7 9AH (1m S of Craven Arms off A49)
☎ 01588 672544

Well-preserved and little altered, this 13th-century
manor house has a romantic setting. It has a fine
timber-framed Jacobean gatehouse, a great hall and a
solar with 17th-century panelling.
Times: Open all year, Apr-Sep, daily 10-6 (Oct 10-5); Nov-28 Mar,
Wed-Sun 10-4, closed 1-2pm Nov-Mar. (Closed 24-26 Dec & 1 Jan).
Fee: £3.50 (ch 5-15 £1.80, under 5's free). Personal stereo tour
included in admission price. **Facilities:** 🅿 & (tape tour for visually
handicapped, ramp for wheelchairs) toilets for disabled ✝

🏛 WESTON-UNDER-REDCASTLE
Map 07 SJ52
HAWKSTONE HISTORIC PARK & FOLLIES
SY4 5UY (3m from Hodnet off A53, follow brown
tourist signs)
☎ 01939 200611 ▤ 01939 200311
e-mail: info@hawkstone.co.uk

Created in the 18th century by the Hill family,
Hawkstone was once one of the greatest historic
parklands. After almost one hundred years of neglect it
has now been restored and designated a Grade 1
historic park. It covers nearly 100 acres of hilly terrain
and vistors are advised to wear sensible shoes and
clothing and to bring a torch. Allow 3-4 hours for the
tour.
Times: Open Apr-2 Jul, Wed-Sun & BHs from 10.30am (10pm wknd).
last admission 4pm. 3 Jul-3 Sep, every day, last admission 5pm. 4 Sep-
29 Oct, Wed-Sun, last admission 4pm. 6 Jan-Mar, wknds from 10am,
last admission 3.30pm **Fee:** Weekdays £4.50 (ch £2.50 pen/students
£3.50.Wknds and BHs £5 (ch £3, pen/student £4). Winter wknds £3.50
(ch £2, pen/student £2.50). Family ticket. **Facilities:** 🅿 💺 ✗ licensed
& (no access to follies due to terrain) toilets for disabled shop ✝ (ex
dogs on lead) 🏷

🏛 WROXETER
Map 07 SJ50
ROMAN TOWN
SY5 6PH (5m E of Shrewsbury, 1m S of A5)
☎ 01743 761330

These excavated remains of the Roman town of
Virconium probably date from AD140 - 150. It was the
fourth largest city in Roman Britain, with impressive
remains of the 2nd-century municipal baths. There is
an interesting museum with educational facilities.
Times: Open all year, Apr-Oct, daily 10-6 (Oct 10-5); Nov-Mar, Wed-
Sun 10-4 (closed 1-2pm). Closed 24-26 Dec & 1 Jan. **Fee:** £3.50 (ch 5-
15 £1.80, under 5's free, con £2.60). Personal stereo tour included in
admission. **Facilities:** 🅿 & shop ✝ ♿

Somerset

Somerset is rich with history and legend, as well as having some beautiful coastline and countryside. The name of the county comes from the Saxon, and literally translated means 'Land of the Summer People.'

One of the county's most famous landmarks is Glastonbury Tor, a hill that once gave refuge to the ancient Britons. Legend has it that Joseph of Arimathea came to Glastonbury in a bid to convert the English. It is also the place where King Arthur and Gwynevere are said to be buried. (Those interested in Arthurian legend should also visit South Cadbury, an Iron Age hill fort reputed to be the site of Camelot.) In more recent years, the area has been host to a more concrete, if no less fabulous event, Glastonbury Festival.

At the other end of the county lies the timeless, rugged beauty of Exmoor, most of which is now a National Park. R. D. Blackmore's novel *Lorna Doone* is set here.

Bath is the biggest town in Somerset, and is ideal for shopping, spa relaxation and architecture buffs. Jane Austen lived here, and set two of her novels in the town.

The seaside resorts of Minehead, Burnham-on-Sea and Weston-super-Mare are great places to enjoy a family holiday. Dunster is further inland and walking through it is a little like taking a time machine through 900 years of history. The town is overshadowed by the Norman splendour of Dunster Castle, owned by the National Trust.

In the heart of Somerset lies Wells, the smallest city in England, with only 10,000 inhabitants. The cathedral was begun in the late 12th century, and completed in the mid-13th. It is well known for its stone figures, and its 600-year old clock.

Top: Hadspen Garden

EVENTS & FESTIVALS

May
4th-6th Bath Annual Spring Flower Show, Royal Avenue
17th-2nd June Bath International Music Festival
29th-1st June The Royal Bath & West Show, Shepton Mallet
tbc Bath Fringe Festival (various venues)

June
17th May-2nd Bath International Music Festival
29th May-1st The Royal Bath & West Show, Shepton Mallet
tbc Glastonbury Festival of Contemporary Performing Arts, Worthy Farm, Pilton

July
13th Glastonbury Pilgrimage, Glastonbury Abbey
tbc Annual Agricultural Show, Thurlbear
tbc Glastonbury International Dance Festival

August
6th-7th Flower Show, Taunton
24th Town & Country Show, Racecourse, Taunton

September
28th Wellington Carnival

October
19th Taunton Carnival

November
tbc Bridgwater Guy Fawkes Carnival, Bridgwater
tbc Glastonbury Chilkwell Guy Fawkes Carnival

🏛 AXBRIDGE
Map 03 ST45
KING JOHN'S HUNTING LODGE
The Square BS26 2AP
☎ 01934 732012

Nothing to do with King John or with hunting, this jettied and timber-framed house was built around 1500. It gives a good indication of the wealth of the merchants of that time and is now a museum of local history, with old photographs, paintings and items such as the town stocks and constables' staves.
Times: Open 29 Mar-Sep, daily 1-4. **Fee:** Free. **Facilities:** & shop ✙ 😠

🏛 BARRINGTON
Map 03 ST31
BARRINGTON COURT GARDEN
TA19 0NQ (5m NE of Ilminster on B3168)
☎ 01460 241938
e-mail: wbagen@smtp.ntrust.org.uk
Times: Open Mar & Oct: Fri, Sat & Sun 11-4.30; Apr- 29 Jun & Sep: daily ex Fri 11-5.30; Jul & Aug daily 11-5.30. **Facilities:** 🅿 ✗ licensed & (batricars available, braille guides) ✙ 😠 *Details not confirmed for 2002*

🏛 BATH
Map 03 ST76
AMERICAN MUSEUM
Claverton Manor BA2 7BD (2.5m SE)
☎ 01225 460503   📋 01225 480726
e-mail: amibbath@aol.com

Claverton Manor is just south east of Bath, in a beautiful setting above the River Avon. The house was built in 1820 by Sir Jeffrey Wyatville, and is now a museum of American decorative arts. The gardens are well worth seeing, and include an American arboretum and a replica of George Washington's garden at Mount Vernon. The Folk Art Gallery and the New Gallery are among the many exhibits in the grounds along with seasonal exhibitions.
Times: Open 24 Mar-4 Nov, Tue-Sun 2-5. Gardens 1-6. BH Sun & Mon 11-5. **Fee:** £5.50 (ch £3, pen £5). **Facilities:** 🅿 🍽 & toilets for disabled shop 🍷

BATH ABBEY
BA1 1LY (city centre, next to Pump Rooms)
☎ 01225 422462   📋 01225 429990
e-mail: office@bathabbey.org

The 15th-century abbey church was built on the site of the Saxon abbey where King Edgar was crowned in 973. The church is Perpendicular style with Norman arches and superb fan-vaulting. The famous West Front carvings represent the founder-bishop's dream of angels ascending and descending from heaven.
Times: Open all year, Apr-Oct Mon-Sat 9-6; Nov-Mar 9-4.30. Sun all year 1-2.30 & 4.30-5.30. **Fee:** Free. **Facilities:** 🅿 (limited street parking) & toilets for disabled shop ✙

BATH POSTAL MUSEUM
8 Broad St BA1 5LJ
☎ 01225 460333   📋 01225 460333
e-mail: info@bathpostalmuseum.org

Discover how 18th-century Bath influenced and developed the Postal System, including the story of the Penny Post. The first letter sent with a stamp was sent from this very building. Visitors can explore the history of written communication from Egyptian clay tables thousands of years ago, to the first Airmail flight from Bath to London in 1912. See the Victorian Post Office and then visit the tea room and shop. You may know how the Romans took their leisure, but how did they communicate across the Empire? Come and discover the answer at the Bath Postal Museum.
Times: Open all year, Mon-Sat 11-5. Parties by appointment. (Closed Sun, 25-26 Dec & 1 Jan). **Fee:** £2.90 (ch £1.20, ch 7 free, pen, UB40 & students £1.95). Party 10+. **Facilities:** 🅿 (200yds) 🍽 & toilets for disabled shop ✙ 🍷

THE BUILDING OF BATH MUSEUM
Countess of Huntingdons Chapel, The Vineyards, The Paragon BA1 5NA (M4 junct 18 onto A46 towards Bath city centre. Take A4, 2nd exit at mini rdbt.)
☎ 01225 333895   📋 01225 445473
e-mail: admin@bobm.freeserve.co.uk

This new museum relates the fascinating story of how Georgian Bath was created. 17th-century Bath was a medieval market town but in the space of 100 years it was transformed into one of the most beautiful and glamorous cities in Europe. The exhibition depicts elegant society life in "Beau" Nash's spa resort and explains how the houses were constructed. After a visit, the street scene outside seems like an extension of the exhibition. Ring for details of special events.
Times: Open 15 Feb-1 Dec, Tue-Sun & BH's 10.30-5. **Fee:** £4 (ch £1.50, concessions £3). Family ticket £10. Party 10+ **Facilities:** 🅿 (500mtrs) & shop ✙ (ex guide dogs)

HOLBURNE MUSEUM OF ART
Great Pulteney St BA2 4DB (city centre. M4 junct 18, A46/A4. Follow brown tourist signs)
☎ 01225 466569   📋 01225 333121
e-mail: s.e.lucy@bath.ac.uk

This elegant building shows 17th- and 18th-century collections of fine and decorative art, notably silver, porcelain, glass, furniture and Old Masters paintings. There is an annual programme of events and lively lectures. The biggest Gainsborough painting in Britain (of The Byam Family), previously unseen by the general public, is on loan to the museum for three years.
Times: Open mid Feb-mid Dec, Mon-Sat & BHs 10-5, Sun 2.30-5.30 (Closed Mon ex group bookings). **Fee:** £3.50 (ch £1.50, unemployed & student £2, other concessions £3). Family ticket £7. **Facilities:** 🅿 🍽 & (lift to all floors) toilets for disabled shop ✙ (ex guide dogs)

MUSEUM OF BATH AT WORK

Julian Rd BA1 2RH (from city centre, off Lansdown Rd into Julian Rd. Museum is next to church on right)

☎ 01225 318348   🖥 01225 318348

e-mail: mobaw@hotmail.com

The centre houses the Bowler collection, and the entire stock-in-trade of various Victorian craftsmen. Also here is 'The Story of Bath Stone', with a replica of a mine face before mechanisation, and a Bath cabinet-maker's workshop. Horstmann Car Gallery is a new feature, plus a computerised information point on Bath's heritage work.

Times: Open all year, Etr-1 Nov, daily 10-5; Nov-Etr, wknds 10-5. (Closed 25-26 Dec). **Fee:** £3.50 (ch, pen & students £2.50). Family ticket £10. **Facilities:** P (0.25 mile) 🍽 shop ✖

MUSEUM OF COSTUME

Bennett St BA1 2QH (M4 junct 18, follow A46 into Bath. Museum near city centre)

☎ 01225 477785   🖥 01225 477743

e-mail: costume_bookings@bathnes.gov.uk

The Museum of Costume is one of the finest collections of fashionable dress in the world, covering the period from the late 16th-century to the present day. It is housed in Bath's famous 18th-century Assembly Rooms designed by John Wood the Younger in 1771.

Times: Open all year, daily 10-5 (Closed 25 & 26 Dec). Last admission 30 mins before closing. **Fee:** £4.20 (ch £3). Family ticket £11.50. Combined ticket with Roman Baths, £9.50 (ch £5.50)

Facilities: P (5 mins walk) (park & ride recommended) & (audio guides available) toilets for disabled shop ✖ (ex guide dogs) 🍽

NO 1 ROYAL CRESCENT

BA1 2LR

☎ 01225 428126   🖥 01225 481850

e-mail: admin@bobm.freeserve.co.uk

Bath is very much a Georgian city, but most of its houses have naturally altered over the years to suit changing tastes and lifestyles. Built in 1768 by John

Wood the Elder, No 1 Royal Crescent has been restored to look as it would have done some 200 years ago.

Times: Open 15 Feb-29 Oct, Tue-Sun 10.30-5; 31 Oct-26 Nov, Tue-Sun 10.30-4. Open BH Mon & Bath Festival Mon 22 May. (Closed Good Fri). Last admission 30 mins before closing. **Fee:** £4 (concessions £3.50). Family ticket £10. Party 10+. **Facilities:** P (5 mins walk) (street parking with card £1 per hour) shop ✖ (ex guide dogs)

ROMAN BATHS & PUMP ROOM

Abbey Church Yard BA1 1LZ (M4 junct 18, A46 into city centre)

☎ 01225 477785   🖥 01225 477743

e-mail: romanbaths_bookings@bathnes.gov.uk

The remains of the Roman baths and temple give a vivid impression of life nearly 2000 years ago. Built next to Britain's only hot spring, the baths served the sick and the pilgrims visiting the adjacent Temple of Sulis Minerva. Above the Temple Courtyard, the Pump Room became a popular meeting place in the 18th century. The site still flows with natural hot water and no visit is complete without a taste of the famous hot spa water.

Times: Open all year, Mar-Jun & Sep-Oct, daily 9-6; Jul & Aug daily 9am-10pm; Jan-Feb & Nov-Dec, daily 9.30-5.30. (Closed 25 & 26 Dec). Last admission 1hr before closing. **Fee:** £7 (ch £4.20). Family ticket £18.50. Combined ticket with Museum of Costume £9.50 (ch £5.50). Disabled visitors free admission to ground floor areas. **Facilities:** P (5 mins walk) (park & ride recommended) ✖ licensed & (sign language & audio tours) toilets for disabled shop ✖ (ex guide dogs) 💳

ROYAL PHOTOGRAPHIC SOCIETY

The Octagon, Milsom St BA1 1DN

☎ 01225 462841   🖥 01225 448688

e-mail: rps@rps.org

Times: Open all year, daily 9.30-5.30, last admission 4.45pm. (Closed 25-26 Dec). **Facilities:** P (5 mins walk) 🍽 ✖ licensed & (chair lift to all floors) toilets for disabled shop ✖ (ex guide dogs) *Details not confirmed for 2002* 💳

SALLY LUNN'S REFRESHMENT HOUSE & MUSEUM

4 North Pde Passage BA1 1NX (city centre, follow signs, next to Bath Abbey)

☎ 01225 461634 🖹 01225 447090

e-mail: corsham@aol.com

This Tudor building is Bath's oldest house and was a popular 17th-century meeting place. The traditional 'Sally Lunn' is similar to a brioche, and it is popularly believed to carry the name of its first maker who came to Bath in 1680. The bun is still served in the restaurant, and the original oven, Georgian cooking range and a collection of baking utensils are displayed in the museum.

Times: Open all year, Museum - Mon-Fri 10-6, Sat 10-6, Sun 11-6. (Closed 25-26 Dec & 1 Jan). **Fee:** 30p (concessions free) **Facilities:** P 2-3 min walk (cards required for street parking) ♥ ✗ licensed ♿ (braille menu for the blind) shop 🐾 (ex guide dogs) ♥

CASTLE CARY Map 03 ST63

HADSPEN GARDEN & NURSERY

Hadspen House BA7 7NG (2m SE off A371)

☎ 01749 813707 🖹 01749 813707

Times: Open Mar-1 Oct, Thu-Sun & BHs 10-5. **Facilities:** P ✗ ♿ toilets for disabled garden centre 🐾 (ex guide dogs) *Details not confirmed for 2002*

CHARD Map 03 ST30

FORDE ABBEY

TA20 4LU (4m S of Chard, follow brown tourist signs)

☎ 01460 221290 🖹 01460 220296

This 12th-century Cistercian monastery was converted into a private dwelling in the mid-17th century by Cromwell's attorney general. In the house there are good pictures and furniture and an outstanding set of Mortlake tapestries. The large gardens are some of the finest in Dorset and include a kitchen garden, rock garden and bog garden as well as herbaceous borders and many outstanding trees.

Times: Gardens, open all year, daily 10-4.30. Abbey & gardens Apr-Oct Tue-Thu, Sun & BH 1-4.30. **Fee:** Gardens £4 (ch free, pen £3.80). House & Gardens £5.20 (ch free, pen £5). **Facilities:** P ♥ ♿ (wheelchair can be borrowed) toilets for disabled shop garden centre 🐾 (ex in the garden) ♥

CLEVEDON Map 03 ST47

CLEVEDON COURT

Tickenham Rd BS21 6QU (off B3130 1.5m E of Clevedon)

☎ 01275 872257

Clevedon Court is a remarkably complete manor house of around 1320AD. Additions have been made in each century, so it has a pleasing variety of styles, with an 18th-century terraced garden.

Times: Open 31 Mar-29 Sep, Wed-Thu, Sun & BH Mon 2-5. **Fee:** £4.50 (ch £2). Party 20+ by arrangement. **Facilities:** P ♿ (ground floor accessible via 4 steps) 🐾 🍴

CRANMORE Map 03 ST64

EAST SOMERSET RAILWAY

Cranmore Railway Station BA4 4QP (on A361 between Frome & Shepton Mallet)

☎ 01749 880417 🖹 01749 880764

Times: Open daily Mar-24 Dec from 10am. For days when steam trains are operating phone 01749 880417. **Facilities:** P ♥ ✗ licensed ♿ (ramp from road to platform) toilets for disabled shop *Details not confirmed for 2002* ♥

CRICKET ST THOMAS Map 03 ST30

THE WILDLIFE PARK AT CRICKET ST THOMAS

TA20 4DB (3m E of Chard on A30, follow brown signs. Clearly signposted from M5 junct 25)

☎ 01460 30111 🖹 01460 30817

The Wildlife Park offers you the chance to see more than 60 species of animals at close quarters. Visitors can learn about what is being done to save endangered species, take a walk through the Lemur Wood, ride on the Safari Train or visit the Children's Farm. During peak season, park mascot Larry the Lemur stars in his own show.

Times: Open all year, daily 10-6, last admission 4. (Closed 25 Dec). **Fee:** £5.95 (ch 4-14 £4.50 & pen £4.95, under 3's free). Family ticket £19, party 20+ **Facilities:** P ♥ ✗ licensed ♿ (some steep slopes) toilets for disabled shop 🐾 (ex guide dogs) ♥

DUNSTER Map 03 SS94

DUNSTER CASTLE

TA24 6SL (3m SE of Minehead, approach from A39. Approx 2m from Dunster Stn)

☎ 01643 821314 🖹 01643 823000

e-mail: wdugen@smtp.ntrust.org.uk

The castle's picturesque appearance is largely due to 19th-century work, but older features can also be seen, the superb 17th-century oak staircase for example. Sub-tropical plants flourish in the 28-acre park and the terraced gardens are noted for exotica such as a giant lemon tree, yuccas, mimosa and palms.

Times: Open: Castle: 31 Mar-Sep, Sat-Wed 11-5; Oct-4 Nov, Sat-Wed 11-4. Garden & Park: Apr-29 Sep daily 10-5; Oct-Mar 11-4. **Fee:** Castle, Garden & Park £6.20 (ch under 16 £3.10). Family ticket £15.50. Garden & park only £3 (ch under 16 £1.50). Family ticket £7.50. **Facilities:** P ♿ (Braille & audio guides, large print guides & Batricar) toilets for disabled shop 🍴

EAST HUNTSPILL Map 03 ST34

SECRET WORLD-BADGER & WILDLIFE RESERVE CENTRE

New Rd TA9 3PZ (Signed from A38, 1m S of Highbridge)

☎ 01278 783250 🖹 01278 793109

Times: Open Mar-Nov, daily 10-6. Nov-Dec, daily 10-5. Feb- Mar, daily 10-5. **Facilities:** P ♥ ✗ ♿ toilets for disabled shop garden centre *Details not confirmed for 2002*

EAST LAMBROOK   Map 03 ST41
EAST LAMBROOK MANOR GARDEN
TA13 5HH (signed off A303, at South Petherton roundabout)
☎ 01460 240328   📄 01460 242344
e-mail: enquiries@eastlambrook.com

It was the late Margery Fish who created the concept of 'cottage gardening' in the 1930s, and her wonderful Grade I listed gardens are known to garden lovers throughout the world. The gardens are now under extensive restoration and house the National Collection of Geraniums, a specialist plant nursery, a tea shop and art gallery.
Times: Open Feb-Oct, daily 10-5. **Fee:** £2.95 (ch £1 & pen £2.50). Party £2.50 each. **Facilities:** 🅿 💺 ♿ (Gardens partly accessible) shop garden centre ✸ (ex guide dogs) 🍴

FARLEIGH HUNGERFORD   Map 03 ST85
FARLEIGH HUNGERFORD CASTLE
BA3 6RS (3.5m W of Trowbridge on A366)
☎ 01225 754026

The ruined 14th-century castle has a chapel containing wall paintings, stained glass and the fine tomb of Sir Thomas Hungerford who built the castle. His powerful family and the castle are linked with various grim tales.
Times: Open all year, Apr-Sep, daily 10-6 (Oct 10-5); Nov-Mar, Wed-Sun 10-4 (closed 24-26 Dec & 1 Jan. (Reviewed Mar 2002). **Fee:** £2.30 (con £1.70, ch 5-15 £1.20, under 5's free). (Reviewed Mar 2002). **Facilities:** 🅿 ♿ ✸ ♨

GLASTONBURY   Map 03 ST43
GLASTONBURY ABBEY
Abbey Gatehouse, Magdalene St BA6 9EL (on A361 between Frome & Taunton. M5 junct 23 then A39 to Glastonbury)
☎ 01458 832267   📄 01458 832267
e-mail: glastonbury.abbey@dial.pipex.com

Few places in Britain are as rich in myth and legend as Glastonbury. Tradition maintains that the impressive ruins mark the birth place of Christianity in Britain. Joseph of Arimathea is said to have founded a chapel here in AD61, planting his staff in the ground, where it flowered both at Christmas and Easter. Later, it is said, King Arthur and Guinevere were buried here, and the abbey has been a place of pilgrimage since the Middle Ages. The present abbey ruins date mostly from the 12th and 13th centuries and fell into decay after the Dissolution. The display area contains artefacts and a model of the Abbey as it might have been in 1539.
Times: Open all year, daily, Jun-Aug 9-6; Sep-May 9.30-6pm or dusk, whichever is the earliest. Dec-Feb open at 10am. (Closed 25 Dec). **Fee:** £3 (ch 5-15 £1, pen & students £2.50). Family ticket (2ad+2ch) £6.50. **Facilities:** 🅿 (charged) 💺 ♿ (no access in Lady Chapel,audio tape,deaf loop,wheelchairs) toilets for disabled shop ✸ (only if dogs are on leads)

KINGSDON   Map 03 ST52
LYTES CARY MANOR
TA11 7HU (off A303)
☎ 01985 843600

Much of the present house was built in the 16th century although the oldest part, the chapel, dates from 1343. The Great Hall was a 15th-century addition. Unfortunately the gardens did not survive, but the present formal gardens are being restocked with plants that were commonly grown at the time of building.
Times: Open 23 Mar-30 Oct, Mon, Wed & Sat 2-6 or dusk if earlier. Also Fri in Jun, Jul & Aug. **Fee:** £4.60 (ch £2) **Facilities:** 🅿 ♿ (braille guide. scented plants) toilets for disabled ✸ 🐾

MONKSILVER   Map 03 ST03
COMBE SYDENHAM COUNTRY PARK
TA4 4JG
☎ 01984 656284   📄 01984 656273
Times: Open Apr-Sep. Country Park: daily 9-5. Other attractions open by guided tour, Spring BH-Sep, Mon, Thu & Fri at 2pm. **Facilities:** 🅿 (charged) ♿ ✸ (ex in park) *Details not confirmed for 2002*

MONTACUTE   Map 03 ST41
MONTACUTE HOUSE
TA15 6XP (off A3088)
☎ 01935 823289   📄 01935 823289
e-mail: wmogen@smtp.ntrust.org.uk
Times: Open, Garden & Park: Apr-30 Oct daily (ex Tue) 11.30-5.30. Nov-Mar Wed-Sun 11.30-4. House: Apr-30 Oct, daily (ex Tue) 12-5.30.
Facilities: 🅿 ✕ licensed ♿ (Braille guide) toilets for disabled shop garden centre ✸ (ex park) 🐾 *Details not confirmed for 2002*

MUCHELNEY   Map 03 ST42
MUCHELNEY ABBEY
TA10 0DQ
☎ 01458 250664

Encircled by marshes, Muchelney seemed a suitably remote spot in the 8th century for a Benedictine Abbey. The ruins that remain date from the 15th and 16th centuries, however, and there is also a 14th-century priest's house nearby. Exhibitions include Stuart furnishings and examples of the work of modern potter, John Leach.
Times: Open Apr-Oct, daily 10-6 (5pm Oct). (Reviewed Mar 2002) **Fee:** £1.90 (ch 5-15 £1, under 5's free, con £1.40) (Reviewed Mar 2002) **Facilities:** 🅿 ♿ ✸ ♨

NETHER STOWEY   Map 03 ST13
COLERIDGE COTTAGE
35 Lime St TA5 1NQ (At W end of Nether Stowey, on S side of A39, 8m W of Bridgwater)
☎ 01278 732662

It was in this small cottage that Coleridge was most inspired as a poet and here that he wrote *The Rime of the Ancient Mariner,* part of *Christabel* and *Frost at Midnight.* The Coleridge family moved to Nether Stowey
contd.

in 1797 and became friendly with the Wordsworths who lived nearby.
Times: Open Apr-Sep, Tue-Thu & Sun 2-5. **Fee:** £3. (ch £1.50).
Facilities: ⊞ ⊁ ⛵

⌂ NUNNEY
Map 03 ST74
NUNNEY CASTLE
(3.5m SW of Frome, off A361)
Times: Open any reasonable time. **Facilities:** ⅏ ⊞ *Details not confirmed for 2002*

⌂ SPARKFORD
Map 03 ST62
HAYNES MOTOR MUSEUM
BA22 7LH (from A303 follow A359 road towards Castle Cary, the museum is clearly signposted)
☎ 01963 440804 🖹 01963 441004
e-mail: marc@haynesmotormuseum.co.uk
Times: Open all year, Mar-Oct , daily 9.30-5.30; Nov-Feb, 10-4.30. Etr-summer hols open to 6.30pm. (Closed 25 Dec & 1 Jan). **Facilities:** ⊞ ⬤ ⅏ (ramps & loan wheelchairs available) toilets for disabled shop ⊁ (ex guide dogs & in grounds) *Details not confirmed for 2002* 🖚

⌂ STOKE ST GREGORY
Map 03 ST32
WILLOW & WETLANDS VISITOR CENTRE
Meare Green Court TA3 6HY (between North Curry & Stoke St Gregory, signed from A361 & A378)
☎ 01823 490249 🖹 01823 490814
e-mail: phcoate@globalnet.co.uk

The Centre is owned and run by Somerset Basketmakers and willow growers P H Coate & Son. The environmental exhibition gives a fascinating insight into the Somerset Levels and Moors. Guided tours are available.
Times: Open all year, Mon-Fri 9-5 (guided tours 10-4), Sat (no tours) 9-5. Closed Sun. **Fee:** Free. **Facilities:** ⊞ ⬤ ⅏ toilets for disabled shop 🖚

⌂ STOKE-SUB-HAMDON
Map 03 ST41
STOKE-SUB-HAMDON PRIORY
North St TA4 6QP (between A303 & A3088)
☎ 01985 843600

This 15th-century house is built of Ham Hill stone and was once the home of the priests of the chantry belonging to the now vanished Beauchamp Manor. The 14th- and 15th-century farm buildings and the screens passage of the chantry remain.
Times: Open 23 Mar-3 Nov, daily 10-6 or dusk if earlier. Great Hall only open to visitors. **Fee:** Free. ⏐P⏐ (5mtrs) ⛵

⌂ STREET
Map 03 ST43
THE SHOE MUSEUM
C & J Clark Ltd, High St BA16 0YA (M5 junct 23, take A39 to Street, follow signs for Clarks Village)
☎ 01458 842169 🖹 01458 443196

The museum is in the oldest part of the shoe factory set up by Cyrus and James Clark in 1825. It contains shoes from Roman times to the present, buckles, engravings, fashion plates, machinery, hand tools and advertising material.
Times: Open all year. **Fee:** Free. **Facilities:** ⊞ (charged) ⬤ ✕ ⅏ toilets for disabled shop ⊁

⌂ TAUNTON
Map 03 ST22
HESTERCOMBE GARDENS
Cheddon Fitzpaine TA2 8LG (3m N, off A361 near Cheddon Fitzpaine)
☎ 01823 413923 🖹 01823 413727
e-mail: info@hestercombegardens.com

There are three period gardens to enjoy at Hestercombe: the 40-acre Georgian pleasure grounds with woodland walks, temples, Witch House and Great Cascade; the Victorian terrace with its newly restored fountain; and the Edwardian gardens, where the work of Gertrude Jekyll and architect Edwin Lutyens are shown off to full effect.
Times: Open every day, 10-6 (last admission 5). **Fee:** £4 (ch5-15 £1, pen £3.80). **Facilities:** ⊞ ⬤ ⅏ (gardens partially accessible) toilets for disabled shop garden centre (Apr-Oct) ⊁ (ex on lead) 🖚

⌂ TINTINHULL
Map 03 ST41
TINTINHULL HOUSE GARDEN
BA22 9PZ (0.5m S off A303)
☎ 01935 822545
e-mail: wtifxs@smtp.ntrust.org.uk
Times: Open Apr-Sep, Wed-Sun & BH Mons 12-6. **Facilities:** ⊞ ⊁ ⛵ *Details not confirmed for 2002*

WASHFORD   Map 03 ST04
CLEEVE ABBEY
TA23 0PS (0.25m S of A39)
☎ 01984 640377

The now ruined Cistercian abbey was founded at the end of the 12th century. Little remains of the church, but the gatehouse, dormitory and refectory are in good condition, with traceried windows, a fine timbered roof and wall paintings to be seen.
Times: Open all year, Apr-Sep, daily 10-6 (5pm Oct); Nov-Mar, daily 10-1-4. Closed 24-26 Dec & 1 Jan. (Reviewed Mar 2002) **Fee:** £2.60 (con £2, ch 5-15 £1.30, under 5's free). **Facilities:** �[P] & shop ✗ (in certain areas) ‡‡

TROPIQUARIA WILDLIFE PARK
TA23 0QB (on A39, between Williton and Minehead)
☎ 01984 640688   ▤ 01984 640688
e-mail: office@tropiquaria.co.uk

Housed in a 1930s BBC transmitting station, the main hall has been converted into an indoor jungle with a 15-foot waterfall, tropical plants and free-flying birds. (Snakes, lizards, iguanas, spiders, toads and terrapins are caged!) Downstairs is the submarine crypt with local and tropical marine life. Other features include landscaped gardens, the Shadowstring Puppet Theatre, and 'Wireless in the West' museum. Also two new full size pirate adventure ships are moored on the front lawn, accessible to pirates of all ages!
Times: Open Apr-Sep, daily 10-5; Oct, daily 11-5, Nov & Feb-Mar wknds & school hols 11-5. (Closed Dec & Jan). **Fee:** £4.95 (ch £3.75, pen £4.25). **Facilities:** ⊡ ⚑ & shop ✗ (ex guide dogs) ⬤

WELLS   Map 03 ST54
THE BISHOP'S PALACE
Henderson Rooms BA5 2PD (next to cathedral off the Market Sq)
☎ 01749 678691   ▤ 01749 678691

Close to the cathedral is the moated bishop's palace. The early part of the palace, the bishop's chapel and the ruins of the banqueting hall date from the 13th century and the undercroft remains virtually unchanged from this time. There are several state rooms and a long gallery which houses portraits of former Bishops. Events include a Living History re-enactment.
Times: Open Apr-Oct, Tue-Fri & BH's; daily in Aug 10.30-5 Sun 2-5. Gates close at exactly 6pm. **Fee:** £3 (ch 12 accompanied free, UB40's £1.50, pen £2, disabled £1.50) . Party 10+ £2 each. **Facilities:** [P] (100yrds) ⚑ ✗ licensed & (free use of electric wheelchair)

WESTON-SUPER-MARE   Map 03 ST36
THE HELICOPTER MUSEUM
The Heliport, Locking Moor Rd BS24 8PP (outskirts of town on A371, nr M5 junct 21)
☎ 01934 635227   ▤ 01934 645230
e-mail: office@helimuseum.fsnet.co.uk

The world's largest rotary-wing collection and the only helicopter museum in Britain. More than 50 helicopters and autogyros are on display - including examples from France, Germany, Poland, Russia and the United States, from 1935 to the present day - with displays of models, engines and other components explaining the history and development of the rotorcraft. Special events include `Open Cockpit Days', when visitors can learn more about how the helicopter works.
Times: Open all year, Nov-Mar Wed-Sun 10-4. Apr-Oct 10-6. (closed 24-26 Dec & 1 Jan) Open daily during Etr & Summer school hols. **Fee:** £3.75 (ch under 5 free, ch 5-16 £2.75, pen £3.25). Family ticket £11. Party 15+. **Facilities:** [P] ⚑ & toilets for disabled shop ⬤

TIME MACHINE
Burlington St BS23 1PR
☎ 01934 621028   ▤ 01934 612526
e-mail: peterjones@n-somerset.org.uk
Times: Open all year: Mar-Sept daily 10-5, Nov-Dec 10-4 & BH Mon. (Closed 25-26 Dec & 1 Jan). **Facilities:** [P] (800 yds) (some disabled parking outside museum) ⚑ & toilets for disabled shop garden centre ✗ (ex guide dogs) *Details not confirmed for 2002*

WOOKEY HOLE   Map 03 ST54
WOOKEY HOLE CAVES & PAPERMILL
BA5 1BB (M5 junct 22 follow signs via A38 & A371, from Bristol & Bath, A39 to Wells then 2m to Wookey Hole)
☎ 01749 672243   ▤ 01749 677749
e-mail: witch@wookey.co.uk

A 40-minute guided tour leads visitors through this amazing complex of caves, with stalagmites, stalactites and other interesting geological features. There is also a Victorian papermill, with handmade papermaking, and an old penny pier with mirror maze and penny arcade.
Times: Open all year, Mar-Oct 10-5; Nov-Feb 10.30-4.30. (Closed 17-25 Dec). **Fee:** £7.30 (ch £4.30) **Facilities:** [P] ✗ licensed & (Papermill only) toilets for disabled shop ✗ (ex guide dogs) ⬤

YEOVILTON   Map 03 ST52
FLEET AIR ARM MUSEUM
Royal Naval Air Station BA22 8HT (on B3151)
☎ 01935 840565   ▤ 01935 842630
e-mail: info@fleetairarm.com
Times: Open all year, daily (ex 24-26 Dec) 10-5.30 (4.30pm Nov-Mar). **Facilities:** [P] ⚑ ✗ licensed & (wheelchairs available) toilets for disabled shop ✗ (ex guide dogs) *Details not confirmed for 2002* ⬤

Staffordshire

For many, the main attractions of Staffordshire are the rollercoaster entertainment of Alton Towers or the precision craftsmanship of the world-famous potteries of Stoke-on-Trent. Yet the county also has some beautiful countryside and historic sites.

Part of the Peak District National Park – the first in Britain – forms the top right-hand corner of the county, and contains landscape ideal for hiking or pony trekking, as well as more adventurous pastimes such as rock climbing, hang-gliding, potholing, mountain biking, abseiling and orienteering.

Toward the south lies Cannock Chase, 30,000 acres of forest and heathland that was once a royal hunting preserve, and where a large herd of fallow deer still run free. The Chase is also home to cemeteries of fallen servicemen, including 5,000 Germans who died in Britain during two World Wars.

The Vale of Trent is known for its gentle beauty, and provides a welcome contrast to the craggy splendour of the moorland. Miles of rural canals (more than in any other county) are also a welcoming sight.

Staffordshire has many historic attractions, including Lichfield's three-spired cathedral which contains the 7th-century Gospels of St Chad. The town was also the birthplace of Dr Samuel Johnson, who was born in a bookshop, and each year there are celebrations to commemorate the man who gave us the first Dictionary of the English Language.

Burton-upon-Trent is the 'Brewing Capital of England', and the Bass Museum Visitors' Centre will surely provide a certain something to banish the thirst.

EVENTS & FESTIVALS

June
2nd Midland Counties Show, Uttoxeter Racecourse, Wood Lane, Uttoxeter
21st-23rd Lichfield Folk Festival (various venues)
tbc World Toe Wrestling Championships, Ye Olde Royal Oak, Wetton

July
3rd-14th Lichfield International Arts Festival (various venues)

September
9th Abbots Bromley Horn Dance (throughout village)

Top: Sir Henry Doulton, Burslem

🏛 ALTON   Map 07 SK04
ALTON TOWERS
ST10 4DB (signed from M1 junct 23A, M6 junct 15, M1 junct 28 or M6 junct 16)
☎ 08705 204060 📠 01538 704097

Alton Towers offers rides, shows and attractions guaranteed to suit every member of the family. There are enchanting children's areas and the theme park has more thrill rides than any other in Europe. The Alton Towers Hotel displays a wonderful array of artefacts and memorabilia from a bygone age. On top of all this, there are 200 acres of landscaped gardens and the majestic ruins of the Towers themselves.
Times: Open Apr-29 Oct, daily 9.30-5,6 or 7. (Please contact for 2002 dates) **Fee:** Jul & Aug £23 (ch £19, under 4's free); wknds & sch hols £22 (ch £18, under 4's free); wkdays £17 (ch £14, under 4's free). Please telephone for price confirmation **Facilities:** 🅿 ☕ ✖ licensed ⅋ (disabled guest guide books) toilets for disabled shop ✱ (ex guide dogs) ➥

🏛 BIDDULPH   Map 07 SJ85
BIDDULPH GRANGE GARDEN
Grange Rd ST8 7SD (off A527, 0.5m N of Biddulph)
☎ 01782 517999 📠 01782 510624
Times: Open mid Mar-Oct, Wed-Fri 12-6. Sat-Sun & BH Mon 11-6 (last admission 5.30 or dusk if earlier); early Nov-mid Dec, Sat-Sun 12-4 or dusk. **Facilities:** 🅿 ☕ shop ✱ ♨ *Details not confirmed for 2002*

🏛 BURTON-UPON-TRENT   Map 08 SK22
THE BASS MUSEUM
PO Box 220, Horninglow St DE14 1YQ (from N, M1 junct 28, A38, A511; from S, M1 junct 24, A564, A38)
☎ 01283 511000 📠 01283 513509
e-mail: enquires@bass-museum.com

This museum is housed in the original Engineers Dept and Joiners shop, and was opened in 1977, the bi-centenary of the founding of the Bass brewery. Visitors can explore the history of brewing through a wide range of visual and interactive displays, and also visit the majestic Bass Shire horse team. The Bass Museum also plays host to conferences, exhibitions and a variety of entertainment.
Times: Open all year, Mon-Fri 10-5, Sat & Sun 11-5. Last admission 4pm. (Closed 25-26 Dec & 1 Jan). **Fee:** £4.95 (ch £2, pen £3). Family ticket £15. Brewery tours by arrangement only, at extra charge (inc free glass of beer/lager/soft drink) **Facilities:** 🅿 ✖ licensed ⅋ (lift to all floors) toilets for disabled shop ✱ (ex guide dogs) ➥

🏛 CHEDDLETON   Map 07 SJ95
CHEDDLETON FLINT MILL
Beside Caldon Canal, Leek Rd ST13 7HL (3m S of Leek on A520)
☎ 01782 502907

Two water mills complete with wheels are preserved here, and both are in running order. The 17th-century South Mill was used to grind corn, while the North Mill was built to grind flint for the pottery industry. The restored buildings have displays on aspects of the pottery industry. Exhibits include examples of motive power, such as a Robey steam engine, and of transport, such as the restored 70ft horse-drawn narrow boat 'Vienna'.

Cheddleton Flint Mill

Times: Open all year, Sat & Sun 2-5, Mon-Fri 10-5. **Fee:** Free. **Facilities:** 🅿 ⅋

🏛 HALFPENNY GREEN   Map 07 SO89
HALFPENNY GREEN VINEYARDS
DY7 5EP (0.5m off B4176 Dudley to Telford rd)
☎ 01384 221122 📠 01384 221101
e-mail: enquiries@halfpenny-green-vineyards.co.uk

Using German, French and hybrid varieties that can prosper even in the poorest British summer, this small vineyard offers "The complete English wine experience." This includes a self-guided vineyard trail as well as guided tours, wine-tasting, a craft centre and a visitor centre. Visitors can purchase wines with personalised labels for special occasions. Coarse fishing is also available.
Times: Open all year, daily 10.30-5. **Fee:** *Prices not confirmed for 2002* **Facilities:** 🅿 ☕ ⅋ toilets for disabled shop ✱ (ex guide dogs) ➥

🏛 HIMLEY   Map 07 SO89
HIMLEY HALL & PARK
DY3 4DF (off A449, on B4176)
☎ 01902 324093 & 326665 📠 01902 894163
e-mail: himley.pls@mbc.dudley.gov.uk

The extensive parkland offers a range of attractions, including a nine-hole golf course and coarse fishing. The hall is open to the public when exhibitions are taking place. There is a permanent orienteering course, a charge is made for the maps. Guided tours at the hall are available by prior arrangement. Hall available for private hire.
Times: Open Hall: Apr-mid Sep, 2-5. Closed Mon ex BH. Park open all year. **Fee:** Free. **Facilities:** 🅿 (charged) ☕ ⅋ toilets for disabled ✱ (ex guide dogs & in park)

🏛 LICHFIELD
Map 07 SK10

ERASMUS DARWIN CENTRE
Beacon St WS13 7AD (signed Lichfield Cathedral.
Access by foot through the cathedral close)
☎ 01543 306260 🖥 01543 306109
e-mail: erasmus.d@virgin.net
Times: Open Tue-Sat 10-4.30, Sun noon-4.30, BH Mons 10-4.30. Last
admission 3.45. P (200mtrs) ⚹ toilets for disabled shop garden centre
🐕 (ex guide dogs) *Details not confirmed for 2002*

LICHFIELD CATHEDRAL
WS13 7LD (signed from all major roads and within city)
☎ 01543 306240 🖥 01543 306109
e-mail: enquiries@lichfield-cathedral.org

The Cathedral's three spires, known as the Ladies of
the Vale, dominate the landscape. The first cathedral
here was founded in AD700 to house the shrine of St
Chad. The present building, with its elaborate carvings,
has been much restored since it was attacked during
the Civil War. Among its treasures is an 8th-century
illuminated manuscript, the Lichfield Gospels. Many
musical events take place here.
Times: Open daily 7.45-6. **Fee:** Suggested donation of £3 for each
adult visitor. **Facilities:** P (200mtrs) (no parking ex disabled in close)
🍷 ✕ licensed ⚹ (Touch & hearing centre for blind) toilets for
disabled shop 🐕 (ex guide dogs)

LICHFIELD HERITAGE CENTRE
Market Square WS13 6LG
☎ 01543 256611 🖥 01543 414749
Times: Open all year, daily 10-5. Last admission 4.14pm. (Closed Xmas
& New Year) **Facilities:** P (200yds) 🍷 ⚹ (lift) toilets for disabled
shop 🐕 (ex guide dogs) *Details not confirmed for 2002* 🐕

SAMUEL JOHNSON BIRTHPLACE MUSEUM
Breadmarket St WS13 6LG (in city centre market place)
☎ 01543 264972 🖥 01543 414779
e-mail: sjmuseum@lichfield.gov.uk

A statue of Dr Johnson sits at one end of Market Square
facing his birthplace on the corner of Breadmarket
Street. The house, where Samuel's father had a
bookshop, is now a museum containing many of
Johnson's personal relics. His favourite armchair and
walking stick are among the collection. Tableaux show
the house as it was in the 18th century.
Times: Open daily 10.30-4.30. (Closed Xmas, New Year & Sun Nov-
Jan). **Fee:** £2 (ch & pen £1.10). Joint ticket with Lichfield Heritage
Centre £3.20 (ch & pen £2.20). Family ticket £5.40. **Facilities:** P
(500yds) (large print text literature) shop 🐕 (ex guide dogs/in shop)

🏛 MOSELEY

Map 07 SJ90

MOSELEY OLD HALL

WV10 7HY (4m N of Wolverhampton, off A460)
☎ 01902 782808   🖹 01902 782808
e-mail: mmodxl@smtp.ntrust.org.uk
Times: Open 20 Mar-19 Dec; Mar-May Wed, Sat-Sun, BH Mon and
Tue 1.30-5.30 (BH 11-5). June-Oct Wed & Sat-Sun, BH Mon and Tue;
also Tue in July & Aug 1.30-5.30 (BH Mon 11-5); Nov & Dec: Sun 1.30-
4.30 (guided tour only, last tour at 4pm). **Facilities:** 🄿 💺 ✕ licensed
& (braille & large print, 1 wheelchair) toilets for disabled shop 🛏 (ex
guide dogs) ✖ *Details not confirmed for 2002* 🍴

🏛 SHUGBOROUGH

Map 07 SJ92

SHUGBOROUGH ESTATE

ST17 OXB (6m E of Stafford off A513, signed from M6
junct 13)
☎ 01889 881388   🖹 01889 881323
e-mail: promotions@staffordshire.gov.uk

Set on the edge of Cannock Chase, Shugborough is the
magnificent 900-acre seat of the Earls of Lichfield. The
18th-century mansion house contains fine collections
of ceramics, silver, paintings and French furniture. Part
of the house is still lived in by the Lichfield family.
Visitors can enjoy the Grade I listed historic garden and
a unique collection of neo-classical monuments. Other
attractions include the museum and the original
servants quarters, the laundry, kitchens, brewhouse
and coachhouses which have all been restored and are
fully operational. Shugborough Park Farm is a Georgian
farmstead that has an agricultural museum, working
corn mill and rare breeds centre.
Times: Open 25 Mar-1 Oct, daily (ex Mon, but open BH Mon) 11-5.
Sun only during Oct. Site open all year to pre-booked parties. **Fee:** Site
admission £2 per vehicle. Mansion £4.50 (concession £3); County
Museum £4.50 (concession £3); Park Farm £4.50 (concession £3).
Single site family ticket £12. Family Voyager (all 3 sites) £22. Farm
Rover £30 family. **Facilities:** 🄿 (charged) 💺 ✕ licensed & (step
climber for wheelchairs, 2 Batricars) toilets for disabled shop 🛏 (ex
guide dogs & in parkland) ✖ 🍴

🏛 STAFFORD

Map 07 SJ92

SHIRE HALL GALLERY

Market Square ST16 2LD (M6 junct 13 or 14, follow
signs to town centre then signs for Gallery)
☎ 01785 278345   🖹 01785 278327
e-mail: shirehallgallery@staffordshire.gov.uk

A fine gallery housed in the 18th-century Shire Hall –
one of Staffordshire's most magnificent buildings. It
holds exhibitions of contemporary arts, contains
historic courtrooms and a Crafts Council selected craft
shop.
Times: Open all year, Mon & Fri 9.30-6, Tue-Thu 9.30-5, Sat 10-5.
Closed BH. **Fee:** Free. **Facilities:** 🄿 (200yds) 💺 & (minicom
telephone & hearing loop) toilets for disabled shop 🛏 (ex guide dogs)
🍴

🏛 STOKE-ON-TRENT

Map 07 SJ84

CERAMICA

Wedgewood Place, Burslem ST6 3DS (M6 junct 15/16,
A500 then B5051 to Burslem. In Burslem centre)
☎ 01782 832001   🖹 01782 823300

Following the unearthing of Josiah Wedgewood's kiln, a
new attraction celebrating the past, present and future
of British pottery is set to open during the spring. Other
key exhibits include the Arnold Bennett study room,
Bizarreland for children, Magic Carpet Ride and
pavilions illustrating pottery manufacture.
Times: Due to open for Spring 2002. Please contact to confirm dates
& times. **Fee:** Telephone for 2002 admission prices. **Facilities:** 🄿
(charged) & toilets for disabled shop 🛏 (ex guide dogs) 🍴

ETRURIA INDUSTRIAL MUSEUM

Lower Bedford St, Etruria ST4 7AF (M6 junct 16, A500
onto Stoke Rd (A5006))
☎ 01782 233144   🖹 01782 233145
Times: Open all year, Wed-Sun 10-4. (Closed Xmas & New Year).
Facilities: 🄿 💺 & toilets for disabled shop 🛏 (ex guide dogs)
Details not confirmed for 2002

GLADSTONE POTTERY MUSEUM

Uttoxeter Rd, Longton ST3 1PQ (on A50, signposted
from A500 link with M6)
☎ 01782 319232   🖹 01782 598640
e-mail: gladstone@stoke.gov.uk

The last complete Victorian pottery factory from the
days of bottle kilns. Tour the factory and see the pottery
making skills of the craftsmen and craftswomen. The
Museum shop stocks a wide range of gifts with
craftspeople in mind. With its cobbled yard and giant
bottle kilns, Gladstone perfectly captures the City's
atmospheric past. Meet the head clerk of 1910 who will
talk about life in the factory at that time. There is also a
cinema and a 'family-sized' potters' wheel.
Times: Open all year, daily 10-5 (last admission 4pm). Limited
opening Xmas & New Year. **Fee:** £3.95 (ch £2.50, students & pen
£2.95). Family ticket £10 (2ad+2ch 5-16yrs). **Facilities:** 🄿 💺 ✕
licensed & special potters wheel for wheelchair users to experiment on
toilets for disabled shop 🛏 (ex guide dogs) 🍴

ROYAL DOULTON VISITOR CENTRE

Nile St, Burslem ST6 2AJ (M6 junct 15 from S or 16 from
N. Join A500 then A527 for Tunstall, follow tourist
signs)
☎ 01782 292434   🖹 01782 292424
e-mail: visitor@royal-doulton.com

The Centre houses over 1,500 Royal Doulton figures
including many rare models. The Sir Henry Doulton
Gallery restaurant combines magnificent treasures

from the varied Royal Doulton past. Factory tours can be booked from Monday to Friday.
Times: Open all year, Mon-Sat 9.30-5, Sun 10.30-4.30. Factory tours by advance booking Mon-Fri 10.30-2 (1.30 Fri). (Closed Xmas week). No tours during factory holidays. **Fee:** Visitor Centre only £2 (concessions £2.25); Factory Tour & Visitor Centre £4.50 (concessions £5). Parties 12+. **Facilities:** ⓟ ♨ ✕ ᕕ (only Visitor Centre accessible) toilets for disabled shop ✻ (ex guide dogs) ➤

SPODE
Church St ST4 1BX (M6 junct 15, then A500 to Stoke. Ignore city centre signs. Turn left at Stoke roundabout, follow brown tourist signs)
☎ 01782 744011 ᐧ 01782 744012
e-mail: visitorcentre@spode.co.uk

Spode is the oldest English pottery company still on its original site. Here Josiah Spode first perfected the formula for fine bone china. The Spode site houses a restaurant, factory shops, concession outlets, and a visitors' centre with exhibits on the history and heritage of the ceramics industry. Fully guided factory tours are available, pre-booking essential.
Times: Visitor Centre, Museum, Factory Shops, concessions & licensed restaurant. Mon-Sat 9-5, Sun 10-4. Factory Tours by prior appointment weekdays only, not available during factory closures-please ring for details. **Fee:** Visitor Centre & Museum free. Standard factory tours £4.75 (ch over 12 & concessions £3.75). Connoisseur factory tour £7 & £6. Tours by appointment only. **Facilities:** ⓟ (charged) ✕ licensed ᕕ (ramps) toilets for disabled shop ✻ (ex guide dogs) ➤

THE POTTERIES MUSEUM & ART GALLERY
Bethesda St, Hanley ST1 3DE
☎ 01782 232323 ᐧ 01782 232500
e-mail: museums@stoke.gov.uk

Times: Open all year, Mon-Sat 10-5, Sun 2-5. (Closed Xmas-New Year). **Facilities:** ⓟ (500mtrs) ♨ ᕕ (lift, induction loop, 2 wheelchairs available) toilets for disabled shop ✻ (ex guide/helping dogs) *Details not confirmed for 2002* ➤

WEDGWOOD VISITOR CENTRE
Barlaston ST12 9ES (5m S)
☎ 01782 204141 & 204218 ᐧ 01782 204402
Times: Open all year, Mon-Fri 9-5, Sat & Sun 10-5; (Closed Xmas & 1 Jan). **Facilities:** ⓟ ✕ licensed ᕕ toilets for disabled shop ✻ *Details not confirmed for 2002*

⌂ TAMWORTH   Map 07 SK20
DRAYTON MANOR THEME PARK & ZOO
B78 3TW (M42, junct 9, follow brown tourist board signs on A4091)
☎ 01827 287979 ᐧ 01827 288916

A popular family theme park with over 100 rides set in 250 acres of parkland and lakes. There are world-class rides like 'Apocalypse' – the world's first stand-up tower drop, 'Shockwave' – Europe's only stand-up rollercoaster and 'Stormforce 10' (bring your waterproofs!) There are also many children's rides, plus a zoo and exotic creature reserve and 'Dinosaurland'.
Times: Park open end Mar-end Oct, 9-6 daily, Zoo open 10-5, 6 or 7, Rides open 10.30-5, 6, & 7 (depending on season). **Fee:** Admission & rides wristband: £15 (ch >900mm up to 13 £11, ch under 900mm free, pen, wheelchair £6.50) Family ticket £47-£58. **Facilities:** ⓟ ♨ ✕ licensed ᕕ (ramps or lifts to most rides, some rides limited access) toilets for disabled shop garden centre ✻ (ex in park) ➤

TAMWORTH CASTLE
The Holloway, Ladybank B79 7NA (from M42 junct 10 & M6 junct 12, access via A5)
☎ 01827 709626 ᐧ 01827 709630
e-mail: heritage@tamworth.gov.uk

The dramatic Norman motte and bailey castle was once the home of England's Royal Champions and today is (reputedly) haunted by two lady ghosts. Quizzes, dressing-up and brass-rubbing make it a great family destination.
Times: Open all year, Mon-Fri 10-5.30; Sat & Sun 12-5.30. Last admission 4.30. Telephone to confirm opening times before visiting.
Fee: £4.30 (ch £2.20). Family £11.90. Prices subject to change.
Facilities: ⓟ (100yds & 400yds) ᕕ (one wheelchair for use inside the castle) shop ✻ (ex guide dogs & hearing dogs)

WALL
Map 07 SK10

WALL ROMAN SITE
Watling St WS15 0AW (off A5)
☎ 01543 480768

Wall was originally the Roman fort of Letocetum, standing at the crossroads of Watling Street and Rykneild Street. It was an important military base from about AD50. Excavations have revealed the most complete bath house ever found in Britain.
Times: Open Apr-Sep, daily 11-5) **Fee:** £2.40 (ch 5-15 £1.20, under 5's free, con £1.80). **Facilities:** 🏋 ♿ ♨

WESTON PARK
Map 07 SJ81

WESTON PARK
TF11 8LE (on A5 at Weston-under-Lizard, 30min from central Birmingham 3m off M54 junct 3 and 8m off M6 junct 12)
☎ 01952 852100   📠 01952 850430
e-mail: enquiries@weston-park.com

Built in 1671, this fine mansion stands in elegant gardens and a vast park designed by 'Capability' Brown. Three lakes, a miniature railway, and a woodland adventure playground are to be found in the grounds, and in the house itself there is a notable collection of pictures, furniture and tapestries.
Times: Open Etr, May-Jun, wknds & BH's; 30 Jun-2 Sep, daily (Closed 14 Jul, 4 & 17-20 Aug); 8-16 Sep wknds only. **Fee:** Park & Gardens £2.50 (ch £1.50, pen £2). House, £2 (ch £1, pen £1.50). Family ticket (non inc house) £6 (up to 2ad+3ch). **Facilities:** 🅿 ♨ ✕ licensed ♿ (disabled route, access to restaurant & shop) toilets for disabled shop ➾

WHITTINGTON
Map 07 SK10

STAFFORDSHIRE REGIMENT MUSEUM, WHITTINGTON BARRACKS
WS14 9PY (on A51 between Lichfield & Tamworth)
☎ 0121 311 3240/3229   📠 0121 311 3205
Times: Open all year, Tue-Fri 10-4.30 (last admission 4); also Apr-Oct wknds and BH 1-4.30. (Closed Xmas-New Year). Parties at other times by arrangement. **Facilities:** 🅿 ♿ (ramps) toilets for disabled shop 🏋 (outside only ex guide dogs) *Details not confirmed for 2002*

WILLOUGHBRIDGE
Map 07 SJ74

THE DOROTHY CLIVE GARDEN
TF9 4EU (on A51 between Nantwich & Stone)
☎ 01630 647237   📠 01630 647902

This 200-year-old gravel quarry has been converted into a delightful woodland garden. The quarry is at the top of a small hill and the garden has fine views of the countryside and adjoining counties. There is a variety of rare trees and shrubs. The garden provides colour and interest throughout the seasons from spring to glowing autumn tints.
Times: Open Apr-Oct, daily 10-5.30. **Fee:** £3 (ch up to 11 yrs free, ch 11-16 £1, pen £2.50). Party 20+. **Facilities:** 🅿 ♨ ♿ (wheelchairs for use, special route) toilets for disabled

Suffolk

Britain's most easterly county has plenty to offer to visitors, aside from the enviable fact that it has the driest regional climate in England.

Suffolk was once part of the kingdom of East Anglia. Back then the kingdom was protected by almost impenetrable boundaries; sea to the north and east, the undrained Fens to the west, and a barrier of oak forest to the south. However, these natural defences didn't stop invasion from Romans, Angles, Vikings, and Saxons, all of whom have left their mark on the area. In later years Icelandic fisherfolk settled in the coastal towns, and Flemish weavers helped the wool towns boom and also took part in the brewing industry.

Lavenham has some marvellous medieval timber houses as well as a church with a massive tower. John Constable, world-famous painter of *'The Haywain'*, went to school here and was born in nearby East Bergholt. Thomas Gainsborough was another artistic son of Suffolk, born in Sudbury, where a statue of him stands in the village square. Sudbury also features as 'Eatanswill' in Dickens' *The Pickwick Papers*.

Ipswich is said to be the oldest continuously-inhabited Anglo-Saxon town in England, and has some very attractive municipal parks. The dock area has been massively redeveloped after the decline of the town as a major port.

Known as the Sunrise Coast, the resorts of Lowestoft, Kessingland and Southwold have won awards for the cleanliness and safety of their beaches. Lowestoft is Britain's most easterly town and sits between sandy beaches on one side and beautiful broadland on the other. Sparrow's Nest Park is located just below the lighthouse and the town also features a maritime museum, a War Memorial Museum and the Royal Naval Patrol Museum.

EVENTS & FESTIVALS

May
10th-26th Bury St Edmunds Festival, arts festival (various venues)
12th South Suffolk Show, Point-to-Point Course, Ampton Park, Ingham
tbc Mildenhall Air Fete, US Airforce, Mildenhall
tbc Sagitta Guineas Festival, Newmarket Racecourse, Newmarket

June
6th-7th Suffolk Show, Suffolk Showground, Bucklesham Road, Ipswich
7th-23rd Aldeburgh Festival of Music & the Arts, Snape Maltings Concert Hall, Snape
tbc Maritime Ipswich, Ipswich Docks

July
tbc Ipswich Music Day
tbc Suffolk Coast Bike Ride (in aid of Anthony Nolan Bone Marrow Trust)

August
25th-26th Eye Show, Eye Show Ground, Eye

November
1st November Big Night Out, fireworks to music event, Melford Hall Park, Long Melford

Top: Framlingham Castle

🏛 BUNGAY   Map 05 TM38
OTTER TRUST
Earsham NR35 2AF (off A143, 1m W of Bungay)
☎ 01986 893470   📠 01986 892461

The Otter Trust's main aim is to breed this endangered species in captivity in sufficient numbers so that it can re-introduce young otters into the wild wherever suitable habitat remains. This re-introduction programme has been running since 1983. The Otter Trust covers 23 acres on the banks of the River Waveney. As well as otter pens, there are three lakes with a large collection of European waterfowl.
Times: Open Apr (or Good Fri if earlier)-Oct, daily 10.30-6. **Fee:** £5 (ch over 3 £3, pen £4). Disabled person in wheelchair free.
Facilities: 🅿 💺 ⚁ toilets for disabled shop 🏃 (ex guide dogs)

🏛 BURY ST EDMUNDS   Map 05 TL86
MANOR HOUSE MUSEUM
Honey Hill IP33 1HF (edge of town centre, follow signs to Police Station, opposite is museum car park)
☎ 01284 757072   📠 01284 757079

The Georgian mansion specialises in costumes, textiles, horology and fine and decorative art from the 17th to the 20th centuries. There is a temporary exhibition gallery as well as workshops in textiles and horology - a new feature is an interactive horological room and feely pictures and boxes.
Times: Open all year Sat-Sun, Tue-Wed 10-5. Other times by arrangement. **Fee:** £3 (ch £2 con £2). **Facilities:** 🅿 (charged) 💺 ✗ licensed ⚁ (Special tours can be arranged for disabled groups) toilets for disabled shop 🏃 (ex guide dogs) 🍴 ⛴

MOYSE'S HALL MUSEUM
Cornhill IP33 1DX (in town centre)
☎ 01284 757488   📠 01284 757079
Times: Open all year Mon-Sat 10-5, Sun 2-5. (Closed 25-26 Dec & Good Fri). **Facilities:** 🅿 (200yds) ⚁ shop 🏃 (ex guide dogs) *Details not confirmed for 2002* ⛴

🏛 CAVENDISH   Map 05 TL84
THE SUE RYDER FOUNDATION MUSEUM
PO Box 5736 CO10 8RN (on A1092 Long Melford to Clare road)
☎ 01787 282591   📠 01787 280548

The museum shows the work and history of the small but effective international foundation which cares for the sick and disabled. The Home's garden and chapel are also open.
Times: Open all year, daily 10-5.30. (Closed 25 Dec). **Fee:** 80p (ch 12 & pen 40p). Parties by appointment. **Facilities:** 🅿 ✗ ⚁ toilets for disabled shop 🏃

🏛 EASTON   Map 05 TM25
EASTON FARM PARK
IP13 0EQ (signed from A12 at Wickam Market, and from A1120)
☎ 01728 746475   📠 01728 747861
e-mail: easton@eastonfarmpark.co.uk

A Victorian model farm situated in the Deben River Valley. There are lots of breeds of farm animals, including Suffolk Punch horses. A purpose built dairy centre enables visitors to watch the cows being milked every afternoon, and there is the original Victorian Dairy which houses a collection of dairy bygones. Pets paddocks allow children to feed and touch the smaller animals.
Times: Open 19 Mar-30 Sep, daily 10.30-6. Also open Feb & Oct half term hols. Closed Mon ex BHs and Mon in Jul-Aug. **Fee:** £4.75 (ch under 3 free, ch 3-16 £3.24, pen £4.25). Party 20+ **Facilities:** 🅿 💺 ⚁ (special parking) toilets for disabled shop ⛴

🏛 EUSTON   Map 05 TL87
EUSTON HALL
IP24 2QP (on A1088, 3m S of Thetford)
☎ 01842 766366   📠 01842 766764

Home of the Duke and Duchess of Grafton, this 18th-century house is notable for its fine collection of pictures, by Stubbs, Lely, Van Dyck and other Masters. The grounds were laid out by John Evelyn, William Kent and 'Capability' Brown, and include a 17th-century church in the style of Wren.
Times: Open 28 Jun-27 Sep, Thu only & Suns 24 Jun & 2 Sep 2.30-5. **Fee:** £3 (ch 50p, pen £2.50). **Facilities:** 🅿 💺 ⚁ shop 🏃 (guide dogs by permission)

🏛 FLIXTON   Map 05 TM38
NORFOLK & SUFFOLK AVIATION MUSEUM
Buckeroo Way, The Street NR35 1NZ (off A143, take B1062, 2m W of Bungay)
☎ 01986 896644
e-mail: nsam.flixton@virgin.net

Situated in the Waveney Valley, the museum has over 24 historic aircraft. There is also a Bloodhound surface-to-air missile, the 446th Bomb Group Museum, RAF Bomber Command Museum, the Royal Observer Corps Museum, RAF Air-Sea Rescue and Coastal Command and a souvenir shop. Among the displays are Decoy

Sites and Wartime Deception, and Fallen Eagles –
Wartime Luftwaffe Crashes.

Times: Open Apr-Oct Sun-Thu 10-5 (last admission 4); Nov-Mar 10-4 (last admission 3) Tue, Wed, Sun. New year closed 2 weeks either side. **Fee:** Free. **Facilities:** 🅿 ⅋ (helper advised. ramps ex 1small building) toilets for disabled shop 🐾 (ex guide dogs)

⚏ FRAMLINGHAM   Map 05 TM26
FRAMLINGHAM CASTLE
IP13 9BP (on B1116)
☎ 01728 724189

Built by Hugh Bigod between 1177 and 1215, the castle has fine curtain walls, 13 towers and an array of Tudor chimneys. In the 17th century the castle was bequeathed to Pembroke College, Cambridge, which built almshouses inside the walls.

Times: Open all year, Apr-Oct, daily 10-6 (5pm in Oct); Nov-Mar, daily 10-4. Closed 24-26 Dec & 1 Jan. **Fee:** £3.50 (ch 5-15 £1.80, under 5's free, con £2.60). Personal stereo tour included in admission. **Facilities:** 🅿 ⅋ shop 🐾 ⚏

⚏ HORRINGER   Map 05 TL86
ICKWORTH HOUSE, PARK & GARDENS
The Rotunda IP29 5QE (2.5m S of Bury St Edmunds in the village of Horringer on A143)
☎ 01284 735270 ▤ 01284 735175

The eccentric Earl of Bristol created this equally eccentric house, begun in 1795, to display his collection of European art. The Georgian Silver Collection is considered the finest in private hands. 'Capability' Brown designed the parkland, and also featured are a deer enclosure, waymarked walks and an adventure playground.

Times: Open: House 24 Mar-28 Oct, Tue, Wed, Fri, wkends & BH Mons 1-5 (4.30 in Oct) last admission 4.30; Garden open daily 24 Mar-28 Oct 10-5. 29 Oct-Mar 10-4 wkdays; Park daily 7am-7pm. **Fee:** House, Garden & Park £5.70 (National Trust members & ch u5 free, ch £2.50) Garden & park £2.50 (ch 80p). Discount for pre-booked parties. **Facilities:** 🅿 ✗ licensed ⅋ (braille guide batricars stairlift to shop & restaurant) toilets for disabled shop garden centre 🐾 (ex guide dogs & in park) ⚏

⚏ IPSWICH   Map 05 TM14
CHRISTCHURCH MANSION
Soane St IP4 2BE (South side of Christchurch Park)
☎ 01473 253246 & 213761 ▤ 01473 210328

Times: Open all year, Tue-Sat 10-5 (dusk in winter), Sun 2.30-4.30 (dusk in winter). (Closed Good Fri & 24-26 Dec & 1-2 Jan). Open BH Mon. **Facilities:** 🅿 ⅋ (tape guide for partially sighted) shop 🐾 *Details not confirmed for 2002*

IPSWICH MUSEUM
High St IP1 3QH (Follow tourist signs to Crown St car park. Museum 3 mins walk)
☎ 01473 433550 ▤ 01473 433558
e-mail: museum.service@ipswich.gov.uk
Times: Open all year, Tue-Sat 10-5. (Closed Sun, BH's, 24-26 Dec & 1 Jan). **Facilities:** 🅿 (3 min walk) ⅋ (step crawler to first floor) shop 🐾 (ex guide dogs) *Details not confirmed for 2002*

⚏ LAVENHAM   Map 05 TL94
LAVENHAM GUILDHALL
Market Place CO10 9QZ (A1141 & B1071)
☎ 01787 247646
e-mail: almjtg@smtp.ntrust.org.uk

The Guildhall of Corpus Christi is one of the finest timber framed buildings in Britain. It was built around 1530 by the prosperous Corpus Christi Guild, for religious rather than commercial reasons. The hall now houses a local history museum telling the story of Lavenham's 15th- and 16th-century wool-trade riches. Visitors can also see the walled garden with its 19th-century lock-up and mortuary.

Times: Open Mar, Sat, Sun & BH Mons 11-4; Apr-Oct, daily 11-5; Nov, Sat & Sun 11-4. (Closed Good Fri) **Fee:** £3 (accompanied ch free). Parties £2.50 each. School parties by arrangement 60p per ch. **Facilities:** 🅿 (adjacent) ♨ (shop & tea room accessible) shop 🐾 ⚏

⚏ LEISTON   Map 05 TM46
LEISTON ABBEY
(1m N off B1069)
Times: Open any reasonable time. **Facilities:** 🅿 ⅋ ⚏ *Details not confirmed for 2002*

LONG SHOP MUSEUM
Main St IP16 4ES (A12, follow B1119 from Saxmundham to Leiston. Museum in town centre)
☎ 01728 832189 ▤ 01728 832189
e-mail: longshop@care4free.net

Discover the magic of steam through a visit to the world famous traction engine manufacturers. Trace the history of the factory and Richard Garrett engineering. See the traction engines and road rollers in the very place that they were built. Soak up the atmosphere of the Long Shop, built in 1852 as one of the first production line engineering halls in the world. An award-winning museum with three exhibition halls full of items from the glorious age of steam and covering 200 years of local, social and industrial history.

Times: Open Apr-Oct, Mon-Sat 10-5, Sun 11-5. **Fee:** £3 (ch 75p, under 5's free, concessions £2.50) **Facilities:** 🅿 ⅋ toilets for disabled shop 🐾 (ex guide dogs)

⚏ LINDSEY   Map 05 TL94
ST JAMES'S CHAPEL
Rose Green
Times: Open all year. **Facilities:** ⅋ ⚏ *Details not confirmed for 2002*

🏛 LONG MELFORD　　　　Map 05 TL84
KENTWELL HALL
CO10 9BA (signposted off A134)
☎ 01787 310207　📠 01787 379318
Times: Open: Gardens & Farm, Sun during Mar. House, Gardens & Farm: Apr-11 Jun, Sun only; Also 16-28 Apr, 30 May-2 Jun & 12 Jul-24 Sep daily. 27 Sep-29 Oct, Sun only. open 23-27 Oct daily. Historical re-creations on selected wknds & BH through the year. **Facilities:** 🅿 💷 ♿ (wheelchair ramp & 2 wheelchairs for loan) toilets for disabled shop 🐾 (ex guide dogs) *Details not confirmed for 2002* ☕

MELFORD HALL
CO10 9AA (off A134, 3m N of Sudbury, next to village green)
☎ 01787 880286
e-mail: amdklx@smtp.ntrust.org.uk

Queen Elizabeth I was a guest at this turreted, brick-built Tudor house in 1578. It features an 18th-century drawing room, a Regency library and a Victorian bedroom. There is also a large collection of Chinese porcelain, and a display on Beatrix Potter, who was related to the owners and often stayed here. The garden has a Tudor pavilion, which may have been built as a banqueting house.
Times: Open Etr wkend & Etr Mon; Apr & Oct wkends only; May-Sep, daily Wed-Sun (open BH Mon) 2-5.30. **Fee:** £4.40 **Facilities:** 🅿 ♿ (stairlift, braille/large print guides, ramps) toilets for disabled 🐾 (ex guide dogs & dogs in park) 🐾

🏛 LOWESTOFT　　　　Map 05 TM59
EAST ANGLIA TRANSPORT MUSEUM
Chapel Rd, Carlton Colville NR33 8BL (3m SW of Lowestoft, on B1384. Follow brown signs from A12 & A146))
☎ 01502 518459　📠 01502 584658

A particular attraction of this museum is the reconstructed 1930s street scene which is used as a setting for working vehicles: visitors can ride by tram, trolley bus and narrow gauge railway. Other motor, steam and electrical vehicles are exhibited. There is also a woodland picnic area served by trams.
Times: Open Good Fri & Etr Sat 2-4, Etr Sun-Etr Mon 11-5.30. May-Sep, Sun & BH's 11-5.30; Jun-Sep, Wed & Sat 2-5 (last entry 1 hour before closing). **Fee:** £4.50 (ch 5-15 & pen £3). Price includes rides. Party. **Facilities:** 🅿 💷 ♿ toilets for disabled shop ☕

MARITIME MUSEUM
Sparrow Nest Gardens, Whapload Rd NR32 1XG (on A12, 100 metres N of Lowestoft Lighthouse, turn right down Ravine)
☎ 01502 561963　& 511260

Models of ancient and modern fishing and commercial boats, fishing gear and shipwrights' tools are among the exhibits. An exhibition on the evolution of lifeboats, and a replica of the aft cabin of a steam drifter feature. There is also an art gallery.
Times: Open 21 Apr-8 Oct, daily, 10-5. **Fee:** 75p (ch, students 25p, pen 50p) **Facilities:** 🅿 ♿ shop 🐾 (ex guide & small dogs)

PLEASUREWOOD HILLS FAMILY THEME PARK
Leisure Way, Corton NR32 5DZ (off A12 at Lowestoft)
☎ 01502 586000 (Admin)　& 508200 (info)
📠 01502 567393
e-mail: info@pleasurewoodhills.co.uk
Times: Open 16 Apr-1 May; wknds 6-14 May. 20 May-10 Sep & 21-29 Oct, daily; wknds in Sep & Oct. **Facilities:** 🅿 💷 ✕ licensed ♿ all shows accessible. Most ride operators are able to assist toilets for disabled shop 🐾 (ex guide dogs) *Details not confirmed for 2002* ☕

🏛 NEWMARKET　　　　Map 05 TL66
NATIONAL HORSERACING MUSEUM AND TOURS
99 High St CB8 8JL (town centre)
☎ 01638 667333　📠 01638 665600

A chance to meet the horses and stable staff at close quarters, watch the horses on the historic gallops and see them in the equine swimming pool. Retired jockeys will answer questions and let you ride the horse simulator at up to 40mph. Another attraction lets you record your own racing commentary. Ring for details of special tours.
Times: Open Etr-end Oct, Tue-Sun (also BH Mons & Mon in Jul & Aug) 10-5. **Fee:** £4.50 (ch £1.50, con £3.50). 🅿 (300yds) 💷 ✕ licensed ♿ (ramps) toilets for disabled shop 🐾 (ex guide dogs) ☕

🏛 ORFORD　　　　Map 05 TM45
ORFORD CASTLE
IP12 2ND (on B1084)
☎ 01394 450472

Built by Henry II circa 1165, the castle's magnificent keep survives almost intact with three immense towers reaching to 90 feet. Inside there are many rooms to explore.
Times: Open all year, Apr-Sep, daily 10-6; (Oct 10-5); Nov-Mar, Wed-Sun, 10-1 & 2-4. Closed 24-26 Dec & 1 Jan. **Fee:** £3.10 (ch 5-15 £1.60, under 5's free, con £2.30). **Facilities:** 🅿 🐾 ♿

⛪ SAXMUNDHAM
Map 05 TM36

BRUISYARD WINES & HERBS
Church Rd, Bruisyard IP17 2EF (4m W of Saxmundham bypass (A12))
☎ 01728 638281 ☐ 0870 136 3708
e-mail: ian@bruisyardwines.fsnet.co.uk

A vineyard with a winery in traditional Suffolk farm buildings. There are tranquil water and herb gardens with a peaceful, wooded picnic area and children's play area. Visitors can take an audio guided-tour, and buy from a range of wines, many of which can be sampled first.
Times: Open Feb-Xmas, Tue-Sun & BHs. Summer 10.30-5, Winter 11-4.
Fee: Free. **Facilities:** ⬛ & shop garden centre ✝ (ex in vineyard & guide dogs) ⬚ ⬛

⛪ SAXTEAD GREEN
Map 05 TM26

SAXTEAD GREEN POST MILL
The Mill House IP13 9QQ (2.5m NW of Framlingham on A1120)
☎ 01728 685789

Dating from 1854, this is one of the finest examples of a traditional Suffolk post-mill. Machinery and millstones are in perfect order.
Times: Open Apr-Oct, Mon-Sat 10-6 (Oct 10-5). Closed 1-2pm (closed Nov-28mar). **Fee:** £2.10 (ch 5-15 £1.60, under 5's free). (exterior only)
Facilities: ✝ ⌗

⛪ STOWMARKET
Map 05 TM05

MUSEUM OF EAST ANGLIAN LIFE
IP14 1DL (town centre opposite ASDA supermarket, signed from A14 & B1115)
☎ 01449 612229 ☐ 01449 672307

This 70-acre, all-weather museum is set in an attractive river-valley site. There are reconstructed buildings, including a water mill, a smithy and also a wind pump, and the Boby Building houses craft workshops. There are displays on Victorian domestic life, gypsies, farming and industry. These include working steam traction engines, the only surviving pair of Burrell ploughing engines of 1879, and a working Suffolk Punch horse.
Times: Open Apr-Oct. **Fee:** £4.50 (ch 4-16 £3, concession £4). Family ticket £14.75. Party 10+. **Facilities:** ⬛ (adjacent) ⬛ & (wheelchairs available, special vehicle facilities) toilets for disabled shop ⬛

⛪ SUDBURY
Map 05 TL84

GAINSBOROUGH'S HOUSE
46 Gainsborough St CO10 2EU (town centre. Follow pedestrian signs from town centre car parks or from train stn)
☎ 01787 372958 ☐ 01787 376991
e-mail: mail@gainsborough.org

The birthplace of Thomas Gainsborough RA (1727-88). The Georgian-fronted town house, with an attractive walled garden, displays more of the artist's work than any other gallery, together with 18th-century furniture and memorabilia. There's a varied programme of

THE NATIONAL HORSERACING MUSEUM

NEWMARKET, SUFFOLK

The National Horseracing Museum
99 High Street
Newmarket CB8 8JL
www.nhrm.co.uk
Tel: 01638 667333
Fax: 01638 665600

The extraordinary history of the people and horses involved in racing in Britain.

NEW FOR 2002
THE WORLD OF DICK FRANCIS.

•

Practical gallery - meet retired jockeys and trainers and ride the horse simulator.

•

Minibus equine tours led by experts.

•

Gift shop. Cafe.

•

Open
29 March to 31 October
11am to 5pm
(Closed Mondays except in July and August).

exhibitions throughout the year including fine art, craft, photography, printmaking and sculpture.
Times: Open all year - House Tue-Sat 10-5, Sun & BH Mons 2-5; (4pm Nov-Mar). (closed Good Fri & Xmas-New Year). **Fee:** £3 (ch, students & disabled £1.50 pen £2.50). Party rates available. **Facilities:** ⬛ (300 yds) (no parking in Gainsborough Street) & toilets for disabled shop ✝ (ex guide dogs) ⬛

⛪ SUFFOLK WILDLIFE PARK
Map 05 TM58

SUFFOLK WILDLIFE PARK
Kessingland NR33 7SL (S of Gt Yarmouth, just S of Lowestoft off A12)
☎ 01502 740291 ☐ 01502 741104

Take a walk on the wild side at Suffolk's premier wildlife attraction. Set in 100 acres of coastal parkland, you will see giraffes, African lions, cheetahs, chimpanzees, zebra, African antelope, colonies of lemur monkeys living freely on their islands, and the only aardvarks in the country. Animal feeding times are both fun and informative. Other attractions include the Safari Road Train, Explorer Trails, Crazy Golf, Bouncey Castles and large children's play area.
Times: Open all year, daily from 10am. (Closed 25-26 Dec).
Fee: £7.50 (ch 3-14 £5.50) peak season. **Facilities:** ⬛ ⬛ ✕ & (wheelchairs available for hire) toilets for disabled shop ✝ ⬛

🏛 WESTLETON   Map 05 TM46
RSPB NATURE RESERVE MINSMERE
IP17 3BY (signposted from A12 & Westleton)
☎ 01728 648281 📄 01728 648770
e-mail: minsmere@rspb.org.uk

One of the RSPB's most popular sites. It is famous for its nesting avocets, marsh harriers and bitterns. Ideal for families and birdwatchers alike, there are countryside walks of varying lengths, and eight hides. The Visitor Centre provides information about the reserve, and there is a shop and tearoom. Education programmes for school groups are also available.
Times: Open Wed-Mon 9am-9pm (or sunset if earlier). Visitor centre & shop Feb-Oct 9-5, Nov-Jan 9-4. Closed Xmas & Boxing day. **Fee:** £5 (ch £1.50, concessions £3). Family ticket £10. RSPB members free.
Facilities: 🅿 💺 ♿ (ramps, viewing areas, wheelchair) toilets for disabled shop 🐕 (ex guide dogs) 🍽

🏛 WEST STOW   Map 05 TL87
WEST STOW ANGLO SAXON VILLAGE
West Stow Country Park, Icklingham Rd IP28 6HG (off A1101, follow brown tourist signs)
☎ 01284 728718 📄 01284 728277
e-mail: weststow@burybo.stedsbc.gov.uk

The village is a reconstruction of a pagan Anglo-Saxon settlement dated 420-650 AD. Seven buildings have been reconstructed on the site of the excavated settlement. There is a Visitors' Centre and a children's play area. A new Anglo-Saxon Centre houses the original objects found on the site.
Times: Open all year, daily 10-5. Last entry 4pm
Fee: £4.50 (ch £3.50). Family ticket £13. **Facilities:** 🅿 💺 ♿ (ramps) toilets for disabled shop 🐕 (ex guide dogs) 🍽

🏛 WOODBRIDGE   Map 05 TM24
WOODBRIDGE TIDE MILL
Tide Mill Way IP12 4SR (follow signs for Woodbridge off A12, 7m E of Ipswich - Tide Mill is on riverside)
☎ 01473 626618

The machinery of this 18th-century mill has been completely restored. There are photographs and working models on display. Situated on a busy quayside, the unique building looks over towards the historic site of the Sutton Hoo ship burial. Every effort is made to run the machinery for a while whenever the mill is open and the tides are favourable.
Times: Open Etr, then daily May-Sep. Apr, Oct wknds only. 11-5
Fee: £1.50 (con £1, accompanied ch free). 🅿 (400 yds) (no parking or turning in Tide Mill Way) ♿ shop 🐕 (ex guide dogs)

Surrey

Surrey is profoundly affected by its proximity to London, and much of the county has been developed to accommodate affluent commuters to the capital. Despite this, it has the reputation of being Britain's most wooded county, and it has some lovely countryside.

Particularly attractive are the areas around Haslemere and Shere. High points are the North Downs west of Guildford rising to a peak at Box Hill near Dorking, and Leith Hill which is 970 ft (294m) tall, making it the highest point in the southeast of England.

There are a number of attractions located within the area bounded by the M25 motorway. These include Sandown Park and Epsom racecourses, and the south's two huge theme parks, Thorpe Park and Chessington World of Adventures, where you can enjoy all the thrills and spills of white knuckle rides and a variety of themed areas.

Kingston-upon-Thames is the county's administrative headquarters. Other main towns are Woking, Farnham, Dorking and Guildford. The latter has a modern cathedral, consecrated in 1961, and the Keep of the Norman Castle still survives. The castle was frequented by King John, who signed the Magna Carta at Runnymede, a meadow on the south bank of the Thames, in 1215. The castle at Farnham is still in one piece, it dates from 1160 and was occupied until 1927. Farnham is a pleasant town with some graceful Georgian buildings, particularly in Castle Street.

Woking has a peculiar claim to fame. It was here, in 1898, that Martians landed on Horsell Common. The invasion was part of H.G.Wells' classic sci-fi novel *The War of the Worlds*. Wells lived in Woking and Horsell Common is 750 acres of open space that are home to deer, bees and the spider-hunting wasp!

EVENTS & FESTIVALS

June
3rd Surrey County Show, Stoke Park, Guildford

July
tbc Guildford Live Music Festival
tbc Guildford Summer Spectacular (various events throughout the month)

August
4th Cranleigh Show, Showground, Cranleigh
tbc Wisley Flower Show, Royal Horticultural Society, Wisley

October
20th-3rd Nov Guildford Book Festival

November
20th Oct-3rd Guildford Book Festival

Top: Royal Holloway College near Egham.

ASH VALE · ARMY MEDICAL SERVICES MUSEUM
Map 04 SU85

Keogh Barracks GU12 5RQ (M3 junct 4 on A331 to
Mytchett then follow tourist signs)
☎ **01252 340212** ▯ **01252 340224**
e-mail: **museum@keogh72.freeserve.co.uk**
Times: Open all year, Mon-Fri 10-3.30, Fri 9-3. (Closed Xmas, New
Year & BH). Wknds & BH by appointment only. **Facilities:** ▯ & toilets
for disabled shop (large shop selling souvenirs) ✦ (ex guide dogs)
Details not confirmed for 2002

CHERTSEY · THORPE PARK
Map 04 TQ06

Staines Rd KT16 8PN (M25 junct 11 or 13 and follow
signs via A320 to Thorpe Park)
☎ **01932 569393** ▯ **01932 566367**

Set in 500 acres of park, Thorpe Park is the UK's fastest
changing family theme park with the addition of three
white-knuckle rides. Explosive new Detonator,
awesome Vortex and whirlwind Zodiac promise sense-
ational thrills. Plus Tidal Wave - Europe's highest water
drop ride, the Pirates 4D experience and established
favourites like Loggers Leap, Thunder River and
Neptune's Beach provide fun for all ages. The South of
England's biggest firework display takes place end of
October featuring the most awe-inspiring display of
fireworks, pyrotechnics, lasers and special effects. The
world's first ever looping coaster is new for 2002.
Times: Open from Apr-end Oct, call 0870 444 4466 for opening
times. Last admission 1hr before closing. **Fee:** £19 (ch £15). Family
(2ad+2ch under 13) £59. Annual pass £70 per person. **Facilities:** ▯
▆ ✗ licensed & (some rides not accessible, free w.chr loan) toilets
for disabled shop ✦ (ex guide dogs) ◥

EAST CLANDON · HATCHLANDS
Map 04 TQ05

GU4 7RT (E off A246)
☎ **01483 222482** ▯ **01483 223176**
Times: Open House & Gardens 2 Apr-Oct, daily, Tue-Thu & Sun, 2-
5.50 (also open BH & Fri in Aug). Park Walks open Apr-Oct, daily, 11-6.
Facilities: ▯ ✗ licensed & (wheelchair available & special parking)
toilets for disabled shop ✦ (ex guide dogs) ➍ *Details not confirmed*
for 2002

FARNHAM · BIRDWORLD & UNDERWATERWORLD
Map 04 SU84

Holt Pound GU10 4LD (3m S on A325)
☎ **01420 22140** ▯ **01420 23715**
e-mail: **bookings@birdworld.co.uk**

Birdworld is the largest bird collection in the country
and includes toucans, pelicans, flamingoes, ostriches
and many others. Underwater World is a tropical
aquarium with brilliant lighting that shows off
collections of marine and freshwater fish, as well as the
swampy depths of the alligator exhibit. Visitors can also
visit some beautiful gardens, the Jenny Wren farm and
the Heron Theatre.

Birdworld & Underwaterworld

Times: Open all year, daily from 1st wk Jan & mid Feb-end Oct; 8 Jan-
mid Feb & Nov-Dec open wknds only. **Fee:** £8.50 (ch 3-14 £5.50, pen
£6.95) Family ticket £24.95(2 adults & 2 ch). **Facilities:** ▯ ▆ &
(wheelchairs available) toilets for disabled shop ✦ (ex guide dogs)
◥

FARNHAM CASTLE KEEP
Castle Hill GU6 0AG (0.5m N on A287)
☎ **01252 713393**

Built by an 11th-century bishop of Winchester, the
castle made a convenient resting place on the journey
to London. His tower, standing on a mound, was later
encircled by high walls.
Times: Open Apr-Oct, daily 10-6 (Oct 10-5). **Fee:** £2.10 (ch 5-15 £1.10,
under 5's free, con £1.60). **Facilities:** ▯ ✦ ⌗

GREAT BOOKHAM · POLESDEN LACEY
Map 04 TQ15

RH5 6BD (2m S off A246 from Great Bookham)
☎ **01372 452048** ▯ **01372 452023**
e-mail: **spldjd@smtp.n.trust.org.uk**

King George VI and Queen Elizabeth (the Queen
Mother) spent part of their honeymoon here, and
photographs of other notable guests can be seen. The
house is handsomely furnished and full of charm, and it
is set in spacious grounds. There is also a summer
festival, where concerts and plays are performed.
Please phone for details of special events.
Times: Open all year. Grounds, Garden & Landscape walks: daily 11-6.
House: 31 Mar-4 Nov, Wed-Sun 1-5. Also BH Mon 11-5 (last admission
30mins before closing) **Fee:** Ground, Garden & Landscape walks: £4
(Family ticket £10); House: £3 extra (Family £7.50 extra). Ch under 17
half price, ch under 5's free. Party 15+ **Facilities:** ▯ ▆ ✗ licensed &
(braille guide & disabled parking by arrangement) toilets for disabled
shop garden centre ✦ (ex guide dogs or grounds) ➍

🏛 GUILDFORD　　　　Map 04 SU94

DAPDUNE WHARF

Wharf Rd GU1 4RR (off Woodbridge Road to rear of Surrey County Cricket Ground)

☎ 01483 561389　🖥 01483 531667

Times: Open Apr-Oct, Thu, wknds & BHs 11-5. River bus service 11-5 (conditions permitting)

Facilities: 🅿 💺 ♿ (braille guide) toilets for disabled 🛇 (ex on lead) 🐾 *Details not confirmed for 2002*

GUILDFORD CASTLE

GU1 3TU

☎ 01483 444718　🖥 01483 444444

e-mail: dandol@guildford.gov.uk

Times: Open: Grounds daily 8-dusk (Closed 25 Dec); Keep Apr-Sep 10.30-6. **Facilities:** 🅿 (50yds) ♿ *Details not confirmed for 2002*

GUILDFORD HOUSE GALLERY

155 High St GU1 3AJ (N side of High St, opposite Sainsbury's)

☎ 01483 444740　🖥 01483 444742

e-mail: guildfordhouse@ remote.guildford.gov.uk

An impressive building in its own right, Guildford House dates from 1660 and has been Guildford's art gallery since 1959. A changing selection from the Borough's Art Collection is on display, including pastel portraits by John Russell, topographical paintings and contemporary craftwork, as well as temporary exhibitions.

Times: Open Tue-Sat 10-4.45. **Fee:** Free. **Facilities:** 🅿 (100yds) 💺 ♿ shop 🛇

LOSELEY PARK

GU3 1HS (2m SW of Guildford, off A3 onto B3000)

☎ 01483 304440　& 505501　🖥 01483 302036

e-mail: enquiries@loseley-park.com

Sir William More built this house over 400 years ago with stone from the ruins of Waverley Abbey; the house is a fine example of Elizabethan architecture, set in magnificent parkland. The Walled Gardens include a Herb Garden, which illustrates the culinary, medicinal, dyeing and cosmetic uses of herbs and an award-winning rose garden.

Times: Walled Gardens open 7 May-Sep, Wed-Sun & BH 11-5. House open 28 May-27 Aug, Wed-Sun & BH Mon 2-5 (last tour 4pm).

Fee: House & Gardens £6 (ch £3, ch under 5 free, concessions £5). Gardens only £3 (ch £1.50, con £2.50). Party. Garden summer ticket £15, admits ticket holder & guest from May-Sep. **Facilities:** 🅿 💺 ✗ licensed ♿ (wheelchair available, parking outside house) toilets for disabled shop garden centre 🛇 (ex guide dogs)

🏛 HASCOMBE　　　　Map 04 SU94

WINKWORTH ARBORETUM

Hascombe Rd GU8 4AD (2m NW on B2130, follow brown tourist signs from Godalming)

☎ 01483 208477　🖥 01483 208252

e-mail: swagen@smtp.ntrust.org.uk

This lovely woodland covers a hillside of nearly 100 acres, with fine views over the North Downs. The best

times to visit are April and May, for the azaleas, bluebells and other flowers, and October for the autumn colours. A delightful Victorian boat house is open Apr-Oct with fine views over Rowes Flashe lake.

Times: Open all year, daily during daylight hours. (could close when weather is bad) **Fee:** £3.50 (ch £1.75). Family ticket £8.75, additional family member £1.50. **Facilities:** 🅿 💺 ♿ (suggested route, free entry for helpers) toilets for disabled shop 🛇 (ex on leads) 🐾

🏛 OUTWOOD　　　　Map 04 TQ34

OUTWOOD WINDMILL

Outwood Common RH1 5PW (M25 junct 6, take A25 through Godstone towards Redhill, after 1m turn S off A25 at Bletchingly, between The Prince Albert, White Hart, mill 3m on left)

☎ 01342 843458　& 843644　🖥 01342 843458

e-mail: sheila@outwoodwindmill.co.uk

This award-winning example of a post-mill dates from 1665 and is the oldest working windmill in England and one of the best preserved in existence. Standing 400ft above sea level, it is surrounded by common land and National Trust property. Ducks, goats and geese wander freely in the grounds, and there is a small museum of bygones.

Times: Open Etr Sun-last Sun in Oct, Sun & BH Mons only 2-6. Other days & evening tours by arrangement. **Fee:** £2 (ch £1). **Facilities:** 🅿 (10yds) ♿ toilets for disabled shop

🏛 PAINSHILL PARK　　　　Map 04 TQ06

PAINSHILL LANDSCAPE GARDEN

KT11 1JE (W of Cobham, on A245)

☎ 01932 868113　🖥 01932 868001

e-mail: enquiries@painshill.fsbusiness.co.uk

Painshill covers 158 acres and was created by the Hon. Charles Hamilton between 1738 and 1773. Visitors can walk through a series of delightful scenes. There are also: a huge lake, shrubberies, a massive waterwheel, a Gothic temple, a ruined abbey, a Turkish tent and a crystal grotto.

Times: Open Apr-Oct, Tue-Sun & BH, 10.30-4.30. (gates close 4pm). Nov-Mar, Tue-Thu, wknds & BH 11-3 (gates close 4pm). Closed 25-26 Dec. **Fee:** £4.20 (ch 5-16 £1.70, concessions £3.70). Pre-booked adult groups 10+ £3.30. **Facilities:** 🅿 💺 ✗ ♿ (wheelchairs & buggies available - pre-booked) toilets for disabled shop 🛇 (ex guide dogs) 🦮

🏛 REIGATE　　　　Map 04 TQ24

REIGATE PRIORY MUSEUM

Bell St RH2 7RL (off A217)

☎ 01737 222550

Times: Open Wed & Sat 2-4.30 in term time. **Facilities:** 🅿 (50yds) ♿ ("Hands On" facilities) shop 🛇 *Details not confirmed for 2002*

🏛 TILFORD　　　　Map 04 SU84

RURAL LIFE CENTRE

Reeds Rd GU10 2DL (off A287, 3m S of Farnham, sign posted)

☎ 01252 795571　🖥 01252 795571

e-mail: rural.life@psion.net

The museum covers village life from 1750 to 1960. It is

contd.

set in over ten acres of garden and woodland and incorporates purpose-built and reconstructed buildings, including a chapel. Displays show village crafts and trades, such as wheelwrighting, thatching, ploughing and gardening. The historic village playground provides entertainment for children and there is an arboretum featuring over 100 trees from around the world.
Times: Open Apr-Sep, Wed-Sun & BH 11-6. **Fee:** £4 (ch £2 & pen £3). Family ticket £10(2 adults & 2 ch). **Facilities:** 🅿 ☕ ♿ (3 wheelchairs for use) toilets for disabled shop

🏛 WEST CLANDON   Map 04 TQ05
CLANDON PARK
GU4 7RQ (on A247)
☎ 01483 222482 📠 01483 223479
Times: Open House: 2 Apr-31 Oct, Tue, Wed, Thu, Sun & Good Fri, Etr Sat & BH Mons, 11.30-4.30. Last admission 4pm. Garden open daily 9-dusk. Museum open as House, 12-5. Garden open all year daily, 9 until dusk. **Facilities:** 🅿 ☕ ✗ licensed ♿ (wheelchairs, braille guide & disabled parking) toilets for disabled shop 🐾 (ex guide dogs) 🌿
Details not confirmed for 2002

🏛 WEYBRIDGE   Map 04 TQ06
BROOKLANDS MUSEUM
Brooklands Rd KT13 0QN (M25 junct 10/11, museum off B374)
☎ 01932 857381 📠 01932 855465
e-mail: brooklands@dial.pipex.com

Brooklands racing circuit was the birthplace of British motorsport and aviation. From 1907 to 1987 it was a world-renowned centre of engineering excellence. The museum features old banked track and the 1-in-4 Test Hill. Many of the original buildings have been restored including the Clubhouse, the Shell and BP Pagodas, and the Malcolm Campbell Sheds in the Motoring Village. Many motorcycles, cars and aircraft are on display. Ring for details of special events.
Times: Open Tue-Sun & BHs 10-5 (4pm in winter). **Fee:** £7 (ch u5 free, ch 6-16 £5, pen & students £6). Family ticket (2ad+3ch) £18.
Facilities: 🅿 ☕ ♿ toilets for disabled shop 🐾 (ex guide dogs) 🌿

🏛 WISLEY   Map 04 TQ05
RHS GARDEN WISLEY
GU23 6QB (on A3, close to M25 junct 10)
☎ 01483 224234 📠 01483 211750

Covering over 240 acres, Wisley is the flagship of the Royal Horticultural Society demonstrating the very best in gardening practices. The gardens have a wide variety of trees, shrubs and plants, many of which are unusual in Britain. Whatever the season the garden serves as a working encyclopedia for gardeners of all levels.
Times: Open all year, Mon-Fri 10-6 (4.30pm Nov-Feb), opens 9am Sat. Sun members only 9-6 (4.30 Nov-Feb). (Closed 25 Dec). Glasshouses close at 4.15 or sunset Mon-Fri. **Fee:** £5 (ch 6-16 £2). Affiliated society garden entry card £3.50. Party 10+ £4 each. Companion for wheelchair user or visually impaired visitor free.
Facilities: 🅿 ☕ ✗ licensed ♿ (free wheelchairs) toilets for disabled shop garden centre 🐾 (ex guide dogs) 🌿

East Sussex

Natural features of East Sussex include Beachy Head, the highest headland on the South Coast at 590 feet (180m), and the South Downs, the great chalky ridge that once connected England and the Continent, which stretches from Beachy Head into Hampshire.

The heathlands of Ashdown Forest are Winnie the Pooh country, including the bridge where Poohsticks was first played and a monument to A A Milne on Gill's Lap, the Enchanted Place of the much loved Pooh Bear stories.

The coastline is almost entirely built up, and major resorts are Brighton, Hastings and Eastbourne, with Newhaven as the cross channel port. Eastbourne enjoys the reputation of being one of Britain's sunniest seaside destinations, consistently at the top of the sunshine league tables. It is the most respectable of 19th-century resorts with a shingle beach and a fine Victorian pier. Hastings has a fading grandeur, but the Old Town is the most interesting quarter, which can be reached by the West Hill Cliff funicular railway.

Lewes, the county town, is set either side of the River Ouse, where it cuts through the South Downs and provides some dramatic vistas. Attractive streets and lanes known as 'twittens' are overlooked by the Norman castle.

There are castles in abundance in East Sussex: Hastings, Herstmonceux, Pevensey and Bodiam. The town of Battle, six miles (10km) from Hastings, is the site of the famous Battle of Hastings, where the Normans led by William I, defeated Wessex, led by Harold II, on 14 October 1066.

Top: Seven Sisters

EVENTS & FESTIVALS

May
4th-6th Hastings Traditional Jack-in-the-Green Morris Dance Festival
4th-26th Brighton International Festival
12th East Sussex Young Farmers Country Fayre, Laughton
tbc Glyndebourne Festival Opera, Glynde, Lewes
tbc MG Regency Run (London to Brighton run for MG cars)

June
2nd-3rd Battle Medieval Fair, High Street, Battle
9th London to Brighton Classic Car Run

July
28th Battle Abbey Classic Car Show & Country Fayre, Battle (provisional)
tbc Brighton Lions Carnival
tbc Hastings Beer & Music Festival, Dordrecht Way, Hastings

August
tbc Rye Medieval Festival

September
7th-22nd Rye Festival

October
12th-20th Hastings Week
12th Hastings Borough Bonfire Celebrations

November
3rd London to Brighton Veteran Car Run

⛬ ALFRISTON   Map 05 TQ50
ALFRISTON CLERGY HOUSE
The Tye BN26 5TL (4m NE of Seaford, E of B2108, next to church)
☎ 01323 870001   ▤ 01323 871318
e-mail: ksdxxx@smtp.ntrust.org.uk

Step back into the Middle Ages with a visit to this 14th-century thatched Wealden Hall House. Trace the history of this magnificent building – the first to be acquired by the National Trust in 1896 – and discover why the chalk floor is soaked in sour milk! Explore the colourful cottage garden, and savour the idyllic setting beside Alfriston's famous parish church, with stunning views across the meandering River Cuckmere.
Times: Open Apr-Oct Sat-Mon, daily (ex Tue & Fri), 10-5.
Fee: £2.60.(ch £1.30). Family ticket £6.50 **Facilities:** P (0.25 mile) (braille guide) shop ✾ (ex guide dogs) ♨ 🍴

DRUSILLAS PARK
BN26 5QS (off A27)
☎ 01323 874100   ▤ 01323 874101
e-mail: drusilla@drusilla.demon.co.uk

An award-winning small zoo in a stunning valley setting. Animals kept here include meerkats, bats, penguins, monkeys, reptiles and creepy-crawlies. Children are well catered for with keeper talks, animal encounters, extensive play areas and activities such as Panning for Gold and the Zoolympics trail.
Times: Open all year, daily 10-5 (winter 10-4). (Closed 24-26 Dec).
Fee: £7.99 (ch 3-12 £6.99, senior citizens & disabled £5.99). Ch under 3 free. Party 15+. (Subject to change) **Facilities:** P ♨ ✗ licensed & (rear train carriage & sensory trails) toilets for disabled shop ✾ (ex guide dogs) 🍴

⛬ BATTLE   Map 05 TQ71
BATTLE & DISTRICT HISTORICAL SOCIETY MUSEUM (OPPOSITE ABBEY GREEN CAR PARK)
Memorial Hall, High St TN33 0AQ
☎ 01424 775955
e-mail: ann@battlehill.freeserve.co.uk
Times: Open Apr-Sep, daily 10.30-4.30 (Sun 2-5). P (20yds) (stair lift & toilet due to be installed) shop ✾ (ex guide dogs) *Details not confirmed for 2002*

BUCKLEYS YESTERDAY'S WORLD
89-90 High St TN33 0AQ (A21 onto A2100 towards Battle. Opposite Battle Abbey)
☎ 01424 775378   ▤ 01424 775174
e-mail: info@yesterdaysworld.co.uk

Discover a bygone age as the sights and sounds of yesteryear are brought to life by many colourful characters in over 30 shop and room settings including a 1930s Grocer's and a Victorian kitchen. The exhibition contains many rarities from the 1850s and onwards, including some of Queen Victoria's personal effects and letters written by the present Queen.
Times: Open all year, daily 10-6 (last admission 5pm) (Oct to Mar times subject to change). Closed 25-26 Dec & 1 Jan. **Fee:** £4.50 (ch 4-15 £2.99, pen £3.99, disabled £2.20). Family ticket £13.99. Discount for parties of 15+. **Facilities:** P (100yds) (50p per day) ♨ & (limited access for wheelchairs) toilets for disabled shop 🍴

1066 BATTLE OF HASTINGS ABBEY & BATTLEFIELD
High St TN33 0AD (A21 onto A2100)
☎ 01424 773792

Built by William the Conqueror, to atone for the terrible slaughter of the Battle of Hastings in 1066, the Abbey's high altar stood on the spot where Harold fell, and is still marked by a memorial stone. The mile-long Battlefield Walk takes you round the full perimeter of the battlefield itself.
Times: Open all year, Apr-Sep, daily 10-6 (Oct 10-5); Nov-28 Mar, daily 10-4 . Closed 24-26 Dec & 1 Jan. **Fee:** £4.30 (ch 5-15 £2.20, ch u5 free, con £3.20). **Facilities:** P (charged) & shop ✾ (allowed in certain areas) ✿

⛬ BODIAM   Map 05 TQ72
BODIAM CASTLE
TN32 5UA (2m E of A21 Hurst Green)
☎ 01580 830436   ▤ 01580 830398
e-mail: kboxxx@smtp.ntrust.org.uk

With its tall round drum towers at each corner, Bodiam is something of a fairytale castle. It was built in 1386 by Sir Edward Dalnygrigge, for comfort and defence. The walls measure some 6ft 6in thick, and the great gatehouse was defended by gun loops and three portcullises.
Times: Open 16 Feb-Oct, daily 10-6 or dusk if earlier; Nov-15 Feb, Sat & Sun 10-4 or dusk. Last admission 1 hour before closing. **Fee:** £4 (ch £2). Family ticket £10. Car £1.50. **Facilities:** P (charged) ♨ & (Braille/large print guides, special parking on request) toilets for disabled shop ✾ (ex in grounds on a lead) ♨ 🍴

⛪ BRIGHTON
Map 04 TQ30

BOOTH MUSEUM OF NATURAL HISTORY
194 Dyke Rd BN1 5AA (from A27 Brighton by pass,
1.5m NW of town centre, opposite Dyke Rd Park)
☎ 01273 292777   ▤ 01273 292778
e-mail: boothmus@pavilion.co.uk

The museum was built in 1874 to house the bird
collection of Edward Thomas Booth (1840-1890). His
collection is still on display, but the museum has
expanded considerably since Booth's day and now
includes thousands of butterfly and insect specimens,
geology galleries with fossils, rocks and local dinosaur
bones and a magnificent collection of animal skeletons,
largely collected by F W Lucas (1842-1932), a Brighton
solicitor.
Times: Open all year, Mon-Sat (ex Thu) 10-5, Sun 2-5. (Closed Good
Fri, Xmas & 1 Jan). **Fee:** Free. **Facilities:** ℗ (road opposite) (two hour
limit) ♿ shop ✘ (ex guide dogs)

MUSEUM & ART GALLERY
Church St BN1 1UE (in town centre within the pavilion
estate)
☎ 01273 290900   ▤ 01273 292841

The museum is currently closed and undergoing major
restoration and will fully re-open in December 2001.
The new-look museum will feature state-of-the-art
visitor facilities and a series of innovatively redesigned
galleries that will house nationally important
collections of 20th-century art, design and fashion and
world art. Telephone for details.
Times: Open all year, Mon, Tue, Thu, Fri, & Sat 10-5. Sun 2-5. (Closed
Wed, Good Fri, 24, 25 & 26 Dec & 1 Jan). **Fee:** Free. **Facilities:** ℗ (5
mins walk) (Church St NCP & on Street) ▣ ♿ lift,tactile
exhibits,induction loops,ramps & automatic door toilets for disabled
shop ✘ (ex guide dogs)

PRESTON MANOR
Preston Drove BN1 6SD (off A23)
☎ 01273 290900 & 292770   ▤ 01273 292771

This charming Edwardian manor house is beautifully
furnished with notable collections of silver, furniture
and paintings and presents a unique opportunity to see
an Edwardian home both 'upstairs' and 'downstairs'.
The servants' quarters can also be seen, featuring
kitchen, butler's pantry and boot hall. The house is set
in beautiful gardens, which include a pet cemetery and
the 13th-century parish church of St Peter. The newly
restored walled garden enables disabled people to
explore the garden for the first time.
Times: Open all year, Tue-Sat 10-5, Sun 2-5, Mon 1-5 (BH Mons 10-5).
(Closed Good Fri & 25-26 Dec). **Fee:** £3.30 (ch 5-15 £2.05, pen,
students & UB40 £2.80). Family ticket £5.35-£8.65. Party 20+ £2.80
each. Joint ticket with Royal Pavilion £7.40. **Facilities:** ▣ ♿ (access to
ground floor with prior notice) shop ✘ (ex guide dogs)

ROYAL PAVILION
BN1 1EE (town centre at the Old Steine)
☎ 01273 290900   ▤ 01273 292871
e-mail: visitorservices@brighton-hove.gov.uk

Acclaimed as one of the most exotically beautiful
buildings in the British Isles, the Royal Pavilion was the
magnificent seaside residence of George IV. The
breathtaking Regency palace is decorated in Chinese
style, with a romanticised Indian exterior, and
surrounded by restored Regency gardens.
Times: Open all year, Jun-Sep, daily 10-6; Oct-May, daily 10-5. (Closed
25-26 Dec). **Fee:** £5.20 (ch £3.20, concessions £3.75) Family ticket
£8.40-£13.60. Joint ticket with Preston Manor £7.40 Groups 20+.
Facilities: ℗ (5 mins walk) (NCP & on street) ▣ ♿ (tours for the
blind by arrangement, wheelchairs) toilets for disabled shop ✘ (ex
guide dogs) 🍴

SEA LIFE CENTRE
Marine Pde BN2 1TB
☎ 01273 604234 & 604233 (rec info)
▤ 01273 681840
Times: Open all year, daily (ex 25 Dec), 10-5. Last admission 4. (Open
later on wknds in summer & school holidays) **Facilities:** ℗ (200 yds)
▣ ♿ toilets for disabled shop ✘ (ex guide dogs) *Details not
confirmed for 2002* 🍴

⛪ BURWASH
Map 05 TQ62

BATEMAN'S
TN19 7DS (0.5m SW off A265)
☎ 01435 882302   ▤ 01435 882811
e-mail: kbaxxx@smtp.ntrust.org.uk

Rudyard Kipling lived for over 34 years in this 17th-
century manor house and it remains much the same as
it was during his lifetime. His 1928 Rolls Royce Phantom
is on display, and the watermill at the bottom of the
garden grinds wheat into flour on Saturday afternoons.
Times: Open Apr-1 Nov, Sat-Wed 11-5.30, also open Good Fri, (last
admission 4.30pm). House closes at 5pm. **Fee:** £5 (ch £2.50). Family
ticket £12.50. Party 15+. **Facilities:** ▣ ▣ ✗ licensed ♿ (braille
guide/photo tour of rooms) toilets for disabled shop ✘ (ex
guide/hearing dogs) 🐾 🍴

⛪ EASTBOURNE
Map 05 TV69

"HOW WE LIVED THEN" MUSEUM OF SHOPS & SOCIAL HISTORY
20 Cornfield Ter BN21 4NS (just off seafront, between
town centre & theatres)
☎ 01323 737143

Over the last 40 years, Jan and Graham Upton have
collected over 100,000 items which are now displayed
on four floors of authentic old shops and room-settings,
transporting visitors back to their grandparents' era.
Other displays, such as seaside souvenirs, wartime
rationing and Royal mementoes, help to capture 100
years of social history.
Times: Open daily all year, 10-5.30 (last entry 5pm). Winter times
subject to change, telephone establishment. **Fee:** £3 (ch 5-15 £2,
under 5's free, pen £2.50). Party 10+. **Facilities:** ℗ (outside) ♿ (no
charge for disabled) shop

REDOUBT FORTRESS AND MUSEUM

Royal Pde BN22 7AQ
☎ 01323 410300   ▤ 01323 732240
Times: Open Etr-5 Nov, 9.30-5.30. **Facilities:** P (200yds) ☕ shop
Details not confirmed for 2002 ☜

WISH TOWER PUPPET MUSEUM

Martello Tower No 73, King Edward Pde BN21 4BU
(on seafront, W of pier)
☎ 01323 417776   ▤ 01323 644440 or 728319
e-mail: puppet.workshop@virgin.net

This museum hosts a unique display of puppets from all
over the world. From early shadow puppets of Asia,
through over 300 years of Punch and Judy in England to
television and film puppets of today. Puppet shows take
place during the summer.
Times: Open May-mid Jul & Sep, wknds 11-5; mid Jul-Aug, daily 11-5.
Fee: £1.80 (ch16 & pen £1.25, students £1.50) **Facilities:** P (100mtrs)
shop ⚹ ☜

⛪ FIRLE   Map 05 TQ40

FIRLE PLACE

BN8 6LP (off A27, Eastbourne to Brighton road)
☎ 01273 858335   & 858188   ▤ 01273 858188
Times: Open Jun-Sep, Sun, Wed & Thu; also Etr, Spring, May & Aug
BH Sun & Mon 2-4.30. Party 25+. **Facilities:** P ✗ licensed & toilets
for disabled shop ⚹ (ex in garden) *Details not confirmed for 2002*

⛪ GLYNDE   Map 05 TQ40

GLYNDE PLACE

Lewes BN8 6SX (off A27 between Lewes & Eastbourne)
☎ 01273 858224   ▤ 01273 858224

A lovely Elizabethan manor with 18th-century
additions, in a beautiful downland setting. It is still a
family home, lived in by descendants of the original
owner.
Times: Open Jun & Sep, Wed & Sun 2-5, Jul & Aug Wed, Thu & Sun.
Fee: £5 (ch £2.50). **Facilities:** P ☕ shop ⚹

⛪ HAILSHAM   Map 05 TQ50

MICHELHAM PRIORY

Upper Dicker BN27 3QS (off A22 & A27, 2m W of
Hailsham, 8m NW of Eastbourne, signposted from A27
& A22).
☎ 01323 844224   ▤ 01323 844030
e-mail: adminmich@sussexpast.co.uk

Set on a moated island surrounded by gardens,
Michelham Priory is one of the most beautiful historic
houses in Sussex. Founded in 1229 for Augustinian
canons, the Priory is approached through a 14th-
century gatehouse spanning the longest medieval moat
in the country. Most of the original priory was
demolished during the Dissolution, but the remains
were incorporated into a Tudor farm that became a
country house. Outside, the gardens are enhanced by a

working watermill, physic garden, smithy, rope
museum and the dramatic Elizabethan Great Barn.
Times: Open mid Mar-end Oct, Wed-Sun (daily in Aug & BH Mons).
Mar & Oct 10.30-4, Apr- Jul & Sep 10.30-5, Aug 10.30-5.30. **Fee:** £4.70
(ch 5-15 £2.30, pen & student £4). **Facilities:** P ☕ ✗ licensed &
(wheelchairs & braille guide available) shop ⚹ ☜

⛪ HALLAND   Map 05 TQ51

BENTLEY WILDFOWL & MOTOR MUSEUM

BN8 5AF (7m NE of Lewes, signposted)
☎ 01825 840573   ▤ 01825 841322
e-mail: barrysutherland@pavilion.co.uk
Times: Open 20 Mar-Oct, daily (5pm Jul & Aug), House
open from noon, 1 Apr-31 Oct. Nov, Feb & part of Mar, wknds only.
Estate closed Dec & Jan. House closed all winter. **Facilities:** P ☕ &
(wheelchairs available) toilets for disabled shop ⚹ (guide dogs ex in
bird reserve *Details not confirmed for 2002* ☜

⛪ HASTINGS   Map 05 TQ80

HASTINGS EMBROIDERY

White Rock Theatre, White Rock TN34 1JX (on A259,
opposite the pier)
☎ 01424 781010   ▤ 01424 781170
e-mail: whiterocktheatre@hastings.gov.uk
Times: Open Mon-Sun 11-4 (last entry 3.30). Closed during March &
subject to closure for selected events. **Facilities:** P (charged) ☕ ✗
& toilets for disabled shop ⚹ (ex guide dogs) *Details not confirmed
for 2002* ☜

OLD TOWN HALL MUSEUM OF LOCAL HISTORY

Old Town Hall, High St TN34 3EW
☎ 01424 781166   ▤ 01424 781165
e-mail: curator-breathemail.net
Times: Open Apr-Sep, daily 10-5. Oct-Mar, daily 11-4. **Facilities:** P
(150yds) (parking metres in operation) & (lift, evac chair, low-level
displays, audio tour) toilets for disabled shop ⚹ (ex guide dogs)
Details not confirmed for 2002

SMUGGLERS ADVENTURE

St Clements Caves, West Hill TN34 3HY
☎ 01424 422964   ▤ 01424 721483
e-mail: smugglers@tnet.co.uk
Times: Open all year daily, Etr-Sep 10-5.30; Oct-Etr 11-4.30. (Closed
25-26 Dec). **Facilities:** P (500yds) shop ⚹ *Details not confirmed for
2002* ☜

1066 STORY IN HASTINGS CASTLE

Castle Hill Rd, West Hill TN34 3RG
☎ 01424 781111   ▤ 01424 781186
Times: Open Mar-Sep 10-5 (5.30 school holidays). Oct-Feb 11-3.30
(Closed 24-26 Dec). **Facilities:** P (seafront) & shop ⚹ *Details not
confirmed for 2002*

🏛 HERSTMONCEUX   Map 05 TQ61
THE TRUGGERY
Coopers Croft BN27 1QL (from A22 at Hailsham, Boship roundabout, take A271 towards Bexhill for 4m)
☎ 01323 832314   📄 01323 832314
e-mail: sarah@truggery.fsnet.co.uk
Times: Open May-Sep 10-5. Closed all day Sun, Mon ex BHs & Sat pm. Oct-Apr opening times may vary. **Facilities:** 🅿 shop 🚼 *Details not confirmed for 2002* ♨

🏛 HOVE   Map 04 TQ20
BRITISH ENGINEERIUM-MUSEUM OF STEAM & MECHANICAL ANTIQUITIES
off Nevill Rd BN3 7QA
☎ 01273 559583   📄 01273 566403
e-mail: engineerium@mistral.co.uk
Times: Open all year, daily 10-4. In steam first Sun in month & Sun & Mon of BH's. Telephone for details of days closed prior to Xmas.
Facilities: 🅿 ♿ shop 🐕 (ex guide dogs) *Details not confirmed for 2002*

🏛 LEWES   Map 05 TQ41
ANNE OF CLEVES HOUSE MUSEUM
52 Southover High St BN7 1JA (S of town centre off A27/A26/A275)
☎ 01273 474610   📄 01273 486990
e-mail: anne@sussexpast.co.uk

Henry VIII gave this beautiful timber-framed house to Anne of Cleves, his fourth wife, as part of her divorce settlement. Today there are collections of early English furniture, Sussex pottery and stone from Lewes Priory, plus a local social history exhibition. The Wealden Iron Gallery tells the story of the industrial past of Sussex and contains a large collection of iron artefacts.
Times: Open early Jan-mid Feb, Tue, Thu & Sat, 10-5; mid Feb-early Nov daily 10-5 (Sun 12-5); early Nov-mid Dec, Tue & Sat 10-5 (Sun 12-5). **Fee:** £2.60 (ch 5-15 £1.30, pen & student £2.40). Family ticket £6.80 (2ad+2ch) £5.20 (1ad+4ch). **Facilities:** 🅿 (25yds) (on street-2hr restriction) ♿ shop 🐕 (ex guide dogs) ♨

LEWES CASTLE & BARBICAN HOUSE MUSEUM
169 High St BN7 1YE (N of High St off A27/A26/A275)
☎ 01273 486260   📄 01273 486990
e-mail: castle@sussexpast.co.uk

High above the medieval streets stands Lewes Castle, begun soon after the Norman Conquest by William de Warenne as his stronghold in Sussex and added to over the next 300 years, culminating in the magnificent Barbican. Thomas Read Kemp and his family owned and updated the ruins during Georgian times. Barbican House is next to the castle, and now houses a museum covering the area from pre-history to the late medieval period.
Times: Open daily, Mon-Sat 10-5.30, Sun & BH 11-5.30. Last admission 30 mins before closing. **Fee:** £4 (ch £2, pen/student £3.50). Family ticket £10.90/£8. **Facilities:** 🅿 (on street parking) (touch screen) shop 🐕 (ex castle & guide dogs) ♨

🏛 NEWHAVEN   Map 05 TQ40
PARADISE FAMILY LEISURE PARK
Avis Rd BN9 0DH (signposted off A26 & A259)
☎ 01273 512123   📄 01273 616005
e-mail: enquiries@paradisepark.co.uk

A perfect day out for plant lovers whatever the season. Discover the unusual garden designs with waterfalls, fountains and lakes, including the Caribbean garden and the tranquil Oriental garden. The Conservatory Gardens complex contains a large variety of the world's flora divided into several zones. There's also a Sussex history trail and Planet Earth with moving dinosaurs and interactive displays, plus rides and amusements for children.
Times: Open all year, daily 9-6 (Closed 25-26 Dec) **Fee:** £4.99 (ch £3.99). Family ticket £16.99 (2ad+2ch). **Facilities:** 🅿 ♨ ✕ licensed ♿ (all areas level or ramped) toilets for disabled shop garden centre 🐕 (ex guide dogs) ♨

🏛 NORTHIAM   Map 05 TQ82
GREAT DIXTER
TN31 6PH (off A28, signposted)
☎ 01797 252878   📄 01797 252879
e-mail: greatdixter@compuserve.com
Times: Open Apr-29 Oct, Tue-Sun & BH Mon, 2-5.30(last admission 5); Gardens only open from 11am on Sun & Mon BH wknds only.
Facilities: 🅿 ♿ (one wheelchair available free of charge) toilets for disabled shop garden centre 🐕 (ex guide dogs) *Details not confirmed for 2002* ♨

🏛 PEVENSEY   Map 05 TQ60
PEVENSEY CASTLE
BN24 5LE (off A259)
☎ 01323 762604

Witness to 17 centuries of conflict, from its origins as a Roman fortress to its use as a coastal base during the Second World War, this powerful castle has never been taken by force.
Times: Open all year, Apr-Sep, daily 10-6 (Oct 10-5); Nov-Mar, Wed-Sun 10-4. Closed 24-26Dec & 1Jan. **Fee:** £2.50 (ch 5-15 £1.30, ch u5 free, con £1.90). **Facilities:** 🅿 (charged) ♨ ♿ 🐕 (in certain areas) ♿

🏛 RYE   Map 05 TQ92
LAMB HOUSE
West St TN31 7ES (facing W end of Church)
☎ 01892 890651   📄 01892 890110

This 18th-century house was the home of novelist Henry James from 1898 until his death in 1916, and was later occupied by the writer, E F Benson. Some of James' personal posessions can be seen. There is also a charming walled garden.
Times: Open Apr-28 Oct; Wed & Sat 2-6, (last admission 5.30pm).
Fee: Telephone for details. **Facilities:** 🅿 (200m) 🐕 🚼 🌿

RYE CASTLE MUSEUM

3 East St TN31 7JY (on A259 in town centre)
☎ 01797 226728

Part of the museum is housed in a stone tower built as a fortification in 1249. The museum's collection of ironwork, medieval pots and smuggling items are on display here, while the East Street site contains the rest of the collection, including pottery made in Rye, military uniforms, fashions, an eighteenth-century fire engine, toys, cinque port regalia and information on Rye's history.
Times: Open all year Nov-Mar wknds only 10.30-3; Apr-Oct Thu-Mon 10.30-5. (last entry 4.30). **Fee:** Entrance to both sites: £2.90 (ch 7-16 £1.50, concessions £2). Family ticket £5.90. Single entry only: £1.90 (ch 7-16) £1, concessions £1.50). Family ticket £4.50. Party 8+
Ⓟ (30yds) (street limited to 1hr) 丙 (only East Street accessible) toilets for disabled shop ⊁ (ex guide dogs)

🏛 SHEFFIELD PARK   Map 05 TQ42

SHEFFIELD PARK GARDEN

TN22 3QX (5m E of Haywards Heath off A275)
☎ 01825 790231   🖹 01825 791264
e-mail: kshxxx@smtp.ntrust.org.uk
Times: Open Jan-Feb Sat-Sun 10.30-4; Mar-Oct Tue-Sun (open BH Mons) 10.30-6; Nov-Dec Tue-Sun 10.30-4 (Last admission 1 hour before closing). **Facilities:** Ⓟ ⬛ 丙 (powered self drive cars & wheelchairs available) toilets for disabled shop ⊁ (ex guide/hearing dogs) 🐾 *Details not confirmed for 2002* 🍽

🏛 SHEFFIELD PARK STATION   Map 05 TQ42

BLUEBELL RAILWAY

Sheffield Park Station TN22 3QL (4.5m E of Haywards Heath, off A275)
☎ 01825 723777, 722370 & 722008
🖹 01825 724084

A volunteer-run heritage steam railway with nine miles of track running through pretty Sussex countryside. Please note that there is no parking at Kingscote Station. If you wish to board the train here, catch the bus (service 473) which connects Kingscote and East Grinstead.
Times: Open all year, Sat & Sun, daily May-Sep & during school holidays. Santa Specials run Dec. For timetable and information regarding trains contact above. **Fee:** 3rd class return fare £8 (ch £4). Family ticket £21.50. Admission to Sheffield Park Station only £1.60 (ch 80p). Other tickets available on request. **Facilities:** Ⓟ ⬛ ⊁ licensed 丙 (contact for details) toilets for disabled shop 🍽

West Sussex

West Sussex is a county of weald and downland, once dominated by the forest that stretched through The Weald from Kent into Hampshire. The oaks of the forest were used to smelt the local iron ore, and though the forest is now somewhat diminished, the country remains green and lush.

The county town of Chichester, the only city in Sussex, is a gem in its own right. Building on the cathedral began in 1076, and has been added to since then. St Richard was Bishop here in the 13th century, and his shrine was an important pilgrimage centre until its destruction by Henry VIII. South of the city is the headland of Selsey. Selsey was originally an island and is still almost encircled by water, it offers a number of different beaches, including the Witterings and Pagham Harbour which is notable for its birdlife. Pre-Norman Selsey was lost to the sea long ago.

Further east, the county's main seaside resorts are Bognor Regis, Littlehampton and Worthing. Bognor Regis was one of the first bathing resorts in the late 18th century, and Queen Victoria was particularly fond of the place. Bognor gained the addition 'Regis' after George V convalesced there in 1929.

Outside Worthing, at Highdown Hill, there is a Bronze Age settlement beneath an Iron Age hill fort, where the Saxons later buried their dead.

The main towns are Horsham, Haywards Heath, and Crawley. The third of these is the only new town south of London, and is close to Gatwick Airport. Despite its new town status it has several buildings dating back to the 15th century. Arundel is a particularly handsome town, at a crossing point on the River Arun, dominated by the sprawling, much restored castle and the Roman Catholic Cathedral.

Top: Mysterious yew trees in Kingsley Vale

EVENTS & FESTIVALS

March
29th British & World Marbles Championships, Tinsley Green, Crawley

May
29th-30th Corpus Christi Carpet of Flowers & Floral Festival, Arundel

June
3rd Spring Carnival, Crawley
6th-8th Flower Festival, Chichester Cathedral
6th-8th South of England Agricultural Show, Ardingly, Haywards Heath
15th-16th Parham Steam Rally, Pulborough
28th-30th Crawley Folk Festival, Hawth Avenue, Crawley

July
11th Bognor Birdman, Bognor Regis (provisional)
27th-28th Littlehampton Regatta, Littlehampton
tbc Chichester Festivities, various venues
tbc Petworth Festival

August
tbc Arundel Festival

September
14th Findon Great Sheep Fair, Findon (provisional)

October
5th-6th South of England Autumn Show, Haywards Heath

🏛 ARDINGLY   Map 05 TQ32
WAKEHURST PLACE & MILLENNIUM SEED BANK
RH17 6TN (1.5m NW, on B2028)
☎ 01444 894066 🖹 01444 894069
e-mail: wakehurst@kew.org

Woodland and lakes linked by a pretty watercourse make this large garden a beautiful place to walk, and it also has an amazing variety of interesting trees and shrubs, a winter garden, and a rock walk. It is administered and maintained by the Royal Botanic Gardens at Kew. **Times:** Open all year, Nov-Jan 10-4; Feb & Oct 10-5; Mar 10-6; Apr-Sep 10-7. (Closed 25 Dec & 1 Jan). Last admission 30 mins before closing. Mansion Restaurant, shop & exhibition closes one hour before garden & car park. **Fee:** £6.50 (ch under 16, free) **Facilities:** 🅿 ♨ ✕ licensed ♿ (wheelchair available) toilets for disabled shop garden centre ✕ (ex guide dogs) ⬛

🏛 ARUNDEL   Map 04 TQ00
ARUNDEL CASTLE
BN18 9AB (on A27 between Chichester & Worthing)
☎ 01903 882173 🖹 01903 884581
e-mail: arundelcastle@compuserve.com
Times: Open Apr-last Fri in Oct, Sun-Fri 12-5. Last admission 4pm (Closed Sat & Good Fri). **Facilities:** 🅿 ♨ ♿ toilets for disabled shop ✕ (ex guide dogs) *Details not confirmed for 2002* ⬛

WWT ARUNDEL
Mill Rd BN18 9PB (signposted from A27 & A29)
☎ 01903 883355 🖹 01903 884834
e-mail: arundel@wwt.org.uk

More than a thousand ducks, geese and swans from all over the world can be found here, many of which are so friendly that they will even feed from your hand. The wild reserve attracts a variety of birds and includes a reedbed habitat considered so vital to the wetland wildlife it shelters that it has been designated a Site of Special Scientific Interest. Visitors can walk right through this reedbed on a specially designed boardwalk. There is a packed programme of events and activities throughout the year. **Times:** Open all year, daily. Summer 9.30-5; Winter 9.30-4.30. Last admission Summer 5pm; Winter 4pm. (Closed 25 Dec). **Fee:** £5.25 (ch £3.25, pen £4.25). **Facilities:** 🅿 ✕ licensed ♿ (level paths, free wheelchair loan) toilets for disabled shop ✕ (ex guide dogs) ⬛

🏛 ASHINGTON   Map 04 TQ11
HOLLY GATE CACTUS GARDEN
Billingshurst Rd RH20 3BB (off A24, towards Ashington then B2133 towards Billingshurst for 0.5m)
☎ 01903 892930
e-mail: hollygate@tmh.globalnet.co.uk

A mecca for the cactus enthusiast, with more than 30,000 succulent and cactus plants, including many rare types. They come from both arid and tropical parts

of the world, and are housed in over 10,000 sq ft of greenhouses.
Times: Open all year, daily 9-5. (Closed 25-26 Dec). **Fee:** £2 (ch & pen £1.50). Family ticket £6. Party 20+. **Facilities:** 🅿 ♿ shop garden centre ✕ (ex guide dogs)

🏛 BIGNOR   Map 04 SU91
BIGNOR ROMAN VILLA & MUSEUM
RH20 1PH (between A29 & A285)
☎ 01798 869259 🖹 01798 869259
e-mail: bignorromanvilla@care4free.net

Rediscovered in 1811, this Roman house was built on a grand scale. It is one of the largest known, and has spectacular mosaics. The heating system can also be seen, and various finds from excavations are on show. The longest mosaic in Britain (82ft) is on display here in its original position. **Times:** Mar-Apr Tue-Sun & BH 10-5, May 10-5 daily, Jun-Sep 10-6 daily, Oct 10-5 daily **Fee:** £3.50 (ch 5-15 £1.50, pen £2.50). Party 10+. Guided tours by arrangement. **Facilities:** 🅿 ♨ ♿ Most areas accessible shop ✕ (ex guide dogs) ⬛

🏛 BRAMBER   Map 04 TQ11
BRAMBER CASTLE
BN4 3FB (on W side of village off A283)
Times: Open any reasonable time. **Facilities:** 🅿 ❦ *Details not confirmed for 2002*

🏛 CHICHESTER   Map 04 SU80
CHICHESTER CATHEDRAL
West St PO19 1PX (in city centre)
☎ 01243 782595 🖹 01243 536190
e-mail: vo@chicath.freeserve.co.uk

The beauty of the 900-year-old cathedral, site of the shrine of St Richard, is enhanced by many art treasures, ancient and modern. **Times:** Open Etr-mid Sep daily 7.30-7; mid Sep-Etr 7.30-5. Visiting restricted during services and concerts. **Fee:** Free. **Facilities:** 🅿 (within city walls) ♨ ✕ ♿ (touch & hearing centre, loop system) toilets for disabled shop ✕ (ex guide dogs)

MECHANICAL MUSIC & DOLL COLLECTION
Church Rd, Portfield PO19 4HN (1m E, signposted off A27)
☎ 01243 372646 🖹 01243 370299

A unique opportunity to see and hear barrel organs, polyphons, musical boxes, fair organs etc - all fully restored and playing for your pleasure. A magical musical tour to fascinate and entertain all ages. The doll collection contains fine examples of Victorian china and wax dolls, and felt and velvet dolls of the 1920s. **Times:** Open Jun-Sep, Wed 1-4; Group bookings anytime in the year by prior arrangment. **Fee:** £2.50 (ch £1.25). **Facilities:** 🅿 ♿ shop ✕ (ex guide dogs)

PALLANT HOUSE GALLERY
9 North Pallant PO19 1TJ (in city centre off East Street)
☎ 01243 774557   📄 01243 536038
e-mail: pallant@pallant.co.uk

The gallery is housed in a finely furnished, restored Queen Anne townhouse. Important works of Modern British Art are held within the permanent collections, including pieces by (among others): Auerbach, Blake, Bomberg, Caulfield, Freud, Hamilton, Hitchens, Lege, Moore, Nash, Nicholson, Piper, Richards, Severini, Sickert and Sutherland. Telephone for details of temporary exhibitions.
Times: Open all year, Tue-Sat 10-5, Sun & BHs 12.30-5. **Fee:** £4 (ch & W Sussex students free, other students & unemployed £2.50, concessions £3). **Facilities:** P (100 yds) 🍽 ዿ shop ✸ (ex guide dogs)

🏛 EAST GRINSTEAD   Map 05 TQ33
STANDEN
RH19 4NE (2m S of East Grinstead, signposted from B2110)
☎ 01342 323029   📄 01342 316424
e-mail: sstpro@smtp.ntrust.org.uk

Standen is a showpiece of the 19th-century Arts and Crafts movement. It was designed by Philip Webb for the Beale family, and was always meant to be decorated with William Morris wallpapers and fabrics. The interior has been carefully preserved. Webb also designed some of the furniture and details. There is a beautiful hillside garden. For events please contact the property.
Times: House open Apr-Nov, Wed-Sun & BH 12.30-4.30. Garden open same dates as house 11-6 & Nov-mid Dec, Fri-Sun 11-3. **Fee:** House & garden £5.50. Garden only £3. Children half price. Family ticket £13.75. Joint ticket which includes same day entry to Nymans garden £9, available Wed-Fri. **Facilities:** P ✕ licensed ዿ (braille guide & touch list) shop ✸ (ex guide dogs & on wood walk) 🐾 🍽

🏛 FISHBOURNE   Map 04 SU80
FISHBOURNE ROMAN PALACE
Salthill Rd PO19 3QR (Turn off A27 onto A259 into Fishbourne. Turn right into Salthill Rd & right into Roman Way)
☎ 01243 785859   📄 01243 539266
e-mail: adminfish@sussexpast.co.uk

This is the largest known Roman residence in Britain. It was occupied from the 1st to the 3rd centuries AD, and has mosaic floors and painted walls; 25 of these mosaic floors can still be seen in varying states of completeness, including others rescued from elsewhere in the area. Outside, part of the garden has been replanted to its original 1st-century plan. The museum displays a collection of finds from the excavations and tells the story of the site's discovery.
Times: Open all year, daily early Feb-mid Dec. Feb, Nov-Dec 10-4; Mar-Jul & Sep-Oct 10-5; Aug 10-6. Winter wknds 10-4. **Fee:** £4.50 (ch £2.40, pen & students £3.90, registered disabled £3.70). Family ticket £11.70 (2ad+2ch). Group rates available. **Facilities:** P 🍽 ዿ (self guiding tapes & tactile objects for the blind) toilets for disabled shop garden centre ✸ (ex guide dogs) 🍽

🏛 FONTWELL   Map 04 SU90
DENMANS GARDEN
Denmans Ln BN18 0SU (5m E of Chichester off A27 W between Chichester and Arundel, adjacent to Fontwell racecourse)
☎ 01243 542808   📄 01243 544064

A unique 20th-century garden artistically planted with an emphasis on colour, shape and texture. Plants within the garden are allowed to self-seed and ramble. The garden makes much use of gravel throughout, including a gravel 'stream'. A remarkable collection of plants, including glass areas for tender plants, a walled garden and plenty of quiet sitting areas.
Times: Open Mar-Oct daily 9-5. **Fee:** £2.95 (ch £1.75, ch under 4 free, pen £2.65). Party 15+ £2.50 each. **Facilities:** P 🍽 ዿ shop garden centre ✸ (ex guide dogs) 🍽

🏛 GOODWOOD   Map 04 SU81
GOODWOOD HOUSE
PO18 0PX (3m NE of Chichester)
☎ 01243 755000   📄 01243 755005
e-mail: curator@goodwood.co.uk

Ancestral home of the Dukes of Richmond for 300 years. Following refurbishment the State Apartments have taken on new life, including the restored tapestry drawing room. Goodwood was the country home of the scandalous and glamorous Lennox sisters, immortalised in the BBC TV production of *Aristocrats*. Unrivalled as an English ancestral collection, the paintings include works by Van Dyck, Reynolds, Stubbs and Canaletto.
Times: Open 7 May-1 Oct, Sun & Mon; 5 Aug-7 Sep, Sun-Thu 1-5. (Closed 13 & 27 May; 2, 8 & 9 Jul). **Fee:** £6.50 (ch & disabled £3, pen £6). Groups 20+ £5.50 each. **Facilities:** P 🍽 ዿ (ramp at front of house, disabled parking area) toilets for disabled shop ✸ 🍽

🏛 HANDCROSS   Map 04 TQ22
NYMANS GARDEN
RH17 6EB (on B2114)
☎ 01444 400321 & 400777   📄 01444 400253
Times: Open Garden: Mar-29 Oct, daily Wed, Thu & wknds, (also open BH Mon) 11-6 or sunset if earlier. Nov-Mar, wknds, 11-4, restricted according to ground conditions. Closed 25-26 & 30-31 Dec. Phone for more information. House open 29 Mar-29 Oct 12-4.
Facilities: P 🍽 ዿ (wheelchair route, wheelchair available, braille guide) toilets for disabled shop ✸ (ex guide dogs & hearing dogs) 🐾
Details not confirmed for 2002

⛫ HAYWARDS HEATH Map 05 TQ32
Borde Hill Garden
Balcombe Rd RH16 1XP (1.5m N of Hayward Heath on Balcombe Road, 3m from A23)
☎ 01444 450326 📠 01444 440427
e-mail: info@bordehill.co.uk

Borde Hill, set in 200 acres of spectacular Sussex parkland, boasts a fine romantic garden dating from the 1890s, incorporating plants from around the globe. Also on view are several garden 'rooms' and a rose garden designed by RHS Gold Medallist Robin Williams in 1996, among other gardens. Other attractions include fishing and an adventure playground.
Times: Open all year, 10-6 **Fee:** £5.50 (ch 3-15 £3) family £15, Party 20+ **Facilities:** 🅿 🍽 ✕ licensed ♿ (wheelchairs available, audio/braille guides) toilets for disabled shop garden centre ⚘ (ex on leads) ◗

⛫ LOWER BEEDING Map 04 TQ22
Leonardslee Gardens
RH13 6PP (4m SW from Handcross, at junct of B2110 & A281)
☎ 01403 891212 📠 01403 891305
Times: Open Apr-Oct, daily 9.30-6 (May 9.30-8). **Facilities:** 🅿 🍽 ✕ licensed (No wheelchair access. Other disablties are catered for) shop garden centre ⚘ (inc guide dogs) *Details not confirmed for 2002*

⛫ PETWORTH Map 04 SU92
Petworth House & Park
GU28 0AE (in town centre, A272/283)
☎ 01798 342207 & 343929 📠 01798 342963
Times: Open House & Servants Quarters: Apr-1 Nov, Sat-Wed (open Good Fri & every Fri in Jul & Aug). House 1-5.30, last admission 4.30. Park open daily 8-sunset (ex 25-27 Jun). Extra rooms shown on weekdays but not BH. Pleasure Ground & Car Park: 18-19 & 25-26 Mar, 12-4. Apr-1 Nov, 12-6 (11am in Jul, Aug & BH's). **Facilities:** 🅿 (charged) 🍽 ✕ licensed ♿ (wheelchairs available, braille guide) toilets for disabled shop ⚘ (ex guide dogs) 🐾 *Details not confirmed for 2002*

⛫ PULBOROUGH Map 04 TQ01
Parham House & Gardens
Parham Park RH20 4HS (3m SE off A283, between Pulborough & Storrington)
☎ 01903 744888 (info line) 742021
📠 01903 746557
e-mail: parham@dial.pipex.com
Times: Open 4 Apr-Oct, Wed, Thu, Sun & BH. Gardens 12-6; House 2-6 (last entry 5). Guided tours on Wed & Thu mornings and Tue & Fri afternoons by special arrangement. **Facilities:** 🅿 🍽 ♿ (wheelchairs available by arrangement/tape tour) shop garden centre (ex guide dogs & in grounds) *Details not confirmed for 2002* ◗

RSPB Pulborough Brooks Nature Reserve
Uppertons Barn Visitor Centre, Wiggonholt RH20 2EL (signposted on A283, 2m SE of Pulborough & 2m NW of Storrington)
☎ 01798 875851 📠 01798 873816
e-mail: pulborough.brooks@rspb.org.uk

Set in the scenic Arun Valley and easily reached via the visitor centre at Wiggonholt, this is an excellent reserve for year-round family visits. A nature trail winds through hedgerow-lined lanes to viewing hides overlooking water-meadows. Breeding summer birds include nightingales and warblers, ducks and wading birds, and nightjars and hobbies on nearby heathland. Unusual wading birds and hedgerow birds regularly pass through on spring and autumn migration.
Times: Open daily, Reserve: 9-9, (or sunset if earlier). Visitor centre: 10-5. Reserve closed 25 Dec, Visitor Centre closed 25-26 Dec.
Fee: £3.50 (ch 5-16 £1), concessions £2.50) Family £7 (2ad+4ch).
Facilities: 🅿 🍽 ♿ (ramps at some hides/batricar bookable/easy gradient trail) toilets for disabled shop ⚘ (ex guide dogs) ◗

⛫ SINGLETON Map 04 SU81
Weald & Downland Open Air Museum
PO18 0EU (6m N of Chichester on A286)
☎ 01243 811348 📠 01243 811475
e-mail: wealddown@mistral.co.uk

WEALD & DOWNLAND OPEN AIR MUSEUM

Times: Open all year, Mar-Oct, daily 10.30-6 (last admission 5); Nov-Feb, Wed, Sat & Sun 10.30-4, also 26 Dec-1 Jan daily & Feb half term, 10.30-4. **Facilities:** 🅿 🍽 ♿ toilets for disabled shop (ex on leads) *Details not confirmed for 2002* ◗

🏛 SOUTH HARTING   Map 04 SU71
UPPARK
GU31 5QR (1.5m S on B2146)
☎ 01730 825415 825857 🖹 01730 825873
e-mail: sopgen@smtp.ntrust.org.uk
Times: Open 2 Apr-Oct, Sun-Thu. House 1-5. Car park, woodland walk, garden & Exhibition 11.30-5.30. Last admission to house 4pm. Timed tickets will be in operation on BH Sun & Mon & Sun in Jul & Aug. **Facilities:** 🅿 ☕ ㅎ (ramps, lift, stair to exhibition) toilets for disabled shop ✸ (ex woodland walk & car park) 🐾 *Details not confirmed for 2002*

🏛 TANGMERE   Map 04 SU90
TANGMERE MILITARY AVIATION MUSEUM TRUST
PO20 6ES (off A27, 3m E of Chichester)
☎ 01243 775223 🖹 01243 789490
e-mail: admin@tangmere-museum.org.uk

Based at an airfield which played an important role during the World Wars, this museum spans 80 years of military aviation. There are photographs, documents, aircraft and aircraft parts on display along with a Hurricane replica, Spitfire replica and cockpit simulator. A hangar houses a Supermarine Swift and the record-breaking aircraft Meteor and Hunter.
Times: Open Mar-Oct, daily 10-5.30; Feb & Nov, daily 10-4.30. **Fee:** £4 (ch £1.50 & pen £3) Family £9.50 (2ad+2ch). **Facilities:** 🅿 ☕ ㅎ (wheelchairs available) toilets for disabled shop ✸ (ex guide dogs)

🏛 WEST DEAN   Map 04 SU81
WEST DEAN GARDENS
Estate Office PO18 0QZ (on A286, 6m N of Chichester)
☎ 01243 818210 & 811301 🖹 01243 811342
e-mail: gardens@westdean.org.uk

Award winning historic garden of 35 acres in a tranquil downland setting. Noted for its 300ft long Harold Peto pergola, mixed and herbaceous borders, rustic summerhouses and specimen trees. Walled kitchen garden with magnificent collection of 16 Victorian glasshouses and frames. The visitors' centre provides a high level of facilities with a beautiful prospect of the River Lavant and West Dean Park.
Times: Open Mar, Apr & Oct, daily 11-5; May-Sep 10.30-5. Last ticket 4.30pm. **Fee:** £4.50 (ch £2, pen £4). Party+ £4. Family £11.
Facilities: 🅿 ✕ licensed ㅎ (reserved parking, 2 wheelchairs available) toilets for disabled shop ✸ (ex guide dogs) 🚋

Tyne & Wear

Tyne & Wear is a metropolitan county, created by local government reorganisation in 1974. It includes the towns of Newcastle-upon-Tyne, Gateshead, South Shields and Sunderland. It is cut through by the two rivers the Tyne and the Wear, and includes a section of Hadrian's Wall.

Top: Tyne Road Bridge

The area grew prosperous on coal and shipbuilding, and buildings of Victorian grandeur reflect its heyday. George Stephenson established an ironworks here in 1826, and the first engine on the Stockton and Darlington railway was made in Newcastle. Industrial decline has hit hard, but the Geordie spirit survives and brings immense vitality to the place.

Newcastle's 'new castle' is believed to date from the 11th century, though the present keep dates from the 12th. Other ancient buildings include the 14th-century cathedral, and the 17th-century Guildhall. Contemporary constructions include the Metro, which links Newcastle to Gateshead (along with several bridges), and the Metro Centre in Gateshead, Britain's largest shopping centre. The most famous of the bridges are High Level Bridge, a road and rail bridge, built by Robert Stephenson in 1849, and the Tyne Bridge dating from 1929.

Jarrow, five miles east of Newcastle, is remembered for the Jarrow Crusade of 1936, when 200 men marched to London to bring attention to the plight of unemployed shipbuilders. The town was also the home of monk-scholar, the Venerable Bede, whose 8th-century work, *Historia Ecclesiastica Gentis Anglorum*, was the first important history written about the English. He was buried at Jarrow, and his bones remained there until the 11th century when they were moved to Durham. Other notable citizens include footballer Paul "Gazza" Gascoine, singer/songwriter Sting, and writer Vera Brittan.

JARROW   Map 12 NZ36
BEDES WORLD & ST PAUL'S CHURCH
Church Bank NE32 3DY (off A185 near south end of Tyne tunnel)
☎ 0191 489 2106 📠 0191 428 2361
e-mail: visitor.info@bedesworld.co.uk

The Venerable Bede lived over 1300 years ago and was one of early Britain's greatest scholars, author of the "Historia Ecclesiastica Gentis Anglorum" – the definitive history of the early medieval period. As well as exhibits detailing Bede's monastic life and work, the museum re-creates an Anglo-Saxon farm and incorporates the ruins of the medieval monastery. **Times:** Open all year, Apr-Oct, Mon-Sat 10-5.30, Sun noon-5.30; Nov-Mar, Mon-Sat 10-4.30 & Sun 12-4.30; Xmas-New Year opening times vary. Church open Mon-Sat 10-4 & 2.30-4, unless service being held. **Fee:** £4.50 (ch & concessions £2.50). Family ticket £9. UB40 family ticket £6. **Facilities:** 🅿 ♨ ♿ (electric wheelchair on request) toilets for disabled shop 🐾 (ex guide dogs) ♨

NEWCASTLE UPON TYNE   Map 12 NZ26
HANCOCK MUSEUM
Barras Bridge NE2 4PT (Follow exit signs for city centre A167 off the A1(M))
☎ 0191 222 7418 📠 0191 222 6753
e-mail: hancock.museum@ncl.ac.uk

The museum houses geological exhibits and John Hancock's magnificent collection of birds. Land of the Pharaohs explores life and death in Ancient Eygpt. The Earth galleries explore the cosmic and geological processes that have shaped the earth, and investigate the history of life on our planet. **Times:** Open all year, Mon-Sat, 10-5, Sun 2-5. Closed 25 & 26 Dec & 1 Jan. **Fee:** £2.25 (concessions £1.50). Family ticket (2 adults & 2 ch) £6.50. Prices vary with special exhibitions, call 0191 222 7418 for details. **Facilities:** 🅿 ♨ ♿ (stair lift,audio/braille guide, staff trained in sign lang) toilets for disabled shop 🐾 (ex guide dogs) ♨

LIFE INTERACTIVE WORLD
Times Square NE1 4EP (next to Newcastle Central station)
☎ 0191 243 8223 & 0191 243 8210
e-mail: bookings@lifeinteractiveworld.co.uk

This colourful attraction has chosen one of the biggest subjects possible for its theme: life itself. With three spectacular shows that explore the 'Secret of Life', the workings of the brain, and how your body reacts to motion, along with exhibits dealing with cells, the senses, pregnancy, emotion and the beginnings of life, this is an educational as well as entertaining day out. **Times:** Open daily Mon-Sat 10-6, Sun 11-6 . Last entry 4.30pm. Closed 25 Dec & 1 Jan. **Fee:** £6.95 (ch £4.50, concessions £5.50). Family ticket £19.95. **Facilities:** 🅿 (charged) ♨ ♿ (ramps wheelchairs induction loops) toilets for disabled shop 🐾 (ex guide dogs) ♨

MUSEUM OF ANTIQUITIES
The University NE1 7RU (on campus of Newcastle University)
☎ 0191 222 7849 📠 0191 222 8561
e-mail: m.o.antiquities@ncl.ac.uk

Artefacts from north east England from prehistoric times to AD 1600 are on display here. The principal museum for Hadrian's Wall, this collection includes models of the wall, life-size Roman soldiers and a recently refurbished reconstruction of the Temple of Mithras. **Times:** Open all year, daily (ex Sun), 10-5 (Closed Good Fri, 24-26 Dec & 1 Jan). **Fee:** Free. **Facilities:** 🅿 (400yds) ♿ (Large print guide) shop 🐾 (ex guide dogs) ♨

ROWLANDS GILL   Map 12 NZ15
GIBSIDE
NE16 6BG (Turn off A1 western bypass follow brown tourist signs from Gibside & Gibside Chapel, 3m W of Metro Centre & 6m SW of Gateshead, on B6314)
☎ 01207 542255
e-mail: tony.walton@ntrust.org.uk

The important early 18th-century landscaped park contains a chapel - an outstanding example of Palladian architecture, built to a design by James Paine as the mausoleum for members of the Bowes family. It stands at one end of the Great Walk of Turkey oaks, looking towards the column of British Liberty. **Times:** Open: Grounds all year (ex Mon), 10-4.30. Open BH Mon (Mar-Oct 10-5, Nov-Feb 10-3.30). Chapel: Apr-Oct as grounds 11-5, otherwise by prior arrangment. **Fee:** £3 (ch £1.50). Family ticket £8 (single parent family £5). **Facilities:** 🅿 ♨ ♿ (braille guide, wheelchair) shop 🐾 ♨

SOUTH SHIELDS   Map 12 NZ36
ARBEIA ROMAN FORT & MUSEUM
Baring St NE33 2BB (5 mins walk from town centre)
☎ 0191 456 1369 454 4093
📠 0191 427 6862

In South Shields town are the extensive remains of Arbeia, a 2nd-century Roman fort. It was the supply base for the Roman army's campaign against Scotland. On the site of the west gate is a full-scale simulation of a Roman gateway with interior scenes of life at the fort. Archaeological excavations are in progress throughout the summer. **Times:** Open all year, Apr-Sep, Mon-Sat 10-5.30, Sun 1-5; Oct-Mar, Mon-Sat 10-4. Closed 25-26 Dec, 1 Jan & Good Friday. **Fee:** Fort & Museum free of charge ex for 'Timequest'Archaeological Interpretation Gallery £1.50 (ch & concessions 80p). **Facilities:** 🅿 ♿ (Minicom system) toilets for disabled shop ♨

SUNDERLAND   Map 12 NZ35
MUSEUM & WINTER GARDENS
Birdon Rd SR1 1PP
☎ 0191 553 2323 📠 0191 553 7828

The museum's rich collections take in just about everything from the first Nissan car built in Sunderland to fine oils by L.S. Lowry. There are exhibits on the

contd.

prehistoric life of the region, Sunderland's shipbuilding and coal mining past, and local pottery and glassware, to name but a few. The impressive Winter Gardens with their treetop walkway add a further dimension to the museum.

Times: Open all year, Mon 10-4, Tue-Sat 10-5, Sun 2-5. **Fee:** Free. **Facilities:** P (150 yds) ✗ ⟨ (lifts to all floors) toilets for disabled shop ✗ (ex guide dogs) ⬤

NATIONAL GLASS CENTRE
Liberty Way SR6 0GL
☎ 0191 515 5555 ⬔ 0191 515 5556
e-mail: info@nationalglasscentre.com

Housed in a striking modern building, the National Glass Centre celebrates the unique material and explains its history. Visitors can see the changing exhibitions of glass art, featuring pieces by leading artists. There is also the opportunity to witness the glass-making process and learn more about the substance and how it impacts on our lives. The brave can even walk on the glass roof 30 feet above the riverside.

Times: Open daily 10-5 (last admission to glass tour 4pm). Closed 25 Dec & 1 Jan. **Fee:** £5 (concessions £3). Family ticket £12. **Facilities:** P ✗ licensed ⟨ toilets for disabled shop ✗ (ex guide dogs) ⬤

⬛ TYNEMOUTH   Map 12 NZ36
TYNEMOUTH CASTLE & PRIORY
NE30 4BZ (near North Pier)
☎ 0191 257 1090

The castle and priory are a testament to the strategic importance of the site and its great religious significance. The soaring arches of the presbytery are an eloquent reminder of the priory's former wealth, and the Percy Chantry is still almost complete.

Times: Open all year, Apr-Oct, daily 10-6 (Oct 10-5); Nov-Mar, Wed-Sun 10-4 (or dusk if earlier, closed 1-2pm). Closed 24-26 Dec & 1 Jan. **Fee:** £1.90 (ch 5-15 £1, under 5's free, con £1.40). **Facilities:** ⟨ shop ✗ ⬢

⬛ WALLSEND   Map 12 NZ26
SEGEDUNUM ROMAN FORT, BATHS & MUSEUM
Buddle St NE28 6HR (A187 from Tyne Tunnel, signposted)
☎ 0191 236 9347 ⬔ 0191 295 5858

Hadrian's Wall was built by the Roman Emperor Hadrian in 122AD, with the intention of keeping the 'barbarians' of the North from invading the rest of Britain. Segedunum was built as part of the wall, serving as a garrison for 600 soldiers until the collapse of Roman rule in 410AD. This major new historical venture shows what life would have been like then, using artefacts, audio-visuals, reconstructed buildings and a 34m high viewing tower.

Times: Open all year, Apr-Oct, daily 10-5; Nov-Mar, daily 10-3.30. (Closed 25-26 Dec & 1 Jan) **Fee:** £2.95 (ch, pen & concessions £1.95). Family ticket £8.50 **Facilities:** P ⬤ ⟨ toilets for disabled shop ✗ (ex guide dogs) ⬤

⬛ WASHINGTON   Map 12 NZ35
WASHINGTON OLD HALL
The Avenue, Washington Village NE30 7LE (follow signs for District 4 Washington. Beside church in centre of Washington Village)
☎ 0191 416 6879 ⬔ 0191 4192065

The home of George Washington's ancestors from 1183 to 1613, the Old Hall was originally an early medieval manor, but was rebuilt in the 17th century. The house has been restored and filled with period furniture. There are exhibitions on George Washington and American Independence and a formal garden laid out in Jacobean style.

Times: Open Apr-Oct, Sun-Wed; open Good Fri 11-5. Last admission 4.30. (Closed Thu-Sat for pre-booked Weddings). **Fee:** £3 (ch £1.50). Family ticket £7.50. Group £2.50 each. **Facilities:** P ⬤ ⟨ (braille guide, tactile objects in house, handrails, ramps) toilets for disabled shop ✗ (ex guide dogs) ⬢

WWT WASHINGTON
District 15 NE38 8LE (signposted off A195, A1231 & A182)
☎ 0191 416 5454 ⬔ 0191 416 5801
e-mail: washington@wwt.org.uk

In a parkland setting, on the north bank of the River Wear, WWT Washington is the home of a wonderful collection of exotic wildfowl from all over the world. There is also a heronry where visitors can watch a colony of wild Grey Herons on CCTV. The 100-acre site includes an area for wintering wildfowl which can be observed from hides, and a flock of Chilean Flamingos. Other features include a discovery centre, waterfowl nursery, picture windows and a viewing gallery from which to observe the birds.

Times: Open all year, daily 9.30-5 (summer) or 9.30-4 (winter). Closed 25 Dec. **Fee:** £4.90 (ch £2.90, pen £3.90). **Facilities:** P ⬤ ✗ ⟨ (lowered windows in certain hides, wheelchairs to hire free) toilets for disabled shop ✗ (ex guide dogs) ⬤

⬛ WHITBURN   Map 12 NZ46
SOUTER LIGHTHOUSE
Coast Rd SR6 7NH (On A183 coast road, 2m S of South Shields, 3m N of Sunderland)
☎ 0191 529 3161 01670 773966
⬔ 0191 529 0902
e-mail: nslhse@smtp.ntrust.org.uk

When it opened in 1871, Souter was the most advanced lighthouse in the world. Painted red and white and standing at 150ft high, it is a dramatic building and hands-on displays and volunteers help bring it to life. The Engine and Battery Rooms are all in working order and are included in the guided tour, along with the light tower and museum cottage.

Times: Open Apr-Oct daily ex Fri, (open Good Fri), 11-5. Last admission 4.30. Please contact for opening at other times. **Fee:** £3 (ch £1.50) Family ticket £7.50. Parties £2.50 each. National Trust members free. **Facilities:** P ✗ ⟨ braille guide, induction loops, tactile exhibits toilets for disabled shop ✗ (ex guide dogs) ⬢ ⬤

Warwickshire

The countryside of south Warwickshire, located in the Heart of England, was beloved of William Shakespeare. The bard is forever associated with the town of Stratford-upon-Avon, the place of his birth and death, which now has two theatres built in his honour.

These days, the small market town he knew as home is packed with tourists – it is the most visited British tourist destination outside London. North of the county, around Coventry, which is itself officially part of the West Midlands, the scene is much more industrial/urban and seems a world away from this mainly rural area.

Warwickshire has some fine towns, including Warwick itself, the county town, which boasts one of the greatest English castles. The castle is medieval, though it was comprehensively restored in the 19th century, and its enormous bulk dominates the town. The centre of Warwick is mainly Georgian, built following a fire in 1694 that destroyed the earlier medieval buildings, though some do remain on the periphery. The county's other great castle is Kenilworth, a Norman fortress built of sandstone standing to the west of Kenilworth town.

Leamington Spa came to prominence when the fashion for 'taking the waters' was at its height in the late 18th and early 19th centuries. Rugby, however, is best known as the home of one of England's most elevated public schools, immortalised in Thomas Hughes' *Tom Brown's Schooldays*. The school was also the birthplace of the sport that bears its name.

EVENTS & FESTIVALS

February
tbc February Frolics (during lambing), Hatton Country World, February half-term

March
16th-17th Spring Craft Fair, Ragley Hall, Alcester

July
1st-4th The Royal Show, National Agricultural Centre, Stoneleigh Park
3rd-14th Warwick & Leamington Festival (various venues in Warwick, Leamington & Northgate)
26th-28th Warwickshire Folk Festival (various venues)

August
3rd Fireworks & Laser Show, Ragley Hall, Alcester
17th-18th Warwickshire & West Midlands Game Fair, Ragley Hall, Alcester
24th-26th Town & Country Festival, National Agricultural Centre, Stoneleigh

October
19th-20th Autumn Craft Fair, Ragley Hall, Alcester

November
23rd-24th Yuletide Craft Fair, Ragley Hall, Alcester

Top: Warwick Castle

⛪ ALCESTER
Map 04 SP05

RAGLEY HALL
B49 5NJ (off A46/A435)
☎ 01789 762090 🖥 01789 764791
e-mail: ragley.hall@virginnet.co.uk

Ragley Hall is set in 400 acres of parkland and gardens. The Great Hall contains some of England's finest Baroque plasterwork designed by James Gibbs. Graham Rust's mural The Temptation can be seen on the south staircase. Ample picnic areas beside the lake, as well as an adventure playground, maze and woodland walks.
Times: Open mid Apr-early Oct, Thu-Sun & BH Mon. Park & Garden open daily, late Jul-early Sep. **Fee:** House (including garden & park) £5.50 (ch £4, pen £4.50). **Facilities:** 🅿 💺 ⚒ (lift to first floor) toilets for disabled shop (on leads in park only) 🐾

⛪ BADDESLEY CLINTON
Map 04 SP27

BADDESLEY CLINTON HALL
B93 0DQ (0.75m W off A4141, 7.5m NW of Warwick)
☎ 01564 783294 🖥 01564 782706
e-mail: baddesley@smtp.ntrust.org.uk
Times: House open Mar-29 Oct, Wed-Sun & BH Mon (closed Good Fri). Mar-Apr & 1-29 Oct 1.30-5; May-Sep 1.30-5.30. (Last admissions 30 mins before closing). Grounds open 13 Feb-17 Dec, Wed-Sun & BH Mon (open Good Fri). Feb & Nov-17 Dec 12-4.30; Mar-Apr & Oct 12-5; May-Sep 12-5.30. **Facilities:** 🅿 ✗ licensed ⚒ (wheelchairs available, hearing scheme, braille guides) toilets for disabled shop 🐾 (ex guide dogs) 🐕 *Details not confirmed for 2002* 🐾

⛪ CHARLECOTE
Map 04 SP25

CHARLECOTE PARK
CV35 9ER (5m E of Stratford, 1m W of Wellesbourne on B4086)
☎ 01789 470277 🖥 01789 470544
e-mail: charlecote@smtp.ntrust.org.uk
Times: Open 25 Mar-4 Nov, Fri-Tue 12-5. **Facilities:** 🅿 💺 ✗ licensed ⚒ (Braille guides & hearing scheme available) toilets for disabled shop 🐾 🐕 *Details not confirmed for 2002* 🐾

⛪ COUGHTON
Map 04 SP06

COUGHTON COURT
B49 5JA (2m N of Alcester on E side of A435)
☎ 01789 762435 🖥 01789 765544
Times: Open 18 Mar-end Mar & Oct, Sat-Sun. Apr-Sep, Wed-Sun & BH Mon-Tue and all Tues in Jul & Aug. (Closed Good Fri). Oct, Fri & Sat. Open 11.30-5 (BH Mon 11-5). **Facilities:** 🅿 ✗ licensed ⚒ (braille guide, wheelchair available) toilets for disabled shop 🐾 🐕 *Details not confirmed for 2002* 🐾

⛪ FARNBOROUGH
Map 04 SP44

FARNBOROUGH HALL
OX17 1DU (6m N of Banbury, 0.5m W of A423)
☎ 01295 690202
e-mail: upton@smtp.ntrust.org.uk
Times: House, grounds & terrace walk open Apr-Sep, Wed & Sat, & 30 Apr-1 May 2-6. Terrace walk Thu & Fri only, 2-6. Last admission 5.30pm. **Facilities:** 🅿 ⚒ 🐾 (ex guide dogs) 🐕 *Details not confirmed for 2002*

⛪ GAYDON
Map 04 SP35

HERITAGE MOTOR CENTRE
Banbury Rd CV35 0BJ (M40 junct 12 and take B4100. Motor centre is signposted from this junct)
☎ 01926 641188 🖥 01926 641555
e-mail: enquiries@heritagemotorcentre.org.uk

Home to the largest collection of historic British cars anywhere in the world. Set in 63 acres of grounds, the centre boasts a Land Rover demonstration course and has children's quad bikes and electric cars on offer at weekends and during school holidays.
Times: Open all year, daily 10-5. (check for Christmas opening. Closed 24-26, 31 Dec & 1 Jan). **Fee:** £6 (ch 5-16 £4, under 5 free, & senior £5). Family ticket £17. **Facilities:** 🅿 💺 ✗ licensed ⚒ (lifts, wide doors, graded ramps & pathways,wheelchairs) toilets for disabled shop 🐾 (ex guide dogs & hearing dogs) 🐾

⛪ KENILWORTH
Map 04 SP27

KENILWORTH CASTLE
CV8 1NE
☎ 01926 852078

Kenilworth is the largest castle ruin in England, its massive walls towering over the countryside. Originally founded in the 11th century, it was already ancient when Queen Elizabeth I visited her favourite, Robert Dudley, Earl of Leicester, here in 1575; he built a new wing for her use.
Times: Open all year, Apr-Sep daily 10-6 (Oct 10-5); Nov-Mar, daily 10-4. Closed 24-26 Dec & 1 Jan. **Fee:** £4 (ch 5-15 £2, under 5's free, con £3). **Facilities:** 🅿 ⚒ shop 🐾 ♿

STONELEIGH ABBEY
CV8 2LF (Abbey entrance off B4115 close to junction of A46 & A452)
☎ 01926 858535 🖥 01926 850724
e-mail: enquire@stoneleigh.org

Stoneleigh Abbey, in 600 acres of parkland, is one of the finest country house estates in the Midlands and has undergone considerable restoration work. The abbey, founded in the reign of Henry II, is now managed by a charitable trust. Visitors will experience a wealth of architectural styles spanning more than 600 years. The magnificent state rooms and chapel, the medieval Gatehouse and the Regency stables are some of the major areas to be admired.
Times: Open Apr-Oct, Tue-Thu, Sun & BHs for guided tours at 11, 1, 3 & 4pm **Fee:** £5 (one child free with every paying adult, additional ch £2.50, pen £3.50) Party rates available. **Facilities:** 🅿 💺 ⚒ (State rooms are also accessible) toilets for disabled shop

⛪ MIDDLETON
Map 07 SP19

ASH END HOUSE CHILDRENS FARM
Middleton Ln, Middleton B78 2BL (signposted from A4091)
☎ 0121 329 3240 🖥 0121 329 3240
e-mail: childrensfarm@ashendhouse.fsnet.co.uk

Ideal for young children, this is a small family-owned farm with many friendly animals to feed and stroke,

contd.

including some rare breeds. Cafe, shop, gift shop, play areas, picnic barns and lots of undercover activities.
Times: Open daily 10-5 or dusk in winter. (Closed 25-28 Dec & 1 Jan).
Fee: £1.80 (ch £3.60 includes animal feed, badge & pony ride)
Facilities: 🅿 ⬤ ♿ toilets for disabled shop ✗ (ex guide dogs) ☞

MIDDLETON HALL

B78 2AE (M42 junct 9, on A4091 midway between Belfry & Drayton Manor, follow brown signs)
☎ 01827 283095   🖹 01827 285717
Times: Open Apr-Sep, Sun 2-5, BH 11-5. **Facilities:** 🅿 ⬤ ♿ (wheelchairs available) toilets for disabled shop *Details not confirmed for 2002*

🏛 NUNEATON   Map 04 SP39

ARBURY HALL

CV10 7PT (2m SW of Nuneaton, off B4102 Meriden road)
☎ 024 7638 2804   🖹 024 7664 1147
e-mail: brenda.newell@arburyhall.net

The 16th-century Elizabethan house, Gothicised in the 18th century, has been the home of the Newdegate family for over 450 years. It is the finest complete example of Gothic revival architecture in existence, and contains pictures, furniture, and beautiful plasterwork ceilings. The 17th-century stable block, with a central doorway by Wren, houses the tearooms and lovely gardens with lakes and wooded walks.
Times: Open Etr-Sep 2-5.30 (last admission 5pm). Hall & gardens: Sun & Mon of BH weekends only. For other opening days & times, contact the Administrator. **Fee:** £5 (ch £3) gardens only £4. (ch £3.)
Facilities: 🅿 ⬤ ♿ shop ✗ (ex guide dogs & in grounds)

🏛 PACKWOOD HOUSE   Map 07 SP17

PACKWOOD HOUSE

B94 6AT (on unclass road off A34)
☎ 01564 783294   🖹 01564 782706
e-mail: baddesley@smtp.ntrust.org.uk
Times: Open May-Sep, Wed-Sun & BH Mon 1.30-5.30; end Mar-Apr & Oct, Wed-Sun & BH Mon 12.30-4.30. Garden: May-Sep, Wed-Sun & BH Mon 10-5.30; Mar-Apr & Oct, Wed-Sun & BH Mon 10-4.30.
Facilities: 🅿 ♿ (wheelchairs available) toilets for disabled shop ✗ (ex guide dogs) 🐾 *Details not confirmed for 2002* ☞

🏛 RUGBY   Map 04 SP57

THE JAMES GILBERT RUGBY FOOTBALL MUSEUM

5 Saint Matthew's St CV21 3BY (On A428 opposite Rugby School)
☎ 01788 333889   🖹 01788 540795
e-mail: museum@james-gilbert.com

An intriguing collection of rugby football memorabilia is housed in the shop in which Gilbert's have made their world famous rugby balls since 1842. Visitors can watch a craftsman at work, hand-stitching the footballs. Situated near to Rugby School and its famous playing field.
Times: Open all year, Mon-Sat 9-5. Phone for holiday opening times.
Fee: Free. **Facilities:** 🅿 (500 yds) ♿ shop ✗ (ex guide dogs)

🏛 RYTON-ON-DUNSMORE   Map 04 SP37

RYTON ORGANIC GARDENS

CV8 3LG (5m SE of Coventry signposted off A45, on minor road to Wolston)
☎ 024 7630 3517   🖹 024 7663 9229
e-mail: enquiry@hdra.org.uk
Times: Open all year 9-5. (Closed Xmas). **Facilities:** 🅿 ✗ licensed ♿ (wheelchairs available) toilets for disabled shop garden centre ✗ (ex guide dogs) *Details not confirmed for 2002* ☞

🏛 SHOTTERY   Map 04 SP15

ANNE HATHAWAY'S COTTAGE

CV37 9HH (W of Stratford-upon-Avon, between A46 & B439)
☎ 01789 204016   204016
e-mail: info@shakespeare.org.uk

Before her marriage to William Shakespeare, Anne Hathaway lived in this substantial 12-roomed thatched Tudor farmhouse with her prosperous yeoman family. The house now shows many aspects of domestic life in 16th-century England, and has a lovely traditional cottage garden and Shakespeare tree garden.
Times: Open all year, 20 Mar-19 Oct Mon-Sat 9-5, Sun 9.30-4; 20 Oct-19 Mar Mon-Sat 9.30-4, Sun 10-4. (Closed 23-26 Dec). **Fee:** £4.50 (ch £2, concessions £4). Family ticket £11. Inclusive ticket to all 5 Shakespearian properties £12 (ch £6, concessions £11). Family £29.
Facilities: 🅿 (charged) ⬤ ✗ licensed ♿ toilets for disabled shop garden centre ✗ ☞

🏛 STRATFORD-UPON-AVON   Map 04 SP25

BUTTERFLY FARM

Tramway Walk, Swan's Nest Ln CV37 7LS (south bank of River Avon opposite RSC)
☎ 01789 299288   🖹 01789 415878
e-mail: sales@butterflyfarm.co.uk

Europe's largest live Butterfly and Insect Exhibit. Hundreds of the world's most spectacular and colourful butterflies, in the unique setting of a lush tropical landscape, with splashing waterfalls and fish-filled pools. See also the strange and fascinating Insect City, a bustling metropolis of ants, bees, stick insects, beetles and other remarkable insects. See the dangerous and deadly in Arachnoland!
Times: Open daily 10-6 (winter 10-5.30). Closed 25 Dec. **Fee:** £3.95 (ch £2.95, pen & students £3.45). Family £11.50 (2ad+2ch). Party 10+.
Facilities: 🅿 (opposite entrance) (site parking orange badge holders only) ♿ toilets for disabled shop ✗ ☞

HALL'S CROFT

Old Town CV37 6EP (in town centre)
☎ 01789 204016   🖹 01789 296083
e-mail: info@shakespeare.org.uk

A Tudor house with outstanding furniture and paintings where Shakespeare's daughter Susanna, and her husband, Dr John Hall, lived before moving to New Place on the dramatist's death. There is an exhibition on Tudor medicine, and fine walled gardens can also be seen.   *contd.*

Times: Open all year, 20 Mar-19 Oct Mon-Sat 9.30-5; Sun 10-5; 20 Oct-19 Mar, Mon-Sat, 10-4; Sun 10.30-4. (Closed 23-26 Dec).
Fee: £3.50 (ch £1.70 concession £3) Family ticket £8.50.Three In-town Properties ticket: £8.50 (ch £4.20,concession £7.50) Family ticket £20. Five Properties ticket: £12 (ch £6, concession £11) Family ticket £29.
Facilities: P (100metres) (2hr limit on-street parking) ♥ ✗ licensed ♿ (ramp access for garden & lawns) toilets for disabled shop ✖ ♨

NEW PLACE / NASH'S HOUSE

Chapel St CV37 6EP (in town centre)
☎ 01789 204016 ▤ 01789 263138
e-mail: info@shakespeare.org.uk

Only the foundations remain of the house where Shakespeare spent the last five years of his life and died in 1616. The house was destroyed in 1759, but the picturesque garden has been planted as an Elizabethan knot garden. There is a small museum of furniture and local history in the adjacent Nash's House.

Times: Open all year,20 Mar-19 Oct, Mon-Sat, 9.30-5; Sun 10-5; 20 Oct-19 Mar, Mon-Sat, 10-4, Sun 10.30-4. (Closed 23-26 Dec).
Fee: £3.50 (ch £1.70, concessions £3.70) Family ticket £10. Three In-town properties £8.50 (ch £4.20, concessions £7.50) Family ticket £20. Five Properties Ticket £12 (ch £6, concessions £11) Family ticket £29.
Facilities: P (250yds) ♿ toilets for disabled shop ✖ ♨

ROYAL SHAKESPEARE COMPANY COLLECTION

Royal Shakespeare Theatre, Waterside CV37 6BB (M40 junct 14 take A46 S. At 1st rdbt take 1st exit (A439). Follow RSC signs, (park in town centre))
☎ 01789 262870 ▤ 01789 262870
e-mail: info@rsc.org.uk

The RSC gallery is housed in the original Victorian building which was part of Charles Flower's Shakespeare Memorial, opened in 1879, comprising Theatre, Paintings and Sculpture Gallery, Library and Reading Room, the latter were not destroyed when the theatre burnt down in 1926.

Times: Open all year, Mon-Fri 1.30-5.30, Sat 10.30-7.30 & Sun 11.30-4.30. (Closed 24 & 25 Dec).Theatre tours usually Mon-Fri (ex matinee days), 1.30 & 5.30, Sun 12, 1, 2 & 3. **Fee:** Exhibition £2 (ch, pen & students £1.50). Family ticket £4. Theatre Tours £4 (ch, pen & students £3) - advisable to book in advance. **Facilities:** P (200yds) (street parking restricted to 2hrs) ♥ ✗ licensed ♿ services for hearing impaired visitors toilets for disabled shop ✖ (ex guide dogs)

SHAKESPEARE'S BIRTHPLACE

Henley St CV37 6QW (in town centre)
☎ 01789 204016 ▤ 01789 296083
e-mail: info@shakespeare.org.uk

Shakespeare was born in the timber-framed house in 1564. It contains numerous exhibits of the Elizabethan period and Shakespeare memorabilia, and the

contd.

acclaimed exhibition, Shakespeare; His Life and Background.

Times: Open all year, 20 Mar-19 Oct Mon-Sat 9-5, Sun 9.30-5; 20 Oct-19 Mar Mon-Sat 9.30-4. (Closed 23-26 Dec). **Fee:** £6 (ch £2.50, concession £5.50) Family ticket £15. Three In-town Properties Ticket £8.50 (ch £4.20, concessions £7.50) Family ticket £20. Five Properties Ticket £12 (ch £6, concessions £11) Family £29.

Facilities: P (100 yds) (no vehicle access to Henley Street) & toilets for disabled shop ✻ ➘

THE TEDDY BEAR MUSEUM
19 Greenhill St CV37 6LF (M40 junct 15, follow signs to Stratford town centre)
☎ 01789 293160
e-mail: info@theteddybearmuseum.com

Collection of some of the oldest and rarest teddy bears in the world, housed in a small house once owned by Henry VIII. Lots of modern teddy bear stars too, including the original Fozzie Bear, Paddington Bear from the earliest television series, Mr Bean's bear, and many more.

Times: Open all year, daily 9.30-5.30. Closed 25 & 26 Dec. **Fee:** £2.50 (ch £1.50, con £1.95). Family ticket £7.50. Party 20+. **Facilities:** P (30yds & 200yds) (access to ground floor shop only) shop ✻ (ex guide dogs) ➘

🏛 UPTON HOUSE   Map 04 SP34
UPTON HOUSE
OX15 6HT (on A422, 7m NW of Banbury, 12m SE of Stratford)
☎ 01295 670266 🖷 01295 670266
e-mail: upton@smtp.ntrust.org.uk

Times: Open Apr-Oct, Sat-Wed & BH Mon 2-6. Last admission 5.30pm (Oct 5pm). **Facilities:** P ➘ & (Braille guide, parking nr house, buggy for lower garden) toilets for disabled shop ✻ (ex guide dogs) ❧ *Details not confirmed for 2002*

🏛 WARWICK   Map 04 SP26
WARWICK CASTLE
CV34 4QU (2m from M40 junct 15)
☎ 0870 442 2000 🖷 01926 401692
e-mail: customer.information@warwick-castle.com

From the days of William the Conqueror to the reign of Queen Victoria, Warwick Castle has provided a backdrop for many turbulent times. Attractions include the gloomy Dungeon and Torture Chamber, the grand State Rooms, the Great Hall, and a reconstruction of the Royal Weekend Party of 1898, where "Daisy", Countess of Warwick held sway.

Times: Open daily 10-6 (5pm Nov-Mar). Closed 25 Dec. **Fee:** Mar- 11 May & 10 Sep-28 Feb £10.25 (ch £6.25, stu £7.80, pen £7.35) Family £29; 12 May-9 Sep: £11.50 (ch £6.75, stu £8.60, pen £8.20) Family £30. Group rates available. **Facilities:** P (charged) ➘ ✗ licensed & (Free admission to wheelchair bound visitors) toilets for disabled shop ✻ (ex assistance dogs) ➘

WARWICKSHIRE YEOMANRY MUSEUM
The Court House Vaults, Jury St CV34 4EW (on corner of Jury St & Castle St)
☎ 01926 492212 🖷 01926 494837
Times: Open Good Fri-Sep, Fri-Sun 10-1 & 2-4. Other times by prior arrangement. **Facilities:** P (300yds) (2hr max in nearby streets) shop ✻ *Details not confirmed for 2002*

🏛 WILMCOTE   Map 04 SP15
MARY ARDEN'S HOUSE AND THE SHAKESPEARE COUNTRYSIDE MUSEUM
CV37 6BG (3m NW off A34)
☎ 01789 204016 🖷 01789 296083
e-mail: info@shakespeare.org.uk

Mary Arden was William Shakespeare's mother, and this picturesque, half-timbered Tudor house was her childhood home. The house is the main historic feature of an extensive complex of farm buildings which house displays of farming and country life, including a remarkable dovecote, kitchen circa 1900, a smithy and cooper's workshop. Daily demonstrations by The Heart of England Falconry. Rare breeds, duck pond and field walk.

Times: Open all year, 20 Mar-19 Oct Mon-Sat 9.30-5, Sun 10-5; 20 Oct-19 Mar, Mon-Sat 10-4, Sun 10.30-4. (Closed 23-26 Dec).
Fee: £5.50 (ch £2.50, concessions £5) Family ticket £13.50. Five Properties Ticket £12 (ch £6, concessions £11) Family ticket £29.
Facilities: P ➘ & toilets for disabled shop ✻ ➘

West Midlands

At the centre of England, the West Midlands is a metropolitan county with a mainly industrial base. Birmingham is the administrative centre and the other main towns are Coventry, Dudley, Smethick, Walsall, West Bromwich and Wolverhampton.

The area was badly affected by the decline in British manufacturing, but has fought back by diversification into the service sector; impressive conference and exhibition facilities are offered in Birmingham, in the form of the International Convention Centre and National Exhibition Centre, home to many of the country's biggest trade fairs. Industrial heritage museums have blossomed, including the Black Country Museum at Dudley, and Cadbury World, which tells the story of chocolate and the chocolate factory established at Bournville by the renowned Quaker family.

Birmingham, AKA 'Brum', is Britain's second largest city, its position at the hub of things emphasised by the miles of canals criss-crossing the city and its amazing tangle of flyovers. There are some splendid public buildings, notably the Town Hall and the City Museum and Art Gallery. Modern developments include an ongoing rejuvenation of the infamous 60s-designed Bull Ring shopping centre. Birmingham's urban sprawl produced bands Led Zeppelin and Black Sabbath in the 1970s.

The West Midland's multi-racial population gives a buzz to its cultural life, which offers a feast of arts, products, foods and festivals from around the world. In the late 1970s, Coventry was the home of the Two-Tone record label, and band The Specials, mixing punk and ska and gaining plenty of chart success.

Top: Aston Hall, Birmingham

EVENTS & FESTIVALS

March
7th-10th Crufts Dog Show, National Exhibition Centre, Birmingham
17th St Patrick's Day Pageant, Coventry

June
1st Coventry Classic Car Run, War Memorial Park, Coventry
7th-9th Godiva Festival, War Memorial Park, Coventry
19th-23rd BBC Gardeners World Live, Birmingham

July
5th-14th Birmingham International Jazz Festival
13th-14th City of Wolverhampton Show (provisional)
27th-28th Wolvestock Music Festival, Bilston (provisional)

August
22nd-26th Coventry Jazz Festival
tbc Italian Festival, School Street, Wolverhampton
tbc Steam & Vintage Rally, West Park, Wolverhampton

September
29th Aug-2nd Coventry Jazz Festival
tbc Birmingham Arts Festival
tbc Dudley Glass Festival

November
tbc Coombe Fireworks, Coventry
tbc Firework Display, Wolverhampton

🏛 BIRMINGHAM   Map 07 SP08
ASTON HALL
Trinity Rd, Aston B6 6JD (M6 junct 6 follow A38(M)
Aston Expressway towards city centre. Leave at Aston
Waterlinks and follow brown signs to Aston Hall)
☎ 0121 327 0062   📠 0121 327 7162

Built by Sir Thomas Holte, Aston Hall is a fine Jacobean
mansion complete with a panelled Long Gallery,
balustraded staircase and magnificent plaster friezes
and ceilings. King Charles I spent a night here during
the Civil War and the house was damaged by
Parliamentary troops. It was also leased to James Watt
Junior, the son of the great industrial pioneer.
Times: Open Etr-Oct, Tue-Fri 1-4; Sat & Sun 12-4. Closed Mon ex
BH's. **Fee:** Free. **Facilities:** 🅿 💺 ♿ (ground floor only partially
accessible) shop 🐾 (ex guide dogs)

BIRMINGHAM BOTANICAL GARDENS & GLASSHOUSES
Westbourne Rd, Edgbaston B15 3TR (2m W of city
centre, follow signs for Edgbaston, then brown tourist
signs)
☎ 0121 454 1860   📠 0121 454 7835
e-mail: admin@bham-bot-gdns.demon.co.uk

Originally opened in 1832, the gardens include the
Tropical House, which has a 24ft-wide lily pool and
lush vegetation. The Orangery features a wide variety
of citrus fruits and the Cactus House has a desert scene
with its giant agaves and opuntias. Outside, a tour of
the gardens includes rhododendrons and azalea
borders and a collection of over 200 trees.
Times: Open daily all year, wkdays 9-7 or dusk, Sun 10-7 or dusk
whichever is earlier. (Closed 25 Dec). **Fee:** £4.80 (concessions £2.60);
£5.20 summer Sun (concessions £2.60) **Facilities:** 🅿 💺 ✖ licensed
♿ (3 wheelchairs, 2 electric scooters & braille guides) toilets for
disabled shop garden centre 🐾 (ex guide dogs) 💺

BIRMINGHAM MUSEUM & ART GALLERY
Chamberlain Sq B3 3DH
☎ 0121 303 2834   📠 0121 303 1394
Times: Open all year Mon-Thu & Sat 10-5, Fri 10.30-5 and Sun 12.30-5.
Facilities: 🅿 💺 ✖ licensed ♿ (lift) toilets for disabled shop 🐾
Details not confirmed for 2002 💺

THE JEWELLERY QUARTER DISCOVERY CENTRE
75-79 Vyse St, Hockley B18 6HA (turn off A41 into Vyse
St, museum on left after 1st side street)
☎ 0121 554 3598   📠 0121 554 9700
e-mail: Louise-Evans@birmingham.gov.uk

The Museum tells the story of jewellery making in
Birmingham from its origins in the Middle Ages right
through to the present day. Discover the skill of the
jeweller's craft and enjoy a unique tour of an original
jewellery factory frozen in time. For over eighty years
the family firm of Smith and Pepper produced jewellery
from the factory. This perfectly preserved 'time capsule'
workshop has changed little since the beginning of the
century. The Jewellery Quarter is still very much at the
forefront of jewellery manufacture in Britain and the
Museum showcases the work of the city's most exciting
new designers.
Times: Open all year, Mon-Fri 10-4, Sat 11-5. (Closed Sun). Open BHs
but closed Xmas/New Year **Fee:** £2.50 (concessions £2). Family ticket
£6.50. Party 10+ booked in advance. **Facilities:** 🅿 (limited 2hr
stay/pay & display) 💺 ♿ (tours for hearing/visually impaired booked
in advance) toilets for disabled shop 🐾 (ex guide dogs) 💺

SAREHOLE MILL
Cole Bank Rd, Hall Green B13 0BD (M42 junct 4. Take
A34 towards Birmingham. After 5m turn left onto
B4146 Mill on left)
☎ 0121 777 6612   📠 0121 3032891

A working, 18th-century watermill. Corn-grinding
demonstrations every Sunday in August. Once home to
Matthew Boulton and an inspiration to the writer J R R
Tolkein. Displays on rural life and an events
programme – please ring for details.
Times: Open Apr-Oct, Tue-Fri 1-4, Sat-Sun & BH 12-4, Closed Mon
Fee: Free. **Facilities:** 🅿 🐾 (ex guide dogs)

SOHO HOUSE
Soho Av, Handsworth B18 5LB
☎ 0121 554 9122
Times: Open all year, Tue-Sat 10-5 & Sun 12-5; also BH Mon.
Facilities: 🅿 💺 ♿ (induction loop) toilets for disabled shop 🐾 (ex
guide dogs) *Details not confirmed for 2002* 💺

🏛 BOURNVILLE   Map 07 SP08
CADBURY WORLD
Linden Rd B30 2LD (1m S of A38 Bristol Rd, on A4040
ring road)
☎ 0121 451 4159   📠 0121 451 1366
e-mail: cadbury.world@csplc.com

Lots of recent changes have meant Cadbury World now
has much more to see, do and taste. There is the
chance to get involved in the chocolate making
process, and to find out how the chocolate is used to
make famous confectionery. Visitors can learn about
the early struggles and triumphs of the Cadbury
business, and follow the history of Cadbury television
advertising. Besides all this, visitors can relax on the
gentle Cadabra ride, and be a big kid in CadburyLand,
the Fantasy Factory, and on the Cocoa Road. *contd.*

Times: Contact information line 0121 451 4180 for opening times.
Fee: £8.50 (ch £6.50, concessions £6.75) **Facilities:** ▣ ♨ ✗ ♿
(adapted ride & lift to 2nd floor) toilets for disabled shop ✸ (ex guide dogs) ♥

⌂ COVENTRY   Map 04 SP37
COVENTRY CATHEDRAL & VISITOR CENTRE
7 Priory Row CV1 5ES (signposted on all approaches to the city)
☎ 024 7622 7597   ▤ 024 7663 1448
e-mail: information@coventrycathedral.org

Coventry's old cathedral was bombed during an air raid of November 1940 which devastated the city. The remains have been carefully preserved. The new cathedral was designed by Sir Basil Spence and consecrated in May 1962. It contains outstanding modern works of art, including a huge tapestry designed by Graham Sutherland, the West Screen (a wall of glass engraved by John Hutton with saints and angels), bronzes by Epstein, and the Great Baptistry Window by John Piper.
Times: Open all year, daily, Etr-Sep 9.30-6; Oct-Etr 9.30-4.30. Visitor centre open Oct-Apr 11-3, Apr-Oct 10-4. **Fee:** Visitor centre £2 (ch 6 free, ch 6-16, students & pen £1). Party 10+. Cathedral £3 donation. Camera charge £1. Video charge £3. **Facilities:** ▣ (250 yds) ♨ ♿ (lift, touch and hearing centre, paved wheelchair access) toilets for disabled shop ✸ (ex guide dogs)

HERBERT ART GALLERY & MUSEUM
Jordan Well CV1 5QP (in city centre near Cathedral)
☎ 024 7683 2381   & 7683 2565
▤ 024 7683 2410
e-mail: ann.walker@coventry.gov.uk

'Godiva City' tells Coventry's story over 1,000 years, through interactive exhibits, objects, pictures and words. Changing displays of art, craft, social and industrial history. It is Coventry's premier museum and hosts a range of exhibitions and events.
Times: Open all year, Mon-Sat 10-5.30, Sun 12-5. (Closed 25-27 Dec & 1-2 Jan) **Fee:** Free. **Facilities:** ▣ (500yds) ♨ ♿ (disabled parking, automatic doors, tactile/audio displays) toilets for disabled shop ✸ (ex guide/assistance dogs)

JAGUAR DAIMLER HERITAGE CENTRE
Browns Ln, Allesley CV5 9DR (on A45, follow signs for Browns Lane Plant)
☎ 024 7640 2121   ▤ 024 7620 2777
e-mail: tokeeffe@jaguar.com
Times: Open Mon-Fri 9.30-4.30 & last Sun of month 10-4.
Facilities: ▣ ♿ toilets for disabled shop ✸ (ex guide dogs) *Details not confirmed for 2002*

LUNT ROMAN FORT
Coventry Rd, Baginton CV8 3AJ (S side of city, off Stonebridge highway, A45)
☎ 024 7683 2381   & 7683 2565
▤ 024 7683 2410
e-mail: ann.walker@coventry.gov.uk

The turf and timber Roman fort from the end of the 1st

century has been faithfully reconstructed. An Interpretation Centre is housed in the granary.
Times: Open 15 Jul-3 Sep, Thu-Tue 10-5; Spring BH wk daily 10-5; Apr-29 Oct wknds & BH Mons 10-5. **Fee:** £2 (con £1). Audio tour 80p.
Facilities: ▣ ♿ (ramp to Granary Interpretation Centre) toilets for disabled shop ✸ (ex guide/assistancedogs)

MUSEUM OF BRITISH ROAD TRANSPORT
St Agnes Ln, Hales St CV1 1PN (just off ring road junc 1)
☎ 024 7683 2425   ▤ 024 7683 2465
e-mail: museum@mbrt.co.uk

Coventry is the traditional home of the motor industry. The Museum of British Road Transport displays the largest collection of British cars, buses, cycles and motorcycles in the world. Visitors can learn about motoring's early days in 'Memory Lane', how Royalty travelled, and see Thrust 2, the world land speed record story.
Times: Open all year, daily 10-5. (Closed 24-26 Dec). **Fee:** Free.
Facilities: ▣ (adjacent) (pay & display) ♨ ♿ (audio tour, tactile floor & models) toilets for disabled shop ✸ (ex guide dogs) ♥

⌂ DUDLEY   Map 07 SO99
BLACK COUNTRY LIVING MUSEUM
Tipton Rd DY1 4SQ (on A4037, opposite Dudley Guest Hospital)
☎ 0121 557 9643   & 0121 520 8054
▤ 0121 557 4242
e-mail: info@bclm.co.uk
Times: Open all year, Mar-Oct daily 10-5; Nov-Feb, Wed-Sun 10-4. (Telephone for Christmas closing) **Facilities:** ▣ ♨ ♿ (ramps available) toilets for disabled shop ✸ (ex guide dogs) *Details not confirmed for 2002* ♥

DUDLEY ZOO & CASTLE
2 The Broadway DY1 4QB (M5 junct 2 towards Wolverhampton/Dudley. Signposted)
☎ 01384 215313   ▤ 01384 456048
e-mail: marketing@dudleyzoo.org.uk

Set in 40 acres, the castle ruins are an impressive example of feudal splendour, whilst the zoo houses one of the most diverse collections of animals in the country. Home to many endangered species, there is the opportunity to see and learn about animals from every continent.
Times: Open all year, Etr-mid Sep, daily 10-4; mid Sep-Etr, daily 10-3. (Closed 25 Dec). **Fee:** £7 (ch 4-15 £4.75, concessions £5). Family ticket £24.50 (2ad+3ch). Party 15+. **Facilities:** ▣ (charged) ♨ ✗ licensed ♿ (land train from gates-castle, wheelchair hire) toilets for disabled shop ✸ ♥

MUSEUM & ART GALLERY
St James's Rd DY1 1HU (M5 northbound, exit at junct 2. Take A4123 signposted to Dudley)
☎ 01384 815575   ▤ 01384 815576
e-mail: museum.pls@mbc.dudley.gov.uk

The museum houses the Brooke Robinson collection of 17th, 18th and 19th century European painting, furniture, ceramics and enamels. A fine geological

contd.

gallery, 'The Time Trail', has spectacular displays of fossils from the local Wenlock limestone and coal measures.
Times: Open all year, Mon-Sat 10-4. (Closed BHs). **Fee:** Free.
Facilities: P (25mtrs) & (Braille & large print text. Tactile objects) shop ✻ (ex guide dogs)

🏛 SOLIHULL   Map 07 SP17
NATIONAL MOTORCYCLE MUSEUM
Coventry Rd, Bickenhill B92 0EJ (near M42 junct 6, off A45, near NEC)
☎ 01675 443311 📠 0121 711 3153

Five exhibition halls showing British motorcycles built during the Golden Age of motorcycling. Spanning 90 years, the immaculately restored machines are the products of around 150 different factories. Over 700 machines are on show, most are owned by the museum, others are from collections or private owners. Restoration work is carried out by enthusiasts, and new motorcycles are acquired from all over the world.
Times: Open all year, daily 10-6. (Closed 24-26 Dec). **Fee:** £4.50 (ch 12 & pen £3.25). Party 20+. **Facilities:** P ✗ licensed & toilets for disabled shop ✻ (ex guide dogs) 🍴

🏛 STOURBRIDGE   Map 07 SO88
THE FALCONRY CENTRE
Hurrans Garden Centre, Kidderminster Rd South, Hagley DY9 0JB (off A456)
☎ 01562 700014 📠 01562 700014
Times: Open all year, daily 10-5. (Closed 25 & 26 Dec). **Facilities:** P 🍴 & shop garden centre ✻ (ex guide dogs) *Details not confirmed for 2002* 🍴

🏛 WALSALL   Map 07 SP09
NEW ART GALLERY WALSALL
Gallery Square WS2 8LG
☎ 01922 654400 📠 01922 654401
e-mail: info@artatwalsall.org.uk

Largely funded by National Lottery money, this modern art gallery was opened in February 2000. Its unusual tower has a variety of oddly shaped windows, while the main building has six floors of art on display. Includes the Garman Ryan permanent collection and a Discovery Gallery.
Times: Open all year Tue-Sat 10-5, Sun noon-5. Closed Mon ex BH Mons. **Fee:** Free. **Facilities:** P 🍴 ✗ & (lift access to facilties) toilets for disabled shop ✻ (ex guide dogs)

WALSALL LEATHER MUSEUM
Littleton St West WS2 8EQ (on Walsall ring-road on North side of town)
☎ 01922 721153 📠 01922 725827
e-mail: leathermuseum@walsall.gov.uk

Award winning working museum in the saddlery and leathergoods capital of Britain. Watch skilled craftsmen and women at work in this restored Victorian leather factory. Displays tell the story of Walsall's leatherworkers past and present. The large shop stocks

range of Walsall made leathergoods, many at bargain prices. The Saddle Room Café serves delicious home-cooked cakes and light lunches. Groups very welcome, guided tours available.
Times: Open all year, Tue-Sat 10-5 (Nov-Mar 4pm), Sun noon-5 (Nov-Mar 4pm). Open BH Mon. (Closed 24-26 Dec, 1 Jan, Good Fri, Etr Sun & May Day). **Fee:** Free. **Facilities:** P (10metres) 🍴 & (staff with sign language skills,tactile activities,parking) toilets for disabled shop ✻ (ex guide dogs) 🍴

🏛 WOLVERHAMPTON   Map 07 SO99
WIGHTWICK MANOR
WV6 8EE (3m W, beside Mermaid Inn)
☎ 01902 761400 📠 01902 764663
Times: Open Mar-Dec, Thu, Sat & BH Sun & Mon 2.30-5.30.
Facilities: P 🍴 & (car parking call 01902 761400 for details) shop (on leads) 🐾 *Details not confirmed for 2002*

🏛 WORDSLEY   Map 07 SO88
STUART CRYSTAL
Red House Glassworks DY8 4AA (1m from Stourbridge on A491 Stourbridge to Wolverhampton road)
☎ 01384 828282 & 261777 📠 01384 70463
Times: Open all year, daily. (Closed 25-26 Dec & 1 Jan). Tours:Mon-Thu on the hour 10-4(not 12),Fri 10,11 & 1; Shop open Mon-Sat, 9-5, Sun 10-4; Glass Blowing: Wed-Sat. **Facilities:** P 🍴 & (Cone/Museum accessible- factory tours are not) shop ✻ (ex guide dogs) *Details not confirmed for 2002* 🍴

Isle of Wight

Despite its size, – less than 23 miles (39km) across at its widest point – the Isle of Wight offers plenty of scenic variety, and is popular as a holiday destination because of its lovely countryside, pleasant resorts and mild climate.

There's lots to see and do, with an abundance of museums, children's activity parks, and leisure facilities including watersports, riding, cycling, paragliding, golf, and sea and freshwater fishing. Local specialities are freshly caught crab and lobster, which can be enjoyed with a glass of wine from one of the island's five vineyards.

A chalk ridge runs east to west of the island, popular with walkers for the fine views afforded from its vantage points. The interesting coastline takes in the chalky pinnacles of The Needles, some splendid cliffs, and the curious multi-coloured sand at Alum Bay, which can be bought bottled in colourful layers from local souvenir shops. Coastal paths follow the shoreline from Totland to St Lawrence on the south coast, and Yarmouth to Cowes on the north coast.

The east coast has the most developed seaside resorts, with Ryde, Sandown, Shanklin and Ventnor, and their sandy beaches. Newport, the island's capital, is the only inland town and is a good shopping centre.

In addition to its natural features, the island has some fine castles and historic houses. Chief among these are medieval Carisbrooke Castle outside Newport, Osborne House at East Cowes, Brading Roman Villa, and lovely manor houses at Arreton, Barton, Haseley, Nunwell, Appuldurcombe and Morton.

EVENTS & FESTIVALS

May
tbc Isle of Wight Garden Show
tbc Isle of Wight Walking Festival

June
tbc Isle of Wight Cycling Festival

July
20th-21st Isle of Wight County Show, Northwood Show Ground, Newport Road, Northwood, Cowes

August
3rd-10th Cowes Week, sailing event, Cowes

August
18th-19th Isle of Wight Garlic Festival, Newchurch
23rd-26th The Island Steam Show, Havenstreet

October
White Air Extreme Sports Festival

Top: Alum Bay

⛰ ALUM BAY Map 04 SZ38
THE NEEDLES OLD BATTERY
West High Down PO39 0JH (0.75m SW)
☎ 01983 754772
Times: Open 26 Mar-29 Jun Sun-Thu & Jul-Aug daily 10.30-5. Property closes in bad weather. **Facilities:** P (0.75m) 🍴 shop 🐕 *Details not confirmed for 2002*

THE NEEDLES PARK
PO39 0JD (signposted, on B3322)
☎ 0870 458 0022 🖷 01983 755260
e-mail: info@theneedles.co.uk

Overlooking the Needles on the western edge of the Island, the park has attractions for all the family: from traditional fairground rides and open-top bus rides to a state-of-the-art simulator ride. Visitors can ride the spectacular chairlift to the beach, and enjoy views of the rocks, the Lighthouse and the world-famous coloured sands.
Times: Open Apr-early Nov, daily 10-5. Hours extended in high season. **Fee:** No admission charged for entrance to Park. Supersaver Attraction Discount ticket £6.50 (ch £4.50), or chargeable attractions individually priced. **Facilities:** P (charged) 🍴 ✕ licensed ♿ toilets for disabled shop 🐾

⛰ ARRETON Map 04 SZ58
HASELEY MANOR
PO30 3AN (on Sandown to Newport road)
☎ 01983 865420 🖷 01983 867547
Times: Open Etr-Sep, Mon-Fri 10-5.30. (Closed Sat & Sun).
Facilities: P 🍴 ✕ licensed ♿ (wheelchair ramps) toilets for disabled shop *Details not confirmed for 2002* 🐾

ROBIN HILL COUNTRY PARK
Downend PO38 2QT
☎ 01983 527352 🖷 01983 527347

Set in 88 acres of downland and woods, Robin Hill offers a Tree Top Trail, Mazes, Snake Slides, Troll Island, Toboggan Run Ride, Squirrel Tower, Forest Sculptures and a Countryside Centre.
Times: Open 25 Mar-3 Nov, daily 10-5 (last admission 4). **Fee:** Over 1.1m £5.50 (under 1.1m £3.50, pen £5, disabled £3). **Facilities:** P 🍴 ♿ most areas are accessible toilets for disabled shop 🐕 (ex on leads) 🐾

⛰ BEMBRIDGE Map 04 SZ68
BEMBRIDGE WINDMILL
PO30 4EB (0.5m S of Bembridge on B3395)
☎ 01983 873945
Times: Open 27 Mar-Jun & Sep-27 Oct, Sun-Fri (Closed Sat ex Etr Sat) & Jul-Aug, daily 10-5. Last admission 4.45. **Facilities:** P shop 🐕 🐕
Details not confirmed for 2002

⛰ BLACKGANG Map 04 SZ47
BLACKGANG CHINE FANTASY PARK
PO38 2HN (from Ventnor follow signs for Whitnell & Niton. From Niton follow signs for Blackgang)
☎ 01983 730330 🖷 01983 731267
e-mail: vectisventureltd@btinternet.com

Opened as scenic gardens in 1843 covering some 40 acres, the park has imaginative play areas, water gardens, a maze and coastal gardens. Set on the steep wooded slopes of the chine are the themed areas Smugglerland, Nurseryland, Dinosaurland, Fantasyland and Frontierland. St Catherine's Quay has a maritime exhibition showing the history of local and maritime affairs.
Times: Open 26 Mar-28 Oct daily, 10-5.30. Whitsun & high season floodlit every evening (phone for details). **Fee:** Combined ticket to chine, sawmill & quay £6.50 (ch 3-13 & pen £5.50, disabled £3.50). Family £21.50. Return within 4 days - £1 each. **Facilities:** P (charged) 🍴 ✕ ♿ (some paths steep) toilets for disabled shop 🐾

⛰ BRADING Map 04 SZ68
ISLE OF WIGHT WAXWORKS
46 High St PO36 0DQ (on A3055)
☎ 01983 407286 🖷 01983 402112
e-mail: waxworks@
bradingisleofwight.fsnet.co.uk

Rub shoulders with famous and infamous characters through 2000 years of the island's colourful fantasies, legends and facts - brought to life in dramatic scenes with sound, light and animation. Visitors can also see the Ancient Rectory mansion (c1066 AD), the Chamber of Horrors, set in the castle dungeons, and adjacent Animal World of Natural History.
Times: Open all year, Summer 10-9; Winter 10-5. Telephone for Dec opening times. **Fee:** £4.95 (ch £3.35, under 5 free, pen £4). Family £15 (2a+2ch), Family £17.50 (2ad+3ch). Party 20+. Includes free entry into "Chamber of Horrors" & Animal World of Natural History. **Facilities:** P ♿ (Disabled route planner) shop 🐾

LILLIPUT ANTIQUE DOLL & TOY MUSEUM
High St PO36 0DJ (A3055 Ryde/Sandown road)
☎ 01983 407231
e-mail: lilliput.museum@btconnect.com

This private museum contains one of the finest collections of antique dolls and toys in Britain. There are over 2000 exhibits, ranging in age from 2000BC to 1945 with examples of almost every seriously collectable doll, many with royal connections. Also dolls' houses, teddy bears and rare and unusual toys.
Times: Open all year, daily, 10-5. **Fee:** £1.95 (ch & pen £1, ch under 5 free). Party. **Facilities:** P (200 yds) ♿ (ramps provided on request) shop 🐾

MORTON MANOR
PO36 0EP (off A3055, well signposted)
☎ 01983 406168

The manor dates back to 1249, but was rebuilt in 1680 with further changes during the Georgian period. The house contains furniture of both the 18th and 19th centuries, but its main attraction lies in the gardens and vineyard. The garden is landscaped into terraces, with ornamental ponds, a sunken garden and a traditional Elizabethan turf maze. Morton Manor has an established vineyard and winery.
Times: Open Apr-Oct, daily 10-5.30 (Closed Sat) Last admissions 4.30.
Fee: £4.25 (ch £1.75, pen £3.75). Party 15+ £3.25 each. **Facilities:** 🅿 ♥ ✗ licensed ⅃ shop garden centre ✹ (ex in garden on lead)

NUNWELL HOUSE & GARDENS
Coach Ln PO36 0JQ (off Ryde-Sandown Rd, A3055)
☎ 01983 407240

Set in beautiful gardens, Nunwell is an impressive, lived-in and much loved house where King Charles I spent his last night of freedom. It has fine furniture and interesting collections of family militaria. In summer, concerts are occasionally held in the music room and Shakespeare plays performed in the garden.
Times: Open House & Gardens: 27-28 May then 2 Jul-5 Sep, Mon-Wed 1-5. Groups welcome when house open & at other times by appointment. **Fee:** £4 inc guide book. **Facilities:** 🅿 shop ✹ (ex guide dogs)

🏛 CARISBROOKE   Map 04 SZ48
CARISBROOKE CASTLE
PO30 1XY (1.25m SW of Newport, off B3401)
☎ 01983 522107

This is the only medieval castle on the island and its most famous resident was King Charles I who was imprisoned here. There are two medieval wells: the one in the keep can be reached by climbing down 71 steps; the one in the courtyard had winding gear traditionally driven by a donkey, and demonstrations of it working are still given.
Times: Open all year, Apr-Sep, daily 10-6; Oct, daily 10-5; Nov-28 Mar, daily 10-4. (Closed 24-26 Dec & 1 Jan). **Fee:** £4.50 (ch u5 free, ch £2.30 & con £3.40). Family ticket (2 adults & 3 ch) £11.30.
Facilities: 🅿 ♥ ⅃ shop ⌨

🏛 FRESHWATER   Map 04 SZ38
DIMBOLA LODGE
Terrace Ln, Freshwater Bay PO40 9QE (off A3054)
☎ 01983 756814   🗎 01983 755578
e-mail: administrator@dimbola.co.uk

Times: Open all year 10-5 (Closed 5 days at Xmas). **Facilities:** 🅿 ✗ ⅃ toilets for disabled shop ✹ *Details not confirmed for 2002*

🏛 HAVENSTREET   Map 04 SZ58
ISLE OF WIGHT STEAM RAILWAY
The Railway Station PO33 4DS (between Ryde & Newport. Well signposted)
☎ 01983 882204   🗎 01983 884515
e-mail: havenstreet@iwsteamrailway.co.uk

When the Newport to Ryde railway was closed, Haven Street Station was taken over by a private company, the Isle of Wight Steam Railway. A number of volunteers restored the station, locomotives and rolling stock, and steam trains now run the five miles from Wootton, via Haven Street to Smallbrook Junction where there is a direct interchange with the Ryde-Shanklin electric trains.
Times: Open selected days Mar-Oct (Jun-Sep daily). **Fee:** Return Fares £7 (ch 5-15 £4). Family ticket £19. **Facilities:** 🅿 ♥ ⅃ (with assistance) toilets for disabled shop ☕

🏛 NEWPORT   Map 04 SZ48
ROMAN VILLA
Cypress Rd PO30 1EX (S of Newport, signed Roman Villa')
☎ 01983 529720   🗎 01983 823841
Times: Open Etr-Oct, daily 10-4.30. Other times by appointment.
Facilities: 🅿 (100 yds) ⅃ shop ✹ *Details not confirmed for 2002*

🏛 NEWTOWN   Map 04 SZ49
OLD TOWN HALL
Town Ln PO30 4PA (1m N of A3054)
☎ 01983 531785
Times: Open 27 Mar-end Jun, Sep-25 Oct, Mon Wed & Sun (also open Good Fri & Etr Sat); Jul & Aug Sun-Thu, 2-5. Last admission 4.45pm. **Facilities:** 🅿 (Braille guide books available) ✹ 🐾 *Details not confirmed for 2002*

⌂ OSBORNE HOUSE   Map 04 SZ59
OSBORNE HOUSE
PO32 6JY (1m SE of East Cowes)
☎ 01983 200022

Designed by Prince Albert and Thomas Cubitt in the mid-19th century, Osborne was Queen Victoria's favourite home, especially after the death of Prince Albert. She died here in 1901. The interior of the house is largely unchanged since Victorian times, and is a fascinating insight into the private life of the Royal family of that day.
Times: House open Apr-Sep, daily 10-5. Grounds 10-6. Oct 10-5. Pre booked tours of house only 1 Nov-9 Dec & Feb-28 Mar, Sun-Thu.
Fee: House & Grounds: £7.20 (ch 5-15 £3.60, under 5's free, con £5.40). Grounds: £3.80 (ch £1.10, ch u5 free, con £2.90)
Facilities: 🅿 ⬤ ⚅ shop ✸ ♨

⌂ SHANKLIN   Map 04 SZ58
SHANKLIN CHINE
12 Pomona Rd PO37 6PF (A3055 into Chine Hollow, Shanklin Old Village or from Shanklin Esplanade)
☎ 01983 866432   📠 01983 874215
e-mail: jill@shanklinchine.co.uk

Shanklin Chine is a natural gorge of great scenic beauty with a spectacular 45ft waterfall. A path winds down through the gorge, overhanging trees, ferns and other flora that cover its steep sides. The Heritage Centre is home to the exhibition 'A Century of Solent Sea and Sail'. Other features of historic interest include sections of PLUTO (pipeline under the ocean), which carried petrol to the Allied troops in Normandy.
Times: Open 28 Mar-23 May 10-5; 24 May-22 Sep 10-10 (illuminated at night); 23 Sept-3 Nov 10-5, (opening period may be extended depending on weather conditions). **Fee:** £2.50 (ch £1, pen & students £1.50, disabled £1). Family ticket £6.50 (2ad+2ch), £7.25 (2ad+3ch).
Facilities: 🅿 (450 yds) ⬤ shop

⌂ SHORWELL   Map 04 SZ48
YAFFORD WATER MILL FARM PARK
PO30 3LH (on B3399, Shorwell to Brightstone road)
☎ 01983 740610 & 741125   📠 01983 740610
Times: Open all year, daily 10-6 or dusk in winter. (Last admission 5pm). **Facilities:** 🅿 ⬤ ⚅ toilets for disabled shop ✸ (ex guide dogs) *Details not confirmed for 2002*

⌂ VENTNOR   Map 04 SZ57
MUSEUM OF THE HISTORY OF SMUGGLING
Botanic Gardens PO38 1UL (on A3055, 1m W of Ventnor)
☎ 01983 853677

Situated underground in extensive vaults, this unique museum shows methods of smuggling used over a 700-year period. Also an adventure playground.
Times: Open Apr-Sep, daily 10-5. **Fee:** £2.40 (ch & pen £1.20). Parties by arrangement. **Facilities:** 🅿 (charged) ⬤ ✗ licensed shop garden centre

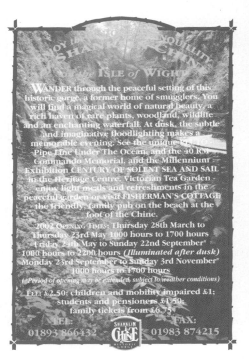

VENTNOR BOTANIC GARDEN
Undercliff Dr PO38 1UL
☎ 01983 855397   📠 01983 856154
Times: Details not confirmed. **Facilities:** 🅿 (charged) ✗ licensed ⚅ toilets for disabled shop ✸ (ex in garden) *Details not confirmed for 2002* ⬤

⌂ WROXALL   Map 04 SZ57
APPULDURCOMBE HOUSE
PO38 3EW (off B3327, 0.5 miles W)
☎ 01983 852484

The manor began life as a priory in 1100, but when it came into the hands of the Worsley family they demolished it and built this Palladian house on the site. Now ruined, it stands in beautiful grounds, landscaped in the 18th century by 'Capability' Brown.
Times: Open 2 Jan-Apr 10-4, May-Sep, daily 10-5. **Fee:** £2 (ch £1 & concessions £1.50). **Facilities:** 🅿 ⚅ ♨

⌂ YARMOUTH   Map 04 SZ38
YARMOUTH CASTLE
Quay St PO41 0PB (adjacent to car ferry terminal)
☎ 01983 760678

Modern buildings surround this well preserved castle, the last addition to Henry VIII's coastal defences, completed in 1547. Fine views of the harbour.
Times: Open Apr-Sep, daily 10-6 (Oct 10-5). **Fee:** £2.20 (ch 5-15 £1.10, ch u5 free, con £1.70). 🅿 (200yds) ⚅ ✸ ♨

Wiltshire

To many visiting the county, Wiltshire has three attractions: Salisbury, Stonehenge and Longleat. While these are all worthwhile, (indeed Stonehenge could be rightly called one of the wonders of the world) there is still plenty more to be discovered in the county.

After seeing Stonehenge, those interested in prehistoric sites should visit Avebury, where the stones are more approachable. Even though there is a lot of tourist activity in the village, the area remains relatively untouched, mostly given over to farmland and moor. This is also a good area for encountering crop circles.

Stonehenge and the Avebury circles seem to be part of a larger complex which still baffles investigators, and includes nearby features such as Windmill Hill with the remains of an earthwork camp some 5,500 years old; Silbury Hill, a man-made mound of earth which covers 5.5 acres; West Kennet Long Barrow, a burial mound; and possibly the chalk-carved White Horses on surrounding hillsides.

Miss Matilda Talbot left the village of Lacock to the National Trust in the 1940s. Another Talbot, William Henry Fox, produced the first-ever photographic negative here in 1831. The village was also used for the recent BBC production of Jane Austen's *Pride & Predjudice.*

Malmesbury in Northern Wiltshire is the oldest borough in England and is home to a partially ruined 12th-century abbey, notable for a very impressive porch carving of the Apostles.

Top: Stonehenge

EVENTS & FESTIVALS

May
1st-11th Swindon Festival of Literature
4th Downton Cuckoo Fair
24th-9th June Salisbury Festival (various venues)
31st-3rd June Chippenham Folk Festival
tbc Swindon Kite Festival

June
24th May-9th Salisbury Festival (various venues)
22nd-29th Corsham Festival
31st May-3rd Chippenham Folk Festival

July
8th-9th Calne Country Music Festival
13th-15th Marlborough International Jazz Festival
26th-28th North Wiltshire Festival, Monkton Park, Chippenham
tbc Festival of Free Flight (hang gliding & paragliding), Wroughton Airfield, Swindon
tbc Marlborough Festival Open Studios, artists' studios within 8 mile radius

August
tbc Wiltshire Festival (music), Lydiard Park, Lydiard Tregoze, West Swindon

October
tbc Calne Music & Arts Festival
tbc Cricklade Festival
tbc North Wilts Classic Car Tour

⚏ AVEBURY
Map 04 SU06

ALEXANDER KEILLER MUSEUM
High St SN8 1RF (from A4 take A4361/B4003)
☎ 01672 539250 ▤ 01672 539388
e-mail: wavgen@smtp.ntrust.org.uk

This is one of the most important prehistoric sites in Europe, and was built before Stonehenge. An avenue of great stones leads to the site, which must have been a place of great religious significance. A barn gallery has recently been added. This interactive museum uses the latest interpretative techniques to explain the history of the Avebury landscape. **Times:** Open Apr-Oct, daily 10-6 or dusk if earlier; Nov-Mar, 10-4. (Closed 24-26 Dec & 1 Jan). **Fee:** £3.50 (ch £1.50). **Facilities:** ▣ ☙ ✗ licensed ᵹ toilets for disabled shop ✖ (ex guide dogs) ♨ ☙ ➽

AVEBURY MANOR
SN8 1RF (from A4 take A4361/B4003)
☎ 01672 539250 ▤ 01672 539388
e-mail: wavgen@smtp.ntrust.org.uk

Avebury Manor has a monastic origin, and has been much altered since then. The present buildings date from the early 16th century, with notable Queen Anne alterations and Edwardian renovation. The flower gardens contain medieval walls, and there are examples of topiary. **Times:** Open: House 2 Apr-Oct, Tue-Wed, Sun & BH Mon 2-5.30 (last admission 5pm or dusk if earlier). Garden 2 Apr-Oct daily ex Mon & Thu (open BH Mon). **Fee:** Manor & garden £3.50 (ch £1.70). Garden £2.50 (ch £1.20). **Facilities:** ▣ ᵹ shop ✖ ☙ ➽

⚏ BRADFORD-ON-AVON
Map 03 ST86

GREAT CHALFIELD MANOR
SN12 8NJ (3m SW of Melksham)
☎ 01225 782239 ▤ 01225 783379
Times: Open 4 Apr-Oct, Tue-Thu, guided tours only at 12.15, 2.15, 3, 3.45, 4.30. **Facilities:** ▣ ✖ ☙ *Details not confirmed for 2002*

TITHE BARN
Times: Open all year, daily 10.30-4. (Closed 25 Dec). Keykeeper. **Facilities:** ▣ ᵹ ✖ ♨ *Details not confirmed for 2002*

⚏ CALNE
Map 03 ST97

BOWOOD HOUSE & GARDENS
SN11 0LZ (off A4 Chippenham to Calne road, in Derry Hill village)
☎ 01249 812102 ▤ 01249 821757
e-mail: houseandgardens@bowood-estate.co.uk

Built in 1624, the house was finished by the first Earl of Shelburne, who employed celebrated architects, notably Robert Adam, to complete the work. Adam's library is particularly admired, and also in the house is the laboratory where Dr Joseph Priestley discovered oxygen in 1774. The chief glory of Bowood, however, is its 2000-acre expanse, 100 acres of which are pleasure gardens. They were laid out by 'Capability' Brown in the 1760s and are carpeted with daffodils, narcissi and bluebells in spring. For the under 12s, the adventure playground is full of thrills and excitement. **Times:** Open Apr-Oct, daily 11-6, including BH. Rhododendron Gardens (separate entrance off A342) open 6 weeks during mid Apr-early Jun 11-6. **Fee:** House & Grounds £5.90 (ch £3.70 & pen £4.90). Rhododendrons only £3.25 **Facilities:** ▣ ☙ ✗ licensed ᵹ (parking by arrangement) toilets for disabled shop ✖ (ex guide & hearing dogs) ➽

⚏ CORSHAM
Map 03 ST87

CORSHAM COURT
SN13 0BZ (4m W of Chippenham off A4)
☎ 01249 701610 ▤ 01249 701610

The Elizabethan manor was built in 1582, and then bought by the Methuen family in the 18th century to house their collections of paintings and statues. 'Capability' Brown made additions to the house and laid out the park, and later John Nash made further changes. There is furniture by Chippendale, Adam, Cobb and Johnson inside, as well as the Methuen collection of Old Masters paintings. The garden has flowering shrubs, herbaceous borders, a Georgian bath house and peacocks. **Times:** Open Summer: 20 Mar-Sep daily ex Mon but incl BH's 2-5.30. Winter: Oct-19 Mar open wknds only 2-4.30pm. Last admission 30 minutes before closing. (Closed December). Open throughout year by appointment for groups 15+. **Fee:** *Prices not confirmed for 2002* **Facilities:** ▣ ☙ ᵹ shop ✖

⚏ HOLT
Map 03 ST86

THE COURTS
BA14 6RR (3m N of Trowbridge, on B3107)
☎ 01225 782340
Times: Open 2 Apr-15 Oct, daily (ex Sat) 1.30-5.30. Out of season by appointment. ᵹ ✖ ☙ *Details not confirmed for 2002*

⚏ LACOCK
Map 03 ST96

LACKHAM COUNTRYSIDE CENTRE
SN15 2NY (3m S of Chippenham, on A350)
☎ 01249 466800 ▤ 01249 466818
e-mail: adavies@lackcoll.ac.uk

Various visitor attractions are situated within the 210-hectare estate of Wiltshire College – Lackham. Thatched and refurbished farm buildings accommodate the farm museum and the grounds feature a walled garden, glasshouses, and a farm park. The largest citron (large lemon), which earned a place in the Guinness Book of Records, was grown in this garden. **Times:** Open Etr-Aug, Sun & BH Mon 10-5. Last admission 4pm. **Fee:** £2 (concessions £2, up to 2 ch under 16 free). **Facilities:** ▣ ☙ ✗ ᵹ (wheelchair available) toilets for disabled shop

LACOCK ABBEY
SN15 2LG (3m S of Chippenham, E of A350)
☎ 01249 730227 (abbey) 730459 (museum)
Times: Museum, Cloisters & Grounds, 26 Feb-29 Oct, daily 11-5.30. Closed Good Fri. Abbey, Apr-29 Oct daily, ex Tue, 1-5.30. Closed Good Fri. Museum open winter wknds, but closed 23-24 Dec-7 Jan. **Facilities:** ▣ ᵹ (taped guides) toilets for disabled shop ✖ ♨ *Details not confirmed for 2002*

🏛 LONGLEAT

Map 03 ST84

LONGLEAT

The Estate Office BA12 7NW (from A36 Bath-Salisbury take A362 Warminster-Frome).
☎ 01985 844400 📠 01985 844885
e-mail: longleat@longleat.co.uk

Nestling within magnificent 'Capability' Brown landscaped grounds in the heart of Wiltshire, Longleat House is widely regarded as one of the most beautiful stately homes open to the public. Longleat House was built by Sir John Thynne and completed in 1580. It has remained the home of the same family ever since. Many treasures are contained within the house: paintings by Tintoretto and Wooton, exquisite Flemish tapestries, fine French furniture and elaborate ceilings by John Dibblee Crace. The murals in the family apartments in the West Wing were painted by Alexander Thynn, the present Marquis, and are fascinating and remarkable additions to the collection. Apart from the ancestral home, Longleat is also renowned for its safari park, the first of its kind in the UK. Here, visitors have the rare opportunity to see hundreds of animals in a natural woodland and parkland setting. Among the most magnificent sights are the famous pride of lions, white tiger, wolves, rhesus monkeys, elephants and zebra. Other attractions which ensure a fun family day out include the 'World's Longest Hedge Maze', the 'Adventure Castle', 'Longleat Railway', 'Pets' Corner' and the 'Safari Boats'. For details of events at Longleat, visit the website at www.longleat.co.uk.

Times: Open Attractions: 16 Mar-3 Nov. House: 16 Mar-Dec daily (ex Xmas Day). Ring to confirm opening arrangements out of season. **Fee:** Longleat passport: under review **Facilities:** 🅿 💺 ✗ licensed ♿ (Informative leaflet available or see website) toilets for disabled shop (free kennels for Safari park) 🍴

🏛 LUDGERSHALL

Map 04 SU25

LUDGERSHALL CASTLE

SP11 9QR (7m NW of Andover on A342)
Times: Open all reasonable times. **Facilities:** 🅿 ♿ 🎯 *Details not confirmed for 2002*

CORSHAM COURT

HOME OF THE METHUEN FAMILY

Corsham Court is one of England's finest Stately Homes. It was a Royal Manor in the days of the Saxon Kings, and the present building is based upon an Elizabethan Manor dating from 1582. Magnificent Georgian State Rooms were added in 1760. It houses one of the oldest and most distinguished collections of Old Masters and Furniture in the country, and with its 'Capability' Brown gardens and arboretum, and architecture by John Nash and Thomas Bellamy, Corsham Court provides the visitor with a wonderful opportunity to enjoy the many delights of the historic and beautiful Stately Home.

Tel/Fax: 01249 701610

For opening times see gazetteer entry

🏛 LYDIARD PARK

Map 04 SU18

LYDIARD PARK

Lydiard Tregoze SN5 9PA (from M4 junct 16. Follow brown tourist signs)
☎ 01793 770401 📠 01793 877909

Set in country parkland, Lydiard Park belonged to the St John family (the Bolingbrokes) for 500 years up until 1943 when it was purchased by the Swindon Corporation. Since then the house has been restored and many of the original furnishings returned together with a family portrait collection dating from Elizabethan to Victorian times. Exceptional plasterwork, early wallpaper, a rare painted glass window, and a room devoted to the talented 18th-century amateur artist, Lady Diana Spencer (Beauclerk), can also be seen.

Times: Open all year, House: Mon-Fri 10-1 & 2-5, Sat 10-5, Sun 2-5 (last Sun in every month, 11-5). Winter closing 4pm (Nov-Feb). Park: all year, daily closing at dusk each day. **Fee:** £1.40 (ch 70p).

Facilities: 🅿 💺 ♿ (telephone 01793 770401 for access information sheet) toilets for disabled shop 🐕 (ex guide dogs in house)

🏛 MARLBOROUGH

Map 04 SU16

CROFTON BEAM ENGINES

Crofton Pumping Station, Crofton SN8 3DW (signposted from A338/A346/B3087 at Burbage)
☎ 01672 870300

The oldest working beam engine in the world still in its original building and still doing its original job, the

contd.

Boulton and Watt 1812, is to be found in this rural spot. Its companion is a Harvey's of Hayle of 1845. Both are steam driven, from a hand-stoked, coal-fired boiler, and pump water into the summit level of the Kennet and Avon Canal with a lift of 40ft.

Times: Open daily May-Sep. Telephone for dates of steaming wknds. **Fee:** Steaming weekend: £3.50 (ch £1, under 5 free & pen £2.50). Family ticket £7. Non-steaming days £2 (ch 50p, pen £1.50). **Facilities:** 🅿 ⬤ ♿ (phone warden in advance, sighted guides provided) shop 🐾

🏛 MIDDLE WOODFORD   Map 04 SU13
Heale Gardens, Plant Centre & Shop
SP4 6NT (4m N of Salisbury, between A360 & A345)
☎ 01722 782504

Heale House and its eight acres of beautiful garden lie beside the River Avon at Middle Woodford. Much of the house is unchanged since King Charles II sheltered here after the Battle of Worcester in 1651. The garden provides a wonderfully varied collection of plants, shrubs, and musk and other roses, growing in the formal setting of clipped hedges and mellow stonework.

Times: Open all year, daily 10-5. **Fee:** £3.25 (ch 5-15 £1.50 under 5's free). Party 20+. **Facilities:** 🅿 ⬤ ♿ shop garden centre 🐾 (ex guide dogs) ⬤

🏛 SALISBURY   Map 04 SU12
The Medieval Hall (Secrets of Salisbury)
Cathedral Close SP1 2EY (follow signs in Cathedral Close)
☎ 01722 412472 & 324731 🖷 01722 339983
e-mail: medihall@aol.com

Visit the historic 13th century Medieval Hall and watch the fascinating 40 minute sound and picture guide to the city and region. A witty and informative soundtrack, specially composed music and some startling effects accompany hundreds of images to provide an insight into Salisbury's extraordinary past, the colourful city of today, and many of the attractions in the area. Enjoy refreshments while you watch. Contact the Hall for full details of special events.

Times: Open Apr-Sep, from 11-5. Also open throughout year for pre-booked groups. **Fee:** £1.50 (ch u6 free, ch 7-18 £1). Family tickets available **Facilities:** 🅿 (charged) ♿

Mompesson House
Chorister's Green, Cathedral Close SP1 2EL
☎ 01722 335659 🖷 01722 335659
e-mail: wmpkxr@smtp.ntrust.org.uk
Times: Open Apr-Oct, daily (ex Thu & Fri) 12-5.30. **Facilities:** 🅿 ⬤ ♿ shop 🐾 🦌 *Details not confirmed for 2002*

Old Sarum
Castle Rd SP1 3SD (2m N on A345)
☎ 01722 335398

Impressive remains of an Iron-Age camp surround what was the original site of Salisbury cathedral and its

thriving community. It was abandoned in medieval times, and the bishop and his flock moved to found a new cathedral where the present city stands. However, for many hundreds of years after its desertion, until the Reform Bill of 1832, ten voters continued to return two MPs to parliament at Westminster.

Times: Open all year, Apr-Sep daily 10-6 (from 9am Jul & Aug; Oct 10-5); Nov-28 Mar, daily 10-4. (Closed 24-26 Dec & 1 Jan). (Reviewed Mar 2002) **Fee:** £2 (ch 5-15 £1, under 5's free, con £1.50). (Reviewed Mar 2002) **Facilities:** 🅿 ♿ 🎫

Salisbury Cathedral
33 The Close SP1 2EJ (south of city centre & Market Sq)
☎ 01722 555120 🖷 01722 555116
e-mail: visitors@salcath.co.uk

Built in one phase between 1220 and 1258, the Cathedral is probably Britain's finest piece of medieval architecture. The spire is 123 metres tall, making it the highest in England. The Chapter House displays a frieze depicting scenes from Genesis and Exodus, and also the finest surviving Magna Carta. The Choir continues a tradition that began around 750 years ago, with performances at daily services. They are accompanied by Europe's finest romantic church organ. The surrounding Cathedral Close contains two museums, two small stately homes and acres of lawn.

Times: Open all year, Jan-May, Sep-Dec, daily 7.15-6.15; Jun-Aug, Mon-Sat 7.15-8.15. **Fee:** Suggested Voluntary Donations: £3.50 (ch £2, pen & students £2.50). Family £8. **Facilities:** 🅿 (100yds) (limited spaces) ⬤ 🗡 licensed ♿ (loop system, interpretative model for blind, wheelchairs) toilets for disabled shop ⬤

Salisbury & South Wiltshire Museum
The King's House, 65 The Close SP1 2EN (in Cathedral Close)
☎ 01722 332151 🖷 01722 325611
e-mail: museum@
salisburymuseum.freeserve.co.uk

One of the most outstanding of the beautiful buildings in Cathedral Close houses this local museum. Galleries include Stonehenge, History of Salisbury, the Pitt Rivers collection, ceramics and pictures and the Wedgwood

contd.

room, a reconstruction of a pre-NHS surgery, and a costume, lace and embroidery gallery.
Times: Open all year Mon-Sat 10-5; also Suns Jul & Aug, 2-5. (Closed Xmas). **Fee:** £3.50 (under 5's free, ch £1, pen, students & UB40s £2.30). Party. Season saver tickets available. **Facilities:** P (100 metres) (nearby parking charge) ✗ ᘓ parking by prior arrangement,induction loop in lecture hall toilets for disabled shop ✗ (ex guide dogs) ◀

⛫ STONEHENGE Map 04 SU14
STONEHENGE
SP4 7DE (2m W of Amesbury at junct of A303 and A344/A360)
☎ 01980 624715

One of the most famous prehistoric monuments in Europe, the henge was started about 5,000 years ago, but redesigned several times during the following 1,500 years. Enormous sarsens, each weighing more than 50 tons, were dragged from the Marlborough Downs, and were then worked into the design we see today - an outer ring of upright stones with lintels, and an inner horseshoe of five pairs of uprights, also with lintels. The axis of the horseshoe points towards the midsummer sunrise.
Times: Open all year, daily, 16 Mar-May & Sep-15 Oct 9.30-6; Jun-Aug, 9-7; 16-23 Oct 9.30-5; 24 Oct-15 Mar 9.30-4. Closed 24-26 Dec. Last admission no later than 30 mins before the advertised closing time. Stonehenge will close promptly 20 mins after the advertised closing time. **Fee:** £4.20 (ch u5 free, ch 5-15 £2.20, con £3.20). **Facilities:** P ◪ ᘓ shop ✗ ✿

⛫ STOURHEAD Map 03 ST73
STOURHEAD HOUSE & GARDEN
Estate Office BA12 6QD (off B3092, 3m NW Mere, follow brown tourist signs)
☎ 01747 841152 ▤ 01747 841152
e-mail: wstest@smtp.ntrust.org.uk

The Palladian house was built in 1720. What makes Stourhead especially memorable is the superb gardens, laid out in 1741. They feature a grotto, a temple to Flora around two springs and the magnificent pantheon with statues and stone reliefs.
Times: Open - House 23 Mar-3 Nov, Sat-Wed 12-5.30 or dusk if earlier. Garden daily all year 9-7 or dusk if earlier. King Alfreds Tower, 23 Mar-3 Nov, Tue-Sun (but open BH Mon), Tue-Fri 2-5.30, Sat-Sun & BH Mon 11.30-5.30 or dusk if earlier. **Fee:** House or garden Mar-Oct £4.90 (ch £2.70). Family £12, Party 15+ £4.40 each. Garden only Nov-Feb £3.80 (ch £1.90). Family £10. Combined House & Garden ticket £8.60 (ch £4.10) Family ticket £20. Parties 15+ £8.10 each. King Alfred's Tower £1.60 (ch 80p) Family £4. **Facilities:** ◪ ◪ ✗ licensed ᘓ (wheelchairs, electric buggy, telephone in advance) toilets for disabled shop garden centre ✗ (ex in gardens Nov-Feb only) ⚘ ◀

⛫ STOURTON Map 03 ST73
STOURTON HOUSE FLOWER GARDEN
Stourton House BA12 6QF (3m NW of Mere, on A303)
☎ 01747 840417

Times: Open Apr-end Nov, Wed, Thu, Sun & BH Mon 11-6 (or dusk if earlier). Also open Dec-Mar, wkdays for plant/dried flower sales.
Facilities: ◪ ◪ ᘓ (wheelchairs available) toilets for disabled shop (plants for sale) garden centre ✗ (ex by arrangement) *Details not confirmed for 2002*

⛫ SWINDON Map 04 SU18
STEAM - MUSEUM OF THE GREAT WESTERN RAILWAY
Kemble Dr SN2 2TA (from M4 junct 16 & A420 follow brown signs to 'Outlet Centre')
☎ 01793 466646 ▤ 01793 466615
e-mail: lsmith@swindon.gov.uk

This brand new museum celebrates the people who built, operated and travelled on the Great Western Railway. Using interactive exhibits, displays, and many original locomotives, one of England's most important historic railways is brought to life.
Times: Open Nov-Mar, Mon-Sat 10-5, Sun 11-5. Apr-Oct, Mon-Sat 10-5.30, Sun 11-5.30. **Fee:** £5.70 (ch £3.60, pen £3.70) Family ticket £14 (2ad+2ch). **Facilities:** P (100 yds) (disabled parking only at establishment) ◪ ᘓ audio guide, wheelchair or scooter can be pre-booked toilets for disabled shop ✗ (ex guide dogs) ◀

⛫ TEFFONT MAGNA Map 03 ST93
FARMER GILES FARMSTEAD
SP3 5QY (11m W of Salisbury, off A303 at Teffont)
☎ 01722 716338 ▤ 01722 716993
e-mail: tdeane6995@aol.com

Set in 175 acres of Wiltshire downland, this is a real working dairy farm. You can watch the cows being milked, bottle feed lambs and get to know a host of other animals and pets. There is an adventure playground with tractors and a relaxing walk along the picturesque Beech belt, meeting Highland cattle and

contd.

Shire horses along the way. There are also exhibition areas and a restaurant.
Times: Open 18 Mar-5 Nov, daily 10-6, wknds in winters, 10-dusk. Party bookings all year. **Fee:** £3.95 (ch £2.85, under 2's free & pen £3.50) Family ticket £13. **Facilities:** ▣ ✗ licensed ㅕ (complete access for disabled/wheelchairs available for use) toilets for disabled shop ➹

⛪ TISBURY   Map 03 ST92
OLD WARDOUR CASTLE
SP3 6RR (2m SW)
☎ 01747 870487

Substantial remains of this hexagonal 14th-century castle are still standing, with walls 60ft high. It was twice besieged, and finally ruined during the Civil War. These ruins are considered among the most attractive in England.
Times: Open all year, Apr-Oct, daily 10-6 (Oct 10-5); Nov-Mar Wed-Sun 10-4, (closed 1-2pm) . Closed 24-26 Dec & 1 Jan. (Reviewed Mar 2002) **Fee:** £2.50 (ch 5-15 £1.30, ch u5 free, con £1.50) (Reviewed Mar 2002) **Facilities:** ▣ ㅕ ✿

⛪ WESTBURY   Map 03 ST85
WOODLAND PARK & HERITAGE CENTRE
Brokerswood BA13 4EH (turn off A36 at Bell Inn, Standerwick. Follow brown tourist signs)
☎ 01373 822238 & 823880 ᐧ 01373 858474
e-mail: woodland.park@virgin.net
Times: Open all year; Park open daily 10-6. Museum open Mon-Fri 10-5 (summer), 12-3 (winter); Sat 2-6, Sun 10-6 (summer); Sun 2-4.30 (winter). Free admission for wheelchair users. **Facilities:** ▣ ♨ ㅕ shop *Details not confirmed for 2002*

⛪ WESTWOOD   Map 03 ST85
WESTWOOD MANOR
BA15 2AF (1.5m SW of Bradford on Avon, off B3109)
☎ 01225 863374
Times: Open Apr-Sep, Sun, Tue & Wed 2-5 **Facilities:** ▣ ✟ ♘
Details not confirmed for 2002

⛪ WILTON (near Salisbury)   Map 04 SU03
WILTON HOUSE
SP2 0BJ (3m W of Salisbury, on A30, 10m from Stonehenge & A303)
☎ 01722 746720 & 746729(24 hr line)
ᐧ 01722 744447
e-mail: tourism@wiltonhouse.com

Built on the site of a 9th century nunnery founded by King Alfred, the Tudor origins of the house can still be seen in the tower which survived the 1647 fire and is now incorporated within the splendid 17th-century house, based on designs by Inigo Jones. Wilton House boasts a world famous art collection with over 230 paintings on show. Outside there are 21 acres of landscaped parkland, rose and water gardens, woodland and riverside walks.
Times: Open 4 Apr-28 Oct daily 10.30-5.30. Last admission 4.30.
Fee: £7.25 (ch 5-15 £4.50, under 5 free, stu & pen £6.25). Family ticket £20. **Facilities:** ▣ ♨ ✗ licensed ㅕ (induction loop) toilets for disabled shop garden centre ✟ (ex guide dogs) ➹

⛪ WOODHENGE   Map 04 SU14
WOODHENGE
(1.5m N of Amesbury, off A345 just S of Durrington)
Times: Open all reasonable times. **Facilities:** ▣ ㅕ ✿ *Details not confirmed for 2002*

Worcestershire

In Worcestershire, the fertile plains of the Vale of Evesham and the Severn Valley climb to the Malvern Hills in the west, and the Cotswolds in the south. To the north of the county lies the industrialised area of the Black Country, in sharp contrast to the south's rural idyll.

Worcester is the county town, and home to the Worcestershire County Cricket Club, which has what some regard as the most attractive grounds in the country, in a delightful setting with views of Worcester Cathedral. Worcester Racecourse is one of the oldest in the country, in Pitchcroft Park, close to the city, beside the River Severn.

Sir Edward Elgar was a Worcester man, and his statue stands in the High Street of the city, facing the cathedral. The cottage where he was born, in Lower Broadheath just west of Worcester, is now open as a museum. He has also recently been commemorated on the new £20 note.

Southeast of Worcester is the Vale of Evesham, the main fruit-growing area of the country, dotted with orchards and market gardens – a picture in the spring with the blossom in the trees. The main town in this area is Evesham, set in a loop of the River Avon.

The Malverns, Great and Little, set on the slopes of the Malvern Hills, are renowned for their refinement. Great Malvern, terraced on its hillside site, came to prominence as a genteel spa for well-to-do Victorians, rivalling the likes of Bath, Buxton and Cheltenham with its glorious surroundings.

EVENTS & FESTIVALS

May
3rd-6th Upton Folk Festival (various venues), Upton-upon-Severn
9th-12th Spring Garden Show, Three Counties Showground, Malvern

June
15th-17th Three Counties Show, Three Counties Showground, Malvern
28th-30th Upton Jazz Festival (various venues), Upton-upon-Severn

July
tbc Worcester Carnival

September
28th-29th The Malvern Autumn Show, Three Counties Showground, Malvern

October
tbc Worcester Male Voice Choir Concert

December
tbc Victorian Christmas Fayre

Top: Sunrise over the Malverns

🏛 BEWDLEY
Map 07 SO77

SEVERN VALLEY RAILWAY
Comberton Hill
☎ 01299 403816   🖨 01299 400839
(For full entry see Kidderminster)

WEST MIDLAND SAFARI & LEISURE PARK
Spring Grove DY12 1LF (on A456 between
Kidderminster & Bewdley)
☎ 01299 402114   🖨 01299 404519

Located in the heart of rural Worcestershire, this 200-acre site is the home to a drive-through safari and Tiger World. There is a variety of rides, amusements and live shows suitable for all members of the family. Other features include Pets Corner, Hippo Lakes, Goat Walk and Seal Aquarium.
Times: Open Apr-Oct, daily from 10am including BH's. **Fee:** £5.95 (ch 4 free). Multi ride wristband £7. Junior restricted £5 (restricted rides only). Ride tickets £1 each from machines (various no of tickets per ride). **Facilities:** 🅿 💺 ✗ licensed ৬ (most area accessible slopes/tarmac paths) shop 🍴

🏛 BROADWAY
Map 04 SP03

BROADWAY TOWER & ANIMAL PARK
WR12 7LB (off A44, 1m SE of village)
☎ 01386 852390   🖨 01386 858038
e-mail: broadway-tower@clara.net
Times: Open Apr-Oct, daily 10.30-5. Nov-Mar (tower only) wknds weather permitting 11-3 or by prior booking. **Facilities:** 🅿 💺 ✗ licensed ৬ toilets for disabled shop *Details not confirmed for 2002*

🏛 BROMSGROVE
Map 07 SO97

AVONCROFT MUSEUM OF HISTORIC BUILDINGS
Stoke Heath B60 4JR (2m S, off A38)
☎ 01527 831886   🖨 01527 876934
e-mail: avoncroft1@compuserve.com

A visit to Avoncroft takes you through nearly 700 years of history. Here you can see 25 buildings rescued from destruction and authentically restored on a 15-acre rural site. There are 15th- and 16th-century timber framed buildings, 18th-century agricultural buildings and a cockpit. There are industrial buildings and a working windmill from the 19th century, and from the 20th, a fully furnished pre-fab.
Times: Open Jul-Aug daily 10.30-5; Apr-Jun & Sep-Oct 10.30-4.30 (wknds 5.30), (Closed Mon); Mar & Nov 10.30-4, (Closed Mon & Fri). Open BHs. **Fee:** £5 (ch £2.50, pen £4). Family ticket £13.50. **Facilities:** 🅿 💺 ৬ (ramps, wheelchair available) toilets for disabled shop 🍴

🏛 EVESHAM
Map 04 SP04

THE ALMONRY HERITAGE CENTRE
Abbey Gate WR11 4EJ (on A4184, opposite Merstow Green)
☎ 01386 446944   🖨 01386 442348
e-mail: almonry@eveshamtc.ndirect.co.uk
Times: Open all year, Mon-Sat & BHs (ex Xmas & Sun in Nov, Dec & Jan) 10-5, Sun 2-5. **Facilities:** 🅿 (110yds) shop ✗ *Details not confirmed for 2002*

🏛 GREAT WITLEY
Map 03 SO76

WITLEY COURT
WR6 6JT (on A433)
☎ 01299 896636

Spectacular ruins of a once great house. An earlier Jacobean manor house was converted in the 19th-century into a vast Italianate mansion with porticoes by John Nash. The adjoining church by James Gibbs has a remarkable 18th-century baroque interior. The gardens were equally elaborate and contained immense stone fountains which still survive today, the largest is the Poseidon Fountain
Times: Open all year Apr-Sep, daily 10-6, (Oct 10-5); Nov-Mar, Wed-Sun 10-4. Closed 24-26 Dec & 1 Jan. **Fee:** £3.80 (ch 5-15 £1.90, under 5's free, con £2.90) **Facilities:** 🅿 💺 ৬ 🏳

🏛 HANBURY
Map 03 SO96

HANBURY HALL
School Rd WR9 7EA (4.5m E of Droitwich, 1m N of B4090 and 1.5m W of B4091)
☎ 01527 821214   🖨 01527 821251
e-mail: hanbury@smtp.ntrust.org.uk
Times: Open 2 Apr-29 Oct, Sun-Wed Hall 2-6 & Gardens 12.30-5.30. Last admission 5.30 (dusk if earlier). **Facilities:** 🅿 💺 ৬ (Braille guide) toilets for disabled shop ✗ (ex in park) 🍴 *Details not confirmed for 2002* 🍴

🏛 KIDDERMINSTER
Map 07 SO87

SEVERN VALLEY RAILWAY
Comberton Hill (on A448, clearly signposted)
☎ 01299 403816   🖨 01299 400839

The leading standard gauge steam railway, with one of the largest collections of locomotives and rolling stock in the country. Services operate from Kidderminster and Bewdley to Bridgnorth through 16 miles of picturesque scenery along the River Severn. Special steam galas and "Day out with Thomas" Weekends take place during the year along with Santa Specials.
Times: Trains operate wknds throughout year, daily early May to end Sep, plus school holidays & half terms, Santa Specials, phone for details. **Fee:** Subject to Review.(Train fares vary according to journey. Main through ticket £9.60 return, Family ticket £25) **Facilities:** 🅿 💺 ৬ (some specially adapted trains, call for details) toilets for disabled shop (at Kidderminster/Bridgnorth) 🍴

WORCESTERSHIRE COUNTY MUSEUM
Hartlebury Castle, Hartlebury DY11 7XZ (4m S of Kidderminster clearly signed from A449)
☎ 01299 250416   🖨 01299 251890
e-mail: museum@worcestershire.gov.uk

Housed in the north wing of Hartlebury Castle, the County Museum contains a delightful display of crafts and industries. There are unique collections of toys, costume, domestic life, room settings and horse-drawn

contd.

vehicles as well as a reconstructed forge, schoolroom, wheelwright's and tailor's shop.
Times: Open Feb-Nov, Mon-Thu 10-5, BH's 11-5, Fri & Sun 2-5. (Closed Sat & Good Fri). **Fee:** £2.50 (ch & pen £1.20). Family ticket £6.50. **Facilities:** ☐ ♥ ♿ (car parking close to main building) toilets for disabled shop ✱ (ex guide dogs & in grounds) ☜

⛫ REDDITCH
Map 03 SP06

FORGE MILL NEEDLE MUSEUM & BORDESLEY ABBEY VISITOR CENTRE
Forge Mill, Needle Mill Ln, Riverside B98 8HY (N side of Redditch, off A441. M42 junct 2)
☎ 01527 62509
e-mail: museum@redditchbc.gov.uk

The Needle Museum tells the fascinating and sometimes gruesome story of how needles are made. Working, water-powered machinery can be seen in an original needle-scouring mill. The Visitor Centre is an archaeological museum showing finds from excavations at the nearby Bordesley Abbey.
Times: Open Etr-Sep, Mon-Fri 11-4.30, Sat-Sun 2-5; Feb-Etr & Oct-Nov, Mon-Thu 11-4 & Sun 2-5. Parties by arrangement. **Fee:** £3.50 (ch 50p, pen £2.50). Family ticket £7.50. Reduced admission charge for holders of a Reddicard. **Facilities:** ☐ ♿ (wheelchair available) toilets for disabled shop ✱ (ex guide dogs) ☜

⛫ SPETCHLEY
Map 03 SO85

SPETCHLEY PARK GARDENS
Spetchley Park WR5 1RS (3m E of Worcester, off A422)
☎ 01905 345213 or 345224 🖹 01453 511915
e-mail: hb@spetchleygardens.co.uk

The 110-acre deer park and the 30-acre gardens surround an early 19th-century mansion (not open), with sweeping lawns and herbaceous borders, a rose lawn and enclosed gardens with low box and yew hedges. There is a large collection of trees (including 17th-century Cedars of Lebanon), shrubs and plants, many of which are rare or unusual.
Times: Open 29 Apr-Sep, Tue-Fri 11-5, Sun 2-5; BH Mons 11-5. Other days by appointment. **Fee:** £3.50 (ch £1.80). Party 25+ £3.30. **Facilities:** ☐ ♥ ♿ (most of garden accessible) ✱

⛫ STONE
Map 07 SO87

STONE HOUSE COTTAGE GARDENS
DY10 4BG (2m SE of Kidderminster, on A448)
☎ 01562 69902 🖹 01562 69960
e-mail: louisa@shcn.co.uk

A beautiful walled garden with towers provides a sheltered area of about one acre for rare shrubs, climbers and interesting herbaceous plants. Adjacent to the garden is a nursery with a large selection of unusual plants.
Times: Open Gardens & nursery Mar-end Sep, Wed-Sat 10-5.30. **Fee:** £2.50 (ch free). **Facilities:** ☐ ♿ garden centre ✱

SEVERN VALLEY RAILWAY

the line for all seasons

The best way to see the beauty of the River Severn is from a steam-hauled train on the Severn Valley Railway.

Kidderminster-Bewdley-Bridgnorth

Open every weekend throughout the year, DAILY from early May to late September, plus local school holidays and half-terms.

THE RAILWAY STATION, BEWDLEY, WORCESTERSHIRE, DY12 1BG
Tel: 01299 403816
www.svr.co.uk

⛫ WORCESTER
Map 03 SO85

CITY MUSEUM & ART GALLERY
Foregate St WR1 1DT (in city centre, 150mtrs from Foregate St railway station)
☎ 01905 25371 🖹 01905 616979

The gallery has temporary art exhibitions from both local and national sources. Museum exhibits cover geology, local and natural history. Of particular interest is a complete 19th-century chemist's shop. There are collections relating to the Worcestershire Regiment and the Worcestershire Yeomanry Cavalry.
Times: Open all year, Mon, Tue-Fri 9.30-5.30, Sat 9.30-5.(Closed 25-26 Dec & 1 Jan also Good Fri) **Fee:** Free. **Facilities:** ℗ (city centre) ♥ ♿ (lift, induction loop) toilets for disabled shop ✱ ☜

THE COMMANDERY
Sidbury WR1 2HU (M5 junct 7, A44, signposted)
☎ 01905 361821 🖹 01905 361822
e-mail: thecommandery@cityof worcester.gov.uk

The headquarters of Charles II's army during the Battle of Worcester in 1651. The Commandery is an impressive complex of medieval timber framed buildings. Various exhibitions include 'Civil War',which details the events of England's bloody revolution.
Times: Open all year, Mon-Sat 10-5, Sun 1.30-5. (Closed 25-26 Dec & 1 Jan) **Fee:** £3.90 (con £2.75) Family ticket £9.95. **Facilities:** ℗ (100yds) shop ✱ (ex guide dogs) ☜

ELGAR'S BIRTHPLACE MUSEUM

Crown East Ln, Lower Broadheath WR2 6RH (3m W,
signposted off A44 to Leominster)
☎ 01905 333426 🖷 01905 333426
e-mail: birthplace@elgar.org

The cottage where composer Sir Edward Elgar was
born in 1857 is now a museum. Housed here is a
unique collection of photographs, manuscripts and
personal memorabilia recording his life and
achievements. See the views of the Malvern Hills that
inspired much of Elgar's music, learn about his wide-
ranging interests and how he composed works such as
'Enigma Variations'.
Times: Open daily 11-5, last admission 4.15, (closed Xmas Day-end
Jan). **Fee:** £3.50 (ch £1.50, stu £1.75 & pen £2.60). Family ticket £8.50.
Party rates available. **Facilities:** 🅿 ♿ (large print guides, audio
facilities, wheelchair access) toilets for disabled shop ✸ (ex guide
dogs) ◥

HAWFORD DOVECOTE

(3m N on A449)
☎ 01684 850051
Times: Open Apr-1 Nov, daily 9-6 or sunset. (Closed Good Fri). Other
times by prior appointment only. **Facilities:** 🅿 (on street parking) ✸
❊ *Details not confirmed for 2002*

MUSEUM OF LOCAL LIFE

Friar St WR1 2NA (city centre, 5min walk from
Cathedral)
☎ 01905 722349

This interesting 500-year-old timber-framed house has
a squint and an ornate plaster ceiling. It is now a
museum of local life and displays show life here over
the last 200 years.
Times: Open all year, Mon-Wed & Fri-Sat 10.30-5. Also BH's. (Closed
25-26 Dec & 1 Jan). **Fee:** Free. 🅿 (200yds) ♿ toilets for disabled shop
✸

MUSEUM OF WORCESTER PORCELAIN

Severn St WR1 2NE (M5 junct 7, follow signs to city
centre, at 5th lights take 1st left into Edger St, bear left
into Severn St. At T-junct bear right. 100yds take 1st
left)
☎ 01905 23221 🖷 01905 617807
e-mail: museum@royal-worcester.co.uk

The Victorian buildings lead into the heart of a world
famous porcelain industry and was founded in 1751.
The guided tours and the Museum of Worcester
Porcelain take visitors on a design journey through
time. Exhibits include room settings, dining scenes and
shop fronts in the Georgian, Victorian and 20th-century
galleries.
Times: Open all year, Mon-Sat 9-5.30, Sun 11-5. **Fee:** Museum: £3
(concessions £2.25), family £6.50. Guided factory tour £5. Special all-
in-one £8 (concessions £6.75), family £20. **Facilities:** 🅿 (charged) ✗
licensed ♿ (ex factory) toilets for disabled shop ✸ ◥

WORCESTER CATHEDRAL

WR1 2LH
☎ 01905 28854 & 21004 🖷 01905 611139
Times: Open all year, daily 7.30-6. **Facilities:** 🅿 (500yds) ♨ ♿
(limited access due to nature of building) toilets for disabled shop ✸
(ex guide dogs) *Details not confirmed for 2002*

East Riding of Yorkshire

From the imposing chalk cliffs at Flamborough, to the rolling green pastures of the Yorkshire Wolds, and the flourishing port of Hull, the East Riding of Yorkshire boasts some of the finest unspoilt countryside in England, and some wonderful places to visit.

Beverley Minster is big enough to be a cathedral. Among its treasures are a 1000-year old sanctuary chair and some wonderfully intricate wooden carvings. The magnificent Percy Tomb is a fine example of 14th-century stonemasonry. Beverley is also home to the Museum of Army Transport.

Driffield is known as the 'Capital of the Wolds', and is home to a livestock auction that attracts farmers from all around. Close by is Sledmere House, an impressive manor house set among parkland designed by `Capability' Brown.

Coastal areas of the East Riding can be a little daunting. Flamborough Head is a plateau of rolling turf 150ft high, surrounded on three sides by the sea. The Heritage Coast Project puts on a wide range of events which includes lectures, guided walks and nature expeditions. The lighthouse has defied the elements since 1806.

Further down the coast, Spurn Head is an unusual sand and shingle peninsula curving across the mouth of the Humber, formed of deposits washed from the crumbling cliffs of Holderness a few miles to the north. The earliest record of Spurn is from 670 AD, when a monastery was established there. Since then the spit has been broken down and rebuilt by the sea three times.

Top: Groynes at Spurn Head

EVENTS & FESTIVALS

April
26th-7th May Bridlington Arts Festival (various venues)
27th-28th East Riding of Yorkshire Classic Cycle Race, Beverley (provisional)

May
5th-6th East Riding Garden & Kite Festival, Beverley
23rd-27th Beverley & East Riding Early Music Festival
26th April-7th Bridlington Arts Festival (various venues)

June
21st-23rd Beverley & East Riding Folk Festival

July
4th-6th Hornsea Music Festival, various venues
17th Driffield Agricultural Show, Driffield Showground

August
10th-11th Driffield Steam & Vintage Rally, Driffield
tbc International Sea Shanty Festival, Hull Marina, Hull
tbc Bridlington Harbour Gala, Garrison Square, Bridlington

September
tbc Beverley & East Riding Chamber Music Festival
tbc International Sequence Dance Festival, Royal Hall Ballroom, Bridlington

October
tbc Hull Fair, Hull

November
tbc Hull Literature Festival

🏛 BEMPTON
Map 08 TA17
RSPB NATURE RESERVE
YO15 1JD (take cliff road from B1229, Bempton and follow brown tourist signs)
☎ 01262 851179 🖪 01262 851533

Part of the spectacular chalk cliffs that stretch from Flamborough Head to Speeton, this is one of the sites in England to see thousands of nesting seabirds including gannets and puffins at close quarters. Viewpoints overlook the cliffs which are best visited from April to July. Enormous numbers of seabirds nest on these cliffs and this is the only gannetry on the English mainland. Many migrants pass off-shore and frequent the clifftop on migration. Grey seal and porpoise are sometimes seen offshore. Please phone for details of events.
Times: Open for visitor centre daily, Mar-Nov 10-5. Winter wknds only 9.30-4. Closed Jan **Fee:** £3 per car, £5 per minibus, £8 per coach **Facilities:** 🅿 (charged) 🍽 & toilets for disabled shop 🐾 (ex on a leash in reserve) 🍹

🏛 BEVERLEY
Map 08 TA03
MUSEUM OF ARMY TRANSPORT
Flemingate HU17 0NG
☎ 01482 860445 🖪 01482 872767

The museum tells the story of army transport from horse drawn wagons to the recent Gulf conflict: everything from prototype vehicles to Montgomery's Rolls Royce and the last Blackburn Beverley aircraft. There are also other exhibits to be explored including 'Monty's Men and D-Day Dodgers".
Times: Open all year, daily 10-5. (Closed 24-26 Dec). **Fee:** £4.50 (ch 5-15, pen & student £3). Family ticket £12 (2 adults & 2 ch). Under 5's free. **Facilities:** 🅿 (charged) 🍽 & (parking next to entrance) toilets for disabled shop 🐾 (ex guide dogs)

🏛 BURTON AGNES
Map 08 TA16
BURTON AGNES HALL
Estate Office YO25 0ND (on A166)
☎ 01262 490324 🖪 01262 490513

Built in 1598, this is a magnificent Elizabethan house, with furniture, pictures and china amassed by the family owners over four centuries. There is a walled garden with maze, potager, herbaceous borders, clematis, campanula and geranium collections, and jungle garden, as well as woodland walks.
Times: Open Apr-Oct, daily 11-5. **Fee:** Hall & grounds £4.80 (ch £2.40, pen £4.30). Grounds only £2.40 (ch £1, pen £2.15). Party 30+.
Facilities: 🅿 🍽 & (scented garden for the blind) toilets for disabled shop garden centre 🍹

NORMAN MANOR HOUSE
Times: Open all year. ✿ *Details not confirmed for 2002*

🏛 HORNSEA
Map 08 TA14
HORNSEA MUSEUM
11 Newbegin HU18 1AB (turn off A165 onto B1244)
☎ 01964 533443

A former farmhouse whose outbuildings now illustrate local life and history. There are 19th-century period rooms and a dairy, plus craft tools and farming implements. Photographs, local personalities and industries are also featured.
Times: Open Etr-mid Oct, Mon-Sat 11-5, Sun 2-5 (last admission 4) **Fee:** £2 (concessions £1.50). Family ticket £6 **Facilities:** 🅿 (50yds) & toilets for disabled shop 🐾

🏛 HULL
Map 08 TA02
MAISTER HOUSE
160 High St HU1 1NL (city centre)
☎ 01482 324114 🖪 01482 227003

The house is a mid18th-century rebuilding, notable for its splendid stone and wrought-iron staircase, ornate stucco work and finely carved doors. Only the staircase and entrance hall are open.
Times: Open all year, Mon-Fri 10-4 (Closed BH). **Fee:** 80p (incl guide book). **Facilities:** 🅿 🐾 ♿ 🐕

MARITIME MUSEUM
Queen Victoria Square HU1 3DX (from M62 follow A63 to town centre, museum is in pedestrian area of town centre)
☎ 01482 613902 🖪 01482 613710
e-mail: museums@hullcc.gov.uk

Hull's maritime history is illustrated here, with displays on whales and whaling, ships and shipping, and other aspects of this Humber port. There is also a Victorian courtroom which is used for temporary exhibitions. The restored dock area, with its fine Victorian and Georgian buildings, is well worth exploring too.
Times: Open all year, Mon-Sat 10-5 & Sun 1.30-4.30. (Closed 25-2 Jan & Good Fri). **Fee:** Free. **Facilities:** 🅿 (100yds) & shop 🐾 (ex guide dogs)

'STREETLIFE' - HULL MUSEUM OF TRANSPORT
High St HU1 1PS (A63 from M62, follow signs for Old Town)
☎ 01482 613902 🖪 01482 613710
e-mail: museums@hullcc.gov.uk

This purpose built museum uses a 'hands-on' approach to trace 200 years of transport history. With a vehicle

contd.

collection of national importance, state of the art animatronic displays and authentic scenarios, you can see Hull's Old Town brought vividly to life. The mail coach ride uses the very latest in computer technology to recreate a Victorian journey by four-in-hand. **Times:** Open all year, Mon-Sat 10-5, Sun 1.30-4.30. (Closed 24-25 Dec & Good Fri). **Fee:** Free. **Facilities:** P (500m) & toilets for disabled shop ✷ (ex guide dogs)

WILBERFORCE HOUSE
23-25 High St HU1 1NE (A63 from M62 or A1079 from York, follow signs for Old Town)
☎ 01482 613902 ▤ 01482 613710
e-mail: museum@hullcc.gov.uk

The early 17th-century Merchants house was the birthplace of William Wilberforce, who became a leading campaigner against slavery. There are Jacobean and Georgian rooms and displays on Wilberforce, and the anti-slavery campaign. The house also has secluded gardens. There are special exhibitions throughout the year. **Times:** Open all year, Mon-Sat 10-5 & Sun 1.30-4.30. (Closed 25-26 Dec, 1 Jan & Good Fri). **Fee:** Free. **Facilities:** P (500m) (meters on street) & (large print, video area & audio guides) shop ✷ (ex guide dogs)

⛫ POCKLINGTON   Map 08 SE84
BURNBY HALL GARDEN & STEWART COLLECTION
The Balk YO42 2QF (off A1079 at turning for Pocklington off B1247)
☎ 01759 302068
Times: Open 31 Mar-Sep, daily 10-6. (last admission 5pm). **Facilities:** P ☛ & (free wheelchair hire) toilets for disabled shop ✷ (ex guide dogs) *Details not confirmed for 2002*

⛫ SEWERBY   Map 08 TA16
SEWERBY HALL & GARDENS
YO15 1EA
☎ 01262 677874 ▤ 01262 674265
e-mail: sewerbyhall@yahoo.com

Sewerby Hall and Gardens, set in 50 acres of parkland overlooking Bridlington Bay, dates back to 1715. The Georgian House, with its 19th-century Orangery, contains art galleries, archaeological displays and an Amy Johnson Room with a collection of her trophies and mementoes. The grounds include magnificent walled Old English and Rose gardens and host many events throughout the year. Activities for all the family include a Children's Zoo and play areas, golf, putting, bowls, plus woodland and clifftop walks. Phone for details of special events.
Times: Estate open all year, dawn-dusk. Hall - contact office for further details **Fee:** £3.10 (ch 5-15 £1, pen £2.30). Family ticket £7.20. Group 10+ **Facilities:** P ☛ & toilets for disabled shop ☛

⛫ SPROATLEY   Map 08 TA13
BURTON CONSTABLE HALL
HU11 4LN (1.5m N of Sproatley. 14m from Beverley - follow A165 Bridlington road)
☎ 01964 562400 ▤ 01964 563229
e-mail: burtonconstable@btclick.com

This superb Elizabethan house was built in 1570, but much of the interior was remodelled in the 18th century. There are magnificent reception rooms and a Tudor long gallery with a pendant roof: the contents range from pictures and furniture to a unique collection of 18th-century scientific instruments. Outside are 200 acres of parkland landscaped by 'Capability' Brown, with oaks and chestnuts, and a lake with an island.
Times: Open, Hall & grounds Etr Sun-end Oct. Grounds 12.30-5, Hall 1-5. **Fee:** House £4 (ch £1.50, pen £3.70). Family £9. **Facilities:** P ☛ & (stair list to first foor, wheelchairs) toilets for disabled shop

North Yorkshire

England's largest county, North Yorkshire has a stunning natural landscape, encompassing part of the Pennines, the rolling farmlands of the Vale of York, the Cleveland Hills and the North York Moors, plus the Yorkshire Dales National Park, which includes Swaledale and Wensleydale.

The coastline offers its own treasures, from the fishing villages of Staithes and Robin Hood Bay to Scarborough, one time Regency spa and Victorian bathing resort.

York, traditionally the capital of the North of England, was second only to London prior to the Industrial Revolution. It is a city of immense historical significance: capital of the British province under the Romans in AD 71 and a Viking settlement in the 10th century. In the Middle Ages its prosperity depended on the wool trade. The city's earliest surviving building is the Roman Multangular Tower, and the city walls, dating from the 14th century, are among the finest in Europe, including four gates or 'bars'. However, the gothic Minster is York's crowning glory, built between 1220 and 1470.

Northallerton, rather than York, is the administrative centre of the county. Harrogate, another celebrated North Yorkshire town, is a traditional spa resort renowned for its gentility and excellent tea rooms. Its handsome stone buildings and lovely gardens have earned it the title of Floral Resort of England. To the south of the town, an area of some 200 acres of common land known as The Stray is popular for walking and picnicking.

The Georgian Theatre
BUILT BY ACTOR-MANAGER
Samuel Butler
1788

Top: Askrigg

EVENTS & FESTIVALS

February
2nd-5th Harrogate Winter Antiques Fair, Harrogate
18th Kall Kwick National Rally, Pickering

March
9th-16th Eskdale Festival of the Arts, Whitby
29th-5th April Harrogate International Youth Music Festival (various venues)

April
31st March-1st Selby Game Fair, Carlton, Goole

May
10th-12th Teeside Garden & Woodland Festival, Yarm

June
14th-29th Grassington Festival, Grassington
21st-7th July Nidderdale Festival
tbc North Yorkshire County Show, South Otterington

July
9th-11th Great Yorkshire Show, Harrogate
18th-3rd August Harrogate International Festival
tbc Northern Aldeborough Festival

August
10th Ripley Show, Ripley
tbc Yorkshire Air Spectacular

September
7th-8th Autumn Gold Garden & Woodland Festival, Yarm
7th-15th Ripon International Festival of Music & the Arts

🏛 ALDBOROUGH
ROMAN TOWN
Map 08 SE46

YO51 9ES (0.75m SE of Boroughbridge, on minor road off B6265 within 1m of junction of A1 & A6055)
☎ 01423 322768

The pretty present-day village occupies the site of the northernmost civilian Roman town in Britain. Remains include two mosaic pavements and part of the town walls.
Times: Open Apr-Sep, daily 10-1 & 2-6 (Oct 10-1 & 2-5). (Closed Nov-28 Mar) **Fee:** £1.80 (ch 5-15 90p, under 5's free, con £1.40)
Facilities: 🍴 🎪

🏛 AYSGARTH
NATIONAL PARK CENTRE
Map 07 SE08

DL8 3TH (off A684, Leyburn to Hawes road at Falls junct & continue down hill over river, centre 500yds on left)
☎ 01969 663424 📠 01969 663105
e-mail: aysgarth@ytbtic.co.uk

A visitor centre for the Yorkshire Dales National Park, with maps, guides, walks and local information. Displays explain the history and natural history of the area.
Times: Open Apr-Oct, daily 10-5; Winter, wknds only. **Fee:** Free.
Facilities: 🅿 (charged) 🍴 ✗ ♿ toilets for disabled shop 🍴 (ex guide dogs) 🚼 🍵

YORKSHIRE CARRIAGE MUSEUM
Yore Mill DL8 3SR (1.75m E on unclass rd N of A684. Right at Palmer Flatt Hotel, museum 300yds)
☎ 01969 663399
Times: Open Apr-Oct, daily 9.30-7.30, other times 9.30-dusk. Closed 24 Dec-12 Jan. **Facilities:** 🅿 (150 yds) 🍵 shop *Details not confirmed for 2002*

🏛 BEDALE
BEDALE MUSEUM
Map 08 SE28

DL8 1AA (on A684, 1.5m W of A1 at Leeming Bar)
☎ 01677 423797 📠 01677 425393

Situated in a building dating back to the 17th-century, the Bedale is a fascinating museum. The central attraction is the Bedale fire engine, which dates back to 1742. Other artefacts include documents, toys, craft tools and household utensils, which all help to give an absorbing picture of the lifestyle of the times.
Times: Tue & Fri 10-12.30 & 2-4, Wed 2-4, Thu-Sat 10-12 **Fee:** Free.
Facilities: 🅿 ♿ 🍴 (ex guide dogs)

🏛 BENINGBROUGH
BENINGBROUGH HALL
Map 08 SE55

YO6 1DD (off A19, 8m NW of York. Entrance at Newton Lodge)
☎ 01904 470666 📠 01904 470002
e-mail: ybbrgb@smtp.ntrust.org.uk

Beningbrough was built around 1716. It houses 100 pictures from the National Portrait Gallery in London. Ornately carved wood panelling is a feature of several of the rooms. The other side of country house life can be seen in the restored Victorian laundry.
Times: Open 31 Mar-Jun & Sep-Oct, Sat-Wed & Good Fri. Also Fris during Jul & Aug daily except Thu. House 12-5. Last admission 4.30pm. Grounds 11am-5.30pm. Last admission 5pm. **Fee:** House, Garden & Exhibition: £5.20 (ch £2.60) Family ticket £13 (2+3 or 1+4). Garden & Exhibition: £3.60 (ch £1.80) Family £9. Cyclists £1 off any ticket.The house may close for up to 1 hour for wedding ceremonies on Fridays. Garden will remain open. **Facilities:** 🅿 ✗ licensed ♿ (access to Victorian laundry, shop & restaurant) toilets for disabled shop 🍴 🐾

🏛 BRIMHAM
BRIMHAM ROCKS
Map 08 SE26

Summerbridge HG3 4DW (off B6265)
☎ 01423 780688 📠 01423 781020
e-mail: yorkbm@smtp.ntrust.org.uk

A Victorian guidebook describes the rocks as 'a place wrecked with grim and hideous forms defying all description and definition'. The rocks have remained a great attraction, and stand on National Trust open moorland at a height of 950ft. An old shooting lodge in the area is now an information point and shop.
Times: Open all year: 8-dusk. May close in bad weather. **Fee:** Cars £2.30. Minibuses £5. Coaches £10. Motorcycles £1. **Facilities:** 🅿 ♿ (specially adapted path, braille guide) toilets for disabled shop 🐾

🏛 CASTLE BOLTON
BOLTON CASTLE
Map 07 SE09

DL8 4ET (off A684, 6 miles W of Leyburn)
☎ 01969 623981 📠 01969 623332
e-mail: harry@boltoncastle.co.uk
Times: Open Apr-Oct 10-5, Nov-Mar 10-4. **Facilities:** 🅿 🍴 shop 🍴 *Details not confirmed for 2002* 🍵

🏛 CASTLE HOWARD
See Malton

🏛 CLAPHAM
CLAPHAM NATIONAL PARK CENTRE
Map 07 SD76

LA2 8ED (signposted off A65 at Clapham)
☎ 015242 51419

A comprehensive information centre with displays on the local countryside and limestone scenery. A wide range of maps, guides, information leaflets, gifts and souvenirs are stocked and knowledgeable staff are on duty to answer questions.
Times: Open Apr-Oct, daily 10-5.Limited opening Nov-Mar. **Fee:** Free.
Facilities: 🅿 (charged) (Radar key scheme) shop 🍵

🏛 COXWOLD
BYLAND ABBEY
Map 08 SE57

YO6 4BD (2m S of A170 between Thirsk & Helmsley, near Coxwold village)
☎ 01347 868614

The abbey was built for the Cistercians in the 12th and 13th centuries and enough remains of the buildings to
contd.

show how beautiful it most have been. There are well preserved floor tiles, carved stones and other finds. **Times:** Open Apr-Sep, daily 10-6 (Oct 10-5). Closed 1-2pm. **Fee:** £4 (ch £3) family ticket £11.50 **Facilities:** ▣ & garden/grounds partly accessible toilets for disabled ⛌ ⛴

⛰ DANBY　　　　　　　Map 08 NZ70
MOORS CENTRE
Lodge Ln YO21 2NB (S off A171 signed 'Moors Centre Danby'. Right at crossroads in Danby, 2m to Centre on left)
☎ 01287 660654 ▤ 01287 660308
e-mail: moorscentre@ytbtic.co.uk

The ideal place to start exploring the North York Moors National Park. There is an exhibition about the area as well as events, video, a shop and local walks. The Moorsbus service also operates from this site – phone for details. **Times:** Open all year, Apr-Oct, daily 10-5. Nov, Dec & Mar daily 11-4. Jan & Feb wknds only 11-4. **Fee:** Free. **Facilities:** ▣ (charged) ⛴ & (woodland & garden trails, motorised & manual wheelchairs) toilets for disabled shop ⛌ (ex guide dogs & in grounds)

⛰ EASBY　　　　　　　Map 08 NZ10
EASBY ABBEY
(1m SE of Richmond off B6271)
Times: Open any reasonable time. **Facilities:** ▣ ⛌ *Details not confirmed for 2002*

⛰ ELVINGTON　　　　　Map 08 SE74
YORKSHIRE AIR MUSEUM & ALLIED AIR FORCES MEMORIAL
Halifax Way YO41 4AU (from York take A1079 then immediate right onto B1228, museum is signposted on right)
☎ 01904 608595 ▤ 01904 608246

The Yorkshire Air Museum is based on a part of the site of a typical World War II bomber base and its aim is to preserve it as a Memorial to the Allied Air Force air and ground crews who served in World War II. Visitors can see aircraft including one of the last of the RAF's Victor tankers, a Lightning and two Buccaneers. **Times:** Open all year, Mon-Fri 10.30-4, Sat & Sun 10.30-5, BH's 10.30-5. In winter times vary, telephone establishment. **Fee:** £4 (ch & pen £3). **Facilities:** ▣ ⛴ ✗ licensed & toilets for disabled shop

⛰ FAIRBURN　　　　　　Map 08 SE42
RSPB NATURE RESERVE
Fairburn Ings, The Visitor Centre, Newton Ln WF10 2BH (W of A1, N of Ferrybridge. Signed from Allerton Bywater off A656. Signed Fairburn Village off A1)
☎ 01977 603796
e-mail: chris.drake@rspb.org.uk

One-third of the 700-acre RSPB reserve is open water, and over 270 species of bird have been recorded. A visitor centre provides information, and there is an elevated boardwalk, suitable for disabled visitors. **Times:** Access to the reserve via car park, open 9-dusk. Centre open 10-5 weekends and 11-4 weekdays (closed 25-26 Dec). **Fee:** Free. **Facilities:** ▣ & (raised boardwalk for wheelchair) toilets for disabled shop (ex guide dogs)

⛰ GRASSINGTON　　　　Map 07 SE06
NATIONAL PARK CENTRE
Colvend, Hebden Rd BD23 5LB (follow B6265 to Grassington, located in car park on B6265 (Hebden Rd), towards Pateley Bridge)
☎ 01756 752774 ▤ 01756 753358
e-mail: grassington@ytbtic.co.uk

The centre is a useful introduction to the Yorkshire Dales National Park. It has a video and a display on 'Wharfedale - Gateway to the Park', and maps, guides and local information are available. There is also a 24-hr public access information service through computer screens and a full tourist information service. **Times:** Open Apr-Oct daily, 9.30-5. Also limited wknds Nov-Mar. **Fee:** Free. **Facilities:** ▣ (charged) & (Radar key scheme) toilets for disabled shop ⛴

⛰ GUISBOROUGH　　　　Map 08 NZ61
GISBOROUGH PRIORY
TS14 6HG (next to parish church)
☎ 01287 633801
Times: Open all year Apr-Sep, Tue-Sun 9-5; Oct-Mar, Wed-Sun 9-5. (Closed 24 Dec & 1 Jan). **Facilities:** & ✗ ⛌ *Details not confirmed for 2002*

⛰ HARROGATE　　　　　Map 08 SE35
RHS GARDEN, HARLOW CARR
Crag Ln, Otley Rd HG3 1QB (off B6162,1.5 miles from Harrogate centre)
☎ 01423 565418 ▤ 01423 530663
e-mail: admin@harlowcarr.fsnet.co.uk

The gardens were begun in 1950 on a rough site of pasture and woodland. Today there are 68 impressive acres of ornamental and woodland gardens, including the northern trial grounds. Courses, demonstrations and practical workshops are held in the Study Centre. **Times:** Open all year, daily 9.30 until dusk. **Fee:** £4.50 (ch under 11 free, 11-16 £1, pen £3.50, students £2). **Facilities:** ▣ ⛴ ✗ licensed & (electric wheelchairs available) toilets for disabled shop garden centre ⛌ (ex guide dogs)

THE ROYAL PUMP ROOM MUSEUM
Crown Place HG1 2RY
☎ 01423 556188 ▤ 01423 556130
e-mail: ig23@harrogate.gov.uk
Times: Open all year, Apr-Oct, Mon-Sat 10-5, Sun 2-5, (Nov-Mar close at 4pm). (Closed 25-26 Dec & 1 Jan). **Facilities:** ℗ (100yds) (restricted to 3hrs, need parking disc) & toilets for disabled shop ⛌ (guide dogs only) *Details not confirmed for 2002* ⛴

⛫ HAWES   Map 07 SD88
DALES COUNTRYSIDE MUSEUM CENTRE
Station Yard DL8 3NT (Off A684 in the Old Station Yard)
☎ 01969 667450 & 667494   🖹 01969 667165
e-mail: hawes@ytbtic.co.uk

Fascinating museum telling the story of the people and landscape of the Yorkshire Dales. Static steam loco and carriages with video and displays. Interactive area. **Times:** Open all year 10-5. **Fee:** Museum: £3 (concessions £2). Family £8 (2 adults+2children). National park centre free. **Facilities:** 🅿 (charged) & toilets for disabled shop ✟ (ex guide dogs) 🍴

⛫ HELMSLEY   Map 08 SE68
DUNCOMBE PARK
YO62 5EB (1m from town centre, off A170)
☎ 01439 770213 & 771115   🖹 01439 771114
e-mail: sally@duncombepark.com
Times: Open: Apr & Oct Sun-Thu; May-Sep Sun-Fri 10.30-6 (tours every hour). **Facilities:** 🅿 💺 ✗ licensed & toilets for disabled shop ✟ (ex park) *Details not confirmed for 2002* 🍴

HELMSLEY CASTLE
YO5 5AB
☎ 01439 770442

The ruined castle dates from the 12th century and later; it stands within enormous earthworks. It was besieged in the Civil War, and destroyed in 1644.
Times: Open all year, Apr-Sep, daily 10-6 (Oct 10-5); Nov-mid Mar, Wed-Sun 10-4 . Closed 1-2pm all year, 24-26 Dec & 1 Jan. **Fee:** £2.40 (ch £1.20, under 5's free, con £1.80). **Facilities:** 🅿 (charged) ✟ (in certain areas) 🎫

⛫ KIRBY MISPERTON   Map 08 SE77
FLAMINGO LAND THEME PARK & ZOO
The Rectory YO17 6UX (off A169 & A64)
☎ 01653 668287   🖹 01653 668280
Times: Open 28 Mar-26 Sep, as well as weekends and full half term week in Oct. **Facilities:** 🅿 💺 ✗ & (parking) toilets for disabled shop *Details not confirmed for 2002* 🍴

⛫ KIRKHAM   Map 08 SE76
KIRKHAM PRIORY
Whitwell-on-the-Hill YO6 7JS (5m SW of Malton on minor road off A64)
☎ 01653 618768

The ruins of this former house of Augustinian canons stand on an entrancing site on the banks of the River Derwent. The remains of the finely sculpted 13th-century gatehouse and lavatorium, where the monks washed in leaded troughs, are memorable.
Times: Open Apr-Sep, daily 10-6, (Oct,10-5). **Fee:** £1.70 (ch 5-15 90p, under 5's free, con £1.30) **Facilities:** 🅿 & ✟ 🎫

⛫ KNARESBOROUGH   Map 08 SE35
KNARESBOROUGH CASTLE & MUSEUM
Castleyard HG5 8AS
☎ 01423 556188   🖹 01423 556130
e-mail: ig23@harrogate.gov.uk
Times: Open Good Fri-Sep, daily 10.30-5. Guided tours regulary available. **Facilities:** 🅿 (100 metres) (disabled parking in adjacent car park) & toilets for disabled shop ✟ (ex guide dogs) *Details not confirmed for 2002*

⛫ MALHAM   Map 07 SD96
MALHAM NATIONAL PARK CENTRE
BD23 4DA (Turn off A65 at Gargrave, opposite petrol station. Malham 7m)
☎ 01729 830363
e-mail: malham@ytbtic.org

The national park centre has maps, guides and local information together with displays on the remarkable natural history of the area, local community and work of conservation bodies. Audio-visuals are provided for groups and a 24-hour teletext information service is available.
Times: Open Apr-Oct, daily 10-5. Limited winter opening. **Fee:** Free. **Facilities:** 🅿 (charged) & (Radar key scheme for toilet) toilets for disabled shop 🍴

⛫ MALTON   Map 08 SE77
CASTLE HOWARD
YO60 7DA (15m NE of York, off A64)
☎ 01653 648333   648444   🖹 01653 648501
e-mail: house@castlehoward.co.uk

In its dramatic setting of lakes, fountains and extensive gardens, this 18th-century palace was designed by Sir John Vanbrugh. Castle Howard was begun in 1699 for the 3rd Earl of Carlisle, Charles Howard. The interior has a 192ft Long Gallery, as well as a Chapel with magnificent stained glass windows by the 19th-century artist, Edward Burne-Jones. The Castle contains a portrait of Henry VIII by Holbein and works by Rubens, Reynolds and Gainsborough. The grounds include the

contd.

domed Temple of the Four Winds by Vanbrugh, and the family Mausoleum.

Times: Open 16 Mar-4 Nov, grounds, exhibition wing, plant centre & stable court yard, daily from 10. House 11. Last admissions 4.30pm. Grounds close 6.30. **Fee:** £7.50 (ch £4.50, pen £6.75). Grounds only £4.50(ch £2.50). **Facilities:** 🅿 💺 ✗ licensed ♿ (chairlift, free adapted transport to house) toilets for disabled shop garden centre 🍴 (ex in grounds & guide dogs) 🐕

EDEN CAMP MODERN HISTORY THEME MUSEUM

Eden Camp YO17 6RT (junct of A64 & A169, between York & Scarborough)
☎ 01653 697777   ▤ 01653 698243
e-mail: admin@edencamp.co.uk

The story of war on the Home Front unfolds in this museum devoted to civilian life in World War II. The displays, covering the blackout, rationing, the Blitz, the Homeguard and others, are housed in a former prisoner-of-war camp built in 1942 for German and Italian soldiers. Hut 13, part of a Millennium project, covers the conflicts that Britain has been involved with from 1945 to present day.

Times: Open 2nd Mon in Jan-23 Dec, daily 10-5. Last admission 4pm. Allow at least 3-4hrs for a visit. **Fee:** £4 (ch & pen £3) Party 10+. **Facilities:** 🅿 💺 ♿ (taped tours, Braille guides) toilets for disabled shop

MALTON MUSEUM

Old Town Hall, Market Place YO17 7LP (from A64, follow signs for Malton town centre)
☎ 01653 695136

The extensive Roman settlements in the area are represented and illustrated in this museum, including collections from the Roman fort of Derventio. There are also displays of local prehistoric and medieval finds plus changing exhibitions of local interest.

Times: Open Etr Sat-Oct, Mon-Sat 10-4. **Fee:** £1.50 (ch, pen & students £1) Family ticket £4 (2 adults & 2 ch). **Facilities:** 🅿 (adjacent) (pay & display-2hrs) ♿ shop 🍴 (ex guide dogs)

🏛 MIDDLEHAM   Map 07 SE18

MIDDLEHAM CASTLE

DL8 4RJ (2m S of Leyburn on A6108)
☎ 01969 623899

The historic town of Middleham is dominated by the 12th-century keep which saw its great days during the Wars of the Roses. The seat of the Neville family, Earls of Warwick, it was the home for a time of the young King Richard III, then Duke of Gloucester.

Times: Open all year, Apr-Sep, daily 10-6 (Oct 10-5); Nov-Mar, Wed-Sun 10-4 (or dusk if earlier). Closed 1-2pm during winter season & 24-26 Dec & 1 Jan)

Fee: £2.40 (ch 5-15 £1.20, under 5's free, con £1.80). **Facilities:** 🅿 ♿ (ex tower) shop ⌗

🏛 MIDDLESBROUGH   Map 08 NZ42

CAPTAIN COOK BIRTHPLACE MUSEUM

Stewart Park, Marton TS7 6AS (3m S on A172)
☎ 01642 311211   ▤ 01642 317419
e-mail: jeanette_grainger@
middlesbrough.gov.uk

Opened to mark the 250th anniversary of the 1728 birth of the voyager, this museum illustrates the early life of James Cook and his discoveries with permanent and temporary exhibitions. Located in spacious and rolling parkland, the site also offers outside attractions. The museum has a special resource centre which has fresh approaches to presentation with computers, films, special effects, interactives and educational aids.

Times: Open all year: Tue-Sun, Summer hrs 10am-5.30pm. Winter hrs 9am-4pm. Last entry 45 mins before closure. (Closed Mon except BH, 25-26 Dec & 1 Jan). **Fee:** £2.40 (ch & pen £1.20). Family ticket £6. **Facilities:** 🅿 💺 ♿ (lift to all floors, car parking) toilets for disabled shop 🍴 (ex guide dogs) 🐕

🏛 NEWBY HALL & GARDENS   Map 08 SE36

NEWBY HALL & GARDENS

HG4 5AE (4m SE of Ripon & 2m W of A1(M), off B6265, between Boroughbridge and Ripon)
☎ 01423 322583   ▤ 01423 324452
e-mail: info@newbyhall.com

This late 17th-century house had its interior and additions designed by Robert Adam, and contains an important collection of classical sculpture and Gobelin tapestries. Twenty-five acres of award-winning gardens include a miniature railway, an adventure garden for children, and a woodland discovery walk.

Times: Open Apr-Sep, Tue-Sun & BH's; Gardens 11-5.30; House 12-5. Last admission 5pm (gardens), 4.30pm (house), **Fee:** *Prices not confirmed for 2002* **Facilities:** 🅿 💺 ✗ licensed ♿ (wheelchairs available, maps of wheelchair routes) toilets for disabled shop garden centre 🍴 (ex guide dogs) 🐕

🏛 NORTH STAINLEY   Map 08 SE27

LIGHTWATER VALLEY THEME PARK

HG4 3HT (3m N of Ripon on A6108)
☎ 0870 458 0060 458 0040   ▤ 01765 635359
e-mail: leisure@lightwatervalley.co.uk

Set in 175 acres of country park and lakeland, Lightwater Valley offers a selection of rides and attractions. Enjoy the white-knuckle thrills of the world's longest roller coaster 'The Ultimate' as well as the Beaver Rapids Log Flume and Treetop Twister spinning roller coaster or, for the less adventurous, there are the Ladybird, boating lake, and children's visitor farm.

Times: Open 7 Apr-22 Apr & 26 May-3 Sep, wknds only; 28 Apr-20 May, 8 Sep-14 Oct & 20-28 Oct, daily. **Fee:** £12.95 over 1.1 metres, £10.50 under 1.1 metres, free under 0.9m; senior citizens £5.95. Family ticket £42 (2ad+2ch) or (1ad+3ch u16), additional members £10.50. **Facilities:** 🅿 💺 ✗ licensed ♿ (even pathways) toilets for disabled shop 🍴 (ex guide dogs) 🐕

🏛 NUNNINGTON
Map 08 SE67

NUNNINGTON HALL
YO6 5UY (4.5m SE of Helmsley)
☎ 01439 748283 📠 01439 748284
e-mail: yorknu@smtp.ntrust.org.uk

This large 16th- to 17th-century house has panelled rooms and a magnificent staircase. The Carlisle collection of miniature rooms is on display.
Times: Open 31 Mar, Sep-4 Nov: daily (ex Mon/Tue but open BH Mon); Jun-Aug: daily (ex Mon & Tue but open BH Mon): Jun-Aug: daily May-end Sep 1.30-5. **Fee:** House £4.50 (ch £2) Family ticket £11. Gardens only £2 (ch free). Party £4 **Facilities:** 🅿 💺 & (ramps, w/chairs, braille guide, garden scents, parking) toilets for disabled shop 🍴 🐾

🏛 ORMESBY
Map 08 NZ51

ORMESBY HALL
TS7 9AS (3m SE of Middlesborough, W of A19 take A174 to A172. Follow signs for Ormesby Hall. Car entrance on Ladgate Lane)
☎ 01642 324188 📠 01642 300937
e-mail: yorkor@smtp.ntrust.org.uk

An 18th-century mansion, Ormesby Hall has stables attributed to John Carr of York. Plasterwork, furniture and 18th-century pictures are on view.
Times: Open Apr-4 Nov; Tue-Thu & Sun 2-5. BH Mons and Good Fri. **Fee:** House & Gardens £3.50 (ch £1.70) Family ticket £8.50 (2+3). Garden only £2.20 (ch £1). Party. **Facilities:** 🅿 💺 & (parking) toilets for disabled shop 🍴 🐾

🏛 OSMOTHERLEY
Map 08 SE49

MOUNT GRACE PRIORY
DL6 3JG (1m NW)
☎ 01609 883494
Times: Open all year, Apr-Sep, daily 10-6; Oct, daily 10-5; Nov-Mar, Wed-Sun 10-1 & 2-4. Last admission 30mins before closing. (Closed 24-26 Dec & 1 Jan). **Facilities:** 🅿 & shop 🍴 ⚙ 🐾 Details not confirmed for 2002

🏛 PARCEVALL HALL GARDENS
Map 07 SE06

PARCEVALL HALL GARDENS
BD23 6DE (Off B6265 between Grassington and Pateley Bridge)
☎ 01756 720311 📠 01756 720311
e-mail: jomakin@parcevallhallgardens.co.uk
Times: Open Apr-Oct, daily 10-6. Winter visitors by appointment.
Facilities: 🅿 💺 Details not confirmed for 2002

🏛 PATELEY BRIDGE
Map 07 SE16

STUMP CROSS CAVERNS
Greenhow HG3 5JL
☎ 01756 752780 📠 01756 752780

Discovered by the brothers Mark and William Newbould in 1860, Stump Cross Caverns have been an attraction for visitors since 1863 when one shilling was charged for entrance. Among the few limestone show caves in Britain, these require no special clothing, experience or equipment, as walkways are level and

Newby Hall & Gardens
Ripon, North Yorkshire

This graceful country house presents Robert Adam at his very best and the spectacular gardens are a must.

Come and Enjoy
- The famous Adam house
- 25 acres of award-winning gardens
- National Collection of CORNUS (dogwoods)
- Exciting Children's Adventure Garden
- Miniature Railway (10¼" gauge)
- Quality licensed Garden Restaurant
- Irresistible Shop and Plant Centre
- Enchanting Woodland Discovery Walk

Open daily except Mondays (but including Bank Holidays) 1st April – end September from 11am.

Full visitor information
Tel: 01423 322583
Fax: 01423 324452
Email: info@newbyhall.com
Web site: www.newbyhall.com

Simply a great day out!

floodlighting is provided. Stalagmites, stalagtites and calcite precipitation make this an eerie day out.
Times: Open daily until 4 Nov, then wknds 10-4 until end of Feb. **Fee:** £4.50 (ch £2.30)
Facilities: 🅿 💺 shop 🍴 ⚙ 🍺

🏛 PICKERING
Map 08 SE78

NORTH YORKSHIRE MOORS RAILWAY
Pickering Station YO18 7AJ
☎ 01751 472508 📠 01751 476970
e-mail: admin@nymr.demon.co.uk

Operating through the heart of the North York Moors National Park between Pickering and Grosmont, steam

contd.

trains cover a distance of 18 miles. The locomotive sheds at Grosmont are open to the public. Events throughout the year include 'Day Out with Thomas' events, Steam Gala, Santa Specials.
Times: Open Apr-5 Nov, daily; Dec, Santa specials and Christmas to New Year running. Further information available from Pickering Station.
Fee: Return: £10 (ch £5, pen £8.50). Family ticket £27 (2ad+3ch), others on request). All-line ticket £10 (ch £8, pen £8.50). Party 20+.
Facilities: 🅿 (charged) 🍽 ✕ licensed ♿ (ramp for trains) toilets for disabled shop (at Pickering, Goathland & Grosmont) 🥄

PICKERING CASTLE
YO6 5AB
☎ 01751 474989

Standing upon its mound high above the town, the 12th-century keep and baileys are among the interesting remains of what was once a favourite royal hunting lodge. An exhibition tells the castle's history.
Times: Open all year, Apr-Sep, daily 10-6 (Oct 10-5); Nov-Mar, Wed-Sun 10-4.Closed 1-2pm all year. Closed 24-26 Dec & 1 Jan. **Fee:** £2.40 (ch 5-15 £1.20 under 5's free, con £1.80). **Facilities:** 🅿 ♿ (ex motte) shop 🍴 🚻

🏛 REDCAR   Map 08 NZ62
RNLI ZETLAND MUSEUM
5 King St TS10 3AH (on corner of King St and The Promenade)
☎ 01642 485370 & 471813

The museum portrays the lifeboat, maritime, fishing and local history of the area, including its main exhibit 'The Zetland' - the oldest lifeboat in the world dating from 1802. There is also a replica of a fisherman's cottage c1900 and almost 2000 other exhibits. The museum is housed in an early lifeboat station, now a listed building.
Times: Open May-Sep, Mon-Fri 1-4, Sat & Sun 12-4. Also Etr. Other times by appointment. **Fee:** Free. **Facilities:** 🅿 (20m) (50p per hour) ♿ (ground floor accessible only) shop

🏛 RICHMOND   Map 07 NZ10
GREEN HOWARDS MUSEUM
Trinity Church Square, Market Place DL10 4QN (From A1, between Catterick & South Corner, follow signs to Richmond. Located in centre cobbled market square, in Old Trinity Church)
☎ 01748 822133 📧 01748 826561

This award-winning museum traces the military history of the Green Howards from the late 17th century onwards. The exhibits include uniforms, weapons, medals and a special Victoria Cross exhibition. Regimental and civic plate is displayed, and there is CD ROM and touch screen video of the First World War Western Front and the Green Howards in the Second World War. Audio guide available.
Times: Open Feb, Mon-Fri 10-4.30; Mar, Mon-Fri 10-4.30; mid Apr-Oct, Mon-Sat 9.30-4.30 & Sun 2-4.30; Nov, Mon-Sat 10-4.30. **Fee:** £2 (ch 5-16 £1, pen £1.50). Family ticket £5. **Facilities:** 🅿 (in market place) (disk parking, 2hr max) ♿ (stairlift for access to all floors) shop 🍴

RICHMOND CASTLE
DL10 4QW
☎ 01748 822493

Built high upon sheer rocks overlooking the River Swale, the castle dates from 1071. Its splendid keep and curtain walls, with two massive towers, are among the impressive remains. Scollard's Hall, built in 1080, may well be the oldest domestic building surviving in Britain.
Times: Open all year, Apr-Sep, daily 10-6 (Oct 10-5); Nov-Mar, daily 10-4 (or dusk if earlier, closed 1-2pm). Closed 24-26 Dec & 1 Jan.
Fee: £2.70 (ch 5-15 £1.40, under 5's free, con £2). **Facilities:** 🅿 (800 yds) ♿ shop 🍴 🚻

🏛 RIEVAULX   Map 08 SE58
RIEVAULX ABBEY
YO6 5LB (2.25m W of Helmsley on minor road off B1257)
☎ 01439 798228

The site for this magnificent abbey was given to a small group of Cistercian monks in 1131; building was completed by the end of the century. In its heyday, this was a prosperous foundation, but its fortunes later declined. Surrounded by wooded hills, the site is beautiful and the remains impressive. From Rievaulx Terrace, at the top of the hill, there is an excellent bird's eye view of the abbey ruins.
Times: Open all year, Apr-Sep, daily 10-6 (Oct 10-5); Jul-Aug, 9.30-7; Nov-Mar, daily 10-4 (or dusk if earlier). Closed 24-26 Dec & 1 Jan.
Fee: £3.60 (ch 5-15 £1.80, under 5's free, con £2.70) **Facilities:** 🅿 ♿ shop 🍴 🚻

RIEVAULX TERRACE & TEMPLES
YO6 5LJ (2m NW of Helmsley on B1257)
☎ 01439 798340 📧 01439 748284

This curved terrace, half a mile long, overlooks the abbey, with views of Ryedale and the Hambleton Hills. It has two mock-Greek temples, one built for hunting parties, the other for quiet contemplation. There are also remarkable frescoes by Borgnis, and an exhibition on English landscape design.
Times: Open Apr-end Oct daily 10.30-5 (4 in Oct). May-Sept daily 10.30-6pm. Last admission one hour before closing. **Fee:** £3.30 (ch £1.50). Family £8. Party £2.80 **Facilities:** 🅿 ♿ (w/chair/runaround vehicle/braille guide/ramp) shop 🥄

🏛 RIPLEY   Map 08 SE26
RIPLEY CASTLE
HG3 3AY (off A61, Harrogate to Ripon road)
☎ 01423 770152 📧 01423 771745
e-mail: enquiries@ripleycastle.co.uk

Ripley Castle has been home to the Ingilby family since 1320, and stands at the heart of an estate with deer park, lake and Victorian walled gardens. The Castle has a rich history and a fine collection of Royalist armour housed in the 1555 tower. There are also walled

contd.

gardens, tropical hot houses, woodland walks, pleasure grounds and the National Hyacinth collection in spring.

Ripley Castle

Times: Open Sep-May & Tue, Thu, Sat & Sun 10.30-3; Jun-Aug daily 10.30-3, also BH and school holidays. Groups any day by prior arrangement. **Fee:** Castle & Gardens £5.50 (ch £3, pen £4.50). Gardens only £3 (ch £1.50, pen £2.50). Party 25+. **Facilities:** ⓟ ⬤ ✕ licensed ⓑ toilets for disabled shop garden centre ✸ (ex guide dogs) ⬤

🏛 RIPON   Map 08 SE37
Fountains Abbey & Studley Royal
HG4 3DY (4m W off B6265)
☎ 01765 608888 ▤ 01765 608889

Founded by Cistercian monks in 1132, Fountains Abbey is the largest monastic ruin in Britain. It was acquired by William Aislabie in 1768, and became the focal point of his landscaped gardens at Studley. Other interesting features include Fountains Hall, built between 1598 and 1611 using the stone from the abbey ruins.
Times: Open all year. daily (except Fri in Nov, Dec & Jan); Apr-Sep, 10-7 (closes at 4pm some days in July & one day in Aug); Oct-Mar 10-5 or duk if earlier. Last admission one hour before closing. **Fee:** £4.50 (ch £2.30). Family ticket £11 (2+3). Party 31+ £3.40 (ch £1.90). **Facilities:** ⓟ ⬤ ✕ licensed ⓑ toilets for disabled shop ⚘

Norton Conyers Hall
HG4 5EQ (from Ripon take A61 to Thirsk. At top of hill just outside Ripon, turn sharp left onto Wath Road)
☎ 01765 640333 ▤ 01765 692772
Times: Open - House & garden Etr Sun & Mon; BH Sun & Mon;Sun between 7 May-3 Sep. Open daily 3-8 Jul. House open 2-5, garden open 11.30-5. Telephone for further details. **Facilities:** ⓟ ⓑ (ramp at entrance) toilets for disabled shop ✸ (ex guide dogs or lead) *Details not confirmed for 2002*

🏛 SALTBURN-BY-THE-SEA   Map 08 NZ62
Saltburn Smugglers Heritage Centre
Old Saltburn TS12 1HF (adjoining Ship Inn, on A174)
☎ 01287 625252 ▤ 01287 625252

Set in old fisherman's cottages, this centre skillfully blends costumed characters with authentic sounds and smells. Follow the story of John Andrew "King of

Smugglers", who was at the heart of illict local trade 200 years ago.
Times: Open 3 Apr-Sep, daily 10-6; Winter open by arrangement only telephone 01642 444318. **Fee:** £1.85 (ch £1.35). Family ticket £5.50. Party. **Facilities:** ⓟ (200 mtrs) (charged) shop ✸

🏛 SCARBOROUGH   Map 08 TA08
Scarborough Castle
Castle Rd YO1 1HY (E of town centre)
☎ 01723 372451

The ruins of Scarborough Castle stand on a narrow headland which was once the site of British and Roman encampments. The curtain wall is thought to have pre-dated the keep, the shell of which, with the later barbican and remains of medieval buildings, are all that remain.
Times: Open all year, Apr-Sep, daily 10-6 (Oct 10-5); Nov-Mar, daily 10-4. Closed 24-26 Dec & 1 Jan. **Fee:** £2.50 (ch 5-15 £1.20, under 5's free, £1.80). **Facilities:** ⓟ (100 yds) ⓑ (ex in keep) ⧉

Sea Life & Marine Sanctuary
Scalby Mills Rd, North Bay YO12 6RP (follow brown signs after entering Scarborough. Centre is in North Bay Leisure Parks area of town)
☎ 01723 376125 ▤ 01723 376285

Now in its 10th year, this fascinating marine sanctuary has just launched a pan-European SOS Conservation & Rescue campaign as part of its continued conservation programme. The centre is home to seahorses, a seal hospital, otters, seapool creatures, sharks, and a home for convalescent Sea Turtles.
Times: Open daily ex 25 Dec. **Fee:** Prices to be confirmed. **Facilities:** ⓟ (charged) ⬤ ⓑ (lift to cafe) toilets for disabled shop ✸ ⬤

🏛 SKINNINGROVE   Map 08 NZ71
Tom Leonard Mining Museum
Deepdale TS13 4AP (just off A174 between Middlesbrough and Whitby)
☎ 01287 642877 ▤ 01287 642970
e-mail: visits@ironstonemuseum.co.uk

On the site of the old Loftus Mine, this museum offers visitors a glimpse into the underground world of Cleveland's ironstone mining past. Discover the special skills and customs of the miners who helped make Cleveland the most important ironstone mining district in Victorian and Edwardian England.
Times: Open Apr-Oct, daily from 1 (last admission 3.45pm). Nov-Mar, schools & parties only. Parties by arrangement. **Fee:** £3 (ch £1.50). Pre-booked parties 12+. **Facilities:** ⓟ (telephone for details) shop ✸ (ex guide dogs)

🏛 SKIPTON
Map 07 SD95

SKIPTON CASTLE
BD23 1AQ (town centre at top of High Street)
☎ 01756 792442 📄 01756 796100
e-mail: info@skiptoncastle.co.uk

Skipton is one of the most complete and well-preserved medieval castles in England. Some of the castle dates from the 1650s when it was rebuilt after being partially damaged during the Civil War. However, the original castle was erected in Norman times and became the home of the Clifford family in 1310 and remained so until 1676. Illustrated tour sheets are available in a number of languages.
Times: Open all year, daily from 10am (Sun noon). Last admission 6pm (4pm Oct-Feb). (Closed 25 Dec). **Fee:** £4.40 (inc illustrated tour sheet) (ch under 18 £2.20, under 5 free, concessions £3.80). Family ticket £11.90. Party 15+. **Facilities:** P (200m) 🍴 shop 🥡

🏛 SUTTON-ON-THE-FOREST
Map 08 SE56

SUTTON PARK
YO61 1DP (on B1363 York to Helmsley road)
☎ 01347 810249 & 811239 📄 01347 811251
e-mail: suttonpark@fsbdial.co.uk
Times: Open - Gardens 2 Apr-end Sept, daily 11am-5pm. House open 2 Apr-27 Sep, Wed & Sun, also Good Fri, Etr Mon and all BH Mons.
Facilities: P 🍴 & 🐕 (ex guide dogs in garden) *Details not confirmed for 2002*

🏛 WHITBY
Map 08 NZ81

WHITBY ABBEY
YO22 4JT (on clifftop E of Whitby town centre)
☎ 01947 603568

Dominating the skyline above the fishing port of Whitby the haunting ruins of the 13th-century Benedictine abbey are an impressive site. St Hilda built the first abbey here in 657.
Times: Open all year, Apr-Sep, daily 10-6; (Oct 10-5); Nov-Mar, daily 10-4. Closed 24-26 Dec & 1 Jan. **Fee:** £1.80 (ch 5-15 90p, under 5's free, con £1.40). **Facilities:** P (charged) shop ♿

🏛 YORK
Map 08 SE65

THE ARC
St Saviourgate YO1 8NN (city centre, follow pedestrian signposts for Archaeological Resource Centre)
☎ 01904 643211 📄 01904 627097
e-mail: jorvik@jvcyork.demon.co.uk

The ARC is a 'hands-on' experience of archaeology, housed in the beautifully restored medieval church of St Saviour. Be an archaeologist yourself - sift through the remains of centuries - bones, shell, pottery and much more.
Times: Open: School holidays Mon-Sat 11-3.30. Closed mid Dec-early Jan. Open for schools & groups all year Mon-Fri 10-3.30. **Fee:** £4.50. (ch, stu & pen £4) Family £15. Group rates available on request.
Facilities: P (50yds) & (induction loop, sensory gaden, hands on) toilets for disabled shop 🐕 (except guide dogs) 🥡

BORTHWICK INSTITUTE OF HISTORICAL RESEARCH
St Anthony's Hall, Peasholme Green YO1 7PW
☎ 01904 642315

Originally built in the second half of the 15th century for the Guild of St Anthony, the hall was later used as an arsenal, a workhouse, a prison and the Bluecoat School from 1705 to 1946. Now part of York University, it houses ecclesiastical archives and exhibitions of documents.
Times: Open all year, Mon-Fri 9.30-12.50 & 2-4.50. Closed Etr & Xmas. **Fee:** Free. **Facilities:** P (max 5mins walk) (public car park) 🐕 🚻

CLIFFORD'S TOWER
Tower St YO1 1SA
☎ 01904 646940

Named after the unfortunate Roger de Clifford, who was hung in chains from the castle, the tower was unused for centuries, as the first castle burned down and its replacement cracked from top to bottom as a result of subsidence. The walk around the old city walls offers the best way of seeing the ancient city.
Times: Open all year, Apr-Sep, daily 10-6; Aug 9.30-7; (Oct 10-5); Nov-Mar, Wed-Sun 10-4 or dusk if earlier. Closed between 1-2pm and 24-26 Dec & 1 Jan. **Fee:** £2 (ch 5-15 £1, under 5's free, con £1.50). **Facilities:** P 🐕 🚻 ♿

FAIRFAX HOUSE
Castlegate YO1 9RN (city centre, close to Jorvik Centre and Clifford's Tower)
☎ 01904 655543 📄 01904 652262
e-mail: peterbrown@fairfaxhouse.co.uk

An outstanding mid 18th-century house with a richly decorated interior, Fairfax House was acquired by the York Civic Trust in 1983 and restored. The house contains fine examples of Georgian furniture, porcelain, paintings and clocks which were donated by Mr Noel Terry, the great grandson of the founder of the York-based confectionery business. There is a special display

contd.

of a recreated meal dating from 1763 in the dining room and kitchen.
Times: Open 20 Feb-5 Jan, Mon-Sat 11-5, (Fri guided tours only at 11am & 2pm). Sun 1.30-5. Last admission 4.30pm. **Fee:** £4 (ch £1.50, pen & student £3.50) **Facilities:** P (50yds) (3hr short stay) & (with assistance, phone before visit) shop 🍴 🍵

GUILDHALL
Off Coney St YO1 9QN (5mins walk from the rail station)
☎ 01904 613161 ▤ 01904 552015

The hall dates from 1446 but in 1942 an air raid virtually destroyed the building. The present Guildhall was carefully restored as an exact replica and was re-opened in 1960. There is an interesting arch-braced roof decorated with colourful bosses and supported by 12 solid oak pillars. There are also some beautiful stained-glass windows.
Times: Open all year, May-Oct, Mon-Fri 9-5, Sat 10-5, Sun 2-5; Nov-Apr, Mon-Fri 9-5.(Closed Good Fri, Spring BH, 25-26 Dec & 1 Jan).
Fee: Free. **Facilities:** P (15-20 mins walk) & (electric chair lift/ramps) toilets for disabled 🍴 (ex guide dogs) 🚼

JORVIK VIKING CENTRE
Coppergate YO1 9WT (in Coppergate shopping area follow signs)
☎ 01904 643211 ▤ 01904 627097
e-mail: jorvik@jvcyork.demon.co.uk

Deep beneath the streets of central York, archaeologists discovered the remains of a place that the Vikings once called home. The archaeological evidence was used to create one of the world's most famous reconstructions of the Viking age. Following 20 years of research and £5 million of investment, the 10th century has been recaptured better than ever, bringing New Jorvik, the trading hub of the Viking world, dramatically to life.
Times: Open all year, Apr-Oct daily 9-5.30; Nov-Mar daily 10-4.30 (Closed 25 Dec). Opening times subject to change, please telephone for up to date details. **Fee:** £6.95 (ch 5-15 £4.95, under 5 free, student & pen £5.95) Family £21.50. Telephone bookings on 01904 543403 (£1 booking fee). **Facilities:** P (400 yds) (limited to 3 hours) 🍵 & (lift & time car designed to take wheelchair, hearing loop) toilets for disabled shop 🍴 🍵

MERCHANT ADVENTURERS' HALL
Fossgate YO1 9XD
☎ 01904 654818 ▤ 01904 654818
e-mail: the.clerk@mahall-york.demon.co.uk

The medieval guild hall of the powerful Merchant Adventurers' Company was built between 1357 and 1361 and is one of the finest in Europe. The Great Hall contains early furniture, one piece dating from the 13th century, paintings, silver, and weights and measures.
Times: Open all year, end Mar-early Nov, daily 9-5 (ex Sun 12-4); early Nov-late Mar, Mon-Sat 9-3.30 (Closed Sun). (Closed 10 days Xmas).
Fee: £2 (ch u7 free, ch 70p, pen & students £1.70). **Facilities:** P (500yds) & toilets for disabled 🍴

NATIONAL RAILWAY MUSEUM
Leeman Rd YO26 4XJ (Signposted from A1(M))
☎ 01904 557216 ▤ 01904 611112
e-mail: nrm@nmsi.ac.uk

Among the impressive exhibits are a reconstruction of Stephenson's Rocket; the record-breaking Mallard; a life-size section of the Channel Tunnel; a Japanese bullet train and Royal Palaces on Wheels. The new wing features the Workshop, the Warehouse, and the Working Railway Gallery.
Times: Open all year, Mon-Sun 10-6,(Closed 24-26 Dec). **Fee:** £7.50 (ch under 16 & pen free, concessions £5). Party £6.50 each.
Facilities: P (charged) 🍵 🍴 licensed & ("Please Touch" evenings) toilets for disabled shop 🍴 (ex guide dogs & hearing dogs) 🍵

ST WILLIAMS COLLEGE
5 College St YO1 7JF (adjacent to east end of York Minster)
☎ 01904 557233 ▤ 01904 557234
e-mail: info@yorkminster.org
Times: Open all year 10-5 for viewing of medieval rooms subject to private bookings - phone for details. Closed 24-26 Dec & Good Fri.
Facilities: P 🍵 🍴 licensed shop 🍴 *Details not confirmed for 2002*

TREASURER'S HOUSE

Chapter House St YO1 2JD (in Minster Yard, on N side of Minster)

☎ 01904 624247 🖹 01904 647372

e-mail: yorkth@smtp.ntrust.org.uk

There has been a house on this site since Roman times and in the basement of this elegant 17th-century building is an exhibition of its history. The house was improved during the 18th century with the addition of a fine staircase. Restored between 1897 and 1930, it was left, with its fine furniture, to the National Trust.

Times: Open Apr-Oct, daily except Friday. 10.30-4.30pm. **Fee:** £3.70 (ch £2). Family ticket £9.50 (2+3). **Facilities:** P (400 yds) ✕ licensed (braille guide/tactile pictures/induction loop/scented path) 🍴 🐾

YORK CASTLE MUSEUM

The Eye of York YO1 1RY (city centre, next to Clifford's Tower)

☎ 01904 653611 🖹 01904 671078

Times: Open all year, Apr-Oct Mon-Sat 9.30-5.30, Sun 10-5.30; Nov-Mar, Mon-Sat 9.30-4, Sun 10-4. (Closed 25-26 Dec & 1 Jan).

Facilities: 🍴 ♿ toilets for disabled shop 🍴 *Details not confirmed for 2002* 🥄

YORK CITY ART GALLERY

Exhibition Square YO1 7EW (3min walk from the Minster)

☎ 01904 551861 🖹 01904 551866

e-mail: art.gallery@york.gov.uk

The gallery is remarkable for the range and quality of its collections that provide a survey of most developments in Western European painting over the past six centuries, something that most regional galleries cannot claim to do. Works by Parmigianino, Bellotto, Lely, Reynolds, Frith, Boudin, Lowry and Nash and nudes by Etty are on permanent display. There are also fine collections of watercolours and pottery.

Times: Open all year, daily 10-5. (Closed 25 & 26 Dec & 1 Jan). **Fee:** £2 (con £1.50). **Facilities:** P (500mtrs) ♿ (chair lift) toilets for disabled shop 🍴 (ex guide dogs) 🥄

THE YORK DUNGEON

12 Clifford St YO1 9RD (from A64/A19/A59 towards city centre)

☎ 01904 632599 🖹 01904 612602

e-mail: yorkdungeons@
merlin-entertainments.com

Deep in the heart of historic York, buried beneath it's very paving stones, lies the North's most chillingly famous museum of horror. The York Dungeon brings more than 2,000 years of gruesomely authentic history vividly back to life...and death. As you delve into the darkest chapters of our grim and bloody past, recreated in all its dreadful detail, remember that everything you experience really happened. A warning – in the dungeon's dark catacombs it always pays to keep your wits about you. The 'exhibits' have an unnerving habit of coming back to life...

Times: Open all year, daily 10.30-5.30 (4.30 Oct-Mar). Closed 25 Dec. **Fee:** £6.95 (ch £4.95, students £5.95, pen £4.95). Family £21 (2ad+2ch). **Facilities:** P (500yds) ♿ (wheelchair ramps, stairlifts, award winning access) toilets for disabled shop 🥄

YORK MINSTER

Deangate YO1 7HH (access via A19, A1 or A64)

☎ 01904 557216 🖹 01904 557218

e-mail: visitors@yorkminster.org

It is believed that Edwin King of Northumbria built the first church on this site in 627. Since then both Saxons and Normans built cathedrals here, and parts of the latter survive in many places in the present structure. From 1220 to 1472 the present church was built to replace the romanesque one. It is notable for its size – the largest medieval church north of the Alps – and for its wealth of stained glass, most of which is original. Daily worship has been conducted on this site for 13 centuries. Events include York Mystery Plays (22 Jun-22 Jul).

Times: Open daily, Mon-Sat 7-6 (later in summer), Sun after 1pm. **Fee:** Free admission (donation requested) but following parts charged; Undercroft, Treasury & Crypt £3 (ch £1, pen & students £2.60); Chapter House £1 (ch free); Central Tower £3 (ch £1). **Facilities:** P (440yds) ♿ (loop system, tactile model, braille guide) toilets for disabled shop 🍴 (ex guide dogs)

YORK MODEL RAILWAY

Tearoom Square, York Station YO2 2AB (next to York Station)

☎ 01904 630169

Times: Open daily, Mar-Oct 9.30-6, Nov-Feb 10.30-5 (Closed 25-26 Dec). **Facilities:** P (100 yds) ♿ shop *Details not confirmed for 2002* 🥄

YORKSHIRE MUSEUM

Museum Gardens YO1 7FR (park & ride service from 4 sites near A64/A19/A1079 & A166, also 3 car parks within short walk)

☎ 01904 551800 🖹 01904 551802

e-mail: yorkshire.museum@york.gov.uk

Yorkshire Museum is set in 10 acres of botanical gardens in the heart of the historic City of York, and displays some of the finest Roman, Anglo-Saxon, Viking and Medieval treasures ever discovered in Britain. The Middleham jewel, a fine example of English Gothic jewellery, is on display, and in the Roman Gallery visitors can see a marble head of Constantine the Great. The Anglo-Saxon Gallery houses the delicate silver-gilt Ormside bowl and the Gilling sword.

Times: Open all year, daily 10-5. **Fee:** £3.95 (concessions £2.50) Family ticket £11.50. **Facilities:** P (5 mins walk) ♿ (ramps & lift) toilets for disabled shop 🍴 🥄

South Yorkshire

South Yorkshire is an industrial area and all the main towns are traditionally steel and coal producing centres. Both of these industries have declined in recent years and have been replaced to some extent by other forms of manufacturing.

Barnsley is the county's administrative centre, located on of one Britain's richest coalfields. The town has an entry in the Domesday Book, and was built on land belonging to the priories of Pontefract and Monk Bretton.

Doncaster, originally a Roman station, is set on the River Don. It is known particularly for its racecourse. The best known race on its calender is the celebrated St Leger, which is held in September. In 1875, Charles Dickens watched it from the 18th-century Italianate grandstand at the Town Moor racecourse. The Lincolnshire Handicap is held in March. The town also possesses some fine Georgian architecture, particularly James Paine's house which was built in 1748.

Rotheram, on the outskirts of Sheffield, has a fine 15th-century church, and a bridge with an old chapel over the Don river.

South Yorkshire claims part of the Peak District National park, whose hills and dales provide relief to the millions of city dwellers within its vicinity.

EVENTS & FESTIVALS

January
5th The Ancient Haxey Hood Game, Doncaster

May
2nd-3rd Sheffield Mayfest, Hillsborough Park (provisional)

June/July
tbc Sheffield Children's Festival

July
6th Dore Gala, Sheffield
6th Stannington Carnival, Sheffield
7th Abbey Field Park Multicultural Festival
tbc City Centre Carnival, Sheffield
tbc Our City, The World Sheffield's Multicultural Festival, Devonshire Green, Sheffield
tbc South Yorkshire Festival, Wortley Hall, Sheffield

August
tbc The Sheffield Show, Graves Park, Sheffield

October
tbc Off the Shelf Literature Festival, Sheffield
tbc Sheffield International Documentary Festival

Top: Watermill in Worsbrough Country Park

🏛 BARNSLEY — Map 08 SE30
MONK BRETTON PRIORY
S71 5QD (1m E of Barnsley town centre, off A633)
☎ 01226 204089
Times: Open all year, Apr-Sep, daily 10-6; Oct, daily 10-5; Nov-Mar, daily 10-4. Keykeeper. **Facilities:** 🅿 & ♨ *Details not confirmed for 2002*

🏛 CONISBROUGH — Map 08 SK59
CONISBROUGH CASTLE
DN12 3HH (NE of town centre off A630)
☎ 01709 863329
Times: Open all year, Apr-Sep, Mon-Sat 10-5, Sun 10-6; Oct-Mar, daily 10-4. Last admission 40mins before closing. (Closed 24-26 Dec & 1 Jan). **Facilities:** 🅿 & ⚓ ♨ *Details not confirmed for 2002*

🏛 CUSWORTH — Map 08 SE50
THE MUSEUM OF SOUTH YORKSHIRE LIFE
CUSWORTH HALL
Cusworth Ln DN5 7TU (3m NW of Doncaster)
☎ 01302 782342 📠 01302 782342
e-mail: margaret@doncaster.gov.uk

The Museum of South Yorkshire is located in Cusworth Hall, an 18th-century country house set in a landscaped park. It has displays which illustrate the way local people here lived, worked and entertained themselves over the last 200 years.
Times: Open all year, Mon-Fri 10-5, Sat 11-5 & Sun 1-5. (4pm Dec & Jan). Closed Good Fri, Xmas & 1 Jan. **Fee:** Free. **Facilities:** 🅿 ♨ & (wheelchair available) toilets for disabled shop ⚓ (ex guide dogs)

🏛 DONCASTER — Map 08 SE50
BRODSWORTH HALL
Brodsworth DN5 7XJ (between A635 & A638)
☎ 01302 7222598 📠 01302 337165

Brodsworth Hall is a Victorian country house which has survived largely intact. The faded grandeur of the family rooms contrasts with the functional austerity of the servants' wing. There are fine gardens.
Times: Open 31 Mar-4 Nov, Tue-Sun & BH's; gardens 1-6, (last admission 5pm); Nov-Mar, 11-4, Mar Gardens, tearooms & shops only.
Fee: House and gardens £5 (ch 5-15 £2.50, under 5's free, con £3.80). **Facilities:** 🅿 ♨ & toilets for disabled shop (12-6) ⚓ ♨ ⚓

DONCASTER MUSEUM & ART GALLERY
Chequer Rd DN1 2AE (off inner ring road)
☎ 01302 734293 📠 01302 735409
e-mail: museum@doncaster.gov.uk

The wide-ranging collections include fine and decorative art and sculpture. Also ceramics, glass, silver, and displays on history, archaeology and natural history. The historical collection of the King's Own Yorkshire Light Infantry is housed here. Temporary exhibitions are held.
Times: Open all year, Mon-Sat 10-5, Sun 2-5. (Closed Good Fri, 25-26 Dec & 1 Jan). **Fee:** Free. **Facilities:** 🅿 & (lift, hearing loop in lecture room) toilets for disabled shop ⚓ (ex guide dogs)

EARTH CENTRE
Denaby Main DN12 4EA
☎ 01709 513933 📠 01709 512010
e-mail: info@earthcentre.org.uk
Times: Open early Apr-early Nov 10-6 (last entry 4pm). During summer holidays 10-8 (last entry 6pm). **Facilities:** 🅿 ♨ ✕ licensed & toilets for disabled shop ⚓ (ex guide dogs) *Details not confirmed for 2002* ⚓

🏛 MALTBY — Map 08 SK59
ROCHE ABBEY
S66 8NW (1.5m S off A634)
☎ 01709 812739

The walls of the South and North Transepts of this 12th-century Cistercian abbey still stand to their full height, providing a dramatic sight for the visitor. There is also a fine gatehouse.
Times: Open Apr-Sep, daily 10-6 (Oct 10-5). **Fee:** £1.70 (ch 5-15 90p, under 5's free, con £1.30) **Facilities:** 🅿 & ♨

🏛 ROTHERHAM — Map 08 SK49
CLIFTON PARK MUSEUM
Clifton Park, Clifton Ln S65 2AA (follow signs from inner ring road)
☎ 01709 382121 ext 3635 📠 01709 823631
e-mail: guy.kilminster@rotherham.gov.uk
Times: Open all year, Mon-Thu & Sat 10-5, Sun 1.30-5 (4.30 Oct-Mar). (Closed Xmas & New Year). Building work during 2001 may limit opening hours. Contact for details. **Facilities:** 🅿 & toilets for disabled shop ⚓ (ex guide dogs) *Details not confirmed for 2002*

MAGNA SCIENCE ADVENTURE CENTRE
Sheffield Rd, Templeborough S60 1DX (M1 junct 34 , follow Templeborough sign off rdbt, then follow brown tourist signs)
☎ 01709 720002 📠 01709 820092
e-mail: jeyre@magnatrust.co.uk

The UK's first Science Adventure Centre is divided into seven sections: Air, Fire, Water, Earth, Face of Steel, Big Melt, and Play. Hands-on activities allow children to learn about science and industry whilst playing, and breaking all the rules – underage driving is permitted and you are advised to stand really, really close to a tornado!
Times: Open daily 10-5. Closed 24-25 Dec. **Fee:** £5.99 (ch £4.50, concessions £4.50). Family ticket £17.99. Party. **Facilities:** 🅿 ♨ ✕ licensed & (lifts) toilets for disabled shop ⚓ (ex guide dogs) ⚓

🏛 SHEFFIELD — Map 08 SK38
BISHOPS HOUSE
Meersbrook Park, Norton Lees Ln S8 9BE (2m S of Sheffield, on A61 Chesterfield road)
☎ 0114 278 2600
e-mail: info@sheffieldgalleries.org.uk

This 15th and 16th-century yeoman's house has been restored and opened as a museum of local and social history. Several rooms have been furnished and there are displays of life in Tudor and Stuart times. Special

contd.

educational facilities can be arranged for schools and colleges. Please ring for details. **Times:** Open Sat 10-4.30. **Fee:** Free. **Facilities:** P (roadside parking on nearby streets) & shop ✗

CITY MUSEUM & MAPPIN ART GALLERY

Weston Park S10 2TP (on A57 Sheffield-Manchester road, close to Children's Hospital)
☎ 0114 278 2600   🖥 0114 275 0957
e-mail: info@sheffieldgalleries.org.uk

The Mappin Art Gallery is home to paintings from the City's collection of 16th-19th-century art. It is also a major regional venue for contemporary art displays. At the City Museum visitors can discover Sheffield's fascinating archaeology, natural history, decorative arts and social history collections.
Times: Open all year, Tue-Sat 10-5, Sun 11-5 also BH Mons. (Closed 25 Dec & 1 Jan). Please telephone prior to visit to confirm opening times. **Fee:** Free. **Facilities:** P (on street parking only) ✇ & (Inductive loop). Handling sessions for pre-booked groups) toilets for disabled shop ✗ (ex guide dogs)

KELHAM ISLAND MUSEUM

Alma St S3 8RY (0.5m NW of city centre, take A61 N to West Bar, follow signs)
☎ 0114 272 2106   🖥 0114 275 7847
e-mail: postmaster@simt.co.uk

The story of Sheffield, its industry and life. With the most powerful working steam engine in Europe, reconstructed workshops, working cutler and craftspeople demonstrating traditional 'made in Sheffield' skills – this is a 'living' museum. During the year Kelham Island stages events, displays and temporary exhibitions culminating in the annual Christmas Victorian Market.
Times: Open Mon-Thu 10-4, Sun 11-4.45.Closed Fri and Sat. Check opening days/times at Christmas & New Year before travelling. **Fee:** £3.50 (ch £2, pen £2.50). Family ticket £8. **Facilities:** P ✇ & (wheelchair on request) toilets for disabled shop ✗

MILLENNIUM GALLERIES

Arundel Gate S1 2PP
☎ 0114 278 2600   🖥 0114 278 2604
e-mail: info@sheffieldgalleries.org.uk

A newly opened museum bringing some of the nation's finest treasures to Sheffield. The four separate galleries are entitled: Special Exhibitions, Metalwork, Craft & Design and the Ruskin Gallery. The Metalwork Gallery offers visitors the chance to make their own hallmark or build a penknife, as well as displaying internationally important pieces of metalwork. The Ruskin Gallery displays John Ruskin's personal collection of painting and design oriented work and minerals. Exhibitions regularly change in the other galleries. Phone for details.
Times: Open daily Mon-Sat 10-5 (Wed until 9pm), Sun 11-5. **Fee:** £4 (ch 5-16 £2, concessions £3). Family ticket £9. **Facilities:** P ✇ ✗ licensed & (hearing loop) toilets for disabled shop ✗ (ex guide dogs)
🖃

West Yorkshire

EVENTS & FESTIVALS

March
8th-22nd Bradford Film
Festival
9th-17th Daffodil Week,
Haworth
23rd-24th Complementary
Medicine Festival, Ilkley

April
1st World Coal Carrying
Championship, Ossett
20th Leeds Dollshouse &
Miniatures Fair

May
8th-11th Todmorden Gang
Show, Todmorden
tbc Wharfedale Music
Festival, Ilkley

June
22nd-23rd Celtic
Weekend, Howarth

July
5th-7th Cleckheaton Folk
Festival (various venues)
tbc Hebden Bridge Arts
Festival (various venues)

September
26th-6th Oct Leeds
International Film Festival

October
19th-20th Complementary
Medicine Festival, Ilkley

November
23rd-24th Scroggling the
Holly, Haworth
30th-1st Dec Masquerade
Weekend, Haworth

December
20th Nov-1st Huddersfield
Contemporary Music Festival
Christmas Festival

The West Riding has long been industrialised, and not only produced coal but was also home to the wool industry. The tall mill chimneys, set against the Pennine Hills, are characteristic of its industrial heritage.

The county includes the towns of Wakefield, Halifax, Huddersfield and Bradford, centres of the wool industry from the 13th century. Huddersfield is known particularly for its fine wool worsted.

Leeds sprawls over its hilly site and includes a great variety of manufacturing and other industries, notably clothing. It is also home to the celebrated Yorkshire County Cricket Club at Headingley.

Many visitors to the region come in the wake of the extraordinary Brontë family. A motherless family with the curate of Haworth, Patrick Brontë, at its head. The children, Charlotte, Branwell (Patrick), Emily and Anne created a rich fantasy world, feeding their literary imaginations. Their poems and novels evoked the nature of their moorland home, particularly Emily's *Wuthering Heights*, published in December 1847, a year before her death from consumption at the age of 30. The Brontë Society was founded in 1893. In 1926 the American publisher Henry Houston Bonnell bequeathed his collection to the society, who bought the parsonage, the Brontë's former home to accommodate it.

Natural features of the county encompass Ilkley Moor, Haworth Moor, and parts of the Peak District National Park.

*Top: The Corn
Exchange, Leeds*

🏛 BRADFORD
Map 07 SE13

BOLLING HALL
Bowling Hall Rd BD4 7LP (1m from city centre off A650)
☎ 01274 723057   📠 01274 726220
e-mail: abickley@legend.co.uk
Times: Open all year, Wed-Fri 11-4, Sat 10-5, Sun 12-5. (Closed Mon ex BH, Good Fri, 25 & 26 Dec). **Facilities:** 🅿 ♿ shop ✘ *Details not confirmed for 2002*

BRADFORD INDUSTRIAL MUSEUM AND HORSES AT WORK
Moorside Rd, Eccleshill BD2 3HP (off A658)
☎ 01274 631756   📠 01274 636362
Times: Open all year, Tue-Sat 10-5, Sun 12-5. (Closed Mon ex BH)
Facilities: 🅿 ♨ ♿ (induction loop in lecture theatre) toilets for disabled shop ✘ *Details not confirmed for 2002*

CARTWRIGHT HALL ART GALLERY
Lister Park BD9 4NS (1m from city centre on A650)
☎ 01274 751212   📠 01274 481045
Times: Open all year Apr-Sep, Tue-Sat 10-5, Sun 1-5. (Closed Mon ex BH, Good Fri, 25 & 26 Dec). **Facilities:** ♨ ♿ (wheelchair available) toilets for disabled shop ✘ *Details not confirmed for 2002*

COLOUR MUSEUM
Perkin House, 1 Providence St BD1 2PW (from city centre follow signs for B6144(Haworth), then follow brown tourist signs)
☎ 01274 390955   📠 01274 392888
e-mail: museum@sdc.org.uk

Europe's only Museum of Colour comprises two galleries packed with visitor-operated exhibits demonstrating the effects of light and colour, including optical illusions and the story of dyeing and textile printing. There is a programme of special exhibitions and events. Please telephone for details.
Times: Open Jan-late Dec, Tue-Sat, 10-4. **Fee:** £1.75 (concessions £1.25). Family ticket £4 **Facilities:** 🅿 (300 yds) ♿ (lift from street level) toilets for disabled shop ✘ (ex guide dogs) ♨

NATIONAL MUSEUM OF PHOTOGRAPHY, FILM & TELEVISION
BD1 1NQ (2m from end of M606, follow signs for city centre)
☎ 01274 202030   📠 01274 394540
e-mail: talk.nmpft@nmsi.ac.uk

The past, present and future of the media explored with interactive displays and dramatic reconstructions - ride on a magic carpet, become a newsreader for the day or try your hand at vision mixing. At the heart of the Museum is IMAX, a cinema screen more than five storeys high.

National Museum of Photography, Film & Television
Times: Open all year, BH's & main school hols 10-6. (Closed Mon). **Fee:** Admission to permanent galleries free, IMAX Cinema £5.80 (concessions £4). Groups 20% discount. **Facilities:** 🅿 (adjacent) ♨ ✘ licensed ♿ (tailored tours,braille signs,induction loop,cinema seating) toilets for disabled shop ✘ (ex guide dogs) ♨

🏛 BRAMHAM
Map 08 SE44

BRAMHAM PARK
LS23 6ND (on A1, 14m S of Wetherby, take Bramham/Thorner slip road and follow signs)
☎ 01937 846002   📠 01937 846001
e-mail: lucy.finucane@bramhampark.co.uk

This fine Queen Anne house was built by Robert Benson and is the home of his descendants. The garden has ornamental ponds, cascades, temples and avenues.
Times: Open Apr-Sep, daily 10.30-5.30. **Fee:** Gardens only £4 (ch under 16 & pen £2, under 5's free). House open by appointment only.
Facilities: 🅿 ♿ toilets for disabled ✘ (ex guide dogs)

🏛 GOMERSAL
Map 08 SE22

RED HOUSE
Oxford Rd BD19 4JP (M62 junct 26, take A58 towards Leeds then right onto A651)
☎ 01274 335100   📠 01274 335105

A delightful house decorated as the 1830s home of a Yorkshire wool clothier and merchant. The house and family were frequently visited by Charlotte Brontë in the 1830s and featured in her novel *Shirley*. The gardens have been reconstructed in the style of the period and there are exhibitions on the Brontë connection and local history.
Times: Open all year, Mon-Fri 11-5, Sat-Sun 12-5. Telephone for Xmas opening. (Closed Good Fri & 1 Jan). **Fee:** Free. **Facilities:** 🅿 ♿ (Braille & tape guide available) toilets for disabled shop ✘ (ex guide dogs) ♨

HALIFAX Map 07 SE02

BANKFIELD MUSEUM

Boothtown Rd, Akroyd Park HX3 6HG (on A647, 0.5m from Halifax town centre)
☎ 01422 354823 & 352334 🖷 01422 349020
e-mail: bankfield-museum@calderdale.gov.uk

Built by Edward Akroyd in the 1860s, this Renaissance-style building houses an outstanding collection of costumes and textiles from many periods and parts of the world, including a new gallery featuring East European textiles. There is also a section on toys, and the museum of the Duke of Wellington's Regiment is housed here. Temporary exhibitions are held and there is a lively programme of events and workshops.
Times: Open all year, Tue-Sat 10-5, Sun 2-5, BH Mon 10-5. **Fee:** Free. **Facilities:** P ♿ audio guide & tactile objects toilets for disabled shop 🐕 (ex guide dogs)

EUREKA! THE MUSEUM FOR CHILDREN

Discovery Rd HX1 2NE (M62 junct 24 follow brown tourist signs to centre(A629))
☎ 01422 330069 01426 983191
🖷 01422 330275
e-mail: info@eureka.org.uk
Times: Open all year, daily 10-5 (except 24-26 Dec) **Facilities:** P (charged) ☕ ♿ (lift, staff trained in sign language, audio guide, workshop) toilets for disabled shop 🐕 (ex guide dogs) *Details not confirmed for 2002*

PIECE HALL

HX1 1RE (follow brown tourist signs)
☎ 01422 358087 🖷 01422 349310
e-mail: karen.belshaw@calderdale.gov.uk

The merchants of Halifax built the elegant and unique hall in 1779, and it has over 300 merchants' rooms around a courtyard, now housing an industrial museum, art galleries and shops selling antiques, books etc. There is an open market on Friday and Saturday, and a flea market on Thursday. There is a lively programe of exhibitions, workshops, activities and events throughout the year, and a festival in the summer, please ring for details.
Times: Open all year daily (Closed 25-26 Dec). Art Gallery ; Tue-Sun & BH Mons 10-5. **Fee:** Free. **Facilities:** P (50 yds) ☕ ♿ (lifts, shopmobility on site & audio guide available) toilets for disabled shop

SHIBDEN HALL

Lister's Rd HX3 6XG (2km E of Halifax on A58)
☎ 01422 352246 & 321455 🖷 01422 348440
e-mail: shibden.hall@calderdale.gov

The house dates back to the early 15th century, and its rooms have been laid out to illustrate life in different periods of its history. Craft weekends, featuring over 30 craftworkers demonstrating historic skills are held, and there's a lively programme of craft events, workshops and family activities. Please phone for details.
Times: Open Mar-Nov, Mon-Sat 10-5, Sun 12-5. Dec-Feb, Mon-Sat 10-4, Sun 12-4 **Fee:** £2.50 (ch & con £1.50) Family £6. Groups ring for details. **Facilities:** P ☕ ♿ (garden only partially accesible) toilets for disabled shop 🐕

HAREWOOD Map 08 SE34

HAREWOOD HOUSE & BIRD GARDEN

LS17 9LQ (junc A61/A659 Leeds/Harrogate Rd)
☎ 0113 218 1010 🖷 0113 218 1002
e-mail: business@harewood.org

The Yorkshire home of the Earl and Countess of Harewood containing fine furniture, porcelain and paintings. The landscaped grounds offer lakeside and woodland walks. The Bird Garden has aviaries for over 150 species. Numerous special events take place throughout the year, telephone for details.
Times: Open 14 Mar-4 Nov, daily Bird Garden from 10am, House from 11am. Grounds & Bird Garden open wknds Nov-Dec.
Fee: 'Freedom ticket' (house, grounds, bird garden, terrace gallery) £8 (ch/student £5, pen £7) Family £28. Bird garden, grounds, terrace gallery £6.25 (ch/student £3.50 pen £5.25) Family £19. Group rate 15+
Facilities: P ☕ ✕ licensed ♿ (electric ramp, lift, free audio tour) toilets for disabled shop garden centre 🐕 (ex in gardens on lead)

HAWORTH Map 07 SE03

BRONTË PARSONAGE MUSEUM

BD22 8DR (A629 & A6033 follow signs for Haworth, take Rawdon Rd, pass 2 car parks, next left, then right)
☎ 01535 642323 🖷 01535 647131
e-mail: bronte@bronte.prestel.co.uk

Haworth Parsonage was the lifelong family home of the Brontës. An intensely close-knit family, the Brontës saw the parsonage as the heart of their world and the moorland setting provided them with inspiration for their writing. The house contains much personal memorabilia, including the furniture Charlotte bought with the proceeds of her literary success, Branwell's portraits of local worthies, Emily's writing desk and Anne's books and drawings.
Times: Open Apr-Sep, daily 10-5.30; Oct-Mar daily 11-5 (final admission 30 min before closing). Closed 24-27 Dec & 8 Jan-3 Feb.
Fee: £4.80 (ch 5-16 £1.50, concessions £3.50). Family ticket £10.50.
Facilities: P (charged) ♿ (Information in large type & braille) shop 🐕 (ex guide dogs)

KEIGHLEY & WORTH VALLEY RAILWAY & MUSEUM

Keighley BD22 8NJ (1m from Keighley on A629 Halifax rd, follow brown tourist signs)
☎ 01535 645214 & 677777 🖷 01535 647317

The line was built mainly to serve the valley's mills, and goes through the heart of Brontë country. Beginning at Keighley (shared with Railtrack), it climbs up to Haworth, and terminates at Oxenhope, which has a storage and restoration building. At Haworth there are locomotive workshops and at Ingrow West, an award-winning museum.
Times: All year weekend service, but daily all BH wks & 19 Jun-1 Sep.
Fee: Full line return ticket £6 reduced fares for ch & pen. Family return ticket £16. Day rover (unlimited travel) £8, Family day rover £20. Under 5's free. Party rates. **Facilities:** P (charged) ☕ ♿ (wheelchairs can be accommodated in brake car). toilets for disabled shop

contd.

⚏ HUDDERSFIELD
Map 07 SE11

HUDDERSFIELD ART GALLERY
Princess Alexandra Walk HD1 2SU
☎ 01484 221964 ext 1962 📄 01484 221952
Times: Open all year, Mon-Fri 10-5, Sat 10-4. (Closed Sun & BH's).
Facilities: P ৬ toilets for disabled shop ✻ (ex guide dogs) *Details not confirmed for 2002*

TOLSON MEMORIAL MUSEUM
Ravensknowle Park, Wakefield Rd HD5 8DJ (on A629)
☎ 01484 223830 📄 01484 223843
Times: Open all year. Mon-Fri 11-5, Sat & Sun noon-5. (Closed Xmas).
Facilities: P ৬ toilets for disabled shop ✻ *Details not confirmed for 2002*

⚏ ILKLEY
Map 07 SE14

MANOR HOUSE GALLERY & MUSEUM
Castle Yard, Church St LS29 9DT (behind Ilkley Parish Church, on A65)
☎ 01943 600066 📄 01943 817079
Times: Open all year, Wed-Sat 11-5, Sun 1-4. (Closed Good Fri, 25-28 Dec). **Facilities:** ৬ shop ✻ *Details not confirmed for 2002*

⚏ KEIGHLEY
Map 07 SE04

CLIFFE CASTLE MUSEUM & GALLERY
Spring Gardens Ln BD20 6LH (NW of town off A629)
☎ 01535 618230 📄 01535 610536
Times: Open all year, Tue-Sat 10-5, Sun 12-5. Also open BH Mon. (Closed Good Fri & 25-28 Dec). **Facilities:** P ✺ ৬ toilets for disabled shop ✻ *Details not confirmed for 2002*

EAST RIDDLESDEN HALL
Bradford Rd BD20 4EA (1m NE of Keighley on south side of Bradford Rd)
☎ 01535 607075 📄 01535 691462
e-mail: yorker@smtp.ntrust.org.uk

This charming 17th-century Yorkshire manor house is typical of its kind, although the plasterwork and oak panelling are contemporary. A small secluded garden is found in the grounds, which also feature one of the largest medieval tithe barns in the north of England.
Times: Open 31 Mar-4 Nov, Tue-Wed, Sat-Sun & Good Fri & BH Mon & Mon in Jul & Aug; 12-5 (Sat 1-5). **Fee:** £3.50 (ch £1.80). Family ticket £8.80. **Facilities:** P ✺ ৬ shop ✻ ⚘

⚏ LEEDS
Map 08 SE33

ABBEY HOUSE MUSEUM
Abbey Walk, Abbey Rd, Kirkstall LS5 3EH (3m W of Leeds city centre on A65)
☎ 0113 230 5492 📄 0113 230 5499

Displays at this museum include an interactive childhood gallery, a look at Kirkstall Abbey, and an exploration of life in Victorian Leeds. Three reconstructed streets allow the visitor to take in the sights and sounds of the late 19th century.
Times: Open all year Tue-Fri 10-5, Sat noon-5, Sun 10-5. Closed Mon
Fee: £3 (ch £1 accompanied by an adult, concessions £2). Family ticket £5 **Facilities:** P ✺ ✕ licensed ৬ (braille plaques on wall) toilets for disabled shop ✻ (ex guide dogs) ⚘

CITY ART GALLERY
The Headrow LS1 3AA (city centre, next to town hall and library)
☎ 0113 247 8248 📄 0113 244 9689

Home to one of the best collections of 20th-century British art outside London, as well as Victorian and late 19th-century pictures, an outstanding collection of English watercolours, a display of modern sculpture and temporary exhibitions focusing on the contemporary.
Times: Open all year, Mon-Sat 10-5, Wed until 8, Sun 1-5.Closed BHs.
Fee: Free. P ✺ ✕ licensed ৬ (restricted access to upper floor) toilets for disabled shop ✻ (ex guide dogs)

KIRKSTALL ABBEY
Abbey Rd, Kirkstall LS5 3EH (off A65, W of city centre)
☎ 0113 275 5821

The most complete 12th-century Cistercian Abbey in the country stands on the banks of the River Aire. Many of the original buildings can still be seen, including the cloister, church and refectory. Tours take visitors to areas not normally accessible to the public. In summer the Abbey hosts plays, fairs and musical events.
Times: Open all year. Abbey site open dawn-dusk. **Fee:** Free.
Facilities: P ৬ toilets for disabled shop ✻

LEEDS INDUSTRIAL MUSEUM AT ARMLEY MILLS
Canal Rd, Armley LS12 2QF (2m W of city, off A65)
☎ 0113 263 7861

Once the world's largest woollen mill, Armley Mills shows the progress of wool from the sheep to knitted clothing. The museum also has its own 1930s cinema illustrating the history of cinema projection, including the first moving pictures taken in Leeds. There is a printing gallery, and demonstrations of static engines and steam locomotives.
Times: Open all year, Tue-Sat 10-5, Sun 1-5. Last entry 1 hr before closing. (Closed Mon ex BHs). **Fee:** £2 (ch 50p pen, students & UB40's £1) Friends & Family ticket £5 (2 adults & 3 ch). **Facilities:** P ৬ (chair-lifts between floors) toilets for disabled shop ✻ ⚐

MIDDLETON RAILWAY
Moor Rd, Hunslet LS10 2JQ (M621 junct 5 or follow signs from A61)
☎ 0113 271 0320 (ansaphone)
📄 01977 620585
e-mail: info@middletonrailway.org.uk

This was the first railway authorised by an Act of Parliament (in 1758) and the first to succeed with steam locomotives (in 1812). Steam trains run each weekend in season from Tunstall Road roundabout to Middleton Park. There is a programme of special events.
Times: Moor Road Station open for viewing every wknd. Trains run Sat, Sun & BH, Apr-Dec. **Fee:** Entry to station free. £2.50 (ch £1.50) Return train fare. Family ticket £7. **Facilities:** P ✺ ৬ (ramped access to all areas) toilets for disabled shop ⚐

ROYAL ARMOURIES MUSEUM

Armouries Dr LS10 1LT (off A61, follow brown tourist signs)

☎ 0113 220 1999 & 0990 106 666

🖥 0113 220 1934

e-mail: enquiries@armouries.org.uk

The museum is an impressive contemporary home for the renowned national collection of arms and armour. The collection is divided between five galleries: War, Tournament, Self-Defence, Hunting and Oriental. The Hall of Steel features a 100ft-high mass of 3000 pieces of arms and armour. Extensive interactive displays, dramatisations of jousting tournaments etc. and the chance to see leather workers and armourers at work.
Times: Open daily, from 10-5. (Closed Xmas eve & day)
Fee: £4.90 (u17, over 60 & con free) Couples £9. Annual passes available. Party 10+ £2.50 each. **Facilities:** 🅿 (charged) 🍽 ✗ licensed ᵫ (induction loops, wheelchairs, signers) toilets for disabled shop 🐾 (ex guide/hearing dogs) 🥤

TEMPLE NEWSAM HOUSE & PARK

LS15 0AE (off A63)

☎ 0113 264 7321 (House) & 264 5535 (Park)

🖥 0113 260 2285

This Tudor and Jacobean mansion boasts extensive collections of decorative arts in their original room settings, including the incomparable Chippendale collection. There's a Rare Breeds Centre, and the 'Capability' Brown grounds have a magnificent display of rhododendrons. Major refurbishment is taking place over the next year so telephone in advance to avoid disappointment.
Times: Open all year. House: Tue-Sat 10-5, Sun 1-5; Nov-28 Dec & Mar, Tue-Sat 10-4, Sun 12-5. Open Bank Hols. Home Farm: 10-4 (3 in winter) ; Gardens: 10-dusk. Estate: daily, dawn-dusk. Closed Jan-Feb re-opens 28 Feb. **Fee:** £2 (concessions £1). Accompanied children 50p. Friends & Family ticket £5 (2 adults & 3 ch). **Facilities:** 🅿 (charged) 🍽 ᵫ (ramps giving full accesss to parkland,wheelchairs for hire) toilets for disabled shop 🐾 🥤

THACKRAY MEDICAL MUSEUM

Beckett St LS9 7LN (next to St James Hospital)

☎ 0113 244 4343   🖥 0113 247 0219

e-mail: medical_museum@msn.com

Times: Open all year, Tue-Sun & BH Mons 10-5.30. Closed 25-26 Dec & 1 Jan. **Facilities:** 🅿 (charged) 🍽 ᵫ (wheelchair loan, induction loop) toilets for disabled shop 🐾 (ex guide dogs) *Details not confirmed for 2002* 🥤

THWAITE MILLS WATERMILL

Thwaite Ln, Stourton LS10 1RP (2m S of city centre, off A61)

☎ 0113 249 6453   🖥 0113 246 5561

A guide will take you on a tour of this water-powered mill which sits between the River Aire and the Aire and Calder Navigation. Two great wheels drive a mass of cogs and grinding wheels which crushed stone for putty and paint throughout the 19th century.
Times: Open Tues-Sat 10am-5pm & Sun 1-5pm. Nov-Dec & March Tues-Sat 10am-4pm, Sun 12-4pm. Open BH Mon. Closed Jan & Feb. **Fee:** £2 (ch 50p, £1 concessions). Family & Friends ticket £5 (2 adults & 3 ch). **Facilities:** 🅿 ᵫ (wheelchair lifts) toilets for disabled shop 🐾 🥤

TROPICAL WORLD

Canal Gardens, Roundhay Park LS8 2ER (3m N of city centre off A58 at Oakwood)

☎ 0113 266 1850   🖥 0113 237 0077

The atmosphere of the tropics is re-created here as visitors walk among exotic trees. A waterfall cascades into a rock-pool and other pools contain terrapins and carp. There are reptiles, insects and more than 30 species of butterfly. There is also a Nocturnal House, a South American Rainforest, and a Desert House.
Times: Open daily, 10-early evening (dusk in winter). Closed 25 Dec
Fee: £1.50 (ch 8-15 75p, ch under 8 & Leeds card holders free). **Facilities:** 🅿 🍽 ᵫ toilets for disabled shop 🐾 (ex guide dogs) 🥤

🏛 LOTHERTON HALL   Map 08 SE43
LOTHERTON HALL
Aberford LS25 3EB (off A1, 0.75m E of junct with B1217)
☎ 0113 281 3259

Built in Edwardian times, the museum contains furniture, pictures, silver and ceramics from the Gascoigne collection, and works of art on loan from Leeds galleries. Outside, the Edwardian garden, bird garden and deer park are delightful places in which to stroll. **Times:** Open Tue-Sat 10-5. Sun 1-5. Bank Hols. Nov-Dec & Mar Tue-Sat 10-4, Sun 12-4. **Fee:** Hall, £2 (ch, pen & students £1, unaccompanied ch 50p). Family & Friends ticket £5 (2 adults & 3 ch). Party 15+. Free admission to Bird Garden, Gardens & Parkland. Free admission to house for driver. **Facilities:** ▣ (charged) ♥ ✗ licensed ᐇ shop ✸ (ex in park) ⬗

🏛 MIDDLESTOWN   Map 08 SE21
NATIONAL COAL MINING MUSEUM FOR ENGLAND
Caphouse Colliery, New Rd WF4 4RH (on A642)
☎ 01924 848806 🖹 01924 840694
e-mail: info@ncm.org.uk

A unique opportunity to go 450ft underground down one of Britain's oldest working mine shafts, guided by an ex-miner. Models and machinery depict methods and conditions of mining from the early 1800s to the present day. You are strongly advised to wear sensible footwear and warm clothing. **Times:** Open all year, daily 10-5. (Closed 24-26 Dec & 1 Jan). **Fee:** £5.75 (ch, pen free, con £4.85). **Facilities:** ▣ ♥ ✗ licensed ᐇ (nature trail not accessible) toilets for disabled shop ⬗

🏛 NOSTELL PRIORY   Map 08 SE41
NOSTELL PRIORY
Doncaster Rd WF4 1QE (6m SE of Wakefield towards Doncaster, off A638)
☎ 01924 863892 🖹 01924 865282
e-mail: yorknp@smtp.ntrust.org.uk

Built by Paine in the middle of the 18th century, the priory has an additional wing built by Adam in 1766. It contains a notable saloon and tapestry room and displays pictures and Chippendale furniture. There is a lake in the grounds. **Times:** Open 31 Mar-4 Nov: daily (ex Mon/Tue open BH Mon); 1-5.30. 10 Nov-9 Dec: Sat/Sun, 12-4.30. Grounds: open same days as house 11-6 **Fee:** House & Grounds £4.50 (ch £2.20). Family ticket £11. Grounds only £2.50 (ch £1.20). **Facilities:** ▣ ♥ ᐇ (lift) toilets for disabled shop ✸ (ex around vista) ♨

🏛 OAKWELL HALL   Map 08 SE22
OAKWELL HALL
Nutter Ln, Birstall WF17 9LG (6m SE of Bradford, off M62 junct 26/27, follow brown tourist signs)
☎ 01924 326240 🖹 01924 326249

A moated Elizabethan manor house, furnished as it might have looked in the 1690s. Extensive 110-acre country park with visitor information centre, period gardens, nature trails, arboretum and children's adventure playground.
Times: Open all year, daily (ex Good Fri, 24 Dec-1 Jan). **Fee:** £1.40 (ch 50p). Family ticket £3. **Facilities:** ▣ ♥ ᐇ (herb garden for the blind, large print & braille guide) toilets for disabled shop ✸ (park only ex guide dogs) ⬗

🏛 WAKEFIELD   Map 08 SE21
WAKEFIELD ART GALLERY
Wentworth Ter WF1 3QW (N of city centre by Wakefield College and Clayton Hospital)
☎ 01924 305796 🖹 01924 305770

Wakefield was home to two of Britain's greatest modern sculptors - Barbara Hepworth and Henry Moore. The art gallery, which has an important collection of 20th-century paintings and sculptures, has a special room devoted to these two local artists. There are frequent temporary exhibitions.
Times: Open all year, Tue-Sat 10.30-4.30, Sun 2-4.30. **Fee:** Free. **Facilities:** ℙ (on street) (on street parking restricted to 2hrs) shop ✸ (ex guide dogs)

🏛 WEST BRETTON   Map 08 SE21
YORKSHIRE SCULPTURE PARK
WF4 4LG (1m from M1 junct 38. A637 to West Bretton, left at war monument)
☎ 01924 830302 🖹 01924 830044
e-mail: office@ysp.co.uk

One of Europe's leading sculpture parks, set in over 500 acres of beautiful parkland. There are changing displays from the loan collection including work by Barbara Hepworth, William Tucker, Grenville Davey and Sol Le Witt. In the adjacent Bretton Country Park there is a permanent exhibition of works by Henry Moore.
Times: Open all year 10-6 (summer) 10-4 (winter). (Closed 24 & 25 Dec). **Fee:** Free. **Facilities:** ▣ (charged) ♥ ᐇ (free scooters, parking, trail accessible for wheelchairs) toilets for disabled shop

Guernsey

Top: Jerbourg Point, St Martin

If it's sunshine, shopping and sea you're interested in, then the island of Guernsey is the ideal location for a break that combines the feeling of being abroad with the familiarity of the English language and British ways of life.

When William conquered England, he didn't need to conquer Guernsey. It was already part of the Duchy of Normandy. The strategic importance of the island has been recognised through the centuries, from the 13th-century Castle Cornet to the fortifications of the German occupying forces during WWII. There are also many ancient structures, some of which are believed to be among the oldest in Europe.

Guernsey enjoys some 2,000 hours of sunshine a year. This makes its 27 beaches great places to spend time. No matter which way the wind is blowing, you'll be sure to find one that's sheltered.

The island is also known for its conservation. Both the National Trust and the home-grown La Société Guernesiaise maintain beautiful areas, including a wooded valley and a number of fields.

Shopping is a major attraction on Guernsey, not necessarily for what's on sale, although the shops cover a wide variety and there are some local specialities including Guernsey sweaters and flowers. The real attraction is the low local taxation and lack of VAT, which makes the island a bargain hunter's paradise.

Close to Guernsey are three smaller islands well worth visiting. Sark, Alderney and Aurigny. Sark was the setting for Mervyn Peake's novel, *Mr Pye*. It was also the location for the TV version starring Derek Jacobi. During the 1850s Victor Hugo was exiled in Guernsey, and wrote *Les Miserables* there.

🏛 FOREST
GERMAN OCCUPATION MUSEUM
Map 16

GY8 0BG
☎ 01481 238205

The museum has the Channel Islands' largest collection of Occupation items, with tableaux of a kitchen, bunker rooms and a street during the Occupation. Liberation Day (9th May) will be celebrated with special events.
Times: Open Apr-Oct 10-5, Nov-Mar 10-1 (Closed Jan). **Fee:** £3 (ch £1.50). **Facilities:** 🅿 ♨ ♿ (ramps & handrails)

🏛 ROCQUAINE BAY
FORT GREY AND SHIPWRECK MUSEUM
Map 16

GY7 9BY
☎ 01481 265036 📄 01481 263279
e-mail: education@museum.guernsey.net

The fort is a Morello tower, nicknamed the 'Cup and Saucer' because of its appearance. It houses a museum devoted to ships wrecked on the treacherous Hanois reef nearby.
Times: Open Apr-Oct, 10-5. **Fee:** £2 (pen £1). Joint ticket with Castle Cornet & Guernsey Museum £7 (pen £4). Students & children free.
Facilities: 🅿 (opposite fort) shop 🅇 ♨

🏛 ST ANDREW
GERMAN MILITARY UNDERGROUND HOSPITAL & AMMUNITION STORE
Map 16

La Vassalerie GY6 8XR
☎ 01481 239100

The largest structure created during the German Occupation, a concrete maze of about 75,000 sq ft, which took slave workers three-and-a-half years to complete, at the cost of many lives. Most of the equipment has been removed, but the central heating plant, hospital beds and cooking facilities can be seen.
Times: Open Jul-Aug, daily 10-noon & 2-4.30; May-Jun & Sep, daily 10-noon & 2-4; Apr & Oct, daily 2-4; Mar & Nov, Sun & Thu 2-3.
Fee: £2.60 (ch 60p). **Facilities:** 🅿 ♿ shop

🏛 ST MARTIN
SAUSMAREZ MANOR
Map 16

Sausmarez Rd GY4 6SG
☎ 01481 235571 📄 01481 235572
e-mail: peter@lesausmarez.fsnet.co.uk

The Manor has been owned by the same family for centuries. There are collections of Oriental, French and English furniture and paintings. The Formal Garden has herbaceous borders, and the Woodland Garden is set around two small lakes and a stream.
Times: Open Etr-Oct 10.30 & 11.30, Mon-Thu; Jun-Aug 10.30, 11.30 & 2 Mon-Thu; Or by appointment. **Fee:** House £4.90 (ch £2, pen £4.50). Woodland Garden £2.50 (accompanied ch £1, pen £2, disabled free). Dolls House Collection £2.50 (ch £1, stu & pen £1.50). Family ticket £5. Sculpture Park £2.50 (accompanied ch £1, pen £2, disabled free).
Facilities: 🅿 ♨ ♿ (free admission, partial access to garden, wheelchair loan) shop 🅇 (ex assist dogs)

🏛 ST PETER PORT
CASTLE CORNET
Map 16

GY1 UG
☎ 01481 721657 📄 01481 715177
e-mail: education@museum.guernsey.net

The history of this magnificent castle spans eight centuries and its buildings now house several museums. Soldiers fire the noonday gun in a daily ceremony. Look for the Maritime Museum that charts Guernsey's nautical history, the 'Story of Castle Cornet'.
Times: Open Apr-Oct, daily 10-5. **Fee:** £5 (students/pen £3). Joint ticket with Fort Grey & Guernsey Museum £7 (pen £4). Accompanied children under 12, students & educational groups free
Facilities: 🅿 (100 yds) (2 hr time zone, 10hr within 200 yards) ♨ shop 🅇 (ex guide dogs) ♨

GUERNSEY MUSEUM & ART GALLERY
Candie Gardens GY1 1UG
☎ 01481 726518 📄 01481 715177
e-mail: education@museum.guernsey.net

The museum tells the story of Guernsey and its people. There is an audio-visual theatre and special exhibitions. It is surrounded by beautiful gardens with superb views.
Times: Open all year, daily 10-5 (summer), 10-4 (winter). **Fee:** £3 (pen £2). Joint ticket with Castle Cornet & Fort Grey £7 (pen £4). Students & children free. **Facilities:** 🅿 (outside museum) (2hr & 5hr) ♨ ♿ toilets for disabled shop 🅇 (ex guide dogs) ♨

🏛 VALE
ROUSSE TOWER
Map 16

Rousse Tower Headland
☎ 01481 726611 📄 01481 721246
e-mail: louise.cain@gov.gg

One of the original 15 towers built in 1778-9 in prime defensive positions around the coast of Guernsey. Musket fire could be directed on invading forces through the loopholes. Replica guns are displayed in the interpretation centre.
Times: Open Apr-Oct 9-dusk, Nov-Mar Wed, Sat & Sun 9-4. **Fee:** Free.
Facilities: 🅿 ♨ 🅇 (ex guide dogs)

Jersey

EVENTS & FESTIVALS

April
2nd-5th Jersey Jazz Festival
(various venues around the island)

May
11th-19th Jersey International Food
Festival (various events around the
island)
24th-27th Jersey International Air
Rally

June
3rd-9th La Fête Nouomande
(Jersey Norman French Festival)
7th-9th Jersey Festival of Motoring
12th-13th Early Summer Flower
Show, Howard Davis Park, St
Helier

July
8th-14th Jersey Garden Festival
(various venues around the
island)
13th-14th Jersey West Show,
traditional country fair in
the Parish of St Peter

August
8th-9th Jersey Battle of
Flowers (centenary year)
14th-15th Summer Flower
Show, Howard Davis Park,
St Helier

September
tbc International Air Display over St
Aubins Bay

October
3rd-6th Jersey Festival of World
Music (various venues around the
island)
6th-13th International Choir
Festival of Jersey

December
tbc Fête dé Noué (Christmas
festival)

The Channel Islands are renowned for their hospitality, prosperity and beauty, with their fine cliffs, sandy beaches, splendid harbours and impressive marinas.

The mild climate is conducive to enjoyable holidays, and ensures an abundance of flowers, fruit and vegetables. Notably the Channel Island tomato and the deliciously earthy early Jersey Royal potato, a delicacy in its own right with a knob of Jersey butter.

Like Guernsey, Jersey has its own breed of cow, and its own sweater, the jersey, incorporating an anchor into its design under the neckline at the front. Agriculture and fishing are traditional industries. The conger eel is particularly associated with the island, and conger eel soup is a popular local dish.

Jersey is the largest of the Channel Islands, and the most southerly, just 30 miles (48km) from St Malo. The unique combination of the French and British ways of life contributes much to the island's undoubtable charm. The island is infused with Gallic culture, as you can see by the names of the streets and the baguettes in the bakers'. The local language is traditionally a Norman-French Patois, though this is in decline and English is generally spoken. The islands also have their own banknotes, though the currency is sterling.

The financial industry has transformed the lives of islanders, bringing great prosperity to its economy. Banks of all nationalities are in residence on the island, taking advantage of its low-tax base and proximity to the City of London. Checking out the multi-million pound properties of the rich and famous tax exiles is part of the sightseeing itinerary.

Top: Jersey States chamber, St Helier

🏛 GOREY
Map 16

MONT ORGUEIL CASTLE
JE3 6ET (A3 or coast road to Gorey)
☎ 01534 853292 📄 01534 854303
e-mail: marketing@jerseyheritagetrust.org
Times: Open daily throughout the year 9.30-6; Last admission 5pm. Times in winter change (Fri-Mon 10-dusk) **Facilities:** P (200 yds) (discs required at harbour) shop 🐾 (ex guide dogs) *Details not confirmed for 2002* 🗨

🏛 GREVE DE LECQ BAY
Map 16

GREVE DE LECQ BARRACKS
☎ 01534 483193
Times: Open Etr wknd & 2 May-15 Oct, Tue-Sat 11-5 & Sun 2-5. (Closed Mon). **Facilities:** P & shop 🐾 (ex guide dogs) 🍴 *Details not confirmed for 2002*

🏛 GROUVILLE
Map 16

LA HOUGUE BIE
JE2 7UA (A6 or A7 to Five Oaks then Prines Tower Rd)
☎ 01534 853823 📄 01534 856472
e-mail: marketing@jerseyheritagetrust.org
Times: Open 29 Mar-Oct, daily 10-5. **Facilities:** P & shop 🐾 (ex guide dogs) *Details not confirmed for 2002* 🗨

🏛 ST BRELADE
Map 16

JERSEY LAVENDER FARM
Rue du Pont Marquet JE3 8DS (on B25 from St.Aubin's Bay to Redhouses)
☎ 01534 742933 📄 01534 745613
e-mail: jerseylavender@localdial.com
Times: Open 22 May-23 Sep, Mon-Sat 10-5. **Facilities:** P ♨ & (wheelchair loan, wide doors, grab rails etc) toilets for disabled shop garden centre *Details not confirmed for 2002* 🗨

🏛 ST CLEMENT
Map 16

SAMARÈS MANOR
JE2 6QW (2m E of St Helier on St Clements Inner Road)
☎ 01534 870551 📄 01534 768949

The manor stands in 14 acres of beautiful gardens. The Japanese Garden occupies an artificial hill, and has a series of waterfalls cascading over Cumberland limestone. There's a craft centre, farm animals and a children's play area. Falconry displays mornings and afternoons except Sundays.
Times: Open 6 Apr-14 Oct. **Fee:** £4.20 (ch under 16 £1.90, pen £3.50).
Facilities: P ♨ ✗ licensed & toilets for disabled shop garden centre 🐾 (ex guide dogs) 🗨

🏛 ST HELIER
Map 16

ELIZABETH CASTLE
JE2 3WU (access by causeway or amphibious vehicle)
☎ 01534 723971 📄 01534 610338
e-mail: marketing@jerseyheritagetrust.org
Times: Open 29 Mar-Oct, daily 9.30-6. Last admission 5. **Facilities:** P ♨ & shop 🐾 (ex guide dogs) *Details not confirmed for 2002* 🗨

JERSEY MUSEUM
The Weighbridge JE2 3NF (near bus station on weighbridge)
☎ 01534 633300 📄 01534 633301
e-mail: marketing@jerseyheritagetrust.org
Times: Open all year, daily 10-5. Winter daily 10-4. (Closed 24-26 Dec & 1 Jan). **Facilities:** P (100yds) (paycard at most public parking) ✗ licensed & (audio loop, audio guide for partially sighted, car park) toilets for disabled shop 🐾 (ex guide dogs) *Details not confirmed for 2002* 🗨

MARITIME MUSEUM & OCCUPATION TAPESTRY GALLERY
New North Quay JE2 3ND (alongside Marina, opposite Liberation Square)
☎ 01534 811043 📄 01534 874099
e-mail: marketing@jerseyheritagetrust
Times: Open all year, daily 10-5 (winter closing at 4pm). **Facilities:** P (paycards in public car parks) & (braille books, audio guide etc) toilets for disabled shop 🐾 (ex guide dogs) *Details not confirmed for 2002* 🗨

🏛 ST LAWRENCE
Map 16

FLYING FLOWERS
Jersey Flower Centre JE3 1GX
☎ 01534 865553 📄 01534 866000
Times: Open Apr-Oct, daily 10-5. **Facilities:** P ♨ ✗ & (Wheelchairs available) toilets for disabled shop 🐾 (ex guide dogs) *Details not confirmed for 2002*

GERMAN UNDERGROUND HOSPITAL
Les Charrieres Malorey JE3 1FU
☎ 01534 863442 📄 01534 865970

On 1 July 1940 the Channel Islands were occupied by German forces, and this vast complex dug deep into a hillside is an evocative reminder of that Occupation. A video presentation, along with a large collection of memorabilia, illustrates the lives of the islanders at war. A further exhibition records their impressions during 1945, the year of liberation.
Times: Open 12 Mar-5 Nov, daily 9.30-5.30 Last admission 4.15. (Closed 9 May & restricted hours 10 Aug & 14 Sep). **Fee:** £6.20 (ch £3). **Facilities:** P ♨ ✗ licensed & (ramp to restaurant & lift in Visitor Centre to restaurant) toilets for disabled shop 🐾 (ex guide dogs) 🗨

HAMPTONNE COUNTRY LIFE MUSEUM
La Rue de la Patente JE3 1HS (5m from St Helier on A1, A10 & follow signs)
☎ 01534 863955 📄 01534 863935
e-mail: marketing@jerseyheritagetrust.org
Times: Open 29 Mar-Oct, daily 10-4. **Facilities:** P ♨ & toilets for disabled shop 🐾 (ex guide dogs) *Details not confirmed for 2002* 🗨

⛫ ST OUEN
Map 16

THE CHANNEL ISLANDS MILITARY MUSEUM
Smile Rd (at rear of the Chateau complex)
☎ 01534 723136 📄 01534 485647
e-mail: damienhorn@jerseymail.co.uk

German uniforms, motorcycles, weapons, documents, photographs and other items from the 1940-45 occupation are displayed in a wartime bunker that was part of the Nazis' Atlantic defences. Many of the items on display are unique to this museum.
Times: Open week before Etr-Oct **Fee:** £2.50 (ch £1). **Facilities:** 🅿 ☕ 🚹 (All parts accessible ex 1 small room) toilets for disabled shop 🐾 (ex guide dogs)

KEMPT TOWER VISITOR CENTRE
Five Mile Rd
☎ 01534 483651 & 483140 📄 01534 485289
Times: Open BH's & Apr & Oct, Thu & Sun only 2-5; May-Sep, daily (ex Mon) 2-5. **Facilities:** 🅿 shop 🐾 *Details not confirmed for 2002*

⛫ ST PETER
Map 16

JERSEY MOTOR MUSEUM
St Peter's Village JE3 7AG (junct off A12 & B41)
☎ 01534 482966

The museum has a fine collection of motor vehicles from the early 1900s. There are also Allied and German military vehicles of World War II, a Jersey Steam Railway section, aero-engines and other items.
Times: Open end Mar-late Oct, daily 10-5. (Last admission 4.40). **Fee:** £3 (ch £1.50). Wheelchair users free. **Facilities:** 🅿 🚹 (access doors) shop 🐾 (ex guide dogs)

THE LIVING LEGEND
Rue de Petit Aleval JE3 7ET
☎ 01534 485496 📄 01534 485855

Pass through the granite archways into the landscaped gardens and the world of the Jersey Experience where the island's exciting past is recreated in a three dimensional spectacle. Learn of the heroes and villains, the folklore and the links with the UK and the struggles with Europe. Other attractions include an adventure playground, street entertainment and the Jersey craft and shopping village.
Times: Open Apr-Oct, daily 9.30-5.30; Mar & Nov, Mon-Wed & Sat-Sun 10-5. **Fee:** £5.95 (ch £3.95, pen £5.60). **Facilities:** 🅿 ✗ licensed 🚹 (wheelchair available) toilets for disabled shop 🐾 (ex guide dogs)

LE MOULIN DE QUETIVEL
St Peters Valley JE3 3EN (on B58 off A11)
☎ 01534 483193
Times: Open May-mid Oct, Tue-Thu 10-4. **Facilities:** 🅿 🚹 shop 🐾 (ex guide dogs) 🚌 🐗 *Details not confirmed for 2002*

⛫ TRINITY
Map 16

DURRELL WILDLIFE CONSERVATION TRUST
Les Augres Manor JE3 5BP
☎ 01534 860000 📄 01534 860001
Times: Open all year, daily 9.30-6 (dusk in winter). (Closed 25 Dec). **Facilities:** 🅿 ✗ licensed 🚹 (trail for the blind, auditory loop in pavilion) toilets for disabled shop 🐾 *Details not confirmed for 2002*

Isle of Man

Going to the Isle of Man is, in many ways, like visiting a foreign country. The island is not ruled by the British monarch, and has its own parliament (the Tynwald) which makes laws that apply only to the island.

The Isle of Man is only 33 miles by 13, yet packs in so much. Celtic crosses, ancient Viking burial grounds and medieval castles are all around, and the history of the island is well chronicled by the award-winning Manx Museum. Inside, visitors can explore the National Art Gallery, the Map Gallery with its large-scale relief map of the island, and see a specially-produced film, 'Story of Mann'.

One of the island's main attractions is its railway network, which began in 1895 and still runs a regular service. 19th-century electric and mountain railways are also still in operation. The Snaefell Mountain Railway is the only electric mountain railway in Britain, and starts its journey from Laxey, home of the world's largest working waterwheel. Douglas also has horse trams, which have been in continuous operation since 1876, except for wartime breaks.

The island is probably best known for its TT (Tourist Trophy) racing, which is staged in May-June each year. The race, originally for cars only, has been run since 1904, and with motorbikes only since 1911. Other races include the Ramsey Sprint, the Manx Grand Prix, the Manx International Car Rally, and the Kart Racing Grand Prix.

The Isle of Man also serves as something of a celebrity retirement colony, currently being the home of British comic actor Norman Wisdom, and keyboard wizard Rick Wakeman.

EVENTS & FESTIVALS

June
tbc Mananan International Festival of Music (various venues)

July
25-27 Irish National Sheepdog Trials
tbc Yn Chruinnaght Inter-Celtic Festival (various venues)
tbc Manx Heritage Flower Show (various venues)

August
tbc International Jazz Festival, Villa Marina, Douglas
tbc Mannin Angling Festival (various venues)
tbc Manx Grand Prix Motorcycle Fortnight (various venues)

September
tbc Mananan Opera Festival, Erin Arts Centre, Port Erin
tbc Manx International Car Rally (various venues)

Top: The Cashtal-Yn-Ard Long burial chamber, Maughold

🏛 BALLAUGH — Map 06 SC39
CURRAGHS WILD LIFE PARK
IM7 5EA (on main road halfway between Kirk Michael & Ramsey)
☎ 01624 897323   📄 01624 897327
e-mail: curraghswlp@gov.im

This park has been developed adjacent to the reserve area of the Ballaugh Curraghs and a large variety of animals and birds can be seen. A walk through the enclosures lets visitors explore the world of wildlife, including local habitats along the Curraghs nature trail. The miniature railway runs on Sundays.
Times: Open all year Etr-Oct, daily 10-6. Last admission 5.15pm. Oct-Etr, Sat & Sun 10-4. **Fee:** £4 (ch £2, pen £2.70). Party. **Facilities:** 🅿 💺 ♿ (loan of wheelchair & electric wheelchair) toilets for disabled shop 🐾 (ex guide dogs by arrangement)

🏛 CASTLETOWN — Map 06 SC26
CASTLE RUSHEN
☎ 01624 648000   📄 01624 648001
Times: Open Apr-Oct, daily 10-5. **Facilities:** 🅿 (100 yds) ♿ shop 🐾 *Details not confirmed for 2002*

NAUTICAL MUSEUM
☎ 01624 648000   📄 01624 648001
Times: Open Apr-Oct, daily 10-5. **Facilities:** 🅿 (50 yds) ♿ shop 🐾 *Details not confirmed for 2002*

OLD GRAMMAR SCHOOL
☎ 01624 648000   📄 01624 648001
Times: Open Apr-Oct, daily 10-5. **Facilities:** 🅿 ♿ shop 🐾 *Details not confirmed for 2002*

🏛 CREGNEISH — Map 06 SC16
CREGNEASH VILLAGE FOLK MUSEUM
(2m from Port Erin/Port St Mary)
☎ 01624 648000   📄 01624 648001
Times: Open Apr-Oct, daily 10-5. **Facilities:** 🅿 💺 ✕ ♿ shop 🐾 (ex in grounds) *Details not confirmed for 2002*

🏛 DOUGLAS — Map 06 SC37
MANX MUSEUM
IM1 3LY
☎ 01624 648000   📄 01624 648001
Times: Open all year, Mon-Sat 10-5. (Closed Sun, Xmas, New Year, am of Tynwald Day 5 Jul). **Facilities:** 🅿 ✕ licensed ♿ toilets for disabled shop 🐾 *Details not confirmed for 2002*

SNAEFELL MOUNTAIN RAILWAY
Banks Circus IM1 5PT
☎ 01624 663366   📄 01624 663637

Snaefell is the Isle of Man's only mountain. Running up it is Britain's oldest working mountain railway, which was laid in 1895. From the top of Snaefell, on a clear day, England, Ireland, Scotland and Wales are all visible.
Times: Open mid Apr-28 Sep **Fee:** Various fares charged.
Facilities: 🅿 💺 shop 🔖

🏛 LAXEY — Map 06 SC48
GREAT LAXEY WHEEL & MINES TRAIL
☎ 01624 648000   📄 01624 648001
Times: Open Apr-Oct, daily 10-5. **Facilities:** 🅿 ♿ shop 🐾 *Details not confirmed for 2002*

🏛 PEEL — Map 06 SC28
HOUSE OF MANANNAN
(on quayside)
☎ 01624 648000   📄 01624 648001
Times: Open daily 10-5. (Closed Xmas & New Year). **Facilities:** 🅿 ♿ toilets for disabled shop 🐾 *Details not confirmed for 2002*

PEEL CASTLE
(on Patricks Isle, facing Peel Bay)
☎ 01624 648000   📄 01624 648001
Times: Open Apr-Oct, daily 10-5. **Facilities:** 🅿 shop 🐾 *Details not confirmed for 2002*

🏛 RAMSEY — Map 06 SC49
'THE GROVE' RURAL LIFE MUSEUM
(on W side of Andreas Road)
☎ 01624 648000   📄 01624 648001
Times: Open Apr-Oct, daily 10-5. **Facilities:** 🅿 💺 ✕ licensed ♿ shop 🐾 *Details not confirmed for 2002*

Glenfinnan viaduct on the Mallaig to Fort William line above the Finnan river

Scotland

EVENTS & FESTIVALS

January
1st Men's & Boy's 'Ba', mass football game, Kirkwall, Orkney Isles
16th Celtic Connections Festival, Glasgow Royal Concert Hall
25th Burns Night (celebrations throughout Scotland)
27th-28th Great British Snow Rally at Glen Forest Park, Aviemore
30th Up Helly Aa, Lerwick, Shetland Islands

February
2nd Six Nations Rugby – Scotland v England, Murrayfield Stadium
10th-11th Antique & Collectors Fair, Ingliston, Edinburgh

March
5th-10th Scottish Curling Championships, Glasgow
16th Six Nations Rugby – Scotland v France, Murrayfield Stadium
23rd-31st World Irish Dancing Championships, Glasgow (venue to be confirmed)
23rd-31st Festival of Folk, Music, Arts & Crafts (various venues), Castle Douglas

April
6th-7th City of Dundee Flower Show, Dundee
6th-16th Edinburgh International Science Festival
19th-20th Ladbroke Casinos Scottish Grand National, Ayr Racecourse, Ayr

May
4th-5th Orkney Country Club Festival of Country & Irish Music
tbc Isle of Bute Jazz Festival (various venues)
tbc Shetland Folk Festival (various venues), Lerwick
27th-2nd June Scottish International Children's Festival, Edinburgh
29th-30th Angus Show, Haughmuir by Brechin, Angus
tbc Atholl Gathering & Highland Games, Blair Atholl, Perth & Kinross

June
2nd Borders Historic Motoring Extravaganza, Borders
6th Lanimer Day, Lanark, South Lanarkshire
27th May-2nd Scottish International Children's Festival, Edinburgh
9th Forfar Highland Games, Forfar, Angus
20th-23rd Royal Highland Show, Edinburgh (provisional)
21st-26th St Magnus Festival, Orkney

29th-30th Moffat Classic Car Rally, Dumfries & Galloway
tbc Dundee Jazz Festival, Dundee Rep Theatre, Tay Square, Dundee

July
14th Stirling Highland Games, Stirlingshire
26th Langholm Common Riding, Dumfries & Galloway
29th-30th Traditional Boat Festival, Portsoy, Aberdeenshire
31st Stranraer Show, Dumfries & Galloway
31st-10th Aug Aberdeen International Youth Festival
tbc Dundee Blues Bonanza, various venues in Dundee
tbc Glasgow International Jazz Festival

August
2nd-24th Edinburgh Military Tattoo
3rd Aboyne Highland Games, Aberdeenshire
8th Highland Games, Monaltrie Park, Aberdeenshire
8th Blairgowrie Highland Games, Perth & Kinross
10th Arbroath Seafest, Arbroath, Angus
11th-25th Edinburgh International Film Festival
11th-31st Edinburgh International Festival
14th Battle of Britain Airshow, Leuchars, Fife
tbc Kirriemuir Festival of Traditional Music & Song, Kirriemuir, Angus
tbc Stirling Festival
tbc Crieff Highland Gathering, Perth & Kinross
tbc Perth Highland Games, Perth & Kinross
tbc Border Gathering Day, Gretna Green, Dumfries & Galloway
tbc Peebles Art Festival (various venues), Borders
tbc Sanquar Riding of the Marches, Dumfries & Galloway

September
7th Braemar Gathering, Princess Royal & Duke of Fife Memorial Park, Braemar, Aberdeenshire
6th-15th Techfest, Aberdeen (various venues)
tbc Borders Festival of Jazz & Blues, Hawick (various venues), Borders

November
tbc Dundee Mountain Film Festival, Bonar Hall, Dundee

December
31st Stonehaven Fireballing Festival (various venues), Aberdeenshire

Above: Robert the Bruce

ABERDEEN CITY

⛫ ABERDEEN
Map 15 NJ90

ABERDEEN ART GALLERY
Schoolhill AB10 1FQ (in city centre)
☎ 01224 523700 📄 01224 632133
e-mail: info@aagm.co.uk

One of the city's most popular tourist attractions Aberdeen's splendid art gallery houses an important fine art collection with many 19th- and 20th-century works.
Times: Open all year ex Xmas/New Year. Mon-Sat 10-5, Sun 2-5.
Fee: Free. **Facilities:** 🅿 (500yds) 🍽 ᵹ toilets for disabled shop ⚹ (ex guide dogs)

ABERDEEN MARITIME MUSEUM
Shiprow AB11 5BY (in city centre)
☎ 01224 337700
e-mail: info@aagm.co.uk

The museum is in Provost Ross's House, Aberdeen's oldest building (1593). It highlights the city's maritime history, its oil industry, and its shipbuilding.
Times: Open all year (ex Xmas & New Year). Mon-Sat 10-5, Sun 12-3. Telephone for details. **Fee:** Free. **Facilities:** 🅿 (250yds) 🍽 ✗ licensed ᵹ toilets for disabled shop ⚹ 🍴

CRUICKSHANK BOTANIC GARDEN
University of Aberdeen, St Machur Dr AB24 3UU (enter by gate in Chanonry, in Old Aberdeen)
☎ 01224 272704 📄 01224 272703
e-mail: pss@abdn.ac.uk

Developed at the end of the 19th century, the 11 acres include rock and water gardens, a rose garden, a fine herbaceous border, an arboretum and a patio garden. There are collections of spring bulbs, gentians and alpine plants, and a fine array of trees and shrubs.
Times: Open all year, Mon-Fri 9-4.30; also Sat & Sun, May-Sep 2-5.
Fee: Free. **Facilities:** 🅿 (200metres) (residents only in immediate vicinity) ᵹ ⚹

PROVOST SKENE'S HOUSE
Guestrow, (off Broad St) AB10 1AS
☎ 01224 641086
e-mail: info@aagm.co.uk

Experience the epitome of style and elegance in this 16th-century townhouse, furnished and decorated in the styles of earlier times. See changing fashions in the Costume Gallery and view an important cycle of religious paintings in the gallery.
Times: Open all year Mon-Sat 10-5, Sun 1-4. closed Xmas & New Year). Telephone for details. **Fee:** Free. **Facilities:** 🅿 (200yds) 🍽 ᵹ ⚹ (ex guide dogs)

SATROSPHERE ("HANDS-ON" SCIENCE & TECHNOLOGY CENTRE)
179 Constitution St AB24 5TU (5mins from town centre, and close to Aberdeen Beach Esplanade)
☎ 01224 640340 📄 01224 622211
e-mail: info@satrosphere.net

Satrosphere is different from many museums or exhibition centres. Displays aren't locked in glass cases and there are certainly no *Do Not Touch* signs. The emphasis is on doing and finding out, not just looking and standing back.
Times: Open all year, Mon & Wed-Fri 10-4, Sat 10-5, Sun 1.30-5. School holidays Mon-Sat 10-5, Sun 1.30-5. (Closed 25-26 Dec & 1-2 Jan). **Fee:** £5 (ch, pen £3). **Facilities:** 🅿 (charged) 🍽 ✗ ᵹ toilets for disabled shop ⚹ 🍴

⛫ PETERCULTER
Map 15 NJ80

DRUM CASTLE
AB31 5EY (3m W, off A93)
☎ 01330 811204 📄 01330 811962
e-mail: aclipson@nts-scot.demon.co.uk

The great 13th-century Square Tower is one of the three oldest tower houses in Scotland and has associations with Robert the Bruce. The handsome mansion, added in 1619, houses a collection of family memorabilia. The grounds contain the 100-acre Old Wood of Drum, a natural oak wood and an old rose garden.
Times: Open mid Apr-May & Sep, daily 1.30-5.30; Jun-Aug, daily 11-5.30; wknds in Oct 1.30-5.30. Last admission 4.45. Grounds open all year 9.30-sunset. **Facilities:** 🅿 🍽 ᵹ (wheelchair available) shop ⚹ (ex guide dogs) 🐾 *Details not confirmed for 2002*

ABERDEENSHIRE

⛫ ALFORD
Map 15 NJ51

ALFORD VALLEY RAILWAY
AB33 8AD (on A944)
☎ 019755 62326 & 62811 📄 019755 63182

Narrow-gauge passenger railway in two sections: Alford–Haughton Park and Haughton Park–Murray Park (approx. one mile each). Steam on peak weekends. Diesel traction. Exhibitions.
Times: Open Apr, May & Sep wknds 1-5, Jun-Aug daily from 1pm (30 min service). Party bookings also available at other times. **Fee:** £2 (ch £1) return fare. **Facilities:** 🅿 ᵹ (ramps at station platforms) toilets for disabled

🏛 BALMORAL
Map 15 NO29
BALMORAL CASTLE GROUNDS & EXHIBITION
AB35 5TB (on A93 between Ballater & Braemar)
☎ 013397 42334 & 42335 📠 013397 42271
e-mail: info@balmoral-castle.co.uk

Times: Open 12 Apr-Jul, daily 10-5. **Facilities:** P (150yds) 🍽 & (wheelchairs available & free parking enquire at main gate) toilets for disabled shop 🐾 (ex guide dogs/in grounds) *Details not confirmed for 2002* 🍸

🏛 BANCHORY
Map 15 NO69
BANCHORY MUSEUM
Bridge St AB31 5SX
☎ 01771 622906 📠 01771 622884
e-mail: heritage@aberdeenshire.gov.uk

The museum has displays on Scott Skinner (The 'Strathspey King'), natural history, royal commemorative china, local silver artefacts and a variety of local history displays.
Times: Open: May, Jun & Sep, Mon-Sat 11-1 & 2-4.30. Jul-Aug, Mon-Sat 11-1, 2-4.30 & Sun 2-4.30. Tel. for Apr & Oct opening times.
Fee: Free. **Facilities:** P (100yds) (limited) & (toilet in staff area, ask attendant) toilets for disabled shop 🐾 (ex guide dogs)

🏛 BANFF
Map 15 NJ66
BANFF MUSEUM
High St AB45 1AE
☎ 01771 622906 📠 01771 622884
e-mail: heritage@aberdeenshire.gov.uk

Displays of geology, natural history, local history, Banff silver, arms and armour, and displays relating to James Ferguson (18th-century astronomer) and Thomas Edward (19th-century Banff naturalist).
Times: Open Jun-Sep, Mon-Sat 2-4.30. **Fee:** Free. **Facilities:** P (200yds) & shop 🐾 (ex guide dogs)

DUFF HOUSE
AB45 3SX (0.5m S, access south of town)
☎ 01261 818181
Times: Telephone for details of opening dates and times.
Facilities: P ✕ & toilets for disabled shop 🐾 ▮ *Details not confirmed for 2002*

🏛 CORGARFF
Map 15 NJ20
CORGARFF CASTLE
AB36 8YL (8m W of Strathdon village)
☎ 01975 651460
Times: Open all year, Apr-Sep, daily 9.30-6.30; Oct-Mar, wknds only. (Closed 25-26 Dec). **Facilities:** P shop ▮ *Details not confirmed for 2002*

🏛 CRATHES
Map 15 NO79
CRATHES CASTLE & GARDENS
AB31 3QJ (On A93, 3m E of Banchory)
☎ 01330 844525 📠 01330 844797

This impressive 16th-century castle with magnificent interiors has royal associations dating from 1323. There is a large walled garden and a notable collection of unusual plants, including yew hedges dating from 1702. The grounds contain six nature trails, one suitable for disabled visitors, and an adventure playground.
Times: Open: Castle & Visitor Centre Apr-Sep, daily 10.30-5.30; Oct, daily 10.30-4.30 (last admission 45 mins before closing). Other times by appointment only. Garden & grounds open all year, daily 9.30-sunset. Admission to castle by timed ticket arrangement, (entry may be delayed on busy days). Grounds may be closed at short notice on busy days due to parking limitations. **Facilities:** P ✕ licensed & (tape for visually impaired) toilets for disabled shop 🐾 (ex guide dogs) 🍸 *Details not confirmed for 2002*

🏛 FETTERCAIRN
Map 15 NO67
FASQUE
AB30 1DN (0.5m N on B974)
☎ 01561 340569 & 340202 📠 01561 340325 & 340569

Fasque has been the home of the Gladstone family since 1829, and W E Gladstone, four times Prime Minister, lived here from 1830 to 1851. There are impressive state rooms and a handsome, sweeping staircase, as well as extensive servants' quarters. The spacious park has red deer and Soay sheep.
Times: Open Jul-Aug, daily 11-5. (Closed 5.30). Groups at all other times by arrangement at any other time all year round. **Fee:** £4 (ch £1.50, concessions £3). Party & guided tours by arrangement.
Facilities: P 🍽 & (wheelchairs available) shop 🐾

🏛 HUNTLY
Map 15 NJ53
BRANDER MUSEUM
The Square AB54 8AE (in town centre museum on ground floor of library building)
☎ 01771 622906 📠 01771 622884
e-mail: heritage@aberdeenshire.gov.uk

The museum has displays of local and church history, plus the 19th-century Anderson Bey and the Sudanese campaigns. Exhibits connected with George MacDonald, author and playwright, can also be seen.
Times: Open all year, Tue-Sat 2-4.30. **Fee:** Free. **Facilities:** P (25yds) & (access very difficult due to 3 large steps at enterance) shop 🐾 (ex guide dogs)

HUNTLY CASTLE
AB54 4SH
☎ 01466 793191

The original medieval castle was rebuilt a number of times and destroyed, once by Mary, Queen of Scots. It was rebuilt for the last time in 1602, in palatial style, and is now an impressive ruin, noted for its ornate heraldic decorations. It stands in wooded parkland.
Times: Open all year, Apr-Sep, daily 9.30-6.30; Oct-Mar, Mon-Sat 9.30-4.30, Sun 2-4.30. (Closed Thu pm, Fri in winter & 25-26 Dec).
Fee: £2.50 (ch £1, concessions £1.90). **Facilities:** ▣ shop ▮

▥ INVERURIE　　　　　Map 15 NJ72
CARNEGIE MUSEUM
Town House, The Square AB51 3SN (in town centre, on R side of Townhouse building, above library)
☎ 01771 622906　▤ 01771 622884
e-mail: heritage@aberdeenshire.gov.uk

This fine museum contains displays on local history and archaeology, including Pictish stones, Bronze Age material and the great North of Scotland Railway.
Times: Open all year, Mon & Wed-Fri 2-4.30, Sat 10-1 & 2-4. (Closed Tue & public holidays) **Fee:** Free. **Facilities:** ℗ (50yds) shop ⊁ (ex guide dogs)

▥ KEMNAY　　　　　Map 15 NJ71
CASTLE FRASER
AB51 7LD (off A944, 4m N of Dunecht)
☎ 01330 833463
e-mail: aclipson@nts-scot.demon.co.uk

The massive Z-plan castle was built between 1575 and 1636 and is one of the grandest of the Castles of Mar. The interior was remodelled in 1838 and decoration and furnishings of that period survive in some of the rooms. A formal garden inside the old walled garden, estate trails, a children's play area and a programme of concerts are among the attractions.
Times: Open - Castle Etr-May, daily 1.30-5.30 Jun-Aug, daily, 11-5.30; wknds in Oct 1.30-5.30 (last admission 4.45). Garden all year, daily 9.30-6; grounds all year daily 9.30-sunset. **Facilities:** ▣ ▆ & shop garden centre ⊁ (ex guide dogs, certain areas) ⛾ *Details not confirmed for 2002*

▥ KILDRUMMY　　　　　Map 15 NJ41
KILDRUMMY CASTLE
AB54 7XT (10m SW of Alford)
☎ 01975 571331

An important part of Scottish history, at least until it was dismantled in 1717, this fortress was the seat of the Earls of Mar. Now it is a ruined, but splendid, example of a 13th-century castle, with four round towers, a hall and chapel all discernible. Some parts of the building, including the Great Gatehouse, are from the 15th and 16th centuries.
Times: Open Apr-Sep, daily 9.30-6.30. **Fee:** £2 (ch 75p, concessions £1.50). **Facilities:** ▣ & toilets for disabled shop ▮

KILDRUMMY CASTLE GARDENS
AB33 8RA (on A97)
☎ 019755 71277　& 71203　▤ 019755 71277
Times: Open Apr-Oct, daily 10-5. **Facilities:** ▣ ▆ & toilets for disabled shop *Details not confirmed for 2002*

▥ MARYCULTER　　　　　Map 15 NO89
STORYBOOK GLEN
AB12 5FT (5m W of Aberdeen on B9077)
☎ 01224 732941　▤ 01224 732941

This is a children's fantasy land, where favourite nursery rhyme and fairytale characters are brought to life. Grown-ups can enjoy the nostalgia and also the 20 acres of Deeside country, full of flowers, plants, trees and waterfalls.
Times: Open Mar-Oct, daily 10-6; Nov-Feb, Sat & Sun only 11-4.
Fee: £3.80 (ch £1.90, pen £2.90). **Facilities:** ▣ ▆ ✕ licensed & toilets for disabled shop ⊁ (ex guide dogs) ⬳

▥ METHLICK　　　　　Map 15 NJ83
HADDO HOUSE
AB41 7EQ (off B999, 4m N of Pitmedden)
☎ 01651 851440　▤ 01651 851888
e-mail: aclipson@nts-scot.demon.co.uk

Haddo House is renowned for its association with the Haddo Choral Society and is the venue for international concerts. It is a splendid Palladian-style mansion built in the 1730s to designs by William Adam. Home to the Earls of Aberdeen, the house was refurbished in the 1880s in the 'Adam Revival' style. The adjoining country park offers beautiful woodland walks.
Times: Open - House mid Apr-Sep, daily 1.30-5.30; wknds in Oct 1.30-5.30 (last admission 4.45). Garden daily, Apr-Oct 9.30-6; Nov-Mar 9.30-4. Country park open all year, daily 9.30-sunset. Occasionally some rooms may be closed to public view due to family occupation. **Facilities:** ▣ & (lift to first floor of house & wheelchair) toilets for disabled shop ⊁ (ex in grounds & guide dogs) ⛾ *Details not confirmed for 2002*

▥ MINTLAW　　　　　Map 15 NJ94
ABERDEENSHIRE FARMING MUSEUM
Aden Country Park AB42 5FQ (1m W of Mintlaw on A950)
☎ 01771 622906　▤ 01771 622884
e-mail: heritage@aberdeenshire.gov.uk

Housed in 19th-century farm buildings, once part of the estate which now makes up the Aden Country Park. Two centuries of farming history and innovation are illustrated, and the story of the estate is also told. The reconstructed farm of Hareshowe shows how a family in the North-East farmed during the 1950s - access by guided tour only.
Times: Open May-Sep, daily 11-4.30; Apr & Oct, wknds only noon-4.30. Last admission 30 mins before closing. Park open all year, Apr-Sep 7-10, winter 7-7. To be confirmed. **Fee:** Free. **Facilities:** ▣ ▆ & (sensory garden) toilets for disabled shop ⊁ (ex guide dogs)

🏛 OLD DEER
Map 15 NJ94

DEER ABBEY
(10m W of Peterhead)
☎ 0131 668 8800

The remains of the Cistercian Abbey, founded in 1218, include the infirmary, Abbot's House and the southern claustral range. The University Library at Cambridge now houses the famous Book of Deer.
Times: Open at all reasonable times. **Fee:** Free. **Facilities:** 🅿 ✝ ▮

🏛 OYNE
Map 15 NJ62

ARCHAEOLINK
Berryhill AB52 6QP (1m off A96 on B9002)
☎ 01464 851500   📄 01464 851544
Times: Open Apr-Oct, daily 10-5. **Facilities:** 🅿 ♨ ✗ licensed ⅗ toilets for disabled shop ✝ (ex guide dogs) *Details not confirmed for 2002* 🍴

🏛 PETERHEAD
Map 15 NK14

ARBUTHNOT MUSEUM & ART GALLERY
St Peter St AB42 1QD (in town centre, at St. Peter's & Queen St. crossroads, above library)
☎ 01771 622906   📄 01771 622884
e-mail: heritage@aberdeenshire.gov.uk

Specialising in local exhibits, particularly those relating to the fishing industry, this museum also displays Arctic and whaling specimens and a British coin collection. The regular programme of exhibitions changes approximately every six weeks.
Times: Open all year, Mon, Tue & Thu-Sat 11-1 & 2-4.30, Wed 11-1. (Closed Sun and BHs). **Fee:** Free. **Facilities:** 🅿 (150 yds) shop ✝ (ex guide dogs)

🏛 PITMEDDEN
Map 15 NJ82

PITMEDDEN GARDEN
AB41 7PA (1m W of Pitmedden on A920)
☎ 01651 842352   📄 01651 843188
e-mail: aclipson@nts.scot.demon.co.uk

The fine 17th-century walled garden, with sundials, pavilions and fountains dotted among the parterres, has been authentically restored. There is a Museum of Farming Life and a woodland walk.
Times: Open - Garden, Museum of Farming Life & Visitor Centre open May-Sep, daily 10-5.30, (last admission 5pm). **Facilities:** 🅿 ♨ ⅗ (2 wheelchairs available) toilets for disabled shop 🍴 *Details not confirmed for 2002*

TOLQUHON CASTLE
AB41 7LP (2m NE off B999)
☎ 01651 851286

Now roofless, this late 16th-century quadrangular mansion encloses an early 15th-century tower. There is a fine gatehouse and a splendid courtyard.
Times: Open all year, Apr-Sep, daily 9.30-6.30; Oct-Mar, wknds only. (Closed 25-26 Dec). **Fee:** £1.80 (ch 75p, concessions £1.30). **Facilities:** 🅿 ⅗ toilets for disabled shop ✝ ▮

🏛 RHYNIE
Map 15 NJ42

LEITH HALL & GARDEN
Kennethmont AB54 4NQ (on B9002, 1m W of Kennethmont)
☎ 01464 831216   📄 01464 831594
e-mail: aclipson@nts.scot.demon.co.uk

Home of the Leith family for over 300 years, the house dates back to 1650, and has a number of Jacobite relics and fine examples of needlework. It is surrounded by charming gardens and extensive grounds.
Times: Open - House Good Fri-Etr Mon & May-Sep, daily 1.30-5.30; wknds in Oct 1.30-5.30. (Last admission 45 mins before closing). Gardens and grounds all year 9.30-sunset. **Facilities:** 🅿 ♨ ⅗ (parking next to hall, scented garden for the blind) toilets for disabled ✝ (ex guide dogs) 🍴 *Details not confirmed for 2002*

🏛 STONEHAVEN
Map 15 NO88

DUNNOTTAR CASTLE
AB39 2TL (2m S of Stonehaven on A92)
☎ 01569 762173

This once-impregnable fortress, now a spectacular ruin, was the site of the successful protection of the Scottish Crown Jewels from the might of Cromwell.
Times: Open all year, summer Mon-Sat 9-6, Sun 2-5; Nov & Feb 9-4, Dec & Jan 9-3, Mar 9-5. Last entry 30 minutes before closing. (Closed 25-26 Dec/New Year). **Fee:** £3.50 (ch 5-15 £1) **Facilities:** 🅿 ✝ (ex on lead)

TOLBOOTH MUSEUM
Old Pier AB39 2JU (on harbour front)
☎ 01771 622906   📄 01771 622884
e-mail: heritage@aberdeenshire.gov.uk

Built in the late 16th century as a storehouse for the Earls Marischal at Dunnottar Castle, the building was the Kincardineshire County Tollbooth from 1600-1767. Displays feature local history and fishing.
Times: Open Jun-Sep, Wed-Mon, 1.30-4.30. (Closed Tue). Tel for May/Oct opening times. **Fee:** Free. **Facilities:** 🅿 (20yds) ⅗ shop ✝ (ex guide dogs)

🏛 TURRIFF
Map 15 NJ75

FYVIE CASTLE
Fyvie AB53 8JS (8m SE of Turriff on A947)
☎ 01651 891266   📄 01651 891107
e-mail: aclipson@nts.scot.demon.co.uk

This superb castle, founded in the 13th century, has five towers, each built in a different century, and is one of the grandest examples of Scottish Baronial architecture. It contains the finest wheel stair in Scotland, and a 17th-century morning room, lavishly furnished in Edwarian style. The collection of portraits is exceptional, and there are also displays of arms and armour and tapestries.
Times: Open 21 Apr-May & Sep daily 1.30-5.30. Jun-Aug daily 11-5.30, wknds Oct 1.30-5.30. (last admission 4.45). Grounds open all year, daily 9.30-sunset. **Facilities:** 🅿 ♨ ⅗ (small lift, braille sheets) toilets for disabled shop ✝ (ex guide dogs) 🍴 *Details not confirmed for 2002*

ANGUS

⚏ ARBROATH
Map 12 NO64

ARBROATH ABBEY
DD11 1EG
☎ 01241 878756

The `Declaration of Arbroath' - declaring Robert the Bruce as king - was signed at the 12th-century abbey on 6 April 1320. The abbot's house is well preserved, and the church remains are also interesting.
Times: Open all year, Apr-Sep, daily 9.30-6.30; Oct-Mar, Mon-Sat 9.30-4.30, Sun 2-4.30. (Closed Thu pm, Fri in winter & 25-26 Dec). **Fee:** £2 (ch 75p, concessions £1.50). **Facilities:** ⊞ ౪ ⚹ ▮

ARBROATH MUSEUM
Signal Tower, Ladyloan DD11 1PU (on A92)
☎ 01241 875598   ▤ 01241 439263
e-mail: signal.tower@angus.gov.uk
Times: Open all year, Mon-Sat 10-5; Jul-Aug, Sun 2-5.(Closed 25-26 Dec & 1-2 Jan). **Facilities:** ⊞ ౪ (induction loop) shop ⚹ (ex guide dogs) *Details not confirmed for 2002*

⚏ BARRY
Map 12 NO53

BARRY MILL
DD7 7RJ (2m W of Carnoustie)
☎ 01241 856761

This restored 18th-century mill works on a demonstration basis. Records show that the site has been used for milling since the 16th century. Displays highlight the important place the mill held in the community. There is a waymarked walk and picnic area.
Times: Open Apr-Sep, daily 11-5; wknds in Oct, 11-5. **Facilities:** ⊞ ౪ ramp from car park to mill toilets for disabled (grounds only) ౪ *Details not confirmed for 2002*

⚏ EDZELL
Map 15 NO56

EDZELL CASTLE
DD9 7UE (on B966)
☎ 01356 648631

The 16th-century castle has a remarkable walled garden built in 1604 by Sir David Lindsay. Flower-filled recesses in the walls are alternated with heraldic and symbolic sculptures of a sort not seen elsewhere in Scotland. There are ornamental and border gardens and a garden house.
Times: Open all year, Apr-Sep, daily 9.30-6.30; Oct-Mar, Mon-Sat 9.30-4.30, Sun 2-4.30. (Closed Thu pm, Fri in winter & 25-26 Dec). **Fee:** £2.50 (ch £1, concessions £1.90). **Facilities:** ⊞ ౪ shop ▮

⚏ FORFAR
Map 15 NO45

THE MEFFAN ART GALLERY & MUSEUM
20 West High St DD8 1BB
☎ 01307 464123   ▤ 01307 468451
e-mail: the.meffan@angus.gov.uk
Times: Open all year. (Closed 25-26 Dec & 1-2 Jan). **Facilities:** ℗ (150yds) ౪ toilets for disabled shop ⚹ (ex guide dogs) *Details not confirmed for 2002* ⬛

⚏ GLAMIS
Map 15 NO34

ANGUS FOLK MUSEUM
Kirkwynd Cottages DD8 1RT (off A94, in Glamis)
☎ 01307 840288   ▤ 01307 840233

A row of stone-roofed, late 18th-century cottages now houses the splendid Angus Folk Collection of domestic equipment and cottage furniture. Across the wynd, an Angus stone steading houses 'The Life on the Land' exhibition.
Times: Open Jul-Aug, daily 10-5; Apr-Jun & Sep, daily 11-5; Oct, wknds 11-5 (last admission 4.30). **Facilities:** ⊞ ౪ toilets for disabled ⚹ (ex guide dogs) ౪ *Details not confirmed for 2002*

GLAMIS CASTLE
DD8 1RJ (5m W of Forfar on A94)
☎ 01307 840393   ▤ 01307 840733
e-mail: glamis@great-houses-scotland.co.uk

Glamis Castle is the family home of the Earls of Strathmore and Kinghorne and has been a royal residence since 1372. It is the childhood home of HM The Queen Mother, the birthplace of HRH Princess Margaret and the legendary setting of Shakespeare's play 'Macbeth'.
Times: Open Apr-Oct, 10.30-5 (Times may change). Last admission 4.45pm. **Fee:** Castle & grounds £6.20 (ch £3.10, pen & students £4.70). Family ticket £17. Grounds only £3.10 (ch, pen & students £1.60). Group 20+ **Facilities:** ⊞ ✕ licensed ౪ toilets for disabled shop ⚹ (ex in grounds) ⬛

⚏ KIRRIEMUIR
Map 15 NO35

BARRIE'S BIRTHPLACE
9 Brechin Rd DD8 4BX (on A90/A926 6m NW of Forfar)
☎ 01575 572646
e-mail: aclipson@nts.scot.demon.co.uk

The creator of Peter Pan, Sir James Barrie, was born in Kirriemuir in 1860. The upper floors of No 9 Brechin Road are furnished as they may have been when Barrie lived there, and the adjacent house, No 11, houses an exhibition about him. The wash-house outside was his first 'theatre' and gave him the idea for Wendy's house in 'Peter Pan'.
Times: Open Apr-Sep, Mon-Sat 11-5.30 & Sun 1.30-5.30; wknds in Oct 11-5.30, Sun 1.30-5.30. Last admission 5pm. **Facilities:** ℗ (100yds) ⬛ ౪ (stairlift, audio programmes) shop ⚹ (ex guide dogs) ౪ *Details not confirmed for 2002*

⚏ MONTROSE
Map 15 NO75

HOUSE OF DUN
DD10 9LQ (on A935, 3m W of Montrose)
☎ 01674 810264   ▤ 01674 810722
e-mail: aclipson@nts.scot.demon.co.uk

This Georgian house, overlooking the Montrose Basin, was built for Lord Dun in 1730 and is noted for the exuberant plasterwork of the interior. Family portraits, fine furniture and porcelain are on display, plus royal mementos connected with a daughter of King William IV and the actress Mrs Jordan, who lived here in the

contd.

19th century. There is a walled garden, and woodland walks.
Times: Open mid Apr-Jun & Sep, daily 1.30-5.30; Jul-Aug, daily 11-5.30; wknds in Oct 1.30-5.30. (last admission 5). Garden & grounds, all year daily 9.30-sunset. **Facilities:** 🅿 ✖ ᕝ (braille sheets, house wheelchair & stair lift) toilets for disabled shop 🍴 (ex guide dogs) ᕤ *Details not confirmed for 2002*

MONTROSE MUSEUM & ART GALLERY
Panmure Place DD10 8HE (opposite Montrose Academy)
☎ 01674 673232 & 875598 (pm)
e-mail: montrose.museum@angus.gov.uk
Times: Open all year, Mon-Sat 10-5. (Closed 25-26 Dec & 1-2 Jan).
Facilities: 🅿 ᕝ shop 🍴 (ex guide dogs) *Details not confirmed for 2002*

ARGYLL & BUTE

⛰ ARDUAINE
Map 10 NM71
ARDUAINE GARDEN
PA34 4XQ (20m S of Oban, on A816)
☎ 01852 200233 🖹 01852 200233

An outstanding 18-acre garden on a promontory bounded by Loch Melfort and the Sound of Jura, climatically favoured by the North Atlantic Drift. It is famous for its rhododendrons and azalea species and other rare trees and shrubs.
Times: Open all year, daily 9.30-sunset. **Facilities:** 🅿 ᕝ toilets for disabled 🍴 (ex guide dogs) ᕤ *Details not confirmed for 2002*

⛰ ARROCHAR
Map 10 NN20
ARGYLL FOREST PARK
Forest Enterprise, Ardgartan Visitor Centre G83 7AR (on A83 at the foot of "The Rest and Be Thankful")
☎ 01301 702597 🖹 01301 702597
e-mail: fekilmun@forestry.gov.uk
Times: Open all year. **Facilities:** 🅿 shop *Details not confirmed for 2002* ᕝ

⛰ AUCHINDRAIN
Map 10 NN00
AUCHINDRAIN TOWNSHIP-OPEN AIR MUSEUM
PA32 8XN (5.5m SW of Inverarary on A83)
☎ 01499 500235

Auchindrain is an original West Highland township of great antiquity, and the only communal tenancy township to have survived on its centuries-old site. The buildings are furnished and equipped to present a fascinating glimpse of Highland life in the last century.
Times: Open Apr-Sep, daily 10-5. **Fee:** £3.80 (ch £1.80, pen £3). Family ticket £9.50. **Facilities:** 🅿 shop

⛰ BARCALDINE
Map 10 NM94
BARCALDINE CASTLE
Benderloch PA37 1SA (9m N of Oban on A828 Oban-Fort William road. Take left turn to Tralee in Benderloch)
☎ 01631 720598 🖹 01631 720598
e-mail: barcaldine.castle@tesco.net

The 16th-century home of the Campbells of Barcaldine. The last of the seven castles built by Black Duncan to

be held in Campbell hands, and associated with the Appin Murder and Glencoe Massacre. Said to be haunted by the Blue Lady, the castle has secret passages and bottle dungeon; there is also a family quiz trail.
Times: Open Jul-Aug afternoons. **Fee:** £3.25 (ch £1.70, concessions £2.85) **Facilities:** 🅿 ᕤ shop 🍴 ᕥ ᕤ

SCOTTISH SEALIFE & MARINE SANCTUARY
PA37 1SE (10m N of Oban on A828, Oban to Fort William road)
☎ 01631 720386 🖹 01631 720529
e-mail: oban@sealife.fsbusiness.co.uk

Set in one of Scotland's most picturesque locations, the Scottish Sea Life & Marine Sanctuary provides dramatic views of native undersea life including stingrays, seals, octopus and catfish. There are daily talks and feeding demonstrations and during the summer young seals can be viewed prior to their release back into the wild. There is a restaurant, gift shop, children's play park and a nature trail.
Times: Open all year, Feb-Nov, daily 9.30-5. Dec & Jan, Sat/Sun & school holidays only. **Fee:** £6.50 (ch £4.50, pen £5.50). Party 10+.
Facilities: 🅿 ✖ licensed ᕝ (assistance available for wheelchairs) toilets for disabled shop 🍴 (ex guide dogs) ᕤ

⛰ BENMORE
Map 10 NS18
BENMORE BOTANIC GARDEN
PA23 8QU (7m N of Dunoon on A815)
☎ 01369 706261 🖹 01369 706369

From the formal garden, through the hillside woodlands, follow the paths to a stunning viewpoint with a spectacular outlook across the garden and the Holy Loch to the Firth of Clyde and beyond. Amongst many highlights are the stately conifers, the magnificent avenue of Giant Redwoods, and an extensive magnolia collection.
Times: Open Mar-Oct, daily, 9.30-6. Other times by arrangement.
Fee: £3 (ch £1, concessions £2.50). Family £7. Season ticket and group rates available. **Facilities:** 🅿 ᕤ ✖ licensed ᕝ toilets for disabled shop garden centre ᕤ

⛰ CARNASSARIE CASTLE
Map 10 NM80
CARNASSARIE CASTLE
PA31 8RQ (2m N of Kilmartin off A816)
☎ 0131 668 8800

Built in the 16th-century by John Carswell, first Protestant Bishop of the Isles, the castle was taken and partly destroyed in Argyll's rebellion of 1685. It consists of a tower house with a courtyard built around.
Times: Open at all reasonable times. **Fee:** Free. **Facilities:** 🅿 🍴 ▮

⛰ GIGHA ISLAND
Map 10 NR64
ACHAMORE GARDENS
PA41 7AD
☎ 01583 505267 & 505254 🖹 01583 505244
e-mail: william@isle-of-gigha.co.uk
Times: Open all year, daily. **Facilities:** 🅿 ᕝ *Details not confirmed for 2002*

⛪ INVERARAY — Map 10 NN00
BELL TOWER OF ALL SAINTS' CHURCH
The Avenue PA32 8YX
☎ 01499 302259
Times: Open mid May-Sep, daily 10-1 & 2-5. **Facilities:** P (adjacent to tower) & shop ⊁ (ex guide dogs) *Details not confirmed for 2002*

INVERARAY CASTLE
PA32 8XE
☎ 01499 302203 📠 01499 302421
e-mail: enquiries@inveraray-castle.com

The third Duke of Argyll engaged Roger Morris to build the present castle in 1743; in the process the old Burgh of Inveraray was demolished and a new town built nearby. The beautiful interior decoration was commissioned by the 5th Duke; the great armoury hall and staterooms are of particular note.
Times: Open Apr to mid Oct. Apr-Jun, Sep & Oct, Mon-Thu & Sat 10-1 & 2-5.45. Sun 1-5.45; Jul & Aug, Mon-Sat 10-5.45, Sun 1-5.45. Last admission 12.30 & 5. **Fee:** £5.50 (ch under 16 £3.50, concessions £4.50) Family ticket £14. School parties. Groups 20+. **Facilities:** P ⚌ & shop ⊁ (ex guide dogs) ⬳

INVERARAY JAIL
Church Sq PA32 8TX (on main Campbeltown Road, A83)
☎ 01499 302381 📠 01499 302195
e-mail: inverarayjail.@btclick.com

Enter Inveraray Jail and step back in time. See furnished cells and experience prison sounds and smells. Ask the `prisoner' how to pick oakum. Turn the heavy handle of an original crank machine, take 40 winks in a hammock or listen to Matron's tales of day-to-day prison life. Visit the magnificent 1820 courtroom and hear trials in progress. Imaginative exhibitions including `Torture, Death and Damnation' and `In Prison Today'.
Times: Open all year, Nov-Mar, daily 10-5 (last admisssion 4); Apr-Oct, daily 9.30-6 (last admission 5pm). (Closed 25 Dec & 1 Jan). **Fee:** £4.90 (ch £2.40, pen £3.10). Family ticket £13.40. Party 10+ **Facilities:** P (100 yds) & (wheelchair ramp at rear, induction loop in courtroom) toilets for disabled shop ⬳

⛪ KILMARTIN — Map 10 NR89
DUNADD FORT
(1m W of Kilmichael Glassary)
☎ 0131 668 8800
Times: Open & accessible at all reasonable times. **Fee:** Free.
Facilities: ⊁ ◪

⛪ LOCHAWE — Map 10 NN12
CRUACHAN POWER STATION
Dalmally PA33 1AN (A85 18m E of Oban)
☎ 01866 822618 📠 01866 822509
Times: Open Etr-Nov, daily 9.30-5 (last tour 4.15). Jul-Aug 9.30-6 (last tour 5.15) **Facilities:** P ⚌ & toilets for disabled shop ⊁ (ex guide dogs) *Details not confirmed for 2002*

⛪ OBAN — Map 10 NM83
CAITHNESS GLASS VISITOR CENTRE
The Waterfront, Railway Pier PA34 4LW (town centre on pier beside train station)
☎ 01631 563386 📠 01631 563386
Times: Open all year, Mon-Sat 9-5 (open late Jun-Sep). Etr-Nov Sun 11-5; Nov-Mar 10-5 Mon-Sat. **Facilities:** P (100yds) & shop ⊁ (ex guide dogs) *Details not confirmed for 2002*

DUNSTAFFNAGE CASTLE
PA37 1PZ (3m N on peninsula)
☎ 01631 562465

Now ruined, this four-sided stronghold has a gatehouse, two round towers and walls 10ft thick. It was once the prison of Flora MacDonald.
Times: Open all year, Apr-Sep, daily 9.30-6.30; Oct-Mar, Sat-Wed. (Closed 25-26 Dec). **Fee:** £2 (ch 75p, concessions £1.50). **Facilities:** ◪ shop ◪

⛪ TAYNUILT — Map 10 NN03
BONAWE IRON FURNACE
PA35 1JQ (0.75m NE off B845)
☎ 01866 822432

The furnace is a restored charcoal blast-furnace for iron-smelting and making cast-iron. It was established in 1753 and worked until 1876. The works exploited the Forest of Lorne to provide charcoal for fuel.
Times: Open Apr-Sep, daily 9.30-6.30. **Fee:** £2.50 (ch £1, concessions £1.90). **Facilities:** ◪ & toilets for disabled shop ◪

CITY OF EDINBURGH

⛪ BALERNO — Map 11 NT16
MALLENY GARDEN
EH14 7AF (off Lanark Rd (A70))
☎ 0131 449 2283

The delightful gardens are set round a 17th-century house (not open). Shrub roses, a woodland garden, and a group of four clipped yews, survivors of a group planted in 1603, are among its notable features. The National Bonsai Collection for Scotland is also at Malleny.
Times: Open Apr-Oct, daily 9.30-7; Nov-Mar, daily 9.30-4. House not open. **Facilities:** ◪ & ⊁ (ex guide dogs) ⬳ *Details not confirmed for 2002*

⛪ EDINBURGH — Map 11 NT27
BRASS RUBBING CENTRE
Trinity Apse, Chalmers Close, High St EH1 1SS
☎ 0131 556 4364 📠 0131 557 3364
Times: Open Apr-Sep, Mon-Sat 10-5 (during Edinburgh Festival Sun 12-5). **Facilities:** P (250mtrs) shop ⊁ (ex guide dogs) *Details not confirmed for 2002*

CAMERA OBSCURA

Castlehill, Royal Mile EH1 2LZ (next to Edinburgh Castle)

☎ 0131 226 3709   🖹 0131 225 4239

e-mail: info@camera-obscura.co.uk

A unique view of Edinburgh – as the lights go down a brilliant moving image of the surrounding city appears. The scene changes as a guide operates the camera's system of revolving lenses and mirrors.
Times: Open all year, daily, Apr-Oct 9.30-6; Nov-Mar 10-5. (Closed 25 Dec). Open later Jul-Aug, phone for details. **Fee:** £4.25 (ch £2.10, students £3.40, pen £2.70) Family ticket £12. **Facilities:** P (300mtrs) shop 🌟 (ex guide dogs) 🍴

CITY ART CENTRE

2 Market St EH1 1DE

☎ 0131 529 3993   🖹 0131 529 3986

e-mail: enquiries@city-art-centre.demon.uk
Times: Open Mon-Sat 10-5 (& Sun 12-5 Jul-Aug). **Facilities:** P (500yds) 🍴 ⅙ (induction loop, lifts, braille signage) toilets for disabled shop 🌟 (ex guide dogs) *Details not confirmed for 2002* 🍴

CRAIGMILLAR CASTLE

EH16 4SY (2.5m SE, off A68)

☎ 0131 661 4445

Mary, Queen of Scots retreated to this 14th-century stronghold after the murder of Rizzio, and the plot to murder Darnley, her second husband, was also hatched here. There are 16th- and 17th-century apartments.
Times: Open all year, Apr-Sep, daily 9.30-6.30; Oct-Mar, Mon-Sat 9.30-4.30. Sun 2-4.30. (Closed Thu pm & Fri in winter & 25-26 Dec). **Fee:** £2 (ch 75p, concessions £1.50). **Facilities:** P ⅙ toilets for disabled shop ▪

DEAN GALLERY

73 Belford Rd EH4 3DS (20 min walk from Edinburgh Haymarket station & Princes Street)

☎ 0131 624 6200   🖹 0131 343 3250

e-mail: enquiries@natgalscot.ac.uk

The Dean Gallery provides a home for the Eduardo Paolozzi gift of sculpture and graphic art, the Gallery of Modern Art's renowned Dada and Surrealist collections, a major library and archive centre, and temporary exhibition space for modern and contemporary art.
Times: Open all year, Mon-Sat 10-5, Sun 12-5. (extended opening during Edinburgh Festival). (closed 25-26 Dec). **Fee:** Admission to permanent collections free, charge may be made for special exhibitions. **Facilities:** P 🍴 ⅙ (ramps & lift) toilets for disabled shop 🌟 (ex guide dogs) 🍴

DYNAMIC EARTH

Holyrood Rd EH8 8AS (on edge of Holyrood Park, opposite the Palace of Holyrood House)

☎ 0131 550 7800   🖹 0131 550 7801

Times: Open Apr-Oct, daily 10-6; Nov-Mar, Wed-Sat 10-5. (Closed 24-25 Dec). **Facilities:** P (charged) 🍴 ✗ licensed ⅙ (audio guides, large print transcripts) toilets for disabled shop 🌟 (ex guide dogs) *Details not confirmed for 2002* 🍴

EDINBURGH CASTLE

EH1 2NG

☎ 0131 225 9846

This historic stronghold stands on the precipitous crag of Castle Rock. One of the oldest parts is the 11th-century chapel of the saintly Queen Margaret, but most of the present castle evolved later, during its stormy history of seiges and wars, and was altered again in Victorian times. The Scottish crown and other royal regalia are displayed in the Crown Room. Also notable is the Scottish National War Memorial.
Times: Open Apr-Sep, daily 9.30-6; Oct-Mar, daily 9.30-5. Last ticket sold 45 mins before closing time. (Closed 25-26 Dec). **Fee:** £7 (ch £2, concessions £5). **Facilities:** P (charged) 🍴 ✗ licensed ⅙ (free transport to top of Castle Hill lift) toilets for disabled shop 🌟 ▪

EDINBURGH ZOO

Murrayfield EH12 6TS (3m W of city centre on A8 towards Glasgow)

☎ 0131 334 9171   🖹 0131 316 4050

e-mail: marketing@rzss.org.uk
Times: Open all year, Apr-Sep, daily 9-6. (Closes 4.30pm Oct-Mar). **Facilities:** P (charged) 🍴 ✗ licensed ⅙ (wheelchair loan free, 1 helper free - phone in advance) toilets for disabled shop 🌟 (ex guide dogs) *Details not confirmed for 2002* 🍴

GENERAL REGISTER HOUSE

(East end of Princes St) EH1 3YY

☎ 0131 535 1314   🖹 0131 535 1360

e-mail: enquiries@nas.gov.uk

The headquarters of the National Archives of Scotland and repository for public and many private records; designed by Robert Adam and founded in 1774. The historical and legal search rooms are available to researchers, and changing exhibitions are held.
Times: Open Mon-Fri 9-4.45. Exhibitions 10-4. (Closed certain BHs & part of Nov). **Fee:** No charge for historical searches or exhibitions. **Facilities:** ⅙ toilets for disabled shop 🌟 (ex guide dogs) 🚽 🍴

GEORGIAN HOUSE

7 Charlotte Square EH2 4DR (2 mins walk W end of Princes Street)

☎ 0131 226 3318   🖹 0131 226 3318

The house is part of Robert Adam's splendid north side of Charlotte Square, the epitome of Edinburgh New Town architecture. The lower floors of No 7 have been restored in the style of the early 1800s, when the house was new. There also videos of life in the New Town, and this house in particular.
Times: Open Apr-Oct, Mon-Sat 10-5, Sun 2-5. Last admission 4.30pm. **Facilities:** P (100 yds) (meters. disabled directly outside) ⅙ (induction loop for hard of hearing) shop 🌟 (ex guide dogs) 🍴
Details not confirmed for 2002

GLADSTONE'S LAND
477b Lawnmarket EH1 2NT (5 mins walk from Princes Street via Mound)
☎ 0131 226 5856 ▤ 0131 226 4851

Built in 1620, this six-storey tenement, once a merchant's house, still has its arcaded front - a rare feature now. Visitors can also see unusual tempera paintings on the walls and ceilings. It is furnished as a typical 17th-century merchant's home, complete with ground-floor shop front and goods of the period.
Times: Open Apr-Oct, Mon-Sat 10-5, Sun 2-5. Last admission 4.30pm. **Facilities:** P (440yds) (outside for disabled) ዹ (tours for the blind can be arranged) shop ✻ (ex guide dogs) ♨ *Details not confirmed for 2002*

HUNTLY HOUSE MUSEUM
142 Canongate, Royal Mile EH8 8DD
☎ 0131 529 4143 ▤ 0131 557 3346
Times: Open all year, Mon-Sat 10-5. (During Festival period only, Sun 2-5). **Facilities:** P (200yds) ዹ shop ✻ (ex guide dogs) *Details not confirmed for 2002*

JOHN KNOX HOUSE
The Netherbow, 43-45 High St EH1 1SR (between The Castle and Holyrood House)
☎ 0131 556 9579 ▤ 0131 557 5224

John Knox the Reformer is said to have died in the house, which was built by the goldsmith to Mary, Queen of Scots. Renovation work has revealed the original floor in the Oak Room, and a magnificent painted ceiling.
Times: Open all year, Mon-Sat 10-5 & Sun in Aug 12-4. (Closed Xmas). **Fee:** £2.25 (ch 75p, under 7's free, concessions £1.75). **Facilities:** P (paying car park) ▆ ዹ (House on 3 levels) toilets for disabled shop ✻ (ex guide dogs) ◥

LAURISTON CASTLE
Cramond Rd South, Davidson's Mains EH4 6AG (NW outskirts of Edinburgh, 1m E of Cramond)
☎ 0131 336 2060 ▤ 0131 557 3346
Times: Open all year by guided tour only; Apr-Oct, 11-1 & 2-5; Nov-Mar, wknds 2-4. (Closed Fri). **Facilities:** P ዹ shop ✻ (ex guide dogs) *Details not confirmed for 2002*

MUSEUM OF CHILDHOOD
42 High St (Royal Mile) EH1 1TG
☎ 0131 529 4142 ▤ 0131 558 3103
Times: Open all year, Mon-Sat, Jun-Sep 10-6; Oct-May 10-5; (also Sun 12-5 in Jul-Aug). **Facilities:** P ዹ (3 floors only) toilets for disabled shop ✻ (ex guide dogs) *Details not confirmed for 2002* ◥

MUSEUM OF SCOTLAND
Chambers St EH1 1JF
☎ 0131 247 4422 ▤ 0131 220 4819
Times: Open all year - Mon, Wed-Sat 10-5, Tue 10-8 & Sun 12-5. **Facilities:** P ▆ ✗ licensed ዹ toilets for disabled shop ✻ (ex guide dogs) *Details not confirmed for 2002* ◥

NATIONAL GALLERY OF SCOTLAND
The Mound EH2 2EL (off Princes Street. 10 min walk from Edinburgh train/bus stations)
☎ 0131 624 6200 ▤ 0131 343 3250
e-mail: enquiries@natgalscot.ac.uk

Occupying a handsome neo-classical building designed by William Playfair, the gallery is home to Scotland's greatest collection of European paintings and sculpture from the Renaissance to Post-Impressionism. It contains notable collections of works by Old Masters, Impressionists and Scottish artists.
Times: Open all year, Mon-Sat 10-5, Sun 12-5; (Extended opening hours during the Edinburgh Festival period). (Closed 25-26 Dec) **Fee:** Free. Admission charged to some major exhibitions. **Facilities:** P (150yds) ዹ (ramps & lift, room A1 not accessible) toilets for disabled shop ✻ (ex guide dogs) ◥

NELSON MONUMENT
Calton Hill
☎ 0131 556 2716 ▤ 0131 557 3346
Times: Open all year, Apr-Sep, Mon 1-6 & Tue-Sat 10-6; Oct-Mar Mon-Sat 10-3. **Facilities:** P shop ✻ (ex guide dogs) *Details not confirmed for 2002*

NEWHAVEN HERITAGE MUSEUM
24 Pier Place, Newhaven EH6 4LP
☎ 0131 551 4165 ▤ 0131 557 3346
Times: Open all year, Mon-Sun 12-5. (Closed 25-26 Dec & 1-2 Jan) **Facilities:** P ዹ shop ✻ (ex guide dogs) *Details not confirmed for 2002*

PALACE OF HOLYROODHOUSE
EH8 8DX (at east end of Royal Mile)
☎ 0131 556 7371 & 0131 556 1096
▤ 0131 557 5256
e-mail: holyroodhouse@royalcollection.org.uk

The Palace grew from the guesthouse of the Abbey of the Holyrood, said to have been founded by David I after a miraculous apparition. Mary, Queen of Scots had her court here from 1561 to 1567, and 'Bonnie' Prince Charlie held levées at the Palace during his occupation of Edinburgh. The Palace is still used by the Royal Family, but can be visited when they are not in residence. There are fine 17th-century state rooms, and the picture gallery is notable for its series of Scottish monarchs.
Times: Open - daily, Apr-Oct 9.30-5.15, Nov-Mar 9.30-3.45. (Closed 25-26 Dec and when Queen in residence). **Fee:** *Prices not confirmed for 2002* **Facilities:** P (charged) ዹ (first floor by lift, wheelchair available) toilets for disabled shop ✻ (ex guide dogs) ◥

PARLIAMENT HOUSE
Supreme Courts, 2-11 Parliament Square EH1 1RQ (behind St Giles Cathedral)
☎ 0131 225 2595 ▤ 0131 240 6755
Times: Open all year, Mon-Fri 10-4. **Facilities:** P (400 mtrs) ▆ ✗ ዹ toilets for disabled ✻ (ex guide dogs) *Details not confirmed for 2002*

THE PEOPLE'S STORY

Canongate Tolbooth, 163 Canongate EH8 8BN

☎ 0131 529 4057   🖹 0131 557 3439

Times: Open, Mon-Sat 10-5. Also, open Sun during Edinburgh Festival 2-5. **Facilities:** P (100yds) meters & (first floor accessible by lift) toilets for disabled shop 🏠 (ex guide dogs) *Details not confirmed for 2002*

ROYAL BOTANIC GARDEN EDINBURGH

20A Inverleith Row EH3 5LR (1m N of city centre)

☎ 0131 552 7171   🖹 0131 248 2901

e-mail: press@rbge.org.uk

Established in 1670, on an area the size of a tennis court, the Garden is now over 70 acres of beautifully landscaped grounds. Spectacular features include the Rock Garden and the Pringle Chinese Collection. The amazing Glasshouse Experience features Britain's palm house and the magnificent woodland gardens and arboretum.

Times: Open all year, daily; Apr-Aug, 9.30-7; Mar & Sep, 9.30-6; Feb & Oct, 9.30-5; Nov-Jan, 9.30-4. (Closed 25 Dec & 1 Jan) **Fee:** Free. **Facilities:** P (restricted at certain times) 🍽 ✗ licensed & (wheelchairs available at east/west gates) toilets for disabled shop garden centre 🏠 (ex guide dogs) 🍽

ROYAL MUSEUM

Chambers St EH1 1JF

☎ 0131 247 4219 (info)   🖹 0131 220 4819

Times: Open all year, Mon-Sat 10-5, Sun 12-5 (Tue late opening till 8). (Closed 25 Dec. Phone for times on 26 Dec/1 Jan). **Facilities:** P 🍽 ✗ licensed & (induction loops) toilets for disabled shop 🏠 (ex guide dogs) *Details not confirmed for 2002* 🍽

ROYAL OBSERVATORY VISITOR CENTRE

Blackford Hill EH9 3HJ

☎ 0131 668 8405   🖹 0131 668 8429

e-mail: vis@roe.ac.uk

There are excellent views of Edinburgh from the rooftop here, and one of Scotland's largest telescopes. Play with light, lenses, and prisms, and learn about the history of the Observatory and its current work in Hawaii and Australia. Public observing on Friday evenings (end Oct to Mar, weather permitting).

Times: Open all year, Mon-Sat 10-5, Sun noon-5. (Closed 22 Dec-2 Jan). **Fee:** £3.50 (ch £2.50, concessions £2). Family ticket £8. **Facilities:** 🅿 🍽 ✗ & (lift-most floors, no access to dome telescopes) toilets for disabled shop 🏠 (ex guide dogs) 🍽

THE ROYAL YACHT BRITANNIA

Ocean Dr, Leith EH6 6JJ

☎ 0131 555 5566   🖹 0131 555 8835

e-mail: enquiry@try-britannia.co.uk

Times: Open all year 10.30-4.30 with extended hours in summer and some restrictions in winter. **Facilities:** 🅿 🍽 & (lift to ship, all areas ramped) toilets for disabled shop 🏠 (ex guide dogs) *Details not confirmed for 2002* 🍽

SCOTCH WHISKY HERITAGE CENTRE

354 Castlehill, The Royal Mile EH1 2NE

☎ 0131 220 0441   🖹 0131 220 6288

e-mail: enquiry@whisky-heritage.co.uk

Times: Open daily, 10-5.30 (extended in summer). (Closed 25 Dec). **Facilities:** P (.25m) 🍽 & (braille script) toilets for disabled shop 🏠 (ex guide dogs) *Details not confirmed for 2002* 🍽

SCOTTISH NATIONAL GALLERY OF MODERN ART

Belford Rd EH4 3DR (in the West End, 20min walk from Edinburgh Haymarket station)

☎ 0131 624 6200   🖹 0131 343 3250

e-mail: enquiries@natgalscot.ac.uk

An outstanding collection of 20th-century painting, sculpture and graphic art. Includes major works by Matisse, Picasso, Bacon, Moore and Lichtenstein and an exceptional group of Scottish paintings. Set in leafy grounds with a sculpture garden.

Times: Open all year, Mon-Sat 10-5 & Sun 12-5. (Extended opening hours during the Edinburgh Festival). (Closed 25-26 Dec) **Fee:** Free. Admission charged to some major exhibitions. **Facilities:** 🄿 🍽 & (ramps & lift) toilets for disabled shop 🏠 (ex guide dogs) 🍽

SCOTTISH NATIONAL PORTRAIT GALLERY

1 Queen St EH2 1JD (parallel to Princes Street, just behind St Andrew Square)

☎ 0131 624 6200   🖹 0131 558 3691

e-mail: enquiries@natgalscot.ac.uk

The collection provides a visual history of Scotland from the 16th century to the present day, told through the portraits of the people who shaped it. Among the most famous are Mary, Queen of Scots, Ramsay's portrait of David Hume and Raeburn's Sir Walter Scott. The building also houses the National Collection of Photography.

Times: Open all year, daily, Mon-Sat 10-5, Sun 12-5. Extended opening hours during the Edinburgh Festival. (Closed 25-26 Dec). **Fee:** Free. Admission charged to some major exhibitions. **Facilities:** P (200yds) 🍽 & (ramps & lift) toilets for disabled shop 🏠 (ex guide dogs) 🍽

SCOTTISH UNITED SERVICES MUSEUM

Edinburgh Castle EH1 2NG (in Edinburgh Castle)

☎ 0131 225 7534   🖹 0131 225 3848

e-mail: alc@nms.ac.uk/scw@nms.ac.uk

Times: Open all year, Apr-Oct, Mon-Sat 9.30-6, Sun 11-6; Nov-Mar, Mon-Sat 9.30-5, Sun 12.30-5 **Facilities:** P & toilets for disabled shop 🏠 *Details not confirmed for 2002*

WEST REGISTER HOUSE

Charlotte Square EH1 3YY

☎ 0131 535 1314   🖹 0131 535 1360

e-mail: enquiries@nas.gov.uk

The former church of St George (1811) was designed by Robert Reid in Greco-Roman style and is now the modern record branch of the National Archives of Scotland. It houses the exhibition `The Face of the

contd.

Country', Scottish rural landscape from historic plans, and the Search Room is available to researchers.
Times: Open Mon-Fri 9-4.45. Exhibitions 10-4. (Closed certain PHs & part of Nov). **Fee:** No charge for historical searches or exhibitions.
Facilities: ⚓ toilets for disabled shop ✖ (ex guide dogs) 🚃 ⬤

THE WRITERS' MUSEUM
Lady Stair's House, Lady Stair's Close, Lawnmarket
EH1 2PA
☎ 0131 529 4901   ▤ 0131 557 3346
e-mail: enquiries@
writersmuseum.demon.co.uk
Times: Open all year, Mon-Sat 10-5. (During Festival period only, Sun 2-5). **Facilities:** ℗ (500mtrs) shop ✖ (ex guide dogs) *Details not confirmed for 2002*

🏛 GOGAR   Map 11 NT17
SUNTRAP GARDEN OATRIDGE COLLEGE
HORTICULTURAL CENTRE
43 Gogarbank EH12 9BY (between A8 & A71 W of city bypass)
☎ 0131 339 7283   & 01506 854387
▤ 01506 853373
Times: Open all year: Apr-Sep, daily 9.30-4.30; Oct-Mar, Mon-Fri 9.30-4.30. (Closed 2 wks Xmas & New Year). **Facilities:** ℗ ⚓ toilets for disabled *Details not confirmed for 2002*

🏛 SOUTH QUEENSFERRY   Map 11 NT17
DALMENY HOUSE
EH30 9TQ
☎ 0131 331 1888   ▤ 0131 331 1788
e-mail: events@dalmeny.co.uk
This is the home of the Earl and the Countess of Rosebery, whose family have lived here for over 300 years. The house, however, dates from 1815 when it was built in Tudor Gothic style. There is fine French furniture and tapestries and porcelain from the Rothschild Mentmore collection. Early Scottish furniture is also shown, with 18th-century portraits, Rosebery racing mementoes, a display of pictures and one of the world's most important Napoleonic collections.
Times: Open Jul-Aug, Sun, Mon & Tue 2-5.30. Last admission 4.45. Open other times by arrangement for groups. **Fee:** £4 (ch 10-16 £2, pen £3.50, students £3). Party 20+. **Facilities:** ℗ ⬤ ⚓ toilets for disabled ✖ (ex guide dogs or in grounds)

HOPETOUN HOUSE
EH30 9SL (2m W of Forth Road Bridge, off A904)
☎ 0131 331 2451   ▤ 0131 319 1885
Times: Open 2 Apr-26 Sep, daily, wknds in Oct 10-5.30 (last admission 4.30). **Facilities:** ℗ ⬤ ✖ licensed ⚓ toilets for disabled shop *Details not confirmed for 2002* ⬤

INCHCOLM ABBEY
Inchcolm Island (1.5m S of Aberdour. Access by ferry Apr-Sep)
☎ 01383 823332
Situated on a green island on the Firth of Forth, the Augustinian abbey was founded in about 1192 by

Alexander I. The well-preserved remains include a fine 13th-century octagonal chapter house and a 13th-century wall painting.
Times: Open Apr-Sep, daily 9.30-6.30. **Fee:** £2.50 (ch £1, concessions £1.90). Additional charge for ferry trip. **Facilities:** ⚓ toilets for disabled shop ✖ ⬤

QUEENSFERRY MUSEUM
53 High St EH30 9HP
☎ 0131 331 5545   ▤ 0131 557 3346
The museum commands magnificent views of the two great bridges spanning the Forth and traces the history of the people of Queensferry and Dalmeny, the historic passage to Fife, the construction of the rail and road bridges and the wildlife of the Forth estuary. An ancient annual custom, in August, is Burry Man; clad from head to toe in burrs, he parades through the town.
Times: Open all year, Mon & Thu-Sat 10-1, 2.15-5 (Sun noon-5)
Fee: Free. ℗ (0.25m) shop ✖ (ex guide dogs)

CITY OF GLASGOW

🏛 GLASGOW   Map 11 NS56
BURRELL COLLECTION
Pollok Country Park G43 1AT (2m S of city centre)
☎ 0141 649 7151   ▤ 0141 636 0086
Times: Open all year, Mon-Sat 10-5, Sun 11-5. **Facilities:** ℗ (charged) ✖ licensed ⚓ (wheelchairs available, tape guides for blind) toilets for disabled shop ✖ *Details not confirmed for 2002*

CATHEDRAL
Castle St G4 0QZ
☎ 0141 552 6891
Times: Open all year, Apr-Sep, Mon-Sat 9.30-6, Sun 2-5; Oct-Mar, Mon-Sat 9.30-4, Sun 2-4. (Closed 25-26 Dec). **Facilities:** ⚓ shop ✖ ⬤ *Details not confirmed for 2002*

GALLERY OF MODERN ART
Queen St G1 3AZ
☎ 0141 229 1996   ▤ 0141 204 5316
Times: Open all year, Mon-Thu & Sat 10-5, Fri & Sun 11-5.
Facilities: ℗ (200yds) ✖ licensed ⚓ toilets for disabled shop ✖ *Details not confirmed for 2002*

GLASGOW ART GALLERY & MUSEUM
Kelvingrove G3 8AG (1m W of city centre)
☎ 0141 287 2699   ▤ 0141 287 2690
Times: Open all year, Mon-Thu & Sat 10-5, Fri & Sun 11-5.
Facilities: ℗ ⬤ ✖ licensed ⚓ toilets for disabled shop ✖ *Details not confirmed for 2002*

GLASGOW BOTANIC GARDENS
730 Great Western Rd G12 0UE (on A82)
☎ 0141 334 2422   ▤ 0141 339 6964
Times: Open all year. Gardens open daily 7am-dusk. Kibble Palace & main range of glasshouses Mon-Fri 10-4.45 (4.15 in winter), wknds afternoon only. **Facilities:** ⬤ ⚓ toilets for disabled ✖ (ex in grounds) *Details not confirmed for 2002*

GLASGOW SCIENCE CENTRE

50 Pacific Quay G51 1EA
☎ 0141 420 5000   📠 0141 420 5001
e-mail: admin@gsc.org.uk
Times: Open daily, all year. **Fee:** Science Mall £6.50 (ch & concessions £4.50). Family ticket £12-£16. Glasgow Tower £5.50 (ch & concessions £4). Family ticket £12-£16. Discounts available for tickets to more than one attraction. **Facilities:** 🅿 🍴 ♿ toilets for disabled shop

GREENBANK GARDEN

Flenders Rd, Clarkston G76 8RB (off A726 on southern outskirts of the city)
☎ 0141 639 3281

The spacious, walled woodland gardens are attractively laid out in the grounds of an elegant Georgian house, and best seen between April and October. A wide range of flowers and shrubs are grown, with the idea of helping private gardeners to look at possibilities for their own environment. A greenhouse and garden designed for the disabled gardener also displays specialised tools.
Times: Garden open all year, daily 9.30-sunset. (Closed 25-26 Dec & 1-2 Jan). House open Apr-Oct Sun only 2-4. Shop & Tearoom open Apr-Oct, daily 11-5; Nov-Mar, Sat & Sun 2-4. **Facilities:** 🅿 🍴 ♿ (wheelchairs available) toilets for disabled shop (& plant sales) 🐕 (ex guide dogs) 🍽 *Details not confirmed for 2002*

HOUSE FOR AN ART LOVER

10 Dumbreck Rd, Bellahouston Park G41 5BW (Exit M8 W J23 signed B768 & turn L at top of slip road onto Dumbreck road. Take first R into Bellahouston Park)
☎ 0141 353 4770   📠 0141 353 4771
e-mail: info@houseforanartlover.co.uk

Originally designed by Glasgow's most celebrated architect, Charles Rennie Mackintosh, in 1901, this unusual cultural, corporate and academic resource began construction in 1989 and was completed in 1996. Contains art galleries and rooms that can be hired for conferences.
Times: Open Apr-Sep, Sun-Thu 10-4 & Sat 10-3; Oct-Mar, Sat-Sun 10-4, telephone for wkday opening details. **Fee:** *Prices not confirmed for 2002* **Facilities:** 🅿 🍴 ✗ licensed ♿ (lift to 2nd floor) toilets for disabled shop 🐕 (ex guide dogs) 🍽

HUNTERIAN ART GALLERY

The University of Glasgow G12 8QQ
☎ 0141 330 5431   📠 0141 330 3618
e-mail: hunter@museum.gla.ac.uk

The founding collection is of paintings bequeathed in the 18th century by Dr William Hunter, including works by Rembrandt and Stubbs. The Gallery now has works by James McNeill Whistler, major displays of paintings by the Scottish Colourists and a graphics collection holding some 300,000 prints. A popular feature of the Charles Rennie Mackintosh collection is the reconstruction of the interiors of The Mackintosh House.

Hunterian Art Gallery

Times: Open all year. Main gallery Mon-Sat 9.30-5. Mackintosh House Mon-Sat 9.30-12.30 & 1.30-5. Telephone for BH closures. **Fee:** Free. **Facilities:** 🅿 (500 yds) (pay & display) ♿ (lift, wheelchair available) toilets for disabled shop 🐕 (ex guide dogs) 🍽

HUNTERIAN MUSEUM

The University of Glasgow G12 8QQ (2m W of city centre)
☎ 0141 330 4221   📠 0141 330 3617
e-mail: rpurss@museum.gla.ac.uk

Named after the 18th-century physician, Dr William Hunter, who bequeathed his large and important collections of coins, medals, fossils, geological specimens and archaeological and ethnographic items to the university. The exhibits are shown in the main building of the university, and temporary exhibitions are held.
Times: Open all year, Mon-Sat 9.30-5. (Closed certain BH's phone for details). **Fee:** Free. **Facilities:** 🅿 (100yds) ♿ (access by lift, prior arrangement) toilets for disabled shop 🐕 (ex guide dogs) 🍽

HUTCHESONS' HALL

158 Ingram St G1 1EJ
☎ 0141 552 8391   📠 0141 552 7031

This handsome early 19th-century building was designed by David Hamilton and houses a visitor centre and shop. There is a video about Glasgow's merchant city, and the Hall can be booked for functions. Telephone for details of concerts, recitals, etc.
Times: Open from 21 Apr, Mon-Sat 10-5. (Closed PH's & 24 Dec-6 Jan). Hall on view subject to functions in progress. **Facilities:** 🅿 (on street) (meters)(outside for disabled) ♿ toilets for disabled shop 🐕 🍽 *Details not confirmed for 2002*

McLELLAN GALLERIES

270 Sauchiehall St G2 3EH
☎ 0141 331 1854   📠 0141 332 9957
Times: Open Mon-Thu & Sat 10-5, Fri & Sun 11-5. Closed 25-26 Dec & 1-2 Jan. **Facilities:** 🅿 (500mtrs) ♿ (assistance available) toilets for disabled shop 🐕 *Details not confirmed for 2002* 🍽

MUSEUM OF TRANSPORT
Kelvin Hall, 1 Bunhouse Rd G3 8DP (1.5m W of city centre)
☎ 0141 287 2000   ▤ 0141 287 2692
Times: Open all year, Mon-Sat 10-5, Sun 11-5. **Facilities:** ℙ (charged) ✗ licensed & (assistance available) toilets for disabled shop ✻
Details not confirmed for 2002

PEOPLE'S PALACE
Glasgow Green G40 1AT (1m SE of city centre)
☎ 0141 554 0223   ▤ 0141 550 0892
Times: Phone for details of opening times. **Facilities:** ℙ ■ & toilets for disabled shop garden centre ✻ *Details not confirmed for 2002*

POLLOK HOUSE
Pollok Country Park G43 1AT (2m S of city centre)
☎ 0141 616 6410   ▤ 0141 649 0823
Times: Open Mon-Sat 10-5; Sun 11-5. **Facilities:** ℙ ■ & shop ✻
Details not confirmed for 2002

PROVAND'S LORDSHIP
3 Castle St G4 0RB (1m E of city centre)
☎ 0141 552 8819   ▤ 0141 552 4744
Times: Open all year, Mon-Sat 10-5, Sun 11-5. **Facilities:** ℙ shop ✻
Details not confirmed for 2002

ST MUNGO RELIGIOUS LIFE & ART MUSEUM
2 Castle St G4 0RH (1m NE of city centre)
☎ 0141 553 2557   ▤ 0141 552 4744
Times: Open all year, Mon-Sat 10-5; Sun 11-5. **Facilities:** ℙ (charged) ■ & (taped information & lift) toilets for disabled shop ✻ *Details not confirmed for 2002*

THE TALL SHIP AT GLASGOW HARBOUR
100 Stobcross Rd G3 8QQ
☎ 0141 339 0631   ▤ 0141 341 0506
e-mail: info@thetallship.com

Built in 1896, the S.V. Glenlee is one of the last remaining Clyde-built sailing ships still afloat. A new exhibit uses audio-visual and interactive elements to tell the story of the Glenlee and the Tall Ship offers children's activities. Visitors can also walk round a museum of Glasgow's shipyards in the Pumphouse, and travel the river on the Frances Mary.
Times: Open daily Apr-Sep 10-5, Oct-Mar 11-4. **Fee:** £4.50 (concessions £3.25, 1 ch free with paying adult/concession, additional ch £2.50). **Facilities:** ℙ ■ ✗ licensed & toilets for disabled shop ✻ (ex guide dogs) ◥

TENEMENT HOUSE
145 Buccleuch St, Garnethill G3 6QN
(N of Charing Cross)
☎ 0141 333 0183

This shows an unsung but once-typical side of Glasgow life: it is a first-floor flat, built in 1892, with a parlour, bedroom, kitchen and bathroom, furnished with the original recess beds, kitchen range, sink, and coal bunker, among other articles. The home of Agnes

Toward from 1911 to 1965, the flat was bought by an actress who preserved it as a `time capsule'.
Times: Open Mar-Oct, daily 2-5. (Last admission 30 mins before closing); weekday morning visits by educational & other groups (not to exceed 15), by advance booking only. **Facilities:** ℙ (100yds) (v.restricted, recommend parking in town (braille guide) ✻ (ex guide dogs) ◥ *Details not confirmed for 2002*

UNIVERSITY OF GLASGOW VISITOR CENTRE
University Av G12 8QQ
☎ 0141 330 5511   ▤ 0141 330 5225
Times: Open all year, Mon-Sat 9.30-5. Also May-Sep, Sun 2-5. In summer guided tours of the university start from the Visitor Centre at 11am & 2pm on Wed, Fri & Sat, telephone 0141 330 5511.
Facilities: ℙ ■ & toilets for disabled shop ✻ *Details not confirmed for 2002* ◥

CLACKMANNANSHIRE

🏛 ALLOA   Map 11 NS89
ALLOA TOWER
Alloa Park FK10 1PP (on A907)
☎ 01259 211701   ▤ 01259 218744

Beautifully restored, the tower, completed in 1467, is the only remaining part of the ancestral home of the Earls of Mar. The structure retains rare medieval features, notably the complete timber roof structure and groin vaulting. A superb loan collection of portraits and chattels of the Erskine family includes paintings by Raeburn.
Times: Open Apr-Sep & wknds in Oct, daily 1.30-5.30. **Facilities:** ℙ & toilets for disabled ✻ ◥ *Details not confirmed for 2002*

🏛 ALVA   Map 11 NS89
MILL TRAIL VISITOR CENTRE
Glentana Mill, West Stirling St FK12 5EN (on A91) approx 8m E of Stirling)
☎ 01259 769696   ▤ 01259 763100
Times: Open all year, Jan-Jun 10-5; Jul-Sep 9-6; Oct-Dec 10-5.
Facilities: ℙ ■ & toilets for disabled shop ✻ (ex guide dogs) *Details not confirmed for 2002*

🏛 DOLLAR   Map 11 NS99
CASTLE CAMPBELL
FK14 7PP (10m E of Stirling on A91)
☎ 01259 742408
Times: Open all year, Apr-Sep, daily 9.30-6.30; Oct-Mar, Mon-Sat 9.30-4.30, Sun 2-4.30. (Closed Thu pm, Fri in winter & 25-26 Dec).
Facilities: ℙ ✗ shop ▮ ◥ *Details not confirmed for 2002*

DUMFRIES & GALLOWAY

🏛 ARDWELL   Map 10 NX14
ARDWELL HOUSE GARDENS
DG9 9LY (10m S of Stranraer, on A716)
☎ 01776 860227   ▤ 01776 860288

Country house gardens and grounds with flowering

contd.

shrubs and woodland walks. Plants for sale. House not open to the public.
Times: Open Mar-Oct, 10-5. Walled garden & greenhouses close at 5pm. **Fee:** £2 (ch & pen £1). **Facilities:** ▣ garden centre

�🏛 CAERLAVEROCK   **Map 11 NY06**
CAERLAVEROCK CASTLE
Glencaple DG1 4RU (8m SE of Dumfries, on B725)
☎ 01387 770244

This ancient seat of the Maxwell family is a splendid medieval stronghold dating back to the 13th century. It has high walls and round towers, with machicolations added in the 15th century.
Times: Open all year, Apr-Sep, daily 9.30-6.30; Oct-Mar, Mon-Sat 9.30-4.30, Sun 2-4.30. (Closed 25-26 Dec). **Fee:** £2.50 (ch £1, concessions £1.90) **Facilities:** ▣ ✗ ᕼ toilets for disabled shop ▮

WWT CAERLAVEROCK
Eastpark Farm DG1 4RS (9m SE of Dumfries, signposted from A75)
☎ 01387 770200   ▤ 01387 770539
e-mail: caerlaverock@wwt.org.uk

This internationally important wetland is the winter habitat of the entire Svalbard population of Barnacle Geese which spends the winter on the Solway Firth. Observation facilities include twenty hides, three towers and a heated observatory. A wide variety of other wildlife can be seen, notably the rare Natterjack Toad and a family of Barn Owls which can be observed via a CCTV system.
Times: Open daily 10-5. (Closed 25 Dec). **Fee:** £4 (ch £2.50 & con £3.25). **Facilities:** ▣ ♥ ᕼ toilets for disabled shop ✗

�🏛 CARDONESS CASTLE   **Map 11 NX55**
CARDONESS CASTLE
DG7 2EH (1m SW of Gatehouse of Fleet off A75)
☎ 01557 814427

A 15th-century stronghold overlooking the Water of Fleet. It was once the home of the McCullochs of Galloway. The architectural details inside the tower are of very high quality.
Times: Open all year, Apr-Sep, daily 9.30-6.30; Oct-Mar, wknds only. (Closed 25-26 Dec). **Fee:** £2 (ch 75p, concessions £1.50).
Facilities: ▣ shop ▮

�🏛 CASTLE DOUGLAS   **Map 11 NX76**
THREAVE CASTLE
DG7 1RX (3m W on A75)
☎ 0411 223101

Archibald the Grim built this lonely castle in the late 14th century. It stands on an islet in the River Dee, and is four storeys high with round towers guarding the outer wall. The island is reached by boat.
Times: Open Apr-Sep, daily 9.30-6.30. **Fee:** £2 (ch 75p, concessions £1.50). Charge includes ferry trip. **Facilities:** ▣ ✗ ▮

THREAVE GARDEN & ESTATE
DG7 1RX (1m W of Castle Douglas off A75)
☎ 01556 502575   ▤ 01556 502683

The best time to visit is in spring when there is a dazzling display of daffodils. The garden is a delight in all seasons, however, and is home to the National Trust for Scotland's School of Practical Gardening.
Times: Open all year - Garden: daily 9.30-sunset. Walled garden & glasshouses: daily 9.30-5. Visitor centre, Shop & Exhibition: Apr-Oct, daily 9.30-5.30. (Last entry 30 minutes before closing). **Facilities:** ▣ ✗ licensed ᕼ (wheelchairs available incl. electric wheelchair) toilets for disabled shop garden centre ✗ (ex guide dogs) ♥ *Details not confirmed for 2002*

�🏛 CREETOWN   **Map 11 NX45**
CREETOWN GEM ROCK MUSEUM
Chain Rd DG8 7HJ (follow signs from A75, located at Creetown bypass)
☎ 01671 820357 & 820554   ▤ 01671 820554
e-mail: gem.rock@btinternet.com

A world famous collection of gems, crystals, minerals and fossils. Interactive computer displays provide an opportunity to learn more, and audio visual displays explain how minerals are formed.
Times: Open Etr-Sep, daily 9.30-5.30; Oct-Nov & Mar-Etr, daily 10-4; Dec-Feb, wknds 10-4 or by appointment wkdays. (Closed 23 Dec-Jan). **Fee:** £2.90 (ch £1.75, concessions £2.40). Family ticket £7.55 (2 adults & 3 ch). Party. **Facilities:** ▣ ♥ ᕼ toilets for disabled shop ✗ (ex guide dogs) ♥

�🏛 DRUMCOLTRAN TOWER   **Map 11 NX86**
DRUMCOLTRAN TOWER
(7m NE of Dalbeattie)
☎ 0131 668 8800
Times: Open at any reasonable time. **Facilities:** ✗ ▮ *Details not confirmed for 2002*

�🏛 DUMFRIES   **Map 11 NX97**
BURNS HOUSE
Burns St DG1 2PS
☎ 01387 255297   ▤ 01387 265081
e-mail: info@dumfriesmuseum.demon.co.uk

It was here that Robert Burns spent the last three years of his short life; he died here in 1796. The house retains much of its 18th-century character and contains many fascinating items connected with the poet. There is the chair in which he wrote his last poems, many original letters and manuscripts, and the famous Kilmarnock and Edinburgh editions of his work.
Times: Open all year, Apr-Sep, Mon-Sat 10-5, Sun 2-5; Oct-Mar Tue-Sat 10-1 & 2-5. **Fee:** Free. **Facilities:** Ⓟ (100yds) shop

BURNS MAUSOLEUM
St Michael's Churchyard
☎ 01387 255297   ▤ 01387 265081
e-mail: info@dumfriesmuseum.demon.co.uk

The mausoleum is in the form of a Greek temple, and contains the tombs of Robert Burns, his wife Jean

contd.

Armour, and their five sons. A sculptured group shows the Muse of Poetry flinging her cloak over Burns at the plough.
Times: Unrestricted access. **Fee:** Free. **Facilities:** P (100yds) &
(visitors with mobility difficulties tel 01387 255297)

DUMFRIES MUSEUM & CAMERA OBSCURA

The Observatory DG2 7SW
☎ 01387 253374 ⊜ 01387 265081
e-mail: postmaster@
dumfriesmuseum.demon.co.uk
Times: Open all year, Apr-Sep Mon-Sat 10-5, Sun, 2-5; Oct-Mar, Tue-Sat 10-1 & 2-5. **Facilities:** P & (camera obscura not accessible, parking available) toilets for disabled shop *Details not confirmed for 2002*

OLD BRIDGE HOUSE MUSEUM

Mill Rd DG2 7BE
☎ 01387 256904 ⊜ 01387 265081
e-mail: info@dumfriesmuseum.demon.co.uk

The Old Bridge House was built in 1660, and is the oldest house in Dumfries. A museum of everyday life in the town, it has an early 20th-century dentist's surgery, a Victorian nursery and kitchens of the 1850s and 1900s.
Times: Open Apr-Sep, Mon-Sat 10-5 & Sun 2-5. **Fee:** Free.
Facilities: P & shop

ROBERT BURNS CENTRE

Mill Rd DG2 7BE
☎ 01387 264808 ⊜ 01387 265081
e-mail:
postmaster@dumfriesmuseum.demon.co.uk
Times: Open all year, Apr-Sep, daily 10-8 (Sun 2-5); Oct-Mar, Tue-Sat 10-1 & 2-5. **Facilities:** P ⚇ & (induction loop hearing system in auditorium) toilets for disabled shop *Details not confirmed for 2002*
⬎

⛪ DUNDRENNAN Map 11 NX74

DUNDRENNAN ABBEY

DG6 4QH (6.5m SE of Kirkcudbright, on A711)
☎ 01557 500262

The now ruined abbey was founded for the Cistercians. The east end of the church and the chapter house are of exceptional architectural quality. Mary, Queen of Scots is thought to have spent her last night in Scotland here on 15 May 1568, before seeking shelter in England, where she was imprisoned and eventually executed.
Times: Open all year, Apr-Sep, daily 9.30-6.30; Oct-Mar, closed Thu pm & Fri. (Closed 25-26 Dec). **Fee:** £1.80 (ch 75p, concessions £1.30).
Facilities: P & ⵓ ⴲ

⛪ GLENLUCE Map 10 NX15

GLENLUCE ABBEY

DG8 0AF (2m NW, off A75)
☎ 01581 300541

The abbey was founded for the Cistercians in 1192 by

Roland, Earl of Galloway. The ruins include a vaulted chapter house, and stand in a beautiful setting.
Times: Open all year, Apr-Sep, daily 9.30-6.30; Oct-Mar, wknds only. (Closed 25-26 Dec). **Fee:** £1.80 (ch 75p, concessions £1.30).
Facilities: P ⵓ & ⴲ ⴲ

⛪ KIRKCUDBRIGHT Map 11 NX65

BROUGHTON HOUSE & GARDEN

12 High St DG6 4JX (off A711/A755)
☎ 01557 330437
e-mail: aclipson@nts.scot.demon.co.uk

An 18th-century house where Edward A Hornel, one of the 'Glasgow Boys' group of artists, lived and worked from 1901–1933. It features a collection of his work, an extensive library of local history, including rare editions of Burns' works, and a Japanese-style garden that he created.
Times: Open daily, Apr-Jun & Sep-Oct 1-5.30; Jul & Aug, 11-5.30 (last admission 4.45pm). **Facilities:** P (on street) (limited space) ⴲ (ex guide dogs) ⵓ *Details not confirmed for 2002*

MACLELLAN'S CASTLE

(in Kirkcudbright on A711)
☎ 01557 331856

This handsome structure has been a ruin since the mid-18th century. It was once an imposing castellated mansion, elaborately planned with fine architectural detail. Something of its 16th-century grandeur still remains.
Times: Open Apr-Sep, daily 9.30-6.30; (Closed 25-26 Dec). **Fee:** £1.80 (ch 75p, concessions £1.30). **Facilities:** P shop ⴲ ⵓ ⴲ

STEWARTRY MUSEUM

Saint Mary St DG6 4AQ (from A711 through town, pass the parish church, museum in approx 200mtrs on right)
☎ 01557 331643 ⊜ 01557 330005
e-mail: DavidD@dumgal.gov.uk
Times: Open Mar-Oct, Mon-Sat 11-4 (5pm in May, Jun & Sep; 6pm in Jul & Aug also Sun 2-5); Nov-Feb, Mon-Sat 11-4. **Facilities:** P (outside) & shop ⴲ *Details not confirmed for 2002*

TOLBOOTH ART CENTRE

High St DG6 4JL (From A711, through town, pass parish church & Stewarty Museum, take 1st right into High St)
☎ 01557 331556 ⊜ 01557 331643
e-mail: DavidD@dumgal.gov.uk
Times: Open Mar & Oct, Mon-Sat 11-4; May-Jun & Sep, Mon-Sat 10-6; Nov-Feb, Mon-Sat 11-4. Open Sun Jun-Sep 2-5. **Facilities:** P (on street parking) ⵓ & (lift) toilets for disabled shop ⴲ *Details not confirmed for 2002*

⛪ MONIAIVE Map 11 NX79

MAXWELTON HOUSE TRUST

DG3 4DX (A76 from Dumfries to Thornhill, after 2m take B729 to Monaive, 11m along road to House)
☎ 01848 200385
Times: Open last Sun in May-Sep, Sun-Fri 11-5. Etr-May by booking only. **Facilities:** P shop *Details not confirmed for 2002*

NEW ABBEY
Map 11 NX96

NEW ABBEY CORN MILL
DG2 8BX (7m S of Dumfries on A710)
☎ 01387 850260

Built in the late 18th century, this water-driven corn mill is still in working order, and regular demonstrations are held.
Times: Open all year, Apr-Sep, daily 9.30-6.30; Oct-Mar, Mon-Sat 9.30-4.30, Sun 2-4.30. (Closed Thu pm & Fri in winter & 25-26 Dec).
Fee: £2.50 (ch £1, concessions £1.90). **Facilities:** P (100yds) shop ✹ ◪

SWEETHEART ABBEY
DG2 8BU (on A710)
☎ 01387 850397

Lady Devorgilla of Galloway founded Balliol College, Oxford in memory of her husband John Balliol; she also founded this abbey in his memory in 1273. When she died in 1289 she was buried in front of the high altar with the heart of her husband resting on her bosom; hence the name 'Sweetheart Abbey'. The abbey features an unusual precinct wall of enormous boulders.
Times: Open all year, Apr-Sep, daily 9.30-6.30; Oct-Mar, Mon-Sat 9.30-4.30, Sun 2-4.30. (Closed Thu pm & Fri in winter & 25-26 Dec).
Fee: £1.50 (ch 50p, concessions £1.10). **Facilities:** P ⅃ (with assistance) ✹ ◪

PALNACKIE
Map 11 NX85

ORCHARDTON TOWER
(6m SE of Castle Douglas)
☎ 0131 668 8800
Times: Open all reasonable times, on application to key keeper. (Closed 25-26 Dec). **Facilities:** P ✹ ◪ *Details not confirmed for 2002*

PORT LOGAN
Map 10 NX04

LOGAN BOTANIC GARDEN
DG9 9ND (on B7065, 14m S of Stranraer)
☎ 01776 860231 ▤ 01776 860333

Logan's exceptionally mild climate allows a colourful array of tender plants to thrive out-of-doors. Amongst the many highlights are tree ferns, cabbage palms, unusual shrubs, climbers and tender perennials found within the setting of the walled, water, terrace and woodland gardens.
Times: Open Mar-Oct, daily 9.30-6. **Fee:** £3 (ch £1, concessions £2.50). Family ticket £7. **Facilities:** P ✹ licensed ⅃ (access limited, wheelchairs available for loan) toilets for disabled shop garden centre ✹ (ex guide dogs) ▼

RUTHWELL
Map 11 NY16

RUTHWELL CROSS
(off B724)
☎ 0131 668 8800
Times: Open all reasonable times. Key from Key Keeper, Kirkyett Cottage, Ruthwell. **Facilities:** P ✹ ◪ *Details not confirmed for 2002*

SAVINGS BANKS MUSEUM
Ruthwell
(*Signposted on the Galloway Tourist Route between Annan and Dumfries*).
Trace the life of the Father of Savings Banks
Rev. Dr Henry Duncan.
Also featured are family and social records. Information is available on the mediaeval
Ruthwell Cross which Dr Duncan restored.
No admission charge.
Open daily. 10am-1pm and 2-5pm.
In winter closed Sundays and Mondays.
Tel: 01387 870640
www.lloydstsb.com/savingsbanksmuseum

SAVINGS BANKS MUSEUM
DG1 4NN (off B724, 10m E of Dumfries & 6m W of Annan)
☎ 01387 870640
e-mail: tsbmuseum@btinternet.com

Housed in the building where savings banks first began, the museum traces their growth and development from 1810 up to the present day. The museum also traces the life of Dr Henry Duncan, father of savings banks, and restorer of the Ruthwell Cross. Multi-lingual leaflets available.
Times: Open all year, daily (ex Sun & Mon Oct-Etr), 10-1 & 2-5. **Fee:** Free. **Facilities:** P ⅃ (touch facilities for blind, guide available) ✹ (ex guide dogs)

SANQUHAR
Map 11 NS70

SANQUHAR TOLBOOTH MUSEUM
High St DG4 6BN (on A76 - Dumfries-Kilmarnock road)
☎ 01659 250186 ▤ 01387 265081
e-mail: info@dumfriesmuseum.demon.co.uk

Housed in the town's fine 18th-century tollbooth, the museum tells the story of the mines and miners of the area, its earliest inhabitants, native and Roman, the history and customs of the Royal Burgh of Sanquhar and local traditions.
Times: Open Apr-Sep, Tue-Sat 10-1 & 2-5, Sun 2-5. **Fee:** Free. **Facilities:** P shop

🏛 STRANRAER   Map 10 NX06
CASTLE KENNEDY GARDENS
Stair Estates DG9 8BX (5m E on A75)
☎ 01776 702024   🖹 01776 706248

Situated on a peninsula between two lochs, the gardens around the Old Castle were first laid out in the early 18th century. Noted for their rhododendrons and azaleas (at their best May and early Jun) and walled kitchen garden with fine herbaceous borders (best in Aug and Sep). The gardens contain many avenues and walks amid beautiful scenery. **Times:** Open Apr-Sep, daily 10-5. **Fee:** *Prices not confirmed for 2002* **Facilities:** 🅿 ☕ & toilets for disabled shop garden centre 🍴

🏛 THORNHILL   Map 11 NX89
DRUMLANRIG CASTLE
DG3 4AQ (4m N of Thornhill off A76)
☎ 01848 330248   🖹 01848 331682
e-mail: bre@drumlanrigcastle.org.uk

This unusual pink sandstone castle was built in the late 17th century in Renaissance style. It contains a collection of paintings by Rembrandt, Da Vinci, Holbein, and many others. There is also French furniture, as well as silver and relics of Bonnie Prince Charlie. The old stable block has a craft centre with resident craft workers, and the grounds offer extensive gardens, working forge and woodland walks. Phone for details of special events. **Times:** Open early May-late Aug, Castle open seven days a week. Guided tours and restricted route may operate at various times, please verify before visiting. **Fee:** £6 (ch £2 & pen £4); grounds only £3. Party 20+ **Facilities:** 🅿 ✖ licensed & (lift for wheelchair users) toilets for disabled shop 🍴 (ex in park on lead) 🍴

🏛 WANLOCKHEAD   Map 11 NS81
MUSEUM OF LEAD MINING
ML12 6UT (on B797 at N end of Mennock Pass)
☎ 01659 74387   🖹 01659 74481
e-mail: ggodfrey@goldpan.co.uk

Wanlockhead is Scotland's highest village, set in the beautiful Lowther Hills. Visitors can see miners'

cottages and the miners' library as well as the 18th-century lead mine, and there is a Gold Panning Centre. **Times:** Open Apr-Oct, daily 11-4.30, Jul/Aug 10.30-5 **Fee:** £3.95 (ch £2.50, concessions £2.70). Family ticket £9.80 (2 adults & 3 ch) **Facilities:** 🅿 ☕ & toilets for disabled shop 🍴 (ex guide dogs) 🍴

🏛 WHITHORN   Map 10 NX44
WHITHORN-CRADLE OF CHRISTIANITY
45-47 George St DG8 8NS (From Newton Stewart or Glenluce follow directions S from A75. In main street of Whithorn)
☎ 01988 500508
e-mail: enquiries@whithorn.com

The Whithorn Dig is the site of the first Christian settlement in Scotland - the Candida Casa of St Ninian. Friendly guides explain the excavation, and there's a museum of Early Christian stones. **Times:** Open daily, Apr-Oct 10.30-5. **Fee:** £2.70 (ch, pen & UB40's £1.50). Family ticket £7.50. Season ticket. Party. **Facilities:** 🅿 ☕ & (one short staircase with 'stairmatic') toilets for disabled shop 🍴

WHITHORN PRIORY
DG8 8PY (on A746)
☎ 01988 500508

The first Christian church in Scotland was founded here by St Ninian in 397AD, but the present ruins date from the 12th century. The ruins are sparse but there is a notable Norman door, the Latinus Stone of the 5th century and other early Christian monuments. **Times:** Open Etr-Oct, daily 10.30-5. **Fee:** Admission charged, please telephone for details. **Facilities:** 🅿 & 🍴 🎏

DUNDEE CITY

🏛 DUNDEE   Map 11 NO43
BROUGHTY CASTLE MUSEUM
Broughty Ferry DD5 2TF (Turn S off A930 at traffic lights by Eastern Preliminary in Broughton Ferry)
☎ 01382 436916   🖹 01382 436950
e-mail: broughty@dundeecity.gov.uk

The 15th-century castle was rebuilt to defend the estuary in the 19th century. It now houses displays on Dundee's whaling history, arms and armour, local history and seashore life. There are superb views across the Tay estuary from the observation room. **Times:** Open all year. Apr-Sep Mon-Sat 10-4, Sun 12.30-4, Oct-Mar Tue-Sat 10-4, Sun 12.30-4, (Closed Mons, 25-26 Dec & 1-3 Jan). **Fee:** Free. **Facilities:** 🅿 (unsuitable for wheelchairs) shop 🍴 (ex guide dogs)

CAMPERDOWN COUNTRY PARK
DD2 4TF (A90 to Dundee, onto A923 Coupar Angus rd, turn left at 1st rdbt to Park)
☎ 01382 432659   🖹 01382 433211

The 19th-century mansion of Camperdown House was built for the son of Admiral Lord Duncan, who defeated

contd.

the Dutch at the Battle of Camperdown in 1797. The house is set in nearly 400 acres of fine parkland which includes a wildlife centre, an adventure play area and an extensive network of footpaths and forest trails to follow.
Times: Open all year - park. Wildlife Centre - daily, Apr-Sep 10-3.45, Oct-Mar 10-2.45. **Fee:** Park - free admission. Wildlife Centre charged. **Facilities:** 🅿 ♿ (ramps) toilets for disabled shop ⚑ (ex guide dogs)

DISCOVERY POINT & RRS DISCOVERY
Discovery Quay DD1 4XA (in Dundee follow tourist signs for Historic Ships)
☎ 01382 201245 📠 01382 25891
e-mail: info@dundeeheritage.sol.co.uk

Discovery Point is the home of RRS Discovery, Captain Scott's famous Antarctic ship. Spectacular lighting, graphics and special effects re-create key moments in the Discovery story. The restored bridge gives a captain's view over the ship and the River Tay. Learn what happened to the ship after the expedition, during the First World War and the Russian Revolution, and find out about her involvement in the first survey of whales' migratory patterns.
Times: Open all year, Apr-Oct, Mon-Sat 10-5, Sun 11-5; Nov-Mar, Mon-Sat 10-4, Sun 11-4. Venue closes 1 hr after last entry. (Closed 25 Dec & 1-2 Jan). **Fee:** £5.95 (ch £3.85, pen & con £4.45). Family ticket £17 (2 adults & 2 ch). Party. Joint ticket with Verdant Works. **Facilities:** 🅿 (charged) ♨ ♿ (in-house wheelchairs & lifts, parking, ramps onto ship) toilets for disabled shop ⚑ (ex guide/hearing dogs) 🍴

CASTLE KENNEDY GARDENS
STRANRAER : WIGTOWNSHIRE

The Gardens are situated on a peninsula between two lochs and are nationally famous for their rhododendrons, azaleas, magnolias and embothriums. They are set in extensive grounds and offer a range of interesting and varied walks.

OPEN DAILY EASTER TO END SEPTEMBER 10am to 5pm
Situated 5 miles east of Stranraer on the A75 Stranraer-Dumfries road
PLANT CENTRE
Light refreshments
Admission: Adults £3.00, OAPs £2.00, Child £1.00 (2001 Prices)
Discount for groups over 20 people
Further information please see Editorial entry

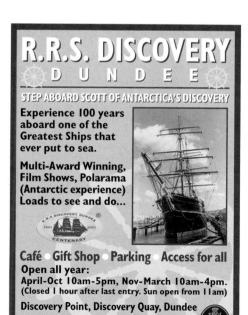

HM Frigate Unicorn

Victory Dock DD1 3JA (From W follow A85 from A90 at Invergowrie. From E follow A92. Located near N end of Tay Road Bridge)

☎ 01382 200900 & 200893

e-mail: frigateunicorn@hotmail.com

The *Unicorn* is the oldest British-built warship afloat, and Scotland's only example of a wooden warship. Today she houses a museum of life in the Royal Navy during the days of sail, with guns, models and displays. **Times:** Open all year: Apr-Oct daily 10-5. Nov-Mar daily 10-5 (closed Mon/Tue & 2 weeks at Xmas & New Year) **Fee:** £3.50 (concessions £2.50). Family ticket £7.50-£9.50. Groups 10+ **Facilities:** 🅿 🍺 ♿ shop ✸ (no exceptions)

McManus Galleries

Albert Square DD1 1DA (Turn off A90 & follow signs for Dundee city centre. In city centre)

☎ 01382 432084 📠 01382 432052

e-mail: arts.heritage@dundeecity.gov.uk

A remarkable Gothic building housing one of Scotland's most impressive collections of fine and decorative art. There are also displays on local archaeology, civic and social history, trades and industries and wildlife and the environment. Touring exhibitions are a regular feature. **Times:** Open all year. Mon-Sat 10.30-5, Thu 10.30-7, Sun 10.30-4. (closed 25-26 Dec & 1-3 Jan) **Fee:** Free. **Facilities:** 🅿 (100 yds) 🍺 ♿ (wheelchair available & high arm chairs, audio loop) toilets for disabled shop ✸ (ex guide dogs)

Mills Observatory

Balgay Park, Glamis Rd DD2 2UB (Turn off A90 towards Dundee Airport. Left at small roundabout near airport towards Botanic Gdns, onto next large roundabout, Observatory signed)

☎ 01382 435846 📠 01382 435962

e-mail: jeff.lashley@dundeecity.gov.uk

The observatory was built in 1935, and has a Victorian 10in Cooke refracting telescope among its instruments. The gallery has displays on astronomy and space exploration; visitors can view a safe projection of the sun on bright days. There is a small planetarium for booked groups only. Open nights during the winter months, children's activities during the summer holidays. **Times:** Open all year, Apr-Sep, Tue-Fri 11-5, Sat/Sun 12.30-4; Oct-Mar, Mon-Fri 4-10, Sat/Sun 12.30-4. (Closed 25-26 Dec & 1-3 Jan). **Fee:** Free except for Planetarium Shows £1 (ch 50p). **Facilities:** 🅿 shop ✸ (ex guide dogs)

Verdant Works

West Henderson's Wynd DD2 5BT (in city follow brown tourist signs)

☎ 01382 225282 📠 01382 221612

e-mail: info@dundeeheritage.sol.co.uk

Dating from 1830, this old jute mill covers 50,000 sq ft and has been restored as a living museum of Dundee and Tayside's textile history and an award winning

European Industrial Museum. Phase I explains what jute is, where it comes from and why Dundee became the centre of its production. Working machinery illustrates the production process from raw jute to woven cloth. Phase II deals with the uses of jute and its effects on Dundee's social history. **Times:** Open Apr-Oct, Mon-Sat 10-5, Sun 11-5. Nov-Mar, Mon-Sat 10-4, Sun 11-4. Venue closes 1 hr after last entry. (Closed 25 Dec & 1-2 Jan). **Fee:** £5.95 (ch £3.85, pen & con £4.45). Family ticket (2 adults & 2 ch) £17. **Facilities:** 🅿 (charged) ♿ (wheelchairs, induction loops) toilets for disabled shop ✸ (ex guide/hearing dogs) 🍺

EAST AYRSHIRE

🏛 GALSTON   Map 11 NS53

Loudoun Castle Theme Park

KA4 8PE (signposted from A74(M), A77, A71)

☎ 01563 822296 📠 01563 822408

e-mail: loudouncastle@btinternet.com

Times: Open Apr-Aug & following days in Sep 3, 9-10, 16-17, 22-25, 29-30. Also 1-2, 7-8, 14-22 Oct. **Facilities:** 🅿 🍺 ✗ licensed ♿ toilets for disabled shop ✸ (ex guide dogs) *Details not confirmed for 2002* 🍺

🏛 KILMARNOCK   Map 10 NS43

Dean Castle Country Park

Dean Rd KA3 1XB

☎ 01563 522702 📠 01563 572552

Times: Open: Country Park all year, dawn to dusk. Dean Castle daily noon-5. Visitor centre & Tearoom 11-5(summer), 11-4(winter). Rare Breeds centre 1-5(summer), 1-4(winter). **Facilities:** 🅿 🍺 ♿ (disabled garden, car parks, ramps & level paths) toilets for disabled shop ✸ (ex guide dogs inside) *Details not confirmed for 2002* 🍺

Dick Institute Museum & Art Galleries

Elmbank Ave KA1 3BU (Follow brown tourist signs from A77 S of Glasgow, into Kilmarnock town centre. Parking at front of building)

☎ 01563 554343 📠 01563 554344

Temporary and permanent exhibitions spread over two floors of this grand Victorian building. Fine art, social and natural history feature upstairs, whilst the downstairs galleries house temporary exhibitions of art and craft. **Times:** Open all year, Gallery & Museum: Mon-Tue, Thu-Fri 10-8, Wed & Sat 10-5. (Closed Sun & BH's). **Fee:** Free except for special exhibitions when a charge may be made. **Facilities:** 🅿 ♿ (wheelchair available) toilets for disabled shop ✸ (ex guide dogs) 🍺

EAST DUNBARTONSHIRE

🏛 BEARSDEN   Map 11 NS57

Roman Bath-House

Roman Rd G61 2SG

☎ 0131 668 8800

Times: Open all reasonable times. **Facilities:** ♿ ✸ 🏳 *Details not confirmed for 2002*

🏛 MILNGAVIE   Map 11 NS57
MUGDOCK COUNTRY PARK
Craigallion Rd G62 8EL (N of Glasgow on A81, signed)
☎ 0141 956 6100 🖷 0141 956 5624
e-mail: lain@mcp.ndo.co.uk

Times: Open all year, daily. **Facilities:** 🅿 💺 ♿ shop garden centre
Details not confirmed for 2002 ⬛

EAST LOTHIAN

🏛 ABERLADY   Map 12 NT47
MYRETON MOTOR MUSEUM
EH32 0PZ (1.5m from A198, 2m from A1)
☎ 01875 870288
Times: Open all year, daily 10-6 (summer); 10-5 (winter). (Closed 25
Dec & 1 Jan). **Facilities:** 🅿 ♿ shop 🐾 (ex guide dogs) *Details not
confirmed for 2002*

🏛 DIRLETON   Map 12 NT58
DIRLETON CASTLE
EH39 5ER (on A198)
☎ 01620 850330

The oldest part of this romantic castle dates from the
13th century. It was besieged by Edward I in 1298,
rebuilt and expanded, and then destroyed in 1650. Now
the sandstone ruins have a beautiful mellow quality.
Within the castle grounds is a garden established in the
16th century, with ancient yews and hedges around a
bowling green.
Times: Open all year, Apr-Sep, daily 9.30-6.30; Oct-Mar, Mon-Sat 9.30-
4.30, Sun 2-4.30. (Closed 25-26 Dec). **Fee:** £2.50 (ch £1, concessions
£1.90). **Facilities:** 🅿 shop 🔴

🏛 EAST FORTUNE   Map 12 NT57
MUSEUM OF FLIGHT
East Fortune Airfield EH39 5LF (Signposted from A1
near Haddington. Turn onto B1347, past
Athelstaneford)
☎ 01620 880308 🖷 01620 880355
e-mail: museum_of_flight@sol.co.uk

Situated on 63 acres of one of Britain's best preserved
wartime airfields, the museum has three hangars, with

more than 50 aeroplanes, plus engines, rockets and
memorabilia. Items on display include two Spitfires, a
Vulcan bomber and Britain's oldest surviving
aeroplane, built in 1896; recent exhibits include a
phantom jet fighter and harrier jump-jet.

Times: Open daily, 10.30-5; Jun-Jul until 6. (Closed 25 & 31 Dec,
1 Jan). **Fee:** £3 (ch free, concessions £1.50). Season ticket available.
Facilities: 🅿 💺 ♿ toilets for disabled shop 🐾 (ex guide dogs) ⬛

🏛 EAST LINTON   Map 12 NT57
HAILES CASTLE
(1m SW on unclass rd)
☎ 0131 668 8800
Times: Open at all reasonable times. **Facilities:** 🍴 🏳 *Details not confirmed for 2002*

PRESTON MILL & PHANTASSIE DOOCOT
EH40 3DS (signposted from A1)
☎ 01620 860426

This attractive mill, with conical, pantiled roof, is the oldest working water-driven meal mill to survive in Scotland, and was last used commercially in 1957. Nearby is the charming Phantassie Doocot (dovecote), built for 500 birds.
Times: Open Apr-Sep, Mon-Sat 11-1 & 2-5, Sun 1.30-5; Oct, wknds 1.30-4. Last entry 20 mins before closing morning and afternoon. **Facilities:** 🅿 ᪲ toilets for disabled shop 🍴 (ex guide dogs) 💥 *Details not confirmed for 2002*

🏛 INVERESK   Map 11 NT37
INVERESK LODGE GARDEN
EH21 7TE (A6124 S of Musselburgh)
☎ 01721 722502

This charming terraced garden, set in the historic village of Inveresk, specialises in plants, shrubs and roses suitable for growing on small plots. The 17th-century house makes an elegant backdrop.
Times: Open all year, Apr-Oct, Mon-Fri 10-4.30, Sat-Sun 2-5. (Closed Sat Nov-Mar). **Facilities:** 🅿 ᪲ 🍴 (ex guide dogs) 💥 *Details not confirmed for 2002*

🏛 NORTH BERWICK   Map 12 NT58
SCOTTISH SEABIRD CENTRE
The Harbour EH39 4SS
☎ 01620 890202   🖶 01620 890222
e-mail: info@seabird.org
Times: Open - Summer, daily 10-6; Winter, daily 10-4. **Facilities:** 🅿 💺 ✗ ᪲ toilets for disabled shop 🍴 (ex guide dogs) *Details not confirmed for 2002*

TANTALLON CASTLE
EH39 5PN (3m E, off A198)
☎ 01620 892727
Times: Open all year, Apr-Sep, daily 9.30-6.30; Oct-Mar, Mon-Sat 9.30-4.30, Sun 2-4.30. (Closed Thu pm & Fri in winter & 25-26 Dec). **Facilities:** 🅿 shop 🍴 🏳 *Details not confirmed for 2002*

🏛 PRESTONPANS   Map 11 NT37
PRESTONGRANGE MUSEUM
Prestongrange (on B1348)
☎ 0131 653 2904   🖶 01620 828201
e-mail: elms@elothian-museums.demon.co.uk
Times: Open end Mar-mid Oct, daily 11-4. Last tour 3pm. **Facilities:** 🅿 ᪲ ᪲ toilets for disabled shop 🍴 (ex guide dogs) *Details not confirmed for 2002*

🏛 BIRKHILL   Map 11 NS97
THE BIRKHILL FIRECLAY MINE
(A706 from Linlithgow, A904 from Grangemouth)
☎ 01506 825855   🖶 01506 828766
e-mail: mine@srps.org.uk
Times: Open Apr-22 Oct wknds only; Jul-27 Aug Tue-Sun. BH Mon's, 1 & 29 May. **Facilities:** 🅿 *Details not confirmed for 2002* 🍴

🏛 BO'NESS   Map 11 NT08
BO'NESS & KINNEIL RAILWAY
Bo'ness Station, Union St EH51 9AQ (A904, signposted)
☎ 01506 822298   🖶 01506 828233
e-mail: railway@srps.org.uk

Historic railway buildings, including the station and train shed, have been relocated from sites all over Scotland. The Scottish Railway Exhibition tells the story of the development of railways and their impact on the people of Scotland. Take a seven mile return trip by steam train to the tranquil country station at Birkhill. Special events take place throughout the year.
Times: Open Apr-Jun & Sep-Oct, Sat-Sun; Steam trains depart 11 (ex Apr), 12.15, 1.45, 3 & diesel at 4.15. Jul-Aug, Tue-Sun; 23 May-27 Jun, special timetable, ring for details. **Fee:** Return fare £4.50 (ch 5-15 £2, concessions (disabled & pen) £3.50). Family ticket £11. Ticket for return train fare and tour of Birkhill Fireclay Mine £7.50 (ch £3.50, concessions £5.30), Family ticket £17.50. **Facilities:** 🅿 💺 ✗ ᪲ (ramps to stn, and adapted carriage) toilets for disabled shop 🍴

KINNEIL MUSEUM & ROMAN FORTLET
Duchess Anne Cottages, Kinniel Estate EH51 0PR (Follow tourist signs from Heritage Railway, off M9. Museum at E end of town accessed via Dean Road)
☎ 01506 778530

The museum is in a converted stable block of Kinniel House. The ground floor has displays on the industrial history of Bo'ness, while the upper floor looks at the history and environment of the Kinneil estate. The remains of the Roman fortlet can be seen nearby. An audio visual presentation shows 2000 years of history.
Times: Open all year, Mon-Sat 12.30-4. **Fee:** Free. **Facilities:** 🅿 ᪲ shop 🍴 (ex guide dogs)

🏛 FALKIRK   Map 11 NS88
CALLENDAR HOUSE
Callendar Park FK1 1YR (from W M80 junct 4; from E M9 junct 4/5; A803 to Falkirk, follow signs into Callendar Park)
☎ 01324 503770   🖶 01324 503771

Mary, Queen of Scots, Oliver Cromwell, Bonnie Prince Charlie, noble earls and wealthy merchants all feature in the history of Callendar House. Costumed interpreters describe early 19th-century life in the kitchens and the 900-year history of the house is illustrated in the 'Story of Callendar House' exhibition. The house is set in parkland, offering boating and woodland walks. Christmas at Callendar House will

contd.

include spitroasting goose in the kitchen, traditional tree and carols in the main hall.

Callendar House

Times: Open all year, Mon-Sat 10-5. Apr-Sep Sun 2-5. **Fee:** £3 (ch & pen £1.50). **Facilities:** 🅿 💺 ✗ ⅙ (ramps & lift) toilets for disabled shop 🍴 (ex guide dogs) 🍴

ROUGH CASTLE
(1m E of Bonnybridge)
☎ 0131 668 8800
Times: Open any reasonable time. **Facilities:** 🅿 🍴 ♜ *Details not confirmed for 2002*

FIFE

⛪ ABERDOUR　　　　　　　Map 12 NT18
ABERDOUR CASTLE
KY3 0SL (5m E of Forth Bridges on A921)
☎ 01383 860519

The earliest surviving part of the castle is the 14th-century keep. There are also later buildings, and the remains of a terraced garden, a bowling green and a fine 16th-century doocot (dovecote).
Times: Open all year, Apr-Sep, daily 9.30-6.30; Oct-Mar, Mon-Sat 9.30-4.30, Sun 2-4.30. (Closed Thu pm, Fri in winter & 25-26 Dec). **Fee:** £2 (ch 75p, concessions £1.50). **Facilities:** 🅿 ✗ ⅙ (w/chairs) toilets for disabled shop ♜

⛪ ANSTRUTHER　　　　　　Map 12 NO50
SCOTTISH FISHERIES MUSEUM
St Ayles, Harbour Head KY10 3AB
☎ 01333 310628　📠 01333 310628
e-mail: andrew@scottish-fisheries-museum.org

This National Museum depicts the history of the Scottish fishing industry, with actual boats and many fine models, photographs and paintings. There is also a reconstruction of a fisherman's cottage.
Times: Open all year, Apr-Sep, Mon-Sat 10-5.30, Sun 11-5; Oct-Mar, Mon-Sat 10-4.30, Sun 12-4.30. (Closed 25-26 Dec & 1-2 Jan). Last admission 45 mins before closing. **Fee:** £3.50 (concessions £2.50). Family ticket £10. Party 12+. **Facilities:** 🅿 (20yds) (charge in summer) 💺 ⅙ (ramps) toilets for disabled shop 🍴 (ex guide dogs)

⛪ BURNTISLAND　　　　　　Map 11 NT28
BURNTISLAND EDWARDIAN FAIR MUSEUM
102 High St KY3 9AS (in the centre of Burntisland)
☎ 01592 412860　📠 01592 412870

Burntisland Museum has recreated a walk through the sights and sounds of the town's fair in 1910, based on a painting of the scene by local artist Andrew Young. See reconstructed rides, stalls and side shows of the time.
Times: Open all year, Mon, Wed, Fri & Sat 10-1 & 2-5; Tue & Thu 10-1 & 2-7pm. Closed public holidays. **Fee:** Free. 🅿 (on street parking) 🍴

⛪ CULROSS　　　　　　　　Map 11 NS98
CULROSS PALACE, TOWN HOUSE & THE STUDY
West Green House KY12 8JH (off A985, 3m E of Kincardine Bridge)
☎ 01383 880359　📠 01383 882675

A royal burgh, Culross dates from the 16th and 17th centuries and has remained virtually unchanged since. It prospered from the coal and salt trades, and when these declined in the 1700s, Culross stayed as it was. It owes its present appearance to the National Trust for Scotland, which has been gradually restoring it. In the Town House there is a visitor centre and exhibition; in the building called The Study a drawing room with a Norwegian painted ceiling can be seen, and the Palace has painted rooms and terraced gardens.
Times: Open - Palace & Town House: Apr-May & Sep, daily 1-5; Jun-Aug, daily 10-5; Oct, wknds 1-5 (last admission to Palace 4pm, Town House 4.30pm). Study: same dates, 1-5. Groups at other times by appointment. **Facilities:** 🅿 💺 ⅙ toilets for disabled shop 🍴 (ex guide dogs) 🍴 *Details not confirmed for 2002*

⛪ CUPAR　　　　　　　　　Map 11 NO31
HILL OF TARVIT MANSIONHOUSE & GARDEN
KY15 5PB (2.5m S of Cupar, off A916)
☎ 01334 653127　📠 01334 653127

Built in the first decade of the 20th century, the Mansionhouse is home to a notable collection of paintings, tapestries, furniture and Chinese porcelain. The grounds include formal gardens, and there is a regular programme of concerts and art exhibitions.
Times: Open- House: 21 Apr-Jun & Sep, daily 1.30-5.30; Jul-Aug, daily 11-5.30; Oct, wknds 1.30-5.30 (last admision 4.45). Garden & grounds: Apr-Sep, daily 9.30am-9pm; Oct-Mar, daily 9.30-4.30. **Facilities:** 🅿 💺 ⅙ toilets for disabled shop 🍴 (ex guide dogs) 🍴 *Details not confirmed for 2002*

RANKEILOUR PARK - THE SCOTTISH DEER CENTRE
Bow-of-Fife KY15 4NQ (3m W of Cupar on A91)
☎ 01337 810391　📠 01337 810477
Times: Open daily, Etr-Oct 10-6, Nov-Etr 10-5. **Facilities:** 🅿 ✗ ⅙ (special parking bay, loan of wheelchairs) toilets for disabled shop 🍴 (ex guide dogs) *Details not confirmed for 2002* 🍴

🏛 DUNFERMLINE   Map 11 NT08

ABBOT HOUSE HERITAGE CENTRE

Abbot House, Maygate KY12 7NE (city centre)
☎ 01383 733266   📠 01383 624908
e-mail: dht@abbothouse.fsnet.co.uk

Housed in one of Dunfermline's most historic buildings, which was formerly attached to the first Benedictine abbey in Scotland, Abbot House holds an interesting collection of artefacts and painstakingly created displays describing 1000 years of Scottish history.
Times: Open daily 10-5. Last entry to upper exhibitions 4.15pm. (Closed 25 Dec & 1 Jan). **Fee:** *Prices not confirmed for 2002*
Facilities: 🅿 (150yds) (disabled parking at establishment) 🍽 ✕ & (parking on site, videos of inaccesible areas) toilets for disabled shop ✸ (ex guide dogs) ☜

ANDREW CARNEGIE BIRTHPLACE MUSEUM

Moodie St KY12 7PL (400yds S from Dunfermline Abbey)
☎ 01383 724302   📠 01383 721862
e-mail: carnegiebirthplace@hotmail.com

The museum tells the story of the handloom weaver's son, born here in 1835, who created the biggest steel works in the USA and then became a philanthropist on a huge scale. The present-day work of the philanthropic Carnegie Trust is also explained.
Times: Open Apr-Oct, Mon-Sat 11-5, Sun 2-5. **Fee:** £2 (ch 16 free, concessions £1). **Facilities:** 🅿 & toilets for disabled shop ✸ (ex guide dogs)

DUNFERMLINE ABBEY

Pittencrieff Park
☎ 01383 739026
Times: Open all year, Apr-Sep, daily 9.30-6.30: Oct-Mar, Mon-Sat 9.30-4.30, Sun 2-4.30. (Closed Thu pm, Fri in winter & 25-26 Dec).
Facilities: 🅿 shop ✸ ▌ *Details not confirmed for 2002*

PITTENCRIEFF HOUSE MUSEUM

Pittencrieff Park KY12 8QH
☎ 01383 722935 & 313838   📠 01383 313837
Times: Open daily Apr-Sep 11-5, Oct-Mar 11-4. **Facilities:** 🅿 & (ramp) toilets for disabled shop ✸ (ex guide dogs) *Details not confirmed for 2002*

🏛 FALKLAND   Map 11 NO20

FALKLAND PALACE & GARDEN

KY15 7BU (off A912, 11m N of Kirkcaldy)
☎ 01337 857397   📠 01337 857980

The hunting palace of the Stuart monarchs, this fine building, with a French-Renaissance style south wing, stands in the shelter of the Lomond Hills. The beautiful Chapel Royal and King's Bedchamber are its most notable features, and it is also home to the oldest royal tennis court in Britain (1539). The garden has a spectacular delphinium border. Recorded sacred music

is played hourly in the Chapel. Please telephone for details of concerts, recitals etc.
Times: Open Jun-Aug, Mon-Sat 10-5.30, Sun 1.30-5.30. (last admission to palace 4.30, to garden 5). Apr-May & Sep-Oct, Mon-Sat 11-5.30, Sun 1.30-5.30. Groups at other times by appointment. Town Hall, by appointment only. **Facilities:** 🅿 & shop ✸ (ex guide dogs) ☜ *Details not confirmed for 2002*

🏛 KELLIE CASTLE & GARDENS   Map 12 NO50

KELLIE CASTLE & GARDENS

KY10 2RF (3m NW of Pittenweem on B9171)
☎ 01333 720271   📠 01333 720326
e-mail: aclipson@nts-scot.demon.co.uk

The oldest part dates from about 1360, but it is for its 16th- and 17th-century domestic architecture that Kellie is renowned. It has notable plasterwork and painted panelling, and there are also interesting Victorian gardens.
Times: Open - Castle Good Fri-Etr Mon & May-Sep, daily 1.30-5.30; wknds in Oct 1.30-5.30 (last admission 4.45). Gardens & grounds open all year, Apr-Oct, daily 9.30-sunset. **Facilities:** 🅿 & (Induction loop for the hard of hearing) shop ✸ (ex guide dogs) ☜ *Details not confirmed for 2002*

🏛 KIRKCALDY   Map 11 NT29

KIRKCALDY MUSEUM & ART GALLERY

War Memorial Gardens KY1 1YG (next to Kirkcaldy train station)
☎ 01592 412860   📠 01592 412870

Set in the town's lovely memorial gardens, the museum houses a collection of fine and decorative art, including 18th- to 21st-century Scottish paintings, among them the works of William McTaggart and S J Peploe. An award-winning display 'Changing Places' tells the story of the social, industrial and natural heritage of the area.
Times: Open all year, Mon-Sat 10.30-5, Sun 2-5. (Closed local hols).
Fee: Free. **Facilities:** 🅿 🍽 & (ramp to main entrance & lift to 1st floor galleries) toilets for disabled shop ✸ (ex guide dogs)

🏛 NORTH QUEENSFERRY   Map 11 NT17

DEEP SEA WORLD

KY11 1JR (from N, M90 take exit for Inverkeithing. From S follow signs to Forth Road Bridge, first exit left)
☎ 01383 411880   📠 01383 410514
e-mail: info@deepseaworld.co.uk

The world's longest underwater tunnel gives you a diver's eye view of an underwater world. Come face to face with Sand Tiger sharks, and watch divers hand feed a wide array of sea life. Visit the Amazon experience with ferocious Piranhas and electric eels and the amazing amphibian display featuring the world's most poisonous frog. The really brave will enjoy the dangerous animals tank.
Times: Open all year, daily, 27 Mar-Jun Mon-Fri 10-6; Jul-Aug, Mon-Fri 10-6.30; Sep-1 Nov, Mon-Fri 10-6; 2 Nov-26 Mar, Mon-Fri 11-5. Wknds, BH & school holidays 10-6. **Fee:** £6.50 (ch 3-5 £4.25, concessions £5). Family ticket & group discounts available. **Facilities:** 🅿 🍽 & (ramps & disabled parking) toilets for disabled shop ✸ (ex guide dogs) ☜

⚏ ST ANDREWS   Map 12 NO51
BRITISH GOLF MUSEUM
Bruce Embankment KY16 9AB (opposite Royal &
Ancient Golf Club)
☎ 01334 460046   ▤ 01334 460064
e-mail: hwebster@randagc.org

A visit to the museum will transport you down a
pathway of surprising facts and striking feats from 500
years of golf history. Using diverse displays and exciting
exhibits, the museum traces the history of the game,
both in Britain and abroad, from the middle ages to the
present day. There are also displays exploring St
Andrews' golfing heritage. Find out more about the
growth of the St Andrews clubmakers as well as the
impact these businesses made upon the city.
Times: Open all year, Etr-mid Oct daily 9.30-5.30; mid Oct-Etr Thu-
Mon 11-3. (closed Tue & Wed). **Fee:** £3.75 (ch 15 £1.50, pen &
students £2.75). Family ticket £9.50. Group 10+ **Facilities:** ▣
(charged) ₺ toilets for disabled shop ↟ (ex guide dogs)

CASTLE & VISITOR CENTRE
KY16 9AR
☎ 01334 477196
Times: Open all year, Apr-Sep, daily 9.30-6.30; Oct-Mar, Mon-Sat 9.30-
4.30, Sun 2-4.30. (Closed 25-26 Dec). **Facilities:** ℙ ₺ toilets for
disabled shop ↟ ▮ Details not confirmed for 2002

CATHEDRAL (& MUSEUM)
KY16 9QU
☎ 01334 472563
Times: Open all year, Apr-Sep, daily 9.30-6.30; Oct-Mar, Mon-Sat 9.30-
4.30, Sun 2-4.30. (Closed 25-26 Dec). **Facilities:** ℙ shop ↟ ▮ Details
not confirmed for 2002

HIGHLAND

⚏ AVIEMORE   Map 14 NH81
STRATHSPEY STEAM RAILWAY
Aviemore Station, Dalfaber Rd PH22 1PY (off B970)
☎ 01479 810725
e-mail: laurence.grant@strathspey-
railway.freeserve.co.uk

This steam railway covers the five and a half miles from
Boat of Garten to Aviemore. The journey takes about 20
minutes, but allow around an hour for the round trip.
Timetables are available from the station and the
tourist information centre.
Times: Open end May-Sep, daily; late Mar-Oct, Wed-Thu, Sat-Sun.
Fee: £6 Basic return; £15 Family return. **Facilities:** ▣ ☕ ₺ (ramps)
toilets for disabled shop ☕

⚏ BALMACARA   Map 14 NG82
BALMACARA (LOCHALSH WOODLAND GARDEN)
IV40 8DN (3m E of Kyle of Lochalsh, off A87)
☎ 01599 566325   ▤ 01599 566359

The Balmacara estate comprises some 5600 acres and
seven crofting villages, and includes Plockton, a
conservation area. There are excellent views of Skye,
Kintail and Applecross. The main attraction is the
Lochalsh Woodland Garden, but the whole area is
excellent for walking.
Times: Open all year, daily 9-sunset. **Facilities:** ▣ ☕ Details not
confirmed for 2002

⚏ BETTYHILL   Map 14 NC76
STRATHNAVER MUSEUM
KW14 7SS
☎ 01641 521418
Times: Open Apr-Oct, Mon-Sat 10-1 & 2-5; Nov-Mar restricted
opening. **Facilities:** ▣ ₺ shop ↟ (ex guide dogs) Details not
confirmed for 2002

⚏ BOAT OF GARTEN   Map 14 NH91
RSPB NATURE RESERVE ABERNETHY FOREST
Forest Lodge, Nethybridge PH25 3EF (nr Strathspey.
Signposted from B970 & A9 at Aviemore, follow 'RSPB
Ospreys' signs)
☎ 01479 831694   ▤ 01479 821069

Home of the Loch Garten Osprey site, this reserve holds
one of most important remnants of Scots Pine forest in
the Highlands. Within its 30,760 acres are forest bogs,
moorland, mountain top, lochs and crofting land. In
addition to the regular pair of nesting ospreys, there are
breeding Scottish crossbills, capercaillies, black grouse
and many others. The ospreys can be viewed through
telescopes and there is a live CCTV link to the nest.
Times: Reserve open at all times. Osprey Centre daily, Apr-Aug 10-6.
Fee: £2.50 (ch 50p, concessions £1.50) Family ticket £5. **Facilities:** ▣
₺ toilets for disabled shop ↟ (ex guide dogs in centre)

⚏ CARRBRIDGE   Map 14 NH92
**LANDMARK HIGHLAND HERITAGE &
ADVENTURE PARK**
PH23 3AJ (off A9 between Aviemore & Inverness)
☎ 01479 841613 & 0800 731 3446
▤ 01479 841384
e-mail: landmark@compuserve.com

This innovative centre is designed to provide a fun and
educational visit for all ages. Microworld is a journey
into inner space, a close up look at the incredible
microscopic world around us. There is a 65ft forest
viewing tower, a working steam-powered sawmill and
various exhibitions. There are demonstrations of timber
sawing and log hauling by a Clydesdale horse
throughout the day. Attractions include the new 3-track
Watercoaster, a maze and an adventure play area.
Times: Open all year, daily, Apr-mid Jul 10-6; mid Jul-mid Aug 10-7;
Sep-Oct 10-5.30; Nov-Mar 10-5. **Fee:** Apr £4.85 (ch £3.45); May-Jun
£6.65 (ch £4.65); Jul-Oct £6.90 (ch £4.85); Nov-Mar £3.75 (ch £2.65).
Family tickets available. **Facilities:** ▣ ☕ ✗ licensed ₺ toilets for
disabled shop ☕

🏛 CAWDOR
Map 14 NH85

CAWDOR CASTLE
IV12 5RD (on B9090 off A96)
☎ 01667 404615   🖷 01667 404674
e-mail: info@cawdorcastle.com

Home of the Thanes of Cawdor since the 14th century, this lovely castle has a drawbridge, an ancient tower built round a tree, and a freshwater well inside the house. Gardens Weekend takes place in June - guided tours of gardens and Bluebell Walk in Cawdor Big Wood.
Times: Open 1 May-13 Oct, daily 10-5.30. (Last admission 5pm). **Fee:** £6.10 (ch 5-15 £3.30, pen £5.10). Family ticket £18. Party 20+ £5.30. Gardens, grounds & nature trails only £3.20. **Facilities:** 🅿 🍴 ✗ licensed ♿ toilets for disabled shop 🐾 (ex guide dogs)

🏛 CLAVA CAIRNS
Map 14 NH74

CLAVA CAIRNS
(6m E of Inverness)
☎ 0131 668 8800
Times: Open at all reasonable times. **Facilities:** 🅿 🐾 ▮ *Details not confirmed for 2002*

🏛 CROMARTY
Map 14 NH76

HUGH MILLER'S COTTAGE
Church St IV11 8XA
☎ 01381 600245

The cottage houses an exhibition on the life and work of Hugh Miller, a stonemason born here in 1802 who became an eminent geologist and writer. It was built by his great-grandfather around 1698, and now has a charming cottage garden.
Times: Open May-Sep, Mon-Sat 11-1 & 2-5, Sun 2-5. **Facilities:** 🅿 (5mins) (disabled is directly outside) ♿ 🐾 (ex guide dogs) 🍽 *Details not confirmed for 2002*

🏛 CULLODEN MOOR
Map 14 NH74

CULLODEN BATTLEFIELD
IV2 5ED (5m E of Inverness)
☎ 01463 790607   🖷 01463 794294

A cairn commemorates the last battle fought on mainland Britain, on 16 April 1746, when 'Bonnie' Prince Charles Edward Stuart's army was routed by the Duke of Cumberland's forces. The battlefield has been restored to its state on the day of the battle, and in summer there are 'living history' enactments. This is a most atmospheric evocation of tragic events. Telephone for details of guided tours.
Times: Open - site always. Visitor Centre open Feb-Mar & Nov-30 Dec, daily 10-4. (Closed 25 & 26 Dec, shop closed 1-7 Nov); Apr-Oct, daily 9-6; Audio visual show closed 30 mins before Visitor Centre.
Facilities: 🅿 ✗ ♿ (wheelchair, induction loop, raised map) toilets for disabled shop 🐾 (ex guide dogs) 🍽 *Details not confirmed for 2002*

🏛 DRUMNADROCHIT
Map 14 NH52

OFFICIAL LOCH NESS MONSTER EXHIBITION CENTRE
IV3 6TU (on A82, 12m S Inverness)
☎ 01456 450573 & 450218   🖷 01456 450770
e-mail: brem@loch-ness-scotland.com

A fascinating and popular multi-media presentation lasting 30 minutes. Seven themed areas cover the story from the pre-history of Scotland, through the cultural roots of the legend in Highland folklore, and into the 50-year controversy which surrounds it. The latest technology in computer animation, lasers and multi-media projection systems is featured.
Times: Open all year; Etr-May 9.30-5.30; Jun-Sep 9.30-6 (9-8.30 Jul & Aug); Winter 10-4. Last admission 30min before closing. **Fee:** £5.95 (ch £3.50, pen & students £4.50, ch under 7 & disabled free). Family ticket £14.95. Group. **Facilities:** 🅿 🍴 ✗ licensed ♿ (parking) toilets for disabled shop 🐾 (ex in grounds) 🍽

URQUHART CASTLE
IV63 6XJ (on A82)
☎ 01456 450551

The castle was once Scotland's biggest and overlooks Loch Ness. It dates mainly from the 14th century, when it was built on the site of an earlier fort, and was destroyed before the 1715 Jacobite rebellion.
Times: Open all year, Apr-Sep, daily 9.30-6.30; Oct-Mar, daily 9.30-4.30. Last admission 45mins before closing. (Closed 25-26 Dec).
Fee: £3.80 (ch £1.20, concessions £2.80). **Facilities:** 🅿 shop 🐾 ▮

🏛 DUNBEATH
Map 15 ND12

LAIDHAY CROFT MUSEUM
KW6 6EH (1m N on A9 off Dunbeath)
☎ 01593 731244

The museum gives visitors a glimpse of a long-vanished way of life. The main building is a thatched Caithness longhouse, with the dwelling quarters, byre and stable all under one roof. It dates back some 200 years, and is furnished as it might have been 100 years ago. A collection of early farm tools and machinery is also shown. Near the house is a thatched winnowing barn with its roof supported on three 'Highland couples', or crucks.
Times: Open Etr-mid Oct, daily 10-6. **Fee:** £1 (ch 50p) **Facilities:** 🅿 🍴 ♿ toilets for disabled

🏛 ELPHIN
Map 14 NC21

HIGHLAND & RARE BREEDS FARM
IV27 4HH (on A835 in Elphin)
☎ 01854 666204   🖷 01854 666204
Times: Open mid May-Sep, daily 10-5. **Facilities:** 🅿 ♿ (assistance available) toilets for disabled shop 🐾 *Details not confirmed for 2002*

⌂ FORT GEORGE Map 14 NH75
FORT GEORGE
IV1 2TD (11m NE of Inverness)
☎ 01667 462777

Built following the Battle of Culloden as a Highland fortress for the army of George II, this is one of the most outstanding artillery fortifications in Europe and is still an active army barracks.
Times: Open all year, Apr-Sep, daily 9.30-6.30; Oct-Mar, Mon-Sat 9.30-4.30, Sun 2-4.30. Last admission 45mins before closing. (Closed 25-26 Dec). **Fee:** Summer: £4 (ch £1.50, concessions £3); Winter: £3.50 (ch £1.20, concessions £2.60). **Facilities:** ₽ ✕ ᵹ toilets for disabled shop ✵ ▮

QUEEN'S OWN HIGHLANDERS REGIMENTAL MUSEUM COLLECTION
IV2 7TD
☎ 01463 224380 🖷 01463 224380

Fort George has been a military barracks since it was built in 1748-1769, and was the Depot of the Seaforth Highlanders until 1961. The museum of the Queen's Own Highlanders (Seaforth and Camerons) is sited in the former Lieutenant Governor's house, where uniforms, medals and pictures are displayed.
Times: Open Apr-Sep, daily 10-6; Oct-Mar, Mon-Fri 10-4. (Closed Good Fri-Etr Mon, Xmas, New Year & BH). **Fee:** Free. (Admission charged by Historic Scotland for entry to Fort George). **Facilities:** ₽ (500yds) ᵹ (stair lift to 1st floor, wheelchair on 1st floor) toilets for disabled shop ✵ (ex guide dogs)

⌂ FORT WILLIAM Map 14 NN17
INVERLOCHY CASTLE
PH33 6SN (2m NE)
☎ 0131 668 8800
Times: Open Apr-Sep. Key available from keykeeper. **Facilities:** ✵ ▮
Details not confirmed for 2002

WEST HIGHLAND MUSEUM
Cameron Square PH33 6AJ (follow signs to tourist office, museum is next door)
☎ 01397 702169 🖷 01397 701927

The displays illustrate traditional Highland life and history, with numerous Jacobite relics. One of them is the 'secret portrait' of Bonnie Prince Charlie, which looks like meaningless daubs of paint but reveals a portrait when reflected in a metal cylinder.
Times: Open all year - Jun-Sep, Mon-Sat 10-5 (also Sun 2-5 Jul-Aug); Oct-May, Mon-Sat 10-4. **Fee:** £2 (ch 50p, concessions £1.50)
Facilities: ₽ (100yds) (charge May-Oct, max. 2hrs stay) ᵹ toilets for disabled shop ✵ (ex guide dogs)

⌂ GAIRLOCH Map 14 NG87
GAIRLOCH HERITAGE MUSEUM
Auchtercairn IV21 2BP (on junct of A382 & B8021. Nr police station & public car park)
☎ 01445 712287
e-mail: jf@gairlochheritagemuseum.org.uk

A converted farmstead now houses the award-winning museum, which shows the way of life in this typical West Highland parish from early times to the 20th century. There are hands-on activities for children and reconstructions of a croft house room, a school room, a shop, and a smugglers' cave. You can also view Gairloch through one of the largest lenses assembled by the Northern Lighthouse Board.
Times: Open Apr-Sep, Mon-Sat 10-5; Oct, Mon-Fri 10-1.30 **Fee:** £2.50 (ch 50p & pen £2). Group 10+ £ 1.50 **Facilities:** ₽ ₩ ✕ licensed ᵹ shop ✵ (ex guide dogs)

⌂ GLENCOE Map 14 NN15
GLENCOE & NORTH LORN FOLK MUSEUM
PH49 4HS (turn off A82 at Glencoe crossroads then immediately L again into Glencoe Village)
☎ 01855 811664

Two heather-thatched cottages in the main street of Glencoe now house items connected with the Macdonalds and the Jacobite risings. A variety of local domestic and farming exhibits, dairy and slate-working equipment, costumes and embroidery is also shown.
Times: Open mid May-Sep, Mon-Sat 10-5.30. **Fee:** £2 (ch free, concessions £1.50). **Facilities:** ₽ ᵹ shop

GLENCOE VISITOR CENTRE
PA39 4HX (on A82, 17m S of Fort William)
☎ 01855 811307 & 811729 🖷 01855 811772

Glencoe has stunning scenery and some of the most challenging climbs and walks in the Highlands. Red deer, wildcats, eagles and ptarmigan are among the wildlife. It is, however, also forever known as a place of treachery and infamy. The Macdonalds of Glencoe were hosts to a party of troops who, under English orders, fell upon them, men, women and children, in a bloody massacre in 1692. The Visitor Centre tells the story.
Times: Open - Site all year, daily. Visitor Centre May-Aug, daily 9.30-5.30; Mar-Apr & Sep-Oct, daily 10-5; (last admission 30 mins before closing). **Facilities:** ₽ ₩ ᵹ (induction loop in video programme room) toilets for disabled shop ✵ (ex guide dogs) ₩ *Details not confirmed for 2002*

HIGHLAND MYSTERYWORLD
PA39 4HL (on A82, 10m S of Fort William)
☎ 01855 811660 🖷 01855 821463
e-mail: monster@mysteryworld.co.uk
Times: Open Etr-Oct, daily, 10-5 (last entry 4.30). **Facilities:** ₽ ₩ ✕ licensed ᵹ toilets for disabled shop (ex guide dogs) *Details not confirmed for 2002* ◥

GLENFINNAN   Map 14 NM98
GLENFINNAN MONUMENT
PH37 4LT (on A830, 18.5m W of Fort William)
☎ 01397 722250

The monument commemorates Highlanders who fought for Bonnie Prince Charlie in 1745. It stands in an awe-inspiring setting at the head of Loch Shiel. There is a visitor centre with information (commentary in four languages) on the Prince's campaign.
Times: Open - Site all year. Visitor Centre, Apr-18 May & Sep-Oct, daily 10-5; 19 May-Aug, daily 9.30-6. **Facilities:** ☒ ☕ ఉ (information centre only) shop ⚑ *Details not confirmed for 2002*

GOLSPIE   Map 14 NH89
DUNROBIN CASTLE
KW10 6SF (1m NE on A9, from Golspie)
☎ 01408 633177 & 633268 🖹 01408 633800

The ancient seat of the Earls and Dukes of Sutherland is a splendid, gleaming, turreted structure, thanks largely to 19th-century rebuilding, and has a beautiful setting overlooking the sea. Paintings, furniture and family heirlooms are on display, and the gardens are on a grand scale to match the house.
Times: Open 1Apr-15 Oct, Mon-Sat 10.30-5.30, Sun 12-5.30. Closes 1 hr earlier Apr, May & Oct. Last admission half hour before closing.
Fee: £6 (ch & pen £5.50). Family ticket £17. Party. **Facilities:** ☒ ☕ ఉ (access by arrangement only) shop ✹

HELMSDALE   Map 14 ND01
TIMESPAN
Dunrobin St KW8 6JX (off A9 in centre of village, by Telford Bridge)
☎ 01431 821327 🖹 01431 821058
e-mail: admin@timespan.org.uk

Located in a historic fishing village, this museum relates to the social and natural history of the area, and the art gallery has changing exhibitions of contemporary art and works by local artists. The garden has over 100 varieties of herbs and plants. There is a gift shop, and a café with beautiful views of Telford Bridge.
Times: Open Apr-Oct, Mon-Sat 9.30-5, Sun 2-5. Last admission to museum 4pm. **Fee:** £3.50 (ch £1.75 pen & student £2.80). Family ticket £8.75. **Facilities:** ☒ ☕ ఉ (lifts) toilets for disabled shop garden centre ✹ (ex guide dogs) ⚑

KINCRAIG   Map 14 NH80
HIGHLAND WILDLIFE PARK
PH21 1NL (on B9152, 7m S of Aviemore)
☎ 01540 651270 🖹 01540 651236
e-mail: wildlife@rzss.org.uk

Times: Open throughout the year, weather permitting. Apr-Oct, 10-6; Jun-Aug 10-7; Nov-Mar 10-4. last entry 2 hours before closing.
Facilities: ☒ ☕ ఉ toilets for disabled shop ✹ *Details not confirmed for 2002* ⚑

KINGUSSIE   Map 14 NH70
HIGHLAND FOLK MUSEUM
Duke St PH21 1JG (12m SW of Aviemore off A9 at Kingussie)
☎ 01540 661307 🖹 01540 661631
e-mail: highland.folk@highland.gov.uk

Established on Iona in 1935 this was Britain's first open air museum. It is an extensive collection of everyday domestic objects together with major exhibits providing an insight into the social history of the Highland people. Visitors will see domestic and agricultural items and trade and craft tools.
Times: Open Apr-29 Sep, Mon-Sat 9.30-5.30, Oct-Mar guided tours Mon-Fri, check for details. **Fee:** £1 (ch & pen 50p). **Facilities:** ☒ ఉ toilets for disabled shop ✹ (ex guide dogs) ⚑

RUTHVEN BARRACKS
(0.5m SE of Kingussie)
☎ 0131 668 8800
Times: Open at any reasonable time. **Facilities:** ☒ ✹ ▮ *Details not confirmed for 2002*

KIRKHILL   Map 14 NH54
MONIACK CASTLE (HIGHLAND WINERY)
IV5 7PQ (7m from Inverness on A862, near village of Beauly, on S side of Beauly Firth)
☎ 01463 831283 🖹 01463 831419
Times: Open all year, Mon-Sat 10-5. (11-4 in winter). **Facilities:** ☒ shop ✹ *Details not confirmed for 2002* ⚑

Highland – Inverclyde

NEWTONMORE Map 14 NN79
CLAN MACPHERSON HOUSE & MUSEUM
Main St PH20 1DE
☎ 01540 673332
Times: Open May-Oct, Mon-Sat 10-5.30, Sun 2.30-5.30. Other times by appointment. **Facilities:** 🅿 & toilets for disabled shop 🐾 *Details not confirmed for 2002*

HIGHLAND FOLK MUSEUM
Aultlarie Croft PH20 1AY (on A86, follow signs off A9)
☎ 01540 661307 ᐧ 01540 661631
e-mail: highland.folk@highland.gov.uk

An early 18th-century farming township has been reconstructed at this award-winning 85-acre museum. The turf houses are furnished with items made using traditional methods, which are demonstrated along with dance, song and buttermaking. The museum also contains a Victorian water-powered sawmill, clockmaker's workshop, and vintage transport.
Times: Open Apr-Aug, Mon-Sun 10.30-5.30; Sep-Oct , Mon-Fri 11-4.30 **Fee:** £5 (ch & pen £3) **Facilities:** 🅿 💺 & (vintage bus with full disabled access) toilets for disabled shop 🐾 (ex guide dogs) 🐟

POOLEWE Map 14 NG88
INVEREWE GARDEN
IV22 2LG (6m NE of Gairloch, on A832)
☎ 01445 781200 ᐧ 01445 781497
e-mail: aclipson@nts.scot.demon.co.uk

The influence of the North Atlantic Drift enables this remarkable garden to grow rare and sub-tropical plants. At its best in early June, but full of beauty from March to October, Inverewe has a backdrop of magnificent mountains and stands to the north of Loch Maree.
Times: Open - Garden all year, mid Mar-Oct, daily 9.30-9. Nov-mid Mar 9.30-5. Visitor Centre mid Mar-Oct, daily 9.30-5.30. Guided walks mid Apr-mid Sep Mon-Fri at 1.30. **Facilities:** 🅿 ✕ licensed & (some paths difficult) toilets for disabled shop 🐾 (ex guide dogs) 💺 *Details not confirmed for 2002*

STRATHPEFFER Map 14 NH45
HIGHLAND MUSEUM OF CHILDHOOD
The Old Station IV14 9DH (take A9 N of Inverness, at Tore rdbt, follow signs to Dingwall. Strathpeffer 5m W of Dingwell on A834)
☎ 01997 421031 ᐧ 01997 421031
e-mail: info@hmoc.freeserve.co.uk

Located in a renovated Victorian railway station of 1885, the museum tells the story of childhood in the Highlands amongst the crofters and townsfolk; a way of life recorded in oral testimony, displays, and evocative photographs. An award-winning video, "A Century of Highland Childhood" is shown. There are also doll and toy collections.
Times: Open Apr-Oct, daily 10-5, (Sun 2-5) also Jul & Aug evenings open to 7pm. Other times by arrangement. **Fee:** £1.50 (ch, pen & students £1). Family ticket £3.50 (2 adults & 3 children). **Facilities:** 🅿 💺 & tape tour with induction loop for partially sighted shop 🐾 (ex guide dogs) 🐟

TORRIDON Map 14 NG85
TORRIDON COUNTRYSIDE CENTRE
The Mains IV22 2EZ (N of A896)
☎ 01445 791221 ᐧ 01445 791378
e-mail: aclipson@nts.scoy.demon.co.uk.

Set amid some of Scotland's finest mountain scenery, the centre offers audio-visual presentations on the local wildlife. At the Mains nearby there are deer to be seen.
Times: Open - Countryside Centre May-Sep, Mon-Sat 10-5, Sun 2-5. Estate and Deer Museum daily all year. **Facilities:** 🅿 & toilets for disabled 💺 *Details not confirmed for 2002*

WICK Map 15 ND34
CAITHNESS GLASS FACTORY & VISITOR CENTRE
Airport Industrial Estate KW1 5BP (on N side of Wick, beside Airport on A99 towards John O'Groats)
☎ 01955 602286 ᐧ 01955 605200
Times: Open all year, Factory shop & Restaurant Mon-Sat 9-5 (Sun, Etr-Dec 11-5). Glassmaking Mon-Fri 9-4.30. **Facilities:** 🅿 ✕ licensed & toilets for disabled shop 🐾 *Details not confirmed for 2002* 🐟

CASTLE OF OLD WICK
(1m S)
☎ 0131 668 8800 ᐧ 0131 668 8888
Times: Open except when adjoining rifle range is in use.
Facilities: 🐾 🚩 *Details not confirmed for 2002*

WICK HERITAGE CENTRE
20 Bank Row KW1 5HS (close to the harbour)
☎ 01955 605393 ᐧ 01955 605393

The heritage centre is near the harbour in a complex of eight houses, yards and outbuildings. The centre illustrates local history from Neolithic times to the herring fishing industry. In addition, there is a working 19th-century lighthouse, and the famous Johnston collection of photographs.
Times: Open Jun-Sep, Mon-Sat 10-5. (Closed Sun). **Fee:** £2 (ch 50p).
Facilities: 🅿 & toilets for disabled

INVERCLYDE

GREENOCK Map 10 NS27
McLEAN MUSEUM & ART GALLERY
15 Kelly St PA16 8JX (close to Greenock West Railway Station)
☎ 01475 715624 ᐧ 01475 715626

James Watt was born in Greenock, and various exhibits connected with him are shown. The museum also has an art collection, and displays on shipping, local and
contd.

natural history, Egyptology and ethnography.
Temporary exhibition gallery.

McLean Museum & Art Gallery

Times: Open all year, Mon-Sat 10-5. (Closed local & national PH).
Fee: Free. **Facilities:** P (200mtrs) & (induction loop) toilets for disabled shop ✱ (ex guide & service dogs)

⚏ PORT GLASGOW   Map 10 NS37
NEWARK CASTLE
PA14 5NH (on A8)
☎ 01475 741858

The one-time house of the Maxwells, dating from the 15th and 17th centuries. The courtyard and hall are preserved. Fine turrets and the remains of painted ceilings can be seen, and the hall carries an inscription of 1597.
Times: Open Apr-Sep, daily 9.30-6.30. **Fee:** £2 (ch 75p, concessions £1.50). **Facilities:** P shop ∎

MIDLOTHIAN

⚏ CRICHTON   Map 11 NT36
CRICHTON CASTLE
EH37 5QH (2.5m SW of Pathhead, off A68)
☎ 01875 320017

The castle dates back to the 14th century, but most of what remains today was built over the following 300 years. A notable feature is the 16th-century wing built by the Earl of Bothwell in Italian style, with an arcade below.
Times: Open Apr-Sep, daily 9.30-6.30. **Fee:** £1.80 (ch 75p, concessions £1.30). **Facilities:** P ∎

⚏ DALKEITH   Map 11 NT36
EDINBURGH BUTTERFLY & INSECT WORLD
Dobbies Garden World, Lasswade EH18 1AZ (0.5m S of Edinburgh City bypass at Gilmerton junct)
☎ 0131 663 4932   ▤ 0131 654 2774
e-mail: ebiw@compuserve.com

Richly coloured butterflies from all over the world can be seen flying among exotic rainforest plants, trees and flowers. The tropical pools are filled with giant waterlilies and colourful fish, and are surrounded by lush vegetation. Also scorpions, leaf cutting ants, beetles, tarantulas and other remarkable creatures. There is a unique honeybee display and daily insect handling sessions.
Times: Open Summer daily 9.30-5.30; winter daily 10-5. (Closed 25-26 Dec & 1-2 Jan). **Fee:** £4.25 (ch, concessions & students £3.25). Family ticket £13 (2 adults & 2 ch). Party 10+. **Facilities:** P ▣ & toilets for disabled shop garden centre ✱ (ex guide dogs) ◥

⚏ NEWTONGRANGE   Map 11 NT36
SCOTTISH MINING MUSEUM
Lady Victoria Colliery EH22 4QN (10m S of Edinburgh City on A7, signposted from Edinburgh City bypass)
☎ 0131 663 7519   ▤ 0131 654 1618
e-mail: enquiries@scottishminingmuseum.com

Britains' finest Victorian colliery. Guided tours with miners, magic helmets, exhibitions, theatres, interactive displays and a visit to the coal face all feature. Home to Scotland's largest steam engine.
Times: Open all year, daily 10-5. **Fee:** £4 (ch & concessions £2.20). Family ticket £10. Party 20+. **Facilities:** P ▣ & toilets for disabled shop ✱ (ex guide dogs) ◥

⚏ PENICUIK   Map 11 NT26
'THE GLASSHOUSE' AT EDINBURGH CRYSTAL
Eastfield EH26 8HB (on A701 towards Peebles)
☎ 01968 675128   ▤ 01968 674847
e-mail: visitorcentre@edinburgh-crystal.co.uk

Watch skilled craftsmen as they take molten crystal and turn it into intricately decorated glassware. Not only can you talk to the craftsmen themselves but there is video footage, story boards, artefacts and audio listening posts to help you understand the history of glassmaking. The shop includes the largest selection of Edinburgh crystal plus seconds at bargain prices.
Times: Open Mon-Sat 10-5, Sun 11-5. **Fee:** Tours £3 (concessions £2). Family ticket £7.50. Party 12+. **Facilities:** P ▣ & (ramp to first floor) toilets for disabled shop ✱ (ex guide dogs) ◥

MORAY

⚏ BALLINDALLOCH   Map 15 NJ13
THE GLENLIVET DISTILLERY
AB37 9DB (off B9008 10m N of Tomintoul)
☎ 01542 783220   ▤ 01542 783218
e-mail: linda_brown@seagram.com

The visitor centre includes a guided tour of the whisky production facilities and a chance to see inside the vast bonded warehouses where the spirit matures. The new multimedia exhibition and interactive presentations communicate the unique history and traditions of Glenlivet Scotch Whisky.
Times: Open: Apr-Oct, Mon-Sat 10-4, Sun 12.30-4. **Fee:** £3 for over 18's which includes minimum £2 voucher redeemable in distillery shop against the purchase of a 70cl bottle of whisky. This charge covers entry to exhibition, guided tour of Distillery & a free dram of whisky. (ch18 free, under 8's not admitted to production areas) **Facilities:** P ▣ & toilets for disabled shop ✱ (ex guide dogs) ◥

🏛 BRODIE CASTLE   Map 14 NH95
BRODIE CASTLE
IV36 2TE (4.5m W of Forres, off A96)
☎ 01309 641371   🖨 01309 641600

The Brodie family lived here for hundreds of years before passing the castle to the NTS in 1980. It contains many treasures, including furniture, porcelain and paintings. The extensive grounds include a woodland walk and an adventure playground. Wheelchairs for disabled visitors are available. Please telephone for details of recitals, concerts, open air theatre etc. **Times:** Open Apr-Sep, Mon-Sat 11-5.30, Sun 1.30-5.30; wknds in Oct, Sat 11-5.30, Sun 1.30-5.30 (last admission 4.30). Grounds open all year, 9.30-sunset. Other times by appointment. **Facilities:** 🅿 ☕ �&. (audio tape & information sheet in Braille) toilets for disabled shop 🎫 (ex guide dogs) ☕ *Details not confirmed for 2002*

🏛 BUCKIE   Map 15 NJ46
BUCKIE DRIFTER MARITIME HERITAGE CENTRE
Freuchny Rd AB56 1TT (1m off A98 between Elgin and Fraserburgh, signposted)
☎ 01542 834646   🖨 01542 835995

Times: Open Apr-Oct, Mon-Sat 10-5, Sun 12-5. **Facilities:** 🅿 ✗ licensed ⅙ (car parking, touch display on lower floor) toilets for disabled shop 🎫 (ex guide dogs) *Details not confirmed for 2002*

🏛 CRAIGELLACHIE   Map 15 NJ24
SPEYSIDE COOPERAGE VISITOR CENTRE
Dufftown Rd AB38 9RS (1m S of Craigellachie on A941)
☎ 01340 871108   🖨 01340 881437
e-mail: info@speyside-coopers.demon.co.uk

A working cooperage with unique visitor centre, where skilled coopers and their apprentices practise this ancient craft. Each year they repair around 100,000 oak casks which will be used to mature many different whiskies. The 'Acorn to Cask' exhibition traces the history and development of the coopering industry. **Times:** Open all year, Mon-Fri 9.30-4.30. (Closed Xmas & New Year). **Fee:** £2.95 (ch £1.75 & pen £2.45). Family ticket £7.95. Party 15+. **Facilities:** 🅿 ☕ ⅙ (Special picnic table) toilets for disabled shop 🎫 (ex guide dogs) ☕

🏛 DUFFTOWN   Map 15 NJ34
BALVENIE CASTLE
AB55 4DH (on A941)
☎ 01340 820121

The ruined castle was the ancient stronghold of the Comyns, and became a stylish house in the 16th century. **Times:** Open Apr-Sep, daily 9.30-6.30. **Fee:** £1.20 (ch 50p, concessions 90p). **Facilities:** 🅿 ⅙ toilets for disabled 🎫

GLENFIDDICH DISTILLERY
AB55 4DH (N of town, off A941)
☎ 01340 820373   🖨 01340 822083
Times: Open all year Mon-Fri 9.30-4.30, also Etr-mid Oct Sat 9.30-4.30, Sun 12-4.30. (Closed Xmas & New Year). **Facilities:** 🅿 ⅙ (ramp access to production area & warehouse gallery) toilets for disabled shop 🎫 (ex guide dogs) *Details not confirmed for 2002*

🏛 DUFFUS   Map 15 NJ16
DUFFUS CASTLE
(off B9012)
☎ 0131 668 8800
Times: Open at all reasonable times. **Facilities:** 🅿 🎫 🎫 *Details not confirmed for 2002*

🏛 ELGIN   Map 15 NJ26
ELGIN CATHEDRAL
North College St IV30 1EL
☎ 01343 547171

Founded in 1224, the cathedral was known as the Lantern of the North and the Glory of the Kingdom because of its beauty. In 1390 it was burnt down, along with most of the town. Although it was rebuilt, it fell into ruin after the Reformation. The ruins are quite substantial, however, and there is still a good deal to admire, including the fine west towers and the octagonal chapter house. **Times:** Open all year, Apr-Sep, daily 9.30-6.30; Oct-Mar, Mon-Sat 9.30-4.30, Sun 2-4.30. (Closed Thu pm, Fri in winter & 25-26 Dec). **Fee:** £2.50 (ch £1, concessions £1.90). **Facilities:** 🅿 ⅙ shop 🎫

ELGIN MUSEUM
1 High St IV30 1EQ (east end of High Street, opposite 'Safeway'. Follow brown signs)
☎ 01343 543675   🖨 01343 543675
e-mail: curator@elginmuseum.org.uk

This award-winning museum is internationally famous for its fossil fish and fossil reptiles, and for its Pictish stones. The displays relate to the natural and human history of Moray. **Times:** Open Apr-Oct, Mon-Fri 10-5, Sat 11-4, Sun 2-5. **Fee:** £2 (ch 50p, pen, students & UB40 £1). Family ticket £4.50. **Facilities:** 🅿 (50mtrs) ⅙ (handrails inside & out. All case displays at sitting level) toilets for disabled shop 🎫 (ex guide dogs)

Pluscarden Abbey
IV30 8UA (6m SW on unclass road)
☎ 01343 890257 📠 01343 890258

The original monastery, founded by Alexander II in 1230, was burnt down, probably by the Wolf of Badenoch who also destroyed Elgin Cathedral. It was restored in the 14th and 19th centuries, and reoccupied in 1948 by Benedictines from Prinknash. Once more a religious community, retreat facilities are available for men and women. All services (with Gregorian chant) are open to the public.
Times: Open all year, daily 4.45-8.30pm. **Fee:** Free. **Facilities:** P ♿ (induction loop, ramps to shop) toilets for disabled shop garden centre 💳

FOCHABERS — Map 15 NJ35

Baxters Highland Village
IV32 7LD (1m W of Fochabers on A96)
☎ 01343 820666 📠 01343 821790
e-mail: highland.village@Baxters.co.uk

The Baxters food firm started here over 130 years ago and now sells its products in over 60 countries. Visitors can see the shop where the story began, watch an audio-visual display, and visit four shops. See the great hall, audio-visual theatre, cooking theatre and food tasting area.
Times: Open all year, Jan-Mar 10-5, Apr-Dec 9-5.30. **Fee:** Free. **Facilities:** P ✕ licensed ♿ (parking facilities) toilets for disabled shop 🐕 (ex guide dogs) 💳

Fochabers Folk Museum
High St IV32 7EP
☎ 01343 821204 📠 01343 821291
Times: Open May-Sep 10.30-4. **Facilities:** P ♿ shop 🐕 *Details not confirmed for 2002*

FORRES — Map 15 NJ05

Dallas Dhu Distillery
IV36 2RR (1m S of Forres, off A940)
☎ 01309 676548

A perfectly preserved time capsule of the distiller's art. It was built in 1898 to supply malt whisky for Wright and Greig's 'Roderick Dhu' blend. Visitors are welcome to wander at will through this fine old Victorian distillery, or to take a guided tour, dram included.
Times: Open all year, Apr-Sep, daily 9.30-6.30; Oct-Mar, Mon-Sat 9.30-4.30, Sun 2-4.30. (Closed Thu pm, Fri in winter & 25-26 Dec). **Fee:** £3 (ch £1, concessions £2.30). **Facilities:** P ♿ toilets for disabled shop 🐕 🔖

Falconer Museum
Tolbooth St IV36 1PH (on A96)
☎ 01309 673701 📠 01309 675863
e-mail: museums@moray.gov.uk

Founded by bequests made by two brothers, Alexander and Hugh Falconer. Hugh was a distinguished scientist, friend of Darwin, recipient of many honours and Vice-President of the Royal Society. On display are fossil mammals collected by him, and items relating to his involvement in the antiquity of mankind. Other displays are on local wildlife, geology, archaeology and history. Also you can see the Forres Quincentennial Time Capsule.
Times: Open all year - Apr-Oct, Mon-Sat 10-5; Nov-Mar, Mon-Thu 11-12.30 & 1-3.30. (Closed Good Fri & May Day). **Fee:** Free. **Facilities:** P (on premises now) ♿ (induction loop system) shop 🐕 (ex guide dogs)

Suenos' Stone
☎ 0131 668 8800
Times: Open - accessible at all times. **Facilities:** P 🐕 🔖 *Details not confirmed for 2002*

KEITH — Map 15 NJ45

Strathisla Distillery
Seafield Av AB55 5BS (follow A96 Aberdeen to Inverness road, Strathisla is signposted in the town)
☎ 01542 783044 📠 01542 783039
e-mail: jeanett_grant@seagram.com

Tour the oldest distillery in the highlands, founded in 1786. Discover the art of the blender before sipping a dram in luxurious comfort.
Times: Open 1Apr-End Oct, Mon-Sat 10-4, Sun 12.30-4 **Fee:** £4 including £2 voucher redeemable in the distillery shop against the purchase of 70cl bottle of whisky. (ch18 free, children under 8 are not admitted to production areas, but are welcome in the centre) **Facilities:** P (access is very limited) shop 🐕 (ex guide dogs) 💳

MARYPARK — Map 15 NJ13

Glenfarclas Distillery
AB37 9BD (4m W of Aberlour on A95 to Grantown-on-Spey)
☎ 01807 500245 & 500257 📠 01807 500234
e-mail: J&GGrant@glenfarclas.demon.co.uk

Established in 1836 Glenfarclas Distillery is proud of its independence. There is a guided tour illustrating the whisky's history and production, followed by a dram in the splendour of the Ships Room or a chance to browse in the gift shop.
Times: Open Jan-Mar, Mon-Fri 10-4, Apr-Sep, Mon-Fri 10-5 & Jul-Sep, also Sat 10-5, Oct-Dec, Mon-Fri 10-4. (Closed Sun). **Fee:** £3.50 per adult. Free admission to under 18's.Party. **Facilities:** P ♿ (only visitor centre is accessible) toilets for disabled shop 🐕 (ex guide dogs in vis. centre) 💳

ᗗ ROTHES
Map 15 NJ24
GLEN GRANT DISTILLERY
AB38 7BS (on A941, in Rothes)
☎ 01542 783318 & 783303 ☝ 01542 783304
e-mail: jennifer_robertson@seagram.com

Founded in 1840 in a sheltered glen by the two Grant brothers. Discover the secrets of the distillery, and enjoy a dram in the delightful Victorian garden originally created by Major Grant and now restored to its former glory.
Times: Open Apr-Oct, Mon-Sat 10-4, Sun 12.30-4. **Fee:** £3 includes minimum £2 voucher redeemable in the distillery shop against 70cl bottle of whisky. Inclusive charge for garden visit & distillery tour. A free dram is offered to over 18s. (ch18 free, children under 8 not admitted to production areas, but are welcome in centre & garden) **Facilities:** ᗜ ᔑ (reception centre & still house) toilets for disabled shop ⁺⁺ (ex guide dogs) ◥

ᗗ SPEY BAY
Map 15 NJ36
TUGNET ICE HOUSE
Tugnet IV32 7PJ (8m E of Elgin on A96, then onto B9104 towards Spey Bay, establishment in 1m)
☎ 01309 673701 ☝ 01309 675863
e-mail: museums@moray.gov.uk

The largest ice house in Scotland, built in 1830.
Times: Please phone for details. **Fee:** Free. **Facilities:** ᗜ ⁺⁺ (ex guide dogs)

ᗗ TOMINTOUL
Map 15 NJ11
TOMINTOUL MUSEUM
The Square AB37 9ET (on A939, 13m E of Grantown)
☎ 01309 673701 ☝ 01309 675863
e-mail: museums@moray.gov.uk

Situated in one of the highest villages in Britain, the museum features a reconstructed crofter's kitchen and smiddy, with other displays on the local wildlife, the story of Tomintoul, and the local skiing industry.
Times: Open Apr, May & Oct Mon-Fri 9.45-12 & 2-4, 2 Jun-Aug Mon-Sat 9.30-12 & 2-4, 1-29 Sep Mon-Sat 9.45-12 & 2-4. (Closed Good Fri & May Day). **Fee:** Free. **Facilities:** ᗜ ᔑ (handling display for visually impaired) shop ⁺⁺ (ex guide dogs)

NORTH AYRSHIRE

ᗗ HUNTERSTON
Map 10 NS15
HUNTERSTON POWER STATION
KA23 9QJ (off A78, S of Largs)
☎ 0800 838557 ☝ 01294 826008
Times: Open - Mar-Sep, daily, 9.30-4.30; Oct-Feb, Mon-Fri 9.30-4.30, Sat & Sun 1-4.30. Tours - Mar-Sep 10.30, 1.30 & 3.30; Oct-Feb 1.30 & 3.30 (Closed 10 Dec-10 Jan). **Facilities:** ᗜ ᔑ (trained guides for visually impaired visitors) toilets for disabled shop ⁺⁺ (ex guide dogs)
Details not confirmed for 2002

ᗗ IRVINE
Map 10 NS34
THE BIG IDEA
The Harbourside KA12 8XX (follow tourist signs)
☎ 08708 404030 ☝ 08708 403130
e-mail: net@bigidea.org.uk
Times: Open all year, daily 10-6. (Closed 25 Dec & 1 Jan). **Facilities:** ᗜ ⁓ ᔑ toilets for disabled shop ⁺⁺ (ex guide dogs)
Details not confirmed for 2002 ◥

SCOTTISH MARITIME MUSEUM
Harbourside KA12 8QE (Follow AA signs from Irvine)
☎ 01294 278283 ☝ 01294 313211

The museum has displays which reflect all aspects of Scottish maritime history. Vessels can be seen afloat in the harbour and undercover. Experience life in a 1910 shipyard worker's tenement flat. Visit the Linthouse Engine Shop, which was originally built in 1872, is being developed and holds a substantial part of the museum's collection in open store.
Times: Open all year, daily 10-5, (ex Xmas & New Year). **Fee:** £2.50 (ch & pen £1.75). Family ticket £5. **Facilities:** ᗜ ⁓ ᔑ (audio tapes for blind) toilets for disabled shop ⁺⁺ (ex guide dogs)

VENNEL GALLERY
10 Glasgow Vennel KA12 0BD
☎ 01294 275059 ☝ 01294 275059
e-mail: vennel@globalnet.co.uk

The Vennel Gallery has a reputation for exciting and varied exhibitions, ranging from international to local artists. Behind the museum is the Heckling Shop where Robert Burns, Scotland's most famous poet, spent part of his youth learning the trade of flax dressing. In addition to the audio-visual programme on Burns, there is a reconstruction of his lodgings at No.4 Glasgow Vennel.
Times: Open all year Mon-Sat 10-5. (Closed Wed). **Fee:** Free. **Facilities:** ᗜ (residential area) ᔑ shop ⁺⁺ (ex guide dogs)

ᗗ LARGS
Map 10 NS25
KELBURN CASTLE AND COUNTRY CENTRE
Fairlie KA29 0BE (on A78 2m S of Largs)
☎ 01475 568685 ☝ 01475 568121
e-mail: admin@kelburncountrycentre.com
Times: Open all year, Apr-Oct, daily 10-6; Nov-Mar, 11-5. **Facilities:** ᗜ ⁓ ⁎ licensed ᔑ (Ranger service to assist disabled) toilets for disabled shop *Details not confirmed for 2002* ◥

VIKINGAR!
Greenock Rd KA30 8QL (opposite RNLI lifeboat station on A78, 0.5m into Largs)
☎ 01475 689777 ☝ 01475 689444
e-mail: anyone@vikingar.co.uk

A multi-media experience that takes you from the first Viking raids in Scotland to their defeat at the Battle of
contd.

Largs. Additional facilities include a swimming pool, a 500-seat theatre and cinema, café and theatre bar.
Times: Open daily, Apr-Sep, Mon-Fri & Sun 10.30-5.30, Sat 12.30-3.30. Oct-Mar, Mon-Fri & Sun 10.30-3.30, Sat 10.30-3.30, Nov/Feb, Wkends only, Sat 12.30-3.30, Sun 10.30-3.30. (Closed Dec/Jan). **Fee:** £3.80 (ch 4-15 £2.90). Family ticket £10.50 (2 adults + 2 ch / 1 adult + 3 ch)
Facilities: 🅿 💺 ♿ toilets for disabled shop 🦮 (ex guide dogs) ☜

🏛 SALTCOATS　　　　　　Map 10 NS24
NORTH AYRSHIRE MUSEUM
Manse St, Kirkgate KA21 5AA
☎ 01294 464174　📠 01294 464174
e-mail: namuseum@globalnet.co.uk

This museum is housed in an 18th-century church, and features a rich variety of artefacts from the North Ayrshire area, including archaeological and social history material. There is a continuing programme of temporary exhibitions.
Times: Open all year, Mon-Sat (ex Wed) 10-1 & 2-5. **Fee:** Free.
Facilities: 🅿 (100 mtrs) ♿ toilets for disabled shop 🦮 (ex guide dogs)

NORTH LANARKSHIRE

🏛 COATBRIDGE　　　　　　Map 11 NS76
SUMMERLEE HERITAGE TRUST
Heritage Way, West Canal St ML5 1QD (in town centre, adjacent to Coatbridge central station)
☎ 01236 431261　📠 01236 440429

A 20-acre museum of social and industrial history centring on the remains of the Summerlee Ironworks which were put into blast in the 1830s. The exhibition hall features displays of social and industrial history including working machinery and recreated workshop interiors. Outside, Summerlee operates the only working tram in Scotland, a coal mine and reconstructed miners' rows with interiors dating from 1840.
Times: Open daily 10-5. (Closed 25-26 Dec & 1-2 Jan). Nov-Mar 10-4.
Fee: Free. **Facilities:** 🅿 💺 ♿ (wheelchair available & staff assistance) toilets for disabled shop 🦮 (ex guide dogs)

🏛 MOTHERWELL　　　　　　Map 11 NS75
MOTHERWELL HERITAGE CENTRE
High Rd ML1 3HU (M74 junct 6, A723 for town centre. At top of hill, turn left, before railway bridge)
☎ 01698 251000　📠 01698 268867
Times: Open daily 10-5, Sun noon-5. (Closed Xmas/New Year).
Facilities: 🅿 ♿ toilets for disabled shop 🦮 (ex guide dogs) *Details not confirmed for 2002*

PERTH & KINROSS

🏛 ABERFELDY　　　　　　Map 14 NN84
DEWAR'S WORLD OF WHISKY
Aberfeldy Distillery PH15 2EB (from A9 turn off for Aberfeldy on A827 at Ballinluig)
☎ 01887 822010　📠 01887 822012
e-mail: enquiries@DewarsWorldofWhisky

Tradition and the latest technology are combined here to tell the story of Dewar's White Label Whisky. Visitors are able to sample the product in the Nosing and Tasting Bar, and have a guided tour of the Aberfeldy distillery, where they can see traditional techniques being employed by skilled craftsmen.
Times: Open Apr-Oct, Mon-Sun 10-6, Sun noon-4; Nov-Mar, Mon-Fri 10-4. (Closed Xmas & New Year). **Fee:** £3.95 (ch £2.50, concession £3). Family ticket £10. Party by arrangement. **Facilities:** 🅿 💺 ♿ (visitor centre only accessible) toilets for disabled shop 🦮 (ex guide dogs) ☜

🏛 BLAIR ATHOLL　　　　　　Map 14 NN86
BLAIR CASTLE
PH18 5TL (7m NW of Pitlochry, off A9)
☎ 01796 481207　📠 01796 481487
e-mail: office@blair-castle.co.uk

Home of the Dukes of Atholl and the Atholl Highlanders, the Duke's unique private army. The castle dates back to the 13th century but was altered in the 18th, and later given a castellated exterior. The oldest part is Cumming's Tower, built in about 1270. There are paintings, Jacobite relics, lace, tapestries, and Masonic regalia. The extensive grounds include a deer park, and a restored 18th-century walled garden and children's play area. Events are held throughout the year, including the annual parade of the Duke's Private Army (ring for details).
Times: Open Apr-25 Oct, daily 10-6. Last admission 5pm. **Fee:** £6.25 (ch £4, stu £5, disabled £2, pen £5.25). Family ticket £18. Party.
Facilities: 🅿 💺 ✗ licensed ♿ (toilets- not suitable for severely disabled, parking) shop ☜

🏛 BRUAR　　　　　　Map 14 NN86
CLAN DONNACHAIDH (ROBERTSON) MUSEUM
PH18 5TW (approx 4m N of Blair Atholl, on B8079)
☎ 01796 483264　📠 01796 483338
e-mail: donkey3@freenetname.co.uk
Times: Open Apr-Oct, Mon-Sat 10-5, Sun 11-5 (Jun-Aug closes at 5.30).
Facilities: 🅿 ♿ shop 🦮 (ex guide dogs) *Details not confirmed for 2002*

🏛 CRIEFF　　　　　　Map 11 NN82
GLENTURRET DISTILLERY
The Hosh PH7 4HA (1.5m NW off A85)
☎ 01764 656565　📠 01764 654366
e-mail: glenturret@highlanddistillers.co.uk

The distillery dates from 1775 and is the oldest in Scotland.
Times: Open Feb-Dec, Mon-Sat 9.30-6 (last tour 4.30), Sun 12-6 (last tour 4.30); Jan, Mon-Fri 11.30-4 (last tour 2.30). (Closed 25-26 Dec & 1-2 Jan) **Fee:** Guided tours and Audio visual exhibition £3.50 (ch 12-17 £2.30 ch under 12 free). **Facilities:** 🅿 ✗ licensed ♿ toilets for disabled shop 🦮

INNERPEFFRAY LIBRARY

PH7 3RF (4.5m SE on B8062)
☎ 01764 652819
e-mail: library@innerpeff.fsnet.co.uk

This is Scotland's oldest free lending library. It was founded in 1680 and is still open every day except Thursdays. It is housed in a late 18th-century building, and contains a notable collection of bibles and rare books. Adjacent is St Mary's Chapel, the original site for the library.

Times: Open all year, Mon-Wed & Fri-Sat 10-12.45 & 2-4.45, Sun 2-4. (Closed Thu). **Fee:** £2.50 (ch u15 50p) **Facilities:** ⊡ ☞ ⋏

⛫ DUNKELD   Map 11 NO04
THE ELL SHOP & LITTLE HOUSES
The Cross PH8 0AN (off A9, 15m N of Perth)
☎ 01350 727460

The National Trust owns two rows of 20 houses in Dunkeld, and has preserved their 17th/18th-century character. They are not open to the public, but there is a display and audio-visual show in the Information Centre.

Times: Open Ell Shop Jun-Aug, Mon-Sat 10-5.30, Sun 1.30-5.30; Apr-May & Sep, Mon-Sat 10-5.30; Oct-23 Dec, Mon-Sat 10-4.30. Exterior of Little Houses can be viewed all year. **Facilities:** ⊡ (300yds) ⅍ toilets for disabled shop ⋏ ⩗ *Details not confirmed for 2002*

⛫ GLENGOULANDIE DEER PARK
Map 14 NN75
GLENGOULANDIE DEER PARK
PH16 5NL (8m NW of Aberfeldy on B846)
☎ 01887 830261   🖹 01887 830261
e-mail: helenmcadam@supanet.com

Various native birds and animals are kept in surroundings as similar to their natural environment as possible, and there are herds of red deer and Highland cattle. Pets must not be allowed out of cars.

Times: Open May-Oct, 9am-1hr before sunset. **Fee:** £1. Cars £6.
Facilities: ⊡ shop ⋏

⛫ KILLIECRANKIE   Map 14 NN96
KILLIECRANKIE VISITOR CENTRE
NTS Visitor Centre PH16 5LG (3m N of Pitlochry on B8079)
☎ 01796 473233   🖹 01796 473233
e-mail: aclipson@nts.scot.demon.ac.uk

The visitor centre features an exhibition on the battle of 1689, when the Jacobite army routed the English, although the Jacobite leader, 'Bonnie Dundee', was mortally wounded in the attack. The wooded gorge is a notable beauty spot, admired by Queen Victoria, and there are some splendid walks.

Times: Visitor Centre, Exhibition, shop & snack bar Apr-Oct, daily 10-5.30. Site all year daily. **Facilities:** ⊡ ☞ ⅍ (visitor centre only) toilets for disabled shop ⩗ *Details not confirmed for 2002*

A GREAT DAY
INSIDE AND OUT

Blair Castle, Scotland's most visited private Historic House, where you can experience 700 years of history in one day.

Open daily 10am to 6pm (last entry 5pm) from 28th March to 25th October 2002. Winter Tours by Arrangement (Nov-Mar).

★ Browse through 30 rooms of fascinating treasures.
★ Explore the beautiful grounds.
★ Marvel at our 'Hercules Walled Garden' project.
★ Licensed Restaurant & Summer Terrace, Gift Shop & Children's Playground. Picnic Area.
A Perfect Venue for Weddings, Conferences & Functions.

BLAIR CASTLE Blair Atholl, Pitlochry, Perthshire.
For information, leaflets or party booking information, telephone: **01796 481 207**
www.blair-castle.co.uk   www.blaircastleshop.co.uk

⛫ KINROSS   Map 11 NO10
KINROSS HOUSE GARDENS
KY13 8ET (M90 junct 6 to Kinross, signposted in village)
☎ 01577 862900   🖹 01577 863372
e-mail: jm@kinrosshouse.com
Times: Gardens only open May-Sep, daily 10-7. **Facilities:** ⊡ ⅍ ⋏ *Details not confirmed for 2002*

LOCH LEVEN CASTLE
Castle Island KY13 7AR (on an Island in Loch Leven accessible by boat from Kinross)
☎ 01786 450000

Mary Queen of Scots was imprisoned here in this five-storey castle in 1567 - she escaped 11 months later and gave the 14th-century castle its special place in history.

Times: Open Apr-Sep, daily 9.30-6.30. **Fee:** £3 (ch £1, concessions £2.30). Charge includes ferry trip. **Facilities:** ⊡ shop ⋏ █

RSPB NATURE RESERVE VANE FARM
By Loch Leven KY13 7LX (on southern shore of Loch Leven, accessed from B9097 to Glenrothes, 2m E M90 junct 5)
☎ 01577 862355   🖹 01577 862013

Well placed beside Loch Leven, with a nature trail and hides overlooking the Loch and a woodland trail with stunning panoramic views. Noted for its pink-footed geese, the area also attracts whooper swans, greylag

contd.

geese, long-eared owls and great spotted woodpeckers amongst others. Details of special events are available from the visitors' centre.
Times: Open daily, 10-5. **Fee:** £3 (ch 50p, concessions £2) Family (2 adults + all ch) £6, members free. **Facilities:** 🅿 🍴 ♿ (visitor centre/shop/coffee shop & obs room accessible) toilets for disabled shop 🚼 (ex guide dogs) 🍽

⚏ MILNATHORT   Map 11 NO10
BURLEIGH CASTLE
KY13 7XZ
☎ 0131 668 8800
Times: Open at all reasonable times. **Facilities:** 🚼 ▮ *Details not confirmed for 2002*

⚏ MUTHILL   Map 11 NN81
DRUMMOND CASTLE GARDENS
PH7 4HZ (2m S of Crieff on A822)
☎ 01764 681257 & 681433   🖷 01764 681550

The gardens of Drummond Castle were originally laid out in 1630 by John Drummond, 2nd Earl of Perth. In 1830, the parterre was changed to an Italian style. The multi-faceted sundial was designed by John Mylne, Master Mason to Charles I.
Times: Open - Gardens May-Oct, daily 2-6 (Last admission 5pm). Also Etr for 4 days. **Fee:** £3.50 (ch £1.50 & pen £2.50). **Facilities:** 🅿 ♿ toilets for disabled shop

⚏ PERTH   Map 11 NO12
BLACK WATCH REGIMENTAL MUSEUM
Balhousie Castle, Hay St PH1 5HR (follow signs to Perth & Black Watch Museum, approach via Dunkeld Road)
☎ 0131 310 8530   🖷 01738 643245

The treasures of the 42nd/73rd Highland Regiment from 1739 to the present day are on show in this museum, together with paintings, silver, colours, uniforms and weapons.
Times: Open all year. May-Sep, Mon-Sat 10-4.30 (Closed last Sat in Jun); Oct-Apr, Mon-Fri, 10-3.30 (Closed 23 Dec-6 Jan). Other times & Parties 16+ by appointment. **Fee:** Donations. **Facilities:** 🅿 ♿ (1 bay parking for disabled) shop 🚼 (ex guide dogs)

BRANKLYN GARDEN
116 Dundee Rd PH2 7BB (on A85)
☎ 01738 625535
e-mail: aclipson@nts.scot.demon.co.uk

The gardens cover two acres and are noted for their collections of rhododendrons, shrubs and alpines. Garden tours and botanical painting courses are held.
Times: Open Mar-Oct, daily 9.30-sunset. **Facilities:** 🅿 🚼 (ex guide dogs) 🍽 *Details not confirmed for 2002*

CAITHNESS GLASS FACTORY & VISITOR CENTRE
Inveralmond Industrial Est PH1 3TZ (on Perth Western Bypass, A9, at Inveralmond Roundabout)
☎ 01738 637373   🖷 01738 622494
Times: Open all year, Factory shop & restaurant Mon-Sat 9-5, Sun 10-5 (Nov-Mar, Sun 11-5). Glassmaking Mon-Fri 9-4.30. **Facilities:** 🅿 ✗ licensed ♿ (wheelchair available) toilets for disabled shop 🚼 (ex guide dogs) *Details not confirmed for 2002* 🍽

HUNTINGTOWER CASTLE
PH1 3JL (2m W)
☎ 01738 627231

Formerly known as Ruthven Castle and famous as the scene of the so-called 'Raid of Ruthven' in 1582, this structure was built in the 15th and 16th centuries and features a painted ceiling.
Times: Open all year, Apr-Sep, daily 9.30-6.30; Oct-Mar, Mon-Sat 9.30-4.30, Sun 2-4.30. (Closed Thu pm, Fri in winter & 25-26 Dec). **Fee:** £2 (ch 75p, concessions £1.50). **Facilities:** 🅿 shop 🚼 ▮

PERTH MUSEUM & ART GALLERY
78 George St PH1 5LB (centrally situated)
☎ 01738 632488   🖷 01738 443505
e-mail: museum@pkc.gov.uk

This purpose-built museum houses collections of fine and applied art, social and local history, natural history and archaeology. Temporary exhibitions are held throughout the year.
Times: Open all year, Mon-Sat 10-5. (Closed Xmas-New Year). **Fee:** Free. **Facilities:** 🅿 (adjacent) ♿ toilets for disabled shop 🚼 (ex guide dogs)

⚏ PITLOCHRY   Map 14 NN95
EDRADOUR DISTILLERY
PH16 5JP (2.5m E of Pitlochry on A924)
☎ 01796 472095   🖷 01796 472002
e-mail: lwilliamson@campbell-distillers.co.uk

It was in 1825 that a group of local farmers founded Edradour, naming it after the bubbling burn that runs through it. It is Scotland's smallest distillery and is virtually unchanged since Victorian times. Have a dram of whisky while watching an audio-visual display in the malt barn and then take a guided tour through the distillery itself.
Times: Open, early Mar-end Oct, Mon-Sat 9.30-5, Sun 12-5. Winter months, Mon-Sat 10-4, shop only. Tours by arrangement in winter months. **Fee:** Free. **Facilities:** 🅿 ♿ toilets for disabled shop 🚼 (ex guide/hearing dogs)

FASKALLY
(1m N on the B8019)
☎ 01350 727284   🖷 01350 728635
e-mail: peter.fullarton@frestry.gsi.gov.uk

On the northern shores of Loch Faskally, the forest walks meander through a wide mix of tree species, some plants are 200 years old. These woodlands were once used for training young foresters at the Forestry

contd.

Commission school, so they could repair British forests ravaged by the felling of trees for the war effort.
Times: Open all year-dawn to dusk. **Fee:** Free. **Facilities:** 🅿 ♿ (smooth, level, path around Loch Dunmore, 700m) toilets for disabled 🚻

SCOTTISH & SOUTHERN ELECTRIC VISITOR CENTRE, DAM & FISH PASS

PH16 5ND (Turn off A9, 24m N of Perth)
☎ 01796 473152   📧 01882 634709

The visitor centre features an exhibition showing how electricity is brought from the power station to the customer, and there's access to the turbine viewing gallery. The salmon ladder viewing chamber allows you to see the fish as they travel upstream to their spawning ground.
Times: Open Apr-Oct, daily 10-5.30. **Fee:** *Prices not confirmed for 2002* **Facilities:** 🅿 ♿ (monitor viewing of salmon fish pass) toilets for disabled shop 🐕 (ex guide dogs) 🍴

🏛 QUEEN'S VIEW   Map 14 NN85

QUEEN'S VIEW VISITOR CENTRE
PH16 5NR (7m W of Pitlochry on B8019)
☎ 01350 727284   📧 01350 728635
e-mail: peter.fullarton@forestry.gsi.gov.uk

Queen Victoria admired the view on a visit here in 1866; it is possibly one of the most famous views in Scotland. The area, in the heart of the Tay Forest Park, has a variety of woodlands that visitors can walk or cycle in. A new exhibition and audio-visual display 'The Cradle of Scottish Forestry' tells the history of the people and the forests of highland Perthshire.
Times: Open Apr-Oct, daily 10-6. **Fee:** Free. **Facilities:** 🅿 (charged) 🅿 ♿ toilets for disabled shop 🍴

🏛 SCONE   Map 11 NO12

SCONE PALACE
PH2 6BD (2m NE of Perth on A93)
☎ 01738 552300   📧 01738 552588
e-mail: visits@scone-palace.co.uk

Scottish kings were crowned at Scone until 1651; and it was the site of the famous coronation Stone of Destiny from the 9th century until it was seized by the English in 1296. The castellated edifice of the present palace dates from 1803 but incorporates the 16th-century and earlier buildings. The grounds include a pinetum, the original Douglas Fir, the unique Murray Star Maze, woodland walks and herbaceous plantings. Also David Douglas Trail.
Times: Open 1Apr-31Oct. **Fee:** Palace & Grounds £5.90 (ch £3.30, students & pen £4.80). Grounds only £2.80 (ch £1.70) Family £17. **Facilities:** 🅿 🍴 ✖ licensed ♿ toilets for disabled shop 🍴

Drummond Castle Gardens Perthshire

Featured in United Artists *Rob Roy*

Scotland's most important formal gardens, among the finest in Europe. The terraces overlook a magnificent parterre celebrating the saltire and family heraldry, surrounding the famous multiplex sundial by John Milne, Master Mason to Charles I.

Tel: 01764 681257/433 Fax: 01764 681550
Email: thegardens@drummondcastle.sol.co.uk

Open Easter weekend, then daily May 1st to October 31st, 2pm-6pm (last entry 5pm).

🏛 WEEM   Map 14 NN84

CASTLE MENZIES
PH15 2JD (Follow signs from A9)
☎ 01887 820982   📧 01887 820982
e-mail: menziesclan@tesco.net

Restored seat of the Chiefs of Clan Menzies, and a fine example of a 16th-century Z-plan fortified tower house. Prince Charles Edward Stuart stayed here briefly on his way to Culloden in 1746. The whole of the 16th-century building can be explored, and there's a small clan museum.
Times: Open Apr-13 Oct, Mon-Sats 10.30-5, Sun 2-5. **Fee:** £3.50 (ch £2, pen £3). **Facilities:** 🅿 🍴 ♿ toilets for disabled shop 🐕 (ex guide dogs)

RENFREWSHIRE

🏛 KILBARCHAN   Map 10 NS46

WEAVER'S COTTAGE
The Cross PA10 2JG (off A737, 12m SW of Glasgow)
☎ 01505 705588
e-mail: aclipson@nts.scot.demon.co.uk

The weaving craft is regularly demonstrated at this delightful 18th-century cottage museum, and there is a collection of weaving equipment and other domestic utensils.
Times: Open Good Fri-Sep, daily, 1.30-5.30; wknds in Oct, 1.30-5.30 (last admission 5). **Facilities:** 🅿 🐕 (ex guide dogs) 🍴 *Details not confirmed for 2002*

🏛 LANGBANK   Map 10 NS37

FINLAYSTONE COUNTRY ESTATE
PA14 6TJ (on A8 W of Langbank, 10m W of Glasgow
Airport, follow Thistle signs)
☎ 01475 540505 ▤ 01475 540285
e-mail: info@finlaystone.co.uk

The house, open by arrangement for groups, is set in
gardens of renowned natural beauty; there are formal
gardens, walled gardens, and woodland walks. The
'Dolly Mixture', an international collection of dolls, can
be seen in the visitor centre.
Times: Open all year. Woodland & Gardens daily, 10-5. **Fee:** Garden &
Woods £3 (ch & pen £2). 'The Dolly Mixture' Doll Museum 50p.
Facilities: ▣ ▼ ⓫ (lift to second floor pathways for wheelchairs)
toilets for disabled shop

🏛 LOCHWINNOCH   Map 10 NS35

LOCHWINNOCH COMMUNITY MUSEUM
High St PA12 4AB
☎ 01505 842615 ▤ 0141 889 9240
Times: Open all year, Mon 10-1, 2-5 & 6-8; Sat 10-1 & 2-5.
Facilities: ▣ ⓫ ✹ (ex guide dogs) *Details not confirmed for 2002*

RSPB LOCHWINNOCH NATURE RESERVE
Largs Rd PA12 4JF (on A760, Largs road, opposite
Lochwinnoch station, 16m SW of Glasgow)
☎ 01505 842663 ▤ 01505 843026
e-mail: Lochwinnoch@rspb.org.uk

The reserve, part of Clyde Muirshiel Regional Park and
a Site of Special Scientific Interest, comprises two
shallow lochs fringed by marsh which in turn is
bordered by scrub and woodland. There are two trails
leading to three hides and a visitor centre with a
viewing tower.
Times: Open all year, daily 10-5. (Closed Xmas & New Year). **Fee:** £2
(ch 50p, concessions £1). Family ticket £4. **Facilities:** ▣ ⓫
(wheelchairs available, access 3 hides) toilets for disabled shop ✹ ➤

🏛 PAISLEY   Map 11 NS46

COATS OBSERVATORY
49 Oakshaw St West PA1 2DE (M8 junct 27, 28 or 29)
☎ 0141 889 2013 ▤ 0141 889 9240
Times: Open all year, Tue-Sat 10-5, Sun 2-5. Last entry 15 minutes
before closing. **Facilities:** ▣ 150yds (meters/limited street parking)
shop ✹ (ex guide dogs) *Details not confirmed for 2002*

PAISLEY MUSEUM & ART GALLERIES
High St PA1 2BA
☎ 0141 889 3151 ▤ 0141 889 9240
Times: Open all year, Tue-Sat 10-5, Sun 2-5. BH 10-5. **Facilities:** ▣
(200yds) ⓫ (parking on site) toilets for disabled shop ✹ (ex guide
dogs) *Details not confirmed for 2002*

🏛 COLDSTREAM   Map 12 NT84

HIRSEL
Douglas & Angus Estates, Estate Office, The Hirsel
TD12 4LP (0.5m W on A697)
☎ 01890 882834 & 882965 ▤ 01890 882834

The seat of the Home family, the grounds of which are
open all year. The focal point is the Homestead Museum,
craft centre and workshops. From there, nature trails
lead around the lake, along the Leet Valley and into
woodland noted for its rhododendrons and azaleas.
Times: Open all year. Museum 10-
5. Craft Centre Mon-Fri, 10-5, wknds noon-5. **Fee:** £2 per car.
Facilities: ▣ (charged) ▼ ⓫ toilets for disabled shop ✹ (ex dogs on
lead)

🏛 DRYBURGH   Map 12 NT53

DRYBURGH ABBEY
TD6 0RQ (5m SE of Melrose on B6404)
☎ 01835 822381

The abbey was one of the Border monasteries founded
by David I, and stands in a lovely setting on the River
Tweed. The ruins are equally beautiful, and the church
has the graves of Sir Walter Scott and Earl Haig.
Times: Open all year, Apr-Sep, daily 9.30-6.30; Oct-Mar, Mon-Sat 9.30-
4.30, Sun 2-4.30. (Closed 25-26 Dec). **Fee:** £2.50 (ch £1, concessions
£1.90). **Facilities:** ▣ ⓫ shop ✹ ▮

🏛 DUNS   Map 12 NT75

JIM CLARK ROOM
44 Newtown St TD11 3AU
☎ 01361 883960 ▤ 01361 884104
Times: Open Etr-Sep, Mon-Sat 10.30-1 & 2-4.30, Sun 2-4; Oct, Mon-Sat
1-4. **Facilities:** ▣ (on street) ⓫ (ramps, wheelchair space, large print
notices etc) shop ✹ (ex guide dogs) *Details not confirmed for 2002*

MANDERSTON
TD11 3PP (2m E of Duns on A6105)
☎ 01361 883450 ▤ 01361 882010
e-mail: palmer@manderston.co.uk
Times: Open 11 May-28 Sep, Thu & Sun 2-5.30 (also late Spring & Aug
English BH Mons). **Facilities:** ▣ ▼ ⓫ shop ✹ (ex guide dogs & in
gardens) *Details not confirmed for 2002*

🏛 EYEMOUTH   Map 12 NT96

EYEMOUTH MUSEUM
Auld Kirk, Manse Rd TD14 5JE (from A1 onto A1107,
follow signs to town centre)
☎ 018907 50678

The museum was opened in 1981 as a memorial to the
129 local fishermen lost in the Great Fishing Disaster of
1881. Its main feature is the 15ft Eyemouth tapestry,
which was made for the centenary. There are also
displays on local history.
Times: Open Apr-Jun & Sep, Mon-Sat 10-5, Sun 11.30-1.30; Jul-Aug,
Mon-Sat 9.30.5.30; Sun 11.30-4.30; Oct, Mon-Sat 10-4, (closed Sun).
Fee: £2 (concessions £1.50). 1 accompanied ch free. Party. **Facilities:**
▣ (250yds) (45min on street outside) ⓫ shop

⛪ GALASHIELS
Map 12 NT43

LOCHCARRON OF SCOTLAND VISITOR CENTRE
Waverley Mill, Huddersfield St TD1 3BA
☎ 01896 752091 & 751100 ▤ 01896 758833
e-mail: quality@lochcarron.com

The museum brings the town's past to life and the focal point is a display on the woollen industry. Guided tours of the mill take about 40 minutes.
Times: Open all year, Mon-Sat 9-5, Sun (Jun-Sep) 12-5. Mill tours Mon-Thu at 10.30, 11.30, 1.30 & 2.30, Fri am only. **Fee:** Museum free. Mill tour £2.50 (ch 14 free). **Facilities:** ▣ & toilets for disabled shop ◥

⛪ GORDON
Map 12 NT64

MELLERSTAIN HOUSE
TD3 6LG (5m E of Earlston, on unclass road)
☎ 01573 410225 ▤ 01573 410636
e-mail: mellerstain.house@virgin.net

One of Scotland's finest Georgian houses, begun by William Adam and completed by his son Robert in the 1770s. It has beautiful plasterwork, period furniture and pictures, terraced gardens and a lake.
Times: Open Etr, then May-Sep, Sun-Fri 12.30-5 (Last admission 4.30pm). **Fee:** £4.50 (ch £2, pen £3.50) Party 20+. **Facilities:** ▣ ☕ & shop garden centre ↟ (ex guide dogs)

⛪ HAWICK
Map 12 NT51

DRUMLANRIG'S TOWER
1 Tower Knowe TD9 7JL
☎ 01450 373457 ▤ 01450 378526
Times: Open Mar-Oct, Mon-Sat 10-6, Sun 12-6; other times Mon-Sat 10-5, Sun 12-5. Family research room open Wed-Fri 10-12 & 1-3.
Facilities: ▣ & toilets for disabled shop ↟ (ex guide dogs) *Details not confirmed for 2002*

⛪ HERMITAGE
Map 12 NY59

HERMITAGE CASTLE
TD9 0LU (5.5m NE of Newcastleton, on B6399)
☎ 01387 376222

A vast, eerie ruin of the 14th and 15th centuries, associated with the de Soulis, the Douglases and Mary Queen of Scots. Much restored in the 19th century.
Times: Open Apr-Sep, daily 9.30-6.30. **Fee:** £1.80 (ch 75p, concessions £1.30). **Facilities:** ▣ & ▮

⛪ INNERLEITHEN
Map 11 NT33

ROBERT SMAIL'S PRINTING WORKS
7/9 High St EH44 6HA
☎ 01896 830206

These buildings contain a Victorian office, a paper store with reconstructed waterwheel, a composing room and a press room. The machinery is in full working order and visitors may view the printer at work and experience typesetting in the composing room.
Times: Open Etr & May-Sep Mon-Sat 10-1 & 2-5, Sun 2-5; wknds in Oct: Sat 10-1 & 2-5, Sun only 2-5. (Last tour 45mins before closing morning & afternoon). **Facilities:** ℗ (300yds) & shop ↟ (ex guide dogs) ☕ *Details not confirmed for 2002*

⛪ JEDBURGH
Map 12 NT62

JEDBURGH ABBEY
☎ 01835 863925

Standing as the most complete of the Border monasteries (although it has been sacked and rebuilt many times) Jedburgh Abbey has been described as 'the most perfect and beautiful example of the Saxon and early Gothic in Scotland'. It was founded as a priory in the 12th century by David I and remains of some of the domestic buildings have been uncovered during excavations.
Times: Open all year, Apr-Sep, daily 9.30-6.30; Oct-Mar, Mon-Sat 9.30-4.30, Sun 2-4.30. (Closed 25-26 Dec). **Fee:** £3 (ch £1, concessions £2.30). **Facilities:** ▣ & (limited access) toilets for disabled shop ↟ ▮

⛪ KELSO
Map 12 NT73

FLOORS CASTLE
Roxburghe Estates Office TD5 7SF (from town centre follow Roxburghe Street to main gates)
☎ 01573 223333 ▤ 01573 226056
e-mail: marketing@floorscastle.com

The home of the 10th Duke of Roxburghe. The Castle's lived-in atmosphere enhances the superb collection of French furniture, tapestries and paintings. The house was designed by William Adam in 1721 and enjoys a magnificent setting overlooking the River Tweed and the Cheviot Hills beyond.
Times: Open 28 Mar-27 Oct, daily 10-4.30. (last admission 4)
Fee: £5.50 (ch u5 free, ch 5-16 £3.25, pen £4.75). Family ticket £15. Group rates for 20+. **Facilities:** ▣ ☕ ✗ licensed & (lift) toilets for disabled shop garden centre ◥

KELSO ABBEY
☎ 0131 668 8800
Times: Open at any reasonable time. **Facilities:** & ▮ *Details not confirmed for 2002*

⛪ LAUDER
Map 12 NT54

THIRLESTANE CASTLE
TD2 6RU (off A68, follow signs)
☎ 01578 722430 ▤ 01578 722761
e-mail: admin@thirlestanecastle.co.uk

One of the seven "Great Houses of Scotland" this fairy-tale castle has been the home of the Maitland family, the Earls of Lauderdale, since the 12th century. Some of the most splendid plasterwork ceilings in Britain may be seen in the 17th-century state rooms. The family nurseries house a sizeable collection of antique toys and dolls. There is a vaulted dungeon display. The informal riverside grounds, with their views of the grouse moors, include a woodland walk, picnic tables and an adventure playground.
Times: Open Apr-Oct daily 10.30-5 except Sat. Last admission 4.15
Fee: £5.20. Family ticket £13. Grounds only £1.50. Party £4.50.
Facilities: ▣ ☕ shop ↟ (ex guide dogs)

🏛 MELROSE
Map 12 NT53

ABBOTSFORD
TD6 9BQ (2m W off A6091, on B6360)
☎ 01896 752043 🖃 01896 752916

Set on the River Tweed, Sir Walter Scott's romantic mansion remains much the same as it was in his day. Inside there are many mementoes and relics of his remarkable life and also his historical collections, armouries and library, with some 9000 volumes. The mansion was built by Scott between 1811 and 1822, and he lived here until his death ten years after its completion.
Times: Open daily from 3rd Mon in Mar-Oct, Mon-Sat 9.30-5. Sun in Mar-May & Oct 2-5. Sun Jun-Sep 9.30-5. **Fee:** £4 (ch £2). Party £3 (ch £1.50). **Facilities:** 🅿 💺 ⴄ (parking at private entrance) toilets for disabled shop 🐾 (ex guide dogs & hearing dogs)

HARMONY GARDEN
St Mary's Rd TD6 9LJ
☎ 01721 722502 🖃 01721 724700

Set around the early 19th-century Harmony Hall (not open to visitors), this attractive walled garden has magnificent views of Melrose Abbey and the Eildon Hills. The garden comprises lawns, herbaceous and mixed borders, vegetable and fruit areas, and a rich display of spring bulbs.
Times: Open Apr-Sep, Mon-Sat 10-5.30, Sun 1.30-5.30. **Facilities:** 🅿 ⴄ 🐾 ⴟ *Details not confirmed for 2002*

MELROSE ABBEY & ABBEY MUSEUM
TD6 9LG
☎ 01896 822562

The ruin of this Cistercian abbey is probably one of Scotland's finest, and has been given added glamour by its connection with Sir Walter Scott. The abbey was repeatedly wrecked during the Scottish wars of independence, but parts survive from the 14th century. The heart of Robert the Bruce is buried somewhere within the church.
Times: Open all year, Apr-Sep, daily 9.30-6.30; Oct-Mar, Mon-Sat 9.30-4.30, Sun 2-4.30. (Closed 25-26 Dec). **Fee:** £3 (ch £1, concessions £2.30). **Facilities:** 🅿 ⴄ shop 🐾 🍴

PRIORWOOD GARDEN & DRIED FLOWER SHOP
TD6 9PX (off A6091, in Melrose, adjacent to abbey. On National Cycle Route 1)
☎ 01896 822493 🖃 01896 822965

This small garden specialises in flowers suitable for drying. It is formally designed with herbaceous and everlasting annual borders, and the attractive orchard has a display of `apples through the ages'. Dried flowers are on sale in the shop.
Times: Open Garden & Shop; Apr-Sep, Mon-Sat 10-5.30, Sun 1.30-5.30; Oct-24 Dec, Mon-Sat 10-4, Sun 1.30-4. Shop in Abbey St only; 9 Jan-Mar, Mon-Sat 12-4; Apr-24 Dec, Mon-Sat 10-5.30, Sun 1.30-5.30. (Closed 31 Oct-7 Nov). **Fee:** Honesty box £2, con £1. **Facilities:** 🅿 ⴄ (ramps, paths) shop ⴟ

🏛 PEEBLES
Map 11 NT23

KAILZIE GARDENS
EH45 9HT (2.5m SE on B7062)
☎ 01721 720007 🖃 01721 720007

These extensive grounds, with their fine old trees, provide a burnside walk flanked by bulbs, rhododendrons and azaleas. A walled garden contains herbaceous, shrub rose borders, greenhouses and a formal rose garden. A garden for all seasons – don't miss the snowdrops. A large stocked trout pond and rod hire available, and an 18-hole putting green opens in 2002.
Times: Open 25 Mar-Oct, daily 11-5.30. Grounds close 5.30pm. Garden open all year. **Fee:** Mid Oct-mid Mar, honesty box; mid Apr-mid Oct £2.50 (ch 5-15 75p). **Facilities:** 🅿 💺 ✗ licensed ⴄ (ramps in garden & gravel paths) toilets for disabled shop

NEIDPATH CASTLE
EH45 8NW (1m W on A72)
☎ 01721 720333 🖃 01721 720333
Times: Open mid Apr-early May, Mon-Sat 11-5, Sun 11-5; Jul-mid Sep, Mon-Sat 11-6, Sun 1-5. **Facilities:** 🅿 (charged) shop *Details not confirmed for 2002*

🏛 SELKIRK
Map 12 NT42

BOWHILL HOUSE AND COUNTRY PARK
TD7 5ET (3m W of Selkirk off A708)
☎ 01750 22204 🖃 01750 22204
e-mail: bht@buccleuch.com

An outstanding collection of pictures, including works by Van Dyck, Canaletto, Reynolds, Gainsborough and Claude Lorraine, are displayed here. Memorabilia and relics of people such as Queen Victoria and Sir Walter Scott, and a restored Victorian kitchen add further interest inside the house. Outside, the wooded grounds are perfect for walking. A small theatre provides a full programme of music and drama.
Times: Open, Park: Apr-Aug daily 12-5 (ex Fri). House & park: Jul, daily 1-4.30. **Fee:** House & grounds £4.50 (ch under 5 & wheelchair users free, pen & groups £4). Grounds only £2. **Facilities:** 🅿 💺 ✗ licensed ⴄ (guided tours for the blind) toilets for disabled shop (Jul) 🐾 (ex in park) 🍴

HALLIWELLS HOUSE MUSEUM
Halliwells Close, Market Place TD7 4BC (off A7 in town centre)
☎ 01750 20096 🖃 01750 23282
e-mail: museums@scotborders.gov.uk

A row of late 18th-century town cottages converted into a museum. Displays recreate the building's former use as an ironmonger's shop and home, and tells the story of the Royal Burgh of Selkirk. The Robson Gallery hosts a programme of contemporary art and craft exhibitions.
Times: Open Apr-Oct, Mon-Sat 10-5 (Jul & Aug until 6), Sun 2-4. **Fee:** Free. **Facilities:** 🅿 (charged) ⴄ (hopefully installing lift to 2nd floor) toilets for disabled shop 🐾 (ex guide dogs)

SIR WALTER SCOTT'S COURTROOM
Market Place TD7 4BT (on A7 in town centre)
☎ 01750 20096 ▤ 01750 23282
e-mail: museums@scotborders.gov.uk

Built in 1803-4 as a sheriff court and town hall this is where the famous novelist, Sir Walter Scott dispensed justice when he was Sheriff of Selkirkshire from 1804-1832. Displays tell of Scott's time as Sheriff, and of his place as a novelist, as well as those of his contemporaries James Hogg and Mungo Park.
Times: Open Apr-Sep, Sat 10-4, Jun-Sep, Sun 2-4; Oct, Mon-Sat 1-4. **Fee:** Free. **Facilities:** P (100mtrs) (30min-onstreet, car park 50p 2 hr) ⬤ shop ⊁ (ex guide dogs)

▥ SMAILHOLM   Map 12 NT63
SMAILHOLM TOWER
TD5 7RT (6m W of Kelso on B6937)
☎ 01573 460365

An outstanding example of a classic Border tower-house, probably erected in the 15th century. It is 57ft high and well preserved. The tower houses an exhibition of dolls and a display based on Sir Walter Scott's book *'Minstrels of the Border'*.
Times: Open Apr-Sep, daily 9.30-6.30; Oct-Mar, Sat-Sun only. (Closed 25-26 Dec). **Fee:** £2 (ch 75p, concessions £1.50). **Facilities:** P shop ⊁ ▮

▥ STOBO   Map 11 NT13
DAWYCK BOTANIC GARDEN
EH45 9JU (8m SW of Peebles on B712)
☎ 01721 760254 ▤ 01721 760214

From the landscaped walks of this historic arboretum an impressive collection of mature specimen trees can be seen - some over 40m tall and including the unique Dawyck beech-stand. Notable features include the Swiss Bridge, a fine estate chapel and stonework/terracing produced by Italian craftsmen in the 1820s.
Times: Open Mar-18 Nov (Nov 10-4). **Fee:** £3 (ch £1, concessions £2.50). Family ticket £7. **Facilities:** P ⬤ ♿ toilets for disabled shop garden centre ⊁ (ex guide dogs) ◥

▥ TRAQUAIR   Map 11 NT33
TRAQUAIR HOUSE
EH44 6PW (At Innerleithen take B709, house is 1m S of Innerleithen)
☎ 01896 830323 & 830785 ▤ 01896 830639
e-mail: enquiries@traquair.co.uk

27 Scottish monarchs have stayed at Traquair House, said to be Scotland's oldest inhabited house, dating back to the 12th century. William the Lion Heart held court here, and the house has associations with Mary, Queen of Scots and the Jacobite risings. The Bear Gates were closed in 1745, not to be reopened until the Stuarts should once again ascend the throne. There is croquet, a maze and woodland walks by the River Tweed, craft workshops and a children's mini

adventure playground. Also a brewery museum and shop, and antique shop.
Times: Open 30 Mar-Oct. **Fee:** £5.50 (ch £3 pen £5.20) Family £16 (2+3). Grounds only £2.50 (ch £1). **Facilities:** P ⬤ ✗ licensed ♿ toilets for disabled shop ◥

SOUTH AYRSHIRE

▥ ALLOWAY   Map 10 NS31
BURN'S COTTAGE
Burns National Heritage Park KA7 4PY (2m S of Ayr, M77/A77 from Glasgow)
☎ 01292 441215 ▤ 01292 441750
e-mail: dotmckay@aol.com
Times: Open all year, Apr-Oct 9-6; Nov-Mar 10-4 (Sun 12-4).
Facilities: P ⬤ ♿ toilets for disabled shop ⊁ (ex guide dogs)
Details not confirmed for 2002 ◥

BURN'S MONUMENT
KA7 4PQ (2m S of Ayr, follow signs for Burns' National Heritage Park in Alloway)
☎ 01292 443700 ▤ 01292 441750
e-mail: dotmckay@aol.com
Times: Open as for Burns' Cottage. (Closed Oct-Etr). **Facilities:** P ♿
Details not confirmed for 2002

TAM O'SHANTER EXPERIENCE
Burns National Heritage Park, Murdoch's Lone KA7 4PQ (2m S of Ayr)
☎ 01292 443700 ▤ 01292 441750

An introduction to the life of Robert Burns, with an audio-visual presentation – a multi-screen 3D experience describing the Tale of Tam O'Shanter. There are also tranquil landscaped gardens. Please telephone for details.
Times: Open all year, Apr-Sep 9-5.30, Oct-Mar 9-5. **Fee:** £1.40 (pen & ch £0.70). **Facilities:** P ⬤ ✗ licensed ♿ (wheelchair available) toilets for disabled shop ⊁ (ex guide/hearing dogs) ◥

▥ CULZEAN CASTLE   Map 10 NS21
CULZEAN CASTLE & COUNTRY PARK
KA19 8LE (4m W of Maybole, off A77)
☎ 01655 884455 ▤ 01655 884503

This 18th-century castle stands on a cliff in spacious grounds and was designed by Robert Adam for the Earl of Cassillis. It is noted for its oval staircase, circular drawing room and plasterwork. The Eisenhower Room explores the American general's links with Culzean. The 563-acre country park has a wide range of attractions – shoreline, woodland walks, parkland, an adventure playground and gardens.
Times: Country park open all year, daily 9.30-sunset. Castle & visitor centre open Apr-Oct, 10.30-5.30. Last admission 5pm. Other times by appointment. **Facilities:** P ⬤ ✗ licensed ♿ (wheelchairs available, lift in castle) toilets for disabled shop garden centre (ex castle, ex guide dogs) ♨ *Details not confirmed for 2002*

KIRKOSWALD
Map 10 NS20

SOUTER JOHNNIE'S COTTAGE
Main Rd KA19 8HY (on A77, 4m SW of Maybole)
☎ 01655 760603
e-mail: aclipson@nts.scot.demon.co.uk

`Souter' means cobbler and the village cobbler who lived in this 18th-century cottage was the inspiration for Burns' character Souter Johnnie, in his ballad *Tam O'Shanter*. The cottage is now a Burns museum and life-size stone figures of the poet's characters can be seen in the restored ale-house in the cottage garden.
Times: Open Good Fri-Sep daily 11.30-5; wknds in Oct, 11.30-5. Last admission 4.30 **Facilities:** P (75yds) & (only one small step into cottage) ✸ (ex guide dogs) ♨ *Details not confirmed for 2002*

MAYBOLE
Map 10 NS20

CROSSRAGUEL ABBEY
KA19 5HQ (2m S)
☎ 01655 883113

The extensive remains of this 13th-century Cluniac monastery are impressive and architecturally important. The monastery was founded by Duncan, Earl of Carrick and the church, claustral buildings, abbot's house and an imposing castellated gatehouse can be seen.
Times: Open Apr-Sep, daily 9.30-6.30. **Fee:** £1.80 (ch 75p, concessions £1.30). **Facilities:** P ✸ ▮

OLD DAILLY
Map 10 NX29

BARGANY GARDENS
KA26 9PH (4m NE on B734 from Girvan)
☎ 01465 871249 ▤ 01465 871282

Woodland walks with a fine show of azaleas and rhododendrons. Plants on sale from the gardens.
Times: Open Gardens Sat, Sun & Mon, May weekends only 10-5
Fee: £1.50 per person requested (chu12 free)
Facilities: P & (only rock garden not accessible)

TARBOLTON
Map 10 NS42

BACHELORS' CLUB
Sandgate St KA5 5RB (on B744, 7.5m NE of Ayr)
☎ 01292 541940
e-mail: aclipson@nts.scot.demon.co.uk

In this 17th-century thatched house, Robert Burns and his friends formed a debating club in 1780. Burns attended dancing lessons and was initiated into freemasonry here in 1781. The house is furnished in the period style.
Times: Open Apr-Sep, daily 1.30-5.30; wknds in Oct 1.30-5.30, last admission 5pm. **Facilities:** P (in village) & ✸ (ex guide dogs) ♨ *Details not confirmed for 2002*

SOUTH LANARKSHIRE

BIGGAR
Map 11 NT03

GLADSTONE COURT MUSEUM
ML12 6DT (entrance by 113 High St)
☎ 01899 221573 & 221050 ▤ 01899 221050
e-mail: margaret@bmtrust.co.uk

An old-fashioned village street is portrayed in this museum, which is set out in a century-old coach-house. On display are reconstructed shops, complete with old signs and advertisements - a bank, telephone exchange, photographer's booth and other interesting glimpses into the recent past.
Times: Open Etr-Oct, Mon-Sat 10.30-5, Sun 2-5. **Fee:** £2 (ch £1, pen £1.50). Family ticket £4. Party £1.25. **Facilities:** P & shop ✸ (ex guide dogs)

GREENHILL COVENANTERS HOUSE
Burn Braes ML12 6DT
☎ 01899 221572 & 221050 ▤ 01899 221050
e-mail: margaret@bmtrust.co.uk

This 17th-century farmhouse was brought, stone by stone, ten miles from Wiston and reconstructed at Biggar. It has relics of the turbulent `Covenanting' period, when men and women defended the right to worship in Presbyterian style. Audio presentations.
Times: Open mid May-Sep, daily 2-5. **Fee:** £1 (ch 50p, pen 70p). Family ticket £2.50. Party 70p. **Facilities:** P & ✸ (ex guide dogs)

MOAT PARK HERITAGE CENTRE
ML12 6DT (On A702, 30m from Edinburgh)
☎ 01899 221050 ▤ 01899 221050
e-mail: margaret@bmtrust.co.uk

The centre illustrates the history, archaeology and geology of the Upper Clyde and Tweed valleys with interesting displays.
Times: Open all year, Apr-Oct, daily 10.30-5, Sun 2-5; Nov-Feb, wkdays during office hours. Other times by prior arrangement. **Fee:** £2 (ch £1, pen £1.50). Family ticket £4. Party £1.25. **Facilities:** P & (upper floor with assistance on request) toilets for disabled shop ✸ (ex guide dogs)

BLANTYRE
Map 11 NS65

DAVID LIVINGSTONE CENTRE
165 Station Rd G72 9BY (M74 junct 5 onto A725, to A724, follow signs for Blantyre, right at lights, Centre at foot of hill)
☎ 01698 823140 ▤ 01698 821424

Share the adventurous life of Scotland's greatest explorer, from his childhood in the Blantyre Mills to his explorations in the heart of Africa, dramatically illustrated here in the historic tenement where he was born. Various events are planned throughout the season.
Times: Open Mon-Sat 10-5, Sun 12.30-5. (Last admission 4.30). Opening hours may be reduced in winter (contact for details).
Facilities: P ✦ & toilets for disabled shop ✸ (ex guide dogs/lead grounds) ♨ *Details not confirmed for 2002* ◣

BOTHWELL — Map 11 NS75

Bothwell Castle

G71 8BL (from Uddingston direction, off B7071)

☎ 01698 816894

Besieged, captured and 'knocked about' several times in the Scottish-English wars, the castle is a splendid ruin. Archibald the Grim built the curtain wall; later, in 1786, the Duke of Buccleuch carved graffiti - a coronet and initials - beside a basement well.

Times: Open all year, Apr-Sep, daily 9.30-6.30; Oct-Mar, Mon-Sat 9.30-4.30, Sun 2-4.30. (Closed Thu pm, Fri in winter & also 25-26 Dec). **Fee:** £2 (ch 75p, concessions £1.50). **Facilities:** P shop

EAST KILBRIDE — Map 11 NS65

Museum of Scottish Country Life

Wester Kittochside EH28 8NB (From Glasgow take A749. From Edinburgh M8 to Glasgow, exit at junct 6 onto A725 to East Kilbride. Kittochside is signposted)

☎ 01355 224181 Fax 01355 571290

e-mail: kittochside@nms.ac.uk

A fascinating museum built on a 170-acre farm and offering an insight into the working lives of people in rural Scotland. The museum runs a programme of events throughout the year, demonstrating its working collection and contrasting modern and traditional farming methods.

Times: Open daily 10-5 (closed Xmas & New Year) **Fee:** £3 (ch u18 free, con £1.50) **Facilities:** P ♿ (disabled parking, exhibition building is fully accessible) toilets for disabled shop (except guide dogs)

HAMILTON — Map 11 NS75

Chatelherault

Ferniegair ML3 7UE (2.5km SE of Hamilton on A72)

☎ 01698 426213 Fax 01698 421532

Designed as a hunting lodge by William Adam in 1732, Chatelherault, built of unusual pink sandstone, has been described as a gem of Scottish architecture. Situated close to the motorway, there is a visitors' centre, shop and adventure playground. Also a herd of white Cadzow cattle.

Times: Open all year, Mon-Sat 10-5, Sun 12-5. House closed all day Fri. **Fee:** Free. **Facilities:** P ♿ (architect designed for disabled person) toilets for disabled shop garden centre (ex in grounds & guide dogs)

Low Parks Museum

129 Muir St ML3 6BJ (By Asda superstore, off M74 junct 6)

☎ 01698 328232 Fax 01698 328412

The museum tells the story of Hamilton and the Clyde Valley, created by linking the former District Museum and The Cameronians (Scottish Rifles) Museum. Housed in the town's oldest building, dating from 1696, the museum features a restored 18th-century assembly room and exhibitions on Hamilton Palace and The Covenanters.

Times: Open Mon-Sat 10-5, Sun 12-5. **Fee:** Free. **Facilities:** P ♿ shop (ex guide dogs)

UDDINGSTON — Map 11 NS66

Glasgow Zoopark

Calderpark G71 7RZ

☎ 0141 771 1185, 771 1186 & 771 1187

Fax 0141 771 2615

Times: Open all year, daily 10-5 (or 6pm depending on season). **Facilities:** P (charged) ♿ (key for toilet at gate) toilets for disabled shop (ex guide dogs) *Details not confirmed for 2002*

STIRLING

BANNOCKBURN — Map 11 NS89

Bannockburn Heritage Centre

Glasgow Rd FK7 0LJ (2m S of Stirling off M80/M9 junct 9)

☎ 01786 812664 Fax 01786 810892

The Heritage Centre stands close to what is traditionally believed to have been Robert the Bruce's command post before the 1314 Battle of Bannockburn, a famous victory for the Scots and a turning point in Scottish history.

Times: Open - Rotunda & site always open. Heritage Centre & Shop; Mar & Nov-23 Dec, daily 11-4.30; Apr-Oct daily 10-5.30. (Last audio-visual showing half hour before closing). **Facilities:** P ♿ (Induction loop for the hard of hearing) toilets for disabled shop (Closed 1-10 Nov) (ex site only) *Details not confirmed for 2002*

BLAIR DRUMMOND — Map 11 NS79

Blair Drummond Safari & Leisure Park

FK9 4UR (M9 junct 10, 4m along A84 towards Callander)

☎ 01786 841456 & 841396 Fax 01786 841491

e-mail: enquiries@safari-park.co.uk

Drive through the wild animal reserves where zebras, North American bison, antelope, lions, tigers, white rhino and camels can be seen at close range. Other attractions include the sea lion show, a ride on the boat safari through the waterfowl sanctuary and around Chimpanzee Island, an adventure playground, giant astraglide, and pedal boats. There are also African elephants, giraffes and ostriches.

Times: Open Apr-1 Oct, daily 10-5.30. Last admission 4.30. **Fee:** £8.50 (ch 3-14 & pen £4.50, ch under 3 free). Party 15+. **Facilities:** P licensed ♿ (special menus & waitress service if booked in advance) toilets for disabled shop (ex guide dogs)

CALLANDER — Map 11 NN60

Rob Roy and Trossachs Visitor Centre

Ancaster Square FK17 8ED (on A84)

☎ 01877 330342 Fax 01877 330784

Times: Open Mar-Dec daily; Mar-May & Oct-Dec 10-5; Jun 9.30-6; Jul-Aug 9-8, Sep 10-6. Jan & Feb wknds only 11-4.30. **Facilities:** P ♿ toilets for disabled shop (ex guide dogs) *Details not confirmed for 2002*

🏛 CAUSEWAYHEAD   Map 11 NS89
NATIONAL WALLACE MONUMENT
Abbey Craig, Hillfoots Rd FK8 2AD (accessed from
A907, Stirling to Alloa road)
☎ 01786 472140 📠 01786 461322
Times: Open all year daily. Jan-Feb & Nov-Dec, 10-4; Mar-May & Oct,
10-5; Jun & Sep 10-6; Jul-Aug 9.30-6.30. **Facilities:** 🅿 💺 (accessible
visitors pavillion at foot of hill) shop 🛏 (ex guide dogs) *Details not
confirmed for 2002* 🗨

🏛 DOUNE   Map 11 NN70
DOUNE CASTLE
FK16 6EA (8m S of Callander on A84)
☎ 01786 841742

The 14th-century stronghold with its two fine towers
has been restored. It stands on the banks of the River
Teith, and is associated with 'Bonnie Prince Charlie'
and Sir Walter Scott.
Times: Open all year, Apr-Sep, daily 9.30-6.30; Oct-Mar, Mon-Sat 9.30-
4.30, Sun 2-4.30. (Closed Thu pm, Fri in winter & 25-26 Dec).
Fee: £2.50 (ch £1, concessions £1.90). **Facilities:** 🅿 shop 🛏

DOUNE MOTOR MUSEUM
The Doune Collection, Carse of Cambus FK16 6HD
(8m NW of Stirling on A84)
☎ 01786 841203 📠 01786 842070
Times: Open Apr-Nov, daily, 10-5. **Facilities:** 🅿 💺 ♿ (ramped areas
to museum & cafeteria) toilets for disabled shop 🛏 *Details not
confirmed for 2002* 🗨

🏛 KILLIN   Map 11 NN53
BREADALBANE FOLKLORE CENTRE
Falls of Dochart FK21 8XE (from A82, at Crianlarich
take A85 towards Perth/Stirling. Then A827 to Killin)
☎ 01567 820254 📠 01567 820764
Times: Open Mar-May & Oct, daily 10-5; Jun & Sep, daily 10-6; Jul-Aug,
daily 9.30-6.30. Feb wknds only 10-4. (Closed Nov-Jan). **Facilities:** 🅿
(30 mtrs) ♿ toilets for disabled shop 🛏 (ex guide dogs) *Details not
confirmed for 2002* 🗨

🏛 PORT OF MENTEITH   Map 11 NN50
INCHMAHOME PRIORY
FK8 3RA (4m E of Aberfoyle, off A81)
☎ 01877 385294

Walter Comyn founded this Augustinian house in 1238,
and it became famous as the retreat of the infant Mary,
Queen of Scots in 1547. The ruins of the church and
cloisters are situated on an island in the Lake of Monteith.
Times: Open Apr-Sep, daily 9.30-6.30. Ferry subject to cancellation in
adverse weather conditions. **Fee:** £3 (ch £1, concessions £2.30).
Admission charge includes ferry trip. **Facilities:** 🅿 shop 🛒

🏛 STIRLING   Map 11 NS79
MAR'S WARK
Broad St FK8 1EE
☎ 0131 668 8800
Times: Open all reasonable times. **Facilities:** 🛒 *Details not confirmed
for 2002*

MUSEUM OF ARGYLL & SUTHERLAND HIGHLANDERS
The Castle FK8 1EH (museum in Stirling Castle)
☎ 01786 75165 📠 01786 446038
e-mail: museum@argylls.co.uk

Situated in the King's Old Building in Stirling Castle, the
museum tells the history of the Regiment from 1794 to
the present day. Displays include uniforms, medals, silver,
paintings, colours, pipe banners, and commentaries.
Times: Open Etr-Sep, Mon-Sat 10-5.30, Sun 11-5; Oct-Etr, Mon-Sun 10-
4. **Fee:** *Prices not confirmed for 2002* **Facilities:** 🅿 (castle esplanade)
shop 🛏

OLD TOWN JAIL
Saint John St FK8 1EA (follow signs for Castle, jail at
top of hill on left)
☎ 01786 450050 📠 01786 471301
e-mail: otjva@aillst.ossian.net
Times: Open daily, Apr-Sep 9.30-5; Oct-Mar 9.30-3.30,
Facilities: 🅿 ♿ (lift to viewpoint) toilets for disabled shop 🛏 (ex
guide dogs) *Details not confirmed for 2002* 🗨

ROYAL BURGH OF STIRLING VISITOR CENTRE
Castle Esplanade FK8 1EH (next to Stirling Castle)
☎ 01786 479901 & 462517 📠 01786 451881
Times: Open all year, Jan-Mar & Nov 9.30-5; Apr-Jun 9.30-6.30; Jul-
Aug, 9-6.30; Sep-Oct 9.30-6. **Facilities:** 🅿 ♿ (Induction loop for the
hard of hearing) toilets for disabled shop 🛏 (ex guide dogs) 🎭
Details not confirmed for 2002

SMITH ART GALLERY & MUSEUM
Dumbarton Rd FK8 2RQ (M9 junct 10, follow signs for
Stirling Castle)
☎ 01786 471917 📠 01786 449523
e-mail: museum@smithartgallery.demon.co.uk

This award-winning museum and gallery presents a
variety of exhibitions drawing on its own rich
collections and works from elsewhere. A range of
programmes and events takes place, ring for details.
Times: Open all year, Tue-Sat 10.30-5, Sun 2-5 (Closed Mon, 25-26
Dec & 1 Jan). **Fee:** Free. **Facilities:** 🅿 💺 ♿ (wheelchair lift, induction
loop in theatre) toilets for disabled shop

STIRLING CASTLE
Upper Castle Hill FK8 1EJ
☎ 01786 450000

Sitting on top of a 250ft rock, Stirling Castle has a
strategic position on the Firth of Forth. As a result it has
been the scene of many events in Scotland's history.
James II was born at the castle in 1430. Mary, Queen of
Scots spent three years there, and it was James IV's
childhood home. Among its finest features are the
splendid Renaissance palace built by James V, and the
Chapel Royal, rebuilt by James VI.
Times: Open all year, Apr-Sep, daily 9.30-6; Oct-Mar, daily 9.30-5. Last
ticket sold 45 mins prior to closing time. **Fee:** £6 (ch £1.50,
concessions £4.50). **Facilities:** 🅿 (charged) ✕ licensed ♿ toilets for
disabled shop 🛏 🛒

WEST DUNBARTONSHIRE

🏛 BALLOCH
Map 10 NS38

BALLOCH CASTLE COUNTRY PARK
G83 8LX (From Glasgow take A82; from Stirling take A811)
☎ 01389 758216   📠 01389 720922
Times: Open: Visitor Centre, Apr-Oct daily 10-5.45. Country Park open all year, 8-dusk. **Facilities:** 🅿 👝 ♿ toilets for disabled shop *Details not confirmed for 2002* 🐾

🏛 DUMBARTON
Map 10 NS37

DUMBARTON CASTLE
G82 1JJ
☎ 01389 732167

The castle, set on the 240ft Dumbarton Rock above the River Clyde, dominates the town (the capital of the Celtic kingdom of Strathclyde) and commands spectacular views. Most of what can be seen today dates from the 18th and 19th centuries, but there are a few earlier remains.
Times: Open all year, Apr-Sep, daily 10-5. **Fee:** £2 (ch 75p, concessions £1.50). **Facilities:** 🅿 shop 🦮 🚩

WEST LOTHIAN

🏛 LINLITHGOW
Map 11 NS97

BLACKNESS CASTLE
EH49 7AL (4m NE)
☎ 01506 834807

Once, this was one of the most important fortresses in Scotland. Used as a state prison during covenanting time, and in the late 19th-century as a powder magazine, it was one of four castles left fortified by the Articles of Union. Most impressive are the massive 17th-century artillery emplacements.
Times: Open all year, Apr-Sep, daily 9.30-6.30; Oct-Mar, Mon-Sat 9.30-4.30, Sun 2-4.30. (Closed Thu pm, Fri in winter & 25-26 Dec). **Fee:** £2 (ch 75p, concessions £1.50). **Facilities:** 🅿 shop 🚩

HOUSE OF THE BINNS
EH49 7NA (4m E of Linlithgow off A904)
☎ 01506 834255
e-mail: aclipson@nts.scot.demon.co.uk

An example of changing architectural tastes from 1612 onwards, this house reflects the transition from fortified stronghold to spacious mansion. The original three-storey building, with small windows and twin turrets, evolved into a fine crenellated house with beautiful moulded plaster ceilings - the ancestral home of the Dalyell family. There is a magnificent display of snowdrops and daffodils in spring.
Times: Open: House, May-Sep, daily (ex Fri), 1.30-5.30 (last admission 5). Parkland, Apr-Oct, daily 10-7; Nov-Mar, daily 10-4 (last admission 30 mins before closing). **Fee:** £3.70 (ch & pen £2.50). Family tickets £9.90. Schools £1. Members of the Royal Scots Dragoon Guards, in uniform, admitted free. **Facilities:** 🅿 ♿ (braille sheets) 🦮 (ex guide dogs) 🐾

LINLITHGOW PALACE
EH49 7AL (off M9)
☎ 01506 842896

The magnificent ruin of a great Royal Palace, set in its own park or `peel'. All the Stewart kings lived here, and work commissioned by James I, III, IV, and VI can be seen. The great hall and the chapel are particularly fine. James V was born here in 1512 and Mary, Queen of Scots in 1542.
Times: Open all year, Apr-Sep, daily 9.30-6.30; Oct-Mar, Mon-Sat 9.30-4.30, Sun 2-4.30. (Closed 25-26 Dec). **Fee:** £2.50 (ch £1, concessions £1.90). **Facilities:** 🅿 shop 🦮 🚩

The Scottish Islands

Both beautiful and daunting, the islands around the Scottish coast reward the braver traveller with incredible unspoilt landscapes, and the satisfaction of journeying to them.

Lewis, Skye and Mull are the largest of the islands, but there are countless others, some of them are tiny, like the sparsely populated Scarp (2500 acres) or the furthest south of the Outer Hebrides, Berneray, which is only 500 acres. The furthest north is Shetland, which is 110 miles north-east of Scotland's north coast. The traditions of this group of islands are more Viking than Scottish, as is demonstrated by Lerwick's annual celebration, the fire feast of 'Up-Helly-Aa'. Held on the last Tuesday of January, the festival is an adaptation of a Norse feast, Uphalliday, marking the end of Yule and the long winter nights. A replica of a 30ft Viking galley is hauled through the streets and ceremonially burned as a prelude to a night of revelry.

Lewis and Harris form a single island that, together with the Uists, Benbecula and Barra, provides a 150-mile long storm-break for the Inner Hebrides and the Western Highlands. Though thousands of people live on Lewis and Harris, the island nevertheless contains huge areas of emptiness. What is not peat-bog and water is mostly rock. The seas are cold, unsurprisingly, but the white sands are lovely to walk on, and there are a number of standing stones near Callanish.

From the sea, Skye's cloud-cap can be seen long before its dark mountains climb over the horizon; so the Norsemen called it Skuyo, 'Isle of Clouds'. Composed mainly of moutain and moor, Skye is a gathering of peninsulas, where crofting is still the main occupation.

Top: Loch Scridain on the Isle of Mull.

ARRAN, ISLE OF

🏛 BRODICK
Map 10 NS03

BRODICK CASTLE, GARDEN & COUNTRY PARK
KA27 8HY (Ferry from Ardrossan-Brodick all year.
Ferry from Kintyre-Lochranza, service limited in winter)
☎ 01770 302202 & 302462 🖨 01770 302312

The site has been fortified since Viking times, but the present castle dating from the 13th century was a stronghold of the Dukes of Hamilton. Splendid silver, fine porcelain and paintings acquired by generations of owners can be seen, including many sporting pictures and trophies. There is a magnificent woodland garden, started by the Duchess of Montrose in 1923, world famous for its rhododendrons and azaleas.
Times: Open - Castle: Jul-Aug, daily 11-5 (last admission 4.30); Apr-Jun & Sep-Oct, daily 11-4.30 (last admission 4). Reception centre: 10-5. Walled garden: open all year, daily 9.30-5. Country park: open all year, daily 9.30-sunset. **Facilities:** 🅿 ✖ & (Braille sheets, motorised buggy, wheelchairs & stairlift) toilets for disabled shop 🎋 (ex guide dogs) 🍴 *Details not confirmed for 2002*

ISLE OF ARRAN HERITAGE MUSEUM
Rosaburn KA27 8DP (from Brodick Pier turn right, approx 1m)
☎ 01770 302636
Times: Open Apr-Oct, Mon-Sat 10-5 high season. Apr-Oct, Mon-Sat 11-4 low season and every Sunday. **Facilities:** 🅿 🍴 & shop *Details not confirmed for 2002*

🏛 LOCHRANZA
Map 10 NR95

ISLE OF ARRAN DISTILLERY VISITOR CENTRE
KA27 8HJ (from Brodick ferry terminal take coast road N for 14m. Distillery on edge of village)
☎ 01770 830264 🖨 01770 830364
e-mail: visitorcentre@arranwhisky.com

Located amidst beautiful surroundings, the distillery was built recently to revive the dormant traditions of Arran single malt whisky production. After a guided tour of the distillery, visitors can now taste some of the first whiskies to be ready after production began in 1995.
Times: Open daily late Mar-Oct, 4 days a week Nov-Dec. (Closed Jan-Mar). **Fee:** £3.50 (ch under 12 free, pen/student £2.50). Party 20+. **Facilities:** 🅿 🍴 ✖ licensed & (ex working distillery, chair lift in visitor centre) toilets for disabled shop 🎋 (ex guide dogs) 🍴

BUTE, ISLE OF

🏛 ROTHESAY
Map 10 NS06

ARDENCRAIG
PA20 9HA (1m off A844, S of Rothesay)
☎ 01700 503331 🖨 01700 504401
e-mail: allan.macdonald@argyll-bute.co.uk

Particular attention has been paid to improving the layout of the garden and introducing rare plants. The greenhouse and walled garden produce plants for floral displays throughout the district. A variety of fish is kept

Ardencraig
Gardens & Aviaries
Rothesay – Isle of Bute

Ardencraig Gardens on the beautiful
Island of Bute where you can sit and
enjoy the sunshine in peace and
tranquillity with views overlooking the
Firth of Clyde.

**You can reach the gardens by car, bus,
or a leisurely stroll through the
Skipper's woods.**

———— Argyll & Bute Council ————

in the ornamental ponds and the aviaries have some interesting birds.
Times: Open May-Sep. **Fee:** Free. **Facilities:** 🅿 🍴 & 🎋 (ex guide dogs)

BUTE MUSEUM
Stuart St PA20 0BR (situated behind the castle)
☎ 01700 502033 (contact) & 505067 (museum)
e-mail: thomas.clegg@btinternet.com

Local and natural history displays, including birds, mammals and seashore items; varied collections of recent bygones, a collection of early Christian crosses, and flints and pots from two Neolithic burial cairns. A special exhibition of local interest is held during Highland Week.
Times: Open all year, Apr-Sep, Mon-Sat 10.30-4.30, Sun 2.30-4.30; Oct-Mar, Tue-Sat 2.30-4.30 (Closed Sun & Mon). **Fee:** £1.20 (ch 40p, pen 70p) **Facilities:** 🅿 & (touch table for blind, ramps) shop 🎋 (ex guide dogs)

ROTHESAY CASTLE
PA20 0DA
☎ 01700 502691

The focal point of Rothesay is this 13th-century castle. It has lofty curtain walls defended by drum towers that enclose a circular courtyard.
Times: Open all year, Apr-Sep, daily 9.30-6.30; Oct-Mar, Mon-Sat 9.30-4.30, Sun 2-4.30. (Closed Thu pm, Fri in winter & 25-26 Dec). **Fee:** £2 (ch 75p, concessions £1.50). **Facilities:** 🅿 shop 🎋

GREAT CUMBRAE ISLAND

🏛 MILLPORT   Map 10 NS15
MUSEUM OF THE CUMBRAES
Garrison House KA28 0DG (from Largs Cal-Mac
Terminal take ferry to Millport. Bus meets each ferry)
☎ 01475 531191   🖃 01294 464174
e-mail: namuseum@globalinet.co.uk

A small museum which displays the history and life of
the Cumbraes. Along with artefacts from the collection,
the museum displays a major exhibition each summer.
There is also a fine collection of local photographs.
Times: Open Jun-Sep, Mon-Sat 11-1 & 1.30-5. **Fee:** Free. **Facilities:** P
(50m) & shop ✿ (ex guide dogs)

LEWIS, ISLE OF

🏛 ARNOL   Map 13 NB34
BLACK HOUSE MUSEUM
PA86 9DB (11m NW of Stornoway on A858)
☎ 01851 710395

A traditional Hebridean dwelling, built without mortar
and roofed with thatch on a timber framework. It has a
central peat fire in the kitchen, no chimney and a byre
under the same roof.
Times: Open all year, Apr-Sep, Mon-Sat 9.30-6.30; Oct-Mar, Mon-Thu
& Sat 9.30-4.30. (Closed 25-26 Dec). **Fee:** £2.50 (ch £1, concessions
£1.90). **Facilities:** P & toilets for disabled shop ✿ ∎

🏛 CALLANISH   Map 13 NB23
CALLANISH STANDING STONES
PA86 9DY (12m W of Stornoway off A859)
☎ 01851 621422

An avenue of 19 monoliths leads north from a circle of
13 stones with rows of more stones fanning out to the
south, east and west. Probably constructed between
3000 and 1500BC, this is a unique cruciform of
megaliths.
Times: Site accessible at all times. Visitor Centre open Apr-Sep, Mon-
Sat 10-7; Oct-Mar, Mon-Sat 10-4. **Fee:** £1.50 (ch 50p, concessions £1).
Facilities: P ✕ & toilets for disabled shop ∎

🏛 CARLOWAY   Map 13 NB24
DUN CARLOWAY BROCH
(1.5m S of Carloway)
☎ 0131 668 8800
Times: Open at all reasonable times. **Facilities:** P ∎ *Details not
confirmed for 2002*

MULL, ISLE OF

🏛 CRAIGNURE   Map 10 NM73
**MULL & WEST HIGHLAND NARROW GAUGE
RAILWAY**
Craignure (old pier) Station PA65 6AY
☎ 01680 812494 (in season) or
01680 300389   🖃 01680 300595

The first passenger railway on a Scottish island, opened
in 1984. Both steam and diesel trains operate on the
ten-and-a-quarter inch gauge line, which runs from
Craignure to Torosay Castle. The 1.25 mile line offers
dramatic woodland and mountain views taking in Ben
Nevis, Glencoe and the Isle of Lismore.
Times: Open 9 Apr-20 Oct. **Fee:** Return £3.50 (ch £2.50); Single £2.50
(ch £1.50). Family ticket return £9.50, single £6. **Facilities:** P &
(provision to carry person seated in wheelchair on trains) shop

TOROSAY CASTLE & GARDENS
PA65 6AY (1.5m S of ferry terminal at Craignure)
☎ 01680 812421   🖃 01680 812470
e-mail: torosay@aol.com

The Scottish Baronial architecture of this Victorian
castle is complemented by the magnificent setting, and
inside the house there are displays of portraits and
wildlife pictures, family scrapbooks and a study of the
Antarctic. The gardens include a statue walk and water
garden, an avenue of Australian gum trees, an Oriental
garden, many rare shrubs, a narrow gauge steam and
diesel railway, a weaver's workshop and a
silversmith's.
Times: Open Etr-mid Oct, daily 10.30-5. Gardens all year. **Fee:** House
& Gardens: £5 (ch £1.75, stu & pen £4) Family £12. Gardens only: £4
(ch £1.25, stu & pen £3) Family £10 **Facilities:** P ₪ & toilets for
disabled shop garden centre ⟁

ORKNEY

🏛 BIRSAY   Map 16 HY22
EARL'S PALACE
KW15 1PD
☎ 0131 668 8800
Times: Open at all reasonable times. **Facilities:** ✿ ∎ *Details not
confirmed for 2002*

🏛 DOUNBY   Map 16 HY22
BROUGH OF BIRSAY
(6m NW)
☎ 0131 668 8800
Times: Open at all reasonable times. **Facilities:** ∎ *Details not
confirmed for 2002*

CLICK MILL
(NE of village, off B9057)
☎ 0131 668 8800
Times: Open at all reasonable time. **Facilities:** ∎ *Details not
confirmed for 2002*

SKARA BRAE
KW16 3LR (19m W of Kirkwall on B9056)
☎ 01856 841815

Engulfed in drift sand, this remarkable group of well-preserved Stone Age dwellings is the most outstanding survivor of its kind in Britain. Stone furniture and a fireplace can be seen.
Times: Open all year, Apr-Sep, daily 9.30-6.30; Oct-Mar, Mon-Sat 9.30-4.30, Sun 2-4.30. (Closed 25-26 Dec). **Fee:** Summer: £4.50 (ch £1.30, concessions £3.30); Winter: £3.50 (ch £1.20, concessions £2.60). **Facilities:** ⊇ ✕ & toilets for disabled shop ✻ ◪

⛫ FINSTOWN   Map 16 HY31
MAES HOWE CHAMBERED CAIRN
(9m W of Kirkwall, on A965)
☎ 01856 761606

The masonry of Britain's finest megalithic tomb is in a remarkable state of preservation. Dating from neolithic times, it contains Viking carvings and runes.
Times: Open all year, Apr-Sep, daily 9.30-6.30; Oct-Mar, Mon-Sat 9.30-4.30, Sun 2-4.30. (Closed Thu pm, Fri in winter & 25-26 Dec). **Fee:** £2.50 (ch £1, concessions £1.90). **Facilities:** ⊇ ✕ shop ✻ ◪

STENNESS STANDING STONES
(3m SW off A965)
☎ 0131 668 8800
Times: Open at any reasonable time. **Facilities:** ⊇ ◪ *Details not confirmed for 2002*

⛫ HARRAY   Map 16 HY31
ORKNEY FARM & FOLK MUSEUM
KW17 2JR
☎ 01856 771411 & 771268 🖹 01856 874615
Times: Open Mar-Oct, Mon-Sat 10.30-1 & 2-5, Sun 2-7. **Facilities:** ⊇ & shop ✻ (ex guide dogs) *Details not confirmed for 2002*

⛫ KIRKWALL   Map 16 HY41
BISHOP'S & EARL'S PALACES
KW15 1PD (in Kirkwall on A960)
☎ 01856 875461

The Bishop's Palace is a hall-house of the 12th century, later much altered, with a round tower built by Bishop Reid in 1541-48. A later addition was made by the notorious Patrick Stewart, Earl of Orkney, who built the adjacent Earl's Palace between 1600 and 1607 in a splendid Renaissance style.
Times: Open Apr-Sep, daily 9.30-6.30. **Fee:** £2 (ch 75p, concessions £1.50). shop **Facilities:** ◪

THE ORKNEY MUSEUM
Broad St KW15 1DH
☎ 01856 873191 🖹 01856 874616
Times: Open all year, Mon-Sat 10.30-12.30 & 1.30-5 (May-Sep Sun 2-5). **Facilities:** ℗ (50yds) & shop ✻ (ex guide dogs) *Details not confirmed for 2002*

⛫ STROMNESS   Map 16 HY20
ORKNEY MARITIME & NATURAL HISTORY MUSEUM
52 Alfred St KW16 3DF
☎ 01856 850025

The museum focuses on Orkney's broad maritime connections, including fishing, whaling, the Hudson's Bay Company, the German Fleet in Scapa Flow, and the award winning Pilot's House extension. The Natural History Gallery gallery is fully restored, displaying a fine collection of curios and rare and interesting exhibits.
Times: Open Apr-Sep, Mon-Sun 10-5; Oct-Mar, Mon-Sat 11-3.30. (Closed Xmas, New Year & 3 wks Feb-Mar). **Fee:** £2.50 (ch 50p concessions £2). Family ticket £5. **Facilities:** ℗ (50yds) & toilets for disabled shop ✻ (ex guide dogs)

PIER ARTS CENTRE
KW16 3AA
☎ 01856 850209 🖹 01856 851462
e-mail: info@pierartscentre.com

The collection is housed in a warehouse standing on its own stone pier. There is a constantly changing programme of exhibitions.
Times: Open all year, Tue-Sat 10.30-12.30 & 1.30-5. **Fee:** Free. **Facilities:** ℗ (100 yds) & shop ✻ (ex guide dogs)

⛫ WESTRAY   Map 16 HY44
NOLTLAND CASTLE
☎ 0131 668 8800
Times: Open all reasonable times. Application to key keeper. ✻ ◪ *Details not confirmed for 2002*

⛫ LERWICK   Map 16 HU44
CLICKHIMIN
ZE1 0QX (1m SW)
☎ 0131 668 8800
Times: Open at all reasonable time. **Facilities:** ◪ *Details not confirmed for 2002*

FORT CHARLOTTE
ZE1 0JN (overlooking harbour)
☎ 0131 668 8800
Times: Open at all reasonable time. **Facilities:** ◪ *Details not confirmed for 2002*

SHETLAND MUSEUM
Lower Hillhead ZE1 0EL
☎ 01595 695057 🖹 01595 696729
e-mail: shetland.museum@sic.shetland.gov.uk

The massive brass propeller blade outside the building is from the 17,000-ton liner *Oceanic*, wrecked off Foula in 1914. The archaeology gallery covers Neolithic burials, axe-making, Bronze Age houses, Iron Age farming and domestic life. There are also agricultural and social history displays, including peat-working, corn harvest, local businesses, medals, bootmaking

contd.

and Shetland weddings. Changing displays of local contemporary art.
Times: Open all year Mon, Wed, Fri 10-7, Tue, Thu, Sat 10-5.
Fee: Free. **Facilities:** ▣ & (lift, wheelchair available) toilets for disabled shop ✝ (ex guide dogs)

▥ MOUSA ISLAND   Map 16 HU42
MOUSA BROCH
(Accessible by boat from Sandwick)
☎ 0131 668 8800
Times: Open at all reasonable time. **Facilities:** ▮ *Details not confirmed for 2002*

▥ SCALLOWAY   Map 16 HU33
SCALLOWAY CASTLE
ZE1 0TP
☎ 0131 668 8800
Times: Open at all reasonable time. **Facilities:** ▣ ▮ *Details not confirmed for 2002*

▥ SUMBURGH   Map 16 HU30
JARLSHOF PREHISTORIC SITE
(At Sumburgh Head, approx 22m S of Lerwick)
☎ 01950 460112

One of the most remarkable archaeological sites in Europe. There are remains of Bronze Age, Iron Age and Viking settlements as well as a medieval farm. There is also a 16th-century Laird's House, once the home of the Earls Robert and Patrick Stewart, and the basis of 'Jarlshof' in Sir Walter Scott's novel *The Pirate*.
Times: Open Apr-Sep, daily 9.30-6.30. **Fee:** £2.50 (ch £1, concessions £1.90). **Facilities:** ▣ shop ▮

SKYE, ISLE OF

▥ ARMADALE   Map 13 NG60
ARMADALE CASTLE GARDENS & MUSEUM OF THE ISLES
IV45 8RS (16m S of Broadford on A851. Well signposted)
☎ 01471 844305 & 844227 ▤ 01471 844275
e-mail: office@cland.demon.co.uk

Armadale Castle and Gardens were built in 1815 as the home of Lord Macdonald. The warming effect of the Gulf Stream allows exotic trees and plants to flourish. Within the 40 acres of gardens is the Museum of the Isles, where visitors can discover the history of the Highlands.
Times: Open daily 9.30-5.30. Garden & Museum open Apr-Oct.
Fee: £4 (con £3). Family ticket £12. Group 8+ £2.60 **Facilities:** ▣ ▾ ✗ licensed & (wheelchairs available) toilets for disabled shop garden centre ◥

▥ DUNVEGAN   Map 13 NG24
DUNVEGAN CASTLE
IV55 8WF (Follow A87 over Skye Bridge. Turn onto A863 at Sligachan, and follow road to Dunvegan)
☎ 01470 521206 ▤ 01470 521205
e-mail: info@dunvegancastle.com

This fortress stronghold set on the sea loch of Dunvegan has been the home of the Chief of Macleod for 800 years. On view are books, pictures, arms and treasured relics of the clan. A pedigree Highland Cattle fold is also an attraction, as is the boat trip to the nearby seal colony.
Times: Open mid Mar-end Oct, Mon-Sun 10-5.30 (last admission 5pm). Winter opening: Nov-mid Mar, Castle & Gardens Mon-Sun 11-4, last admission 3.30pm. **Fee:** Castle & Gardens: £5.50 (ch 5-15 £3, pen, students £5) Family ticket (2 adults & 3 ch) £15. Parties 10+ £5. Gardens only: £3.80 (ch £2) **Facilities:** ▣ ▾ ✗ licensed (restaurant has ramps for wheelchair access) shop ✝ (ex guide dogs & in grounds) ◥

The Pass of Llanberis

Wales

EVENTS & FESTIVALS

March
18th-24th Wrexham Science Festival, Wrexham
26th Conwy Seed Fair, High Street, Conwy (horticultural fair)

April
tbc Country Music Festival, North Wales Theatre, Promenade, Llandudno, Conwy

May
1st-9th St David's Cathedral Festival, St David's, Pembrokeshire
tbc Wrexham Arts Festival, Wrexham

June
1st-9th Beaumaris Festival, Beaumaris, Anglesey
2nd-3rd North Wales Garden Festival & Woodland Festival, Bodelwyddan Castle, St Asaph
tbc Llandudno Festival
tbc Three Peaks Yacht Race, The Quay, Barmouth, Gwynedd

July
5th-7th North Wales Bluegrass Festival, Bodlondeb Field, Llandudno, Conwy
8th-14th Llangollen International Musical Eisteddfod, International Pavilion, Abbey Road, Llangollen, Denbighshire
13th Annual Mountain Bike Bog Snorkelling World Championships, Llanwrtyd Wells (various venues)
20th-27th Fishguard International Music Festival (various venues), Fishguard, Pembrokeshire
22nd-25th Royal Welsh Show, Royal Welsh Showground, Builth Wells
tbc Gower Music Festival, Gower, Swansea (various venues)
tbc Welsh Proms, St David's Hall, The Hayes, Cardiff

August
3rd-10th Royal National Eisteddfod, Llanelli, Carmarthenshire
4th-10th Victorian Week, Talyllyn Railway, Wharf Station, Tywyn, Gwynedd
9th-11th Brecon Jazz Festival (various venues), Brecon, Powys
10th Llangurig & District Show, Tynymaes, Llangurig, Powys
10th Chepstow Agricultural Show, Chepstow Racecourse, Chepstow

13th-14th Anglesey County Show, Anglesey Showground, Gwalchmai, Mona, Anglesey
13th-15th Pembrokeshire County Show, County Showground, Withybush, Haverfordwest, Pembrokeshire
tbc Brecon County Show
tbc Llandrindod Wells Victorian Festival, Llandrindod Wells, Powys
22nd Monmouthshire Show, Vauxhall Fields, Monmouth, Monmouthshire
24th Denbighshire & Flintshire Show, The Green, Denbigh, Denbighshire
28th Vale of Glamorgan Agricultural Show, Fonmon Castle Park, Fonmon
tbc Conwy River Festival, Harbour, Conwy

September
tbc Barmouth Art Festival, Dragon Theatre, Jubilee Road, Barmouth, Gwynedd
tbc Llangollen Hot Air Balloon Festival, International Pavilion, Abbey Road, Llangollen, Denbighshire
tbc North Wales International Music Festival, the Cathedral, St Asaph, Denbighshire
21st-28th Tenby Arts Festival (various venues), Tenby, Pembrokeshire
tbc Cardigan Festival of Walks, Theatr Mwldan, Cardigan, Pembrokeshire
tbc Usk Show, Usk Showground, Gwernesney, Monmouthshire

October
tbc Anglesey Oyster Fair, Anglesey
tbc Bala Autumn Fair Day, Bala, Gwynedd
tbc Snowdonia Marathon, Llanberis, Gwynedd
27th-9th Nov Dylan Thomas – The Celebration, Dylan Thomas Centre, Somerset Place Swansea (50th anniversary of his death this year)

November
tbc Gwyl Ffilm Ryngwladol Cymru - Welsh International Film Festival, Market House, Market Road, Cardiff

December
tbc Royal Welsh Agricultural Winter Fair, Royal Welsh Showground, Builth Wells

BRIDGEND

⛪ BRIDGEND   Map 03 SS97
NEWCASTLE
☎ 01656 659515
Times: Open - accessible throughout the year. Key keeper arrangement. **Facilities:** 🅿 ✱ ⊕ *Details not confirmed for 2002*

⛪ COITY   Map 03 SS98
COITY CASTLE
CF35 6BG
☎ 01656 652021
Times: Open all year, at all times. Key keeper arrangement.
Facilities: 🅿 ✱ ⊕ *Details not confirmed for 2002*

CAERPHILLY

⛪ CAERPHILLY   Map 03 ST18
CAERPHILLY CASTLE
CF8 1JL (on A469)
☎ 029 2088 3143

The concentrically planned castle was begun in 1268 by Gilbert de Clare and completed in 1326. It is the largest in Wales, and has extensive land and water defences. A unique feature is the ruined tower – the victim of subsidence – which manages to out-lean even Pisa! The south dam platform, once a tournament-field, now displays replica medieval siege-engines.
Times: Open: 26 Mar-25 May daily 9.30-5, 26 May-Sep daily 9.30-6, 1-28 Oct daily 9.30-5. 29 Oct-Mar Mon-Sat 9.30-4, Sun 11-4. **Fee:** £2.50 (ch 5-16, pen & students £2). Family ticket £7. **Facilities:** 🅿 ♿ shop ✱ ⊕ 🍽

LLANCAIACH FAWR MANOR
Gelligaer Rd, Nelson CF46 6ER (M4 junct 32, A470 to Merthyr Tydfil. Then on A472 Ystrad Mynach, follow brown tourist signs)
☎ 01443 412248   📠 01443 412688
e-mail: allens@caerphilly.gov.uk

Step back in time to the Civil War period at this fascinating living history museum. The year is 1645 and visitors are invited into the Manor to meet the servants of 'Colonel' Edward Prichard – from the puritanical to the gossipy.
Times: Open Mon-Fri 10-3.30 (last admission), Sat & Sun 10-4.30. (Closed Mon, Nov-Feb, 24 Dec-2 Jan). **Fee:** £4.50 (ch & concessions £3). Family ticket £12. **Facilities:** 🅿 🍽 ✗ licensed ♿ (personal stereo/photo album/braille map) toilets for disabled shop ✱ (ex guide dogs) 🍽

⛪ CWMCARN   Map 03 ST29
CWMCARN FOREST DRIVE
Nantcarn Rd NP11 7FA (8m N of Newport on A467, M4 junct 28, follow brown tourist signs)
☎ 01495 272001   📠 01495 272001
e-mail: tourism@caerphilly.gov.uk

Times: Open Forest Drive: Etr-Oct. Visitor Centre: all year except between Xmas & New Year. **Facilities:** 🅿 🍽 ♿ toilets for disabled shop *Details not confirmed for 2002*

CARDIFF

⛪ CARDIFF   Map 03 ST17
CARDIFF CASTLE
Castle St CF10 3RB (city centre)
☎ 029 2087 8100   📠 029 2023 1417
e-mail: cardiffcastle@cardiff.gov.uk

The Norman castle was built on the site of a Roman fort, and Roman walls some 10ft thick can still be seen. There is also a Norman keep and a 13th-century tower. The character of the castle comes from its transformation in the 19th century, however, when the immensely rich 3rd Marquess of Bute employed William Burges to restore and rebuild it. Together they created a romantic fantasy of a medieval castle. Also here are the military museums of the Royal Regiment of Wales and Queen's Dragoon Guards.
Times: Open all year, daily (ex 25-26 Dec & 1 Jan) including guided tours, Mar-Oct, 9.30-6 (last tour 5pm); Nov-Feb, 9.30-4.30 (last tour 3.15pm). Royal Regiment of Wales Museum closed Tue. Queen's Dragoon Guards Museum closed Fri. **Fee:** Full conducted tour, military museums, green, Roman Wall & Norman Keep £5.25 (ch & pen £3.15). Roman Wall, Norman Keep, & military museum £2.60 (ch & pen £1.60). **Facilities:** 🅿 (200 yds) 🍽 ♿ (access to Castle Green & Museum) toilets for disabled shop ✱ (ex in grounds & guide dogs)

DYFFRYN GARDENS
St Nicholas CF5 6SU (6m W of city centre, off A48)
☎ 029 2059 3328   📠 029 2059 1966
Times: Open all year, 10-dusk **Facilities:** 🅿 🍽 ♿ (wheelchairs, parking) toilets for disabled shop garden centre *Details not confirmed for 2002* 🍽

LLANDAFF CATHEDRAL
Llandaff CF5 2YF (A48, off M4)
☎ 029 2056 4554 📠 029 2056 4554
Times: Open all year. **Facilities:** 🅿 💺 ✗ ♿ (Wheelchair available) toilets for disabled shop 🦮 (ex guide dogs) *Details not confirmed for 2002*

MILLENNIUM STADIUM TOURS
Millenium Stadium, West Gate St CF10 1JA
☎ 029 2082 2009 📠 029 2082 2228

In the late 1990s this massive stadium was completed as part of an effort to revitalise Welsh fortunes. It replaced Cardiff Arms Park, and now hosts major music events, exhibitions, and international rugby and football matches. Its capacity of around 75,000 and its retractable roof make it unique in Europe.
Times: Open Mon-Sat 9-6 (last admission 5pm), Sun & BHs 10-5. Closed pre-event day, event day and post event day; also Good Fri, Xmas & New Year. **Fee:** £5 (ch 5 £2.50, ch under 5 free, concessions £3). Family ticket £15. Party 20+. **Facilities:** 🅿 ♿ (lifts escalators disabled parking) toilets for disabled shop 🦮 (ex guide dogs) 💺

NATIONAL MUSEUM & GALLERY CARDIFF
Cathays Park CF10 3NP (in Civic Centre)
☎ 029 2039 7951 📠 029 2037 3219

This establishment has a vast range of art and science displays. 'The Evolution of Wales' exhibition takes visitors on a spectacular 4600-million year journey, tracing the world from beginning of time and the development of Wales. There are displays of Bronze Age gold, early Christian monuments, Celtic treasures, silver, coins and medals, ceramics, fossils and minerals.
Times: Open all year, Tue-Sun 10-5. (Closed Mon (ex BHs), 24-26 Dec). **Fee:** Free. **Facilities:** 🅿 (charged) 💺 ✗ licensed ♿ (wheelchair available) toilets for disabled shop 🦮 (ex guide dogs) 💺

TECHNIQUEST
Stuart St CF10 5BW (M4 junct 33, follow A4232 to Cardiff Bay)
☎ 029 2047 5475 📠 029 2048 2517
e-mail: info@techniquest.org

Located in the heart of the Cardiff Bay redevelopment area, visitors of all ages will find science and technology made accessible at Britain's leading hands-on discovery science centre. Launch a hot air balloon, see yourself on television and write a Mozart piece with a pair of dice. Fascinating and educational fun.
contd.

Techniquest

Times: Open all year (ex Xmas), Mon-Fri 9.30-4.30; Sat-Sun & BH's 10.30-5. **Fee:** £6.30 (ch 5-16 & con £4.30). Family ticket £17.40 (2 adults & 3 ch). Friend season ticket £44.50. **Facilities:** 🅿 (50m) 💺 ♿ (lift/hearing loop/audio tapes) toilets for disabled shop 🦮 (ex guide dogs) 💺

🏛 ST FAGANS   Map 03 ST17
MUSEUM OF WELSH LIFE
CF5 6XB (4m W of Cardiff, 3m from M4 junct 33, on A4232)
☎ 029 2057 3500 📠 029 2057 3490

A stroll around the indoor galleries and 100 acres of beautiful grounds will give you a fascinating insight into how people in Wales have lived, worked and spent their leisure hours since Celtic times. You can see people practising the traditional means of earning a living, the animals they kept and at certain times of year, the ways in which they celebrated the seasons.
Times: Open all year daily 10-5. Closed 24-26 Dec. **Fee:** Free. **Facilities:** 🅿 💺 ✗ licensed ♿ (wheelchairs available on a 'first come-first served' basis) toilets for disabled shop 🦮 (ex in grounds if on lead) 💺

🏛 TONGWYNLAIS   Map 03 ST18
CASTELL COCH
CF4 7YS (A470 to Tongwynlais junction, then B4262 to castle on top of hill)
☎ 029 2081 0101

Castell Coch is Welsh for red castle, an appropriate name for this fairy-tale building with its red sandstone walls and conical towers. The castle was originally built in the 13th century but fell into ruins, and the present castle is a late-19th-century creation. Inside, the castle is decorated in fantasy style.
Times: Open: 26 Mar-25 May 9.30-5; 26 May-Sep 9.30-6; 1-28 Oct daily 9.30-5; 29 Oct-31 Mar Mon-Sat 9.30-4, Sun 11-4. **Fee:** £2.50 (ch 5-16, pen & students £2). Family ticket £7. **Facilities:** 🅿 shop 🦮 💺

CARMARTHENSHIRE

ABERGWILI
Map 02 SN42

CARMARTHEN MUSEUM
SA31 2JG (2m E of Carmarthen, just off A40, at Abergwili rndbt)
☎ 01267 231691 ▤ 01267 223830
e-mail: cdelaney@carmarthenshire.gov.uk

Housed in the old palace of the Bishop of St David's and set in seven acres of grounds, the museum offers a wide range of local subjects to explore, from geology and prehistory to butter making, Welsh furniture and folk art. Temporary exhibitions are held.
Times: Open all year, Mon-Sat 10-4.30. (Closed Xmas-New Year).
Fee: Free. **Facilities:** ▣ ☕ ዼ toilets for disabled shop ✻ (ex guide dogs)

CARREG CENNEN CASTLE
Map 03 SN61

CARREG CENNEN CASTLE
SA19 6UA (unclassified road from A483 to Trapp village)
☎ 01558 822291

A steep path leads up to the castle, which is spectacularly sited on a limestone crag. It was first built as a stronghold of the native Welsh and then rebuilt in the late 13th century. Most remarkable among the impressive remains is a mysterious passage, cut into the side of the cliff and lit by loopholes. The farm at the site has a rare breeds centre.
Times: Open all year, Apr-28 Oct, daily 9.30-7.30; 11 Nov-Mar, daily, 9.30-dusk. **Fee:** £2.50 (ch 5-16, pen & students £2, disabled free). Family ticket £7. **Facilities:** ▣ ☕ shop ✻ ⊕ ➤

DRE-FACH FELINDRE
Map 02 SN33

MUSEUM OF THE WELSH WOOLLEN INDUSTRY
SA44 5UP (16m W of Carmarthen off A484, 4m E of Newcastle Emlyn)
☎ 01559 370929 ▤ 01559 371592

The museum is housed in the former Cambrian Mills and has a comprehensive display tracing the evolution of the industry from its beginnings to the present day. Demonstrations of the fleece to fabric process are given on 19th-century textile machinery. Special events: please telephone for details.
Times: Open all year, Apr-Sep, Mon-Sat 10-5; Oct-Mar, Mon-Fri 10-5. (Closed 24-26 Dec & 1 Jan). May vary, please call in advance.
Fee: Free. **Facilities:** ▣ ☕ ዼ (Wheelchair access to ground floor & ample seating) toilets for disabled shop garden centre ➤

DRYSLWYN
Map 02 SN52

DRYSLWYN CASTLE
(on B4279)
☎ 029 2050 0200
Times: Open - entrance by arrangement with Dryslwyn Farm.
Facilities: ▣ ✻ ⊕ Details not confirmed for 2002

KIDWELLY
Map 02 SN40

KIDWELLY CASTLE
SA17 5BQ (via A484)
☎ 01554 890104

This is an outstanding example of late 13th-century castle design, with its `walls within walls' defensive system. There were later additions made to the building; the chapel dates from about 1400. Of particular interest are two vast circular ovens.
Times: Open: 26 Mar-25 May daily 9.30-5; 26 May-Sep daily 9.30-6; 1-28 Oct daily 9.30-5; 29 Oct-Mar Mon-Sat 9.30-4, Sun 11-4. **Fee:** £2.50 (ch 5-16, pen & students £2). Family ticket £7. **Facilities:** ▣ ዼ toilets for disabled shop ✻ ⊕ ➤

KIDWELLY INDUSTRIAL MUSEUM
Broadford SA17 4LW (signposted from Kidwelly by-pass)
☎ 01554 891078

Two of the great industries of Wales are represented in this museum: tinplate and coal mining. The original buildings and machinery of the Kidwelly tinplate works, where tinplate was hand made, are now on display to the public. There is also an exhibition of coal mining with pit-head gear and a winding engine, while the more general history of the area is shown in a separate exhibition.
Times: Open Etr, Jun-Aug, PH wknds, Mon-Fri 10-5, Sat-Sun 2-5. Last admission 4pm (5pm Jul-Aug). Other times by arrangement for parties only. **Fee:** Free. **Facilities:** ▣ ☕ ዼ toilets for disabled shop ✻ (ex in grounds)

LAUGHARNE
Map 02 SN31

DYLAN THOMAS' BOAT HOUSE
Dylans Walk SA33 4SD (14m SW of Carmarthen)
☎ 01994 427420 ▤ 01554 747501
Times: Open all year, May-Oct, daily 10-5; Nov-Apr, daily 10.30-3.
Facilities: ▣ (10mins walk) ☕ shop ✻ (ex guide dogs) Details not confirmed for 2002 ➤

LAUGHARNE CASTLE
King St SA33 4SA (on A4066)
☎ 01994 427906

Newly opened to the public, picturesque Laugharne Castle stands on a low ridge overlooking the wide Taff Estuary. A medieval fortress converted into an Elizabethan mansion, it suffered a civil war siege and later became the backdrop for elaborate Victorian gardens, now recreated. Laugharne Castle has also inspired two modern writers - Richard Hughes and Dylan Thomas.
Times: Open: Apr-Sep daily 10-5 (Closed at all other times ex Strata Florida Florida Abbey, Valle Crucis Abbey & Whit which are open sites). **Fee:** £2 (ch 5-16, pen & students £1.50). Family ticket £5.50. ▣ (150 mtrs) ዼ toilets for disabled shop ✻ ⊕ ➤

⛪ LLANARTHNE   Map 02 SN52
NATIONAL BOTANIC GARDEN OF WALES
Middleton Hall SA32 8HG (8m E of Carmarthen on A48
(M4), dedicated intersection - signed)
☎ 01558 667134   🖹 01558 667138
Times: Opening mid May 10-6.30, Jun-Aug 10-7. Sep-Oct 10-5.30,
Nov-Dec 10-4.30. Last admission 1hr before closing time. (Closed 25
Dec). **Facilities:** 🅿 ⬤ ✗ licensed ♿ toilets for disabled shop garden
centre 🐾 (ex guide dogs) *Details not confirmed for 2002* ⬅

⛪ LLANDEILO   Map 03 SN62
DINEFWR PARK
SA19 6RT (off A40, on western outskirts of Llandeilo)
☎ 01558 823902   🖹 01558 822036
Times: Open Apr-Oct, daily (ex Tue & Wed) 11-4.30. Last admission
30 mins before closing. **Facilities:** 🅿 (charged) ⬤ ♿ toilets for
disabled 🐾 (ex outer park on lead) 🐕 *Details not confirmed for 2002*
⬅

⛪ LLANELLI   Map 02 SN50
WWT LLANELLI
Penclacwydd, Llwynhendy SA14 9SH (3m E of Llanelli,
off A484)
☎ 01554 741087   🖹 01554 741087
e-mail: wwtllanelli@aol.com

A wide variety of wild birds, including oystercatchers,
redshanks, curlews, little egrets and occasionally
ospreys, can be seen here during the right season. The
grounds are beautifully landscaped, and include CCTV
transmitting pictures of wild birds on the reserve, a
wetland craft area and a flock of colourful Caribbean
Flamingos. Facilities for the disabled include easy
access on level paths, special viewing areas and
wheelchair loan.
Times: Open summer 9.30-5.30, winter 9.30-4.30. (Closed 24-25
Dec). **Fee:** £5.30 (ch u4 free, ch £3.20, pen £4.25). Family ticket
available. Group rates available. **Facilities:** 🅿 ⬤ ✗ ♿ toilets for
disabled shop 🐾 ⬅

⛪ LLANGATHEN   Map 02 SN52
ABERGLASNEY GARDENS
SA32 8QH (4m W of Llandeilo, follow signs from A40)
☎ 01558 668998   🖹 01558 668998
e-mail: info@aberglasney.org.uk

With a history stretching back to the 15th century,
Aberglasney was reworked by the 17th-century Bishop
of St David's, the 18th-century poet John Dyer and the
19th-century surgeon John Walters Phillips. Falling into
disrepair through the 20th century, the house and its
gardens were eventually rescued in 1995, and are now

largely restored to their original Jacobean splendour. A
mysterious and beautiful day out.

Aberglasney Gardens

Times: Open all year, Apr-Oct, daily 10-6 (last entry 5); Nov-Mar, Mon-
Fri & 1st Sun of month 10.30-3. **Fee:** £5 (ch & disabled £2.50, pen £4).
Party 10+ **Facilities:** 🅿 ⬤ licensed ♿ (wheelchairs available) toilets for
disabled 🐾 (ex guide dogs) ⬅

⛪ LLANSTEFFAN   Map 02 SN31
LLANSTEFFAN CASTLE
(off B4312)
☎ 01267 241756
Times: Open - access throughout the year. **Facilities:** 🐾 ⊕ *Details
not confirmed for 2002*

⛪ PUMSAINT   Map 03 SN64
DOLAUCOTHI GOLD MINES
SA19 8RR (on A482, signposted)
☎ 01558 650359   🖹 01588 822036
e-mail: penpeb@Smpt.NTrust.org.uk
Times: Open 14 Apr-17 Sep, daily 10-5. Guided underground tours
daily. **Facilities:** 🅿 ⬤ ♿ toilets for disabled shop 🐕 *Details not
confirmed for 2002* ⬅

CEREDIGION

⛪ ABERAERON   Map 02 SN46
LLANERCHAERON
SA48 8DG (2.5m E of Aberaeron off A482)
☎ 01545 570200   🖹 01545 571759
Times: Open early Apr-late Oct, Thu-Sun & BH Mons 11-5. Last
admission 30 mins before closing. Park open all year dawn to dusk.
Facilities: 🅿 ♿ toilets for disabled 🐾 (ex on lead) 🐕 *Details not
confirmed for 2002*

ABERYSTWYTH   Map 06 SN58

NATIONAL LIBRARY OF WALES
Penglais Hill SY23 3BU (off Penglais Hill, A487, N
Aberystwyth)
☎ 01970 632800, 623834 & 623837
🖷 01970 615709
e-mail: holi@llgc.org.uk
Times: Open all year, exhibitions, library & reading rooms Mon-Fri
9.30-6, Sat until 5. (Closed BH's & first wk Oct). **Facilities:** 🅿 💷 ৬
toilets for disabled shop ✸ *Details not confirmed for 2002*

CAPEL BANGOR   Map 06 SN68

**RHEIDOL HYDRO ELECTRIC POWER STATION &
VISITOR CENTRE**
Cwm Rheidol SY23 3NF (off A44)
☎ 01970 880667 🖷 01970 880670

A guided tour of the power station and fish farm can be
taken. There is a visitor centre, nature trail and scenic
drive.
Times: Open Apr-Oct, daily 10-4 for free tours of the Power Station,
fish farm & visitor centre. **Fee:** Free. **Facilities:** 🅿 💷 ৬ toilets for
disabled

CENARTH   Map 02 SN24

THE NATIONAL CORACLE CENTRE
Cenarth Falls SA38 9JL (on A484 between Carmarthen
& Cardigan. Beside bridge and river)
☎ 01239 710980
e-mail: martinfowler@btconnect.com

Situated by the beautiful Cenarth Falls, this fascinating
museum has a unique collection from all over the
world, including Tibet, India, Iraq, Vietnam, and North
America. Cenarth has long been a centre for coracle
fishing, and both rides and demonstrations of coracle
building can be arranged. Look out for the salmon leap
by the flour mill.
Times: Open Etr-Oct, Sun- Fri 10.30-5.30. All other times by
appointment. **Fee:** £3 (ch £1, concessions £2.50) **Facilities:** 🅿 💷 ৬
shop 🍴

EGLWYSFACH   Map 06 SN69

RSPB NATURE RESERVE
Cae'r Berllan SY20 8TA (6m S of Machynlleth on A487
in Eglwys-Fach. Signposted from main road)
☎ 01654 781265 🖷 01654 781328

The woodland and marshland of the reserve is home to
an abundance of birds and wildlife. Among the birds
that can be seen here are: pied flycatchers, redstarts,
wood warblers, nut hatches, great and lesser spotted
woodpeckers, buzzards, kestrels, sparrow-hawks, red
kites, peregrines, merlins and hen harriers. Badgers,
polecats and many species of butterfly and dragonfly
also live here.
Times: Open daily, 9am-9pm (or sunset if earlier). Visitor Centre: Apr-
Oct 9-5 daily; Nov-Mar 10-4 (wknds only) **Fee:** £3.50 (ch £1, con
£2.50) Family £7 RSPB members free. **Facilities:** 🅿 ৬ 🍴

FELINWYNT   Map 02 SN25

FELINWYNT RAINFOREST & BUTTERFLY CENTRE
Rhosmaen SA43 1RT (from A487, Blaenannerch Airfield
turning, onto B4333. Signposted 6m N of Cardigan)
☎ 01239 810882 🖷 01239 810465
e-mail: dandjdevereux@btinternet.com

A chance to wander amongst free-flying exotic
butterflies accompanied by the recorded wildlife
sounds of the Peruvian Amazon. A waterfall, ponds and
streams contribute to a humid tropical atmosphere and
provide a habitat for fish and native amphibians. See
the exhibition on the rainforests of the world. Free
paper and crayons to borrow for children.
Times: Open May-Sep. **Fee:** £3.50 (ch 4-14 £1.50, pen £3.25)
Facilities: 🅿 💷 ৬ shop ✸ (ex guide dogs) ◤

GWBERT-ON-SEA   Map 02 SN15

CARDIGAN ISLAND COASTAL FARM PARK
SA43 1PR (signed from A487, Cardigan bypass, 2.5m to
Park)
☎ 01239 612196 🖷 01239 612196
Times: Open: 9.30-7 daily till Nov. Closed for Winter. **Facilities:** 🅿 💷
৬ shop *Details not confirmed for 2002*

PONTERWYD   Map 06 SN78

LLYWERNOG SILVER-LEAD MINE
Llywernog Mine SY23 3AB (11m E of Aberystwyth on
A44)
☎ 01970 890620 🖷 01545 570823
Times: Open Etr-Oct, daily 10-6 (Oct 5pm). Nov-Dec by appointment.
Facilities: 🅿 💷 ৬ shop *Details not confirmed for 2002* ◤

STRATA FLORIDA   Map 03 SN76

STRATA FLORIDA ABBEY
SY25 6BT (unclassified road from Pontrhydfendigaid,
accessed from B4340)
☎ 01974 831261

Little remains of the Cistercian abbey founded in 1164,
except the ruined church and cloister. Strata Florida
was an important centre of learning in the Middle Ages,
and it is believed that the 14th-century poet Dafyd ap
Gwilym was buried here.
Times: Open 3 Apr-30 Sep, daily 10-5; Site open rest of year. **Fee:** £2
(ch 5-16, pen & students £1.50). Family ticket £5.50. **Facilities:** 🅿 ৬
shop ✸ ☺ ◤

CONWY

BETWS-Y-COED   Map 06 SH75

CONWY VALLEY RAILWAY MUSEUM
Old Goods Yard LL24 0AL (signed from A5 into Old
Church Rd, adjacent to train station)
☎ 01690 710568 🖷 01690 710132

The two large museum buildings have displays on both
the narrow- and standard-gauge railways of North
Wales, including railway stock and other memorabilia.
There are working model railway layouts, a steam-
hauled miniature railway in the grounds (which cover

contd.

over four acres) and a 15in-gauge tramway to the woods. The latest addition is the quarter-size steam 'Britannia' loco which is now on display. For children there are self-drive mini-dodgems, Postman Pat, school bus and Toby Tram.
Times: Open Etr-Oct, daily 10-5.30, then wknds until Mar. Museum, large model & gift shop also open on Mon & Tue in winter period. **Fee:** £1 (ch & pen 50p). Family ticket £2.50. Steam train ride £1. Tram ride 80p. **Facilities:** 🅿 💺 ♿ (ramps & clearances for wheelchairs) toilets for disabled shop 🔊

🏛 CERRIGYDRUDION　　　Map 06 SH94
LLYN BRENIG VISITOR CENTRE
LL21 9TT (on B4501 between Denbigh & Cerrigydrudion)
☎ 01490 420463　🗎 01490 420694
e-mail: llyn.brenig@hyder.com

The 1800-acre estate has a unique archaeological trail and round-the-lake walk of ten miles. A hide is available and disabled anglers are catered for with a specially adapted fishing boat and an annual open day. The centre has an exhibition on archaeology, history and conservation and an audio-visual programme.
Times: Open mid Mar-Nov, daily 9-5. **Fee:** Free. **Facilities:** 🅿 (charged) 💺 ♿ (boats for disabled & fishing open days) toilets for disabled shop 🐕 (ex guide dogs)

🏛 CONWY　　　Map 06 SH77
ABERCONWY HOUSE
LL32 8AY (At junction of Castle St & High St)
☎ 01492 592246　🗎 01492 585153
Times: Open 29 Mar-Oct, Wed-Mon 11-5. Last admission 30 mins before closing. **Facilities:** 🅿 (100yds & 0.5 mile) shop 🐕 (ex guide dogs) 🐾 *Details not confirmed for 2002*

CONWY CASTLE
LL32 8AY (accessed from A55 or B5106)
☎ 01492 592358

The castle is a magnificent fortress, built from 1283-7 by Edward I. There is an exhibition on castle chapels on the ground floor of the Chapel Tower. The castle forms part of the same defensive system as the extensive town walls, which are among the most complete in Europe.
Times: Open: 26 Mar-25 May, daily 9.30-5; 26 May-Sep, daily 9.30-6; 1-28 Oct, 9.30-5; 29 Oct-Mar, Mon-Sat 9.30-4, Sun 11-4. **Fee:** £3.60 (ch 5-16, pen & students £2.60). Family ticket £9.80. Joint ticket for both monuments: £6 (ch 5-16, pen & students £5) Family £17. **Facilities:** 🅿 ♿ toilets for disabled shop 🐕 🌀 🔊

CONWY SUSPENSION BRIDGE
LL32 8LO (adjacent to Conwy Castle)
☎ 01492 573282
Times: Open Jul-Aug, daily 10-5; 29 Mar-Jun & Sep-Oct, Wed-Mon 10-5. **Facilities:** 🅿 ♿ 🐕 🐾 *Details not confirmed for 2002*

PLAS MAWR
High St LL32 8DE
☎ 01492 593413

Plas Mawr is an excellent example of an Elizabethan town mansion, and is practically the same as when it was built between 1570 and 1580. Temporary exhibitions are held here.
Times: Open 3 Apr-25 May, daily 9.30-5; 26 May-2 Sep, daily 9.30-6; 3-30 Sep, daily 9.30-5; 1-28 Oct, daily 9.30-4. (Closed Mon ex BH 3 Apr-28 Oct). **Fee:** £4.10 (ch, pen & students £3.10). Family £11.30. joint ticket for both monuments available £6 (ch, pen & students £5) family £17. shop 🔊

SMALLEST HOUSE
The Quay LL32 8BB (from A55 at Conwy signpost, through town, at bottom of High St towards the quay, turn left)
☎ 01492 593484　🗎 01492 593484

The `Guinness Book of Records' lists this as the smallest house in Britain. Just 6ft wide by 10ft high, it is furnished in the style of a mid-Victorian Welsh cottage.
Times: Open Apr-May 10-5, Jun, Sep & Oct, 10-5, Jul & Aug 10-9 or 9.30. **Fee:** 50p (ch under 16 30p, under 5yrs free admission). **Facilities:** 🅿 (100 yds) ♿ shop

🏛 DOLWYDDELAN　　　Map 06 SH75
DOLWYDDELAN CASTLE
LL25 0EJ (on A470 Blaenau Ffestiniog to Betws-y-Coed)
☎ 01690 750366

The castle is reputed to be the birthplace of Llywelyn the Great. It was captured in 1283 by Edward I, who immediately began strengthening it for his own purposes. A restored keep from around 1200, and a 13th-century curtain wall can be seen. An exhibition on the castles of the Welsh Princes is located in the keep.
Times: Open all year, early Apr-late Oct, daily 9.30-6.30; late Oct-Mar, Mon-Sat 9.30-4 & Sun 11-4. (Closed 24-26 Dec & 1 Jan). **Fee:** £2 (ch 5-16, pen & students £1.50). Family ticket £5.50 **Facilities:** 🅿 🐕 🔊

🏛 LLANDUDNO JUNCTION　　　Map 06 SH77
RSPB NATURE RESERVE
LL31 9XZ (off A55, signposted)
☎ 01492 584091　🗎 01492 584091

The visitor centre has a viewing area which overlooks the estuary and Conwy Castle, and there's a nature trail and four hides for viewing lapwings and shelduck among many others. Phone for details of events.
Times: Open daily, 10-5 (or sunset if earlier). **Fee:** Free. **Facilities:** 🅿 ♿ (wheelchair available) toilets for disabled shop 🐕 (ex guide dogs) 🔊

🏛 LLANRWST　　　Map 06 SH86
GWYDYR UCHAF CHAPEL
(0.5m SW off B5106)
☎ 01492 640578
Times: Open any reasonable time. **Facilities:** 🅿 🐕 🚗 🌀 *Details not confirmed for 2002*

PENMACHNO
Map 06 SH75

TY MAWR WYBRNANT
LL25 0HJ (From A5 3m S of Betws-y-Coed take B4406 to Penmachno. House is 2.5m NW of Penmachno by forest road)
☎ 01690 760213
Times: Open 30 Mar-Sep, Thu-Sun & BH Mons 12-5; Oct, Thu, Fri & Sun 12-4. Last admission 30 mins before closing. **Facilities:** P ✱ (ex in grounds) ⛟(minibus access only) ✄ *Details not confirmed for 2002*

TAL-Y-CAFN
Map 06 SH77

BODNANT GARDEN
LL28 5RE (8m S of Llandudno & Colwyn Bay off A470. Also signposted from A55)
☎ 01492 650460 📠 01492 650448

Set above the River Conwy with beautiful views over Snowdonia, these gardens are a delight. Five Italian style terraces were constructed below the house - on the lowest terrace there is a canal pool with an open-air yew hedge stage and a reconstructed Pin Mill. The garden is renowned for its collections of magnolias, camellias, rhododendrons and azaleas and the famous Laburnum Arch. Phone for details of open air theatre.
Times: Open mid Mar-Oct, daily 10-5 (last admission half hour before closing) **Fee:** £5 (ch £2.50). Party 20+ £4.50 **Facilities:** P ✐ & (steep in places with many steps not easy for wheelchairs) toilets for disabled shop garden centre ✱ (ex guide dogs) ✄

TREFRIW
Map 06 SH76

TREFRIW WOOLLEN MILLS
LL27 0NQ (on B5106 in centre of Trefriw, 5m N of Betws-y-Coed)
☎ 01492 640462 📠 01492 641821
e-mail: info@trefriw-woollen-mills.co.uk

Established in 1859, the mill is situated beside the fast-flowing Afon Crafnant, which drives two hydro-electric turbines to power the looms. All the machinery of woollen manufacture can be seen here: blending, carding, spinning, dyeing, warping and weaving. In the Weaver's Garden, there are plants traditionally used in the textile industry, mainly for dyeing. Hand-spinning demonstrations.
Times: Mill open Etr-Oct, Mon-Fri 10-5. Weaving demonstrations & turbine house: open all year, Mon-Fri 10-5. **Fee:** Free. **Facilities:** P (35 yds) ✐ & (access to shop/cafe/weaving & turbine house) shop ✱ (in shop & grounds, not mill) ✄

BODELWYDDAN
Map 06 SJ07

BODELWYDDAN CASTLE
LL18 5YA (adjacent to A55, near St Asaph)
☎ 01745 584060 📠 01745 584563
e-mail: bodelwyddan-castle.co.uk

Set in rolling parkland against the impressive background of the Clwydian Hills, this imposing Victorian country house has been magnificently restored. The lavish interiors reflect various design styles from the 19th century and provide a sumptuous setting for a collection of portraits on loan from the National Portrait Gallery, complemented by furniture from the Victoria and Albert Museum and sculptures from the Royal Academy of Arts.
Times: Open Nov-Mar Tue-Thu, Sat & Sun 10.30-4, Apr-Jun Sat-Thu 10.30-5, Jul-Aug daily 10.30-5, Sep-Oct Sat-Thu 10.30-5. **Fee:** £4 (ch £2.50, pen, UB40, student, disabled £3.50). Family ticket £10.
Facilities: P & (lift to first floor & Braille/Audio Guides) toilets for disabled shop ✱ (ex guide dogs) ✄

CORWEN
Map 06 SJ04

RUG CHAPEL
Rug LL21 9BT
☎ 01490 412025

Rug Chapel was built in 1637 for Colonel William Salusbury, famous Civil War defender of Denbigh Castle. A rare little altered example of a 17th-century private chapel, it reflects the Colonel's High Church religious views. Prettily set in a wooded landscape, the chapel's modest exterior gives little hint of the interior where local artists and carvers were given a free reign, with some spectacular results.
Times: Open mid Apr-Sep, Wed-Sun 10-5. (Closed Mon & Tue, ex BH wknds). **Fee:** £2 (ch 5-16, pen & students £1.50). Family ticket £5.50. **Facilities:** P & toilets for disabled shop ✱ ⚙ ✄

DENBIGH
Map 06 SJ06

DENBIGH CASTLE
(via A525, A543 & B5382)
☎ 01745 813385

The castle was begun by Henry de Lacy in 1282 and has an inspiring and impressive gatehouse, with a trio of towers and a superb archway, which is surmounted by a figure believed to be that of Edward I.
Times: Open: Apr-Oct, Mon-Fri 10-5.30, Sat/Sun 9.30-5.30 (open site at all other times) **Fee:** £2 (ch 5-16, pen & students £1.50). Family ticket £5.50. **Facilities:** P & shop ✱ ⚙ ✄

LLANGOLLEN
Map 07 SJ24

DOCTOR WHO EXHIBITION & MODEL RAILWAY WORLD

Lower Dee Exhibition Centre LL20 8RX (from Llangollen Bridge, 500yds along road towards Wrexham)

☎ 01978 860584 🖥 01978 861928

e-mail: dapol.drwho@btinternet.com

Times: Open 10-5. (Closed 25/26 Dec & 1 Jan). **Facilities:** 🅿 🖤 shop ✗ (ex guide dogs) *Details not confirmed for 2002* 🍴

HORSE DRAWN BOATS CENTRE

The Wharf, Wharf Hill LL20 8TA (A5 turn right at traffic lights over bridge)

☎ 01978 860702 & 01691 690322
🖥 01978 860702

e-mail: sue@horsedrawnboats.co.uk

Take a horsedrawn boat trip along the beautiful Vale of Llangollen, and visit the museum, which illustrates the heyday of canals in Britain. The displays include working and static models, photographs, murals and slides. There is also a narrowboat trip which crosses Pontcysyllte Aqueduct, the largest navigable aqueduct in the world.

Times: Open Mar, wknds; Apr-Oct, daily (limited opening in Oct). **Fee:** Horse Drawn Boat Trip from £3.50 (ch £2.50). Family ticket £10. Narrowboat Trip £6 (ch £5). **Facilities:** 🅿 (400 yds) 🖤 ఊ (alighting/pick-up point available) toilets for disabled shop 🍴

LLANGOLLEN STATION

(At junction of A5 & A539)

☎ 01978 860979 & 860951 timetable
🖥 01978 869247

e-mail: office@llanrail.freeserve.co.uk

Locomotives and rolling stock are displayed, and passenger trains run on a fourteen-and-a-half-mile round trip between Llangollen and Carrog. A special coach for the disabled is sometimes available, as is a dining train. Please ring for details of events.

Times: Open - Station wknds, Steam hauled trains Apr-Oct Sun & daily in early May-late Oct, diesel trains for some off peak services. **Fee:** Station Free, except for special event days when charge of £1 (ch 50p) this is deducted from fare if travelling; 2nd class return fare for full journey £8 (ch £3.80, pen £5.50) Family ticket £18 (2 adults & 2 ch). **Facilities:** 🅿 🖤 ఊ (special coach for disabled parties on some trains) toilets for disabled shop (at Llangollen only) 🍴

PLAS NEWYDD

Hill St LL20 8AW (Follow brown signs from A5, close to Grapes public house in Llangollen)

☎ 01978 861314 🖥 01978 861906

Times: Open Apr-Oct, daily, 10-5. **Facilities:** 🅿 ఊ toilets for disabled ✗ (ex guide dogs or in grounds) *Details not confirmed for 2002*

VALLE CRUCIS ABBEY

LL29 8DD (on B5103, off A5 W of Llangollen)

☎ 01978 860326

Set in a deep, narrow valley, the abbey was founded for the Cistercians in 1201 by Madog ap Gruffydd.

Substantial remains of the church can be seen, and some beautifully carved grave slabs have been found. There is a small exhibition on the Cistercian monks and the abbey.

Times: Open 3 Apr-Sep, daily 10-5, open site. **Fee:** £2 (ch 5-16, pen & students £1.50). Family ticket £5.50. **Facilities:** 🅿 ఊ shop ✗ ♿ 🍴

RHUDDLAN
Map 06 SJ07

RHUDDLAN CASTLE

LL18 5AD

☎ 01745 590777

The castle was begun by Edward I in 1277, on a simple 'diamond' plan with round towers linked by sections of 9ft thick curtain wall. The moat was linked to a deep-water canal, allowing Edward's ships to sail from the sea right up to the castle.

Times: Open 3 Apr-Sep, daily 10-5. (Closed at all other times ex for Strata Florida Abbey, Valle Crucis Abbey & Whit which are open sites). **Fee:** £2 (ch 5-16, pen & students £1.50). Family ticket £5.50. **Facilities:** 🅿 ఊ shop ✗ ♿ 🍴

FLINTSHIRE

EWLOE
Map 07 SJ26

EWLOE CASTLE

(NW of village on B5125)

Times: Open at all times. **Facilities:** ✗ ♿ *Details not confirmed for 2002*

FLINT
Map 07 SJ27

FLINT CASTLE

CH6 5PH

☎ 01352 733078

Times: Open at all times. **Facilities:** 🅿 ✗ ♿ *Details not confirmed for 2002*

HOLYWELL
Map 07 SJ17

BASINGWERK ABBEY

Greenfield Valley Heritage Pk, Greenfield CH8 7GH

☎ 01352 714172

Times: Open all year, daily 9-6. **Facilities:** 🅿 ✗ ఊ (disabled facilities in Heritage Park) toilets for disabled shop ✗ ♿ *Details not confirmed for 2002*

GWYNEDD

BANGOR
Map 06 SH57

PENRHYN CASTLE

LL57 4HN (1m E at Bangor, at Llandegai on A5122, just off A55)

☎ 01248 353084 🖥 01248 371281

e-mail: ppemsn@smtp.ntrust.org.uk

Times: Open 22 Mar-5 Nov, daily (ex Tue) Castle 12-5pm. Grounds and stableblock exhibitions 11-5 (Jul & Aug 10-5.30). Last admission 4.30pm. Last audio tour 4pm. **Facilities:** 🅿 ✗ licensed ఊ (wheelchairs & golf buggies pre bookable) toilets for disabled shop 🐾 *Details not confirmed for 2002*

BEDDGELERT   Map 06 SH54
SYGUN COPPER MINE
LL55 4NE (1m E of Beddgelert on A498)
☎ 01766 510100 🖹 01766 510102
e-mail: sygunmine@cs.com

Times: Open most of the year, daily 10-6. (last tour 5pm).
Facilities: 🅿 & toilets for disabled shop *Details not confirmed for 2002* 🍴

BLAENAU FFESTINIOG   Map 06 SH74
HYDRO CENTRE FFESTINIOG
Ffestiniog Information Centre, First Hydro Company,
Tan-Y-Grisiau LL41 3TP (off A496)
☎ 01766 830465 🖹 01766 833472
e-mail: robertsb@fhc.co.uk

The scheme was the first hydro-electric pumped
storage scheme, and was opened by Her Majesty the
Queen in 1963. Water is released from an upper dam,
through turbines, to generate electricity when needed,
and then pumped back up when demand is low. Guided
tours are available, and the information centre includes
a café.
Times: Open Etr-Oct, Sun-Fri, 10-4.30. Other times by prior
arrangement. **Fee:** *Prices not confirmed for 2002* **Facilities:** 🅿 🍴
shop 🗙 (ex guide dogs)

LLECHWEDD SLATE CAVERNS
LL41 3NB (25m from A55, S on A470. 10m from A5
junct with A470. On A470)
☎ 01766 830306 🖹 01766 831260
e-mail: llechwedd@aol.com
Times: Open all year, daily from 10am. Last tour 5.15 (Oct-Feb 4.15).
(Closed 25-26 Dec & 1 Jan). **Facilities:** 🅿 🍴 ✕ licensed & toilets for
disabled shop (also Victorian shops in the Village) 🗙 (ex on surface)
Details not confirmed for 2002 🍴

CAERNARFON   Map 06 SH46
CAERNARFON CASTLE
LL55 2AY
☎ 01286 677617

Edward I began building the castle and extensive town
walls in 1283 after defeating the last independent ruler
of Wales. Completed in 1328, it has unusual polygonal
towers, notably the ten-sided Eagle Tower. There is a
theory that these features were copied from the walls of
Constantinople, to reflect a legend that Constantine
was born nearby. Edward I's son and heir was born and
presented to the Welsh people here, setting a precedent
that was followed in 1969, when Prince Charles was
invested as Prince of Wales.
Times: Open 26 Mar-25 May, daily 9.30-5; 26 May-Sep, daily, 9.30-6;
1-28 Oct, daily 9.30-5; 29 Oct-Mar, Mon-Sat 9.30-4, Sun 11-4.
Fee: £4.20 (ch 5-16, pen & students £3.20, disabled free). Family ticket
£11.60. **Facilities:** 🅿 shop 🗙 ۞ 🍴

SEGONTIUM ROMAN MUSEUM
Beddgelert Rd LL55 2LN (1m from Caernarfon on A4085
towards Beddgelert)
☎ 01286 675625 🖹 01286 678416

Segontium Roman Museum tells the story of the
conquest and occupation of Wales by the Romans and
displays the finds from the auxiliary fort of Segontium,
one of the most famous in Britain. You can combine a
visit to the museum with exploration of the site of the
Roman Fort, which is in the care of Cadw: Welsh
Historic Monuments. The exciting discoveries displayed
at the museum vividly portray the daily life of the
soldiers stationed in this remote outpost of the Roman
Empire.
Times: Open Apr-Oct, Mon-Sat 10-5, Sun 2-5. Nov-Mar, Mon-Sat 10-4,
Sun 2-4. **Fee:** Free. **Facilities:** 🅿 🗙 (ex guide dogs) 🍴

CRICCIETH   Map 06 SH43
CRICCIETH CASTLE
LL52 0DP (off A497)
☎ 01766 522227

The castle dates from the 13th century and was taken
and destroyed by Owain Glyndwr in 1404. Evidence of
a fierce fire can still be seen. The gatehouse leading to
the inner ward remains impressive, and parts of the
walls are well preserved.
Times: Open: Apr-25 May, daily 10-5; 26 May-Sep, daily 10-6. (Open
site at all other times). **Fee:** £2.50 (ch 5-16, pen & students £2). Family
ticket £7. **Facilities:** 🅿 shop 🗙 ۞ 🍴

CYMER ABBEY   Map 06 SH71
CYMER ABBEY
(2m NW of Dolgellau on A494)
☎ 01341 422854
Times: Open all year, early Apr-Oct, daily 9.30-6; Nov-Mar, daily 9.30-
4. (Closed 24-26 Dec & 1 Jan) **Facilities:** 🅿 & 🗙 ۞ *Details not
confirmed for 2002* 🍴

FAIRBOURNE   Map 06 SH61
FAIRBOURNE RAILWAY
Beach Rd LL38 2PZ (on A493 follow signs for Fairbourne,
main terminus is just past level crossing on left)
☎ 01341 250362 🖹 01341 250240
e-mail: enquiries@fairbourne-railway.co.uk

One of the most unusual of Wales' 'little trains'; built in
1890 as a horse-drawn railway to carry building
materials it was later converted to steam, and now

contd.

covers two-and-a-half miles. Its route passes one of the loveliest beaches in Wales, with views of the beautiful Mawddach Estuary. An enjoyable round trip can be made from Barmouth in summer, crossing the Mawddach by ferry, catching the narrow gauge steam train to Fairbourne and then taking the train – or walking – across the Mawddach Viaduct. At Gorsaf Newydd Terminus visitors can see locomotive sheds.
Times: Open early/mid Apr-mid/late Sep, times vary according to season and events. Trains will run during Oct half term holiday and Santa Specials at Xmas. **Fee:** Return £5.50 (ch £3.40, pen £4.80). Family £15 (2 adults + 3 ch). **Facilities:** P ⚌ ✗ shop ⬟

⛏ GROESLON
Map 06 SH45

INIGO JONES SLATEWORKS
LL54 7ST (on A487, 6m S of Caernarfon towards Porthmadog. Between villages of Groeslin and Penygroes)
☎ 01286 830242 🖥 01286 831247
e-mail: inigojones@netwales.co.uk

Inigo Jones was established in 1861 primarily to make school writing slates. Today the company uses the same material to make architectural, monumental and craft products. A self-guided audio/video tour takes visitors round the slate workshops, and displays the various processes used in the extraction and working of Welsh slate.
Times: Open daily, summer wkdays 9-5, wknds 10-5; winter wkdays 9-5, Sat am 9-12. **Fee:** £3 (ch & pen £2.50) **Facilities:** P ⚌ & toilets for disabled shop ⬟

⛏ HARLECH
Map 06 SH53

HARLECH CASTLE
LL46 2YH (from A496)
☎ 01766 780552

Harlech Castle was built in 1283-81 by Edward I, with a sheer drop to the sea on one side. Owain Glyndwr starved the castle into submission in 1404 and made it his court and campaigning base. Later, the defence of the castle in the Wars of the Roses inspired the song *Men of Harlech*. Today the sea has slipped away, and the castle's great walls and round towers stand above the dunes.
Times: Open 26 Mar-25 May, daily 9.30-5; 26 May-Sep, daily 9.30-6; 1-28 Oct, daily 9.30-5; 29 Oct-Mar, Mon-Sat 9-4, 11-4. **Fee:** £3 (ch 5-16, pen & students £2). Family ticket £8. **Facilities:** P (disabled spaces in car park) shop ⬟ ⊙ ⬟

⛏ LLANBERIS
Map 06 SH56

DINORWIG DISCOVERY
Oriel Eeyri LL55 4TU (on A4086, Llanberis by-pass)
☎ 01286 870636 🖥 01286 871331
Times: Open Mar-Oct, daily, 10-5 peak season, 10.30-3.30 mid-season & 11-3 low season. Booked tours at other times please ring.
Facilities: P (charged) ⚌ & (vehicle with chair lift available for tour) toilets for disabled shop ⬟ *Details not confirmed for 2002* ⬟

DOLBADARN CASTLE
LL55 4UD (A4086)
Times: Open any reasonable time. **Facilities:** P ⬟ ⊙ *Details not confirmed for 2002* ⬟

LLANBERIS LAKE RAILWAY
Padarn Country Park LL55 4TY (off A4086 at Llanberis)
☎ 01286 870549 🖥 01286 870549
e-mail: info@lake-railway.co.uk

Steam locomotives dating from 1889 to 1948 carry passengers on a four-mile return journey along the shore of Padarn Lake. The terminal station is adjacent to the Welsh Slate Museum, in the Padarn Country Park. The railway was formerly used to carry slate.
Times: Open Etr-late Oct. Trains run frequently Sun-Fri (Sat in Jul & Aug), 11-4.30 in peak season. Send for free timetable. **Fee:** £4.50 (ch £3). Family ticket available. Reduced rates for groups. **Facilities:** P (charged) ⚌ & (Disabled carriage available) toilets for disabled shop ⬟ (train & shop) ⬟

SNOWDON MOUNTAIN RAILWAY
LL55 4TY (on A4086, Caernarfon to Capel Curig road. 7.5m from Caernarfon)
☎ 0870 4580033 🖥 01286 872518
e-mail: enquiries@snowdonrailway.co.uk

The journey of just over four-and-a-half miles takes passengers more than 3000ft up to the summit of Snowdon; breathtaking views include, on a clear day, the Isle of Man and the Wicklow Mountains in Ireland. The round trip to the summit and back takes two and a half hours including a half hour at the summit.
Times: Open 15 Mar-1 Nov, daily from 9am (weather permitting). **Fee:** Return £16.90, single £11.90. **Facilities:** P (charged) ⚌ & (some carriages suitable for wheelchairs - must notify) toilets for disabled shop ⬟ (ex off peak) ⬟

WELSH SLATE MUSEUM
Gilfach Ddu, Padarn Country Park LL55 4TY (0.25m off A4086. Museum in Padarn Country Park)
☎ 01286 870630 🖥 01286 871906

Set among the towering quarries at Llanberis, the Welsh Slate Museum is a living, working site located in the original workshops of Dinorwig Quarry, which once employed 15,000 men and boys. You can see the foundry, smithy, workshops and mess room which make up the old quarry, and view original machinery, much of which is still in working order.
Times: Open Etr-Oct, daily 10-5; Nov-Etr, Sun-Fri 10-4. Last admission 1 hour before closing. The site may close Mon (except Bank Holidays). **Fee:** Free. **Facilities:** P (charged) ⚌ & (all parts accessible except patten loft) toilets for disabled shop ⬟

⛏ LLANFIHANGEL-Y-PENNANT
Map 06 SH60

CASTELL-Y-BERE
☎ 029 2050 0200
Times: Open all reasonable times. **Facilities:** ⬟ ⊙ *Details not confirmed for 2002*

🚂 LLANGYBI
Map 06 SH44

St Cybi's Well

☎ 01766 810047

Times: Open at all times. **Facilities:** ♿ ✸ ۞ *Details not confirmed for 2002*

🚂 LLANUWCHLLYN
Map 06 SH83

Bala Lake Railway

The Station LL23 7DD (off A494 Bala to Dolgellau road)

☎ 01678 540666 ▤ 01678 540535

Steam locomotives which once worked in the slate quarries of North Wales now haul passenger coaches for four-and-a-half miles from Llanuwchllyn Station along the lake to Bala. The railway has one of the few remaining double-twist lever-locking framed GWR signal boxes, installed in 1896. Some of the coaches are open and some closed, so passengers can enjoy the beautiful views of the lake and mountains whatever the weather.

Times: Open Etr-1 Oct, daily (except certain Mon & Fri in Apr, May, Jun and Sep) **Fee:** £6.70 return (pen £6.20). Family ticket £16 (2+2). **Facilities:** ▤ ▼ ♿ (wheelchairs can be taken on train) shop

🚂 LLANYSTUMDWY
Map 06 SH43

Lloyd George Museum & Highgate Victorian Cottage

LL52 0SH (on A497 between Pwllheli & Criccieth)

☎ 01766 522071 ▤ 01766 522071

e-mail: amyueddfeydd-museums@ gwynedd.gov.uk

Explore the life and times of David Lloyd George in this museum. His boyhood home is recreated as it would have been when he lived there between 1864 and 1880, as is his uncle Lloyd's shoemaking workshop.

Times: Open Etr, daily 10.30-5; May, Mon-Fri 10.30-5; Jun, Mon-Sat 10.30-5; Jul-Sep daily 10.30-5; Oct, Mon-Fri, 11-4. Other times by appointment, telephone 01286 679098 for details. **Fee:** £3 (ch & pen £2). Family ticket £7. **Facilities:** ▤ ♿ (induction loop, AV theatre, shop & display in cottage) toilets for disabled shop ✸ (ex guide dogs) ▼

🚂 PENARTH FAWR
Map 06 SH43

Penarth Fawr

(3.5m NE of Pwllheli off A497)

☎ 01766 810880

Times: Open at all times. **Facilities:** ♿ ✸ ۞ *Details not confirmed for 2002*

🚂 PLAS-YN-RHIW
Map 06 SH22

Plas-yn-Rhiw

LL53 8AB (12m from Pwllheli signposted from B4413 to Aberdaron)

☎ 01758 780219

This is a small manor house, part medieval, with Tudor and Georgian additions. The ornamental gardens have flowering trees and shrubs including sub-tropical specimens, divided by box hedges and grass paths. There is a stream and waterfall, which descends from the snowdrop wood behind.

Times: Open Mar-14 May, Thu-Mon noon-5; mid May-Oct, Wed-Mon noon-5. **Fee:** £3.20 (ch £1.60). Family ticket £8. P **Facilities:** ▤ ♿ (braille guides/scented plants) toilets for disabled shop ✸ ☘

🚂 PORTHMADOG
Map 06 SH53

Ffestiniog Railway

Harbour Station LL49 9NF (SE end of town, on A487)

☎ 01766 512340 ▤ 01766 514576

e-mail: info@festrail.co.uk

A narrow gauge steam railway running for 13.5 miles through Snowdonia National Park, with breathtaking views and superb scenery. Buffet service on all trains including licensed bar (in corridor carriages). Please telephone for details of special events. The company also runs the Welsh Highland Railway, which will eventually link up with the Ffestiniog Railway.

Times: Open late Mar-early Nov, daily service and also 26 Dec-1 Jan. Limited service Nov-Dec (most days). Limited service Feb & Mar. **Fee:** Full distance return £13.80 (1 child free with each adult, pen £11.10). Other fares available. **Facilities:** ▤ (charged) ✕ licensed ♿ (Wheelchair ramps) toilets for disabled shop (closed 24/25 Dec) ▼

🚂 PORTMEIRION
Map 06 SH53

Portmeirion

LL48 6ET (Off A487 at Minffordd)

☎ 01766 770000 ▤ 01766 771331

e-mail: info@portmeirion-village.com

Welsh architect Sir Clough Williams Ellis built his fairy-tale, Italianate village on a rocky, tree-clad peninsula on the shores of Cardigan Bay. A bell-tower, castle and lighthouse mingle with a watch-tower, grottoes and cobbled squares among pastel-shaded picturesque cottages let as holiday accommodation. The 60-acre Gwyllt Gardens include miles of dense woodland paths and are famous for their fine displays of rhododendrons, azaleas, hydrangeas and sub-tropical flora. There is a mile of sandy beach and a playground for children.

Times: Open all year, daily 9.30-5.30. **Fee:** £5 (ch £2.50, pen £4). Party 15+. **Facilities:** ▤ ▼ ✕ licensed ♿ toilets for disabled shop garden centre ✸ (ex guide dogs) ▼

TYWYN
Map 06 SH50

TALYLLYN RAILWAY
Wharf Station LL36 9EY (A493 Machynlleth to Dolgellau for Tywyn station, B4405 for Abergynolwyn)
☎ 01654 710472   🖷 01654 711755
e-mail: enquiries@talyllyn.co.uk

The oldest 27in-gauge railway in the world, built in 1865 to run from Tywyn on Cardigan Bay to Abergynolwyn slate mine some seven miles inland. The railway climbs the steep sides of the Fathew Valley with stops on the way at Dolgoch Falls and the Nant Gwernol forest. The return trip takes two-and-a-half hours. All scheduled passenger trains are steam hauled.
Times: Open Sun mid Feb-Mar, daily; Apr-early Nov & 26 Dec-1 Jan. Ring for timetable. **Fee:** £9 Day Rover (ch accompanied £2). Intermediate fares available. **Facilities:** 🅿 (charged) 🍽 ♿ (prior notice useful) toilets for disabled shop ⬤

Y FELINHELI
Map 06 SH56

GREENWOOD CENTRE
LL56 4QN (leave A55 at A5 junct, follow Llanberis signs onto B4365, signposted from next rdbt)
☎ 01248 670076   🖷 01248 670069
e-mail: info@greenwood-centre.co.uk

This theme park has a woodland theme and offers an insight into traditional crafts such as wool spinning and reed plaiting. The park also has a sculpture trail, butterfly garden, a rhododendron maze, herb garden, root garden and plenty of play areas for the kids. There are demonstrations in stiltwalking and longbow archery, film shows and a huge great hall made of oak.
Times: Open daily mid Mar-Oct 10-5.30 (Sep/Oct 10-5 & Sun 11-5) **Fee:** Varies with time of year. £3.95-£4.75 (ch & pen £2.95-£3.95). Family ticket £11.95-£21-50. Party. **Facilities:** 🅿 🍽 ♿ (grounds partly accessible) toilets for disabled shop ⬤

ISLE OF ANGLESEY

BEAUMARIS
Map 06 SH67

BEAUMARIS CASTLE
LL58 8AP
☎ 01248 810361

Beaumaris was built by Edward I and took from 1295 to 1312 to complete. In later centuries it was plundered for its lead, timber and stone. Despite this it remains one of the most impressive and complete castles built by Edward I. It has a perfectly symmetrical, concentric plan, with a square inner bailey and curtain walls, round corner towers and D-shaped towers in between. There are also two great gatehouses, but these were never finished.
Times: Open: 26 Mar-25 May daily 9.30-5, 26 May-Sep daily 9.30-6, 1 Oct-28 Oct daily 9.30-5, 29 Oct-Mar Mon-Sat 9.30-4, Sun 11-4.
Fee: £2.50 (ch u5 free, ch 5-16, pen & students £2). Family ticket £7. Party 15+ 10% disc. **Facilities:** 🅿 ♿ shop 🛉 ☺ ⬤

BEAUMARIS GAOL & COURTHOUSE
Steeple Ln LL58 8EW
☎ 01248 810921   & 724444   🖷 01248 750282

With its treadmill and grim cells, the gaol is a vivid reminder of the tough penalties exacted by 19th-century law. The courthouse, built in 1614 and renovated early in the 19th century, is a unique example of an early Welsh court.
Times: Open Etr-Sep, daily 10.30-5. Other times by arrangement only. **Fee:** Gaol £2.75 (ch, pen £1.75). Courthouse £1.50 (ch, pen £1). Combined ticket £3.50 (ch & pen £2.50). Family ticket £7.75. **Facilities:** 🅿 (500yds) ♿ (narrow gates may restrict some wheelchairs) shop 🛉 (ex guide dogs)

MUSEUM OF CHILDHOOD
1 Castle St LL58 8AP (on A545. Opposite Beaumaris Castle)
☎ 01248 712498   🖷 01248 716869

The museum illustrates the life and interests of children and families over 150 years. There are around 2000 items in the museum's collection including money boxes, dolls, educational toys and games, early clockwork trains, cars and aeroplanes, push toys and cycles.
Times: Open daily 10.30-5.30, Sun 12-5. Last admission 4.30, Sun 4. (Closed Nov-2nd wk Mar). **Fee:** *Prices not confirmed for 2002* **Facilities:** 🅿 (50yds) ♿ shop 🛉 (ex guide dogs)

BRYNCELLI DDU
Map 06 SH57

BRYN CELLI DDU BURIAL CHAMBER
(3m W of Menai Bridge off A4080)
☎ 029 2050 0200
Times: Open at all times. **Facilities:** 🅿 🛉 ☺ *Details not confirmed for 2002*

BRYNSIENCYN
Map 06 SH46

ANGLESEY SEA ZOO
LL61 6TQ (follow Lobster signs along A4080 to Zoo)
☎ 01248 430411   🖷 01248 430213
e-mail: fishandfun@seazoo.demon.co.uk

Nestling by the Menai Straits, this all-weather attraction contains a shipwreck bristling with conger eels, a lobster hatchery, a seahorse nursery, crashing waves and the enchanting fish forest.
Times: Open 2 Jan-22 Mar 11-4, 23 Mar-3 Nov 10-6. Last admission 1hr before site closes. **Fee:** *Prices not confirmed for 2002* **Facilities:** 🅿 🍽 ✕ licensed ♿ (wheelchair available) toilets for disabled shop 🛉 (ex guide dogs) ⬤

HOLYHEAD
Map 06 SH28

RSBP NATURE RESERVE SOUTH STACK
South Stack LL65 1YH (A5 or A55 to Holyhead then follow brown tourist signs)
☎ 01407 764973   🖷 01407 764973

High cliffs with caves and offshore stacks backed by the maritime heathland of Holyhead Mountain make this an ideal reserve to watch seabirds. Live video pictures of breeding seabirds are shown in the cliff-top

contd.

information centre during the summer. Choughs, guillemots, razorbills, fulmars and puffins may be seen. **Times:** Open: Visitor Centre daily, Apr-mid Sep, 11-5. Reserve open daily at all times. **Fee:** Free. **Facilities:** ▣

🏛 LLANALLGO   Map 06 SH58
DIN LLUGWY ANCIENT VILLAGE
(1m NW off A5025)
Times: Open at all times. **Facilities:** ✵ ✣ *Details not confirmed for 2002*

🏛 PLAS NEWYDD   Map 06 SH56
PLAS NEWYDD
LL61 6DQ (2m S of Llanfairpwll, on A4080)
☎ 01248 714795 ▤ 01248 713673
e-mail: ppnmsn@smtp.ntrust.org.uk

In a spectacular parkland setting, this elegant 18th-century house was built by James Wyatt. The interior, re-styled in the 1930s, is famous for its association with Rex Whistler. A military museum contains campaign relics of the 1st Marquess of Anglesey who commanded the cavalry at the Battle of Waterloo. Historical cruises and boat trips on the Menai Strait operate weather and demand permitting. The Rhododendron garden is open from April to early June.
Times: Open Apr-Oct, Sat-Wed. House 12-5pm, garden 11am-5.30pm. Last admission 30mins before closing. **Fee:** £4.50 (ch £2.25). Family ticket £11 (2+2). Pre-booked groups (15+) £3.70. Garden only: £2.50 (ch £1.25). **Facilities:** ▣ ✕ licensed ৬ (Close parking, wheelchairs, stairclimber) toilets for disabled shop ✵ ⅏

MERTHYR TYDFIL

🏛 MERTHYR TYDFIL   Map 03 SO00
BRECON MOUNTAIN RAILWAY
Pant Station Dowlais CF48 2UP (follow the Mountain Railway Signs from A470 or A465 N of Merthyr Tydfil)
☎ 01685 722988 ▤ 01685 384854

Opened in 1980, this narrow-gauge railway follows part of an old British Rail route which closed in 1964 when the iron industry in South Wales fell into decline. The present route starts at Pant Station and continues for three-and-a-half miles through the beautiful scenery of the Brecon Beacons National Park, as far as Taf Fechan reservoir. The train is pulled by a vintage steam locomotive and is one of the most popular railways in Wales.
Times: Opening times on application to The Brecon Mountain Railway, Pant Station, Merthyr Tydfil. **Fee:** Fares are under review, please ring for details. **Facilities:** ▣ ☕ ৬ (adapted carriage) toilets for disabled shop ☕

CYFARTHFA CASTLE MUSEUM & ART GALLERY
Cyfarthfa Park CF47 8RE (off A470, N towards Brecon, follow brown signs)
☎ 01685 723112 ▤ 01685 722146

Set in wooded parkland beside a beautiful lake, this imposing gothic mansion now houses a superb

museum and art gallery. Providing a fascinating glimpse into over 3000 years of history, the museum displays wonderful collections of fine art, social history and objects from around the world in a Regency setting.
Times: Open Apr-Sep: Mon-Sun 10-5.30. Oct-Mar: Tue-Fri 10-4, Sat-Sun 12-4. **Fee:** £2 (concessions £1). **Facilities:** ▣ ☕ ৬ (stair lift & wheelchair available) toilets for disabled shop ✵ (ex guide dogs) ☕

MONMOUTHSHIRE

🏛 CAERWENT   Map 03 ST49
CAERWENT ROMAN TOWN
(off A48)
☎ 029 2050 0200
Times: Open - access throughout the year. **Facilities:** ✵ ✣ *Details not confirmed for 2002*

🏛 CALDICOT   Map 03 ST48
CALDICOT CASTLE, MUSEUM & COUNTRYSIDE PARK
Church Rd NP26 4HU (From M4 junct 23A then B4245. From M48 junct 2 follow A48 & B4245. Signposted from B4245)
☎ 01291 420241 ▤ 01291 435094
e-mail: caldicotcastle@monmouthshire.gov.uk

Caldicot Castle's well-preserved fortifications were founded by the Normans and fully developed by the late 14th century. Restored as a family home by a wealthy Victorian, the castle offers the chance to explore medieval walls and towers in a setting of tranquil gardens and wooded country parkland, plus the opportunity to play giant chess or draughts.
Times: Open daily Mar-Oct 11-5 **Fee:** £1.50 (ch, pen & student 85p). Family (2+3) £4. Party 10+. **Facilities:** ▣ ☕ ৬ (taped tour, level trails) toilets for disabled shop ☕

🏛 CHEPSTOW   Map 03 ST59
CHEPSTOW CASTLE
NP6 5EZ
☎ 01291 624065

Built by William FitzOsbern, Chepstow is the first recorded Norman stone castle. It stands in a strategic

contd.

spot above the Wye. The castle was strengthened in the following centuries, but was not besieged (as far as is known) until the Civil War, when it was twice lost to the Parliamentarians. The remains of the domestic rooms and the massive gatehouse with its portcullis grooves and ancient gates are still impressive, as are the walls and towers.
Times: Open 26 Mar-25 May, daily 9.30-5; 26 May-Sep, daily 9.30-6; 1-28 Oct, daily 9.30-5; 29 Oct-Mar, Mon-Sat 9.30-4, Sun 11-4. **Fee:** £3 (ch 5-16, pen & students £2). Family ticket £8. **Facilities:** 🅿 ♿ shop ⚑

GROSMONT
Map 03 SO42
GROSMONT CASTLE
(on B4347)
☎ 01981 240301
Times: Open - access throughout the year. **Facilities:** ♿ ⚑ ☺
Details not confirmed for 2002

LLANTHONY
Map 03 SO22
LLANTHONY PRIORY
☎ 029 2050 0200
Times: Open - access throughout the year. **Facilities:** 🅿 ♿ toilets for disabled ⚑ ☺ *Details not confirmed for 2002*

LLANTILIO CROSSENNY
Map 03 SO31
HEN GWRT
(off B4233)
☎ 029 2050 0200
Times: Open - access throughout the year. **Facilities:** ⚑ ☺ *Details not confirmed for 2002*

MONMOUTH
Map 03 SO51
NELSON MUSEUM & LOCAL HISTORY CENTRE
New Market Hall, Priory St NP25 3XA (town centre)
☎ 01600 713519 🖷 01600 775001
e-mail: nelsonmuseum@
monmouthshire.gov.uk

Commemorative glass, china, silver, medals, books, models, prints and Admiral Nelson's fighting sword feature here. The local history displays deal with Monmouth's past as a fortress market town, and include a section on the co-founder of the Rolls Royce

company, Charles Stewart Rolls, who was also a pioneer balloonist, aviator and, of course, motorist.
Times: Open all year, Mon-Sat 10-1 & 2-5; Sun 2-5. (Closed Xmas & New Year). **Fee:** £1 (pen & students 75p) accompanied ch under 18 free. **Facilities:** 🅿 (200yds) ♿ shop ⚑ (ex guide dogs) ⚑

RAGLAN
Map 03 SO40
RAGLAN CASTLE
NP5 2BT (signposted off A40)
☎ 01291 690228

This magnificent 15th-century castle is noted for its 'Yellow Tower of Gwent'. It was built by Sir William ap Thomas and destroyed during the Civil War, after a long siege. The ruins are still impressive however, and the castle's history is illustrated in an exhibition situated in the closet tower and two rooms of the gate passage.
Times: Open 26 Mar-25 May, daily 9.30-5; 26 May-Sep, daily 9.30-6; 1-28 Oct, daily 9.30-5; 29 Oct-Mar, Mon-Sat 9.30-4, Sun 11-4.
Fee: £2.40 (ch 5-16, pen & students £1.90). Family ticket £6.70.
Facilities: 🅿 ♿ shop ⚑ ☺ ⚑

SKENFRITH
Map 03 SO42
SKENFRITH CASTLE
☎ 029 2050 0200
Times: Open - access throughout the year. Key keeper arrangement.
Facilities: 🅿 ⚑ ☺ ⚘ *Details not confirmed for 2002*

TINTERN
Map 03 SO50
TINTERN ABBEY
NP6 6SE (via A466)
☎ 01291 689251

The ruins of this Cistercian monastery church are still surprisingly intact. The monastery was established in 1131 and became increasingly wealthy until well into the 15th century. During the Dissolution, the monastery was closed and most of the buildings were completely destroyed. During the 18th century many poets and artists came to see the ruins and recorded their impressions.
Times: Open: 26 Mar-25 May daily 9.30-5, 26 May-Sep daily 9.30-6, 1-28 Oct daily 9.30-5, 29 Oct-Mar Mon-Sat 9.30-4, Sun 11-4. **Fee:** £2.50 (ch 5-16, pen & students £2). Family ticket £7. **Facilities:** 🅿 ♿ toilets for disabled shop ⚑ ☺ ⚑

USK
Map 03 SO30
USK RURAL LIFE MUSEUM
Malt Barn, New Market St NP15 1AU
☎ 01291 673777
Times: Open Apr-Oct, daily 10-5 (ex Sat & Sun am) Last admission 4.30. Winter hours contact the Museum. **Facilities:** 🅿 ♿ (special tape recording of tour for deaf) shop *Details not confirmed for 2002*

🏯 WHITE CASTLE   Map 03 SO31

WHITE CASTLE

NP7 8UD (7m NE of Abergavenny, unclass road N of B4233)

☎ **01600 780380**

The impressive 12th- to 13th-century moated stronghold was built by Hubert de Burgh to defend the Welsh Marches. Substantial remains of walls, towers and a gatehouse can be seen. This is the finest of a trio of castles, the others being at Skenfrith and Grosmont.
Times: Open all year, late Apr-late Sep, daily 10-5; site open rest of year. **Fee:** £2 (ch 5-16, pen & students £1.50). Family ticket £5.50.
Facilities: 🅿 ♿ ✸ ۞ 🍴

NEATH PORT TALBOT

🏯 ABERDULAIS   Map 03 SS79

ABERDULAIS FALLS

SA10 8EU (from M4 junct 43, take A465, signposted Vale of Neath)

☎ **01639 636674** 🖥 **01639 645069**
Times: Open: March: Sat & Sun 11am-4pm only. Apr-Oct Mon-Fri 10am-5pm, Sat, Sun & Bank Hols 11am-6pm. **Facilities:** 🅿 ☕ ♿ (lifts for disabled to view falls) toilets for disabled shop ✿ *Details not confirmed for 2002* 🍴

🏯 CRYNANT   Map 03 SN70

CEFN COED COLLIERY MUSEUM

SA10 8SN (1m S of Cryant, on A4109)

☎ **01639 750556** 🖥 **01639 750556**
Times: Open daily, Apr-Oct 10.30-5; Nov-Mar, groups welcome by prior arrangement. **Facilities:** 🅿 ☕ ♿ toilets for disabled shop *Details not confirmed for 2002* 🍴

🏯 CYNONVILLE   Map 03 SS89

SOUTH WALES MINERS MUSEUM

Afan Argoed Country Park SA13 3HG (on A4107 6m NE of Port Talbot, leave M4 at junct 40)

☎ **01639 850564 & 850875** 🖥 **01639 850446**
Times: Open all year daily, Mar-Sep 10.30-5 (Sat & Sun 10.30-6); Oct-Feb 10.30-4 (Sat & Sun 10.30-5). **Facilities:** 🅿 (charged) ☕ ✗ ♿ (mechanical & manual wheel chairs on request) toilets for disabled shop ✸ (ex guide dogs) *Details not confirmed for 2002* 🍴

🏯 MARGAM   Map 03 SS78

MARGAM PARK

SA13 2TJ (Take junct 38 off M4 and follow signs. Approx 300yds on A48 towards Pyle)

☎ **01639 881635** 🖥 **01639 895897**
Times: Open all year, Apr-Sep daily 10-6 (last admission 5pm). Oct-Mar, Wed-Sun 10-5 (last admission 3pm). **Facilities:** 🅿 ☕ ✗ licensed ♿ (free wheelchair loan, garden for disabled) toilets for disabled shop *Details not confirmed for 2002* 🍴

🏯 NEATH   Map 03 SS79

GNOLL ESTATE COUNTRY PARK

SA11 3BS (follow brown tourist signs)

☎ **01639 635808** 🖥 **01639 635694**
Times: Open all year - Country park; Vistor centre, daily from 10am. (Closed Xmas wk). **Facilities:** 🅿 ☕ ♿ toilets for disabled shop ✸ (ex on lead) *Details not confirmed for 2002*

NEATH ABBEY

SA10 7DW

☎ **01639 812387**
Times: Open at all times. Key keeper arrangement. **Facilities:** 🅿 ♿
✸ ۞ *Details not confirmed for 2002*

NEWPORT

🏯 CAERLEON   Map 03 ST39

CAERLEON ROMAN BATHS

NP6 1AE (on B4236)

☎ **01663 422518**

Caerleon was an important Roman military base, with accommodation for thousands of men. The foundations of barrack lines and parts of the ramparts can be seen, with remains of the cookhouse, latrines and baths. The amphitheatre nearby is one of the best examples in Britain.
Times: Open Apr-28 Oct, daily 9.30-5; 29 Oct-Mar, Mon-Sat 9.30-5, Sun 1-5. **Fee:** £2 (ch 5-16, pen & students £1.50, disabled free). Family ticket £5.50. **Facilities:** 🅿 ♿ shop ✸ ۞ 🍴

ROMAN LEGIONARY MUSEUM

High St NP18 1AE (10mins from M4/Severn Bridge. From M4 junct 25 take B4596)

☎ **01633 423134** 🖥 **01633 422869**

The museum illustrates the history of Roman Caerleon and the daily life of its garrison. On display are arms, armour and equipment, with a collection of engraved gemstones, a labyrinth mosaic and finds from the legionary base at Usk. Please telephone for details of children's holiday activities.
Times: Open all year, Apr-Oct, Mon-Sat 10-6, Sun 2-6; Nov-Mar, Mon-Sat 10-4, Sun 2-4.30. **Fee:** Free. 🅿 (100yds) ♿ toilets for disabled shop ✸ (ex guide dogs) 🍴

🏯 NEWPORT   Map 03 ST38

TREDEGAR HOUSE & PARK

Coedkernew NP1 9YW (2m W, signposted from A48/M4 junct 28)

☎ **01633 815880** 🖥 **01633 815895**
e-mail: tredegar.house@newport.gov.uk
Times: Open Good Fri-Sep, Wed-Sun & BHs 11-4. (All week in Aug, wknds only in Oct). Special Hallowe'en & Xmas opening. Also open for group visits at other times. **Facilities:** 🅿 (charged) ☕ ✗ licensed ♿ (wheelchairs for loan) toilets for disabled shop ✸ (ex grounds & guide dogs) *Details not confirmed for 2002* 🍴

PENHOW
Map 03 ST49

PENHOW CASTLE
NP26 3AD (M4 junct 24, on A48 between Newport & Chepstow)
☎ 01633 400800 📠 01633 400990
e-mail: info@penhowcastle.com

The oldest inhabited castle in Wales, originally a small border fortress. The building presents a fascinating picture of castle life through nine centuries. Rooms include the Norman bedchamber, the 15th-century Great Hall with its fine screen and minstrels' gallery, the elegant dining room with original panelling and the cosy Victorian housekeeper's room. Please ring for deatails of special events.
Times: Open Good Fri-end Sep, Wed-Sun & BH 10-5.15 last admission; "Candlelit Tours" by arrangement; Aug open daily; Winter Wed 10-4 Sun 1-4. (Closed Jan-Feb). **Fee:** £3.85 (ch £2.60). Family ticket £10.50. Party 20+ 10%off **Facilities:** 🅿 ♿ (audio-tours for blind) shop 🍴 (ex guide dogs)

PEMBROKESHIRE

AMROTH
Map 02 SN10

COLBY WOODLAND GARDEN
SA67 8PP (1.5 miles inland from Amroth, follow brown signs from A477)
☎ 01834 811885
Times: Open Apr-Oct, daily 10-5. Walled garden Apr-30 Oct 11-5.
Facilities: 🅿 🍽 ♿ (Limited due to terrain) toilets for disabled shop garden centre 🎋 *Details not confirmed for 2002* 🍴

CAREW
Map 02 SN00

CAREW CASTLE & TIDAL MILL
SA70 8SL (on A4075, just off A477 Pembroke to Kilgetty rd)
☎ 01646 651782 📠 01646 651782
e-mail: enquiries@
carewcastle.pembrokeshirecoast.org.uk

This magnificent Norman castle has royal links with Henry Tudor and was the setting for the Great Tournament of 1507. Nearby is the Carew Cross (Cadw), an impressive 13ft Celtic cross dating from the 11th century. Carew Mill is one of only four restored tidal mills in Britain, with records dating back to 1558.
Times: Open Etr-end Oct, daily 10-5. **Fee:** £2.80 (ch & pen £1.90).Family ticket £7.50. Single ticket (castle or mill) £1.90 (ch £1.50).
Facilities: 🅿 ♿ (ramps) toilets for disabled shop 🍴

CILGERRAN
Map 02 SN14

CILGERRAN CASTLE
SA43 2SF (off A484 & A478)
☎ 01239 615007

Set above a gorge of the River Teifi - famed for its coracle fishermen - Cilgerran Castle dates from the 11th to 13th centuries. It decayed gradually after the

Civil War, but its great round towers and high walls give a vivid impression of its former strength.
Times: Open: Apr-Oct, daily 9.30-6.30; Nov-Mar, daily 9.30-4. **Fee:** £2 (ch 5-16, pen & students £1.50). Family ticket £5.50. & shop
Facilities: 🍴 ☺ 🍴

CRYMYCH
Map 02 SN13

CASTELL HENLLYS FORT
Pant-Glas, Meline SA41 3UT (off A487 between Eglwyswrw and Newport)
☎ 01239 891319 📠 01239 891319
e-mail: celts@castellhenllys.freeserve.co.uk
Times: Open Apr-early Nov, daily 10-5. Last entry 4.30 **Facilities:** 🅿 ♿ toilets for disabled shop *Details not confirmed for 2002* 🍴

FISHGUARD
Map 02 SM93

OCEANLAB
The Parrog, Goodwick SA64 0DE (close to Stena Line ferry terminal at harbour)
☎ 01348 874737 📠 01348 872528
e-mail: ocean_lab01@hotmail.com
Times: Open Etr-Oct 10-6, winter opening on request. **Facilities:** 🅿 🍽 ♿ toilets for disabled shop 🍴 (ex guide dogs) *Details not confirmed for 2002* 🍴

LAMPHEY
Map 02 SN00

LAMPHEY PALACE
SA71 5NT (off A4139)
☎ 01646 672224

This ruined 13th-century palace once belonged to the Bishops of St David's.
Times: Open all year, daily 10-5. **Fee:** £2 (ch 5-16, pen & students £1.50, disabled free). Family ticket £5.50. **Facilities:** 🅿 ♿ toilets for disabled shop 🍴 ☺ 🍴

LLANYCEFN
Map 02 SN02

PENRHOS COTTAGE
SA66 7XT (near Maenclochog & Llanycefn, N of Haverfordwest)
☎ 01437 760460 📠 01437 760460
Times: Open mid May-Sep Mon-Fri, by appointment only. Tel: 01437 760460. **Facilities:** 🅿 (roadside) ♿ shop 🍴 (ex in grounds or guide dogs) *Details not confirmed for 2002*

LLAWHADEN
Map 02 SN01

LLAWHADEN CASTLE
☎ 01437 541201
Times: Open at all times. Key keeper arrangement. **Facilities:** ♿ 🍴 ☺ *Details not confirmed for 2002*

NARBERTH   Map 02 SN11
OAKWOOD PARK
Canaston Bridge SA67 8DE (M4 W Junct 49, take A48 to Carmarthen, signposted from Carmarthen)
☎ 0870 1240044, 08453455657
▤ 01834 891408
e-mail: enquiries@oakwood-leisure.com

Wales' premier theme park, featuring: the world's no.1 wooden roller coaster Megafobia, the 50m-high sky coaster Vertig, shot n' drop tower coaster The Bounce, and Snake River Falls. For young children there is KidzWorld featuring The Wacky Factory, The Lost Kingdom, Techniquest and Playtown. In summer there are firework displays and light shows at night.
Times: Open daily 12 Apr-Sep, from 10am. **Fee:** Adults & ch over 10 £11.75, ch 3-9 £10.75, under 2 free, pen & disabled £7.50. Party 20+. Family ticket £42. **Facilities:** ▣ ⬤ ✕ licensed & (wheelchair hire, special access to some rides) toilets for disabled shop ✸ (ex guide dogs) ⬤

NEWPORT   Map 02 SN03
PENTRE IFAN BURIAL CHAMBER
(3m SE from B4329 or A487)
☎ 029 2050 0200
Times: Open - access throughout the year. **Facilities:** ✸ ⊕ *Details not confirmed for 2002*

PEMBROKE   Map 02 SM90
THE MUSEUM OF THE HOME
7 Westgate Hill SA71 4LB (opposite Pembroke Castle)
☎ 01646 681200

A pleasant domestic setting provides an opportunity to view some of the objects that have been part of everyday life over the past three hundred years.
Times: Open May-Sep, Mon-Thu 11-5, other times by arrangement. **Fee:** £1.20 (ch & pen 90p). **Facilities:** ▣ (100 yds) (Public Pay & Display) ✸

PEMBROKE CASTLE
SA71 4LA (west end of main street)
☎ 01646 681510   ▤ 01646 622260
e-mail: pembroke.castle@talk21.com

The birthplace of first Tudor king, Henry VII, Pembroke Castle is a well-preserved Norman fortress with an impressive 75ft circular keep. The Great Gatehouse is home to a number of exhibitions tracing the history of medieval life at the castle. Beneath the Northern Hall is a vast cavern, once occupied by Stone Age cave dwellers and later used as a food and boat store by the Normans.
Times: Open all year, daily, Apr-Sep 9.30-6; Mar & Oct 10-5; Nov-Feb, 10.30-4.30; (Closed 24-26 Dec & 1 Jan). **Fee:** £3 (ch under 16 & pen £2, ch under 5 & wheelchairs free). Family ticket £8. **Facilities:** ▣ (200 yds) ⬤ & toilets for disabled shop ⬤

ST DAVID'S   Map 02 SM72
ST DAVIDS BISHOP'S PALACE
SA62 6PE (on A487)
☎ 01437 720517

These extensive and impressive ruins are all that remain of the principal residence of the Bishops of St Davids. The palace shares a quiet valley with the cathedral, which was almost certainly built on the site of a monastery founded in the 6th century by St David. The Bishop's Palace houses an exhibition: 'Lords of the Palace'.
Times: Open: 26 Mar-25 May daily 9.30-5, 26 May-Sep daily 9.30-6, 1-28 Oct daily 9.30-5, 29 Oct-Mar Mon-Sat 9.30-4, Sun 11-4. **Fee:** £2 (ch 5-16, pen & students £1.50). Family ticket £5.50. **Facilities:** ▣ & toilets for disabled shop ✸ ⊕ ⬤

ST DAVIDS CATHEDRAL
The Close SA62 6PE
☎ 01437 720202   ▤ 01437 721885
e-mail: adminstrator@stdavidscathedral.org.uk

Begun 1181 on the reputed site of St David's 6th century monastic settlement. The present building was altered during the 12th to the 14th centuries and again in the 16th. The ceilings of oak, painted wood and stone vaulting are of considerable interest.
Times: Open all year 8.30-6. **Fee:** Suggested donation of £2.
Facilities: ▣ (300yds) ⬤ & toilets for disabled shop ✸ (ex guide dogs) ⬤

ST FLORENCE   Map 02 SN00
MANOR HOUSE WILDLIFE & LEISURE PARK
Ivy Tower SA70 8RJ (on B4318 between Tenby & St Florence)
☎ 01646 651201   ▤ 01646 651201

The park is set in 35 acres of delightful wooded grounds and award-winning gardens. The wildlife includes exotic birds, reptiles and fish. Also here are a pets' corner, a children's playground with free rides on the astraglide slide and roundabouts. Other attractions include a natural history museum, a go-kart track and a
contd.

model railway exhibition. There are daily falconry displays. Telephone for details of displays and animal feeding times.
Times: Open Etr-end Sep, daily 10-6. Please telephone for late opening Jul/Aug. **Fee:** £4.25 (ch £3.25, pen £3.75, disabled/helpers £2.50) Family ticket £13.50 (2 adults, 2 ch). Party 20+. **Facilities:** ▣ ▼ ₠ toilets for disabled shop ✱

🏛 SCOLTON   Map 02 SM92
SCOLTON VISITOR CENTRE
SA62 5QL (5m N of Haverfordwest, on B4329)
☎ 01437 731328 (Mus) & 731457 (Park)
🖹 01437 731743
Times: Open; Museum Apr-Oct, Tue-Sun & BH's 10.30-5.30; Country Park all year ex 25 & 26 Dec, Etr-Sep 10-7, Oct-Etr 10-4.30.
Facilities: ▣ (charged) ▼ ₠ (disabled parking area near house) toilets for disabled shop ✱ (ex guide dogs & in grounds) *Details not confirmed for 2002*

🏛 TENBY   Map 02 SN10
TENBY MUSEUM & ART GALLERY
Castle Hill SA70 7BP (near town centre above harbour)
☎ 01834 842809 🖹 01834 842809
e-mail: tenbymuseum@hotmail.com
Times: Open all year, Etr-Oct, daily 10-5; Nov-Etr, Mon-Fri 10-5.
Facilities: ▣ ₠ shop ✱ (ex guide dogs) *Details not confirmed for 2002*

TUDOR MERCHANT'S HOUSE
Quay Hill SA70 7BX
☎ 01834 842279
Times: Open 2 Apr-Sep, Mon-Tue, Thu-Sat 10-5, Sun 1-5. Dec Mon-Tue, Thu-Fri 10-3, Sun 12-3. **Facilities:** ℙ (500yds) (no coaches nearby) ₠ (garden could be accessed) ✱ (ex guide or small dogs) ⅏ *Details not confirmed for 2002*

POWYS

🏛 ABERCRAF   Map 03 SN81
DAN-YR-OGOF THE NATIONAL SHOWCAVES CENTRE FOR WALES
SA9 1GJ (M4 J45, midway between Swansea & Brecon on A4067)
☎ 01639 730284 & 730801 🖹 01639 730293
e-mail: info@showcaves.co.uk

This award winning attraction includes three separate caves, a dinosaur park, an Iron Age Farm, a museum, a shire horse centre and a covered children's play area.
Times: Open Apr-Oct, daily from 10am. Please telephone for Oct. **Fee:** £7.50 (ch £4.50). Group rates 15+ **Facilities:** ▣ ▼ shop ◀

🏛 BERRIEW   Map 07 SJ10
GLANSEVERN HALL GARDENS
Glansevern SY21 8AH (on A483 between Welshpool and Newtown)
☎ 01686 640200 🖹 01686 640829
Times: Open May-Sep, BH Mon, Fri-Sat 2-6. Parties other dates by arrangement **Facilities:** ▣ ▼ ₠ (most areas accessible) shop garden centre *Details not confirmed for 2002*

🏛 BRECON   Map 03 SO02
BRECKNOCK MUSEUM & ART GALLERY
Captain's Walk LD3 7DW (near town centre at junction of The Watton & Glamorgan St)
☎ 01874 624121 🖹 01874 611281
e-mail: brecknock.museum@powys.gov.uk

A wealth of local history is explored at the museum, which has archaeological and historical exhibits, with sections on folk life, decorative arts and natural history. Victorian Assize Court is interpreted with life-size figures and there is one of the finest collections of Welsh Lovespoons. The museum also runs a lively programme of Welsh contemporary art exhibitions.
Times: Open all year, Mon-Fri 10-5, Sat 10-1 & 2-4; also open Sun 12-5 Apr-Sep. Nov-Feb, Sat until 4. (Closed Good Fri, Xmas, Boxing Day & New Year's Day). **Fee:** Free. **Facilities:** ▣ ₠ (limited parking, must be accompanied by able-bodied) toilets for disabled shop ✱ (ex guide dogs) ◀

SOUTH WALES BORDERERS (24TH REGIMENT) MUSEUM MUSEUM
The Barracks, The Watton LD3 7EB (close to town centre, well signed)
☎ 01874 613310 🖹 01874 613275
e-mail: swb@rrw.org.uk

The museum of the South Wales Borderers and Monmouthshire Regiment, which was raised in 1689 and has been awarded 23 Victoria Crosses. Amongst the collections is the Zulu War Room, devoted to the war and in particular to the events at Rorke's Drift, 1879, when 121 men fought 4500 Zulus.
Times: Open all year, Apr-Sep daily; Oct-Mar, Mon-Fri 9-5. (Closed Xmas & New Year). **Fee:** £2 (ch 16 £1). **Facilities:** ℙ (town centre) ₠ toilets for disabled shop ✱ (ex guide dogs) ◀

🏛 LLANFAIR CAEREINION   Map 06 SJ10
WELSHPOOL & LLANFAIR LIGHT RAILWAY
SY21 0SF (beside A458, Shrewsbury-Dolgellau road)
☎ 01938 810441 🖹 01938 810861
Times: Open Etr-Oct, phone for timetable enquiries. **Facilities:** ▣ ▼ ₠ (two coachs adapted for wheelchairs) toilets for disabled shop *Details not confirmed for 2002* ◀

🏛 MACHYNLLETH   Map 06 SH70
CELTICA
Y Plas, Aberystwyth Rd SY20 8ER (2 minutes walk S of town clock. Car park entrance off Aberystwyth Rd)
☎ 01654 702702 🖹 01654 703604
e-mail: celtica@celtica.wales.com

Located in a restored mansion house, Celtica is an exciting heritage centre introducing the history and culture of the Celtic people. The sights and sounds of Celtic life are brought alive as you go on a journey portraying the Celtic spirit of the past, present and future. There's an interpretive centre dedicated to Welsh and Celtic history, a children's indoor play area, and conference rooms. Education resources are

contd.

available and groups are welcome. Storytelling, lectures, music and craft events take place.
Times: Open daily 10-6 (last show starts 4.40). Evening opening for pre-booked groups. (Closed 1 Jan, & 14-18 Jan) **Fee:** £4.95 (concessions £3.80). Family ticket £13.75. **Facilities:** 🅿 💺 ✗ licensed & (Lift & ramps to public areas; Induction loop) toilets for disabled shop ⅀ (ex guide dogs) ➷

CENTRE FOR ALTERNATIVE TECHNOLOGY
SY20 9AZ (2.5m N on A487)
☎ 01654 702400   📄 01654 702782
e-mail: help@catinfo.demon.co.uk
Times: Open Mar-Oct; 10-5.30; Nov-Feb; 11-4. (Closed 23-26 Dec & 5-23 Jan). **Facilities:** 🅿 💺 (wheelchair available) shop ⅀ (ex guide dogs) *Details not confirmed for 2002* ➷

🏚 MONTGOMERY   Map 03 SO29
MONTGOMERY CASTLE
☎ 029 2050 0200
Times: Open all year, any reasonable time. **Facilities:** & ⅀ ☺
Details not confirmed for 2002

🏚 PRESTEIGNE   Map 03 SO36
THE JUDGE'S LODGING
Broad St LD8 2AD (In centre of town, off B4362 - signed from A44/A49)
☎ 01544 260650/1   📄 01544 260652
e-mail: info@judgeslodging.org.uk

A restored Victorian town house with integral courtroom, cells and service areas - step back into the 1860s, accompanied by an 'evesdropping' audiotour of voices from the past. Explore the fascinating world of the Victorian judges, their servents & felonious guests at this award winning 'hands on' historic house.
Times: Open daily, Mar-Oct 10-6, Nov-Dec Wed-Sun 10-4. Closed Jan-Feb. **Fee:** £3.75 (ch & concessions £2.75). Family £11. Party rates available. **Facilities:** 🅿 200mtrs & (lift, disabled pack for inacceslble items) shop ⅀ (ex guide dogs)

🏚 TRETOWER   Map 03 SO12
TRETOWER COURT & CASTLE
NP8 2RF (3m NW of Crickhowell, off A479)
☎ 01874 730279

The castle is a substantial ruin of an 11th-century motte and bailey, with a three-storey tower and 9ft-thick walls. Nearby is the Court, a 14th-century fortified manor house which has been altered and extended over the years. The two buildings show the shift from medieval castle to more domestic accommodation over the centuries.
Times: Open early-late Mar, daily 10-4; late Mar-late May & early Sep-late Oct, daily 10-5; late May-early Sep, daily 10-6. **Fee:** £2.50 (ch 5-16, pen & students £2). Family ticket £7. **Facilities:** 🅿 & toilets for disabled shop ⅀ ☺ ➷

🏚 WELSHPOOL   Map 07 SJ20
POWIS CASTLE
SY21 8RF (1m S of Welshpool, signposted off A483)
☎ 01938 551920   📄 01938 554336
e-mail: ppcmsn@smtp.ntrust.org.uk

Laid out in the Italian and French styles, the Garden retains its original lead statues, an Orangery and an aviary on the terraces. The medieval castle contains one of the finest collections of paintings and furniture in Wales and a beautiful collection of treasures from India.
Times: Castle & museum open: Apr-Jun and Sep-Oct, Wed-Sun 1-5; Jul-Aug Tue-Sun 1-5; Open all Bank Hol's in season. Garden is open same days as castle and museum 11-6. Last admission to all parts is 30 mins before closing. **Fee:** Castle, Museum & Gardens £7.50, (ch under 17 £3.75) Family ticket £18.75. Group member £6.50. Garden only: £5 (ch £2.50) Family £12.50, Group member £4. NT members & ch under 5 free. **Facilities:** 🅿 ✗ licensed (photos of interior available from tearoom) shop garden centre ⅀ (ex guide dogs) 🦮 ➷

RHONDDA CYNON TAFF

🏚 TREHAFOD   Map 03 ST09
RHONDDA HERITAGE PARK
Lewis Merthyr Colliery, Coed Cae Rd CF37 7NP (between Pontypridd & Porth, off A470; follow brown tourist signs from M4 junct32)
☎ 01443 682036   📄 01443 687420
e-mail: rhonpark@netwales.co.uk

Based at the Lewis Merthyr Colliery, the Heritage Park is a fascinating 'living history' attraction. You can take the Cage Ride to 'Pit Bottom' and explore the underground workings of a 1950s pit, guided by men who were miners themselves. There are children's activities, an art gallery and a museum illustrating living conditions in the Rhondda Valley. Special events throughout the year, phone for details.
Times: Open all year, daily 10-6. (Closed Mon from Oct-Etr). Last admission 4.30pm. (Closed 25 & 26 Dec). **Fee:** £5.60 (ch £4.30, pen £4.95). Family ticket £16.50. **Facilities:** 🅿 💺 ✗ licensed & (Wheelchair available, accessible parking, lifts) toilets for disabled shop ⅀ (ex guide dogs) ➷

SWANSEA

🏛 LLANRHIDIAN
Map 02 SS49
WEOBLEY CASTLE
SA3 1HB (from B4271 or B4295)
☎ 01792 390012

A 12th- to 14th-century fortified manor house with an exhibition on the history of Weobley and other historic sites on the Gower peninsula.
Times: Open all year, Apr-Oct, daily 9.30-6; Nov-Mar daily 9.30-5 **Fee:** £2 (ch 5-16, pen & students £1.50). Family ticket £5.50.
Facilities: 🅿 ♿ shop 🐾 ☺ 🍴

🏛 OXWICH
Map 02 SS48
OXWICH CASTLE
SA3 1NG (A4118 from Swansea)
☎ 01792 390359

Situated on the Gower peninsula, this Tudor mansion is a striking testament in stone to the pride and ambitions of the Mansel dynasty of Welsh gentry. The E-shaped wing houses an exhibition on historical Gower and 'Chieftains and Princes of Wales'.
Times: Open 3 Apr-Sep, daily 10-5 (Closed at all other times ex Strata Florida Abbey, Valle Crucis Abbey and Whit which are open sites). **Fee:** £2 (ch 5-16, pen & students £1.50). Family ticket £5.50. **Facilities:** 🅿 ♿ (Radar key toilet) toilets for disabled 🐾 ☺ 🍴

🏛 PARKMILL
Map 02 SS58
GOWER HERITAGE CENTRE
Y Felin Ddwr SA3 2EH (Follow signs for South Gower on A4118 W from Swansea. W side of Parkmill village)
☎ 01792 371206 🖨 01792 371471
e-mail:
info@gowerheritagecentre.sagehost.co.uk

Based around a 12th-century water-powered cornmill, the site also contains a number of craft workshops, a museum and a miller's cottage, all set in attractive countryside in an Area of Outstanding Natural Beauty.
Times: Open daily, Mar-Oct 10-6; Nov-Feb 10-5. (Closed 25 Dec). **Fee:** £2.95 (ch, students & pen £1.95). Family ticket £8.50. Party. **Facilities:** 🅿 🍴 ♿ (ramp entrance access) toilets for disabled shop 🍴

🏛 SWANSEA
Map 03 SS69
GLYNN VIVIAN ART GALLERY
Alexandra Rd SA1 5DZ (Turn off M4 J42 along Fabian Way A483 up Wind St. Turn L at train stn opposite library)
☎ 01792 655006 & 651738 🖨 01792 651713
e-mail: glynn.vivian.gallery@business.ntl.com

A broad spectrum of visual arts form the original bequest of Richard Glynn Vivian, including Old Masters and an international collection of porcelain and Swansea china. The 20th century is also well represented with modern painting and sculpture by British and foreign artists, with the emphasis on Welsh artists.
Times: Open all year, Tue-Sun & BH Mon 10-5. (Closed 25, 26 Dec & 1 Jan). **Fee:** Free. **Facilities:** 🅿 (200 yds, NCP) ♿ shop 🐾 (ex guide dogs, hearing dogs) 🍴

SWANSEA MARITIME & INDUSTRIAL MUSEUM
Museum Square, Maritime Quarter SA1 1SN (M4 junct 42, on main rd into Swansea city centre)
☎ 01792 650351 & 470371 🖨 01792 654200
e-mail: swansea.maritime.museum@swansea.gov.uk

This museum complex in the Swansea maritime quarter contains a working woollen mill as well as a selection of floating boats to explore (Apr-Oct). There are displays relating to the Port of Swansea, its industries and environment, transport exhibits, and maritime and agricultural sections. There is a programme of temporary exhibitions.
Times: Open all year, Tue-Sun 10-5.(last admission 4.45pm). Closed Mon except BH Mon, 25, 26 Dec & 1 Jan. **Fee:** Free. **Facilities:** 🅿 (50yds) (charged) 🍴 ♿ shop 🐾 (ex guide dogs) 🍴

TORFAEN

🏛 BLAENAVON
Map 03 SO20
BIG PIT NATIONAL MINING MUSEUM OF WALES
NP4 9XP (M4 junct 26/25, follow signs on A4042 & A4043 to Pontypool & Blaenavon. Signposted off A465)
☎ 01495 790311 🖨 01495 792618
e-mail: pwllmawr@aol.com

The `Big Pit' closed as a working mine in 1980, but today you can don safety helmets and cap lamps, and descend the 300ft shaft to find out what life was like for Welsh miners. There is also an exhibition in the old pithead baths and a reconstructed miner's cottage. Sturdy shoes and warm clothes are recommended for tours of the mine.
Times: Open Mar-Nov, daily 9.30-5, last tour 3.30. Dec-Feb telephone for opening details. **Fee:** Free. **Facilities:** 🅿 🍴 ♿ (underground tours by prior arrangement) toilets for disabled shop (not on underground tours) 🍴 *See advert on p353*

BLAENAVON IRONWORKS
North St
☎ 01495 792615

The Blaenavon Ironworks were a milestone in the history of the Industrial Revolution. Constructed in 1788-99, they were the first purpose-built, multi-furnace ironworks in Wales. By 1796, Blaenavon was the second largest ironworks in Wales, eventually closing down in 1904.
Times: Open Apr-Oct, daily 9.30-4.30. For details of opening outside this period, telephone 01633 648081. **Fee:** £2 (ch 5-16, pen & students £1.50). Family ticket £5.5. **Facilities:** 🅿 ⍟ ⊕ 🍽

CWMBRAN   Map 03 ST29
GREENMEADOW COMMUNITY FARM
Greenforge Way NP44 5AJ (follow signs for Cwmbran then brown tourist signs (with sheep on) to farm)
☎ 01633 862202 📠 01633 489332
e-mail: greenmeadow_community_farm@compuserve.com

This is one of Wales' leading tourist attractions - a community farm that was built during the 1980s on land threatened by developers. There are milking demonstrations, tractor and trailer rides, a dragon adventure play area, a farm trail, a nature trail and lots more. Phone for details of lambing weekends, shearing, country fair and agricultural shows, Halloween and Christmas events.
Times: Open summer 10-6, winter 10-4. (Closed 25 Dec). **Fee:** Adult £3 (ch £2.25) Family (2 adults & 3 children) £12 or Season Family ticket £30. **Facilities:** 🅿 ⍟ & (tractor & trailer rides for wheelchair users) toilets for disabled shop 🍽

VALE OF GLAMORGAN

BARRY   Map 03 ST16
WELSH HAWKING CENTRE
Weycock Rd CF62 3AA (on A4226)
☎ 01446 734687 📠 01446 739620
Times: Open end Mar-end Sep, daily 10.30-5, 1hr before dusk in winter. **Facilities:** 🅿 ⍟ & toilets for disabled shop 🍽 *Details not confirmed for 2002* 🍽

OGMORE   Map 03 SS87
OGMORE CASTLE
☎ 01656 653435
Times: Open - access throughout the year. Key keeper arrangement.
Facilities: 🅿 & ⍟ ⊕ *Details not confirmed for 2002*

PENARTH   Map 03 ST17
COSMESTON LAKES COUNTRY PARK & MEDIEVAL VILLAGE
Cosmeston Lakes Country Park, Lavernock Rd CF64 5UY (on B4267 between Barry and Penarth, close to M4 junct 33)
☎ 029 2070 1678 📠 029 2070 8686

Deserted during the plagues and famines of the 14th century, the original village was rediscovered through archaeological excavations. The buildings have been faithfully reconstructed on the excavated remains, creating a living museum of medieval village life. Special events throughout the year include re-enactments and Living History.
Times: Open all year, daily 11-5 in Summer, 11-4 in Winter. (Closed 25 Dec). Country park open at all times. **Fee:** Entry to Village £3, (concessions £2) Family ticket £7.50. Entry to Country Park is free.
Facilities: 🅿 ⍟ ✕ & (access ramps) toilets for disabled shop

ST HILARY   Map 03 ST07
OLD BEAUPRE CASTLE
(1m SW, off A48)
☎ 01446 773034
Times: Open - access throughout the year. Key keeper arrangement.
Facilities: 🅿 ⍟ ⊕ *Details not confirmed for 2002*

WREXHAM

CHIRK   Map 07 SJ23
CHIRK CASTLE
LL14 5AF (8m S of Wrexham, signposted off A483)
☎ 01691 777701 📠 01691 774706
e-mail: pcwmsn@smtp.ntrust.org.uk
Times: Open 29 Mar-Sep, Wed-Sun & BH Mon 12-5 (castle), 11-6 (gardens); Oct, Wed-Sun 12-4 (castle), 11-5 (gardens). Last admission 30 mins before closing. **Facilities:** 🅿 ✕ licensed & (stairclimber) toilets for disabled shop 🍽 (ex guide dogs) 🐾 *Details not confirmed for 2002*

WREXHAM   Map 07 SJ35
ERDDIG
LL13 0YT (off A525, 2m S of Wrexham & A483/A5152 Oswestry road)
☎ 01978 355314 📠 01978 313333
Times: Open 25 Mar-1 Nov, Sat-Wed (open Good Fri), house 12-5, garden 11-6 (Jul-Aug gardens 10-6); Oct-1 Nov, Sat-Wed, house 12-4, garden 11-5. **Facilities:** 🅿 ✕ licensed & toilets for disabled shop garden centre 🍽 (ex guidance dogs) 🐾 *Details not confirmed for 2002* 🍽

Northern Ireland

The six counties of Ulster are part of the United Kingdom. The greater part of its 1.6 million inhabitants are Protestants, descendants of an influx of settlers from England and Scotland in the 17th century.

Despite well-publicized tensions, the province has consistently drawn tourists, not so much to the cities which are more interesting than attractive, but for the scenery.

The most popular landscapes are linked by the 430 mile (700km) Ulster Way, which would take an intrepid walker though all six counties, taking in the Glens of Antrim with its woods, waterfalls and ruins, and the remarkable Giant's Causeway. Further south near the border with the Republic, the Ulster Way meanders through the Mountains of Mourne, rather gaunt, steep granite hills (highest point Slieve Donard, 2795 ft (852m)). Less strenuous stretches explore the beautiful Lough Erne.

Belfast is more attractive than news reports may have led you to imagine, with its parks, castle, meadows and botanical gardens.

After Belfast, the second city is Londonderry, or Derry, depending on your perspective. The city walls stand virtually complete, a reminder of the siege of 1688 when the Apprentice Boys locked out James II's army. From the walls you can view the sweep of the River Foyle.

Downpatrick, the market town of Down, claims to be the burial place of St Patrick, the patron saint of Ireland. His life is commemorated in the cathedral, and in the converted jail.

For lakes, islands, caves, castles and grand houses, Enniskillen is the place to go. Perched on an island between the Upper and Lower Lough Erne, it offers boat trips, angling, water sports and easy rambling.

Top: Murlough Bay, Co Antrim

BELFAST

⌂ BELFAST
Map 01 D5

BELFAST CASTLE
Antrim Rd BT15 5GR (2.5m from city centre, take
Antrim road towards Glengormley then left into
Innisfayle Park, signed)
☎ 028 9077 6925 ▤ 028 9037 0228
Times: Open all year, daily. Castle open to public viewing. Food &
drink available all day & evening. (closed only 25 Dec) **Facilities:** ℗
☕ ✗ licensed ⅋ (lift to all floors, ramps being installed early '98)
toilets for disabled shop ✸ (ex guide dogs) *Details not confirmed for
2002* ☞

BELFAST ZOOLOGICAL GARDENS
Antrim Rd BT36 7PN (6m N, on A6)
☎ 028 9077 6277 ▤ 028 9037 0578
e-mail: strongej@belfastcity.gov.uk

The 50-acre zoo has a dramatic setting on the face of
Cave Hill, enjoying spectacular views. Attractions
include the award-winning primate house (gorillas and
chimpanzees), penguin enclosure, free-flight aviary,
African enclosure, and underwater viewing of sealions
and penguins. There are also red pandas, free-ranging
lemurs and a group of very rare spectacled bears.
Times: Open all year (ex 25 Dec), daily Apr-Sep 10-5; Oct-Mar 10-2.30.
Fee: Admission charged (ch under 4, pen & disabled free). Party.
(Prices under review) **Facilities:** ℗ ☕ ⅋ (free admission & reserved
parking) toilets for disabled shop ✸ (ex guide dogs) ☞

BOTANIC GARDENS
Stranmillis Rd BT7 1JP
☎ 028 9032 4902 ▤ 028 9023 7070
e-mail: maxwellr@belfastcity.gov.uk

One highlight of the park is the beautiful glass-domed
Victorian Palm House, built between 1839-52. This
palm house predates the one in Kew Gardens and is
one of the earliest curved-glass and iron structures in
the world. Another feature is the Tropical Ravine -
stand on a balcony to get a wonderful view through a
steamy ravine full of exotic plants.
Times: Open all year, Park daily 8-dusk. Tropical ravine and
palmhouse Mon-Fri 10-12.30 & 1-5 (summer), closes 4.30 (winter);
wknds open 1-5 (summer), 1-4 (winter). **Fee:** Free. **Facilities:** ℗
(street) ⅋

GIANT'S RING
(0.75m S of Shaws Bridge)
☎ 028 9023 5000 ▤ 028 9031 0288
Times: Open all times. **Facilities:** ℗ *Details not confirmed for 2002*

ULSTER MUSEUM
Botanic Gardens BT9 5AB (M1/M2 to Balmoral exit)
☎ 028 9038 3000 ▤ 028 9038 3003

Both a national museum and an art gallery, the
collections are Irish and international in origin and
cover antiquities, art, botany and zoology, geology and
local history (including industrial archaeology). An

annual programme of changing temporary exhibitions
and events take place.
Times: Open all year, Mon-Fri 10-5, Sat 1-5, Sun 2-5. Tel for details of
Xmas closures. **Fee:** Free. ℗ (100yds on street) (Clearway 0800-0930
& 1630-1800) ☕ ⅋ (all galleries except one. Loop system, wheelchair
lifts) toilets for disabled shop ✸ (ex guide dogs) ☞

W5 AT ODYSSEY
2 Queens Quay BT3 9QQ
☎ 028 9046 7700 ▤ 028 9046 7707
e-mail: wsonline.co.uk

W5 investigates Who? What? Where? When? Why?...
and that pretty much sums up the intent behind
Ireland's first purpose built discovery centre. Visitors of
any age will want to get their hands on interactive
science and technology displays that include the laser
harp, the fog knife, microscopes, robots and computers.
W5 is part of a massive Millennium Landmark Project
in the heart of Belfast.
Times: Open all year ex 25-26 Dec & 12 Jul. **Fee:** £5 (ch £3,
concessions £3.50). Family ticket £14. **Facilities:** ℗ (charged) ✗
licensed ⅋ (hearing loop) toilets for disabled shop ✸ (ex guide dogs)
☞

CO ANTRIM

⌂ ANTRIM
Map 01 D5

ANTRIM ROUND TOWER
BT41 1BJ (N of town)
☎ 028 9023 5000 ▤ 028 9031 0288
Times: Open all year. **Facilities:** ℗ ⅋ *Details not confirmed for 2002*

⌂ BALLYCASTLE
Map 01 D6

BONAMARGY FRIARY
(E of town, at golf course)
☎ 028 9023 5000 ▤ 028 9031 0288
Times: Open all year. **Facilities:** ℗ ⅋ ♿ *Details not confirmed for
2002*

⌂ BALLYLUMFORD
Map 01 D5

BALLYLUMFORD DOLMEN
(on B90 on NW tip of Island Magee)
☎ 028 9023 5000 ▤ 028 9031 0288
Times: Open all year. **Facilities:** ⅋ *Details not confirmed for 2002*

⌂ BALLYMENA
Map 01 D5

HARRYVILLE MOTTE
(N bank of River Braid)
☎ 028 9023 5000 ▤ 028 9031 0288
Times: Open all year. **Facilities:** ℗ ⅋ ♿ *Details not confirmed for
2002*

⌂ BALLYMONEY
Map 01 C6

LESLIE HILL OPEN FARM
Leslie Hill BT53 6QL (1m NW of Ballymoney on MacFin
Rd)
☎ 028 2766 6803 ▤ 028 2766 6803

An 18th-century estate with a Georgian house,
magnificent period farm buildings and fine grounds

contd.

with paths, lakes and trees. Attractions include an extensive collection of rare breeds, poultry, horsedrawn machinery and carriages, exhibition rooms, a museum, working forge, deer park, walled garden and an adventure playground.
Times: Open Jul-Aug Mon-Sat 11-6, Sun 2-6; Jun Sat-Sun & BH's 2-6; Etr-May & Sep Sun & BH's 2-6, open all Etr wk 11-6. **Fee:** £2.90 (ch £1.90). Family ticket £8.50. **Facilities:** 🅿 💌 ⅃ (ramps) toilets for disabled shop garden centre 🐾 (ex on leads)

🏛 BUSHMILLS   Map 01 C6
OLD BUSHMILLS DISTILLERY
BT57 8XH (on the Castlecatt road)
☎ 028 2073 1521   🖷 028 2073 1339
e-mail: scroskery@idl.ie

Old Bushmills was granted its licence in 1608 and is the oldest licenced whiskey distillery in the world. There's a guided tour, and afterwards you can take part in a comparative tasting session and become a whiskey expert.
Times: Open Apr-Oct, Mon-Sat 9.30-5.30, Sun 12-5.30, last tour 4pm; Nov-Mar, Mon-Fri 5 tours daily, 10.30/11.30/1.30/2.30/3.30. **Fee:** £3.95 (pen & student £3.50, accompanied ch £1.95) Family ticket £11. **Facilities:** 🅿 ✕ ⅃ (AV theatre/shops/restaurant) toilets for disabled shop 🐾 (ex guide dogs) 🍴

🏛 CARRICK-A-REDE   Map 01 D6
CARRICK-A-REDE ROPE BRIDGE AND LARRYBANE VISITORS CENTRE
(E of Ballintoy on B15)
☎ 028 2073 1582   🖷 028 2073 2963
e-mail: unavsm@smtp.ntrust.org.uk

This shaky rope bridge, 80ft above the sea, bridges the 60ft gap between cliffs and a small rocky island. It owes its existence to the salmon who regularly make the dash through the chasm and get netted for their efforts. The bridge has been put across the gap each spring and dismantled every autumn for the last 300 years.
Times: Bridge open Spring-early Sep, daily 10-6; Jul-Aug, daily 10-8. Visitor centre & Tea room open May, wknds & BHs 1-5; Jun-Aug daily 12-6. **Fee:** £2.50 per car, coaches £6. **Facilities:** 🅿 (charged) 💌 ⅃ (information centre) toilets for disabled 🐾

🏛 CARRICKFERGUS   Map 01 D5
CARRICKFERGUS CASTLE
BT38 7BG (on N shore of Belfast Lough)
☎ 028 9335 1273   🖷 028 9336 5190
Times: Open all year, Apr-Sep, weekday 10-6, Sun 2-6; Oct-Mar closes at 4. **Facilities:** 🅿 💌 ⅃ toilets for disabled shop 🐾 *Details not confirmed for 2002*

TOWN WALLS
☎ 028 9023 5000   🖷 028 9031 0288
Times: Visible at all times. **Facilities:** 🅿 ⅃ *Details not confirmed for 2002*

🏛 CHURCHTOWN   Map 01 D5
CRANFIELD CHURCH
(3.75m SW of Randalstown)
☎ 028 9023 5000   🖷 028 9031 0288
Times: Open all year. **Facilities:** 🅿 ⅃ ♿ *Details not confirmed for 2002*

🏛 GIANT'S CAUSEWAY   Map 01 C6
GIANT'S CAUSEWAY CENTRE
44 Causeway Rd BT57 8SU (2m N of Bushmills on B146)
☎ 028 2073 1855   🖷 028 2073 2537
e-mail: causewaytic@hotmail.com

This dramatic rock formation is undoubtedly one of the wonders of the natural world. The Centre provides an exhibition and audio-visual show, and Ulsterbus provides a minibus service to the stones and there are guided walks, and special facilities for the disabled.
Times: Open all year, daily 10-4 (6pm Jun & Sep-Oct; 7pm Jul-Aug). **Fee:** Audio-visual show (12 min) £1 (ch 50p). Family ticket £2.50. Causeway coaster fare to Grand causeway currently £1 return, 60p single, (oap & ch 50% reduction). All prices under review.
Facilities: 🅿 (charged) 💌 ✕ ⅃ (mini bus transport with wheelchair hoist, reserved parking) toilets for disabled shop 🐾 (ex guide dogs) 🍴

🏛 LARNE   Map 01 D5
OLDERFLEET CASTLE
☎ 028 9023 5000   🖷 028 9031 0288
Times: Open at all times. *Details not confirmed for 2002*

🏛 LISBURN   Map 01 D5
DUNEIGHT MOTTE AND BAILEY
(2.3m S beside Ravernet River)
☎ 028 9023 5000   🖷 028 9031 0288
Times: Open all year. *Details not confirmed for 2002*

IRISH LINEN CENTRE & LISBURN MUSEUM
Market Square BT28 1AG (signposted both in and outside town centre)
☎ 028 9266 3377   🖷 028 9267 2624
Times: Open all year, Mon-Sat, 9.30-5. **Facilities:** 🅿 (200m) (limited for disabled and coaches) 💌 ⅃ (lift, induction loop, staff trained in sign language) toilets for disabled shop 🐾 (ex guide dogs) *Details not confirmed for 2002*

🏛 PORTBALLINTRAE   Map 01 C6
DUNLUCE CASTLE
(off A2)
☎ 028 2073 1938   🖷 028 2031 8288
Times: Open all year, Apr-Sep, weekdays 10-7, Sun 2-7; Oct-Mar, Tue-Sat 10-4, Sun 2-4. **Facilities:** 🅿 ⅃ toilets for disabled shop *Details not confirmed for 2002*

▥ TEMPLEPATRICK   Map 01 D5

PATTERSONS SPADE MILL
751 Antrim Rd BT39 0AP (2m SE of Templepatrick on A6)
☎ 028 9443 3619   ▤ 028 9443 3619

This is the last surviving water-driven spade mill in Ireland. It has been completely restored by the National Trust and is now back in production.
Times: Open Etr, Apr-May & Sep, wknds 2-6; Jun-Aug, daily (ex Tue) 2-6, also on BHs. **Fee:** £3 (ch £1.25). Family Ticket £7.25. Party £1.75.
Facilities: ▣ ♿ (ramps wheelchair available) toilets for disabled ✖

TEMPLETOWN MAUSOLEUM
BT39 (in Castle Upton graveyard on A6, Belfast-Antrim road)

Situated in the graveyard of Castle Upton, this family mausoleum is in the shape of a triumphal arch and was designed by Robert Adam.
Times: Open daily during daylight hours. **Fee:** Free. 🚬 ✖

CO ARMAGH

▥ ARMAGH   Map 01 C5

ARMAGH COUNTY MUSEUM
The Mall East BT61 9BE (in centre of City)
☎ 028 3752 3070   ▤ 028 3752 2631
e-mail: acm.um@nics.gov.uk

Housed in a 19th-century schoolhouse, this museum contains an art gallery and library, as well as a collection of local folkcrafts and natural history. Special events are planned thoughout the year.
Times: Open all year, Mon-Fri 10-5, Sat 10-1 & 2-5. **Fee:** Free.
Facilities: ▣ ♿ (ramp/lifts) toilets for disabled shop ✖ (ex guide dogs)

ARMAGH FRIARY
(SE edge of town)
☎ 028 9023 5000   ▤ 028 9031 0288
Times: Open all year. **Facilities:** ▣ ♿ *Details not confirmed for 2002*

ARMAGH PLANETARIUM
College Hill BT61 9DB (on main Armagh-Belfast road close to Mall, city centre)
☎ 028 3752 3689 & 3752 4725
▤ 028 3752 6187
e-mail: ktl@armagh-planetarium.co.uk

The Planetarium is home to The Star Theatre, a multi-media environment equipped with the latest technology including a virtual reality digital system. Also featured are The Hall of Astronomy, the new Eartharium Building and, surrounding the Planetarium, is the Astropark, a 25-acre 'hands on' park.
Times: Open all year, Hall of Astronomy Mon-Fri 10-4.45, shows daily at 3. Also open Sat & Sun 1.15-4.45, shows every Sat 2, 3 & 4. Additional shows during Etr, Xmas & BH's. (Closed Sun). **Fee:** £3.75 (ch, pen & students £2.75). Family ticket £11. Exhibition area £1.
Facilities: ▣ ♿ (Loop system in theatre) toilets for disabled shop ✖ (ex guide dogs) 🚬

NAVAN CENTRE
Killylea Rd BT60 4LD (2m W on A28)
☎ 028 3752 5550   ▤ 028 3752 2323
e-mail: navan@enterprise.net

Navan was once known as Emain Macha, the ancient seat of kings and earliest capital of Ulster. Today it is an impressive archaeological site with its own museum and visitor centre, located in a building that blends into the landscape. The Navan Centre uses audio-visuals and interactive devices to unravel history from myth. The myths include Conor McNessa, Cú Chulainn and the Red Branch Knights.
Times: Open all year Mon-Fri 10-5, Sat 11-5, Sun 12-5. (Closed Xmas week) **Fee:** *Prices not confirmed for 2002* **Facilities:** ▣ ▄ ♿ (loop for hearing aids, parking) toilets for disabled shop ✖ (ex guide dogs)

PALACE STABLES HERITAGE CENTRE
The Palace Demesne BT60 4EL (off Friary Road beside council offices)
☎ 028 3752 9629   ▤ 028 3752 9630
e-mail: stables@armagh.gov.uk

This picturesque Georgian building, set around a cobbled courtyard, has been lovingly restored and now houses a heritage centre. A daily Georgian interpretation is provided by costumed characters. Special events include the Easter Georgian Festival, and an antiques and collectibles fair on the last Sunday of each month.
Times: Open all year, May-Aug, Mon-Sat 10-5.30, Sun 1-6; Sep-Apr, Mon-Sat 10-5, Sun 2-5. Last tour 1hr before closing. **Fee:** £3.50 (ch £2, pen £2.75). Family ticket £9.50. **Facilities:** ▣ ✖ licensed ♿ (ramps & Lift in stables) toilets for disabled shop (dogs courtyard only) 🚬

ST PATRICK'S TRIAN
40 English St BT61 7BA
☎ 028 37 521801   ▤ 028 37 510180
e-mail: info@armagh.gov.uk

This award-winning attraction incorporates three different exhibitions. 'The Armagh Story' traces the city's history; 'Patrick's Testament' examines Armagh's association with Ireland's patron saint; and in 'The Land of Lilliput' a giant tells the story of Gulliver's Travels.
Times: Open all year, Mon-Sat 10-5, Sun 2-5; Jul-Aug, Mon-Sat 10-5. Last tour 1hr before closing. **Fee:** £3.75 (ch £2, pen & student £2.75). Family ticket £9.50. **Facilities:** ▣ (charged) ✖ licensed ♿ (specially designed for disabled) toilets for disabled shop ✖ (ex guide dogs)

▥ CAMLOUGH   Map 01 D5

KILLEVY CHURCHES
(3m S lower eastern slopes of Slieve Gullion)
☎ 028 9023 5000   ▤ 028 9031 0288
Times: Open all year. ♿ *Details not confirmed for 2002*

JONESBOROUGH
Map 01 D5

KILNASAGGART INSCRIBED STONE
(1.25m S)
☎ 028 9023 5000 ▤ 028 9031 0288
Times: Open all year. **Facilities:** P *Details not confirmed for 2002*

MOY
Map 01 C5

ARGORY
Derrycaw Rd BT71 6NA (3m NE)
☎ 028 8778 4753 ▤ 028 8778 9598
e-mail: uagest@smtp.ntrust.org.uk

Originally the home of the McGeough family, this Regency house is situated on a hillside overlooking the Blackwater River. The house is full of period furniture and bric-a-brac. Of particular interest is the very unusual acetylene lighting, installed by the family in 1906.
Times: Open Etr, daily; Apr-May & Sep, wknds & BH; Jun-Aug, daily (ex Tue) 2-6. Open from 1pm on BHs. Last tour 5.15. **Fee:** House & grounds £3 (ch £1.50). Family ticket £7.50. Car park £2.55. Party.
Facilities: P (charged) ☕ ﾖ (special parking facilities, wheelchair available) toilets for disabled shop ﾔ (ex guide dogs) ﾥ ﾒ

NEWRY
Map 01 D5

MOYRY CASTLE
(7.5m S)
☎ 028 9023 5000 ▤ 028 9031 0288
Times: Open all year *Details not confirmed for 2002*

OXFORD ISLAND
Map 01 D5

LOUGH NEAGH DISCOVERY CENTRE
Oxford Island National Nature, Reserve BT66 6NJ (signposted from M1, junct 10)
☎ 028 3832 2205 ▤ 028 3834 7438
e-mail: oxford.island@craigavon.gov.uk

Learn about the history and wildlife of the Lough through a series of exciting audio-visual shows, interactive games and an exhibition, then experience the Island for yourself. In a spectacular setting on the water's edge, discover natural history, wildlife, family walks and much more.
Times: Open Apr-Sep, daily 10-7; Oct-Mar, Wed-Sun 10-5. **Fee:** £1.50 (ch £1, concessions £1.20). Family ticket £4. **Facilities:** P ☕ ﾖ (grounds accessible in part, bird watching hides) toilets for disabled shop ﾔ (ex guide dogs) ﾒ

PORTADOWN
Map 01 D5

ARDRESS HOUSE
Annaghmore BT62 1SQ (7m W on B28)
☎ 028 3885 1236 ▤ 028 3885 1236
e-mail: uagest@smtp.org.uk

A plain 17th-century house, transformed around 1770 by its visionary architect-owner George Ensor, who added elegant wings and superb Adamesque plasterwork. The house has a fine picture gallery on loan from the Earl of Castlestewart. The grounds are

beautifully unspoilt and there is a farmyard with livestock and a display of farm implements.
Times: Open Etr, daily; Apr-May & Sep, wknds & BH's; Jun-Aug, daily (ex Tue) 2-6. **Fee:** House, grounds & farm £2.70 (ch £1.35). Family ticket £6.75. Farmyard only £2.40 (ch £1.20). Family ticket £6. Party.
Facilities: P ﾖ toilets for disabled shop ﾔ (ex guide dogs) ﾥ ﾒ

TYNAN
Map 01 C5

VILLAGE CROSS
☎ 028 9023 5000 ▤ 028 9031 0288
Times: Open all year **Facilities:** P ﾖ *Details not confirmed for 2002*

CO DOWN

ARDGLASS
Map 01 D5

JORDAN'S CASTLE
☎ 028 9023 5000 ▤ 028 9031 0288
Times: Open Jul-Aug; Tue-Sat 10-7, Sun 2-7. Other times on request.
Facilities: ﾔ *Details not confirmed for 2002*

BALLYWALTER
Map 01 D5

GREY ABBEY
(on east edge of village)
☎ 028 9023 5000 ▤ 028 9031 0288
Times: Open Apr-Sep; Tue-Sat 10-7, Sun 2-7. **Facilities:** P ﾖ toilets for disabled *Details not confirmed for 2002*

CASTLEWELLAN
Map 01 D5

DRUMENA CASHEL
(2.25m SW)
☎ 028 9023 5000 ▤ 028 9031 0288
Times: Open all times **Facilities:** P *Details not confirmed for 2002*

COMBER
Map 01 D5

WWT CASTLE ESPIE
Ballydrain Rd BT23 6EA (3m S of Comber, 13m SE of Belfast. Signed from the A22 Comber-Killyleagh-Downpatrick road)
☎ 028 9187 4146 ▤ 028 9187 3857
e-mail: castleespie@wwt.org.uk
Times: Open all year; summer, Mon-Sat 10.30-5, Sun 11.30-6; winter Mon-Fri 11.30-4.15, Sat 11.30-4.30, Sun 11.30-5. (Closed 24 & 25 Dec).
Facilities: P ✕ ﾖ (hides have wheelchair platforms) toilets for disabled shop ﾔ *Details not confirmed for 2002* ﾒ

DONAGHADEE
Map 01 D5

BALLYCOPELAND WINDMILL
(1m W, on B172)
☎ 028 9186 1413 ▤ 028 9131 0288
Times: Open all year Apr-Sep, Tue-Sat 10-7, Sun 2-7; Oct-Mar, Sat 10-4, Sun 2-4. **Facilities:** P shop ﾔ *Details not confirmed for 2002*

DOWNPATRICK
Map 01 D5

DOWN COUNTY MUSEUM
The Mall BT30 6AH (follow brown signs)
☎ 028 4461 5218 ▤ 028 4461 5590
e-mail: museum@downdc.gov.uk

The museum is located in the restored buildings of the 18th-century county gaol. In addition to restored cells

contd.

that tell the stories of some of the prisoners, there are exhibitions on the history of County Down. Plus temporary exhibits, events, tea-room and shop. **Times:** Open all year, Jun-Aug, Mon-Fri 10-5, wknds 2-5; rest of year, Tue-Fri 10-5 & Sat 2-5. Also open all BH's. **Fee:** Free. **Facilities:** P (100yds) ☕ & (wheelchair available, handling boxes on application) toilets for disabled shop ✟ (ex guide dogs)

INCH ABBEY
(0.75m NW off A7)
☎ 028 9023 5000   ▤ 028 9031 0288
Times: Open Apr-Sep 10-7, Sun 2-7. Oct-Mar free access. **Facilities:** P & *Details not confirmed for 2002*

LOUGHINISLAND CHURCHES
(4m W)
☎ 028 9023 5000   ▤ 028 9031 0288
Times: Open all times **Facilities:** P & ⚘ *Details not confirmed for 2002*

MOUND OF DOWN
(on the Quoile Marshes, from Mount Crescent)
☎ 028 9023 5000   ▤ 028 9031 0288
Times: Open all times **Facilities:** P *Details not confirmed for 2002*

STRUELL WELLS
(1.5m E)
☎ 028 9023 5000   ▤ 028 9031 0288
Times: Open all times **Facilities:** P ⚘ *Details not confirmed for 2002*

⛪ DROMARA   Map 01 D5
LEGANANNY DOLMEN
(4m S)
☎ 028 9023 5000   ▤ 028 9031 0288
Times: Open at all times & ⚘ *Details not confirmed for 2002*

⛪ HILLSBOROUGH   Map 01 D5
HILLSBOROUGH FORT
☎ 028 9268 3285   ▤ 028 9031 0288
Times: Open all year; Apr-Sep, Tue-Sat 10-7, Sun 2-7; Oct-Mar, Tue-Fri 10-4, Sat 10-4, Sun 2-4., **Facilities:** P & *Details not confirmed for 2002*

⛪ KILKEEL   Map 01 D4
GREENCASTLE
(4m SW)
☎ 028 9023 5000   ▤ 028 9031 0288
Times: Open Jul-Aug, Tue-Sat 10-7, Sun 2-7. **Facilities:** P & *Details not confirmed for 2002*

⛪ KILLINCHY   Map 01 D5
SKETRICK CASTLE
(3m E on W tip of Sketrick Islands)
☎ 028 9023 5000   ▤ 028 9031 0288
Times: Open at all times. **Facilities:** P & *Details not confirmed for 2002*

⛪ NEWCASTLE   Map 01 D5
DUNDRUM CASTLE
(4m N)
☎ 028 9023 5000   ▤ 028 9031 0288
Times: Open Apr-Sep, Tue-Sat 10-7, Sun 2-7. **Facilities:** P & toilets for disabled *Details not confirmed for 2002*

MAGHERA CHURCH
(2m NNW)
☎ 028 9023 5000   ▤ 028 9031 0288
Times: Open all year. **Facilities:** P & *Details not confirmed for 2002*

⛪ NEWTOWNARDS   Map 01 D5
MOUNT STEWART HOUSE, GARDEN & TEMPLE OF THE WINDS
Greyabbey BT22 2AD (5m SE off A20)
☎ 028 4278 8387   ▤ 028 4278 8569
e-mail: umsest@smtp.ntrust.org.uk

On the east shore of Strangford Lough, this 18th-century house was the work of three architects. In the inspired gardens, which are now a nominated World Heritage Site, many rare and subtropical trees thrive. Located by the shore is the Temple of the Winds, built by James 'Athenian' Stuart in 1782 for the first Marquess.
Times: Open House Etr, daily; May-Sep daily (ex Tue); Apr & Oct wknds, 1-6. Garden: Mar, Sun 2-5 & St Patrick's Day 11-6; Apr-Sep, daily & Oct, wknds 11-6. Temple of the Winds Apr-Oct, wknds 2-5.
Fee: House Garden & Temple: £3.50 (ch £1.75). Family ticket £8.75. Garden: £3 (ch £1.50) Group 15+. **Facilities:** P ☕ & (4 wheelchairs (2 electric) available) toilets for disabled shop ✟ ☕

SCRABO TOWER
Scrabo Country Park, 203A Scrabo Rd BT23 4SJ (1m W)
☎ 028 9181 1491   ▤ 028 9182 0695
Times: Open Etr, May-Sep, Sat-Thu 11-6.30. Country park open all year, daily, 11-6.30. **Facilities:** P shop ✟ *Details not confirmed for 2002*

⛪ PORTAFERRY   Map 01 D5
EXPLORIS AQUARIUM
The Rope Walk, Castle St BT22 1NZ (A20 or A2 or A25 to Strangford Ferry Service)
☎ 028 4272 8062   ▤ 028 4272 8396
e-mail: susan.moore@ards-council.gov.uk

Exploris Aquarium is Northern Ireland's only public

contd.

aquarium and now includes a seal sanctuary. Situated in Portaferry on the shores of Strangford Lough it houses some of Europe's finest displays. The Open Sea Tank holds 250 tonnes of sea water, and the Shoaling Ring, where visitors are surrounded by hundreds of fish, is a tank 6m in diameter. The complex includes a park with duck pond, picnic area, children's playground, caravan site, woodland and bowling green. **Times:** Open all year, Mon-Fri 10-6, Sat 11-6, Sun 1-6. (Sep-Feb closing 1 hr earlier). **Fee:** *Prices not confirmed for 2002* **Facilities:** 🅿 ⬛ ♿ (lift available) toilets for disabled shop 🍴 (ex guide dogs) 🍵

🏛 SAINTFIELD   Map 01 D5
ROWALLANE GARDEN
BT24 7LH (1m S of Saintfield on A7)
☎ 028 9751 0131   🖥 028 9751 1242

Beautiful and exotic 52-acre gardens, started by the Reverend John Moore in 1860, containing exquisite plants from all over the world. They are particularly noted for their rhododendrons and azaleas and for the wonderful floral displays in spring and summer. There are monthly demonstrations on The Art of the Gardener.
Times: Open 17 Mar-Oct, Mon-Fri 10.30-6, Sat & Sun 12-6; Nov-Mar, Mon-Fri 10.30-5. (Closed 25-26 Dec & 1 Jan) **Fee:** Apr-Oct £3 (ch £1.25); Nov-Mar £1.50 (ch 75p). Family £6.25, Party £1.75. **Facilities:** 🅿 ⬛ ♿ (parking facilities) toilets for disabled (dogs on leads) 🐕

🏛 STRANGFORD   Map 01 D5
AUDLEY'S CASTLE
(1.5m W by shore of Strangford Lough)
☎ 028 9023 0560   🖥 028 9031 0288
Times: Open Apr-Sep, daily 10-7. **Facilities:** 🅿 🍴 *Details not confirmed for 2002*

CASTLE WARD
BT30 7LS (0.5m W of Strangford Village on A25)
☎ 028 4488 1204   🖥 028 4488 1729
e-mail: ucwest@smtp.ntrust.org.uk

The curious diversity of styles in this house is due to the fact that its owner and his wife could never agree; so classical themes and a more elaborate Gothic look were both incorporated. The servants' living quarters are reached by an underground passage. Gardens, complete with a small lake and classical summerhouse, are richly planted and especially beautiful in spring.
Times: House open Jun-Aug, daily (ex Thu) 1-6; Apr-May & 18 Sep-Oct, wknds 1-6. **Fee:** House £3 (ch £1.50). Estate £3.50 per car (Nov-Mar £1.75). Family ticket £7.50. Party £2.50. **Facilities:** 🅿 (charged) ⬛ ✕ ♿ (wheelchair available, may be driven to house) toilets for disabled shop 🐕 🍵

STRANGFORD CASTLE
☎ 028 9023 5000   🖥 028 9031 0288
Times: Visable from outside. **Facilities:** 🍴 *Details not confirmed for 2002*

🏛 WARRENPOINT   Map 01 D5
NARROW WATER CASTLE
(1m NW)
☎ 028 9023 5000   🖥 028 9031 0288
Times: Open Jul-Aug, Tue-Sat 10-7, Sun 2-7. **Facilities:** 🅿 *Details not confirmed for 2002*

CO FERMANAGH

🏛 BELLEEK   Map 01 B5
BELLEEK POTTERY
3 Main St BT93 3FY
☎ 028 6865 9300   🖥 028 6865 8625
e-mail: visitorcentre@belleek.ie

Known worldwide for its fine Parian china, Ireland's oldest pottery was started in 1857 by the Caldwell family. Meet the craftspeople at work whilst touring the Pottery and visit the museum, which has exhibits dating back over 140 years.
Times: Open all year, Apr-Sep, Mon-Fri 9-6, Sat 10-6; also Apr-Jun, Sun 2-6 & Jul-Aug, Sun 11-6. Oct-Mar, Mon-Fri 9-5.30. **Fee:** Guided tours £2.00 (ch under 12 free, pen £1). **Facilities:** 🅿 ✕ ♿ (wheelchairs can be provided) toilets for disabled shop 🍴 (ex guide dogs) 🍵

🏛 CASTLE ARCHDALE BAY   Map 01 C5
WHITE ISLAND CHURCH
(in Castle Archdale Bay; ferry from marina)
☎ 028 9023 5000   🖥 028 9031 0288
Times: Open Jul-Aug, Tue-Sat 10-7, Sun 2-7. **Facilities:** 🅿 🍴 🚼 *Details not confirmed for 2002*

🏛 DERRYGONNELLY   Map 01 C5
TULLY CASTLE
(3m N, on W shore of Lower Lough Erne)
☎ 028 9023 5000   🖥 028 9031 0288
Times: Open Apr-Sep Tue-Sat 10-7, Sun 2-7; Oct-Mar 10-4.(2-4 Sun).
Facilities: 🅿 ♿ 🍴 *Details not confirmed for 2002*

🏛 ENNISKILLEN   Map 01 C5
CASTLE COOLE
BT74 (1.5m SE on A4)
☎ 028 6632 2690   🖥 028 6632 5665
e-mail: UCASCO@smtp.ntrust.org.uk

No expense was spared in the building of this mansion. James Wyatt was the architect, the lovely plasterwork ceilings were by Joseph Rose, and the chimneypieces the work of Richard Westmacott. Vast amounts of Portland stone were specially imported, together with an Italian expert in stonework. The house is filled with beautiful Regency furniture.
Times: Open Jun-Aug, Fri-Wed 1-6 (last tour 5.15); Apr-May & Sep, wknds & BH's 1-6. **Fee:** £3 (ch £1.50). Family ticket £8, Party £2.50 **Facilities:** 🅿 ⬛ ♿ (may be driven to house) toilets for disabled shop 🍴 (ex in park & guide dogs) 🐕 🍵

DEVENISH ISLAND
(2m N)
☎ 028 9023 5000   🖷 028 9031 0288
Times: Open Apr-Sep, Tue-Sat 10-7, Sun 2-7. **Facilities:** 🅿 shop ✻
Details not confirmed for 2002

ENNISKILLEN CASTLE
BT74 7HL
☎ 028 6632 2711
Times: Open all year Mon 2-5, Tue-Fri 10-5 (closed 1-2, Oct-Apr), Sat
2-5 May-Aug, Sun 2-5 Jul-Aug, all day BH's. **Facilities:** 🅿 & shop ✻
Details not confirmed for 2002

FLORENCE COURT
BT92 1DB (8m SW of Enniskillen via A4 & A32)
☎ 028 6634 8249   🖷 028 6634 8873
e-mail: UFCEST@smtp.ntrust.org.uk

An 18th-century mansion overlooking wild and
beautiful scenery towards the Mountains of Cuilcagh.
The interior of the house, particularly noted for its
flamboyant rococo plasterwork, was gutted by fire in
1955, but has been miraculously restored. There are
pleasure grounds with an Ice House, Summer House,
Water Powered Sawmill and also a walled garden.
Times: Open Etr, daily 1-6; Apr, May & Sep wknds & BH's 1-6; Jun-
Aug, daily (ex Tue) 1-6. **Fee:** £3 (ch £1.50). Family ticket £8. Estate only
£2 per car. **Facilities:** 🅿 (charged) 🍴 & (electric wheelchair
available/wheelchair path) toilets for disabled shop 🌂 🥤

MARBLE ARCH CAVES
Marlbank Scenic Loop BT92 1EW (off A4 Enniskillen-
Sligo road)
☎ 028 6634 8855   🖷 028 6634 8928
e-mail: mac@fermanagh.gov.uk
Times: Open late Mar-Sep. From 10 daily. **Facilities:** 🅿 🍴 & toilets for
disabled shop ✻ (ex guide dogs) *Details not confirmed for 2002* 🥤

MONEA CASTLE
(6m NW)
☎ 028 9023 5000   🖷 028 9031 0288
Times: Open at any reasonable time. **Facilities:** 🅿 & *Details not
confirmed for 2002*

THE SHEELIN IRISH LACE MUSEUM
Ballanaleck BT92 2BA (from Enniskillen take A4 onto
A509. Thatched Sheelin restaurant on left after 3m,
museum in restaurant car park).
☎ 028 6634 8052   🖷 028 6634 8200
e-mail: rosemary.cathcart@virgin.net

The Irish Lace Museum has the largest and most
comprehensive display of antique lace anywhere in
Ireland. There are around 140 exhibits, representing the
five main types of Irish lace: Inishmacsaint Needlelace,
Crochet, Limerick, Carrickmacross, and Youghal
Needlelace. The history of the Irish lace-making
industry is described, and antique items can be bought
in the museum shop.
Times: Open daily 10-6. **Fee:** £2 (ch under 14 £1, pen £1.50). Party
15+ **Facilities:** 🅿 ✕ licensed & (toilets for disabled in restaurant)
toilets for disabled shop ✻ (ex guide dogs) 🥤

⌂ LISNASKEA   Map 01 C5
CASTLE BALFOUR
☎ 028 9023 5000   🖷 028 9031 0288
Times: Open at all times. **Facilities:** 🅿 & *Details not confirmed for
2002*

⌂ NEWTOWNBUTLER   Map 01 C5
CROM ESTATE
BT92 8AP (3m W)
☎ 028 6773 8174   & 6773 8118
🖷 028 6773 8174
e-mail: ucromw@smtp.ntrust.org.uk

Featuring 770 hectares of woodland, parkland and
wetland, the Crom Estate is one of Northern Ireland's
most important conservation areas. Nature trails are
signposted through woodlands to the ruins of the old
castle, and past the old boat house and picturesque
summer house. Day tickets for pike fishing and boat
hire are available from the Visitor Centre.
Times: Open Apr-Sep, daily 10-6, Sun 12-6. **Fee:** Parking £3
Facilities: 🅿 (charged) 🍴 & toilets for disabled shop 🌂 🥤

CO LONDONDERRY

⌂ COLERAINE   Map 01 C6
HEZLETT HOUSE
Castlerock BT51 4TN (5m W on Coleraine/Downhill
coast road)
☎ 028 7084 8567

A low, thatched cottage built around 1690 with an
interesting cruck truss roof, constructed by using pairs
of curved timbers to form arches and infilling around
this frame with clay, rubble and other locally available
materials.
Times: Open Etr, daily; Apr/May/Sep wknds & BH's; Jun-Aug, daily (ex
Tue) 12-5. **Fee:** £2 (ch 90p). Family ticket £5. Party £1.50. **Facilities:** 🅿
✻ (ex in gardens) 🌂

MOUNT SANDEL
(1.25m SSE)
☎ 028 9023 0560   🖷 028 9031 0288
Times: Open at all times. **Facilities:** 🅿 & *Details not confirmed for
2002*

⌂ COOKSTOWN   Map 01 C5
TULLAGHOGE FORT
(2m S)
☎ 028 9023 5000   🖷 028 9031 0288
Times: Open at all times. **Facilities:** 🅿 *Details not confirmed for
2002*

WELLBROOK BEETLING MILL
Corkhill BT80 9RY (4m W in Co Tyrone, 0.5m off A505)
☎ 028 8675 1735
e-mail: uspest@smtp.ntrust.org.uk

This 18th-century water-powered linen mill was used
for bleaching and, until 1961, for finishing Irish linen.
Beetling was the name given to the final process in

contd.

linen making, when the material was beaten by 30 or so hammers (beetles) to achieve a smooth and slightly shiny finish.
Times: Open Etr, daily; Apr-Jun & Sep, wknds & BH's; Jul-Aug, daily (ex Tue) 2-6. **Fee:** £5 (ch £2). Family & group ticket available.
Facilities: ♿ & toilets for disabled shop (dogs on leads) ⛄

⛪ DOWNHILL   Map 01 C6
MUSSENDEN TEMPLE BISHOP'S GATE AND BLACK GLEN
Mussenden Rd BT51 4RP (1m W of Castlerock off A2)
☎ 028 7084 8725
e-mail: uncwaw@smtp.org.uk

Spectacularly placed on a cliff edge overlooking the Atlantic, this perfect 18th-century rotunda was modelled on the Temple of Vesta at Tivoli. Visitors entering by the Bishop's Gate can enjoy a beautiful glen walk up to the headland where the temple stands.
Times: Open Temple: Etr, daily noon-6; Apr-Jun & Sep, wknds & BH's noon-6; Jul-Aug, daily noon-6. **Fee:** Free. **Facilities:** ♿ & ⛄

⛪ DUNGIVEN   Map 01 C5
BANAGHER CHURCH
(2m SW)
☎ 028 9023 5000   🖷 028 9031 0288
Times: Open at all times. **Facilities:** ♿ & *Details not confirmed for 2002*

DUNGIVEN PRIORY
(SE of town overlooking River Roe)
☎ 028 9023 5000   🖷 028 9031 0288
Times: Open - Church at all times, chancel only when caretaker available. Check at house at end of lane. **Facilities:** ♿ & *Details not confirmed for 2002*

⛪ LIMAVADY   Map 01 C6
ROUGH FORT
(1m W off A2)

Early Christian rath.
Times: Open at all times. **Fee:** Free. 🚻 ⛄

⛪ LONDONDERRY   Map 01 C5
CITY WALLS
☎ 028 9023 5000   🖷 028 9031 0288
Times: Open all times. **Facilities:** ♿ (charged) & *Details not confirmed for 2002*

FOYLE VALLEY RAILWAY MUSEUM
Foyle Rd BT48 6SQ
☎ 028 7126 5234   🖷 028 7137 7633
Times: Open all year, Apr-Sep Mon-Sat 10-5, Sun 2-5; Oct-Mar Mon-Sat 10-4. **Facilities:** ♿ & toilets for disabled shop garden centre 🏵
Details not confirmed for 2002

TOWER MUSEUM
Union Hall Place BT48 6LU
☎ 028 7137 2411   🖷 028 7137 7633
e-mail: towermuseum@dnet.co.uk
Times: Open all year, Sep-Jun Tue-Sat 10-5. Jul-Aug Mon-Sat 10-5, Sun 2-5. Also open all BH Mons. **Facilities:** ⓟ (300 yds) & toilets for disabled shop 🏵 (ex guide dogs) *Details not confirmed for 2002*

⛪ MAGHERA   Map 01 C5
MAGHERA CHURCH
(E approach to the town)
☎ 028 9023 5000   🖷 028 9031 0288
Times: Key from Leisure Centre. **Facilities:** ♿ & *Details not confirmed for 2002*

⛪ MONEYMORE   Map 01 C5
SPRINGHILL
BT45 7NQ (1m from Moneymore on B18 to Coagh)
☎ 028 8674 8210   🖷 028 8674 8210
e-mail: uspest@smtp.ntrust.org.uk

This pleasingly symmetrical manor house dates back to the 17th century. Today much of the family furniture, books and bric-a-brac have been retained. Outside, the laundry, stables, brewhouse, and old dovecote make interesting viewing, as does the excellent costume museum.
Times: Open Etr, Apr-Jun & Sep, wknds & BH's 2-6; Jul-Aug, daily (ex Thu) 2-6. **Fee:** £6.50 (ch £2.50). Family ticket & Party available
Facilities: ♿ 📷 & (photograph album of first floor available) toilets for disabled shop (dogs on leads) ⛄

CO TYRONE

⛪ ARDBOE   Map 01 C5
ARDBOE CROSS
(off B73)
☎ 028 9023 5000   🖷 028 9031 0288
Times: Open at all times. **Facilities:** ♿ & *Details not confirmed for 2002*

⛪ BALLYGAWLEY   Map 01 C5
U S GRANT ANCESTRAL HOMESTEAD & VISITOR CENTRE
Dergenagh, 190 Ballygawley Rd BT70 1TW (off A4, 3m on Dergenagh road, signposted)
☎ 028 8555 7133   🖷 028 8576 7911
Times: Open Etr-Sep, Mon-Sat 12-5, Sun 2-6. Other times by arrangement. (Closed 25-26 Dec & 1 Jan). **Facilities:** ♿ 📷 & (wide doorway to audio-visual area/entrances/exits) shop 🏵 (ex guide dogs) *Details not confirmed for 2002*

⛪ BEAGHMORE   Map 01 C5
BEAGHMORE STONE CIRCLES AND ALIGNMENTS
☎ 028 9023 5000   🖷 028 9031 0288
Times: Open at all times. **Facilities:** ♿ & *Details not confirmed for 2002*

BENBURB
Map 01 C5

BENBURB CASTLE
☎ 028 9023 5000 📄 028 9031 0288
Times: Castle grounds open at all times. Special arrangements, made in advance, necessary for access to flanker tower. **Facilities:** 🅿 � 🍽
Details not confirmed for 2002

CASTLECAULFIELD
Map 01 C5

CASTLE CAULFIELD
☎ 028 9023 5000 📄 028 9031 0288
Times: Open at all times. **Facilities:** 🅿 ⅋ *Details not confirmed for 2002*

NEWTOWNSTEWART
Map 01 C5

HARRY AVERY'S CASTLE
(0.75m SW)
☎ 028 9023 5000 📄 028 9031 0288
Times: Open at all times. 🍽 🏕 *Details not confirmed for 2002*

OMAGH
Map 01 C5

ULSTER AMERICAN FOLK PARK
BT78 5QY (5m NW Omagh)
☎ 028 8224 3292 📄 028 8224 2241
e-mail: uafp@iol.ie

An outdoor museum that traces the history of Ulster's links with America and the emigration of Ulster residents to the US during the 18th and 19th centuries. The 70-acre site is divided into two parts – Old World and New World. There are demonstrations of Old and New World crafts and a visitor centre with exhibitions and audio-visual presentations. The Centre for Emigration Studies is based here, and has a research library and emigration database – please ring for details.
Times: Open Etr-Sep, daily 10.30-6, Sun & BH 11-6.30; Oct-Etr Mon-Fri 10.30-5. Last admission 1hr 30mins before closing. **Fee:** £4 (ch & pen £2.50). Family ticket £10. Children under 5yrs free. **Facilities:** 🅿 ✕ ⅋ toilets for disabled shop 🍽 (ex guide dogs) 🍹

ULSTER HISTORY PARK
Cullion BT79 7SU (7m on B48)
☎ 028 8164 8188 📄 028 8164 8011
e-mail: uhp@omagh.gov.uk

The story of settlement in Ireland, told with the aid of full-scale models of the houses and monuments built through the ages. Exhibitions and audio-visual presentations expand the theme.
Times: Open all year, Jul-Aug daily 10-6.30; Apr-Jun & Sep, daily 10-5.30; Oct-Mar, Mon-Fri 10-5. **Fee:** £3.75 (ch, students, pen & registered disabled £2.50). Family ticket (2 adults & 2 ch) £12. Group 15+
Facilities: 🅿 🍽 ⅋ toilets for disabled shop 🍽 (ex guide dogs) 🍹

STEWARTSTOWN
Map 01 C5

MOUNTJOY CASTLE
Magheralamfield (3m SE, off B161)
☎ 028 9023 5000 📄 028 9031 0288
Times: Open at all times. **Facilities:** 🅿 *Details not confirmed for 2002*

STRABANE
Map 01 C5

GRAY'S PRINTING PRESS
49 Main St BT82 8AU
☎ 028 7188 4094

Strabane was once an important printing and book-publishing centre, the only relic of this is a small shop in Main Street which now houses a museum illustrating the history of Strabane. The Print Museum, in a separate building, contains three 19th-century presses and shows the development of printing techniques over 150 years.
Times: Open Apr-Sep, Tue-Sat 2-5. Other times by prior arrangement. **Fee:** £2 (ch 90p). Family ticket £4.50. Party £1.30. **Facilities:** 🅿 (100yds) ⅋ 🍽 (ex guide dogs) 🍹

Republic of Ireland

No visitor comes here without preconceptions, and while some of these will be confirmed, there are always plenty of surprises, and more to discover.

To be sure it is green - the Emerald Isle is no misnomer - and you're never far from water, from the craggy Atlantic coast, the countless loughs, rivers and bogs, to the regular falls of rain, or Irish mist. And then there are the people.

Certainly this country with its tiny population has brought us an abundance of world-class literary figures, and you will meet the same love of words and ideas in any street, shop or pub. Music too seems to run in the veins - listening to an Irish band, it soon becomes clear that the musicians are playing as much for their own pleasure as for the tourist's. However, this is no quaint backwater; the Republic has enthusiastically embraced its European identity, and will soon be exchanging the Punt for the Euro.

Where to go? It would be hard to miss out on elegant, cosmopolitan Dublin, and in the south there's Cork, vying with the capital for business and cultural supremacy. To explore the west, head for Galway, where Gaelic is still spoken by many inhabitants as a first language, and inland you will not be disappointed by the craft studios and restaurants of Kilkenny.

Further afield there is no end of opportunity for fishing, golfing, walking and relaxing. You can find a quiet charm everwhere you visit, but there are some strikingly unique attractions. The Burren is a naturalist's joy, with exotic flora in every crevice of its strange rockscape, and Newgrange is one of Europe's most important and mysterious prehistoric sites.

CO CLARE

BALLYVAUGHAN
Map 01 B3

AILLWEE CAVE
(3m S of Ballyvaughan. Signposted)
☎ 065 7077036 & 7077067 🖷 065 7077107
e-mail: aillwee@eircom.net

An underground network of caves beneath the world famous Burren. Guided tours take you through large caverns, over bridged chasms and alongside thunderous waterfalls. There is a craftshop, a dairy and a speciality food shop. At Xmas: Santa's workshop; at Easter: an egg hunt in the woods.
Times: Open all Year from 10 . **Fee:** IEP7.50 (ch IEP4.50). Family ticket IEP21-IEP24 **Facilities:** 🍴 ✕ licensed & toilets for disabled shop 🐾 (in cave) 🍵

BUNRATTY
Map 01 B3

BUNRATTY CASTLE & FOLK PARK
(8m from Limerick on N18 to Ennis)
☎ 061 361511 & 360788 🖷 061 361020
e-mail: oconnorm@shannon-dev.ie
Times: Open all year, daily 9.30-5.30 (last admission 4.30pm). Folk Park also open Jun-Aug 9-6.30 (last admission 5.30pm). Last admission to Castle 4pm all year. Closed Good Friday & 24-26 Dec. **Fee:** Castle IEP5.80-IEP7.50 (ch IEP3.31-IEP4.20, pen/student IEP4.20-IEP5.25). Family ticket IEP15.75-IEP19.70. Folk park only IEP4.30-IEP5.25 (ch IEP2.40-IEP3.15). **Facilities:** 🅿 🍴 ✕ licensed & toilets for disabled shop 🍵

LISCANNOR
Map 01 B3

VISITORS CENTRE CLIFFS OF MOHER
(6m NW of Lahinch)
☎ 065 81565 & 061 360788 🖷 061 361020
e-mail: oconnorm@shannon-dev.ie
Times: Open all year, 9.30-5.30 June-Aug 9-8pm (subject to weather conditions). Visitor centre closed Good Friday & 23-27 Dec. O'Briens Tower 9.30-5.30. **Fee:** O'Briens Tower IEP1.05 (ch IEP.65). **Facilities:** 🅿 (charged) 🍴 & toilets for disabled shop 🍵

QUIN
Map 01 B3

THE CRAGGAUNOWEN BRONZE AGE PROJECT
(signed from N18, 10km N from Sixmilebridge)
☎ 061 367178 & 360788 🖷 061 361020
e-mail: oconnorm@shannon-dev.ie
Times: Open Apr-Oct daily 10-6 (last admission 5pm). **Fee:** IEP4.61-IEP5.25 (ch IEP2.85-IEP3.15, pen/students IEP3.70-IEP3.95). Family ticket IEP12.15-IEP13.15. **Facilities:** 🅿 🍴 & toilets for disabled shop 🍵

CO CORK

BALLINCOLLIG
Map 01 B2

BALLINCOLLIG GUNPOWDER MILLS HERITAGE CENTRE
(on Cork/Killarney road)
☎ 021 4874430 🖷 021 4874836
e-mail: ballinco@indigo.ie
Times: Open daily, 25 Apr-Sep 10-6. Last tour at 5.15pm. **Facilities:** 🅿 🍴 & toilets for disabled shop 🐾 (ex guide dogs) *Details not confirmed for 2002*

BLARNEY
Map 01 B2

BLARNEY CASTLE & ROCK CLOSE
(5m from Cork on main road towards Limerick. 30 min from Cork airport. 30min from Ferry Port).
☎ 021 4385252 & 385669 🖷 021 4381518
e-mail: info@blarneyc.iol.ie

The site of the famous Blarney Stone, known the world over for the eloquence it is said to impart to those who kiss it. The stone is in the upper tower of the castle, and, held by your feet, you must lean backwards down the inside of the battlements in order to receive the gift of the gab.
Times: Open - Blarney Castle & Rock Close, Jun-Aug Mon-Sat 9-7.30; May Mon-Sat 9-7; Sep Mon-Sat 9-6.30; Apr & Oct Mon-Sat 9-sunset; summer Sun 9.30-5.30; winter Sun 9.30-sunset. Blarney House & Gardens Jun-mid Sep Mon-Sat noon-6. **Fee:** Blarney Castle & Rock Close IEP3.50 (ch IEP1, pen & students IEP2.50). **Facilities:** 🅿 & shop 🐾 (ex guide dogs)

CARRIGTWOHILL (CARRIGTOHILL)
Map 01 B2

FOTA ARBORETUM & GARDENS
Fota Estate
☎ 021 4812728 🖷 021 4812728
Times: Open Mar-Oct, daily 10-6; Nov-Feb, daily 10-5. (Closed 25 Dec). **Facilities:** 🅿 (charged) & toilets for disabled 🐾 (ex on lead) *Details not confirmed for 2002*

FOTA WILDLIFE PARK
Fota Estate (10km E of Corky. Take Cobh road from N25, Cork - Waterford road)
☎ 021 4812678 🖷 021 4812744
e-mail: info@fotawildlife.ie

Times: Open all year 17 Mar-Sep daily, 10-6 (Sun 11-6) Oct-17 Mar wkends only. Last admission 5. **Facilities:** 🅿 (charged) ✕ & (Ramps where required) toilets for disabled shop 🐾 *Details not confirmed for 2002* 🍵

CLONAKILTY　　Map 01 B2
WEST CORK MODEL VILLAGE RAILWAY
Inchydoney Rd (From Cork N71 left at junct for
Inchydoney Island, signposted at road junction. Village
is at Bay side of Clonakilty)
☎ 023 33224
e-mail: modelvillage@eircom.net

This miniature world depicts Irish towns as they were
in the 1940s, with models of the West Cork Railway and
various animated scenes. The tea room is set in
authentic railway carriages that overlook picturesque
Clonakilty Bay.
Times: Open Feb-Oct daily 11-5, Sat & Sun 1-5; Jul-Aug, daily,
extended hours 10-6. **Fee:** IEP4 (ch IEP2 concessions IEP3). Family
ticket IEP10, Party 12+. **Facilities:** 🅿 🍴 ♿ toilets for disabled shop 🐕
(ex guide dogs) 🍴

COBH　　Map 01 B2
THE QUEENTOWN STORY
Cobh Railway Station (Off N25, follow signs for Cobh.
Centre is at Deepwater Quay, adjacent to Train Stn)
☎ 021 4813591　🖷 021 4813595
e-mail: info@cobheritage.com

A dramatic exhibition of the origins, history and
legends of Cobh. Between 1848 and 1950 over 3 million
Irish people were deported from Cobh on convict ships.
Visitors can explore the conditions onboard these
vessels and learn about the harbour's connections with
the Lusitania and the Titanic.
Times: Open all year 10-6. Last admission 5pm. **Fee:** IEP3.95 (ch12
IEP2, pen & students IEP3.20). Family ticket IEP12. **Facilities:** 🅿 🍴 ✗
♿ toilets for disabled shop 🐕 (ex guide dogs) 🍴

CORK　　Map 01 B2
CORK CITY GAOL
Convent Av, Sundays Well (2km from Patrick St, off
Sunday's Well Rd)
☎ 021 4305022　🖷 021 4307230
e-mail: corkgaol@indigo.ie

A restored 19th century prison building. Furnished
cells, lifelike characters and sound effects combine to
allow visitors to experience day-to-day life for prisoners
and gaoler. There is an audio-visual presentation of the
social history of Cork City. Individual audio tours are
available in a number of languages. A new permanent
exhibition, the Radio Museum Experience, is located in
the restored 1920s broadcasting studio, home to Cork's
first radio station, 6CK. Unfortunately the 1st and 2nd
floors are not accessible to wheelchair users.
Times: Open Mar-Oct, daily 9.30-6; Nov-Feb, daily 10-5. Last
admission 1hr before closing. **Fee:** *Prices not confirmed for 2002*
Facilities: 🅿 🍴 ♿ (customer care policy - individual attention) toilets
for disabled shop 🐕 (ex guide dogs)

CORK PUBLIC MUSEUM
Fitzgerald Park, Mardyke (N of University College)
☎ 021 270679　🖷 021 270931
Times: Open all year, Jun-Aug Mon-Fri 11-1 & 2.15-6, Sun 3-5; Sep-
May Mon-Fri 11-1 & 2.15-5, Sun 3-5. (Closed Sat, BH wknds & PH)
Facilities: 🅿 (100 yds) shop 🐕 (ex guide dogs) *Details not
confirmed for 2002*

GLENGARRIFF　　Map 01 B2
GARINISH ISLAND
(1.5km boat trip from Glengarriff)
☎ 027 63040　🖷 027 63149
Times: Open Jul-Aug, Mon-Sat 9.30-6.30, Sun 11-7; Apr-Jun & Sep,
Mon-Sat 10-6.30, Sun 1-7; Mar & Oct, Mon-Sat 10-4.30, Sun 1-5. Last
landing 1 hour before closing. Charge made by boat operators.
Facilities: 🍴 ♿ (minimal due to boat access) toilets for disabled
(must be on leads) *Details not confirmed for 2002*

KINSALE　　Map 01 B2
CHARLES FORT
☎ 021 772263　🖷 021 774347
e-mail: info@heritageireland.ie
Times: Open all year, mid Mar-Oct, daily 10-6; Nov-mid Mar, Sat-Sun
10-5, wkdays by arrangement. Last admission 45 minutes before
closing. **Facilities:** 🅿 🍴 ♿ toilets for disabled 🐕 (ex guide dogs)
Details not confirmed for 2002

DESMOND CASTLE
Cork St
☎ 021 774855
Times: Open mid Jun-early Oct, daily 10-6; mid Apr-mid Jun, Tue-Sun
& BH Mon 10-6. Last admission 45 mins before closing. **Facilities:** 🅿
🐕 (ex guide dogs) *Details not confirmed for 2002*

MIDLETON　　Map 01 C2
OLD MIDLETON DISTILLERY
(at E end of main street on L. Well signposted)
☎ 021 4613594　🖷 021 4613642

A tour of the Old Midleton Distillery consists of a 15
minute audio/visual presentation, a 35-minute guided
tour of the Old Distillery and then back to the Jameson
Bar for a whiskey tasting - soft drinks are available for
children. The guided tour and audio-visual aids are
available in five languages.
Times: Open Mar-Oct, daily 10-6. Last tour 4. Nov-Feb Mon-Fri, two
tours 12 & 3. Sat-Sun, two tours 2 & 4. (Closed Xmas). **Fee:** IEP4.50 (ch
IEP2). Family ticket (2+3)IEP11.50 **Facilities:** 🅿 🍴 ✗ licensed ♿
toilets for disabled shop 🐕 (ex guide dogs) 🍴

CO DONEGAL

⛪ ARDARA
Map 01 B5

ARDARA HERITAGE CENTRE
The Diamond
☎ 075 41704 🖹 075 41381
Times: Open Apr-Sep, 10-6. **Facilities:** 🅿 ♨ ✗ ♿ toilets for disabled shop 🐾 (ex guide dogs) *Details not confirmed for 2002*

⛪ BALLYSHANNON
Map 01 B5

THE WATER WHEELS
Abbey Assaroe (cross Abbey River on Rossnowlagh Rd, next turning left & follow signs)
☎ 072 51580

Abbey Assaroe was founded by Cistercian Monks from Boyle Abbey in the late 12th century. The Cistercians excelled in water engineering and canalised the river to turn water wheels for mechanical power. Two restored 12th-century mills, one is used as coffee shop and restaurant; the other houses a small museum related to the history of the Cistercians.
Times: Open Etr week & May-Aug, Mon-Sat 10.30-6.30, Sun 1.30-dusk. **Fee:** Free. **Facilities:** 🅿 ♨ ✗ licensed ♿ toilets for disabled shop garden centre

⛪ DONEGAL
Map 01 B5

DONEGAL CASTLE
☎ 073 22405 🖹 073 22436
Times: Open mid Mar-mid Oct, daily 9.30-6.30 (last admission 5.45).
Facilities: 🅿 🐾 (ex guide dogs) *Details not confirmed for 2002*

⛪ LETTERKENNY
Map 01 C5

GLEBE HOUSE & GALLERY
Churchill (signposted from Letterkenny)
☎ 074 37071 🖹 074 37521
Times: Open Etr & mid May-Sep, Sat-Thu 11-6.30. (Last tour of house 5.30). **Facilities:** 🅿 ♨ ♿ toilets for disabled 🐾 (ex guide dogs) *Details not confirmed for 2002*

GLENVEAGH NATIONAL PARK & CASTLE
Churchill
☎ 074 37090 🖹 074 37072
Times: Open daily mid Mar-early Nov, 10-6.30 **Facilities:** 🅿 ♨ ✗ ♿ toilets for disabled *Details not confirmed for 2002*

⛪ LIFFORD
Map 01 C5

CAVANACOR HISTORIC HOUSE & CRAFT CENTRE
Ballindrait (1.5m from town off N14 Strabane/Letterkenny road)
☎ 074 41143 🖹 074 41143
e-mail: joannaok7@hotmail.com

Built in the early 1600s and commanding a view of the Clonleigh valley and the River Deele, Cavanacor House is the ancestral home of James Knox Polk, 11th President of the USA (1845-1849). King James II dined under the sycamore tree in front of the house in 1689. There is a display of the history of the house and the surrounding area and over 10 acres of landscaped gardens and an old-fashioned walled garden. The Art Gallery will feature exhibitions of new work by national and international artists. Please ring for details.
Times: Open Etr & Jun-Aug. **Fee:** IEP3.50 (ch & pen IEP3).
Facilities: 🅿 ♨ ✗ ♿ shop garden centre (on leads) 🐕

CO DUBLIN

⛪ BALBRIGGAN
Map 01 D4

ARDGILLAN CASTLE
(Pass Airport & Swords rdbt, take R127 & follow signs).
☎ 01 8492212 🖹 01 8492786

A large and elegant country manor house built in 1738, set in 194 acres of parkland and overlooking the sea and coast as far as the Mourne Mountains. There is a permanent exhibition of the 17th-century 'Down Survey' maps and various temporary exhibitions. Tours of the Gardens (June, July and August) begin at 3.30pm every Thursday.
Times: Open Apr-Sep, Tue-Sun & BH's 11-6 (daily Jul-Aug); Oct-Mar, Wed-Sun & BH's 11-4.30. (Closed 23 Dec-1 Jan). **Fee:** IEP3 (pen & students IEP2). Family ticket IEP6.50. Party. **Facilities:** 🅿 ♨ ♿ toilets for disabled shop 🐾 (ex guide dogs)

⛪ DONABATE
Map 01 D4

NEWBRIDGE HOUSE AND TRADITIONAL FARM
☎ 01 8436534 & 8462184 🖹 01 8462537
Times: Open Apr-Sep Tue-Sat 10-5, Sun & PH 2-6; Oct-Mar Sat-Sun & PH 2-5. Parties at other times by arrangement. **Facilities:** 🅿 ♨ shop 🐾 *Details not confirmed for 2002*

⛪ DUBLIN
Map 01 D4

THE CASINO
off Malahide Rd, Marino (5km N of City Centre)
☎ 01 8331618 🖹 01 8331618
Times: Open Jun-Sep, daily 10-6; May & Oct, daily 10-5; Apr, Sun, Thu & BH's 12-5; Feb, Mar & Nov, Sun, Thu & BH's 12-4. Last admission 45 mins before closing. (Closed Dec & Jan). **Facilities:** 🅿 ♿ 🐾 (ex guide dogs) *Details not confirmed for 2002*

THE CHESTER BEATTY LIBRARY
Clock Tower, Dublin Castle (10 walk from Trinity College, up Dame St towards Cathedral)
☎ 01 4070750 🖹 01 4070760
e-mail: info@cbl.ie

The contents of this fascinating gallery were bequeathed to Ireland by its first honorary citizen, American mining engineer and collector, Sir Alfred Chester Beatty (1875-1968). The collection includes manuscripts, prints, icons, miniatures, and objets d'art of great importance from 2700BC to the present day. See illuminated copies of the Qu'ran and the Bible, Egyptian papyrus texts, and Buddhist paintings.
Times: Open May-Sep Mon-Fri 10-5, Oct-Apr Tue-Fri 10-5, All year Sat 11-5, & Sun 1-5. (Closed Good Friday, BH Mons, 25/25/26Dec, 1Jan).
Fee: Free. **Facilities:** 🅿 5 min walk ♨ ✗ ♿ toilets for disabled shop garden centre 🐾 (ex guide dogs) 🐕

CHRIST CHURCH CATHEDRAL
Christchurch Place (at the top end of Dame St)
☎ 01 6778099 🖷 01 6798991
e-mail: cccdub@indigo.ie
Times: Open 10-5.30. **Facilities:** 🅿 (100yds) & shop ✻ (ex guide dogs) *Details not confirmed for 2002*

DRIMNAGH CASTLE
Long Mile Rd, Drimnagh
☎ 01 4502530 🖷 01 4505401
Times: Open Apr-Sep, Wed & wknds 12-5; Oct-Mar, Sun 12-5. Last tour 4.15. Other times by arrangement. **Facilities:** 🅿 💷 & (gravel courtyard and garden. steps) ✻ (ex guide dogs) *Details not confirmed for 2002*

DUBLIN CASTLE
Dame St ☎ 01 6777129 🖷 01 6797831
Times: Open all year, Mon-Fri 10-5, Sat-Sun & BH 2-5. (Closed 24-26 Dec & Good Fri). **Facilities:** 🅿 ✗ & toilets for disabled *Details not confirmed for 2002*

DUBLINIA
St Michael's Hill, Christ Church
☎ 01 6794611 🖷 01 6797116
Times: Open Apr-Sep 10-5; Oct-Mar, Mon-Sat 11-4, Sun & BH 10-4.30. (Closed 24-26 Dec). **Facilities:** 🅿 (100yds) 💷 & (2 floors accessible, but bridge and tower are not) toilets for disabled shop ✻ (ex guide dogs) *Details not confirmed for 2002* 🥄

DUBLIN WRITERS MUSEUM
18 Parnell Square North
☎ 01 8722077 🖷 01 8722231
e-mail: writers@dublintourism.ie
Times: Open all year, Mon-Sat 10-5 & Sun & BH 11-5. Jun-Aug, Mon-Fri 10-6pm. **Facilities:** 🅿 (200 yds) (Metered) 💷 ✗ licensed shop ✻ (ex guide dogs) *Details not confirmed for 2002* 🥄

GUINNESS STOREHOUSE
St James's Gate ☎ 01 4084800 🖷 01 4084965
e-mail: guinness-storehouse@guinness.com

Established in 1876, the Storehouse remained crammed with hopsacks until 1957, then it was converted and is now a hi-tech, 21st-century mix of an arts centre, conference facility, restaurant and bar. Visitors can find out about every aspect of the drink's history and creation, and then enjoy a free glass of the stuff.
Times: Open Oct-Mar, Mon-Sat 9.30-5, Sun 10.30-5; Apr-Sep, Mon-Sat 9.30-6, Sun 10.30-6. (Closed 25 &26 Dec & Good Fri) **Fee:** *Prices not confirmed for 2002* **Facilities:** 🅿 💷 ✗ & toilets for disabled shop ✻ (ex guide dogs) 🥄

DUBLIN VIKING ADVENTURE
Essex St West, Temple Bar
☎ 01 6796040 🖷 01 6796033
e-mail: marketing@dublintourism.ie
Details not confirmed for 2002

HOWTH CASTLE RHODODENDRON GARDENS
Howth (9m NE of city centre, by coast road to Howth. Just before Howth signposted for Deer Park Hotel)
☎ 01 8322624 & 8322256 🖷 01 8392405
e-mail: sales@deerpark.iol.ie

On the northern boundary of Dublin Bay, the castle is justly famous for its gardens and especially for its rhododendron walk. The walk is open all year, but is at its best in May and June. There are views north to the Mourne Mountains and to the west of Dublin Bay.
Times: Open all year, daily 8am-dusk. (Closed 25 Dec). **Fee:** Free. **Facilities:** 🅿 & (steep hills unsuitable, ramped entrance) toilets for disabled ✻ (ex guide dogs) 🥄

HUGH LANE MUNICIPAL GALLERY OF MODERN ART
Charlemont House, Parnell Square
☎ 01 8741903 🖷 01 8722182
e-mail: info@hughlane.ie
Times: Open all year, Tue-Thu 9.30-6, Fri-Sat 9.30-5, Sun 11-5. Late night opening Thu until 8, Apr-Aug only. (Closed Mon, Good Fri & 24-25 Dec). **Facilities:** 🅿 (100 metres) (meter parking) 💷 & (Ramp & reserved parking) toilets for disabled shop ✻ (ex guide dogs) *Details not confirmed for 2002*

IRISH MUSEUM OF MODERN ART
Royal Hospital, Kilmainham (from city centre pass Heuston Station, 1st left on St John's Rd)
☎ 01 612 9900 🖷 01 612 9999
e-mail: info@modernart.ie

Housed in the Royal Hospital Kilmainham, an impressive 17th-century building, the museum presents a wide-ranging programme of Irish and International 20th-century art from its own collections. Also temporary exhibitions, talks, seminars and musical events.
Times: Open all year Tue-Sat 10-5.30, Sun & BH's 12-5.30. (Closed 24-26 & 31 Dec & Good Fri). **Fee:** Free. **Facilities:** 🅿 💷 & (wheelchair available) toilets for disabled shop ✻ (ex guide dogs)

JAMES JOYCE CENTRE
35 North Great George's St
☎ 01 8788547 🖷 01 8788488
e-mail: joycecen@iol.ie
Times: Open all year, Mon-Sat 9.30-5, Sun 12.30-5. (Closed Good Fri & 24-26 Dec). **Facilities:** 🅿 (200 mtrs) 💷 & toilets for disabled shop ✻ (ex guide dogs) *Details not confirmed for 2002* 🥄

KILMAINHAM GAOL
Inchicore Rd
☎ 01 4535984 🖷 01 4532037
Times: Access by guided tour only. Open Apr-Sep, daily 9.30-6 (last tour 4.45); Oct-Mar, Mon-Fri 9.30-5 (last tour 4), Sun 10-6 (last tour 4.45). **Facilities:** 🅿 (on street parking only) 💷 & (tours available by prior appointment) toilets for disabled ✻ *Details not confirmed for 2002*

MARSH'S LIBRARY
St Patrick's Close
☎ 01 4543511 ▤ 01 4543511
e-mail: keeper@marshlibrary.ie

The first public library in Ireland, dating from 1701. Designed by William Robinson, the interior has been unchanged for 300 years. The collection is of approximately 25,000 volumes of 16th, 17th and early 18th century books.
Times: Open Mon & Wed-Fri, 10-12.45 & 2-5; Sat 10.30-12.45.
Fee: IEP2 (students & pen IEP1, ch free). **Facilities:** P ✝ ♿

NATIONAL BOTANIC GARDENS
Glasnevin (on Botanic Road, between N1 and N2)
☎ 01 8374388 & 8377596 ▤ 01 8360080
Times: Open all year, summer Mon-Sat 9-6, Sun 11-6; winter Mon-Sat 10-4.30, Sun 11-4.30. **Facilities:** ▣ ♿ (Wheelchair available) toilets for disabled ✝ (ex guide dogs) *Details not confirmed for 2002*

NATIONAL GALLERY OF IRELAND
Merrion Square (situated 5 mins walk from Pearse Station)
☎ 01 6615133 ▤ 01 6615372
e-mail: artgall@eircom.net

The gallery, founded in 1854 by an Act of Parliament, houses the national collections of Irish art and European Old Masters including Caravaggio, Poussin, El Greco, Roderic O'Conor, and the Yeats'. A Yeats museum has recently opened and a new wing to the existing building will be completed by Autumn 2001.
Times: Open Mon-Sat 9.30-5.30 (Thu 9.30-8.30), Sun 12-5.30. (Closed 24-26 Dec & Good Fri). **Fee:** Free. **Facilities:** P (5 mins walk) (meter parking, 2hrs max) ☕ ✘ licensed ♿ (braille/audio tours, lifts, ramps, parking bay) toilets for disabled shop ✝

NATIONAL LIBRARY OF IRELAND
Kildare St
☎ 01 6030200 ▤ 01 6766690
e-mail: info@nli.ie
Times: Open: Mon-Wed 10-9, Thu-Fri 10-5 & Sat 10-1. (Closed Sun, Xmas-New Year, Etr & BH's). **Facilities:** ♿ toilets for disabled shop ✝ (ex guide dogs) ♿ *Details not confirmed for 2002*

NATIONAL PHOTOGRAPHIC ARCHIVE
Meeting House Square, Temple Bar
☎ 01 6030200 ▤ 01 6777451
e-mail: photoarchive@nli.ie
Times: Open all year, Mon-Fri 10-5; Sat 10-2 exhibition area only. (Closed BH's). **Facilities:** ♿ toilets for disabled shop ✝ (ex guide dogs) *Details not confirmed for 2002* ☕

NATURAL HISTORY MUSEUM
Merrion St
☎ 01 6777444 ▤ 01 6766116
Times: Open Tue-Sat 10-5, Sun 2-5. **Facilities:** P (parking meters wkdays) ♿ ✝ *Details not confirmed for 2002*

NEWMAN HOUSE
University College Dublin, 86 St Stephens Green (South side of St Stephen's Green)
☎ 01 7067422 & 4757255 ▤ 01 7067211

Newman House consists of two superb Georgian town houses, containing some of Ireland's finest 18th-century plasterwork and decoration. As the founding home of University College Dublin in 1854, the house has been associated with many famous literary and historical figures, including John Henry Newman, Gerard Manley Hopkins and James Joyce.
Times: Open Jun-Aug, Tue-Fri 12-5. At other times tours by prior arrangement only. **Fee:** IEP3 (concessions IEP2). **Facilities:** P (100yds) ✘ licensed ✝ (ex guide dogs)

NUMBER TWENTY NINE
29 Lower Fitzwilliam St (on the corner of Lower Fitzwilliam St & Upper Mount Sq)
☎ 01 7026165 ▤ 01 7027796
e-mail: numbertwentynine@mail.esb.ie

Number Twenty-Nine is an exhibition of the home life of a middle-class merchant family in Dublin, in the late 18th and early 19th century.
Times: Open all year, Tue-Sat 10-5, Sun 2-5. (Closed Mon & 2 wks prior to Xmas). **Fee:** IEP2.50 (ch under 16 free, other concessions IEP1). **Facilities:** P (on street (1 hour meter) ☕ shop ✝ ☕

PHOENIX PARK VISITOR CENTRE
Phoenix Park
☎ 01 6770095 ▤ 01 8205584
Times: Open Jun-Sep, daily 10-6; Apr-May, daily 9.30-5.30; mid-end Mar & Oct, daily 9.30-5; Jan-mid Mar & Nov-Dec, Sat & Sun 9.30-4.30. Last admission 45 mins before closing. **Facilities:** ▣ ☕ ♿ toilets for disabled ✝ (ex guide dogs) *Details not confirmed for 2002*

GEORGE BERNARD SHAW HOUSE
33 Synge St
☎ 01 4750854 & 8722077 ▤ 01 8722231
e-mail: Dublin-Tourism@msn.com
Times: Open May-Oct, Mon-Sat 10-5, Sun & PH's 11-5. **Facilities:** ▣ (charged) shop garden centre ✝ (ex guide dogs) *Details not confirmed for 2002*

⛁ DUN LAOGHAIRE   Map 01 D4
JAMES JOYCE TOWER
Joyce Tower, Sandycove (1m SE Dun Laoghaire by coast road to Sandycove Point or turn off main Dun Laoghaire-Dalkey road)
☎ 01 2809265 & 8722077 ▤ 2809892
e-mail: enterprises@dublintourism.ie
Times: Open Apr-Oct Mon-Sat 10-5, Sun & PHs 2-6; Nov-Mar by arrangement. **Facilities:** P (100 yds) ♿ shop ✝ (ex guide dogs) *Details not confirmed for 2002* ☕

🏛 MALAHIDE   Map 01 D4

FRY MODEL RAILWAY
Malahide Castle Demesne
☎ 01 8463779 & 8462184 🖷 01 8463723
e-mail: fryrailway@dublintourism.ie
Times: Open all year, Apr-Oct, Mon-Sat 10-5, Sun & PH 2-6; Nov-Mar
Sat-Sun & PH 2-5. Parties at other times by arrangement. **Facilities:** 🅿
♿ shop 🐾 *Details not confirmed for 2002* 🏴

MALAHIDE CASTLE
(From Dublin city centre follow signs for Malahide, then
approaching the village, main entrance to castle is
signposted to right of main rd)
☎ 01 8462184 & 8462516 🖷 01 8462537
e-mail: malahidecastle@dublintourism.ie

One of Ireland's oldest castles, this romantic and
beautiful structure, set in 250 acres of grounds, has
changed very little in 800 years. Tours offer views of
Irish period furniture and historical portrait collections.
Additional paintings from the National Gallery depict
figures from Irish life over the last few centuries.
Times: Open all year, Apr-Oct, Mon-Sat 10-5, Sun & PH 11-6; Nov-Mar,
Mon-Fri 10-5, Sat-Sun & PH 2-5. (Closed for tours 12.45-2pm).
Fee: IEP4 (ch IEP2, con IEP3). Family ticket IEP11. Combined tickets for
related attractions available. **Facilities:** 🅿 🍺 ✗ licensed shop 🐾 🏴

CO GALWAY

🏛 GALWAY   Map 01 B3

GALWAY CITY MUSEUM
Spanish Arch
☎ 091 567641 🖷 091 567641

Galway City Museum is devoted to the city's history.
Features examples of medieval stonework, stone axe
heads and scrapers dating from 3,500 years BC, a peat
fire, a large map of the city in 1651, photographs of
19th-century traditional dress and memorabilia of the
Connaught Rangers Regiment.
Times: Open all year daily, Mar-Oct 10-5.15. Nov-Feb 2-4, times under
review. **Fee:** IEP1. (ch & students IR50p). **Facilities:** 🅿 (100yds)
(parking discs required) ♿ 🐾 (ex guide dogs)

NORA BARNACLE HOUSE MUSEUM
Bowling Green (close to St Nicholas Collegiate Church,
in city centre)
☎ 091 564743

The smallest museum in Ireland, this tiny turn-of-
century house was the home Nora Barnacle,
companion, wife and lifelong inspiration of James
Joyce. It was here in 1909, sitting at the kitchen table
that Joyce first met his darling's mother. Letters,
photographs and other exhibits of the lives of James
Joyce & Nora Barnacle make a visit here a unique
experience.
Times: Open Jun-mid Sep, Tue-Sat 10-1 & 2-5. Opening times may
vary. **Fee:** IEP2 (students IEP1) **Facilities:** 🅿 100yds shop

ROYAL TARA CHINA VISITOR CENTRE
Tara Hall, Mervue (off N17 opp Trappers Rest or left off
N6 after Ryan's Hotel)
☎ 091 751301 🖷 091 757574
e-mail: visitorcentre@royal-tara.com
Times: Open all year, 9-6 (9-8 Jul-Sep, 9-9 Dec). Guided factory tours
Mon-Fri 9.30-3.30. **Facilities:** 🅿 🍺 ✗ ♿ toilets for disabled shop 🐾
(ex guide dogs) *Details not confirmed for 2002* 🏴

🏛 GORT   Map 01 B3

THOOR BALLYLEE
(1km off N18, 1km off N66)
☎ 091 631436 🖷 091 565201
Times: Open Etr-Sep, daily 10-6. **Facilities:** 🅿 🍺 ♿ (audio-visual
presentation) toilets for disabled shop 🐾 *Details not confirmed for
2002* 🏴

🏛 KINVARRA   Map 01 B3

DUNGUAIRE CASTLE
☎ 091 37108 & 061 360788 🖷 061 361020
e-mail: oconnorm@shannon-dev.ie
Times: Open May-mid Oct, daily 9.30-5.30 (last admission 4.30pm).
Fee: IEP3.05-IEP3.15 (ch IEP1.81, pen/student IEP2.10). Family ticket
IEP7.50-IEP7.90 **Facilities:** 🅿 shop 🐾 (ex guide dogs) 🏴

🏛 PORTUMNA   Map 01 B3

PORTUMNA CASTLE & GARDENS
☎ 0509 41658
Times: Open mid Apr-Sep, daily 9.30-6.30. **Facilities:** 🅿 ♿ (access
limited) 🐾 (ex guide dogs) *Details not confirmed for 2002*

🏛 ROUNDSTONE   Map 01 A4

ROUNDSTONE MUSICAL INSTRUMENTS
Craft Centre (Take N59 from Galway towards Clifden.
After approx 50m turn L at Roundstone sign, 7m to
village).
☎ 095 35875 🖷 095 35980
e-mail: bodhran@iol.ie

The Roundstone Music and Craft shop is situated within
the walls of an old Franciscan monastery. Here you can
see Ireland's oldest drum – the Bodhrán – being made
and regular talks and demonstrations are given. There
is an outdoor picnic area alongside the bell tower,
situated in a beautiful location by the water.
Times: Open daily Apr-Oct 9.30-6, Jul-Sep 9-7, Winter 6 days 9.30-6
Fee: Free. **Facilities:** 🅿 🍺 ♿ toilets for disabled shop

CO KERRY

🏛 CASTLEISLAND   Map 01 B2

CRAG CAVE
(1m N, signposted off N21)
☎ 066 7141244 🖷 066 7142352
e-mail: cragcave@eircom.net
Times: Open daily, Mar-Nov 10-6 (Jul-Aug until 6.30). Last tour 30
minutes before closing time. **Facilities:** 🅿 🍺 ✗ licensed ♿ (ramp to
visitor centre) toilets for disabled shop 🐾 (ex guide dogs) *Details not
confirmed for 2002* 🏴

🏛 DUNQUIN   Map 01 A2
THE BLASKET CENTRE
(10m W of Dingle town, on Slea Head Drive)
☎ 066 9156444 & 9156371 🖹 066 9156446
e-mail: mdemordha@eolga.ie

In the early part of the last century a small group of writers from the remote Blasket Island, just off the coast of County Kerry, achieved world renown. They told their own story in their own language; the centre describes the lives of the Islanders before the sad abandonment of the island in 1953. Research and conference facilities also available.
Times: Open daily, Etr-late Oct 10-6 (7 Jul-Aug). Open on request all year for groups over 30. Last admission 45 min before closing
Fee: IEP2.50 (ch & student IEP1, pen IEP1.75). Family ticket IEP6.
Facilities: 🅿 ☻ ✕ licensed ⅏ (reserved parking) toilets for disabled 🐾 (ex guide dogs)

🏛 KILLARNEY   Map 01 B2
KILLARNEY TRANSPORT MUSEUM
Scotts Hotel Gardens (centre of town, opposite railway station)
☎ 064 34677 🖹 064 32638

A unique collection of Irish veteran, vintage and classic cars, motorcycles, bicycles, carriages and fire engines. Exhibits include the 1907 Silver Stream, reputed to be the rarest car in the world, it was designed and built by an Irishman and he only made one!
Times: Open Apr-Oct, daily 10-6. Open at other times by appointment
Fee: IEP3 (ch IEP1.50, students & pen IEP2). Family ticket IEP8.
Wheelchair visitors free. Party. **Facilities:** 🅿 ☻ ✕ licensed ⅏ shop

MUCKROSS HOUSE, GARDENS & TRADITIONAL FARMS
Muckross (4m on Kenmare Road)
☎ 066 31440 & 35571 🖹 066 33926
e-mail: mucros@iol.ie
Times: Open Jul-Aug, daily 9-7; 17 Mar-Jun & Sep-Oct, 9-6; Nov-16 Mar 9-5.30. **Facilities:** 🅿 ✕ licensed ⅏ toilets for disabled shop 🐾 (ex guide dogs) *Details not confirmed for 2002* ☻

🏛 TRALEE   Map 01 A2
KERRY THE KINGDOM MUSEUM
Ashe Memorial Hall, Denny St
☎ (066) 7127777 🖹 066 7127444
e-mail: info@kerrymuseum.com

This museum tells the story of Kerry and Ireland from earliest times. The Geraldine Tralee Experience takes visitors by time car through reconstructed street scenes from the Middle Ages, complete with sounds and smells. There are also many archaeological finds and interactive exhibitions.
Times: Open daily, Mar-Oct 10-5.30; Aug 10-7; Nov-Dec 12-4. (Closed 24-26 Dec). **Fee:** *Prices not confirmed for 2002* **Facilities:** 🅿 (100mtrs) (disc parking area) ☻ ⅏ (enter through tourist office entrance) toilets for disabled shop garden centre 🐾 ☻

🐴🐎🏇

The Irish National Stud Japanese Gardens and St. Fiachra's Garden

TULLY · KILDARE · IRELAND
Tel: 00 353 45 521617 Fax: 00 353 45 522964

Situated just 40 minutes from Dublin via the M/N7, with easy access by rail and bus. Visitors may have a guided tour of the Stud Farm, browse around the world famous Japanese Gardens, visit the Horse Museum which houses the skeleton of the legendary steeplechaser *Arkle* and see our Millennium Garden – dedicated to the Patron Saint of Gardeners – St. Fiachra. Within this garden lies a **Waterford Crystal Garden** emerging from a souterrain or underground passage in a Monastic cell. Restaurant, Craft Shop and Lego area for children. Coach and Car Park – FREE.

Open February-November, 9.30am-6pm, 7 days a week

🏛 VALENTIA ISLAND   Map 01 A2
THE SKELLIG EXPERIENCE
(Ring of Kerry Road, signed after Cahersiveen then Valentia bridge or ferry from Rena Rd Point)
☎ 066 9476306 🖹 066 9476351
Times: Open 25 Mar-Jun & Sep 10-7, Jul-Aug 9.30-7 (last tour 6.15). Oct-mid Nov, Sun-Thu 10-5.30. **Facilities:** 🅿 ☻ ⅏ toilets for disabled shop 🐾 (ex guide dogs) *Details not confirmed for 2002* ☻

CO KILDARE

🏛 CELBRIDGE   Map 01 D4
CASTLETOWN
(13m from Dublin, follow signs to Celbridge from N4)
☎ 01 6288252 🖹 01 6271811
e-mail: castletown@ealga.ie

Ireland's largest and finest Palladian country house, begun c1722 for William Conolly, Speaker of the Irish House of Commons. The state rooms include the 'Pompeian' Long Gallery with its Venetian chandeliers, green silk drawing room and magnificent staircase hall with Lafrancini plasterwork. There is a fine collection of 18th-century Irish furniture and paintings.
Times: Open Etr Day-Sep Mon-Fri 10-6, Sat-Sun & BH 1-6; Oct Mon-Fri 10-5, Sun & BH 1-5; Nov Sun 1-5. Restoration continues. **Fee:** IEP3 (ch & students IEP1.25, pen IEP2). Family ticket IEP7.50. **Facilities:** 🅿 ☻ ⅏ toilets for disabled 🐾 (ex guide dogs)

KILDARE   Map 01 C3
JAPANESE GARDENS
Irish National Stud, Tully (off N7)
☎ 045 521617 & 522963 ▤ 045 522964
e-mail: stud@IRISH-national-stud.ie

Situated in the grounds of the Irish National Stud, the
gardens were established by Lord Wavertree between
1906 and 1910, and symbolise `The Life of Man' in a
Japanese-style landscape. You can also visit the Horse
Museum which includes the skeleton of Arkle. The
Commemorative Millennium Garden of St Fiachra
seeks to capture the power of the Irish landscape in its
rawest state, that of rock and water.
Times: Open 12 Feb-12 Nov, daily 9.30-6, last admission 5. **Fee:** *Prices
not confirmed for 2002* **Facilities:** ▣ ✗ licensed ♿ (all parts of stud
accessible, only small part of gardens) toilets for disabled shop ⚲ (ex
on lead) ◥

CO KILKENNY

KILKENNY   Map 01 C3
KILKENNY CASTLE
☎ 056 21450 ▤ 056 63488
Times: Open all year - Jun-Sep, daily 10-7; Apr-May, daily 10.30-5; Oct-
Mar, Tue-Sat 10.30-12.45 & 2-5, Sun 11-12.45 & 2-5. Last tour 45mins
before closing. (Closed Xmas & Good Fri). **Facilities:** ▣ (charged) ◥
♿ shop ⚲ (ex guide dogs) *Details not confirmed for 2002*

CO LIMERICK

FOYNES   Map 01 B3
FOYNES FLYING BOAT MUSEUM
(on N69 in Foynes, 23m from Limerick)
☎ 069 65416 ▤ 069 65416
e-mail: famm@eircom.net

The museum recalls the era of the flying boats during
the 1930s and early 1940s when Foynes was an
important airport for air traffic between the United
States and Europe. There is a comprehensive range of
exhibits, graphic illustrations and a 1940s style cinema
featuring a 17-minute film – all original footage from
the 30s and 40s. It was here that Irish coffee was first
invented by chef, Joe Sheridan, in 1942.
Times: Open 31 Mar-Oct, daily 10-6. Last admissions 5.15pm.
Fee: IEP3.50 (ch IEP2, student IEP3). Family ticket IEP9. **Facilities:** ▣
◥ ♿ toilets for disabled shop ⚲ (ex guide dogs) ◥

HOLYCROSS   Map 01 C3
LOUGH GUR STONE AGE CENTRE
Bruff Rd (17 km S of Limerick City, off R512 towards
Kilmallock)
☎ 061 385186 & 061 360788 ▤ 061 361020
e-mail: oconnorm@shannon-dev.ie
Times: Open May-Sep, daily 10-6 (last admission 5pm) **Fee:** IEP3.15
(ch IEP1.60, pen IEP1.81). Family ticket IEP6.30. **Facilities:** ▣ ◥ ♿
shop ⚲ (ex guide dogs) ◥

KILCORNAN   Map 01 B3
CELTIC PARK & GARDENS
(N69 Limerick to Tralge road)
☎ 061 394243 ▤ 353 69 64257
Times: Open daily, Mar-Oct 9-7. Last entry 6pm. **Facilities:** ▣ ◥
shop (on lead) *Details not confirmed for 2002*

LIMERICK   Map 01 B3
HUNT MUSEUM
The Custom House, Rutland St (a short walk from
Arthur's Quay)
☎ 061 312833 ▤ 061 312834
e-mail: info@huntmuseum.com

On show at the Hunt Museum is one of Ireland's finest
private collections of art and antiquities. It reflects
Ireland's Celtic past and also features masterworks by
Da Vinci and Renoir. Set in an 18th-century customs
house beside the broad, majestic Shannon.
Times: Open daily Mon-Sat 10-5, Sun 2-5. **Fee:** IEP4.20 (ch IEP2,
concessions IEP3.20). Family ticket IEP10. Party. **Facilities:** ℗ (50
mtrs) (parking discs for street parking) ◥ ✗ licensed ♿ toilets for
disabled shop ⚲ (ex guide dogs) ◥

KING JOHN'S CASTLE
Nicholas St
☎ 061 411201 & 360788 ▤ 061 361020
e-mail: oconnorm@shannon-dev.ie
Times: Open Apr-Oct daily 9.30-5.30 (last admission 4.30); Jul & Aug
open until 6pm; Nov-Mar 10.30-4.30 (last admission 3.30pm). **Fee:**
IEP4.61-IEP5.25 (ch IEP2.85-IEP3.15, pen & students IEP3.70-IEP3.95).
Family ticket IEP12.55-IEP13.15. **Facilities:** ▣ ◥ ♿ (lifts and ramps)
toilets for disabled shop ⚲ (ex guide dogs) ◥

CO LONGFORD

KEENAGH   Map 01 D6
CORLEA TRACKWAY VISITOR CENTRE
(Off R397, 3km from village)
☎ 043 22386 ▤ 043 22442
Times: Open Apr-1 Oct, daily 10-6. Last admission 45 mins before
closing. **Facilities:** ▣ ◥ ♿ toilets for disabled ⚲ (ex guide dogs)
Details not confirmed for 2002

CO MAYO

BALLYCASTLE   Map 01 B5
CÉIDE FIELDS
(5m W on R314)
☎ 096 43325 ▤ 096 43261
Times: Open Jun-Sep, daily 9.30-6.30; mid Mar-May & Oct, daily 10-5;
Nov, daily 10-4.30; other times by arrangement. **Facilities:** ▣ ◥ ♿
toilets for disabled ⚲ (ex guide dogs) *Details not confirmed for 2002*

CO MONAGHAN

INNISKEEN
Map 01 C4

PATRICK KAVANAGH RURAL & LITERARY RESOURCE CENTRE
Candlefort (between Carrickmacross N2 & Dundalk N1)
☎ 042 78560 ▤ 042 78560
e-mail: infoatpkc@tinet.ie

Birthplace of Patrick Kavanagh, one of Ireland's foremost 20th-century poets. The village grew around the ancient monastery of St Daig MacCairill, founded in 562, and its strong, 10th-century round tower still stands. The centre, housed in the former parish Church, chronicles the ancient history of the region and its role in developing Kavanagh's work.
Times: Open all year, Mon Fri 11-5, wknds & BH's 2-6. (Closed Oct-May, wknds & BH's Dec-16 Mar) **Fee:** IEP2 (ch 12 free, concessions IEP1). Kavanagh trail guide map available IR50p. Kavanagh Country Tours - a guided tour with live performances lasting 90 mins, advance booking essential IEP5 including admission to centre. **Facilities:** ▣ ☛ ⓧ toilets for disabled shop

MONAGHAN
Map 01 C5

MONAGHAN COUNTY MUSEUM
1-2 Hill St (near town centre, opposite Tourist Information office)
☎ (047) 82928 ▤ 047 71189
e-mail: moncomuseum@eircom.net
Times: Open all year, Tue- Sat 11-1 & 2-5. **Facilities:** ▣ (near town centre) (restricted on street parking) ⓧ ⓨ *Details not confirmed for 2002*

CO OFFALY

BIRR
Map 01 C3

BIRR CASTLE DEMESNE
(in town square take exit beside Bank of Ireland and bear right. Turn left, entrance is on right, car park on left)
☎ 0509 20336 ▤ 0509 21583
e-mail: info@birrcastle.com

A large landscaped park with a lake, rivers and waterfalls, with important plant collections including magnolias, maples, limes and oaks. The Demesne is particularly colourful in the spring and autumn, and is noted for its formal gardens, containing the tallest box hedges in the world. The Demesne is also home to the Great Birr Telescope, built in 1844, and Ireland's Historic Science Centre, a series of galleries focusing on Ireland's scientific past.
Times: Open all year, 9am-6pm. **Fee:** IEP6.50 (ch IEP3.20, pen & students IEP4.50). Family ticket (2 adults & 2 ch) IEP17.50.
Facilities: ▣ (charged) ☛ ⓨ toilets for disabled shop garden centre ◥

CO ROSCOMMON

BOYLE
Map 01 B4

KING HOUSE
(in town centre, 1km from N4)
☎ 079 63242 ▤ 079 63243
e-mail: kinghouseboyle@hotmail.com
Times: Open Apr-mid Oct, daily 10-6 (last admission 5pm). All other times by appointment. **Facilities:** ▣ ☛ ⓧ ⓨ (lift to all areas) toilets for disabled shop garden centre Ⓚ (ex guide dogs) *Details not confirmed for 2002*

STROKESTOWN
Map 01 C4

STROKESTOWN PARK HOUSE GARDEN & FAMINE MUSEUM
Strokestown Park
☎ 078 33013 ▤ 078 33712
e-mail: info@strokestownpark.ie
Times: Open Apr-Oct, daily 11-5.30. All other times, group bookings only. **Facilities:** ▣ ⓧ licensed ⓨ (Access for ramps) toilets for disabled shop *Details not confirmed for 2002* ◥

CO TIPPERARY

CAHIR
Map 01 C3

SWISS COTTAGE
Kilcommon (1m from town on Ardfinnan road)
☎ 052 41144 ▤ 052 42324
Times: Open mid Mar-Apr & Oct-Nov, Tue-Sun 10-1 & 2-4.30; May-Sep, daily 10-6. Last admission 30mins before closing. **Facilities:** ▣ Ⓚ (ex guide dog) *Details not confirmed for 2002*

CASHEL
Map 01 C3

BRÚ BORÚ HERITAGE CENTRE
☎ 062 61122 ▤ 062 62700
e-mail: bruboru@comhaltas.com

At the foot of the Rock of Cashel, a 4th-century stone fort, this Heritage Centre is dedicated to the study and celebration of native Irish music, song, dance, story, telling, theatre and Celtic studies. There's a Folk Theatre where three performances are held daily in the summer, and in the evening, banquets evoke the Court of Brian Ború, 11th-century High King of Ireland, with songs, poems and sagas.
Times: Open Jan-May & Oct-Dec, Mon-Fri 9.30-5.30; Jun-Sep Tue-Sat 9.30-11, Sun-Mon 9.30-5.30. **Fee:** Admission to centre free. Night show IEP9. Exhibition, 'Sounds of History' £4. **Facilities:** ▣ (charged) ☛ ⓧ licensed ⓨ (wheelchair bay in theatre) toilets for disabled shop Ⓚ (ex guide dogs) ◥

CO WATERFORD

🏛 LISMORE
Map 01 C2

LISMORE CASTLE GARDENS
(on Dungarvan road N72 just near town centre)
☎ 058 54424 📠 058 54896
e-mail: lismoreestates@eircom.net

Lismore castle is the Irish home of the Duke of Devonshire. The beautifully situated walled and woodland gardens contain a fine collection of camellias, magnolias and other shrubs and a remarkable Yew Walk. It is said that Spenser wrote part of his *Faerie Queene* in these gardens.
Times: Open 22 Apr-14 Oct, daily 1.45-4.45. (Open at 11 during Jul/Aug) **Fee:** IEP3 (ch under 16 IEP1.50). Party 20+ IR2.50 (ch under 16 £1.30). **Facilities:** 🅿 🕭 (some of grounds are accessible)

🏛 WATERFORD
Map 01 C2

WATERFORD CRYSTAL VISITOR CENTRE
(on N25, 1m from city centre)
☎ 051 73311 📠 051 78539
Times: Tours of factory: Apr-Oct, daily 8.30-4, gallery daily 8.30-6; Nov-Feb,Mon-Fri 9-3.15, gallery 9-5. **Facilities:** 🅿 🕭 ✕ 🕭 (special tours on request) toilets for disabled shop 🛏 *Details not confirmed for 2002* 🕭

CO WEXFORD

🏛 FERRYCARRIG
Map 01 D3

IRISH NATIONAL HERITAGE PARK
(3m from Wexford, on N11)
☎ 053 20733 📠 053 20911
e-mail: info@inhp.com
Times: Open Apr-Oct daily 9.30-6.30. Last admission 5. Allow 1.5 hour for visit (closing time subject to seasonal change). **Facilities:** 🅿 🕭 ✕ licensed 🕭 toilets for disabled shop 🛏 (ex guide dogs) *Details not confirmed for 2002* 🕭

🏛 NEW ROSS
Map 01 C3

DUNBRODY ABBEY VISITORS CENTRE
Dunbrody Abbey, Campile (10 miles from New Ross at the base of the Hook Peninsular)
☎ 051 88603

The visitor centre is based around the Abbey itself and Dunbrody Castle. There is an intriguing yew hedge maze with 1550 yew trees and a museum. In addition there is a golf pitch and putt course with competitions organised twice a month, and a local craft centre.
Times: Open Apr-Sep 10-6 (7pm Jul-Aug). **Fee:** IEP1.50 (ch IEP1). Family ticket IEP4. Maze/Golf IEP1.50, (ch IEP1). Family IEP4. **Facilities:** 🅿 🕭 🕭 shop garden centre (specialising in conifers & shrubs)

JOHN F KENNEDY ARBORETUM
(12km S of New Ross, off R733)
☎ 051 388171 📠 051 388172

The Arboretum covers 623 acres across the hill of Slievecoiltia which overlooks the Kennedy ancestral home at Dunganstown. There are 4,500 types of tree and shrub representing the temperate regions of the world, laid out in botanical sequence. There's a lake and a visitor centre.
Times: Open daily, May-Aug 10-8; Apr & Sep 10-6.30; Oct-Mar 10-5. Last admission 45 mins before closing. (Closed Good Fri & 25 Dec). **Fee:** IEP2 (ch & student IEP1, pen IEP1.50). Family ticket IEP5. Party 20+ IEP1.50. Heritage card (12month) visits all Heritage Service sites. Adult IEP15 (pen IEP10, ch/student IEP6). Family ticket IEP36 **Facilities:** 🅿 🕭 🕭 toilets for disabled shop (dogs on lead)

🏛 WEXFORD
Map 01 D3

THE IRISH AGRICULTURAL MUSEUM
Johnstown Castle Old Farmyard (4m SW of Wexford town, signposted off N25)
☎ 053 42888 📠 053 42213

This museum has displays on rural transport, farming and the activities of the farmyard and farmhouse; it includes a large exhibition on the history of the potato and the Great Famine (1845-49). Large scale replicas of different workshops, including a blacksmith's, cooper's and basket worker's, and there are displays on dairying, cycling, and sugar-beet harvesting and a collection of Irish country furniture. New permanent exhibitions on gardening and the Ferguson System.
Times: Open all year, Jun-Aug Mon-Fri 9-5 & Sat-Sun 11-5; Apr-May & Sep-14 Nov Mon-Fri 9-12.30 & 1.30-5, Sat-Sun 2-5; 15 Nov-Mar Mon-Fri 9-12.30 & 1.30-5 (Closed 25 Dec-2 Jan). **Fee:** IEP3 (ch & students IEP2). Family ticket IEP10. Parking charge May-Sep. **Facilities:** 🅿 (charged) 🕭 🕭 toilets for disabled shop 🛏 (ex small dogs)

JOHNSTOWN CASTLE GARDENS
Johnstown Castle (4m SW of Wexford, signposted off N25)
☎ 053 42888 📠 053 42004

The 19th-century mansion is closed to the public but visitors can explore the 50 acres of grounds containing over 200 different varieties of trees and shrubs, ornamental lakes with wildfowl, and walled gardens and hothouses. The ruins of Rathlannon Castle, a medieval tower house, can also be seen.
Times: Open all year, daily 9-5.30. (Closed 25 Dec). **Fee:** Car (inc passengers) IEP3. Pedestrians IEP1.50 (ch & students IR50p). **Facilities:** 🅿 🕭 🕭 toilets for disabled

WEXFORD WILDFOWL RESERVE
North Slob (take coast road over bridge for 3km, signs show turning on right)
☎ 053 23129 📠 053 24785
e-mail: cwilson@ealga.ie

The reserve is of international importance for Greenland white-fronted geese, brent geese, Bewick's swans and wigeon. The reserve is a superb place for birdwatching and there are hides and a tower hide available as well as a visitor centre.
Times: Open all year, 15 Apr-Sep 9-6; Oct-14 Apr 10-5. **Fee:** Free. **Facilities:** 🅿 🕭 toilets for disabled 🛏 (ex guide dogs)

CO WICKLOW

🏛 ENNISKERRY
Map 01 D4

POWERSCOURT GARDENS EXHIBITION
Powerscourt Estate (just off N11 S of Bray, next to Enniskerry village)
☎ 01 2046900   🖷 01 2863561
e-mail: gardens@powerscourt.ie

Begun by Richard Wingfield in the 1740s, the gardens are a blend of formal plantings, sweeping terraces, statuary and ornamental lakes together with secret hollows, rambling walks and walled gardens. The house itself incorporates an exhibition which traces the history of the estate, and tells the story of the disastrous fire of 1974 which gutted the house.
Times: Open - Gardens Mar-Oct daily 9.30-5.30; Nov-Feb daily 9.30-dusk. Waterfall Mar-Oct daily 9.30-7; Nov-Feb daily 10.30-dusk.(Please check winter opening times as they are subject to change. Closed 25-26 Dec). **Fee:** *Prices not confirmed for 2002*
Facilities: 🅿 ☕ ✕ licensed ⅋ (Lift to first floor, Wheelchair available) toilets for disabled shop garden centre 🐾 (ex guide dogs) 🛥

🏛 KILQUADE
Map 01 D3

NATIONAL GARDENS EXHIBITIONS CENTRE
Calumet Nurseries (7m S of Bray - turn off N11 at Kilpedder)
☎ 01 2819890   🖷 01 2810359
e-mail: calumet@clubi.ie
Times: Open Feb-22 Dec, Mon-Sat 10-6, Sun 1-6. **Facilities:** 🅿 ☕ ⅋ shop garden centre 🐾 (ex guide dogs) *Details not confirmed for 2002* 🛥

🏛 RATHDRUM
Map 01 D3

AVONDALE HOUSE & FOREST PARK
(1.6km S of town. R752 off N11)
☎ 0404 46111   🖷 0404 46111
e-mail: costelloe_j@coillte.ie

It was here in 1846 that one of the greatest political leaders of modern Irish history, Charles Stewart Parnell, was born. Parnell spent much of his time at Avondale until his death in October 1891. The house is set in a magnificent forest park with miles of forest trails, plus a children's play area and picnic areas.
Times: House: 17 Mar-Oct, 11-6. Outside of these dates group bookings by appointment. Last admission 1 hour before closure. (Closed Good Fri). Park: Open daily. **Fee:** *Prices not confirmed for 2002* **Facilities:** 🅿 (charged) ✕ licensed ⅋ (Special carpark & one forest trail accessible) shop 🐾 (ex guide dogs & on lead) 🛥

County Map

The county map shown here will help you identify the counties within each country. You can look up each county in the guide using the county names at the top of each page. To find towns featured in the guide use the atlas pages and the index at the back of the book.

England

1 Bedfordshire
2 Berkshire
3 Bristol
4 Buckinghamshire
5 Cambridgeshire
6 Greater Manchester
7 Herefordshire
8 Hertfordshire
9 Leicestershire
10 Northamptonshire
11 Nottinghamshire
12 Rutland
13 Staffordshire
14 Warwickshire
15 West Midlands
16 Worcestershire

Scotland

17 City of Glasgow
18 Clackmannanshire
19 East Ayrshire
20 East Dunbartonshire
21 East Renfrewshire
22 Perth & Kinross
23 Renfrewshire
24 South Lanarkshire
25 West Dunbartonshire

Wales

26 Blaenau Gwent
27 Bridgend
28 Caerphilly
29 Denbighshire
30 Flintshire
31 Merthyr Tydfil
32 Monmouthshire
33 Neath Port Talbot
34 Newport
35 Rhondda Cynon Taff
36 Torfaen
37 Vale of Glamorgan
38 Wrexham

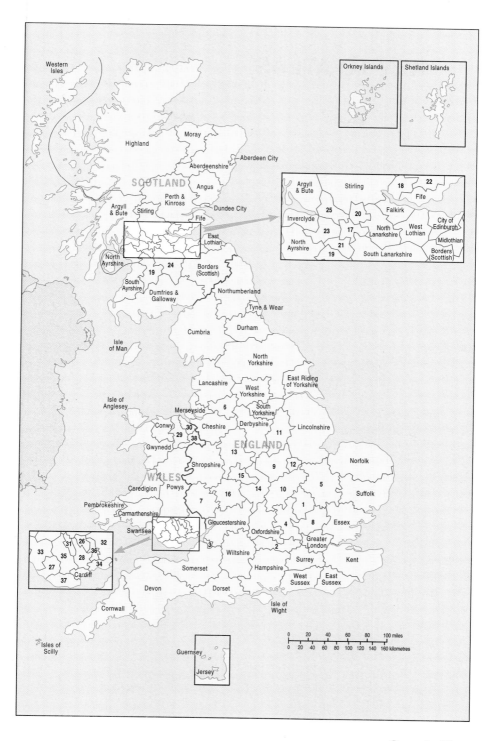

County Map

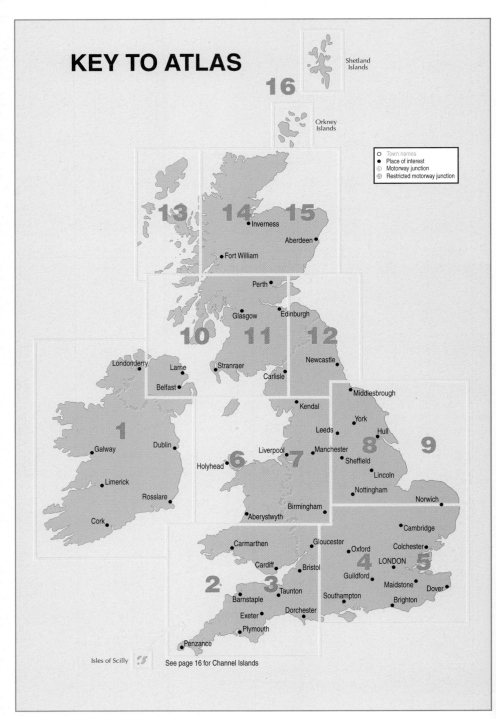

KEY TO ATLAS

Shetland Islands

16

Orkney Islands

○	Town names
●	Place of interest
⊕	Motorway junction
⊕	Restricted motorway junction

13   **14**   **15**

● Inverness

● Aberdeen

● Fort William

● Perth

10   **11**   **12**

● Glasgow   ● Edinburgh

● Londonderry   ● Larne   ● Stranraer   ● Newcastle

● Belfast   ● Carlisle

● Middlesbrough

● Kendal

● York   ● Hull

1   ● Leeds

● Galway   ● Dublin   ● Liverpool   ● Manchester

6   **7**   ● Sheffield   **8**   **9**

● Holyhead   ● Lincoln

● Limerick   ● Nottingham

● Rosslare   ● Norwich

● Cork   ● Birmingham

● Aberystwyth   ● Cambridge

● Carmarthen   ● Gloucester   ● Colchester

● Oxford

● Cardiff   ● Bristol   **4**   LONDON   **5**

2   **3**   ● Guildford   ● Dover

● Barnstaple   ● Taunton   ● Southampton   ● Maidstone

● Dorchester   ● Brighton

● Exeter

● Plymouth

● Penzance

Isles of Scilly   See page 16 for Channel Islands

© Automobile Association Developments Limited 2001

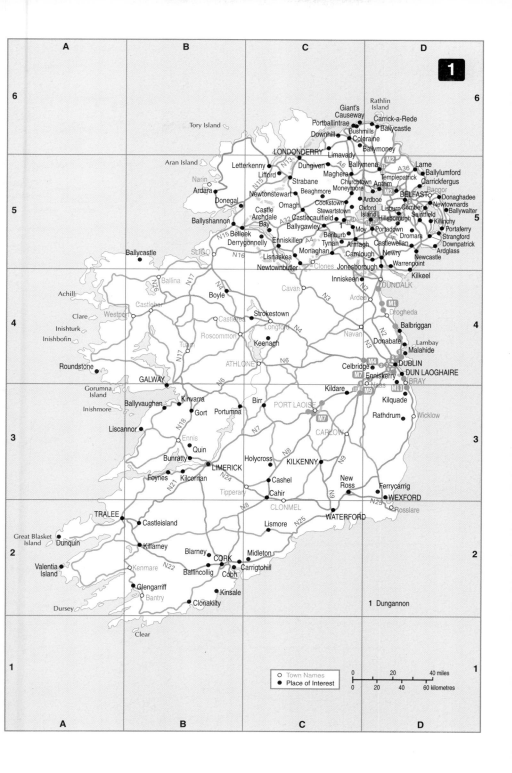

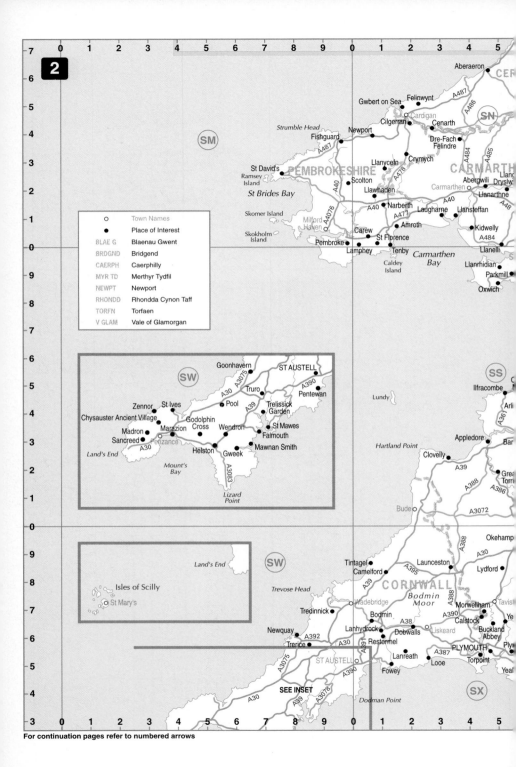

2

Town Names ○
Place of Interest ●

BLAE G	Blaenau Gwent
BRDGND	Bridgend
CAERPH	Caerphilly
MYR TD	Merthyr Tydfil
NEWPT	Newport
RHONDD	Rhondda Cynon Taff
TORFN	Torfaen
V GLAM	Vale of Glamorgan

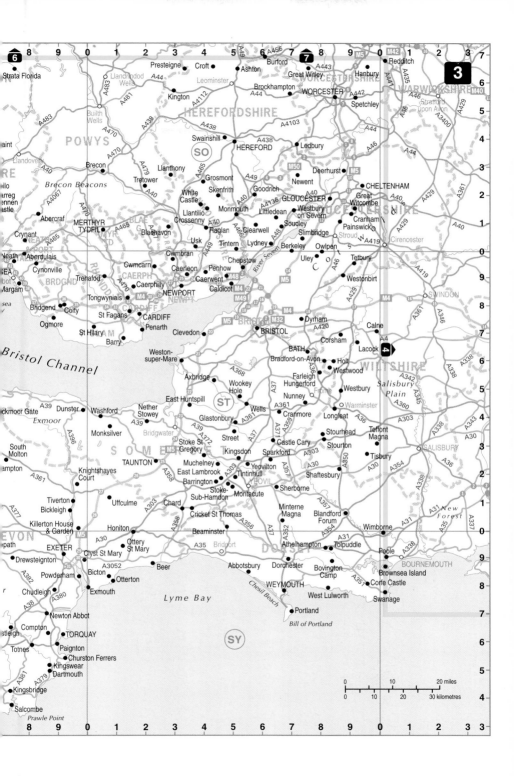

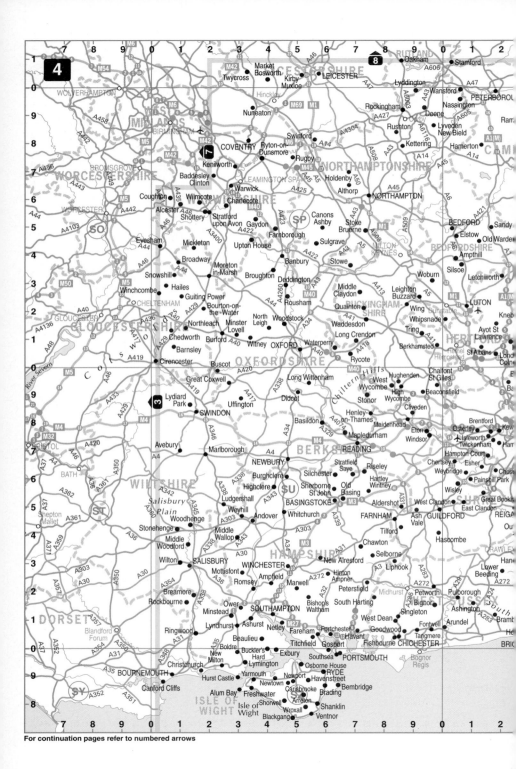

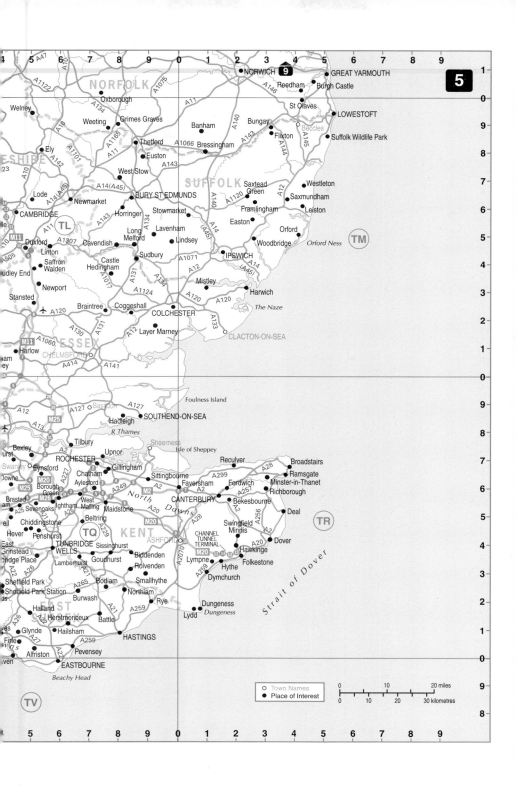

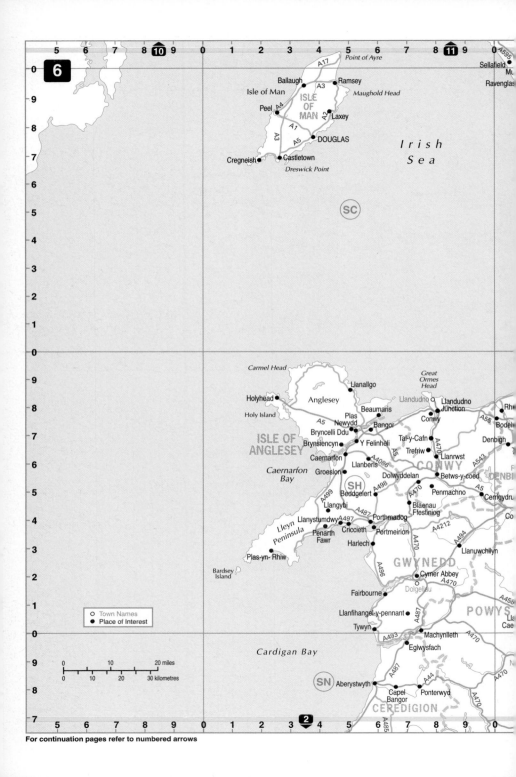

For continuation pages refer to numbered arrows

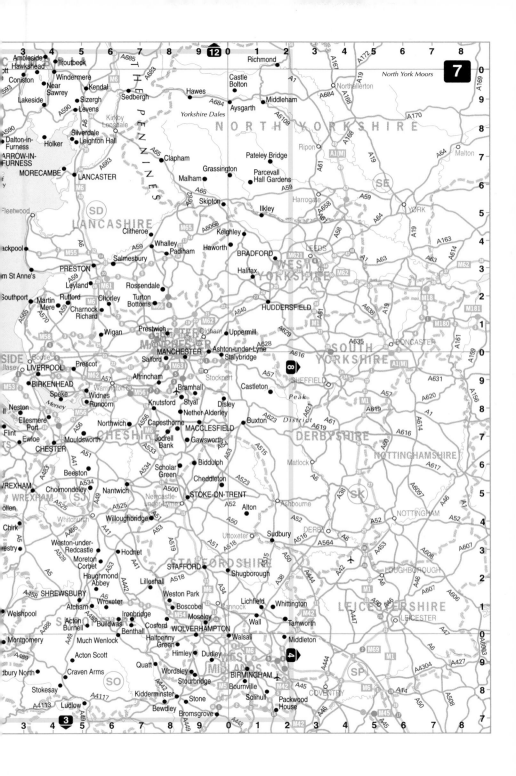

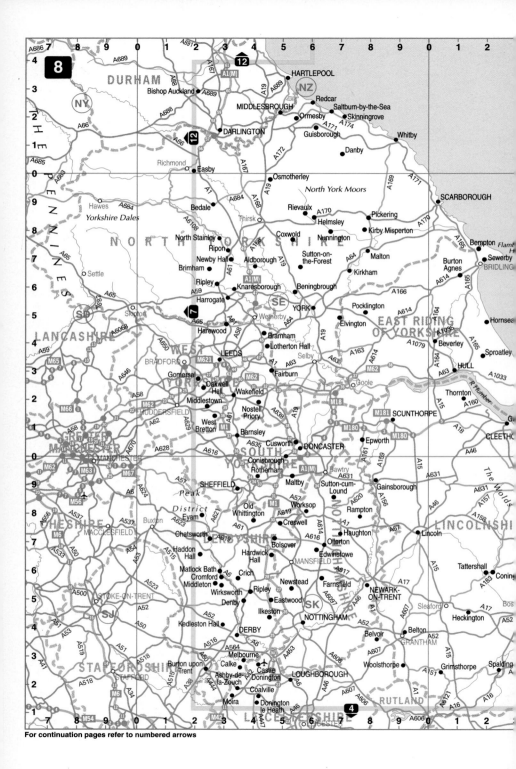

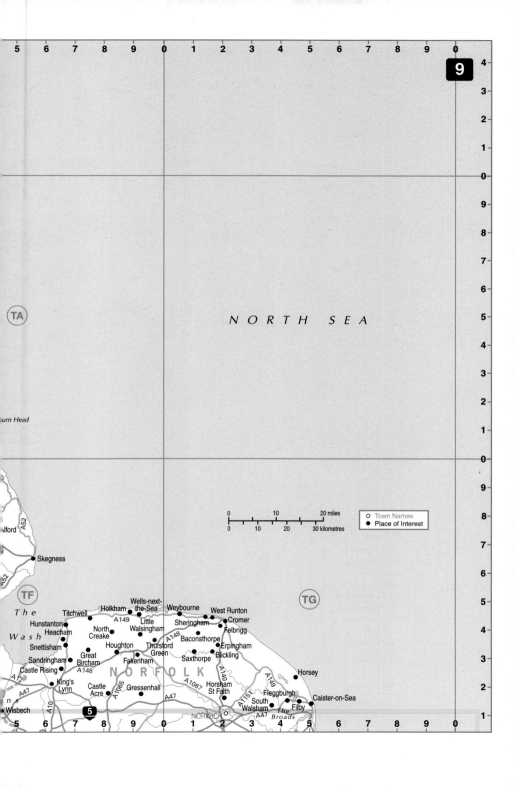

5 6 7 8 9 0 1 2 3 4 5 6 7 8 9 0

4
3
2
1
0

9
8
7
6
5
4
3
2
1
0

TA

N O R T H   S E A

9
8
7
6
5

urn Head

9
8
7
6
5

0 10 20 miles
0 10 20 30 kilometres

○ Town Names
● Place of Interest

TF

TG

Skegness

The
Wash

Titchwell
Holkham
Wells-next-
the-Sea
Weybourne
West Runton

Hunstanton
Heacham
A149
Little
Walsingham
Sheringham
Cromer
Felbrigg

North
Creake
Thursford
A148
Baconsthorpe
Erpingham

Snettisham
Houghton
Green
Saxthorpe
Blickling

Sandringham
Great
Bircham
Fakenham

Castle Rising
A148
N O R F O L K

King's
Lynn
Castle
Acre
A1065
Gressenhall
A1067
Horsham
St Faith
Horsey

Wisbech
A10
5
NORWICH
A47
South
Walsham
Fleggburgh
Filby
Caister-on-Sea
The
Broads

lford
A52

A52

lford

ns

A47

5 6 7 8 9 0 1 2 3 4 5 6 7 8 9 0

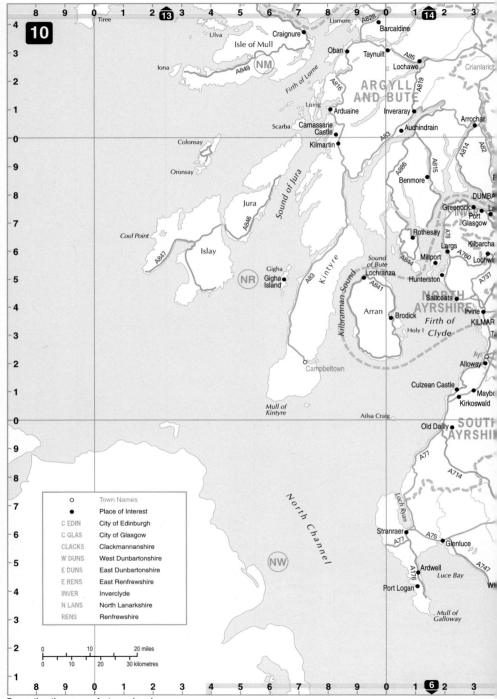

Tiree

Ulva

Isle of Mull

Iona

A849

NM

Firth of Lorne

Lismore

A828

Barcaldine

Oban

Taynuilt

Lochawe

A85

Craignure

Crianlarich

ARGYLL
AND BUTE

A816

A819

Luing

Arduaine

Inveraray

Auchindrain

Arrochar

Scarba

Carnassarie
Castle

Kilmartin

A83

A814

A82

Colonsay

Oronsay

A886

A815

Benmore

DUMBA

Jura

Sound of Jura

A846

Greenock

Port
Glasgow

Le

Coul Point

A847

Rothesay

A78

Kilbarcha

Islay

Gigha

NR

Gigha
Island

A83

Kintyre

Sound
of Bute

A844

Largs

Millport

A760

Lochwir

A737

Lochranza

Saltcoats

NORTH
AYRSHIRE

Kilbrannan Sound

A841

Hunterston

Arran

Brodick

Holy I

Firth of
Clyde

Irvine

KILMAR

Ta

Campbeltown

Ayr

Alloway

Culzean Castle

Maybo

Kirkoswald

Mull of
Kintyre

Ailsa Craig

Old Daily

SOUT
AYRSHI

A77

North Channel

A714

NW

Stranraer

A75

Glenluce

Loch Ryan

A77

Ardwell

A176

Luce Bay

A747

Port Logan

W

Mull of
Galloway

○	Town Names
●	Place of Interest
C EDIN	City of Edinburgh
C GLAS	City of Glasgow
CLACKS	Clackmannanshire
W DUNS	West Dunbartonshire
E DUNS	East Dunbartonshire
E RENS	East Renfrewshire
INVER	Inverclyde
N LANS	North Lanarkshire
RENS	Renfrewshire

0   10   20 miles
0   10   20   30 kilometres

For continuation pages refer to numbered arrows

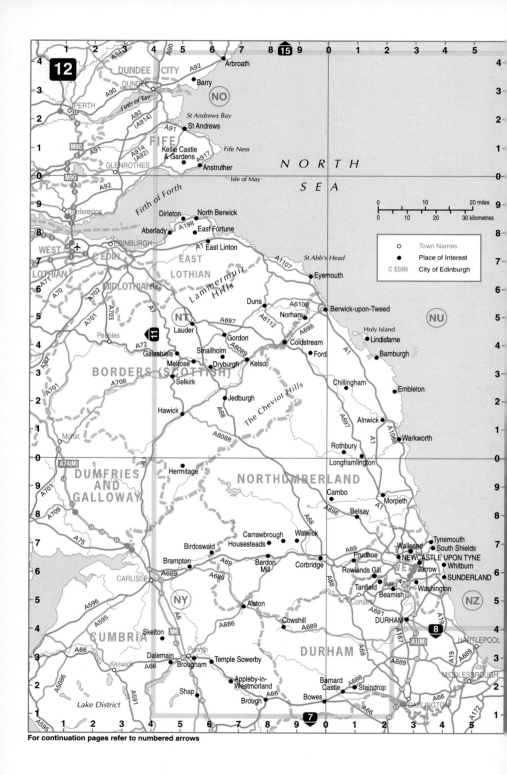

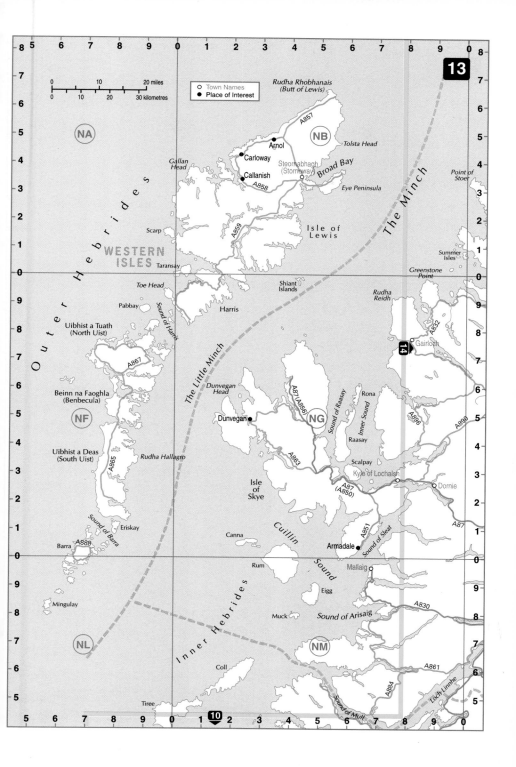

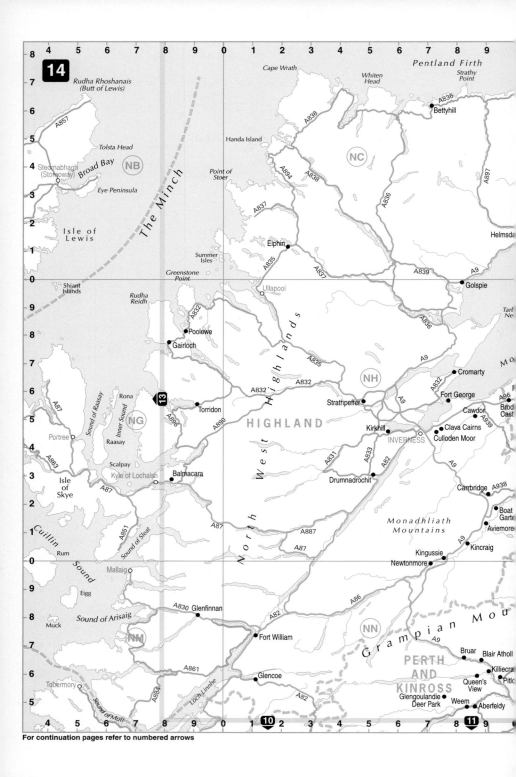

4 5 6 7 8 9 0 1 2 3 4 5 6 7 8 9

Pentland Firth

Cape Wrath

Whiten Head

Strathy Point

Rudha Rhoshanais
(Butt of Lewis)

A857

A836

Bettyhill

Tolsta Head

Broad Bay

NB

Handa Island

A838

NC

A897

Steornabhagh
(Stornoway)

Eye Peninsula

The Minch

Point of Stoer

A894 A838

A836

Helmsda

Isle of
Lewis

Shiant
Islands

Greenstone
Point

Summer
Isles

A837

Elphin

A835

A837

A839

A9

Golspie

Tarl
Ne

Rudha
Reidh

Ullapool

A832

West Highlands

A836

Poolewe

Gairloch

A835

NH

Cromarty

Mo

13

Rona

NG

Torridon

A832

A832

Strathpeffer

Fort George

A832

A96

Cawdor

A939

Brod
Cast

Portree

Sound of Raasay

Inner Sound

A896

A890

HIGHLAND

Kirkhill

Clava Cairns
Culloden Moor

Raasay

INVERNESS

Isle
of
Skye

A863

Scalpay

Kyle of Lochalsh

Balmacara

North

A831

A833

A82

Carrbridge A938

Boat
Garte

A87

A851

Drumnadrochit

Monadhliath
Mountains

Aviemore

Cuillin

Rum

A887

A9

Kincraig

Sound

A87

Kingussie

Mallaig

Eigg

A87

A86

Newtonmore

Muck

Sound of Arisaig

A830 Glenfinnan

A82

NN

Grampian Mou

Tobermory

A861

Fort William

Bruar Blair Atholl

A9

Glencoe

A861

Sound of Mull

A884

Loch Linnhe

A82

PERTH
AND
KINROSS

Killiecra

Queen's
View

Pitlo

Glengoulandie
Deer Park

Weem Aberfeldy

4 5 6 7 8 9 0 1 10 2 3 4 5 6 7 8 11 9

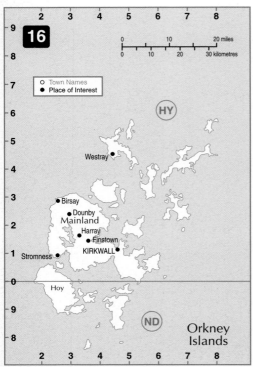

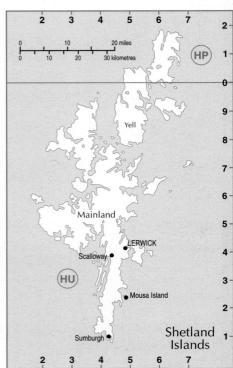

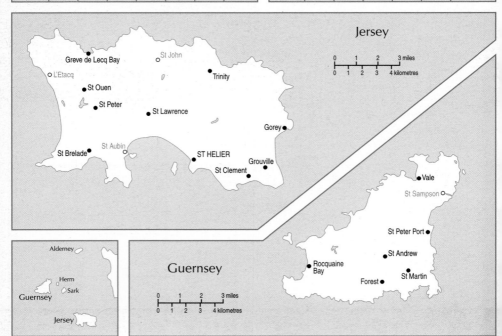

London Postcode Index

**This list of London attractions is in postcode order.
The page numbers are to the right**

London Postcode Index

The main pictures are held in the Automobile Association's own library (AA PHOTO
LIBRARY) and were taken by the following photographers.
AA PHOTO LIBRARY 128b. 330; STUART ABRAHAMS 276b, 278; MARTYN
ADELMAN 86b, 251t; ADRIAN BAKER 190; PETER BAKER 35, 49t, 66t, 173t; VIC
BATES 279t, 279b; JEFF BEAZLEY 72t, 120t; PETE BENNETT 1; M BIRKITT 13t, 13b,
24, 49b, 75t, 75b, 124t, 124b, 127, 128t, 166t, 166b, 177, 184t, 184b, 185, 227t;
JAMIE BLANDFORD 364t; PETER BROWN 219t; IAN BURGUM 186b, 331b, 353; JIM
CARNIE 281t; CHRIS COE 109t. 213t; STEVE DAY 79t, 152t, 152b, 178t, 241t, 267,
268t, 281b; RICHARD ELLIOT 326t; ERIC ELLINGTON 326b; DEREK FORSS 25, 203t,
209t, 213b, 218, 237b; STEPHEN HILL 364b; CAROLINE JONES 16, 21, 29t, 29b,
105t, 105b, 247t; MAX JOURDAN 132t, 132b; S KING 42b; ANDREW LAWSON 55t,
55b; CAMERON LEES 42t, 72b, 169t; S & O MATHEWS 79b, 90b, 109b, 165, 169b,
203b, 224t, 241b; ROGER MOSS 65; JOHN MOTTISHAW 86t, 89, 120b; GEORGE
MUNDAY 354t, 354b; RICH NEWTON 19, 66b, 173b, 251b; ANDREW PERKINS 157t;
ROY RAINFORD 104t; MICHAEL SHORT 178b; 227b; SLIDE FILE 375; TONY SOUTER
2r, 3t, 90t, 223; FORBES STEVENSON 247b; RICK STRANGE 3l, 4l; RICHARD
SURMAN 104b; DAVID TARN 254t; TOM TIMMS 2l, 5; JAMES TIMS 3, 8; MARTIN
TRELAWNY 219b; PETER TRENCHARD 274b, 276t; WYN VOYSEY 3r, 4b, 186t, 209b,
237t, 274t; RONALD WEIR 331t; JONATHON WELSH 197t, 197b, 202, 233t, 233b;
HARRY WILLIAMS 102t, 102b, 208; PETER WILSON 256t, 256b, 268b; TIM
WOODCOCK 157t, 224b, 254b
Abbreviations for terms appearing above. (t) top, (b) bottom, (l) left, (r) right

Thanks also to Alton Towers, Ironbridge Gorge Museums, Our Dynamic Earth, RRS
Discovery, Jim Cartwright/National Space Science Centre, and Simon Burt/Apex
Photo Agency/The Eden Project for use of photos in the introductory pages.

Index

D

E

Index

Index

Index

Index

Please send this form to:
  Head of Guidebooks,
  7th Floor
  Lifestyle Guides,
  The Automobile Association,
  Fanum House,
  Basingstoke RG21 4EA

  or fax: 01256 491647
  or e-mail: lifestyleguides@theAA.com

Readers' Report form

Please use this form to recommend any visitor attraction you have been to, whether it is in the guide or not currently listed. Feedback from readers helps us to keep our guide accurate and up to date. Please note, however, that if you have a complaint to make during a visit, we strongly recommend that you discuss the matter with the establishment management there and then so that they have a chance to put things right before your visit is spoilt. The AA does not undertake to arbitrate between you and the attraction's management, or to obtain compensation or engage in correspondence.

Date:

Your name (block capitals)

Your address (block capitals)

....

....

....

e-mail address: ....

Comments (please include the name & address of the attraction)

....

....

....

....

....

....

....

....

(please attach a separate sheet if necessary)

Please tick here if you DO NOT wish to receive details of AA offers or products ☐

PTO

Have you bought this guide before?   YES   NO

Have you bought any other Days Out guides recently? If yes, which ones?

....

....

Why did you buy this guide? (circle all that apply)

family holiday   short break   school holidays   special occasion

other..

How often do you have a Day Out? (circle one choice)

more than once a month   once a month   once in 2-3 months

once in six months   once a year   less than once a year

Please answer these questions to help us make improvements to the guide:

Which of these factors are most important when choosing a Day Out?

Price   Location   Previous experience   Recommendation

Type of attraction

Other (please state):...

Do you read the editorial features in the guide?   YES   NO

Do you use the location atlas?   YES   NO

Which elements of the guide do you find the most useful when choosing somewhere to visit?

Description   Photo   Advertisement

Can you suggest any improvements to the guide?

....

....

....

....

....

....

Thank you for completing this form

Please send this form to:
Head of Guidebooks,
7th Floor
Lifestyle Guides,
The Automobile Association,
Fanum House,
Basingstoke RG21 4EA

Readers' Report form

or fax: 01256 491647
or e-mail: lifestyleguides@theAA.com

Please use this form to recommend any visitor attraction you have been to, whether it is in the guide or not currently listed. Feedback from readers helps us to keep our guide accurate and up to date. Please note, however, that if you have a complaint to make during a visit, we strongly recommend that you discuss the matter with the establishment management there and then so that they have a chance to put things right before your visit is spoilt. The AA does not undertake to arbitrate between you and the attraction's management, or to obtain compensation or engage in correspondence.

Date:

Your name (block capitals)

Your address (block capitals)

....

....

....

e-mail address: ....

Comments (please include the name & address of the attraction)

....

....

....

....

....

....

....

....

(please attach a separate sheet if necessary)

Please tick here if you DO NOT wish to receive details of AA offers or products ☐

PTO

Readers' Report Form

Have you bought this guide before? YES NO

Have you bought any other Days Out guides recently? If yes, which ones?

....

....

Why did you buy this guide? (circle all that apply)

family holiday short break school holidays special occasion

other...

How often do you have a Day Out? (circle one choice)

more than once a month   once a month   once in 2-3 months

once in six months   once a year   less than once a year

Please answer these questions to help us make improvements to the guide:

Which of these factors are most important when choosing a Day Out?

Price   Location   Previous experience   Recommendation

Type of attraction

Other (please state):...

Do you read the editorial features in the guide? YES NO

Do you use the location atlas? YES NO

Which elements of the guide do you find the most useful when choosing somewhere to visit?

Description   Photo   Advertisement

Can you suggest any improvements to the guide?

....

....

....

....

....

....

Thank you for completing this form

Please send this form to:
  Head of Guidebooks,
  7th Floor
  Lifestyle Guides,
  The Automobile Association,
  Fanum House,
  Basingstoke RG21 4EA

Readers' Report form

or fax: 01256 491647
or e-mail: lifestyleguides@theAA.com

Please use this form to recommend any visitor attraction you have been to, whether it is in the guide or not currently listed. Feedback from readers helps us to keep our guide accurate and up to date. Please note, however, that if you have a complaint to make during a visit, we strongly recommend that you discuss the matter with the establishment management there and then so that they have a chance to put things right before your visit is spoilt. The AA does not undertake to arbitrate between you and the attraction's management, or to obtain compensation or engage in correspondence.

Date:

Your name (block capitals)

Your address (block capitals)

....

....

....

e-mail address: ....

Comments (please include the name & address of the attraction)

....

....

....

....

....

....

....

(please attach a separate sheet if necessary)

Please tick here if you DO NOT wish to receive details of AA offers or products ☐

PTO

Readers' Report Form

Have you bought this guide before? YES   NO

Have you bought any other Days Out guides recently? If yes, which ones?

....

....

Why did you buy this guide? (circle all that apply)

family holiday   short break   school holidays   special occasion

other..

How often do you have a Day Out? (circle one choice)

more than once a month   once a month   once in 2-3 months

once in six months   once a year   less than once a year

Please answer these questions to help us make improvements to the guide:

Which of these factors are most important when choosing a Day Out?

Price   Location   Previous experience   Recommendation

Type of attraction

Other (please state):...

Do you read the editorial features in the guide?   YES   NO

Do you use the location atlas?   YES   NO

Which elements of the guide do you find the most useful when choosing somewhere to visit?

Description   Photo   Advertisement

Can you suggest any improvements to the guide?

....

....

....

....

....

....

Thank you for completing this form